Front Cover: Tavern House, Tetbury, Gloucestershire

Contents

This 'Where to Stay' guide is designed to give you all the information you need to help you find accommodation in

Welcome

England in the right place, at the right price and with the facilities and services that are right for you.

Whatever your reason for staying away from home – holiday, shopping trip, on business or visiting friends or relatives – you're sure to find in this guide accommodation that suits you best.

And to help in your selection, most of the accommodation entries in this guide show their national Crown ratings awarded by the Tourist Board (see pages 4–5).

A unique and helpful feature of this 'Where to Stay' guide is that all the essential information you need is presented in a straightforward and easy-to-read style, along with a brief description of the establishment.

Symbols are used only to give you all the very detailed – but perhaps necessary – information about additional services and facilities. But there's no need to flick back and forth between pages to find out what all the symbols mean – just fold out the back cover and you can check them as you go.

to the Guide

At the back of the guide you will find full-colour maps which not only pinpoint all those cities, towns and villages with accommodation listings, but are also useful as route maps. They show major towns, motorways, main 'A' roads, airports, towns with BR InterCity stations, main ferry routes, and much, much more.

Also at the back is a comprehensive town index to make it easy for you to check out what accommodation is available in a particular place.

And there's more! Each of the 12 regional sections starts with lots of ideas on where to go and what to see in the region. Throughout the guide you'll also find thumbnail town descriptions to give you a quick picture of each place.

To complete the 'Where to Stay' package you'll find the Information

Pages (starting on page 423) full of useful advice on such things as booking, cancellation, complaints, etc.

'Where to Stay' is a series of four guides, all available from your local bookshop:

Hotels & Guesthouses in England £8.95

Bed & Breakfast, Farmhouses, Inns & Hostels in England £7.95

Self-Catering Holiday Homes in England £5.95

Camping & Caravan Parks in Britain £5.95

3

Sure Sign
of Where to Stay

When you see *the Crown or Listed sign at a hotel, guesthouse, farmhouse, inn or B&B, or in its advertising, you can be sure that the establishment has been inspected and found to meet Tourist Board standards for facilities and services.*

Since their introduction *in 1987, the Tourist Board Crown ratings have become recognised as the leading indicator of the standards you can expect to find at your selected accommodation.*

Over 17,000 places *throughout the country now offer the reassurance of a national Crown rating – and the number grows daily.*

To help you find *accommodation that offers even higher standards than those required for a simple Listed or Crown rating, there are now four levels of quality grading – using the terms* **APPROVED, COMMENDED, HIGHLY COMMENDED** *and* **DE LUXE.**

Accommodation establishments *which apply for this additional quality grading are subject to a more rigorous Tourist Board inspection, taking into account such important aspects as warmth of welcome, atmosphere and efficiency of service as well as the quality of furnishings, fitments and equipment. However, if no quality grade appears you can still be sure of high standards of cleanliness and service appropriate to the type of establishment.*

4

Listed You can be sure that the accommodation will be clean and comfortable, but the range of facilities and services may be limited.

You will find additional facilities, including washbasin and chair in your bedroom, and you will have use of a telephone.

There will be a colour TV in your bedroom or in a lounge and you can enjoy morning tea/coffee in your bedroom. By the end of 1993, at least some of the bedrooms will have a private bath (or shower) and WC.

At least one-third of the bedrooms (and, by the end of 1993, one-half) will have private bath (or shower) en-suite. You will also be able to order a hot evening meal.

 Your bedroom will have a colour TV, radio and telephone, there will be lounge service until midnight and evening meals can be ordered up to 2030 hours. Three-quarters of the bedrooms (90% by the end of 1993) will have private bath and/or shower and WC en-suite.

 Every bedroom will have private bath, fixed shower and WC en-suite. The restaurant will be open for breakfast, lunch and dinner (or you can take meals in your room from breakfast until midnight) and you will benefit from an all-night lounge service. A night porter will also be on duty.

A more detailed explanation of what you may expect at accommodation with a Crown rating can be found on pages 429–432.

New "Lodge" Category

The growing popularity of places on motorways and trunk routes offering comfortable, purpose-built accommodation for relatively short stays has led the English Tourist Board to introduce a new "Lodge" category – using Moon symbols – within its national accommodation rating scheme.

Because not all "Lodges" are alike in terms of the facilities offered, they are distinguished by the use of One, Two or Three Moons.

In a One Moon "Lodge", your bedroom will have at least a washbasin and radio or colour TV. Tea/coffee may be from a vending machine in a public area.

Your bedroom in a Two Moon "Lodge" will have colour TV, tea/coffee-making facilities and en-suite bath or shower with WC.

 In a Three Moon "Lodge", you will find colour TV and radio, tea/coffee-making facilities and comfortable seating in your bedroom and there will be a bath, shower and WC en-suite. The reception area will be manned throughout the night.

"Lodges" are not separately identified in this edition of Where to Stay but signs incorporating the Moon symbols will begin to appear on premises around the country during 1993.

AYDON GRANGE

Establishments included *in this "Where to Stay" guide which have achieved the highest quality grade of* **DE LUXE** *for the exceptionally high quality standard of the facilities and services they provide are featured on this page.*

Please use *the Town Index on page 457 to find page numbers for their full entry listings.*

A Look at Some of
the Best

Aydon Grange, *Corbridge, Northumberland*
The Beeches, *Carlisle, Cumbria*
Broadview, *Crewkerne, Somerset*
Holmfield, *Kendal, Cumbria*
The Old Rectory, *Thornton Watlass, N. Yorkshire*
Parkside House, *Hastings, E. Sussex*
Pickett Howe, *Buttermere, Cumbria*

HOLMFIELD

The Upper House, *Wormbridge, Hereford & Worcester*

PICKETT HOWE

Use your *i*'s

When it comes to your next English break, the first stage of your journey could be closer than you think. You've probably got a Tourist Information Centre nearby. But you might not have realised that it's there to serve the local community – as well as visitors.

So make us your first stop. We'll be happy to help you, wherever you're heading.

Many Information Centres can provide you with maps and guides, helping you plan well in advance. And sometimes it's even possible for us to book your accommodation, too.

A visit to your nearest Information Centre can pay off in other ways as well. We can point you in the right direction when it comes to finding out about all the special events which are happening in the local region.

In fact, we can give you details of places to visit within easy reach... and perhaps tempt you to plan a day trip or weekend away.

Across the country, there are more than 600 Information Centres to choose from. So you're never far away. You'll find the address of your nearest Tourist Information Centre in your local Phone Book.

This 'Where to Stay' guide *will make it easy for you to find accommodation to suit your mood and your pocket. The content has been structured to enable you to find a place to stay even if you have only a general idea of the area you are planning to visit. Just follow the notes below and you'll soon find accommodation that's right for you.*

There is a complete *town index at the back which lists all the places with accommodation featured in the guide.*

If you already know *the name of the town in which you wish to stay, simply use the town index to find the relevant page number.*

How to use the guide

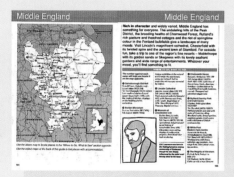

If you are touring *or only know the general area in which you wish to stay, look at the colour maps to find place names in the area and then refer to the town index for page numbers.*

The main body of this guide *is divided into 12 sections corresponding to England's tourist regions. Each regional section begins with a location map and an introduction with ideas on where to go and what to see.*

The region's *cities, towns and villages with their accommodation are then listed alphabetically. Accompanying each place name is a map reference which refers to the colour maps at the back of the guide. This enables you to find the exact location.*

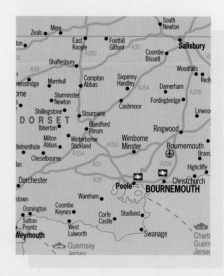

Accommodation information *has been provided by the proprietors of the establishments. Some information is represented by symbols and you will find a key to these inside the back cover flap.*

BLAKENEY

Norfolk
Map ref 3B1

Picturesque village on the north coast of Norfolk and a former port and fishing village, 15th C red bricked Guildhall. Marshy creeks extend towards Blakeney Point (National Trust) and are a paradise for naturalists, with trips to the reserve & to see the seals from Blakeney Quay.

Blakeney H

...0 (last

...ng for 75
Cards accepted: Access, Visa, Diners, Amex

12-120

Changes *may have occurred since the guide went to press or may occur during 1993 – so please check any aspects which are important to you before booking. We also advise you to read the information pages towards the back of the guide, particularly the section on cancellations.*

Enquiry coupons *are included at the back of the guide. One type will help you when contacting establishments about accommodation; the other can be used to request information from advertisers.*

England
at a Glance

England is divided *into 12 tourist regions, each of which has its own section in this guide. The regions are shown on the map and also listed opposite together with an index which identifies the region in which each county is located.*

■ Northumbria

■ Yorkshire & Humberside

■ Cumbria

■ North West

■ Middle England

■ East Anglia

■ Heart of England

■ Thames & Chilterns

■ London

■ South East England

■ South of England

■ West Country

Colour maps *showing all the places with accommodation listed in this guide and an index to the place names can be found at the back of the guide.*

County Index

11

SURE SIGNS

OF WHERE TO STAY

Throughout Britain, the tourist boards now inspect over 30,000 places to stay, every year, to help you find the ones that suit you best.

Looking for a hotel, guesthouse, inn, B&B or farmhouse? Look for the **CROWN**. The classifications: 'Listed', and then **ONE to FIVE CROWN,** tell you the range of facilities and services you can expect. The more Crowns, the wider the range.

Looking for a self-catering holiday home? Look for the **KEY**. The classifications: **ONE to FIVE KEY,** tell you the range of facilities and equipment you can expect. The more Keys, the wider the range.

THE GRADES: **APPROVED, COMMENDED, HIGHLY COMMENDED and DE LUXE,** whether alongside the **CROWNS** or the **KEYS,** show the quality standard of what is provided. If no grade is shown, you can still expect a high standard of cleanliness.

Looking for a holiday caravan, chalet or camping park? Look for the **Q** symbol. The more ✓s in the Q (from one to five), the higher the quality standard of what is provided.

We've checked them out before you check in!

More detailed information on the **CROWNS,** the **KEYS** and the **Q** is given in free *SURE SIGN* leaflets, available at any Tourist Information Centre.

13

Travel and Leisure Guides
from the

There is now a wide range of

books and guides published in

association with the English

Tourist Board, plus, where

appropriate, the National

Tourist Boards for Scotland,

Wales and Northern Ireland.

THE GREAT BRITISH... SERIES
Three books: Railway, Soldier, Countryside.
*The heritage and development of these
fascinating subjects with gazetteer of museums to
visit.*
Published by David & Charles, £14.99

FAMILY LEISURE GUIDE SERIES
Four guides: Golf, Birdwatching, Horse Riding,
Horse Racing.
*Complete guides to sporting and leisure activities
with gazetteer of attractions and places to visit.*
Published by Charles Letts, £9.95

**English
Tourist Board**

Look for the English Tourist Board
logo at your bookshop.

**English
Tourist Board**

**English
Castles**
·A L M A N A C·

English Tourist Board

HEALTHY BREAKS
Complete guide to health farms, spas and centres.
Published by Discovery Press, £8.99

POCKET ALMANAC SERIES
Two guides: English Castles and English Gardens.
Each containing over 100 of the best places to visit. Full colour.
Published by Lochar Publishing, £6.99

CIVIL WAR
The tumultuous years of the 1640's with complete gazetteer of events and places to visit.
Published by Collins & Brown, £10.99

UK ACTIVITY HOLIDAYS
Annual guide to activity, hobby, special interest and children's holidays throughout the UK plus holiday discount vouchers.
Published by Charles Letts, £4.50

STAY ON A FARM
Annual guide to over 1000 farms in membership of the Farm Holiday Bureau.
Published by Charles Letts, £5.95

Country Code

🍀 Enjoy the countryside and respect its life and work
🍀 Guard against all risk of fire🍀 Fasten all gates
🍀 Keep your dogs under close control🍀 Keep to
public paths across farmland 🍀 Use gates and stiles
to cross fences, hedges and walls 🍀 Leave livestock,
crops and machinery alone 🍀 Take your litter home
🍀 Help to keep all water clean🍀 Protect wildlife,
plants and trees 🍀 Take special care on country roads
🍀 Make no unnecessary noise

Advertisers

When requesting further information from
advertisers in this guide, you may find it helpful to
use the advertisement enquiry coupons which
can be found towards the end of the guide.
These should be cut out and mailed direct to
the companies in which you are interested. Do
remember to include your name and address.

Where to Stay in England

Published by: English Tourist Board, Thames Tower, Black's Road, Hammersmith, London W6 9EL. Internal Reference Number: ETB/213/93 AS/1357/47.5M/92

Managing Editor: Sally Marshall Compilation, Design & Production: Guide Associates, Croydon Colour Photography: Nigel Corrie (front cover and page 4); Glyn Williams and Syndication International (pages 1–4, 9, 480 and back cover) Illustrations: Susie Louis Cartoons: Ken Pyne Cartography: Colin Earl Cartography, Alton Typesetting: Computaprint, London, and Guide Associates, Croydon Printing & Binding: Bemrose Security Printing, Derby Advertisement Sales: Madison Bell Ltd, 3 St. Peter's Street, Islington Green, London N1 8JD. Telephone: 071-359 7737.

The information contained in this guide has been published in good faith on the basis of information submitted to the English Tourist Board by the proprietors of the premises listed, who have paid for their entries to appear. The English Tourist Board cannot guarantee the accuracy of the information in this guide and accepts no responsibility for any error or misrepresentation. All liability for loss, disappointment, negligence or other damage caused by reliance on the information contained in this guide, or in the event of bankruptcy, or liquidation, or cessation of trade of any company, individual or firm mentioned, is hereby excluded.

The English Tourist Board

The Board is a statutory body created by the Development of Tourism Act 1969 to develop and market England's tourism. Its main objectives are to provide a welcome for people visiting England; to encourage people living in England to take their holidays there; and to encourage the provision and improvement of tourist amenities and facilities in England. The Board has a statutory duty to advise the Government on tourism matters relating to England and, with Government approval and support, administers the national classification & grading schemes for tourist accommodation in England.

National Accessible Scheme

◆

If you are a wheelchair user or someone who has difficulty walking, look for the national "Accessible" symbol when choosing where to stay.

All the places that display the symbol have been checked by a Tourist Board inspector against criteria that reflect the practical needs of wheelchair users.

At the moment, the Tourist Boards are concentrating their inspections on hotels, guesthouses, inns, B&Bs, farmhouse acommodation and self-catering holiday homes. There are plans to extend the scheme to holiday caravan parks and visitor attractions in 1994.

◆

There are three categories of accessibility:

Category 1: Accessible to all wheelchair users including those travelling independently

Category 2: Accessible to a wheelchair user with assistance

Category 3: Accessible to a wheelchair user able to walk short distances and up at least three steps

◆

The National Accessible Scheme forms part of the Tourism for All campaign that is being promoted by all three national Tourist Boards.

A leaflet giving more information on the scheme is available free from any Tourist Information Centre, whose staff will also be pleased to help with finding suitable accommodation in the area.

Additional help and guidance can be obtained from the Holiday Care Service, 2 Old Bank Chambers, Station Road, Horley, Surrey RH6 9HW.
Tel: (0293) 774535. Fax: (0293) 784647.
Minicom: (0293) 776943 (24-hour answering).

◆

London

A heady mixture of history and heritage, modern architecture and old markets, museums and shopping malls, pageantry and tranquil parks, London is the cocktail that goes to everybody's head, as attractions old and new jostle for attention. Browse around the famous shops, take a river trip to see the regenerated Docklands, visit the magnificently restored Queen's House in historic Greenwich, potter in Portobello Market, stroll in Richmond Park, admire Hampton Court Palace, have a traditional pub lunch, see a show. You'll never run out of ideas in London – and London will always have new delights in store.

WHERE TO GO, WHAT TO SEE

The poet William Blake, who was regarded by his contemporaries as a mad genius, used to take the air on Hampstead Heath

Bankside Gallery
48 Hopton Street, Blackfriars, London SE1 9JH
Tel: 071-928 7521
The home of The Royal Water-colour Society and The Royal Society of Painter-Etchers and Engravers. Changing exhibitions of watercolours and prints.

Bank of England Museum
Bartholomew Lane, London EC2 8AH
Tel: 071-601 5545
History of Bank of England: interactive video illustrating place of the Bank in today's world economy. Bars of gold, banknote gallery.

British Museum
Great Russell Street, London WC1B 3DG
Tel: 071-636 1555
One of the great museums of the world, showing the works of man from all over the world from prehistoric to comparatively modern times.

Cabinet War Rooms
Clive Steps, King Charles Street, London SW1A 2AQ
Tel: 071-930 6961
Suite of 21 historic rooms, including Cabinet Room, transatlantic telephone room, map room and Prime Minister's room. Were in operational use 1939–1945.

Commonwealth Institute
Kensington High Street, London W8 6NQ
Tel: 071-603 4535
Three floors of exhibition galleries where you can discover the history, landscape, wildlife and culture of 50 Commonwealth countries.

Design Museum
Butler's Wharf, Shad Thames, London SE1 2YD
Tel: 071-403 6933
Study collection showing the development of design in mass production. Review of new products, graphics gallery and changing programme of exhibitions.

Fenton House
Windmill Hill, London NW3 6RT
Tel: 071-435 3471
William and Mary house which now contains the Benton

Fletcher collection of early keyboard instruments and the Binning collection of porcelain and furniture.

Freud Museum
20 Maresfield Gardens,
Hampstead, London
NW3 5SX
Tel: 071-435 2002
Library and study of Sigmund Freud's London home. Includes Freud's antiquity collection, library and furniture. Exhibitions and videos.

Guards Museum
Wellington Barracks,
Birdcage Walk, London
SW1E 6HQ
Tel: 071-414 3271
Collection of uniforms, colours and artefacts spanning over 300 years of history of the Foot Guards.

HMS Belfast
Morgans Lane, Tooley Street,
London SE1 2JH
Tel: 071-407 6434
11,500-tonne World War II cruiser, now a floating naval museum, with 7 decks to explore. Many naval exhibitions.

Imperial War Museum
Lambeth Road, London SE1 6HZ
Tel: 071-416 5000
Illustrates and records all aspects of World Wars I and II and other conflicts involving Britain and the Commonwealth since 1914. Blitz Experience, Operation Jericho.

Kensington Palace State Apartments
London W8 4PX
Tel: 071-937 9561
Furniture from the Stuart–Hanoverian periods, 3 rooms from the Victorian era. Works of art from the royal collection, court dress collection.

The 165ft high Chinese pagoda at Kew Gardens was designed by Sir William Chambers in 1761

Kew Bridge Steam Museum
Green Dragon Lane, Brentford,
Middlesex TW8 0EN
Tel: 081-568 4757
Victorian waterworks housing massive steam-powered pumping engines. Steam railway, water history. Tea room, shop.

Museum of London
150 London Wall, London
EC2Y 5HN
Tel: 071-600 3699
The galleries illustrate over 2,000 years of the capital's social history, from prehistoric times to

the 20th C. Regular temporary exhibitions, lunchtime lecture programmes.

Madame Tussauds
Marylebone Road, London
NW1 5LR
Tel: 071-935 6861
World famous collection of wax figures. Exhibits include historic scenes, "super stars", and the Chamber of Horrors. London Planetarium next door.

Museum of the Moving Image
South Bank, London
SE1 8XT
Tel: 071-928 3535
Celebration of cinema and television. 50 exhibition areas, offering plenty of hands-on participation, and a cast of actors to tell visitors more.

National Army Museum
Chelsea, London SW3 4HT
Tel: 071-730 0717
The history of the British army through 5 centuries from 1485, the Indian army up to independence in 1947 and colonial land forces. Battle of Waterloo exhibition.

National Maritime Museum
Romney Road, Greenwich,
London SE10 9NF
Tel: 081-858 4422
Britain's maritime heritage illustrated through actual and model ships, paintings, uniforms, navigation and astronomy instruments, archives and photographs. Queen's house.

National Postal Museum
King Edward Building, King
Edward Street, London EC1A 1LP
Tel: 071-239 5420
One of the most important and extensive collections of postage

London

stamps in the world, including
the Phillips and Berne Collections.
Temporary exhibitions.

Old Royal Observatory
Flamsteed House, Greenwich
Park, Greenwich, London SE10
Tel: 081-858 4422
*Museum of astronomy and time.
Greenwich Meridian, working
telescopes and planetarium,
timeball.*

Pollock's Toy Museum
1 Scala Street, London W1P 1LT
Tel: 071-636 3452
*Toys of all kinds – dolls, dolls'
houses, Victorian nursery, toy
theatres, teddy bears, tin toys,
folk toys worldwide.*

Royal Air Force Museum
Grahame Park Way, Hendon,
London NW9 5LL
Tel: 081-205 2266
*Three halls displaying almost
70 full-size aircraft. "Battle of
Britain Experience", flight
simulator, free film shows. Shop
and restaurant.*

Science Museum
Exhibition Road, South
Kensington, London SW7 2DD
Tel: 071-938 8000
*National Museum of Science and
Industry. Full-size replica of
Apollo II Lunar Lander, launch
pad, Wellcome Museum of the
History of Medicine, flight lab,
food for thought, optics.*

Spitting Image Rubberworks
Cubitts Yard, James Street,
Covent Garden, London
WC2E 8PA
Tel: 071-240 0838
*12-minute show with Mrs
Thatcher, the Queen, etc, in the
form of a TV-style panel game.
Extensive talk with videos about
the making of Spitting Image.*

The Story of
Telecommunications
145 Queen Victoria Street,
London EC4V 4AT

Tel: 071-248 7444
*Museum telling the story of
telecommunications with various
set-pieces and "hands on"
exhibits.*

The Theatre Museum
1E Tavistock Street, Covent
Garden, London WC2
Tel: 071-836 7891
*Five galleries include permanent
display of history of performance
in the United Kingdom.
Collection includes theatre,
ballet, dance, rock and pop
music, musical stage.*

Tower Bridge
London SE1 2UP
Tel: 071-403 3761
*Video film of raising of bridge,
museum with original steam-
powered engines and walkway
with panoramic views of London.
Exhibition on history of bridge.
Gift shop.*

Tower Hill Pageant
1 Tower Hill Terrace, London
EC3N 4EE
Tel: 071-709 0081
*Automatic vehicles transport
visitors past tableaux depicting
the history of the City and its*

port. Display of archaeological
finds. Shop and restaurant.

Victoria and Albert Museum
South Kensington, London
SW7 2RL
Tel: 071-938 8500
*Magnificent Victorian building.
Fine and decorative arts from
15th-20th C, jewellery, silver,
textiles, fashions, ceramics.*

Wimbledon Lawn
Tennis Museum
Wimbledon, London SW19
Tel: 081-946 6131
*Exhibits include Victorian
parlour, racket maker's workshop,
costumes, trophies, equipment.
Films of matches, shop.*

FIND OUT MORE

Further information about
holidays and attractions in the
London region is available from:
**London Tourist Board
and Convention Bureau**
26 Grosvenor Gardens, London
SW1W 0DU
Tel: 071-730 3488

*Little Venice is a secluded basin
of the Grand Union Canal*

London

TOURIST INFORMATION

Tourist and leisure information can be obtained from Tourist Information Centres throughout England. Details of centres and other information services in Greater London are given below. The symbol ⋈ means that an accommodation booking service is provided.

TOURIST INFORMATION CENTRES

CENTRAL LONDON

Victoria Station, Forecourt, SW1 ⋈
Easter–October, daily 0800–1900. November–Easter, Monday–Saturday 0800–1900, Sunday 0800–1600.
The information centre on the station forecourt provides a London and Britain tourist information service, offers a hotel accommodation booking service, stocks free and saleable publications on Britain and London and sells theatre tickets, tourist tickets for bus and underground and tickets for sightseeing tours.

Liverpool Street Underground Station, EC2 ⋈
Monday 0815–1900. Tuesday–Saturday 0815–1800. Sunday 0830–1645.
The information centre at the main entrance from the station to the underground provides a London and Britain information service, offers a hotel accommodation booking service, stocks free and saleable publications on Britain and London and sells theatre tickets and tour and transport tickets.

British Travel Centre ⋈
12 Regent Street, Piccadilly Circus, SW1Y 4PQ
Monday–Friday 0900–1830. Saturday–Sunday 1000–1600 (0900–1700 Saturdays May–

September).
Information on travel, accommodation, events and entertainment in England, Scotland, Wales and Ireland. Booking service for rail, air, coach and car travel, sightseeing tours, theatre tickets and accommodation. Bureau de change, bookshop and gift shop.

Bloomsbury Tourist Information Centre ⋈
35–36 Woburn Place, WC1H 0JR
Tel: 071-636 7175
Daily 0945–1900.
Information on the London area, free literature on London and England, tickets for sightseeing tours and an accommodation booking service.

Selfridges ⋈
Oxford Street, W1. Basement Services Arcade – Duke Street entrance.
Open during normal store hours, this centre supplies tourist information, leaflets, useful publications, tourist tickets for bus and underground and sightseeing tours and provides an accommodation booking service.

GREATER LONDON

Heathrow Terminals 1,2,3 Underground Station Concourse (Heathrow Airport) ⋈
Daily 0800–1800.
This centre provides tourist information on London and Britain, offers a hotel accommodation booking service, stocks free and saleable publications and sells theatre tickets.

Croydon Tourist Information Centre
Katharine Street, Croydon CR9 1ET
Tel: 081-760 5630
Monday 0930–1900. Tuesday–

Friday 0930–1800. Saturday 0900–1700.

Greenwich Tourist Information Centre ⋈
46 Greenwich Church Street, SE10 9BL
Tel: 081-858 6376
Daily 1000–1700.

Harrow Tourist Information Centre
Civic Centre, Station Road, Harrow HA1 2UJ
Tel: 081-424 1103
Monday–Friday 0900–1700.

Hillingdon Tourist Information Centre
Central Library, 14 High Street, Uxbridge UB8 1HD
Tel: Uxbridge (0895) 250706
Monday–Thursday 0930–2000. Friday 0930–1730. Saturday 0930–1600.

Hounslow Tourist Information Centre
24 The Treaty Centre, Hounslow High Street, Hounslow TW3 1ES
Tel: 081-572 8279
Monday, Wednesday 0930–1730. Tuesday, Thursday–Saturday 0930–2000.

Lewisham Tourist Information Centre
Lewisham Library, 366 Lewisham High Street, SE13 6LG
Tel: 081-690 8325
Saturday, Monday 0930–1700. Tuesday, Thursday 0930–2000. Friday 0930–1300.

Redbridge Tourist Information Centre
Town Hall, High Road, Ilford, Essex IG1 1DD
Tel: 081-478 3020
Monday–Friday 0830–1700.

Richmond Tourist Information Centre ⋈
Old Town Hall, Whittaker Avenue, Richmond upon Thames

21

TW9 1TP
Tel: 081-940 9125
Monday–Friday 1000–1800.
Saturday 1000–1700. May–
October, also Sunday 1015–
1615.

**Tower Hamlets Tourist
Information Centre**
Mayfield House, Cambridge
Heath Road, E2 9LL
Tel: 081-980 4831 ext 5313/5
Monday–Friday 0900–1700.

**Twickenham Tourist
Information Centre**
The Atrium, Civic Centre, York
Street, Twickenham, TW1 3BZ
Tel: 081-891 7272
Monday–Friday 0900–1715.

London information:
071-730 3488 (automatic
queueing system).
Monday–Friday 0900–1800.
Saturday 0900–1700.

England information:
071-824 8000.
Monday–Friday 0900–1800.
Saturday 0900–1700.

**Accommodation and tours
reservation service,
guidebook sales (credit card
holders only):**
071-824 8844.
Monday–Friday 0900–1800.
Saturday 0900–1700.

Riverboat information:
071-730 4812.

VISITORCALL

LTB's 'phone guide to London
operates 24 hours a day. To
access a full range of information
call 0839 123456.
To access specific lines dial
0839 123 followed by:
What's on this week – 400
Sunday in London – 407
Rock and pop concerts – 422

Where to take children – 424
Museums – 429
Current exhibitions – 403
Changing the Guard – 411
Theatre – 423
Historic sights – 427
Pubs and restaurants – 485
Calls cost 36p per minute cheap
rate, 48p per minute at all other
times.
To order a Visitorcall card please
call 071-971 0026. Information
for callers using push-button
telephones: 071-971 0027.

**HOTEL ACCOMMODATION
SERVICE**

The London Tourist Board and
Convention Bureau helps visitors
to find and book accommodation
at a wide range of prices in hotels
and guesthouses, including
budget accommodation,
throughout the Greater London
area. Reservations are made with
hotels which are members of LTB
denoted in this guide with the
symbol ♠ by their name.
Reservations can be made by
credit card holders via the
telephone accommodation
reservations service on 071-824
8844 by simply giving the
reservations clerk your card
details (Access or Visa) and room
requirements. LTB takes an
administrative booking fee. The
service operates Monday–Friday
0900–1800, Saturday 0900–1700.
Alternatively, LTB accepts
reservation requests by post.
Please write to the
Accommodation Services
Department at LTB's head office
at 26 Grosvenor Gardens, London
SW1W ODU stating your
requirements.
Reservations on arrival are
handled at the Tourist
Information Centres operated by
LTB at Victoria Station forecourt,
Heathrow Terminals 1,2,3
Underground Station Concourse,
Liverpool Street Station and
Selfridges. Go to any of them on
the day when you need

accommodation. A
communication charge and a
refundable deposit are payable
when making a reservation.

**WHICH PART OF
LONDON?**

The majority of tourist
accommodation is situated in the
central parts of London and is
therefore very convenient for
most of the city's attractions and
night life.
However, there are many hotels
in outer London which provide
other advantages, such as easier
parking. In the "Places to Stay"
pages which follow, you will find
accommodation listed under
INNER LONDON (covering the
E1 to W14 London postal area)
and OUTER LONDON (covering
the remainder of Greater
London). See colour maps 6 and
7 at the back of the guide.

Key to symbols

Information about many of
the services and facilities at
establishments listed in this
guide is given in the form of
symbols. The key to these
symbols is inside the back
cover flap. You may find it
helpful to keep the flap
open when referring to the
entry listings.

London index

If you are looking for accommodation in a particular establishment in London and you know its name, this index will give you the page number of the full entry in the guide.

Places to stay

Accommodation entries in this section are listed under **Inner London** (covering the E1 to W14 London Postal Area) and **Outer London** (covering the remainder of Greater London). See colour maps 6 and 7 at the back of the guide. If you want to look up a particular establishment, use the index to establishments (preceding page) to find the page number.

The symbols at the end of each accommodation entry give information about services and facilities. A 'key' to these symbols is inside the back cover flap, which can be kept open for easy reference.

INNER LONDON

See colour maps 6 & 7

LONDON E7

Grangewood Lodge Hotel ⋔
Listed
104 Clova Road, Forest Gate, London E7 9AF
☎ 081-534 0637 & 503 0941
Comfortable budget accommodation in a quiet road, pleasant garden. Easy access to central London, Docklands and M11. 12 minutes to Liverpool Street station.
Bedrooms: 9 single, 2 double, 6 twin, 3 triple
Bathrooms: 3 public, 1 private shower
Bed & breakfast

per night:	£min	£max
Single	16.00	16.00
Double	24.00	30.00

Parking for 1
Cards accepted: Access, Visa

Westbury Guest House
8 Westbury Road, Forest Gate, London E7 8BU
☎ 081-472 9848
Victorian family house with all modern amenities and close to travel facilities.
Bedrooms: 1 single, 2 twin
Bathrooms: 1 public

Bed & breakfast

per night:	£min	£max
Single	15.00	20.00
Double	30.00	40.00

Parking for 2

LONDON E11

Sans Souci House
11 Chelmsford Road, Leytonstone, London E11 1BT
☎ 081-539 1367
Fax 081-558 9189
Comfortable accommodation with all amenities, in a quiet road near Leytonstone underground station. 20 minutes from central London. Easy access to M11 and M25.
Bedrooms: 2 single, 6 twin
Bathrooms: 2 public

Bed & breakfast

per night:	£min	£max
Single	23.50	
Double	36.80	

Parking for 4
Cards accepted: Access, Visa, Amex

LONDON N1

Kandara Guest House ⋔
Listed
68 Ockendon Road, London N1 3NW
☎ 071-226 5721 & 226 3379

Small family-run guesthouse near the Angel, Islington. Free street parking and good public transport to West End and City.
Bedrooms: 4 single, 1 double, 3 triple
Bathrooms: 2 public

Bed & breakfast

per night:	£min	£max
Single	22.00	24.00
Double	29.00	35.00

LONDON N4

Costello Palace Hotel
374 Seven Sisters Road, Finsbury Park, London N4 2PG
☎ 081-802 6551
Attractive, family-run hotel opposite park and on the main road. Close to Finsbury Park and Manor House undergrounds. Convenient for all amenities. Full English breakfast.
Bedrooms: 18 single, 10 double, 8 twin, 5 triple
Bathrooms: 15 private, 6 public, 9 private showers

Bed & breakfast

per night:	£min	£max
Single	25.00	30.00
Double	35.00	45.00

Parking for 35
Cards accepted: Access, Visa

LONDON N7

Five Kings Guest House ⋔

59 Anson Road, Tufnell Park, London N7 0AR
☎ 071-607 3996 & 607 6466
Privately-run guesthouse in a quiet residential area. 15 minutes to central London. Unrestricted parking in road.
Bedrooms: 6 single, 3 double, 3 twin, 2 triple, 1 multiple
Bathrooms: 5 private, 3 public, 2 private showers

Bed & breakfast

per night:	£min	£max
Single	15.00	16.00
Double	24.00	28.00

Half board

per person:	£min	£max
Weekly	90.00	96.00

Cards accepted: Access, Visa

LONDON N11

Byron Villa
147 Bounds Green Road, New Southgate, London N11 2ED
☎ 081-888 1278
Victorian character guesthouse, 15 minutes from central London, opposite underground and near Alexandra Palace. Singles and

groups welcome. Parking space.
Bedrooms: 1 double, 1 twin, 3 multiple
Bathrooms: 2 public

Bed & breakfast

per night:	£min	£max
Single	22.00	25.00
Double	32.00	34.00

Parking for 4

LONDON N13

Mrs B Connolly
71 Berkshire Gardens,
Palmers Green, London
N13 6AA
☎ 081-888 5573
2-storey house with a garden, 5 minutes' bus ride from Wood Green Piccadilly line underground station. Car parking available.
Bedrooms: 1 single, 1 twin
Bathrooms: 1 private, 1 public

Bed & breakfast

per night:	£min	£max
Single	10.00	11.00
Double	20.00	22.00

Half board

per person:	£min	£max
Daily	13.00	14.00

Lunch available
Parking for 1

LONDON N19

Parkland Walk Guest House
Listed COMMENDED
12 Hornsey Rise Gardens,
London N19 3PR
☎ 071-263 3228
Fax 071-831 9489
Telex 262433
Friendly Victorian family house in residential area Highgate/Crouch End. Near many restaurants and convenient for central London. Non-smokers only please.
Bedrooms: 2 single, 1 twin, 1 triple
Bathrooms: 2 public

Bed & breakfast

per night:	£min	£max
Single	22.00	25.00
Double	40.00	45.00

LONDON N22

Pane Residence
154 Boundary Road, Wood
Green, London N22 6AE
☎ 081-889 3735

In a pleasant location 6 minutes' walk from Turnpike Lane underground station and near Alexandra Palace. Kitchen facilities available.
Bedrooms: 1 single, 1 double, 1 twin
Bathrooms: 1 public

Bed & breakfast

per night:	£min	£max
Single	14.00	15.00

Half board

per person:	£min	£max
Daily	20.00	22.00

Parking for 2

LONDON NW1

Somerset House Hotel ₥
6 Dorset Square, London
NW1 6QA
☎ 071-723 0741
Fax 071-723 6081
Spacious rooms with colour TV. Bridal suites available. Cooked breakfast. Located close to Baker Street station. All rooms with en-suite bathroom.
Bedrooms: 8 single, 8 double, 4 twin, 4 triple, 4 multiple
Bathrooms: 28 private

Bed & breakfast

per night:	£min	£max
Single	29.00	39.00
Double	45.00	55.00

Lunch available
Evening meal 1800 (last orders 2200)
Cards accepted: Access, Visa, Diners, Amex

LONDON NW2

Cricklewood Guest House ₥
19 Cricklewood Lane,
London NW2 1HN
☎ 081-452 1847 & 452 8667
Fax 081-450 1219
Close to fast train, bus and underground services to West End and City, and approximately 3 minutes from beginning of M1.
Bedrooms: 1 double, 1 twin, 3 triple, 1 multiple
Bathrooms: 4 public, 5 private showers

Bed & breakfast

per night:	£min	£max
Single	25.00	30.00
Double	38.00	43.00

Half board

per person:	£min	£max
Daily	26.00	28.50
Weekly	164.00	180.00

LONDON NW3

The Langorf Hotel ₥
😊😊 COMMENDED
20 Frognal, Hampstead,
London NW3 6AG
☎ 071-794 4483
Fax 071-435 9055
Three minutes' walk from Finchley Road underground, this elegant Edwardian residence in Hampstead boasts attractive bedrooms with full facilities. BTA Spencer Award 1992 runners-up.
Bedrooms: 1 single, 22 double, 8 twin
Bathrooms: 30 private

Bed & breakfast

per night:	£min	£max
Single	40.00	61.00
Double	50.00	83.00

Lunch available
Evening meal 1800 (last orders 2300)
Parking for 5
Cards accepted: Access, Visa, Diners, Amex

LONDON NW4

Rilux House ₥
😊😊
1 Lodge Road, London
NW4 4DD
☎ 081-203 0933
Fax 081-203 6446
High standard establishment for 2-3 people, with own shower, WC, kitchen, tea facilities and video. Separate entry and garden. Few minutes' walk from Hendon Central underground and buses.
Bedrooms: 1 double
Bathrooms: 1 private, 1 private shower

Bed & breakfast

per night:	£min	£max
Single	25.00	30.00
Double	45.00	55.00

Parking for 1

The enquiry coupons at the back will help you when contacting proprietors.

LONDON NW6

Charlotte Guest House & Restaurant ₥
221 West End Lane, West
Hampstead, London
NW6 1XJ
☎ 071-794 6476
Fax 071-431 3584
Rooms with private facilities. Restaurant and coffee lounge. French and German spoken. Direct trains to Gatwick, Luton and City Airports. Free London Travel Card for a week's stay.
Bedrooms: 12 single, 12 double, 12 twin, 2 triple
Bathrooms: 19 private, 6 public

Bed & breakfast

per night:	£min	£max
Single	16.00	30.00
Double	25.00	40.00

Lunch available
Evening meal 1800 (last orders 2200)

Mrs M Herbert
88 Charteris Road, Kilburn,
London NW6 7EX
☎ 071-328 0584
Modernised Victorian terraced house with off-street parking. On bus route to Oxford Street.
Bedrooms: 2 double, 1 triple
Bathrooms: 1 public

Bed & breakfast

per night:	£min	£max
Single	15.00	15.00
Double	30.00	30.00

LONDON NW10

J and T Guest House
98 Park Ave North,
Willesden Green, London
NW10 1JY
☎ 081-452 4085
Fax 081-450 2503
Small guesthouse in north west London close to underground. Easy access to Wembley Stadium complex. 5 minutes from M1.
Bedrooms: 1 single, 1 twin, 1 triple
Bathrooms: 2 private, 2 public

Bed & breakfast

per night:	£min	£max
Single	17.00	25.00
Double	32.00	38.00

Parking for 2
Cards accepted: Access, Visa

LONDON SE3

"Anand" (Happiness)
2 Hardy Road, Blackheath,
London SE3 7NR
☎ 081-305 0120 & 305
2203
*Detached Edwardian house in
peaceful surroundings.
Greenwich Park and
Blackheath within walking
distance. 16 minutes train to
Charing Cross and Victoria.
Station 2 minutes' walking
distance.*
Bedrooms: 4 double, 3 twin,
2 triple
Bathrooms: 3 public

Bed & breakfast

per night:	£min	£max
Single	15.00	
Double	30.00	

Half board

per person:	£min	£max
Daily	21.00	

Evening meal from 1930
Parking for 12

Frank & Sylvia's Guest House
143 Shooters Hill Road,
Blackheath, London
SE3 8UQ
☎ 081-853 3216
*Large Victorian house, with
spacious rooms, recently
renovated and redecorated.
Warm reception guaranteed.
Close to Greenwich with easy
access to central London.*
Bedrooms: 1 double, 3 twin,
4 triple, 4 multiple
Bathrooms: 2 public

Bed & breakfast

per night:	£min	£max
Single	20.00	20.00
Double	34.00	34.00

Parking for 1

LONDON SE6

Mrs Freda Ward
Listed
41 Minard Road, Catford,
London SE6 1NP
☎ 081-697 2596
*English home in quiet
residential area off A205
South Circular road. 10
minutes' walk to Hither Green
station for 20 minute journey
to central London.*
Bedrooms: 1 single, 2 twin
Bathrooms: 1 public

Bed & breakfast

per night:	£min	£max
Single	17.00	
Double	34.00	

Evening meal 1700 (last
orders 2000)

Mr and Mrs J H Broughton
31 & 33 Ringstead Road,
Catford, London SE6 2BU
☎ 081-461 0146 & 698
0010
*Convenient for Crystal Palace
(10 minutes by car) and 20
minutes by train to central
London. Greenwich 10
minutes away. Sky TV and
video channel in each
bedroom.*
Bedrooms: 1 single, 3 twin,
1 triple
Bathrooms: 2 private,
2 public, 2 private showers

Bed & breakfast

per night:	£min	£max
Single	20.00	25.00
Double	30.00	35.00

LONDON SE9

Meadow Croft Lodge M
APPROVED
96-98 Southwood Road, New
Eltham, London SE9 3QS
☎ 081-859 1488
*Between A2 and A20, near
New Eltham station with easy
access to London. Warm and
friendly atmosphere. TV in
rooms. British Tourist
Authority London B&B award
1990.*
Bedrooms: 4 single,
3 double, 9 twin, 1 multiple
Bathrooms: 1 private,
4 public, 9 private showers

Bed & breakfast

per night:	£min	£max
Single	20.00	27.00
Double	38.00	42.00

Parking for 9
Cards accepted: Access, Visa

LONDON SE12

Kingsland House
45 Southbrook Road, Lee,
London SE12 8LJ
☎ 081-318 4788
*Detached house in
conservation area, close to
Blackheath and Greenwich
and with easy access to City
and West End. Homely
atmosphere. Cooked breakfast
when required.*
Bedrooms: 2 single, 2 twin
Bathrooms: 1 public

Bed & breakfast

per night:	£min	£max
Single	12.00	14.00
Double	26.00	26.00

LONDON SE21

Diana Hotel
88 Thurlow Park Road,
London SE21 8HY
☎ 081-670 3250
*Small, friendly, family-run
hotel in a pleasant suburb of
Dulwich, 10 minutes from
central London.*
Bedrooms: 2 single,
4 double, 3 twin, 3 triple
Bathrooms: 2 private,
2 public, 2 private showers

Bed & breakfast

per night:	£min	£max
Single	28.00	38.00
Double	40.00	45.00

Evening meal 1800 (last
orders 1930)
Parking for 3

LONDON SE22

Bedknobs
Listed COMMENDED
58 Glengarry Road, East
Dulwich, London SE22 8QD
☎ 081-299 2004
*Victorian family-run house,
carefully restored, providing
modern-day comforts and a
friendly service.*
Bedrooms: 1 single,
1 double, 1 twin, 1 triple
Bathrooms: 2 public

Bed & breakfast

per night:	£min	£max
Single	19.00	25.00
Double	34.00	40.00

LONDON SE26

Be My Guest
79 Venner Road, Sydenham,
London SE26 5HU
☎ 081-659 5413
Fax: 081-776 8151
*Spacious Victorian residence,
15 minutes to central London
from nearby stations. Free
travel in London with
reservations of 3 days or
more. Car and driver service
by arrangement.*
Bedrooms: 1 twin, 2 multiple
Bathrooms: 3 private

LONDON SE21

Bed & breakfast

per night:	£min	£max
Single	35.00	46.00
Double	46.00	54.00

Half board

per person:	£min	£max
Daily	35.00	58.00
Weekly	245.00	406.00

Evening meal 1900 (last
orders 2000)
Parking for 2
Cards accepted: Access, Visa,
Switch

LONDON SW1

Alexander Hotel
13 Belgrave Road, Victoria,
London SW1V 1RB
☎ 071-834 9738
*Family run hotel 5 minutes'
walk from Victoria rail, coach
and air terminal stations.*
Bedrooms: 1 single,
7 double, 2 twin, 2 triple,
1 multiple
Bathrooms: 13 private

Bed & breakfast

per night:	£min	£max
Single	25.00	40.00
Double	35.00	50.00

Cards accepted: Access, Visa

Alexander House Hotel
Listed APPROVED
32 Hugh Street, London
SW1 1RT
☎ 071-834 5320
*Guesthouse with TV in
bedrooms. Full English
breakfast.*
Bedrooms: 2 single,
3 double, 2 twin, 2 triple
Bathrooms: 2 public

Bed & breakfast

per night:	£min	£max
Single	20.00	25.00
Double	28.00	35.00

Caswell Hotel
25 Gloucester Street,
London SW1V 2DB
☎ 071-834 6345
*Pleasant, family-run hotel,
near Victoria coach and rail
stations, yet in a quiet
location.*
Bedrooms: 1 single,
6 double, 6 twin, 3 triple,
2 multiple
Bathrooms: 7 private,
5 public

Bed & breakfast

per night:	£min	£max
Single	27.00	34.00
Double	38.00	62.00

🔶🖃🏠🖐️🕯️🔲⛽📶🚗✖️🚲

Colliers Hotel ⋀⋀
97 Warwick Way, London
SW1V 1QL
☎ 071-834 6931 & 828
0210
Fax 071-834 8439
Telex 24699 KISMET G
*A modern style family hotel
with spacious rooms.*
Bedrooms: 4 single,
6 double, 5 twin, 4 triple
Bathrooms: 1 private,
3 public, 7 private showers

Bed & breakfast

per night:	£min	£max
Single	18.00	28.00
Double	28.00	36.00

Cards accepted: Access, Visa,
Diners, Amex

🔶4🖃🔲🏠📺✖️🚲🐾DAP

Corona Hotel ⋀⋀
♛♛
87-89 Belgrave Road,
Victoria, London SW1V 2BQ
☎ 071-828 9279
Fax 071-931 8576
*Small in stature, but big on
hospitality, Corona offers a
uniquely friendly atmosphere
which has endeared it to
hundreds who regularly stay
here.*
Bedrooms: 8 single,
14 double, 9 twin, 2 triple,
2 multiple
Bathrooms: 29 private,
2 public, 2 private showers

Bed & breakfast

per night:	£min	£max
Single	32.00	46.00
Double	48.00	62.00

Cards accepted: Access, Visa,
Diners, Amex, Switch

🔶🔹🖃🏠🔲📺◐
🗒️🔲✖️DAP🐾SP🅣

Ebury House Hotel ⋀⋀
102 Ebury Street, London
SW1W 9QD
☎ 071-730 1350 & 730
1105
*Close to Buckingham Palace
and the West End. Victoria
train and coach stations
nearby.*
Bedrooms: 3 single,
4 double, 3 twin, 2 triple
Bathrooms: 3 public

Bed & breakfast

per night:	£min	£max
Single	30.00	38.00
Double	40.00	48.00

Cards accepted: Access, Visa
🔶🔹🖃🏠🔲✖️🚲

Edward House Hotel
5 St. George's Drive, London
SW1V 4DP
☎ 071-834 5207 & 828
8456
Fax 071-976 5428
*Near the National Express
coach station, 2 minutes from
Victoria underground and
mainline station. All rooms
have full central heating, TV,
tea-making facilities and
direct-dial telephone.*
Bedrooms: 2 single,
6 double, 3 twin, 9 triple
Bathrooms: 6 private,
3 public, 10 private showers

Bed & breakfast

per night:	£min	£max
Single	20.00	30.00
Double	30.00	45.00

Cards accepted: Access, Visa,
Amex

🔶🔹🏠🔲🕯️🔲◐🔲🗒️
✖️DAP🐾SP🅣

Elizabeth Hotel ⋀⋀
♛
37 Eccleston Square,
London SW1V 1PB
☎ 071-828 6812
*Friendly, quiet hotel
overlooking lovely gardens of
stately residential square
(circa 1835), close to*

*Belgravia and within 5
minutes' walk of Victoria.*
Bedrooms: 10 single,
12 double, 6 twin, 4 triple,
9 multiple
Bathrooms: 24 private,
6 public, 5 private showers

Bed & breakfast

per night:	£min	£max
Single	35.00	55.00
Double	55.00	77.00

🔶🔹🖃🔲✂️🔲📺🔹🔲🏠
🗒️🔆❄️🔲DAP🏮🅣

Ad Display advertisement
appears on this page

Georgian House
Hotel ⋀⋀
♛♛♛
35 St. George's Drive,
London SW1V 4DG
☎ 071-834 1438
Fax 071-976 6085
*Run by the direct descendants
of the master builder who
built the hotel in 1851. All
facilities and extensive
breakfast.*
Bedrooms: 8 single,
14 double, 5 twin, 5 triple,
2 multiple
Bathrooms: 23 private,
3 public, 5 private showers

Bed & breakfast

per night:	£min	£max
Single	15.00	29.50
Double	29.00	44.50

Cards accepted: Access, Visa
🔶🔹🔲🏠🔹🔲🔲S🔲🔲,
🔲✖️DAP🐾SP🏮🅣

Holly House Hotel ⋀⋀
Listed
20 Hugh Street, Victoria,
London SW1V 1RP
☎ 071-834 5671
Fax 071-834 5671
*Small private bed and
breakfast establishment with
colour TV and tea/coffee
facilities in rooms. In the
heart of London, 2 minutes
from Victoria station.*

Bedrooms: 7 single,
6 double, 8 twin, 5 triple
Bathrooms: 1 private,
5 public

Bed & breakfast

per night:	£min	£max
Single	22.00	25.00
Double	32.00	35.00

Cards accepted: Access, Visa,
Diners, Amex
🔶🔹🔲🔲🔲🔲✖️🔲DAP🐾SP

Huttons Hotel ⋀⋀
55 Belgrave Road, London
SW1V 2BB
☎ 071-834 3726
*5 minutes' walk from Victoria
and central London.*
Bedrooms: 5 single,
11 double, 27 twin, 8 triple,
2 multiple
Bathrooms: 26 private,
10 public

Bed & breakfast

per night:	£min	£max
Single	33.00	
Double	41.00	

Cards accepted: Access, Visa,
C.Bl, Diners, Amex
🔶🔹🔹🖃🔲🔲📺◐🔲,
✖️DAP🐾🅂SP

Kirness Hotel
29 Belgrave Road, Victoria,
London SW1V 1RB
☎ 071-834 0030
*Small friendly guesthouse. All
main European languages
spoken. Suitable for students.*
Bedrooms: 4 single, 2 double
Bathrooms: 6 private,
1 public

Bed & breakfast

per night:	£min	£max
Single	20.00	25.00
Double	28.00	35.00

🔶7🔲🔲🔲✖️🚲🐾SP

Marne Hotel
34 Belgrave Road, Victoria,
London SW1V 1RG
☎ 071-834 5195

Continued ▶

LONDON SW1

Continued

Family-run hotel close to Victoria station. Rooms with private shower, toilet and colour television. Japanese and French spoken.
Bedrooms: 3 single, 6 double, 3 twin
Bathrooms: 4 private, 2 public

Bed & breakfast

per night:	£min	£max
Single	20.00	35.00
Double	28.00	45.00

さ占口山内CV◎Ⅲ.ㅁメ

Sidney Hotel M
76 Belgrave Road, London SW1V 4LU
☎ 071-834 2738 & 834 2860
Fax 071-630 0973
Friendly establishment, a few minutes' walk from Victoria rail and coach stations.
Bedrooms: 10 single, 15 double, 7 twin, 5 triple, 3 multiple
Bathrooms: 26 private, 3 public, 7 private showers

Bed & breakfast

per night:	£min	£max
Single	32.00	46.00
Double	48.00	62.00

Cards accepted: Access, Visa, Diners, Amex, Switch
さ占し℡口↓凵内CV◎Ⅲ.ㅁメ DAP ▧ SP T

Simone House Hotel M
Listed
49 Belgrave Road, London SW1V 2BB
☎ 071-828 2474
Near Victoria station and within easy walking distance of numerous sightseeing attractions.
Bedrooms: 2 single, 5 double, 8 twin, 3 triple
Bathrooms: 8 private, 2 public

Bed & breakfast

per night:	£min	£max
Single	18.00	22.00
Double	28.00	44.00

さ占山内CVⅢ.ㅁメ

Stanley House Hotel M
👑👑
19-21 Belgrave Road, London SW1V 1RB
☎ 071-834 5042 & 834 7292
Fax 071-834 8439
Telex 24699 KISMET G

Modern-style family hotel with spacious rooms, all with intercom and radio. Telex available.
Bedrooms: 1 single, 6 double, 13 twin, 11 triple
Bathrooms: 20 private, 4 public

Bed & breakfast

per night:	£min	£max
Single	20.00	30.00
Double	30.00	40.00

Lunch available
Cards accepted: Access, Visa, C.Bl, Diners, Amex
さ占口🄯◫S内CV◎Ⅲ.
メ DAP ▧ SP

Windermere Hotel M
👑👑👑 COMMENDED
142-144 Warwick Way, Victoria, London SW1V 4JE
☎ 071-834 5163 & 834 5480
Fax 071-630 8831
Telex 94017182 WIREG
Winner of "Certificate of Distinction" in the British Tourist Authority's London B and B Awards 1991. A friendly, charming hotel with nicely equipped bedrooms.
Bedrooms: 3 single, 11 double, 5 twin, 1 triple, 3 multiple
Bathrooms: 19 private, 2 public

Bed & breakfast

per night:	£min	£max
Single	38.00	52.00
Double	48.00	71.00

Lunch available
Evening meal 1800 (last orders 2100)
Cards accepted: Access, Visa, Amex
さ占し口🄯◫✕内CV◎Ⅲ.
ㅁメ DAP ▧ SP

LONDON SW3

Uptown Reservations
50 Christchurch Street, Chelsea, London SW3 4AR
☎ 071-351 3445
Fax 071-351 9383
Charming central London bed and breakfast. Selection of other rooms, all with private bathroom and Continental breakfast, in Chelsea, Knightsbridge, Kensington, Belgravia and Little Venice.
Bedrooms: 2 double, 2 twin
Bathrooms: 4 private

Bed & breakfast

per night:	£min	£max
Single	31.50	31.50
Double	62.50	62.50

さ◫↓凵S✕CVⅢ.ㅁ
❋ 🛏 ▧ 🏛

LONDON SW5

Lord Jim Hotel
23-25 Penywern Road, London SW5 9TT
☎ 071-370 6071
Fax 071-373 8919
Telex 27700
A budget priced, well-serviced bed and breakfast, ideally situated for Earl's Court and Olympia Exhibition Halls. Convenient for museums, city and a direct link to Heathrow Airport and Gatwick Airport (via Victoria).
Bedrooms: 8 single, 14 double, 5 triple
Bathrooms: 1 private, 7 public, 7 private showers

Bed & breakfast

per night:	£min	£max
Single	15.00	20.00
Double	24.00	30.00

Cards accepted: Access, Visa, C.Bl, Diners, Amex
さ占◫山S内CV◎◫
Ⅲ.ㅁ

Manor Hotel M
23 Nevern Place, London SW5 9NR
☎ 071-370 6018 & 370 4164
Fax 071-244 6610
Telex 949631 DELTA
Centrally located, a few minutes' walk from Earl's Court underground station. Pleasant atmosphere. Easy access to Heathrow via M4.
Bedrooms: 6 single, 10 double, 8 twin, 3 triple
Bathrooms: 13 private, 4 public, 2 private showers

Bed & breakfast

per night:	£min	£max
Single	19.00	26.00
Double	28.00	36.00

さ占◫口山内CV◎Ⅲ.ㅁ
DAP ▧ SP

Merlyn Court Hotel M
👑👑
2 Barkston Gardens, London SW5 0EN
☎ 071-370 1640
Fax 071-244 8024
Well-established, family-run, good value hotel in quiet Edwardian square, close to Earl's Court and Olympia, with direct underground link to Heathrow, the West End and rail stations.
Bedrooms: 4 single, 4 double, 4 twin, 2 triple, 3 multiple
Bathrooms: 10 private, 6 public, 1 private shower

Bed & breakfast

per night: £min £max

Bed & breakfast

per night:	£min	£max
Single	20.00	30.00
Double	35.00	55.00

Cards accepted: Access, Visa
さ占し口山🄯内CVⅢ.ㅁ
DAP ▧ SP T

Rushmore Hotel M
11 Trebovir Road, London SW5 9LS
☎ 071-370 3839 & 370 6505
Telex 297761 ref. 1933
Each room stylishly and individually themed, making the hotel unique in its category. All rooms have cable colour TV and direct-dial telephone. Within a minute's walk of both Earl's Court underground station and exhibition centre.
Bedrooms: 1 single, 10 double, 6 twin, 2 triple, 3 multiple
Bathrooms: 22 private

Bed & breakfast

per night:	£min	£max
Single	39.00	42.00
Double	49.00	52.00

Parking for 5
Cards accepted: Access, Visa, Diners, Amex
さ占し口↓凵山✕CV
◎Ⅲ.ㅁ▧ SP T

Sara Hotel
15 Eardley Crescent, London SW5 9JS
☎ 071-244 9500 & 373 3708
Fax 071-244 9500
Modern family-run hotel with facilities including en-suite bedrooms (shower and toilet), colour TV and alarm clock. Personally supervised by owner. Two minutes' walk from Earl's Court underground station. Telephone and fax facilities available.
Bedrooms: 5 single, 3 double, 2 twin, 3 triple
Bathrooms: 4 private, 3 public, 8 private showers

Bed & breakfast

per night:	£min	£max
Single	16.00	23.50
Double	24.00	34.95

Cards accepted: Access, Visa, Diners, Amex
さ3口山内CV◎Ⅲ.メ DAP
▧ SP

Swiss House Hotel M
171 Old Brompton Road, London SW5 0AN
☎ 071-373 2769 & 373 9383
Fax 071-373 4983
Very clean, comfortable and conveniently situated hotel

near London museums, shopping/exhibition centres. Gloucester Road underground station is within easy walking distance. Recent winner of BTA award for best value B&B in London.
Bedrooms: 2 single, 6 double, 2 twin, 6 triple
Bathrooms: 11 private, 1 public

Bed & breakfast

per night:	£min	£max
Single	32.00	45.00
Double	48.00	58.00

Cards accepted: Access, Visa, C.Bl, Diners, Amex

Windsor House M

Listed

12 Penywern Road, London SW5 9ST
☎ 071-373 9087
Fax 081-960 7273
Budget-priced bed and breakfast establishment in Earl's Court. Easily reached from airports and motorway. The West End is minutes away by underground.
Bedrooms: 2 single, 5 double, 3 twin, 1 triple, 4 multiple
Bathrooms: 1 private, 5 public, 11 private showers

Bed & breakfast

per night:	£min	£max
Single	18.00	30.00
Double	26.00	40.00

Parking for 10
Cards accepted: Access, Visa, C.Bl, Diners, Amex

York House Hotel M

28 Philbeach Gardens, London SW5 9EA
☎ 071-373 7519 & 373 7579
Fax 071-370 4641
Bed and breakfast hotel, conveniently located close to the Earl's Court and Olympia Exhibition Centres and the West End.
Bedrooms: 20 single, 9 double, 3 twin, 6 triple
Bathrooms: 1 private, 9 public

Bed & breakfast

per night:	£min	£max
Single	25.00	26.00
Double	39.00	40.00

Cards accepted: Access, Visa, Amex

LONDON SW7

Abcone Hotel M

APPROVED

10 Ashburn Gardens, London SW7 4DG
☎ 071-370 3383
Fax 071-373 3082
Telex 926054 ABCONE G
Close to Gloucester Road underground and convenient for High Street Kensington, Knightsbridge, Olympia, Earl's Court, museums and Hyde Park.
Bedrooms: 16 single, 16 double, 3 twin
Bathrooms: 26 private, 3 public

Bed & breakfast

per night:	£min	£max
Single	35.00	69.00
Double	48.00	85.00

Cards accepted: Access, Visa, Diners, Amex

Five Sumner Place Hotel M

HIGHLY COMMENDED

5 Sumner Place, South Kensington, London SW7 3EE
☎ 071-584 7586
Fax 071-823 9962
Awarded the best bed and breakfast in London. Situated in South Kensington, the most fashionable area. This family owned and run hotel offers first-class service and personal attention.
Bedrooms: 3 single, 6 double, 4 twin
Bathrooms: 13 private

Bed & breakfast

per night:	£min	£max
Single	55.00	62.00
Double	70.00	84.00

Cards accepted: Access, Visa, Amex

More House M

53 Cromwell Road, South Kensington, London SW7 2EH
☎ 071-584 2040 & 584 2039
Large Victorian building in Kensington, close to museums and within walking distance of Hyde Park. Available July and August, only.
Bedrooms: 28 single, 20 twin
Bathrooms: 15 public

Bed & breakfast

per night:	£min	£max
Single	20.00	22.00
Double	35.00	38.00

Open July-August

Hotel Number Sixteen M

HIGHLY COMMENDED

16 Sumner Place, London SW7 3EG
☎ 071-589 5232
Fax 071-584 8615
Telex 266638
With atmosphere of a comfortable town house in very attractive street. Secluded award-winning gardens.
Bedrooms: 9 single, 27 double, 27 twin, 3 triple
Bathrooms: 61 private, 1 private shower

Bed & breakfast

per night:	£min	£max
Single	55.00	95.00
Double	85.00	155.00

Cards accepted: Access, Visa, Diners, Amex

LONDON SW13

Mr Paul Northcott

22 Verdun Road, Barnes, London SW13 9AY
☎ 081-741 3392
Georgian-style house in beautiful residential area of village. 2 minutes' walk from River Thames, with pubs and restaurants. 20 minutes from Heathrow and City by underground or BR. En-suite facilities.
Bedrooms: 1 single, 1 twin, 1 triple
Bathrooms: 1 private, 1 public

Bed & breakfast

per night:	£min	£max
Single	15.00	18.00
Double	30.00	36.00

Parking for 3

LONDON SW14

The Plough Inn

APPROVED

42 Christchurch Road, East Sheen, London SW14 7AF
☎ 081-876 7833
A delightful old pub, established 1733. Next to Richmond Park. En-suite accommodation, traditional ales, home-cooked food.
Bedrooms: 7 double
Bathrooms: 7 private

Bed & breakfast

per night:	£min	£max
Single	45.00	48.00
Double	55.00	60.00

Half board

per person:	£min	£max
Daily	50.00	55.00

Lunch available
Evening meal 1930 (last orders 2130)
Parking for 6
Cards accepted: Access, Visa

LONDON SW15

Alnwick

Listed

27 Roehampton Lane, Putney, London SW15 5LS
☎ 081-878 9449
Homely accommodation close to Richmond Park. Central London easily accessible by bus and train.
Bedrooms: 1 single, 1 triple
Bathrooms: 1 private, 1 public

Bed & breakfast

per night:	£min	£max
Single	16.00	18.00
Double	32.00	36.00

Parking for 1

LONDON SW17

Mrs L Catterall

12 Avarn Road, Tooting, London SW17 9HA
☎ 081-767 0584
Family home 8 minutes from Tooting Broadway underground station, 10 minutes from British Rail and 1 minute from buses. Refrigerator in all rooms.
Bedrooms: 1 single, 1 twin, 1 triple
Bathrooms: 1 public

Bed & breakfast

per night:	£min	£max
Single		15.00
Double		30.00

LONDON W1

Astor Court Hotel

20 Hallam Street, London W1N 5LF
☎ 071-636 4133
Telex 268345 ASTOR G
Tourist hotel 5 minutes from Oxford Circus and close to Harley Street and major hospitals.
Bedrooms: 4 single, 34 twin, 7 triple
Bathrooms: 45 private

Continued ▶

LONDON W1

Continued

Bed & breakfast

per night:	£min	£max
Single	60.00	81.50
Double	88.50	95.00

Cards accepted: Access, Visa, Diners, Amex

Bentinck House Hotel ⋒

20 Bentinck Street, London W1M 5RL
☎ 071-935 9141
Fax 071-224 5903
Telex 8954111
Family-run bed and breakfast hotel in the heart of London's fashionable West End, close to Bond Street underground and Oxford Street.
Bedrooms: 8 single, 3 double, 5 twin, 3 triple, 1 multiple
Bathrooms: 18 private, 4 public

Bed & breakfast

per night:	£min	£max
Single	37.00	52.00
Double	59.00	69.00

Half board

per person:	£min	£max
Daily	47.00	62.00
Weekly	260.00	360.00

Evening meal 1800 (last orders 2200)
Cards accepted: Access, Visa, C.Bl, Diners, Amex

Lincoln House Hotel ⋒

COMMENDED

33 Gloucester Place, London W1H 3PD
☎ 071-486 7630
Fax 071-486 0166
Newly refurbished Georgian hotel in heart of West End close to Oxford Street shops, theatres, etc. Ideal location for holiday or business trips. Well-appointed accommodation at economy rates.
Bedrooms: 4 single, 9 double, 5 twin, 4 triple
Bathrooms: 17 private, 1 public

Bed & breakfast

per night:	£min	£max
Single	35.00	45.00
Double	49.00	59.00

Cards accepted: Access, Visa, Diners, Amex, Switch

Wyndham Hotel

Listed

30 Wyndham Street, London W1H 1DD
☎ 071-723 7204 & 723 9400
Small family-run bed and breakfast close to Baker Street and Marylebone stations. Well within walking distance of Oxford Street.
Bedrooms: 6 single, 2 double, 3 twin
Bathrooms: 1 public, 10 private showers

Bed & breakfast

per night:	£min	£max
Single	26.00	28.00
Double	37.00	38.00

LONDON W2

Abbey Court Hotel ⋒

Listed

174 Sussex Gardens, London W2 1TP
☎ 071-402 0704
Fax 071-224 9114
Central London hotel, reasonable prices. Within walking distance of Lancaster Gate, Paddington station and Hyde Park.
Bedrooms: 4 single, 7 double, 3 twin, 10 triple, 2 multiple
Bathrooms: 10 private, 6 public, 6 private showers

Bed & breakfast

per night:	£min	£max
Single	18.00	
Double	26.00	

Parking for 12
Cards accepted: Access, Visa, C.Bl, Amex

Ad Display advertisement appears on page 31

Allandale Hotel

3 Devonshire Terrace, Lancaster Gate, London W2 3DN
☎ 071-723 8311 & 723 7807
Small, select, well-cared for family hotel, close to Hyde Park, West End and Lancaster Gate and Paddington stations. English breakfast.
Bedrooms: 1 single, 11 double, 4 twin, 4 triple, 2 multiple
Bathrooms: 21 private, 1 public

Bed & breakfast

per night:	£min	£max
Single	30.00	36.90
Double	35.00	45.00

Half board

per person:	£min	£max
Weekly	200.00	245.00

Cards accepted: Access, Visa, Diners

Barry House Hotel ⋒

APPROVED

12 Sussex Place, London W2 2TP
☎ 071-723 7340 & 723 0994
Fax 071-723 9775
Family-run bed and breakfast hotel, 4 minutes' walking distance from Paddington station. Hyde Park, Marble Arch and Oxford Street close by.
Bedrooms: 3 single, 2 double, 9 twin, 4 triple
Bathrooms: 14 private, 2 public

Bed & breakfast

per night:	£min	£max
Single	25.00	30.00
Double	44.00	54.00

Cards accepted: Access, Visa, Diners, Amex

Beverley House Hotel ⋒

142 Sussex Gardens, London W2 1UB
☎ 071-723 3380
Fax 071-402 3292
Opened in July 1990, a bed and breakfast hotel offering high standards at low prices. Close to Paddington station, Hyde Park and museums.
Bedrooms: 6 single, 5 double, 6 twin, 6 triple
Bathrooms: 23 private

Bed & breakfast

per night:	£min	£max
Single	35.00	45.00
Double	40.00	57.00

Evening meal 1800 (last orders 2200)
Parking for 2
Cards accepted: Access, Visa, C.Bl, Diners, Amex, Switch

Cambria House Hotel

139 Sussex Gardens, Hyde Park, London W2 2RX
☎ 071-723 5677 & 724 9346
Friendly hotel with comfortable, well-appointed rooms, each with colour TV. Ideal West End location, offering high standards and good value.
Bedrooms: 3 single, 6 double, 2 twin, 8 triple
Bathrooms: 1 private, 2 public

Bed & breakfast

per night:	£min	£max
Single	18.00	20.00
Double	27.00	30.00

Parking for 3
Cards accepted: Access, Visa, Diners

Camelot Hotel ⋒

COMMENDED

45-47 Norfolk Square, Paddington, London W2 1RX
☎ 071-262 1980 & 723 9118
Fax 071-402 3412
Telex 268312 WESCOM G CENTRAL
Beautifully restored 19th C town house "Bed and Breakfast" hotel offering charming, stylish accommodation in central London.
Bedrooms: 14 single, 11 double, 12 twin, 1 triple, 6 multiple
Bathrooms: 36 private, 1 public, 4 private showers

Bed & breakfast

per night:	£min	£max
Single	40.25	55.00
Double	77.00	77.00

Cards accepted: Access, Visa, Switch

Dylan Hotel ⋒

14 Devonshire Terrace, Lancaster Gate, London W2 3DW
☎ 071-723 3280
Fax 071-402 2443
Small hotel in central location. 4 minutes from Paddington and Lancaster Gate underground stations. Marble Arch, Hyde Park and Oxford Street close by. Not just a hotel, a home from home.
Bedrooms: 3 single, 4 double, 7 twin, 3 triple
Bathrooms: 7 private, 3 public, 4 private showers

Bed & breakfast

per night:	£min	£max
Single	25.00	30.00
Double	38.00	50.00

ACCOMMODATION

Central London   *Budget Prices*

WESTPOINT HOTEL
**170 Sussex Gardens, Hyde Park, London W2 1PT.
Tel: 071-402 0281 (Reservations) Fax: 071-224 9114.**

**Most rooms with private shower & toilet, radio/intercom
& colour TV. Children welcome. TV lounge.**

This hotel has long been a popular choice amongst tourists because of its central location,
being near to Hyde Park and only 2 minutes from Paddington and Lancaster Gate tube stations.
The West End's tourist attractions, including theatres, museums and Oxford Street stores,
are within easy reach. Individuals, families and groups are all welcome.

• PRIVATE CAR PARK • DIRECT A2 BUS FROM HEATHROW •

RATES: *Low Season*
Singles from £18 per person.
Doubles from £13 per person.
Family rooms from £11 per person.

High Season
Singles from £24 per person.
Doubles from £14 per person
Family Rooms from £11 per person.

ABBEY COURT HOTEL
**174 Sussex Gardens, Hyde Park, London W2 1TP.
Tel: 071-402 0704 Fax: 071-224 9114.**

*Open all year. Radio Intercom in every room. Children welcome.
Most rooms with private shower, toilet and colour TV.*

• CAR PARKING AVAILABLE • A2 BUS FROM HEATHROW •

Central London hotel in a pleasant avenue near Hyde Park and within 2 minutes' walking distance
of Paddington main line and tube station and Lancaster Gate tube station. The tourist attractions
of the West End including theatres, museums and Oxford Street are within easy reach. Individuals,
families, school parties and groups are all welcome and group tours can be arranged.

TERMS per person:
High season: Single from £28.00, double from £16.00 p.p., family £12.00 p.p.
Low season: Single from £20.00, double from £14.50 p.p., family from £12.00 p.p.

Special Prices
SASS HOUSE HOTEL
*11 Craven Terrace, Hyde Park, London W2 3QD.
Tel: 071-262 2325 Fax: 071-224 9114.*
★ Centrally located – within easy reach of London's most famous tourist attractions.
★ Nearest underground Paddington and Lancaster Gate. ★ Served by a network of bus routes.
★ Colour television lounge. ★ Centrally heated. ★ Radio and intercom in all rooms.
★ Special group and party booking rates. ★ Parking facilities available.
★ A2 bus from Heathrow.
**RATES per person: single room from £16.00. Double room from £11.00 p.p.
and family room or party booking rate from £10.00 p.p. inc. bed & breakfast.**

LONDON W2

Continued

Cards accepted: Access, Visa, Amex

Ⓢ♨⛁☐♿ⓊⓁⓈ♀ⓉⓋ◐ 🛏,☎✕🚭♨ⓈⒻⓉ

Hyde Park Rooms ⋒
137 Sussex Gardens, Hyde Park, London W2 2RX
☎ 071-723 0225 & 723 0965
Small centrally located private hotel with personal service. Within walking distance of Hyde Park and Kensington Gardens. Car parking available.
Bedrooms: 6 single,
10 double, 4 twin, 2 triple,
1 multiple
Bathrooms: 8 private,
3 public
Bed & breakfast

per night:	£min	£max
Single	20.00	24.00
Double	30.00	36.00

Parking for 3
Cards accepted: Access, Visa, C.Bl, Diners, Amex
Ⓢ♨☐♿◐🛏,♨◐Ⓤ ✕ⒹⒶⓅⓈ♿Ⓣ

Kings Arms
254 Edgware Road, Paddington, London W2 1DS
☎ 071-262 8441
Conveniently located for public transport and West End shopping. Recently decorated and furnished to a comfortable standard.
Bedrooms: 3 single,
2 double, 5 twin
Bathrooms: 3 private,
3 public
Bed & breakfast

per night:	£min	£max
Single	15.00	20.00
Double	25.00	35.00

Half board

per person:	£min	£max
Daily	18.00	23.00
Weekly	110.00	140.00

Lunch available
Evening meal 1700 (last orders 2100)
Ⓢ♨ⒾⓈⓉⓋ◐🛏,♨✕ⒹⒶⓅ♿Ⓢ

Nayland Hotel ⋒
♨♨♨♨
132-134 Sussex Gardens, London W2 1UB
☎ 071-723 4615
Fax 071-402 3292
Centrally located, close to many amenities and within walking distance of Hyde Park and Oxford Street. Quality you can afford.

Bedrooms: 11 single,
8 double, 17 twin, 5 triple
Bathrooms: 41 private
Bed & breakfast

per night:	£min	£max
Single	40.00	49.00
Double	46.00	62.00

Evening meal 1800 (last orders 2130)
Parking for 5
Cards accepted: Access, Visa, C.Bl, Diners, Amex, Switch
Ⓢ♨☎♿⛁☐♿♿◐☲🛏, 🛏♨♿Ⓣ

Oxford Hotel
13-14 Craven Terrace, Paddington, London W2
☎ 071-262 9608
Fax 071-706 4318
Telex 24226 ROYAL G
Located in a quiet one-way street, close to underground and bus routes to Oxford Street. 5 minutes' walk from Hyde Park.
Bedrooms: 10 single,
3 double, 13 twin, 2 triple
Bathrooms: 8 public,
2 private showers
Bed & breakfast

per night:	£min	£max
Single		17.50
Double	25.00	30.00

Cards accepted: Access, Visa, Amex
Ⓢ♨12♨♿☐♿Ⓤ✕♀ⓉⓋ 🛏,♨✕🚭ⒹⒶⓅ♿ⓈⓉ

Picton House Hotel
122 Sussex Gardens, London W2 1UB
☎ 071-723 5498 & 723 5479
Small, privately-owned hotel in desirable location near Oxford Street and Hyde Park and convenient for Madame Tussauds. High standard of personal service.
Bedrooms: 1 single,
4 double, 2 twin, 8 triple
Bathrooms: 6 private,
3 public, 4 private showers
Bed & breakfast

per night:	£min	£max
Single	25.00	30.00
Double	35.00	45.00

Cards accepted: Access, Visa, Diners, Amex
Ⓢ♨♨♿Ⓤ✕ⓉⓋ🛏,♨✕ 🚭ⒹⒶⓅ♿Ⓢ

Rhodes House Hotel ⋒
♨♨ APPROVED
195 Sussex Gardens, London W2 2RJ
☎ 071-262 5617 & 262 0537
Fax 071-723 4054
Rooms with private facilities, TV and telephone. Friendly

atmosphere. Families especially welcome. Near transport for sightseeing and shopping.
Bedrooms: 2 single,
4 double, 4 twin, 4 triple
Bathrooms: 11 private,
2 public
Bed & breakfast

per night:	£min	£max
Single	23.50	41.25
Double	35.25	52.87

Cards accepted: Access, Visa
Ⓢ♨♿☐♿ⓊⓁ♀ⓉⓋ🛏,♨ 🚭Ⓢ

Sass House Hotel ⋒
Listed
10 & 11 Craven Terrace, London W2 3QD
☎ 071-262 2325
Fax 071-224 9114
Budget accommodation, convenient for central London, Hyde Park and the West End. Paddington and Lancaster Gate underground stations nearby. Easy access to tourist attractions.
Bedrooms: 4 single,
4 double, 4 twin, 6 triple
Bathrooms: 3 public
Bed & breakfast

per night:	£min	£max
Single	16.00	
Double	22.00	

Cards accepted: Access, Visa, Amex
Ⓢ♨⛁ⓊⓁ♀ⓉⓋ🛏,✕ⒹⒶⓅ♿Ⓢ
Ⓐⓓ Display advertisement appears on page 31

Hotel Slavia ⋒
♨♨♨
2 Pembridge Square, London W2 4EW
☎ 071-727 1316 & 229 0803
Fax 071-229 0803
Telex 917458 SLAVIA
Family-run modernised hotel in a quiet garden square, 150 yards from Bayswater Road and public transport. Portobello antique market nearby.
Bedrooms: 4 single,
6 double, 13 twin, 8 triple
Bathrooms: 31 private
Bed & breakfast

per night:	£min	£max
Single	30.00	45.00
Double	40.00	60.00

Parking for 1
Cards accepted: Access, Visa, Diners, Amex, Switch
Ⓢ♨♿♀ⓉⓋ◐☲🛏,♨ⒹⒶⓅ ♿Ⓢ♿Ⓣ

Springfield Hotel
Listed APPROVED
154 Sussex Gardens, London W2 1UD
☎ 071-723 9898
Fax 071-723 0874
Small hotel close to Hyde Park and Marble Arch.
Bedrooms: 3 single,
4 double, 10 twin, 2 triple,
2 multiple
Bathrooms: 18 private,
5 public
Bed & breakfast

per night:	£min	£max
Single	25.00	28.00
Double	36.00	40.00

Parking for 2
Cards accepted: Access, Visa, Switch
Ⓢ♨♿☐♿ⓊⓁ♀ⓉⓋ🛏,♨ ♿Ⓢ

Westpoint Hotel ⋒
Listed
170-172 Sussex Gardens, London W2 1TP
☎ 071-402 0281
Fax 071-224 9114
Inexpensive accommodation in central London. Close to Paddington and Lancaster Gate underground stations. Easy access to tourist attractions and Hyde Park.
Bedrooms: 2 single,
17 double, 6 twin, 9 triple,
6 multiple
Bathrooms: 23 private,
5 public, 1 private shower
Bed & breakfast

per night:	£min	£max
Single	18.00	
Double	24.00	

Parking for 8
Cards accepted: Access, Visa, C.Bl, Diners, Amex
Ⓢ♨⛁☐♿ⓊⓁ♀ⓉⓋ◐🛏,♨ ✕ⒹⒶⓅ♿Ⓢ
Ⓐⓓ Display advertisement appears on page 31

LONDON W3

Mrs Ann Thomson
49 Twyford Avenue, West Acton, London W3 9PZ
☎ 081-993 4995
Ealing Common, comfortable Edwardian house near tube and North Circular (A406). Easy access to M4, M40, Heathrow and central London.
Bedrooms: 1 single,
1 double, 1 twin
Bathrooms: 1 public
Bed & breakfast

per night:	£min	£max
Single	15.00	20.00
Double	30.00	40.00

Ⓢ♿ⓊⓁ🛏,♨✕🚭Ⓣ

LONDON W4

Elliott Private Hotel
62 Elliott Road, Chiswick,
London W4 1PE
☎ 081-995 9794
*120 metres from Turnham
Green underground station,
principal lines to Victoria
station, Heathrow Airport.
Adjoining park with 7 tennis
courts.*
Bedrooms: 6 single,
2 double, 4 twin, 1 triple
Bathrooms: 2 public

Bed & breakfast

per night:	£min	£max
Single	20.00	22.00
Double	30.00	33.00

Parking for 1

Foubert's Hotel ⋀
162-166 Chiswick High
Road, London W4
☎ 081-994 5202
Fax 081-995 6743
*Family-run hotel close to
Heathrow Airport and central
London. Fully licensed
restaurant and candlelit wine
cellars. Live music at
weekends.*
Bedrooms: 11 single,
2 double, 3 twin, 1 triple
Bathrooms: 4 public

Bed & breakfast

per night:	£min	£max
Single	23.00	28.00
Double	40.00	45.00

Half board

per person:	£min	£max
Daily	30.00	35.00

Lunch available
Evening meal (last orders
2300)
Cards accepted: Access, Visa

LONDON W5

Corfton Guest House
42 Corfton Road, Ealing,
London W5 2HT
☎ 081-998 1120
*Close to Ealing Broadway
station, in a quiet residential
area of considerable
character.*
Bedrooms: 2 single,
5 double, 1 twin, 2 triple
Bathrooms: 4 private,
2 public

Bed & breakfast

per night:	£min	£max
Single	14.00	25.00
Double	22.00	30.00

Parking for 6

Eaton Guesthouse
60 Eaton Rise, London
W5 2HA
☎ 081-998 2157
*In a quiet residential area, 5
minutes' walk from Ealing
Broadway British Rail and
underground stations.*
Bedrooms: 3 single,
2 double, 2 twin, 1 triple
Bathrooms: 1 private,
3 public

Bed & breakfast

per night:	£min	£max
Single	13.00	18.00
Double	24.00	30.00

Parking for 6

Grange Lodge
48-50 Grange Road, Ealing,
London W5 5BX
☎ 081-567 1049
Fax 081-579 5350
*Quiet, comfortable hotel
within a few hundred yards of
the underground station.
Midway between central
London and Heathrow.*
Bedrooms: 7 single,
1 double, 2 twin, 4 triple
Bathrooms: 4 private,
2 public

Bed & breakfast

per night:	£min	£max
Single	25.00	33.00
Double	35.00	43.00

Parking for 10
Cards accepted: Access, Visa

Gresham Hotel
10 Hanger Lane, Ealing,
London W5 3HH
☎ 081-992 0801
Fax 081-993 7468
*Conveniently located family-
run bed and breakfast, ideal
for London Airport, city
centre and Wembley Stadium.
Colour TV with Sky movies,
tea/coffee facilities in all
rooms.*
Bedrooms: 3 single,
2 double, 2 twin, 2 triple,
2 multiple
Bathrooms: 4 private,
3 public

Bed & breakfast

per night:	£min	£max
Single	29.37	58.75
Double	44.65	70.50

Half board

per person:	£min	£max
Weekly	185.00	444.00

Evening meal 1800 (last
orders 2030)
Parking for 14

Cards accepted: Access, Visa,
C.Bl, Diners

Shiva Hotel
4 Tring Avenue, Ealing
Common, London W5 3HH
☎ 081-992 0016
Fax 081-993 7468
*Friendly family-run hotel
close to all amenities.
Convenient for Heathrow
Airport, West End and
Wembley Stadium.*
Bedrooms: 9 single,
3 double, 3 twin, 3 triple
Bathrooms: 8 private,
3 public, 1 private shower

Bed & breakfast

per night:	£min	£max
Single	29.37	58.75
Double	44.65	70.50

Half board

per person:	£min	£max
Weekly	185.00	444.00

Evening meal 1800 (last
orders 2030)
Parking for 6
Cards accepted: Access, Visa,
C.Bl, Diners, Amex

LONDON W6

Premier West Hotel ⋀
28-34 Glenthorne Road,
Hammersmith, London
W6 0LS
☎ 081-748 6181
Fax 081-748 2195
*Friendly hotel with affordable
prices, conveniently situated
for West End, Earl's Court
and Olympia exhibition
centres and Heathrow Airport.*
Bedrooms: 10 single,
4 double, 17 twin, 14 triple,
4 multiple
Bathrooms: 41 private,
4 public

Bed & breakfast

per night:	£min	£max
Single	32.50	65.00
Double	45.00	75.00

Lunch available
Evening meal 1800 (last
orders 2100)
Parking for 6
Cards accepted: Access, Visa,
C.Bl, Diners, Amex

LONDON W7

Wellmeadow Lodge ⋀
COMMENDED
24 Wellmeadow Road,
London W7 2AL
☎ 081-567 7294
Fax 081-566 3468

Cards accepted: Access, Visa,
C.Bl, Diners

Shiva Hotel
4 Tring Avenue, Ealing
Common, London W5 3HH
☎ 081-992 0016
Fax 081-993 7468
*Friendly family-run hotel
close to all amenities.
Convenient for Heathrow
Airport, West End and
Wembley Stadium.*
Bedrooms: 9 single,
3 double, 3 twin, 3 triple
Bathrooms: 8 private,
3 public, 1 private shower

Bed & breakfast

per night:	£min	£max
Single	36.00	45.00
Double	62.00	70.00

Evening meal 1800 (last
orders 1200)
Cards accepted: Access, Visa,
Amex

LONDON W8

Demetriou Guest House ⋀
Listed APPROVED
9 Strathmore Gardens,
London W8 4RZ
☎ 071-229 6709
*Small privately owned
guesthouse close to
Kensington Gardens and
Kensington High Street.
Convenient for Notting Hill
Gate underground.*
Bedrooms: 1 single,
3 double, 3 twin, 2 triple
Bathrooms: 3 public

Bed & breakfast

per night:	£min	£max
Single	27.00	27.00
Double	40.00	

Topaz Hotel
15 Lexham Gardens,
Kensington, London W8 5JJ
☎ 071-373 3466
*Small moderately-priced bed
and breakfast.*
Bedrooms: 4 single,
4 double, 4 twin, 4 triple
Bathrooms: 4 public

Bed & breakfast

per night:	£min	£max
Single		20.00
Double	30.00	35.00

LONDON W11

B & B Flatlets ⋀
72 Holland Park Avenue,
London W11 3QZ
☎ 071-229 9233
Fax 071-221 1077
*Clean, friendly, family-run
guesthouse offering budget
accommodation. Full English
breakfast served to rooms. All
rooms have their own
complete cooking facilities.
Near public transport. Also at*
Continued ►

*Charming establishment
offering high standard of
accommodation and a warm
welcome. Close to tube with
easy access to central London
and Heathrow.*
Bedrooms: 2 single, 2 double
Bathrooms: 2 private,
1 public

33

LONDON W11

Continued

64 Holland Road, London W14.
Bedrooms: 3 twin, 2 triple
Bathrooms: 1 private, 2 public

Bed & breakfast per night:	£min	£max
Single	15.00	22.00
Double	25.00	40.00

Cards accepted: Access, Visa

Holland Park Hotel
6 Ladbroke Terrace, London W11 3PG
☎ 071-792 0216
Economy town house hotel with own secluded garden, furnished with 18th and 19th C antiques. Good clean accommodation. A hotel you would be reluctant to leave.
Bedrooms: 9 single, 7 double, 5 twin, 2 triple
Bathrooms: 11 private, 3 public, 6 private showers

Bed & breakfast per night:	£min	£max
Single	37.60	47.00
Double	47.00	63.45

Cards accepted: Access, Visa, Diners, Amex

Mrs L Stephan
152 Kensington Park Road, London W11 2EP
☎ 071-727 7174
Pleasantly situated Victorian terrace house, close to all amenities. Clients receive individual attention in homely and friendly surroundings.
Bedrooms: 2 double, 1 triple
Bathrooms: 1 public

Bed & breakfast per night:	£min	£max
Double	22.00	

6

LONDON W13

Mrs A M Clark
84 Cleveland Road, Ealing, London W13 8AH
☎ 081-998 3107
Fax 081-998 8861
Attractive turn-of-the-century cottage-style house providing bed and breakfast in a friendly environment. Convenient London and Heathrow Airport.
Bedrooms: 1 single, 1 double, 1 triple
Bathrooms: 2 public

Bed & breakfast per night:	£min	£max
Single	15.00	16.00
Double	30.00	32.00

Half board per person:	£min	£max
Daily	22.00	23.00
Weekly	120.00	130.00

Evening meal 1900 (last orders 2100)
Parking for 2

Mrs Teresa McHugh
68 Cleveland Road, Ealing, London W13 8AJ
☎ 081-991 5142
Large family house in a quiet residential area. Close to Ealing Broadway underground station. Easy access to central London and Heathrow Airport, 10 minutes from M4 and A40.
Bedrooms: 1 single, 2 twin, 1 triple, 2 multiple
Bathrooms: 3 public

Bed & breakfast per night:	£min	£max
Single	15.00	16.00
Double	30.00	32.00

2

LONDON W14

Forrest House
40 Addison Gardens, London W14 0DP
☎ 071-603 5938
Fax 071-602 5609
Convenient for Earl's Court and Olympia. Easy access to Heathrow Airport. French, German, Italian and Spanish spoken. All rooms with private bathroom (WC, shower, washbasin), TV and tea/coffee facilities.
Bedrooms: 1 single, 1 double, 2 twin, 1 triple
Bathrooms: 5 private

Bed & breakfast per night:	£min	£max
Single	30.00	35.00
Double	40.00	48.00

Cards accepted: Access, Visa, Switch
12

Janus Hotel
26 Hazlitt Road, London W14 0JY
☎ 071-603 6915 & 603 3119
Homely hotel quietly but centrally situated within easy reach of the West End. Self-catering facilities available.
Bedrooms: 6 single, 3 double, 3 twin, 3 triple, 3 multiple
Bathrooms: 3 public, 5 private showers

Bed & breakfast per night:	£min	£max
Single	15.00	23.00
Double	20.00	30.00

Cards accepted: Access, Visa

LONDON WC1

Acorns Hotel
42 Tavistock Place, London WC1H 9RE
☎ 071-837 3077 & 837 2723
Grade II listed Victorian house, well-placed between West End and the City, ideal for business or pleasure. Minutes' walk to Russell Square, Euston and King's Cross.
Bedrooms: 2 single, 6 double, 4 twin, 2 triple
Bathrooms: 4 public

Bed & breakfast per night:	£min	£max
Single	20.00	28.00
Double	30.00	38.00

Cards accepted: Access, Visa, C.Bl, Diners, Amex
6

Central Hotel
16-18 Argyle Street, Kings Cross, London WC1H 8EQ
☎ 071-837 9008
Fax 071-278 8682
Clean, family-run newly renovated bed and breakfast close to mainline train stations and conveniently located for all major tourist attractions.
Bedrooms: 16 single, 10 double, 19 twin, 14 triple
Bathrooms: 16 public

Bed & breakfast per night:	£min	£max
Single	18.00	24.00
Double	26.00	30.00

Cards accepted: Access, Visa

Garth Hotel
Listed
69 Gower Street, London WC1E 6HJ
☎ 071-636 5761
Fax 071-637 4854
Family-run bed and breakfast accommodation centrally situated, convenient for shops, theatres and travel. TV lounge. Complimentary tea/coffee on arrival.
Bedrooms: 3 single, 3 double, 4 twin, 3 triple, 2 multiple
Bathrooms: 3 public

Bed & breakfast per night:	£min	£max
Single	22.00	28.00
Double	32.00	40.00

Cards accepted: Access, Visa

Langland Hotel
29-31 Gower Street, London WC1E 6HG
☎ 071-636 5801 & 580 6171
Fax 071-580 2227
Telex 28151 Attn BHA
Family-run bed and breakfast hotel in central London, close to many of the theatres.
Bedrooms: 6 single, 6 double, 7 twin, 8 triple
Bathrooms: 4 public, 6 private showers

Bed & breakfast per night:	£min	£max
Single	22.00	28.00
Double	30.00	38.00

Half board per person:	£min	£max
Daily	30.00	36.00

Evening meal 1800 (last orders 2000)
Cards accepted: Access, Visa

St. Athan's Hotel
20 Tavistock Place, Russell Square, London WC1H 9RE
☎ 071-837 9140 & 837 9627
Fax 071-833 8352
Small family-run hotel.
Bedrooms: 16 single, 15 double, 15 twin, 5 multiple
Bathrooms: 3 private, 12 public

Bed & breakfast per night:	£min	£max
Single	24.00	28.00
Double	34.00	38.00

Cards accepted: Access, Visa, Diners, Amex

LONDON WC2

Hotel Strand Continental
143 The Strand, London WC2R 1JA
☎ 071-836 4880
Small hotel with friendly atmosphere, near theatres and famous London landmarks.
Bedrooms: 10 single, 7 double, 2 twin, 3 triple
Bathrooms: 6 public

Bed & breakfast

per night:	£min	£max
Single	23.00	26.00
Double	29.00	33.00

⌕ ⌖ 📺 ◑ ▥ 🗙 ◰

OUTER LONDON

See colour map 6

Mr F J Edwards

Listed

123 Park Road, Beckenham, Kent BR3 1QJ
☎ 081-650 1281
Modern comfortable home near New Beckenham station. Convenient for central London, National Sports Centre (Crystal Palace) and Bromley.
Bedrooms: 1 single, 2 double
Bathrooms: 1 public

Bed & breakfast

per night:	£min	£max
Single	15.00	
Double	30.00	

Parking for 4

⌕ ⌖ ▯ ▥ ↙ ▥ ◰ ✕ ◰

CROYDON

Iverna

Listed

1 Annandale Road, Addiscombe, Croydon CR0 7HP
☎ 081-654 8639
Large house in a quiet road, close to East Croydon station. London Victoria 15 minutes away. No smoking in public areas.
Bedrooms: 1 single, 2 twin, 1 triple
Bathrooms: 1 public

Bed & breakfast

per night:	£min	£max
Single	18.00	
Double	34.00	

Parking for 1

⌕ ⌖ ▯ ☏ ↙ ▥ ▥ ◰ ◰

Peters Bed and Breakfast Accommodation

99 Broughton Road, Thornton Heath, Croydon CR7 6AJ
☎ 081-665 6748
Bed and breakfast accommodation (cooking facilities available on request). 10 minutes from Croydon town centre. Near Thornton Heath bus station for central London and the city.
Bedrooms: 3 double
Bathrooms: 1 private, 2 public

Bed & breakfast

per night:	£min	£max
Single	17.00	20.00
Double	25.00	30.00

⌕ ⌖ ▯ ↙ ▥ ▥ ◉ ◰ ✕ ▥ SP

HARROW

Harrow Hotel ⋀⋀

♕ ♕ ♕ ♕ APPROVED

12-22 Pinner Road, Harrow, Middlesex HA1 4HZ
☎ 081-427 3435
Fax 081-861 1370
Telex 917898 Hartel G
All en-suite hotel on London underground. Good bar meal menu at budget prices. Always complimented for its friendly staff.
Bedrooms: 52 single, 20 double, 20 twin, 5 triple, 1 multiple
Bathrooms: 97 private

Bed & breakfast

per night:	£min	£max
Single	43.00	79.00
Double	56.00	89.00

Half board

per person:	£min	£max
Daily	55.00	90.00
Weekly	350.00	490.00

Lunch available
Evening meal 1800 (last orders 2130)
Parking for 58
Cards accepted: Access, Visa, Diners, Amex, Switch

⌕ ⌖ ☏ ▤ ▯ ↙ ◑ ▤ S ↙ ▥ 📺 ◑ ▥ ◰ ◰ ⌁6-120 ◱ ▥ SP T

Knights Bed and Breakfast

▥

78 Gayton Road, (off Kenton Road), Harrow, Middlesex HA1 2LS
☎ 081-427 5309 & 863 6401
Family guesthouse near Harrow town centre with easy access to central London.
Bedrooms: 2 twin, 1 triple
Bathrooms: 1 public

Bed & breakfast

per night:	£min	£max
Single	18.00	25.00
Double	25.00	35.00

Parking for 6

⌕ ▯ ↙ ▥ ▮ ◑ ▥ ◰ ✕ ◰

HOUNSLOW

Lampton Guesthouse

4 Lampton Park Road, Hounslow, Middlesex TW3 4HS
☎ 081-572 8622
Detached property with garden at rear. Convenient for the high street,

underground station and Heathrow Airport.
Bedrooms: 3 single, 2 twin
Bathrooms: 2 public, 2 private showers

Bed & breakfast

per night:	£min	£max
Single	23.00	23.00
Double	36.00	36.00

Parking for 6

⌕ 5 ▯ ▥ ▥ 🗙 ◰

ISLEWORTH

Ashleigh

22 Lingwood Gardens, Osterley, Isleworth, Middlesex TW7 5LZ
☎ 081-568 3800
In quiet cul-de-sac, close to Osterley underground station and National Trust house and parkland. Convenient for Heathrow Airport and central London.
Bedrooms: 1 double, 1 twin, 1 triple, 1 multiple
Bathrooms: 1 public

Bed & breakfast

per night:	£min	£max
Single	18.00	22.00
Double	26.00	30.00

Parking for 2

⌕ 3 ▥ ▮ S ▥ 🗙 ◰

PURLEY

Conifer's

Listed

41 Peaks Hill, Purley, Surrey CR8 3JJ
☎ 081-660 6902
Private detached house 15 miles from central London. Golf, tennis, cricket clubs 10-20 minutes' walk away. Near Croydon, Epsom and Wimbledon. Convenient for M23 to Gatwick Airport.
Bedrooms: 2 single, 1 double, 1 twin
Bathrooms: 1 private, 2 public

Bed & breakfast

per night:	£min	£max
Single	16.50	18.00
Double	28.00	35.00

Parking for 4

⌕ ▤ ▯ ↙ ▥ ↙ 📺 ◑ ▥ ◰ ◰ ✕ ◰ SP

Mrs J Stock

Listed COMMENDED

51 Selcroft Road, Purley, Surrey CR8 1AJ
☎ 081-660 3054
Fax 081-660 3054
Central London 20 minutes by train. Convenient for M25, M23 and Gatwick Airport.
Bedrooms: 2 twin, 1 triple
Bathrooms: 1 public

Bed & breakfast

per night:	£min	£max
Single	17.00	18.00
Double	34.00	34.00

Evening meal 1800 (last orders 2100)
Parking for 3
Open January-November

⌕ 10 ▥ ↙ ▯ ▥ ▮ ⌖ 📺 ▥ ◰ ✕ ◰ ◰

ROMFORD

Gidea Park Hotel

115 Main Road, Gidea Park, Romford RM2 5EL
☎ (0708) 746676 & 746628
Fax (0708) 764044
Large Victorian house on the A118, built in 1880. Fine English/French restaurant and ample parking.
Bedrooms: 12 single, 5 double, 3 twin
Bathrooms: 20 private

Bed & breakfast

per night:	£min	£max
Single	39.00	39.00
Double	44.00	59.00

Lunch available
Evening meal 1900 (last orders 2100)
Parking for 20
Cards accepted: Access, Visa, Amex, Switch

⌕ 3 ▥ ↙ ☏ ▤ ▯ ◑ ▮ S ▥ 📺 ▥ ◰ ⌁ ↑ ▶ ◰

TEDDINGTON

Bushy Park Lodge Hotel

♕♕

6 Sandy Lane, Teddington, Middlesex TW11 0DR
☎ 081-943 5428 & 977 4924
Fax 081-943 1917
Close to Kingston Bridge and Hampton Court. Purpose-built in 1989. No restaurant.
Bedrooms: 5 double, 1 twin
Bathrooms: 6 private

Bed & breakfast

per night:	£min	£max
Single	35.00	50.00
Double	45.00	60.00

Parking for 8
Cards accepted: Access, Visa, Diners, Amex

⌕ ▤ ☏ ▤ ▯ ↙ ▮ S ▥ 📺 ▥ ◰ ◱ ▥ SP

WALLINGTON

Mrs J Dixon

▥

17 Osmond Gardens, Wallington, Surrey SM6 8SX
☎ 081-647 1943

Continued ▶

WALLINGTON
Continued

Double/family room with en-suite shower, colour TV, tea/coffee making facilities, London 33 minutes by British Rail, Gatwick 45 minutes' drive.
Bedrooms: 1 triple
Bathrooms: 1 private shower
Bed & breakfast

per night:	£min	£max
Double	36.00	40.00

Parking for 1

WEMBLEY

Elm Hotel ⋔
COMMENDED

1-7 Elm Road, Wembley,
Middlesex HA9 7JA
☎ 081-902 1764
Fax 081-903 8365
Ten minutes' walk (1200 yards) from Wembley Stadium and Conference Centre. 150 yards from Wembley Central underground and mainline station.
Bedrooms: 8 single,
9 double, 9 twin, 4 triple

Bathrooms: 20 private,
4 public
Bed & breakfast

per night:	£min	£max
Single	33.00	44.00
Double	43.00	53.00

Parking for 8
Cards accepted: Access, Visa

Wembley Park Guest House ⋔
Listed

8 Forty Lane, Wembley,
Middlesex HA9 9EB
☎ 081-904 6329
Guesthouse close to Wembley Park station, stadium, arena, conference centre. Easy access to major routes and city. Parking available.
Bedrooms: 3 single, 1 twin,
3 triple
Bathrooms: 1 private,
3 public
Bed & breakfast

per night:	£min	£max
Single	25.00	27.00
Double	35.00	38.00

Evening meal 1800 (last orders 2100)
Parking for 10

Cards accepted: Access, Visa,
Amex

WEST DRAYTON

The Alice House
Listed   APPROVED

9 Hollycroft Close, Sipson,
West Drayton, Middlesex
UB7 OJJ
☎ 081-897 9032
Small, clean and comfortable guesthouse. Convenient for the airport, but with no noise from flight path. Car service to airport available. Evening meal by arrangement. Parking.
Bedrooms: 1 single,
1 double, 1 twin
Bathrooms: 1 public
Bed & breakfast

per night:	£min	£max
Single	28.00	30.00
Double	38.00	40.00

Evening meal 1800 (last orders 2200)
Parking for 4

Apple Tree Cottage
⋔⋔ APPROVED

1a Frays Avenue, West
Drayton, Middlesex UB7 7AF
☎ (0895) 448872
Charming and comfortable accommodation in cottage-style house. 10 minutes to Heathrow, 30 minutes to central London, close to M4, M40, M25.
Bedrooms: 1 single, 2 double
Bathrooms: 1 private,
1 public, 1 private shower
Bed & breakfast

per night:	£min	£max
Single	20.00	25.00
Double	35.00	38.00

Evening meal 1900 (last orders 2130)
Parking for 2

The national
Crown scheme is
explained in full
in the information
pages towards the
back of this guide.

Use your *i*'s

⟮i⟯ Tourist information ⟫

There are more than 600 Tourist Information Centres throughout England offering friendly help with accommodation and holiday ideas as well as suggestions of places to visit and things to do.

In your home town there may be a centre which can help you before you set out. You'll find the address of your nearest Tourist Information Centre in your local Phone Book.

ALMANAC SERIES
English Castles ◆ English Gardens

England's castles and gardens are an integral part of its heritage. They provide a wealth of choice for the visitor. The pocket-sized Almanac guides include a selection of around 100 of the best-known locations open to the public.

Each of the individual entries is illustrated in colour and all the practical details a visitor needs to plan and enjoy a visit are provided. There is information on:

◆ *Opening times and admission charges*

◆ *Location and access*

◆ *Facilities for disabled visitors*

◆ *Special features*

Published in association with the English Tourist Board by Lochar Publishing.

Available in hardback from bookshops, price £6.99.

THE GREAT BRITISH...

The Great British Railway
by Tony Hall-Patch
The Great British Countryside
by Christopher Somerville
The Great British Soldier
by Philip Warner

The Great British... series presents a living history of British life:
The Railway – the development of both the engine and the rail system
The Countryside – how it has been shaped by geological and human influences
The Soldier – the changing lifestyle and experiences of the everyday soldier

◆ *Illustrated throughout with stunning photographs* ◆ *Packed with facts*

◆ *Recommends museums and locations of particular interest*

◆ *Contains a comprehensive gazetteer of the best of British museums*

Published in association with the National Tourist Boards for England, Scotland, Wales and Northern Ireland by David & Charles.
Available in hardback from bookshops, price £14.99.

Cumbria

Cumbria offers many contrasts of scenery, from the breathtaking beauty of the central Lake District to the more relaxed, rolling landscape of east Cumbria and the Pennines, the rich plains of the Border Country to the north and the seascapes of the west coast. Such spectacular scenery

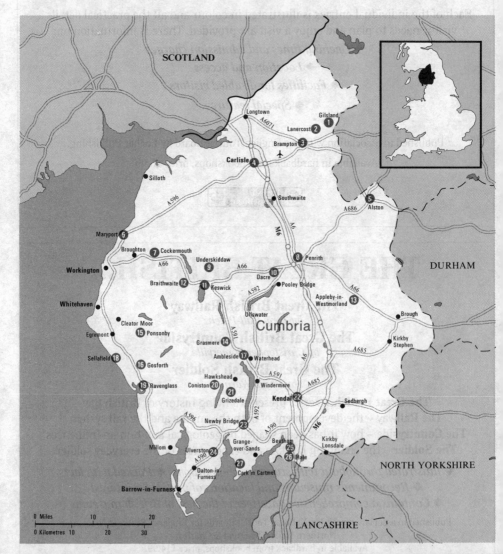

Use the above map to locate places in the "Where to Go, What to See" section opposite.

Use the colour maps at the back of this guide to find places with accommodation.

provides a paradise for outdoor activities all the year round – walking, climbing, riding, golf, cycling, bird-watching and winter sports of every kind. There is as much variety in the heritage of the region, from the remains of Roman settlements to the grandeur of stately homes.

WHERE TO GO, WHAT TO SEE

The number against each name will help you locate it on the map opposite.

❶ Birdoswald Roman Fort
Gilsland, Cumbria
CA6 7DD
Tel: (069 77) 47602
Remains of Roman fort on one of the best parts of Hadrian's Wall with excellent views of the Irthing Gorge. Visitor centre brings to life the story of Birdoswald.

❷ Lanercost Priory
Lanercost, Brampton, Cumbria CA8 2HQ
Tel: Brampton (069 77) 3030
Impressive red sandstone priory made of stones from Hadrian's Wall. Founded in 1166 for Augustinian canons. Ruined nave restored in 18th C as parish church.

❸ Naworth Castle
Brampton, Cumbria
Tel: Brampton (069 77) 3666
Historic border fortress, built in 1335 and renovated in 1602. Great hall, Gobelin tapestries, Pre-Raphaelite library, 14th C dungeons.

❹ Carlisle Castle
Carlisle, Cumbria CA3 8UR
Tel: Carlisle (0228) 31777
Border stronghold – keep built 1092 on site of Roman fort. 12th C keep with vaulted

passages, chambers, staircases and towers. Dungeon. 14th C main gate with portcullis.

❹ Tullie House
Castle Street, Carlisle, Cumbria CA3 8TP
Tel: Carlisle (0228) 34781
Major tourist complex housing museum, art gallery, theatre, shops, restaurant, bars.

❺ South Tynedale Railway
Railway Station, Alston, Cumbria CA9 3JB
Tel: Alston (0434) 381696
2ft gauge railway following part

The poet William Wordsworth – to many people his name is synonymous with the Lake District

of the route of the former Alston to Haltwhistle branch line through South Tynedale.

❻ Senhouse Roman Museum
The Battery, Sea Brows, Maryport, Cumbria CA15 6JD
Tel: Maryport (0900) 816168
Oldest archaeological collection in UK. Large collection of Roman altars and inscriptions.

❼ Wordsworth House
Cockermouth, Cumbria CA13 9RX
Tel: Cockermouth (0900) 824805
Wordsworth's birthplace. Georgian house with 18th C furnishings and personal effects of the poet. Static and tape/slide displays. Garden featured in poems.

❽ Brougham Castle
Penrith, Cumbria CA10 2AA
Tel: Penrith (0768) 62488
Impressive 12th C Norman keep remains by River Eamont, close to Roman fort Brocavum. 14th C fortress of Robert Clifford. Restored by Lady Anne Clifford in 17th C.

Remote mountain valleys – typical of the breathtaking beauty that always surrounds you in England's Lakeland

⑨ Mirehouse
Underskiddaw, Cumbria CA12 4QE
Tel: Keswick (076 87) 72287
Manuscripts and portraits with many literary connections, Victorian schoolroom/nursery, antiques quiz, woodland and lakeside walk, 4 adventure playgrounds.

⑩ Dalemain
Dacre, Cumbria CA11 0HB
Tel: Pooley Bridge (076 84) 86450
Historic house, Georgian furniture, Westmorland and Cumberland Yeomanry Museum. Agricultural bygones, adventure playground, licensed restaurant, gardens.

⑪ Cars of the Stars Motor Museum
Keswick, Cumbria CA12 5LS
Tel: Keswick (076 87) 73757
Cars that have appeared in TV and film or owned by famous personalities, including Bergerac's car, James Bond's car, Chitty Chitty Bang Bang.

⑫ Whinlatter Visitor Centre
Braithwaite, Cumbria CA12 5TW
Tel: Braithwaite (076 87) 82469
Interpretative forestry exhibition with audio-visual presentations. Working model of forest operations, lecture theatre, walks, trails, orienteering.

⑬ Appleby Castle Conservation Centre
Appleby-in-Westmorland, Cumbria CA16 6XH
Tel: Appleby (076 83) 51402
Norman keep. Great hall of house has Clifford family triptych. Large collection of waterfowl, owls, pheasants, rare breeds of farm animals.

⑭ Grasmere and Wordsworth Museum
Grasmere, Cumbria LA22 9SH
Tel: Grasmere (096 65) 544
Wordsworth's home 1799–1808. Poet's possessions, museum with manuscripts, farmhouse reconstruction, paintings and drawings. Special exhibitions throughout the year.

⑮ Ponsonby Farm Park
Ponsonby, Cumbria CA20 1BX
Tel: Beckermet (0946) 841426
Working mixed farm, rare breeds of farm animals, old and modern farm buildings. Tearoom, shop, picnic and play area.

⑯ Gosforth Pottery
Gosforth, Cumbria CA20 1AH
Tel: Gosforth (094 67) 25296
Working country pottery. Demonstrations and supervised opportunity to make a pot. Wide range of hand-made pottery for sale.

⑰ Rydal Mount
Ambleside, Cumbria LA22 9LU
Tel: Ambleside (053 94) 33002
Wordsworth's home for 37 years. First editions, portraits, memorabilia. Garden landscaped by Wordsworth.

⑰ Stagshaw Gardens
Ambleside, Cumbria
Tel: Ambleside (053 94) 32109
Woodland garden on a steep slope overlooking Windermere. Rhododendrons, azaleas, camellias, spring bulbs.

⑱ Sellafield Visitors Centre
Sellafield, Cumbria CA20 1PG
Tel: Seascale (094 67) 27027
Exhibition of nuclear power and the nuclear industry.

⑲ Muncaster Mill
Ravenglass, Cumbria CA18 1ST
Tel: Ravenglass (0229) 717323
Working water-powered corn mill. Early Victorian machinery in daily use producing a range of stone-ground flours and oatmeals.

⑳ Brantwood
Coniston, Cumbria LA21 8AD
Tel: Coniston (053 94) 41396
Beautiful home of John Ruskin. Superb lake and mountain views. Works by Ruskin and contemporaries, memorabilia. Craft and picture galleries.

㉑ Grizedale Forest Park Visitor Centre
Grizedale, Hawkshead, Cumbria LA22 OQJ
Tel: Satterthwaite (0229) 860373
Displays show Grizedale from wildwood to woodland managed by the Forestry Commission for timber, wildlife and people. Trails, walks, hides, orienteering, books, maps.

㉒ Kendal Museum
Kendal, Cumbria LA7 6BZ
Tel: Kendal (0539) 721374
An outstanding natural history gallery with reconstructions of Lake District habitats. World Wildlife Gallery. Local history in Westmorland Gallery.

㉒ Levens Hall
Kendal, Cumbria LA8 OPB
Tel: Sedgwick (053 95) 60321
Elizabethan mansion, incorporating a pele tower.

Famous topiary garden laid out in 1692, steam collection, plants for sale, shop, play area, picnic area.

㉓ Graythwaite Hall Gardens
Newby Bridge, Cumbria LA12 8BA
Tel: Newby Bridge (053 95) 31248
Rhododendrons, azaleas and flowering shrubs. Laid out by T. Mawson 1888–1890.

㉔ Lakeside and Haverthwaite Railway
Ulverston, Cumbria LA12 8AL
Tel: Newby Bridge (053 95) 31594
Standard gauge steam railway which operates a daily seasonal service. Steam and diesel locomotives on display.

㉕ Heron Corn Mill and Paper Museum
c/o Henry Cooke Ltd, Beetham, Cumbria LA7 7AR
Tel: Milnthorpe (053 95) 63363
Restored working corn mill. 14ft high breastshot waterwheel. Museum of paper-making.

㉖ Lakeland Wildlife Oasis
Hale, Cumbria LA7 7BW
Tel: (053 95) 63027
A wildlife exhibition where both living animals and inanimate "hands on" displays are used to illustrate evolution in the animal kingdom. Gift shop.

㉗ Lakeland Motor Museum
Cark in Cartmel, Cumbria LA11 7PL
Tel: Grange-over-Sands (053 95) 58509
Over 100 historic cars, motorcycles, bicycles and engines. 1920s replica garage. Many collections of transport-related items. Esso historic exhibition.

FIND OUT MORE

Further information about holidays and attractions in the Cumbria region is available from:
Cumbria Tourist Board
Ashleigh, Holly Road, Windermere, Cumbria LA23 2AQ
Tel: (053 94) 44444

These publications are available from the Cumbria Tourist Board (post free):
Cumbria The Lake District Touring Map (including tourist information and touring caravan and camping parks) £2.95
Places to Visit and Things to Do in Cumbria The Lake District (over 200 ideas for a great day out) 95p
Short Walks – Good for Families (route descriptions, maps and information for 14 walks in the lesser-known areas of Cumbria) 95p
Wordsworth's Lake District (folded map showing major Wordsworthian sites plus biographical details) 45p

The intricately carved Anglian cross in Irton Churchyard

41

Places to stay

Accommodation entries in this regional section are listed in alphabetical order of place name, and then in alphabetical order of establishment.

The map references refer to the colour maps at the back of the guide. The first figure is the map number; the letter and figure which follow indicate the grid reference on the map.

The symbols at the end of each accommodation entry give information about services and facilities. A 'key' to these symbols is inside the back cover flap, which can be kept open for easy reference.

ALSTON

Cumbria
Map ref 5B2

Alston is the highest market town in England, set amongst the highest fells of the Pennines and close to the Pennine Way in an Area of Outstanding Natural Beauty. Mainly 17th C buildings with steep, cobbled streets.
Tourist Information Centre
☎ *(0434) 381696*

Shield Hill House ⚑
👑👑

Garrigill, Alston CA9 3EX
☎ (0434) 381238
Converted farmhouse with extensive views. In the heart of the North Pennines. Convenient for Borders, Lakes, Northumbria and dales. 3.5 miles from Alston on the B6277 Barnard Castle road. No smoking please.
Bedrooms: 2 double, 2 twin, 1 multiple
Bathrooms: 5 private
Bed & breakfast

per night:	£min	£max
Single	16.25	17.50
Double	32.50	35.00

Half board

per person:	£min	£max
Daily	24.50	26.25
Weekly	162.75	162.75

Evening meal 1930 (last orders 1200)

Parking for 8
Cards accepted: Access, Visa
🖙🏧📭🕭🖵📺 🖴❀✕🚭 🅂🄿

AMBLESIDE

Cumbria
Map ref 5A3

Market town situated at the head of Lake Windermere and surrounded by fells. The historic town centre is now a conservation area and the country around Ambleside is rich in historical and literary association. Good centre for touring, walking and climbing.
Tourist Information Centre
☎ *(05394) 325*

Broadview ⚑
Low Fold, Lake Road, Ambleside LA22 0DN
☎ (053 94) 32431
Spacious, comfortable family Victorian guesthouse. Superb views, easy walk to village and lake.
Bedrooms: 2 double, 1 twin, 3 triple
Bathrooms: 2 public
Bed & breakfast

per night:	£min	£max
Double	28.00	32.00

Open April-October
🖙📭🅂✕🛏✕🚭

Crow How Hotel ⚑
👑👑👑 COMMENDED
Rydal Road, Ambleside LA22 9PN
☎ (053 94) 32193
Victorian country house in a quiet location, with 2 acres of grounds. Only 1 mile from the centre of Ambleside.
Bedrooms: 6 double, 1 twin, 2 triple
Bathrooms: 8 private
Bed & breakfast

per night:	£min	£max
Single	24.50	25.50
Double	49.00	60.00

Half board

per person:	£min	£max
Daily	35.50	41.00
Weekly	223.50	258.00

Evening meal 1930 (last orders 1930)
Parking for 12
Open February-November
Cards accepted: Access, Visa
🖙📭🖵🕭🗏🅂🖴🚭 🅂🄿

Easedale Guest House
👑👑
Compston Road, Ambleside LA22 9DJ
☎ (053 94) 32112
Centrally situated, fine views, car parking, good food, friendly and comfortable.
Bedrooms: 1 single, 4 double, 1 triple
Bathrooms: 2 private, 2 public

Bed & breakfast

per night:	£min	£max
Single	15.00	16.00
Double	30.00	36.00

Half board

per person:	£min	£max
Daily	25.00	26.00

Evening meal 1900 (last orders 1900)
Parking for 8
Open March-December
🖙10📭🕭📭🗏🖵🎏✕🛪
🄳🄰🄿🖎🅂🄿

Foxghyll ⚑
👑👑👑 HIGHLY COMMENDED
Under Loughrigg, Rydal, Ambleside LA22 9LL
☎ (053 94) 33292
Large country house in secluded gardens with direct access to fells. All rooms en-suite, one with spa bath. Ample parking.
Bedrooms: 2 double, 1 twin
Bathrooms: 3 private
Bed & breakfast

per night:	£min	£max
Double	38.00	48.00

Parking for 7
🖙10📭📭🖵🕭🗏🖵✕🗏
🖵🖴🖊❀✕🎏🍴

Glenside ⚑
👑 COMMENDED
Old Lake Road, Ambleside LA22 0DP
☎ (053 94) 32635
17th C farm cottage, comfortable bedrooms with original oak beams. TV lounge. Between town and

lake, ideal centre for walking.
Private parking.
Bedrooms: 2 double, 1 twin
Bathrooms: 1 public

Bed & breakfast

per night:	£min	£max
Single	12.50	15.00
Double	25.00	30.00

Parking for 3
🏵5🖤🛌🎍🌡🍴📺⬛🗙🗿
🅿🆃

High Wray Farm
Listed

High Wray, Ambleside
LA22 0JE
☎ (053 94) 32280
173-acre livestock farm.
Charming 17th C farmhouse
once owned by Beatrix Potter.
In quiet location, ideal centre
for touring or walking.
Panoramic views and lake
shore walks close by.
Bedrooms: 2 double, 1 twin
Bathrooms: 1 private,
1 public

Bed & breakfast

per night:	£min	£max
Single	13.00	15.00
Double	26.00	30.00

Parking for 7
🏵🛌🖤💺🎍📺⬛🗿
🗿🆃

Lattendales ᴹ
🏵🏵

Compston Road, Ambleside
LA22 9DJ
☎ (053 94) 32368
Traditional Lakeland home in
the heart of Ambleside. A
central base for walking or
touring, offering comfortable
accommodation and local
produce.
Bedrooms: 2 single,
1 double, 2 twin, 1 triple
Bathrooms: 4 private,
1 public

Bed & breakfast

per night:	£min	£max
Single	12.00	15.00
Double	30.00	39.00

Half board

per person:	£min	£max
Daily	25.00	30.00
Weekly	169.00	199.00

Evening meal 1830 (last
orders 1700)
Open February-December
🏵🛌🎍💺📺⬛🗿🆃

Old Fisherbeck
Old Lake Road, Ambleside
LA22 0DH
☎ (053 94) 33540
18th C cottage in tiny garden,
near lake and town centre.
On quiet road with quick
access to fells. Log fires,

informal and peaceful.
Bargain breaks available.
Non-smokers only please.
Bedrooms: 1 double, 2 twin
Bathrooms: 2 public

Bed & breakfast

per night:	£min	£max
Double	29.00	32.00

Lunch available
Parking for 3
Open January-October
🏵8🐾🔥🛤🎍🗿🛌📗🍴📺
⬛🚗✿🗿🅿🗿🏵

The Old Vicarage ᴹ
🏵🏵 APPROVED

Vicarage Road, Ambleside
LA22 9DH
☎ (053 94) 33364
Fax (053 94) 34734
Traditional Lakeland-stone
house, pleasantly situated in
own grounds in heart of
village. Quality
accommodation. All en-suite.
Bedrooms: 7 double, 1 twin,
1 triple, 1 multiple
Bathrooms: 10 private

Bed & breakfast

per night:	£min	£max
Single	21.00	25.00
Double	42.00	50.00

Parking for 12
🏵🛌🖤🎍🗿🛌🗿
💺🎍📺🚗🍴🗿✿🗿🗿
🏵🆃

Raaesbeck
🏵🏵

Fairview Road, Ambleside
LA22 9EE
☎ (053 94) 33844
18th C building in the older,
quiet and elevated part of the
village, with a garden and
views of Loughrigg Fell, yet
only 3 minutes' walk from
village.
Bedrooms: 2 double, 1 twin
Bathrooms: 2 public

Bed & breakfast

per night:	£min	£max
Double	25.00	28.00

Parking for 3
Cards accepted: Amex
🏵5🖤🗿🗿📺⬛🚗✿🗙
🗿🗿🏵

Riverside
Millans Park, Ambleside
LA22 9AG
☎ (053 94) 33501
Victorian house on a quiet
road yet near all amenities.
Private parking. Lovely views
over the fells.
Bedrooms: 3 double
Bathrooms: 1 public

Bed & breakfast

per night:	£min	£max
Double	25.00	28.00

Parking for 3
Open February-November
🏵🛤🖤🎍📺⬛🗿🏵

Riverside Lodge
Country House ᴹ
🏵🏵 COMMENDED

Nr. Rothay Bridge,
Ambleside LA22 0EH
☎ (053 94) 34208
Georgian country house of
character with 2 acres of
grounds through which the
River Rothay flows, 500 yards
from the centre of Ambleside.
Bedrooms: 4 double, 1 twin,
1 triple
Bathrooms: 6 private

Bed & breakfast

per night:	£min	£max
Double	42.00	57.00

Parking for 20
Cards accepted: Access, Visa
🏵11🛌🍴💺🎍🗿🖤🚪🍴🗿🚿
🗿🎍⬛🚗🚽🗙🗿🗿🏵

Rowanfield Country
Guesthouse ᴹ
🏵🏵 COMMENDED

Kirkstone Road, Ambleside
☎ (053 94) 33686
Idyllic setting, panoramic lake
and mountain views. Laura
Ashley style decor.
Scrumptious food created by
proprietor/chef. Special break
prices.
Bedrooms: 5 double, 1 twin,
1 triple
Bathrooms: 7 private

Bed & breakfast

per night:	£min	£max
Double	44.00	54.00

Half board

per person:	£min	£max
Daily	32.00	41.00
Weekly	210.00	225.00

Evening meal 1900 (last
orders 1930)
Parking for 8
Open March-December
Cards accepted: Access, Visa
🏵5🖤🗿🛌🖤🗿🗿🍴🎍⬛
🗿🎍🗿🗿🏵

Smallwood House
Hotel ᴹ
🏵🏵

Compston Road, Ambleside
LA22 9DJ
☎ (053 94) 32330
Family-run hotel in central
position, offering warm and
friendly service, good home
cooking and value-for-money
quality and standards.
Bedrooms: 3 single,
6 double, 2 twin, 2 triple,
1 multiple

Bathrooms: 8 private,
3 public

Bed & breakfast

per night:	£min	£max
Single	17.00	25.00
Double	34.00	50.00

Half board

per person:	£min	£max
Daily	26.00	34.00
Weekly	215.00	235.00

Lunch available
Evening meal 1900 (last
orders 2000)
Parking for 11
🏵🛌🖤🗿🗿📺⬛🚗
🅿🗿

Thorneyfield Guest
House ᴹ
🏵 COMMENDED

Compston Road, Ambleside
LA22 9DJ
☎ (053 94) 32464
Cosy family-run guesthouse in
the town centre with friendly
and helpful service. Close to
the park, miniature golf,
tennis and lake. Large family
rooms available.
Bedrooms: 1 single,
2 double, 1 twin, 1 triple,
2 multiple
Bathrooms: 2 public

Bed & breakfast

per night:	£min	£max
Single	13.00	16.00
Double	26.00	32.00

Parking for 3
🏵5🗿🖤🛌🗿📺⬛🗿
🅿🗿

Wanslea Guest
House ᴹ
🏵🏵🏵

Lake Road, Ambleside
LA22 0DB
☎ (053 94) 33884
Spacious, comfortable, family-
run Victorian house offering
good food, wines and fine
views. Easy walk to lake and
village. Honeymoons a
speciality. Brochure available.
Bedrooms: 1 single,
3 double, 3 triple, 1 multiple
Bathrooms: 4 private,
3 public

Bed & breakfast

per night:	£min	£max
Single	16.00	23.00
Double	30.00	50.00

Half board

per person:	£min	£max
Daily	28.00	30.00
Weekly	170.00	190.00

Evening meal 1845 (last
orders 1500)
🏵🛌🗿🗿🎍📺⬛🚗✿🅿
🗿🆃

AMBLESIDE

Continued

Windlehurst Guesthouse ⛰

[♛♛]

Millans Park, Ambleside
LA22 9AG
☎ (053 94) 33137

Elegant Victorian house on a peaceful road in Ambleside, with commanding views of Loughrigg fell. Within easy walking distance of amenities. No-smoking establishment.

Bedrooms: 1 single, 2 double, 2 triple, 1 multiple
Bathrooms: 1 private, 2 public

Bed & breakfast per night:	£min	£max
Single	13.00	17.00
Double	26.00	44.00

Parking for 6
Open January-October and Christmas

🐎 📖 ☕ [UL] 🔒 [S] 🚭 🛋 [TV] 🔥 👔 ✿ 🚐

APPLEBY-IN-WESTMORLAND

Cumbria
Map ref 5B3

Former county town of Westmorland, at the foot of the Pennines in the Eden Valley. The castle was rebuilt in the 17th C, except for its Norman keep, ditches and ramparts. It now houses a Rare Breeds Survival Trust Centre. Good centre for exploring the Eden Valley.
Tourist Information Centre
☎ *(076 83) 51177*

Bongate House ⛰

[♛♛♛] APPROVED

Appleby-in-Westmorland
CA16 6UE
☎ (076 83) 51245

Family-run Georgian guesthouse on the outskirts of a small market town. Large garden. Relaxed friendly atmosphere, good home cooking.

Bedrooms: 1 single, 4 double, 2 twin, 1 triple
Bathrooms: 5 private, 1 public

Bed & breakfast per night:	£min	£max
Single	16.00	16.00
Double	32.00	37.00

Half board per person:	£min	£max
Daily	23.50	26.00
Weekly	150.00	170.00

Evening meal 1900 (last orders 1800)
Parking for 10

🐎 7 ☕ 🔒 [S] 🛋 [TV] 🔥 👔 ∪ ⛳ ✿ [SP] 🏠 [T]

Meadow Ing Farm

[Listed] COMMENDED

Crackenthorpe, Appleby-in-Westmorland CA16 6AE
☎ (076 83) 52543

105-acre dairy farm. Attractive sandstone farmhouse in Eden. Beautiful views, antique-furnished rooms, friendly atmosphere, wholesome food. Private fishing available on the River Eden.

Bedrooms: 1 twin, 1 triple
Bathrooms: 2 public

Bed & breakfast per night:	£min	£max
Single	15.00	
Double	28.00	

Half board per person:	£min	£max
Daily	22.00	24.00
Weekly	154.00	168.00

Evening meal 1830 (last orders 1930)

🐎 📖 ☕ [UL] [▣] [S] 🚭 🛋 [TV] 🔥 👔 🎣 ✿ 🚐

ARNSIDE

Cumbria
Map ref 5A3

Small coastal town situated in an Area of Outstanding Natural Beauty with spectacular views over Kent Estuary of the Lakeland hills. Excellent base for bird watching. The incoming tide creates an impressive tidal bore.

Stonegate Guest House

The Promenade, Arnside, Carnforth, Lancashire
LA5 0AA
☎ (0524) 761171

Peaceful Victorian guesthouse with beautiful views over Kent estuary to Lakeland fells. Traditional and vegetarian cuisine. Charming bedrooms. Non-smoking.

Bedrooms: 1 single, 2 double, 2 triple
Bathrooms: 2 public

Bed & breakfast per night:	£min	£max
Single	16.00	16.00
Double	32.00	36.00

Evening meal 1830 (last orders 1900)
Open February-December

🐎 🖥 ☕ [UL] 🔒 [S] 🚭 🔥 👔 ✿ 🚐 [OAP] ➶

AYSIDE

Cumbria
Map ref 5A3

Browside Cottage ⛰

Ayside, Grange-over-Sands
LA11 6JE
☎ (053 95) 31500
Fax (053 95) 31857

17th C country cottage with fine Lakeland views, set in well established garden. 3 miles from foot of Lake Windermere on A590.

Bedrooms: 1 double, 1 twin
Bathrooms: 1 public

Bed & breakfast per night:	£min	£max
Single	13.50	16.50
Double	27.00	33.00

Half board per person:	£min	£max
Daily	21.00	24.00

Evening meal 2000 (last orders 2000)
Parking for 2

🐎 📖 🖥 ☕ [UL] 🔒 [S] 🚭 🛋 🔥 👔 ✿ 🚐 [OAP] ➶ [SP] 🏠

BARROW-IN-FURNESS

Cumbria
Map ref 5A3

Modern shipbuilding and industrial centre on a peninsula in Morecambe Bay. Ruins of 12th C Cistercian Furness Abbey. Sandy beaches and nature reserves on Walney Island.
Tourist Information Centre
☎ *(0229) 870156*

Inn on the Town

Cornwallis Street, Barrow-in-Furness LA14 2LG
☎ (0229) 821523
Fax (0229) 870669

Lively, comfortable, friendly hotel with nightclub and 3 theme bars. Restaurant, functions.

Bedrooms: 34 single, 11 double, 12 twin, 3 triple
Bathrooms: 60 private

Bed & breakfast per night:	£min	£max
Single	25.00	30.00
Double	35.00	40.00

Half board per person:	£min	£max
Daily	30.00	35.00
Weekly	200.00	280.00

Lunch available
Evening meal 1900 (last orders 2100)
Cards accepted: Visa

🐎 📞 🖥 ☕ 🔒 [S] 🛋 ◐ [⇕] 🔥 👔 [OAP] [SP] 🏠

BASSENTHWAITE

Cumbria
Map ref 5A2

Standing in an idyllic setting, nestled at the foot of Skiddaw and Ullock Pike, this village is just a mile from Bassenthwaite Lake, the one true 'lake' in the Lake District. The area is visited by many varieties of migrating birds.

Brook House Farm

Bassenthwaite, Keswick
CA12 4QP
☎ (076 87) 76393

250-acre mixed farm. 17th C farmhouse retaining many original features including oak beams, in a quiet picturesque village close to a stream. Self-catering cottages also available.

Bedrooms: 1 double, 1 twin
Bathrooms: 2 public

Bed & breakfast per night:	£min	£max
Double	27.00	32.00

Parking for 5
Open February-November
Cards accepted: Access, Visa

🐎 10 ☕ [UL] 🛋 [TV] 🔥 ✈ 🚐 🏠

BOOTLE

Cumbria
Map ref 5A3

An ancient settlement, once a market town, lying close to Blackcombe where the River Annas flows by the roadside. Now a quiet village.

Foldgate Farm

Corney, Bootle Village, Millom LA19 5TN
☎ (065 78) 660 & from Feb 1993 (0229) 718660

170-acre hill farming farm. 19th C farm on a scenic route between Ravenglass and Broughton. Home cooking a speciality.

Bedrooms: 2 double
Bathrooms: 1 public

Bed & breakfast per night:	£min	£max
Single	12.50	15.00
Double	24.00	26.00

Half board

per person:	£min	£max
Daily	19.00	21.00

Evening meal from 1800
Parking for 4
Open January-November
🛇 ⬛ Ⓢ ⧖ ⚄ �📺 🏬 🚗 ✿ 🏍

BORROWDALE

Cumbria
Map ref 5A3

Stretching south of Derwentwater to Seathwaite in the heart of the Lake District, the valley is walled by high crags. It can justly claim to be the most scenically impressive valley in the Lake District. Excellent centre for walking and climbing.
Tourist Information Centre
☎ *(07687) 77294*

Yew Craggs Guest House

Rosthwaite, Keswick
CA12 5XB
☎ (076 87) 77260
Beside Rosthwaite Bridge in the centre of the Borrowdale Valley. Good for walking, superb views in all directions.
Bedrooms: 3 double, 2 triple
Bathrooms: 1 public
Bed & breakfast

per night:	£min	£max
Double	28.00	38.00

Parking for 6
Open February-November
🛇 6 ⬛ ≀ ⌘ 🚗 ✕ 🏍

BRAITHWAITE

Cumbria
Map ref 5A3

Braithwaite nestles at the foot of the Whinlatter Pass and has a magnificent backdrop of the mountains forming the Coledale Horseshoe.

Coledale Inn ⋀

😃😃😃 COMMENDED
Braithwaite, Keswick
CA12 5TN
☎ (076 87) 78272
Victorian country house hotel and Georgian inn, in a peaceful hillside position away from traffic, with superb mountain views.
Bedrooms: 1 single, 5 double, 2 twin, 3 triple, 1 multiple
Bathrooms: 12 private

Bed & breakfast

per night:	£min	£max
Single	16.00	20.00
Double	43.00	51.00

Lunch available
Evening meal 1830 (last orders 2100)
Parking for 15
Cards accepted: Access, Visa
🛇 🚲 ⌘ ⚄ ⬚ ≀ Ⓢ ⧖ 🙰 🏬,
🚗 🍴 ✿ 🏍 🏵 SP 🏰

Thelmlea ⋀

😃😃😃
Braithwaite, Keswick
CA12 5TD
☎ (076 87) 78305
Country house in 1.75 acre grounds. Friendly relaxed atmosphere, log fire, home cooking. Superb views. Ideal base for walkers or touring. Within easy reach of all lakes, coast and Carlisle (30-40 minute drive).
Bedrooms: 1 double, 1 twin, 1 triple, 1 multiple
Bathrooms: 3 private, 2 public
Bed & breakfast

per night:	£min	£max
Double	30.00	38.00

Half board

per person:	£min	£max
Daily	24.00	28.00
Weekly	150.00	185.00

Evening meal from 1830
Parking for 9
🛇 ♿ 2 ⬚ 🙰 ⬛ Ⓢ ⧖ ⚄ 📺 🏬, 🚗
✿ 🏍 OAP SP Ⓣ

BRAMPTON

Cumbria
Map ref 5B2

Pleasant market town whose character has changed very little over the past 150 years. The Moot Hall, in the market square, is a fine octagonal building which stands next to the stocks. A good centre for exploring Hadrian's Wall.
Tourist Information Centre
☎ *(06977) 3433.*

Cracrop Farm ⋀

😃😃 COMMENDED
Kirkcambeck, Brampton
CA8 2BW
☎ Roadhead (076 78) 245
425-acre mixed farm. Superior accommodation on farm which has won prizes in farming and wildlife competition. Farm trails in unspoilt, picturesque countryside. Relax in sauna and spa bath.
Bedrooms: 2 double, 1 twin

Bathrooms: 3 private, 1 public
Bed & breakfast

per night:	£min	£max
Single	20.00	25.00
Double	34.00	38.00

Evening meal 1800 (last orders 1300)
Parking for 4
Cards accepted: Amex
🛇 10 ⬛ ⬚ ≀ ⬚ 🙰 ⧖ ≀
📺 🏬, 🚗 ⎑ ⊘ ✕ 🔍 ∪ ↑ ✿
🏍 SP

Halidon

😃
4 Tree Terrace, Tree Road, Brampton CA8 1TY
☎ (069 77) 2106
Delightfully restored Edwardian terraced house five minutes from town centre. Close to Roman wall amd Talkin Tarn. Home cooking and a warm welcome.
Bedrooms: 1 twin, 1 triple
Bathrooms: 1 public
Bed & breakfast

per night:	£min	£max
Single	13.00	13.00
Double	26.00	26.00

🛇 ♿ ⬚ ⬛ Ⓢ ⧖ ≀ 📺 🏬, 🏍

Hare & Hounds Inn

😃
Talkin Village, Brampton
CA8 1LE
☎ (069 77) 3456
Typical country inn with a cosy atmosphere and real ale, only 500 yards from the golf-course and Talkin Tarn with boating, fishing, swimming, windsurfing and birdwatching.
Bedrooms: 1 single, 2 double, 1 twin
Bathrooms: 2 private, 1 public
Bed & breakfast

per night:	£min	£max
Single	20.00	28.00
Double	30.00	38.00

Half board

per person:	£min	£max
Daily	22.00	35.00

Lunch available
Evening meal 1900 (last orders 2130)
Parking for 18
🛇 ⬚ ≀ ⬚ Ⓢ ⧖ ≀ 📺 🏬, 🚗 ⚄
∪ ↑ SP 🏰 Ⓣ

High Rigg Farm ⋀

😃 APPROVED
Walton, Brampton CA8 2AZ
☎ (069 77) 2117
202-acre mixed farm. 18th C listed farmhouse on roadside, 1 mile from Walton and Roman Wall, 4 miles from Brampton. Family-run with

---

pedigree cattle and sheep, farm trail.
Bedrooms: 1 triple
Bathrooms: 1 public
Bed & breakfast

per night:	£min	£max
Single	14.00	15.00
Double	27.00	28.00

Half board

per person:	£min	£max
Daily	22.00	23.00
Weekly	150.00	155.00

Evening meal 1800 (last orders 1400)
Parking for 4
🛇 ⬚ ⬚ ≀ 🙰 ⬚ 🙰 ⧖ ≀
📺 🏬, 🚗 ≀ ∪ ⎑ ✿ ✕ 🏍
SP 🏰

Howard House Farm ⋀

😃😃 COMMENDED
Gilsland, Carlisle CA6 7AN
☎ Gilsland (069 77) 47285
250-acre livestock farm. Peaceful farm in comfortable and friendly surroundings, 7 miles north-east of Brampton and at centre of Roman wall.
Bedrooms: 1 double, 1 twin, 1 triple
Bathrooms: 1 private, 2 public
Bed & breakfast

per night:	£min	£max
Double	30.00	36.00

Half board

per person:	£min	£max
Daily	24.00	27.00

Evening meal 1800 (last orders 1800)
Parking for 4
🛇 ♿ ⬚ ⬛ 🙰 Ⓢ ⧖ 📺 🏬, ⚄
⎑ ✿ ✕ 🏍 OAP SP

Miller Hill

Listed
The Banks, Brampton
CA6 7DE
☎ Gilsland (069 77) 47298
Situated on Hadrian's Wall, 2.5 miles from Birdoswald, 3 miles from Lanercost Priory. Housesteads and Scottish border within easy reach.
Bedrooms: 1 double, 1 triple
Bathrooms: 1 public
Bed & breakfast

per night:	£min	£max
Single	13.00	14.00
Double	25.00	27.00

Open May-October
🛇 ⬛ 🙰 ⬚ 📺 🏬, ✿ 🏍

The symbols are explained on the flap inside the back cover.

BRIGSTEER

Cumbria
Map ref 5A3

Low Plain Farmhouse

😋😋 APPROVED

Brigsteer, Kendal LA8 8AX
☎ (044 88) 323
*Quiet country farmhouse
nestling in the Lake District
National Park. Evening meal,
traditional English home
cooking available on request.*
Bedrooms: 1 double, 1 twin,
1 triple
Bathrooms: 2 public

Bed & breakfast

per night:	£min	£max
Double	30.00	36.00

Evening meal 1830 (last
orders 2000)
Parking for 4
Open January-October

🛇 ♨ 🖥 ⑤ 🛏 📺 ▥ ▱ ❀ 🤸

BROUGHTON-IN-FURNESS

Cumbria
Map ref 5A3

Old market village whose
historic charter to hold
fairs is still proclaimed
every year on the first day
of August in the market
square. Good centre for
touring the pretty Duddon
Valley.

Broom Hill

Broughton-in-Furness
LA20 6JD
☎ (0229) 716358
*Manor house with large
secluded gardens and fine
views. All usual facilities.*
Bedrooms: 3 double
Bathrooms: 2 private,
1 public

Bed & breakfast

per night:	£min	£max
Single	17.00	18.50
Double	34.00	37.00

Parking for 7
Open April-October

🛇 ♨ ▯ ♨ 🖥 ⑤ ▥ ▱ ◉ 🤸

Cobblers Cottage ⚠

😋 APPROVED

Griffin Street, Broughton-in-Furness LA20 6HH
☎ (0229) 716413
*Quaint 17th C cottage offering
delicious food in a cosy and
relaxed atmosphere. Ideally
situated for exploring South
Lakes and beautiful Duddon
Valley.*
Bedrooms: 2 double, 1 twin
Bathrooms: 1 private,
1 public

Bed & breakfast

per night:	£min	£max
Single	14.50	17.50
Double	29.00	35.00

Half board

per person:	£min	£max
Daily	25.00	28.00
Weekly	168.00	189.00

Evening meal 1900 (last
orders 1700)

🛇 ♨ 🖥 ⑤ 🛏 📺 ▥ ▱ 🤸 ⑤🏠

The Hill Farm ⚠

Heathwaite, Grizebeck,
Kirkby-in-Furness LA17 7XP
☎ (022 989) 706
*100-acre livestock farm.
Beautiful oak-beamed
farmhouse, fully modernised.
Set in peaceful, unspoilt Lake
District valley with
magnificent views, between
Coniston and Broughton-in-
Furness. Home-baked bread
and free-range eggs. TV on
request.*
Bedrooms: 1 double, 1 twin,
1 triple
Bathrooms: 2 public

Bed & breakfast

per night:	£min	£max
Double	30.00	37.00

Parking for 6
Open March-November

🛇 ▯ ♨ 🖥 ⑤ 🛏 📺 ▥ ▱ ❀ ✗ 🤸

BUTTERMERE

Cumbria
Map ref 5A3

Small village surrounded
by high mountains,
between Buttermere lake
and Crummock Water. An
ideal centre for walking
and climbing the nearby
peaks and for touring.

Pickett Howe ⚠

😋😋😋 DE LUXE

Brackenthwaite, Buttermere
Valley, Cockermouth
CA13 9UY
☎ Lorton (0900) 85444
*Well-appointed 17th C
longhouse, peacefully situated
between Crummock and
Loweswater Lakes off the
B5289, 4 miles from
Buttermere. Renowned for
creative cooking and relaxing
atmosphere.*
Bedrooms: 3 double, 1 twin
Bathrooms: 4 private

Bed & breakfast

per night:	£min	£max
Double	58.00	66.00

Half board

per person:	£min	£max
Daily	45.50	49.50
Weekly	318.50	

Evening meal 1915 (last
orders 1915)
Parking for 6
Open March-November and
Christmas
Cards accepted: Access, Visa

🛇 10 ⤵ 🖥 ▯ ♨ 🛏 ⑤ ✂ 🤸 ▥ ▱ ♨ ⟲ 🌙 �📷 ❀ 🤸 ⟲ ⑤ 🏠 ⛃

CALDBECK

Cumbria
Map ref 5A2

Quaint limestone village
lying on the northern
fringe of the Lake District
National Park. John Peel,
the famous huntsman
who is immortalised in
song, is buried in the
churchyard. The fells
surrounding Caldbeck
were once heavily mined,
being rich in lead, copper
and barytes.

Friar Hall ⚠

Listed

Caldbeck, Wigton CA7 8DS
☎ (069 98) 633
*140-acre mixed farm. In the
lovely village of Caldbeck
overlooking the river. Ideal
for touring the Lakes and
Scottish Borders. On Cumbria
Way route.*
Bedrooms: 2 double, 1 triple
Bathrooms: 2 public

Bed & breakfast

per night:	£min	£max
Single	15.00	16.00
Double	28.00	30.00

Parking for 3
Open March-November

🛇 ♨ 🖥 📺 ▱ ✗ 🤸

The Height Farm ⚠

Caldbeck, Wigton CA7 0LU
☎ (069 98) 668
*240-acre livestock farm.
Spacious and comfortable
18th C farmhouse with
panoramic views of the
Skiddaw Fells and Caldbeck
Village. Ideal base for
Hadrian's Wall, Eden Valley,
Solway and Lake District.*
Bedrooms: 1 double, 1 twin,
1 multiple
Bathrooms: 2 public

Bed & breakfast

per night:	£min	£max
Single	13.00	14.00
Double	26.00	28.00

Half board

per person:	£min	£max
Daily	19.00	20.00
Weekly	133.00	140.00

Evening meal 1800 (last
orders 1000)
Parking for 12

🛇 ▯ 🖥 ⑤ 🛏 📺 ▥ ▱ ✕ ❀ 🤸 ⛃

Parkend Restaurant and Country Hotel

😋😋😋 COMMENDED

Parkend, Caldbeck, Wigton
CA7 8HH
☎ (069 98) 494
*17th C farmhouse restaurant
with en-suite rooms, situated
1.5 miles west of Caldbeck.
Birthplace of the legendary
John Peel.*
Bedrooms: 3 double
Bathrooms: 3 private

Bed & breakfast

per night:	£min	£max
Double	45.00	45.00

Lunch available
Evening meal 1900 (last
orders 2200)
Parking for 16
Cards accepted: Access, Visa,
Amex

🛇 ▯ ⤵ ♨ 🖥 ⑤ ✂ 🛏 📺 ▥ ▱ ❀ ⑤ 🏠

CARLISLE

Cumbria
Map ref 5A2

Near Scottish border, this
cathedral city suffered
years of strife through the
centuries, often changing
hands between England
and Scotland. The red
sandstone cathedral is
the second smallest in
England. Castle founded
in 1092 now houses a
museum.
*Tourist Information Centre
☎ (0228) 512444*

Abbey Court

Listed

24 London Road, Carlisle
CA1 2EL
☎ (0228) 28696
*Family-run guesthouse, close
to city centre, central for
Scotland/Lakes, on main
thoroughfare. 5 minutes'
walking distance from station.
Easy access M6 junction 42.*
Bedrooms: 3 single,
3 double, 6 twin, 5 triple
Bathrooms: 6 public

Bed & breakfast

per night:	£min	£max
Single	15.00	20.00
Double	25.00	30.00

Half board

per person:	£min	£max
Daily	20.00	25.00

Evening meal 1800 (last orders 1900)

🛇🍴⌶☐🛎🟦🛏🆂🌀🕭▥, 🍳
🅾🅰🆂🆂🅿🆃⟋

Beech Croft
😃😃 COMMENDED

Aglionby, Carlisle CA4 8AQ
☎ (0228) 513762
Spacious, modern, detached house in a delightful rural setting. 1 mile on the A69 from M6 junction 43. High quality accommodation in a friendly family atmosphere.
Bedrooms: 1 single, 2 double
Bathrooms: 1 private, 2 public

Bed & breakfast

per night:	£min	£max
Single	17.00	17.00
Double	34.00	38.00

Parking for 4

🛇3🕮☐🛏🟦🆂🕭▥,
🍳🆎

The Beeches M
Listed   DE LUXE

Wood Street, Carlisle
CA1 2SF
☎ (0228) 511962
Situated in Carlisle's unique award-winning street and quiet conservation area, an 18th C grade II listed period residence. Laura Ashley furnishings, every attention to detail and comfort. Finalist in English Tourist Board's award of Excellence for Bed and Breakfast 1991. 1 mile from M6 exit 43 and city centre. Private parking.
Bedrooms: 1 double, 2 twin
Bathrooms: 1 public

Bed & breakfast

per night:	£min	£max
Double	30.00	35.00

Parking for 6

🛇🕮☐🛏🟦🛎🆂▥,🍳⟋
🗙🆎🆂🅿

Blue Bell Inn M
😃

Sowerby Row, Carlisle
CA4 0QQ
☎ Raughton Head (069 96) 363
Idyllic 18th C country pub, 8 miles from M6 junction 41. Extensive bar menu offered in homely atmosphere. Walking, fishing, horse riding, shooting available locally.
Bedrooms: 1 double, 1 twin, 1 triple
Bathrooms: 1 public

Bed & breakfast

per night:	£min	£max
Single	14.00	16.50
Double	28.00	33.00

Lunch available
Evening meal 1900 (last orders 2100)
Parking for 30

🛇🕮☐🛏🌀🔌🆎🕭▥,🍳
🝙🕽⟋☼🗙🆎🅰🆎🅿🆏

Craighead M
😃😃

6 Hartington Place, Carlisle
CA1 1HL
☎ (0228) 27443
Attractive Victorian town house with spacious rooms and original features. Minutes' walk to city centre, bus and rail stations. Friendly and comfortable. Fresh farm food.
Bedrooms: 2 double, 1 twin
Bathrooms: 2 public

Bed & breakfast

per night:	£min	£max
Single	15.00	17.00
Double	28.00	32.00

🛇🕮☐🛏🌀🆂🌀🕭▥,🍳
🆎🅿🆏

East View En Suite Guest House M
Listed

110 Warwick Road, Carlisle
CA1 1JU
☎ (0228) 22112
All rooms en-suite, with colour TV. 10 minutes from buses, railway, city centre, restaurants, river walks.
Bedrooms: 2 single, 2 double, 1 twin, 1 triple, 3 multiple
Bathrooms: 9 private

Bed & breakfast

per night:	£min	£max
Single	15.00	20.00
Double	28.00	35.00

Parking for 4

🛇☐🛏🟦🛎🆂🟡▥,🍳🆎

The Gill Farm M
😃

Blackford, Carlisle CA6 4EL
☎ Kirklinton (0228) 75326
124-acre arable & livestock farm. Ideal halfway stopping place or a good base for touring Cumbria's beauty spots. In peaceful countryside, 3 miles from the M6 junction 44. From Carlisle go north to Blackford, fork right at sign for Cliff and Kirklinton, after 100 yards turn right, half a mile turn left, Gill Farm on left on this road.
Bedrooms: 1 double, 1 twin, 1 triple
Bathrooms: 2 public

Bed & breakfast

per night:	£min	£max
Single	15.00	18.00
Double	28.00	33.00

Half board

per person:	£min	£max
Daily	22.00	24.00
Weekly	140.00	145.00

Evening meal 1800 (last orders 1600)
Parking for 6
Open January-November

🛇🔌🟦🅰🔌🕭▥,🍳⟋☼
🆎🆏

Howard House
😃😃😃 COMMENDED

27 Howard Place, Carlisle
CA1 1HR
☎ (0228) 29159
Lawrence and Sandra invite you to their spacious Victorian home in quiet location. City centre, bus/rail stations, riverside walks. Four-poster en-suite rooms. Home cooking. Family historians welcome.
Bedrooms: 1 single, 1 double, 1 twin, 2 multiple
Bathrooms: 2 private, 2 public

Bed & breakfast

per night:	£min	£max
Single	14.00	16.00
Double	28.00	34.00

Half board

per person:	£min	£max
Daily	21.00	23.00
Weekly	140.00	154.00

Evening meal 1800 (last orders 1000)

🛇🆎🕮☐🔌🟦🛎🆂🌀🕭
▥,🍳▸🅿

Kenilworth
34 Lazonby Terrace, London Road, Carlisle CA1 2PZ
☎ (0228) 26179
Small family-run guesthouse which is an excellent base for touring the Lake District and the Borders.
Bedrooms: 1 single, 2 double, 1 twin, 2 multiple
Bathrooms: 2 public

Bed & breakfast

per night:	£min	£max
Single	13.00	15.00
Double	24.00	26.00

Parking for 5

🛇🅼☐🔌🆎🌀🕭▥,🆏

New Pallyards M
😃😃😃 COMMENDED

Hethersgill, Carlisle CA6 6HZ
☎ Nicholforest (0228) 577 308
65-acre mixed farm. 18th C farmhouse, modernised to a good standard, offering a

---

warm welcome in peaceful surroundings. Gold award winner of 1989 Cookery & Food Association's "Great British Breakfast" competition. Filmed for BBC TV's "The Visit".
Bedrooms: 1 single, 2 double, 1 twin, 1 triple
Bathrooms: 3 private, 1 public, 1 private shower

Bed & breakfast

per night:	£min	£max
Single	18.00	20.00
Double	36.00	38.00

Half board

per person:	£min	£max
Daily	28.00	30.00
Weekly	120.00	125.00

Lunch available
Evening meal 1900 (last orders 1930)
Parking for 7

🛇🆎🛏🆂🟡🅰🕭▥,🍳🝙
⟋⟋🆎🆎🆏

Riverston Guest House M
Listed

68 St. James Road, Denton Holme, Carlisle CA2 5PD
☎ (0228) 20825 & 818060
Large Victorian house 15 minutes west of the city centre, in quiet residential area. Close to River Caldew, park, bowling greens, shopping area.
Bedrooms: 2 single, 2 double, 2 twin, 1 multiple
Bathrooms: 2 public

Bed & breakfast

per night:	£min	£max
Single	15.50	
Double	30.00	

Half board

per person:	£min	£max
Daily	21.00	

Evening meal 1800 (last orders 2000)
Parking for 3

🛇☐🔌🟦🆂🟡▥,🍳🗙🆎
🅾🆎🆃

Saffron House
Wetheral, Carlisle CA4 8HL
☎ (0228) 561280
Spacious, private, self-contained suite of rooms in quiet country village. Good English breakfasts, private parking, warm friendly atmosphere.
Bedrooms: 1 double
Bathrooms: 1 private

Bed & breakfast

per night:	£min	£max
Double	30.00	30.00

Parking for 2

🛇🆎☐🔌🔌🟦🛎🟡
▥,🍳☼🗙🆏

CARLISLE

Continued

Streethead Farm ⋀

Listed

Ivegill, Carlisle CA4 ONG
☎ Southwaite (069 74)
73327
*211-acre mixed & dairy farm.
Distant hills, log fires, home
cooking on working farm
between Penrith and Carlisle
(8 miles). 10 minutes from
junctions 41 and 42 of M6.
Ideal for Lakes or Scotland.
Brochure available.*
Bedrooms: 1 double, 1 triple
Bathrooms: 1 public

Bed & breakfast

per night:	£min	£max
Single	13.00	15.00
Double	26.00	28.00

Half board

per person:	£min	£max
Daily	21.00	23.00

Evening meal 1830 (last
orders 1000)
Parking for 2
Open March-October
🐕7 🖿 🛉 S 📺 ⅏ U ✿ ✗
🛵 🏰

CARTMEL

Cumbria
Map ref 5A3

Picturesque conserved
village based on a 12th C
priory with a well-
preserved church and
gatehouse. Just half a
mile outside the National
Park, this is a peaceful
base for walking and
touring, with historic
houses and beautiful
scenery.

Eeabank House ⋀

🍴

123 Station Road, Cark in
Cartmel, Grange-over-Sands
LA11 7NY
☎ Flookburgh (053 95)
58818
*Family-run guesthouse close
to Holker Hall and gardens,
easy access to Lakes, good
country walks. Ideal for
touring.*
Bedrooms: 1 double, 1 twin,
1 triple
Bathrooms: 1 private,
1 public

Bed & breakfast

per night:	£min	£max
Single	14.50	17.00
Double	29.00	34.00

Half board

per person:	£min	£max
Daily	21.00	22.50
Weekly	140.00	155.00

Lunch available
Evening meal 1830 (last
orders 2100)
Parking for 3
Cards accepted: Access, Visa
🐕 👶 📺 🛉 S ⅏ 📺 ⅏ 🍴
🛵 🏰 DAP ✗ SP

CARTMEL FELL

Cumbria
Map ref 5A3

Small village set in
tranquil countryside in an
upland area of great
beauty. Noted for its 16th
C church with 3-tiered
pulpit.

Lightwood Farmhouse ⋀

♛♛♛ COMMENDED

Cartmel Fell, Bowland
Bridge, Grange-over-Sands
LA11 6NP
☎ Newby Bridge (053 95)
31454
*17th C farmhouse with
original oak beams. Extensive
views, large garden with
streams. Home cooking. Just
off the A592 near Bowland
Bridge.*
Bedrooms: 5 double, 3 twin,
1 triple
Bathrooms: 8 private,
1 public

Bed & breakfast

per night:	£min	£max
Double	33.00	

Half board

per person:	£min	£max
Daily	26.50	
Weekly	110.00	

Evening meal 1900 (last
orders 2100)
Parking for 9
Cards accepted: Access, Visa
🐕 👶 🛉 S ⅏ 📺 ⅏ 🍴 🍴 ✿
✗ 🛵 🏰

Individual
proprietors have
supplied all details
of accommodation.
Although we do
check for accuracy,
we advise you to
confirm the
information at the
time of booking.

COCKERMOUTH

Cumbria
Map ref 5A2

An ancient market town
at confluence of Rivers
Cocker and Derwent.
Birthplace of William
Wordsworth in 1770, the
house where he was born
is at the end of the
town's broad, tree-lined
main street and is now
owned by the National
Trust. Good touring base
for the Lakes.
Tourist Information Centre
☎ *(0900) 822634*

Crag End Farm

Listed

Rogerscale, Lorton,
Cockermouth CA13 0RG
☎ (090 085) 658
*250-acre mixed farm. In
lovely surroundings and ideal
for families, this peaceful
working family farm is
convenient for the Lakes, the
shops and many walks. Home
cooking using home-grown
produce.*
Bedrooms: 1 double, 1 twin,
1 multiple
Bathrooms: 2 public

Bed & breakfast

per night:	£min	£max
Single	15.00	
Double	30.00	

Half board

per person:	£min	£max
Daily	22.00	
Weekly	154.00	

Evening meal 1800 (last
orders 1800)
Parking for 10
🐕 ⅏ 🛉 📺 / ✿ ✗ 🛵 🏰

CONISTON

Cumbria
Map ref 5A3

Born from the mining
industry, this village lies at
the north end of Coniston
Water. The scenery to the
rear of the village is
dominated by Coniston
Old Man. Its most famous
resident was John Ruskin,
whose home, Brentwood,
is open to the public.
Good centre for walking.
Tourist Information Centre
☎ *(05394) 41533.*

Arrowfield ⋀

♛♛ HIGHLY COMMENDED

Little Arrow, Coniston
LA21 8AU
☎ (053 94) 41741

*Elegant 19th C Lakeland
house in beautiful rural
setting. Adjacent to Coniston/
Torver road (A593). 2 miles
from Coniston village.*
Bedrooms: 1 single,
2 double, 2 twin
Bathrooms: 2 private,
1 public

Bed & breakfast

per night:	£min	£max
Single	17.00	19.00
Double	32.00	42.00

Half board

per person:	£min	£max
Daily	28.00	33.00
Weekly	186.00	221.00

Evening meal from 1900
Parking for 6
Open March-November
🐕3 ⅏ 🛉 S ✗ ⅏ 📺 🍴 ✿
✗ 🛵 SP

Wilson Arms

Torver, Coniston LA21 8BB
☎ (053 94) 41237
Fax (053 94) 41590
*In the small village of Torver,
2.5 miles from Coniston. Ideal
walking area. Central for all
lakes. Meals available in
restaurant.*
Bedrooms: 5 double, 1 twin,
1 triple
Bathrooms: 7 private

Bed & breakfast

per night:	£min	£max
Single	25.00	25.00
Double	35.00	39.00

Lunch available
Evening meal 1800 (last
orders 2100)
Parking for 20
Cards accepted: Access, Visa
🐕 ⅏ 🛉 S ✗ ⅏ 🍴 🍴 🍴 🍴
✿ ✗ 🛵 SP

Yewdale Hotel ⋀

♛♛♛ COMMENDED

Yewdale Road, Coniston
LA21 8LU
☎ (053 94) 41280
*Built of local materials in
1896 as a bank, now a
modern hotel skilfully
refurbished throughout.
Reduced rate breaks available.*
Bedrooms: 5 double, 2 twin,
3 triple
Bathrooms: 10 private,
2 public

Bed & breakfast

per night:	£min	£max
Single	20.00	30.00
Double	40.00	60.00

Half board

per person:	£min	£max
Daily	31.50	39.00
Weekly	165.00	228.00

Lunch available
Evening meal (last orders
2100)

Parking for 6
Cards accepted: Access, Visa
🐕🍴🖥❄🏃🅿💲✂🎿🛏🅲
🅰🚶🔔🎫 DAP 🔌 SP 🏠

COWGILL
Cumbria
Map ref 5B3

Birk Rigg
♔
Cowgill, Sedbergh LA10 5RH
☎ Dent (058 75) 367
*Thoughtfully renovated
Yorkshire farmhouse. 3.5
miles to the east of Dent, Birk
Rigg enjoys superb panoramic
views of Dentdale.*
Bedrooms: 1 double, 1 twin,
1 triple
Bathrooms: 2 public
Bed & breakfast

per night:	£min	£max
Single	13.50	14.50
Double	27.00	29.00

Parking for 6
🐕🍴❄🅲💲✂📺🛏🅰
🚶❄

CROSTHWAITE
Cumbria
Map ref 5A3

The Punch Bowl Inn
Crosthwaite, Kendal
LA8 8HR
☎ (053 95) 68237
*Coaching inn with bar food,
choice of oak beamed rooms,
log fires. 3 bedrooms with
private facilities and 4-poster
beds. Adjacent to Crosthwaite
Church in the Lyth Valley. 5
miles from Windermere and
Kendal.*
Bedrooms: 3 double
Bathrooms: 3 private
Bed & breakfast

per night:	£min	£max
Single	25.00	25.00
Double	40.00	40.00

Lunch available
Evening meal 1830 (last
orders 2130)
Parking for 100
Cards accepted: Access, Visa
🐕🍴🖥❄💲🛏🔴🚶 SP

CULGAITH
Cumbria
Map ref 5B2

Elm Tree Barn
Culgaith, Penrith CA10 1QW
☎ Penrith (0768) 88730
*300-year-old barn converted to
a high standard, set in
tranquil, picturesque
countryside with views over
Eden Valley, yet just 1 mile
from A66.*

Bedrooms: 1 double, 2 twin
Bathrooms: 2 public
Bed & breakfast

per night:	£min	£max
Single	13.50	13.50
Double	27.00	27.00

Parking for 4
🐕♿❄🆄🅿✂🛏📺🅲🔴♻
🐾🚶🏠

DENT
Cumbria
Map ref 5B3

Very picturesque village
with narrow cobbled
streets lying within the
boundaries of the
Yorkshire Dales National
Park.

Sun Inn ♈
Main Street, Dent, Sedbergh
LA10 5QL
☎ (058 75) 208
*17th C inn with original
beams, in an outstanding
conservation area. Reputation
for good value bar meals and
serves beer from the local
Dent Brewery.*
Bedrooms: 1 double, 1 twin,
1 triple
Bathrooms: 1 public
Bed & breakfast

per night:	£min	£max
Single	15.50	23.00
Double	26.00	31.00

Half board

per person:	£min	£max
Daily	20.50	28.00
Weekly	126.00	126.00

Lunch available
Evening meal 1830 (last
orders 2030)
Parking for 20
Cards accepted: Access, Visa,
Switch
🐕🍴❄🅲💲✂🛏🔴🔵🚶
🐾🎫 DAP SP 🏠 🆃

ELTERWATER
Cumbria
Map ref 5A3

Attractive village at the
foot of Great Langdale
with a small village green
as its focal point.
Elterwater, one of the
smallest lakes in the Lake
District, was named by
the Norsemen as 'Swan
Lake' and swans still
frequent the lake.

Barnhowe ♈
Lane Ends, Elterwater,
Ambleside LA22 9HW
☎ (096 67) 346
*Traditional stone house on
Elterwater Common, with*

*former smithy barns
converted into spinning and
weaving workshops. Spinning
tuition available. Guests asked
not to smoke or to bring dogs
into the house.*
Bedrooms: 1 single,
1 double, 1 twin
Bathrooms: 1 public
Bed & breakfast

per night:	£min	£max
Single	14.00	15.00
Double	28.00	30.00

Parking for 6
Open February-December
🐕🍴❄🆄🅲💲✂📺🛏🔴
❄🚶🏠

Fellside
3 & 4 Lane Ends,
Elterwater, Ambleside
LA22 9HN
☎ Langdale (096 67) 678
*In the heart of the Langdales,
ideal for fell walking and
peaceful holidays.*
Bedrooms: 1 single,
1 double, 1 twin
Bathrooms: 1 public
Bed & breakfast

per night:	£min	£max
Single	14.50	
Double	29.00	

Half board

per person:	£min	£max
Daily	24.50	

Evening meal from 1900
Parking for 4
🐕6🅲🛏🔴🚶🐾🏠

GARRIGILL
Cumbria
Map ref 5B2

Tynehead
Garrigill, Alston CA9
☎ (0434) 381402 & 091-488
1881
*Recently converted 17th C
miners' cottage/barns at head
of South Tyne. Glorious views
of valley, river and waterfalls.*
Bedrooms: 1 double, 1 twin
Bathrooms: 1 public
Bed & breakfast

per night:	£min	£max
Single	14.00	17.50
Double	28.00	35.00

Half board

per person:	£min	£max
Daily	18.00	21.50
Weekly	112.00	133.00

Parking for 3
🐕♻❄🆄💲✂📺🛏🔴
❄🚶🏠

┌─────────────────────┐
│ We advise you to   │
│ confirm your   │
│ booking in writing. │
└─────────────────────┘

GRANGE-OVER-SANDS
Cumbria
Map ref 5A3

This restful seaside resort
overlooks Morecambe
Bay, with pleasant
seafront walks and
beautiful gardens. The
bay attracts many species
of wading birds.
*Tourist Information Centre
☎ (053 95) 34026.*

High Bank
Methven Road, Grange-over-
Sands LA11 7DU
☎ (053 95) 32902
*Spacious Victorian house in
quiet situation, with attractive
and interesting garden and
sea views. Close to all
amenities.*
Bedrooms: 1 single,
1 double, 1 twin
Bathrooms: 1 public
Bed & breakfast

per night:	£min	£max
Single	13.50	13.50
Double	27.00	27.00

Half board

per person:	£min	£max
Daily	20.00	20.00
Weekly	140.00	140.00

Evening meal from 1830
Parking for 2
🐕5❄🆄📺🛏🔴❄🚶🏠

Prospect House Hotel ♈
♔♔ APPROVED
Kents Bank Road, Grange-
over-Sands LA11 7DJ
☎ (053 95) 32116
*Our best advertisement is the
many return visits we receive
every year. Imaginative meals
and a friendly welcome are
guaranteed.*
Bedrooms: 5 double, 2 twin
Bathrooms: 6 private,
1 public
Bed & breakfast

per night:	£min	£max
Single	20.00	25.50
Double	36.50	42.00

Half board

per person:	£min	£max
Daily	27.50	32.00
Weekly	180.00	198.00

Evening meal 1845 (last
orders 1530)
Parking for 5
🐕6🍴🖥❄🅲💲✂🛏🔴
❄🐾🔌 SP

GRASMERE

Cumbria
Map ref 5A3

Described by William Wordsworth as 'the loveliest spot that man hath ever found', this village is in a beautiful setting overlooked by Helm Crag, famed for its gingerbread. Wordsworth lived at Dove Cottage. The cottage and museum are open to the public. *Tourist Information Centre ☎ (05394) 35245.*

Bramriggs
Listed   APPROVED

Grasmere, Ambleside
LA22 9RU
☎ (053 94) 35360
Small country house with garden bordering footpath to Helvellyn. Tranquil setting, spectacular views of almost entire valley. 1 mile north of Grasmere village. Lovely walking country.
Bedrooms: 1 single,
1 double, 1 twin
Bathrooms: 1 public
Bed & breakfast

per night:	£min	£max
Single	16.00	17.00
Double	32.00	36.00

Parking for 7
ᗧᓍᏉ⊡🖤⊞🅸🆂 ⊤🆅 ⊞, 🖉 ❄ 🐾

Craigside House ⋀
😄😄 COMMENDED

Grasmere, Ambleside
LA22 9SG
☎ (053 94) 35292
Delightfully furnished Victorian house on the edge of the village near Dove Cottage. In a large, peaceful garden overlooking the lake and hills.
Bedrooms: 2 double, 1 twin
Bathrooms: 3 private

Bed & breakfast

per night:	£min	£max
Single	25.50	49.00
Double	51.00	57.50

Parking for 6
ᗧᓍᏉ⊡🖤⊞🅸⋀⊞,🖉❄🗡 🐾🍃

Fairy Glen Guest House
Swan Lane, Grasmere, Ambleside LA22 9RH
☎ (053 94) 35620
Well situated, fine views of surrounding fields and fells. Ample facilities. Two rooms with own shower. Large sitting room. Fully heated. Private parking.
Bedrooms: 1 double, 2 twin
Bathrooms: 1 public,
2 private showers
Bed & breakfast

per night:	£min	£max
Double	32.00	36.00

Parking for 3
🖤⊞🅸⋀⊤🆅⊞,❄🐾🅂🄿

Harwood Hotel ⋀
Red Lion Square, Grasmere, Ambleside LA22 9SP
☎ (053 94) 35248
Family-run hotel in the heart of Grasmere. Comfortable rooms all with private facilities and TV. Ideal for exploring the Lake District.
Bedrooms: 1 single,
5 double, 1 twin
Bathrooms: 7 private
Bed & breakfast

per night:	£min	£max
Single	23.50	27.50
Double	47.00	55.00

Evening meal 1900 (last orders 1930)
Parking for 8
Open January-November
Cards accepted: Access, Visa
ᗧᓍᏉ⊡🖤🅸🆂⊬⋀⊞,🖉🗡 🐾🅂🄿

Travellers Rest ⋀
Grasmere, Ambleside
LA22 9RR
☎ (053 94) 35604
Charming 17th C inn nestling in the heart of Lakeland and with superb views. Cumbrian hospitality includes good food, lovely ales, open fires and comfortable accommodation.
Bedrooms: 1 single,
3 double, 2 twin, 1 triple
Bathrooms: 2 public
Bed & breakfast

per night:	£min	£max
Single	19.50	22.50
Double	39.00	43.00

Half board

per person:	£min	£max
Daily	24.50	34.50
Weekly	157.50	180.00

Lunch available
Evening meal 1900 (last orders 2130)
Parking for 45
ᗧᏄ⊑🖤🅸🆂⊞,🖉🍷❄ 🐾🖎🅂🄿

GRAYRIGG

Cumbria
Map ref 5B3

Punchbowl House
Grayrigg, Kendal LA8 9BU
☎ (053 984) 345 & Early 93 (0539) 824345
Renovated spacious Victorian farmhouse with log fires, ideal for Howgills and east Lakes. Non-smokers only please.
Bedrooms: 2 double, 1 twin
Bathrooms: 1 private,
1 public
Bed & breakfast

per night:	£min	£max
Single	15.50	15.50
Double	31.00	37.00

Parking for 6
ᗧ5⊡🖤🄿⊡🅸🆂⊬⋀⊞, 🖉🗡🐾🅂🄿

GREAT ASBY

Cumbria
Map ref 5B3

Asby Grange
Listed

Great Asby, Appleby-in-Westmorland CA16 6HF
☎ Appleby (076 83) 52881
300-acre mixed farm. 18th C farmhouse in beautiful and peaceful countryside. Ideal for touring Lakes and Yorkshire Dales. Convenient for M6.
Bedrooms: 2 double
Bathrooms: 1 public
Bed & breakfast

per night:	£min	£max
Double	24.00	28.00

Parking for 4
Open April-October
ᗧ🖤⊞🅸⋀⊤🆅⊞,🐾

GREENODD

Cumbria
Map ref 5A3

Machell Arms
Greenodd Village, Ulverston LA12 7QZ
☎ (0229) 861 246
Family-run pub in hillside village. 5 miles Windermere, 5 miles Coniston Water. Log fire, home-made food and real ale. Warm welcome.
Bedrooms: 2 triple,
1 multiple
Bathrooms: 1 public
Bed & breakfast

per night:	£min	£max
Single	13.50	15.00
Double	24.00	28.00

Half board

per person:	£min	£max
Daily	17.00	22.00
Weekly	112.00	150.00

Lunch available
Evening meal 1800 (last orders 2030)
Parking for 7
ᗧᏄ⊡🖤🅸🆂🖉🍷

the BIRKS

A secluded and peaceful 17th century Lakeland farmhouse set in two acres of gardens and surrounded by the beautiful scenery of the unspoilt Lyth Valley. A family-run guesthouse with a warm welcome.

Underbarrow is a small village within the National Park. It nestles in an enchanting location yet is only 6 miles from Lake Windermere, and is convenient for access to all parts of the Lake District. The area is ideal for walking and cycling and has many varied routes. Non-smoking. Please phone for brochure.

The Birks, Underbarrow, Cumbria LA8 8HJ
Tel : (053 95) 68360

HAVERTHWAITE

Cumbria
Map ref 5A3

Set in the Levens Valley
south-west of Newby
Bridge, on the north bank
of River Leven.
Headquarters of the
Lakeside and
Haverthwaite Railway
Company.

The Coach House ⋒

Hollow Oak, Haverthwaite,
Ulverston LA12 8AD
☎ (053 95) 31622
*Friendly and comfortable
coach house with original
beams. Garden. Convenient
for Holker Hall, Coniston and
Windermere. Non-smokers
only please.*
Bedrooms: 2 double, 1 twin
Bathrooms: 2 public

Bed & breakfast

per night:	£min	£max
Double	24.00	30.00

Parking for 3
Open March-October
🛁🕯💷🌡☂📺🛏❄✗✦🚲

HAWKSHEAD

Cumbria
Map ref 5A3

Lying near Esthwaite
Water, this village has
great charm and
character. Its small
squares are linked by
flagged or cobbled alleys
and the main square is
dominated by the market
house or Shambles where
the butchers had their
stalls in days gone by.
Tourist Information Centre
☎ *(05394) 36525.*

Balla Wray Cottage ⋒

High Wray, Ambleside
LA22 0JQ
☎ (053 94) 32401
*Lakeland stone cottage on
west side of Windermere lake
in quiet secluded position
with views over the lake.
Balla Wray is shown on
Ordnance Survey map
(reference SD378999).*
Bedrooms: 1 double, 1 twin
Bathrooms: 2 private

Bed & breakfast

per night:	£min	£max
Double	50.00	50.00

Parking for 2
🛁🖃🕯💷🎖§✗🛏🚲❄🚲

Foxgloves ⋒

Hawkshead, Ambleside
LA22 0NR
☎ (053 94) 36352
*Comfortable accommodation
quietly situated on the edge of
the village. Home cooking.
Superb views from every
room. Visitors' lounge with
colour TV. Non-smokers only,
please.*
Bedrooms: 2 double, 1 twin
Bathrooms: 1 private,
1 public

Bed & breakfast

per night:	£min	£max
Double	29.00	36.00

Half board

per person:	£min	£max
Daily	22.00	26.00
Weekly	147.00	168.00

Evening meal from 1800
Parking for 3
🛁🕯💷🖃§🎖📺🛏 🚲 OAP SP

High Grassings ⋒

Sunny Brow, Outgate,
Ambleside LA22 0PU
☎ (053 94) 36484
*Traditional farmhouse in 7
acres with magnificent
mountain views. Comfortable
lounge with log fire, large
selection of books and TV.*
Bedrooms: 3 double, 1 twin,
1 triple
Bathrooms: 5 private

Bed & breakfast

per night:	£min	£max
Double		37.00

Parking for 8
🛁4🕯💷🖃§🎖📺🛏🚲
❄✗🚲

Kings Arms Hotel ⋒

The Square, Hawkshead,
Ambleside LA22 0NZ
☎ (053 94) 36372
*Cosy old world inn
overlooking the square. Oak
beams, open fire, real ale.
Lakeland cottage annexe.
Happy, informal atmosphere.*
Bedrooms: 7 double, 2 twin,
2 triple
Bathrooms: 7 private,
1 public

Bed & breakfast

per night:	£min	£max
Single	19.00	28.50
Double	33.00	52.00

Half board

per person:	£min	£max
Daily	27.00	38.50

Lunch available
Evening meal 1800 (last
orders 2100)
Cards accepted: Access, Visa
🛁🕿🖃🕯§🎖🛏❄🚲🚲
SP 🏛

Silverholme ⋒

Graythwaite, Ulverston
LA12 8AZ
☎ Newby Bridge (053 95)
31332
*Set in its own grounds,
overlooking Lake
Windermere, this small
mansion house provides a
quiet, comfortable, relaxed
atmosphere. Home cooking.*
Bedrooms: 1 single, 3 double
Bathrooms: 2 public

Bed & breakfast

per night:	£min	£max
Single	17.50	19.50
Double	35.00	39.00

Half board

per person:	£min	£max
Daily	27.00	29.00

Evening meal 1900 (last
orders 1700)
Parking for 6
🛁🕯💷🖃§🎖📺🛏🚲❄
🚲🏛

Walker Ground Manor ⋒

Hawkshead, Ambleside
LA22 0PD
☎ (053 94) 36219
*Traditional bed and breakfast,
specialising in preserving its
16th C charm. Home cooking,
log fires, 4-poster beds, idyllic
country setting. No smoking.
Adults only, no pets.*
Bedrooms: 2 double, 1 twin
Bathrooms: 1 private,
2 public

Bed & breakfast

per night:	£min	£max
Double	50.00	90.00

Evening meal from 1900
Parking for 6
🖃🕯🕿💷§🎖📺🛏🚲
🕾▶✗❄🚲🏛

HESKET NEWMARKET

Cumbria
Map ref 5A2

Attractive village
comprising a cluster of
18th C houses around a
green and a market cross,
in the quieter, northern
fells.

Wood House ⋒

Hesket Newmarket, Wigton
CA7 8HR
☎ (069 98) 207
*17th C farmhouse close to
northern fells. Warm welcome
assured at all times. Peaceful
location, ideal walking,
touring base. At junction 41
of M6 take Wigton road
(B5305), after 6 miles left for
Hesket Newmarket - farm is 1
mile before village.*

Terrace Farm

Listed

High Lorton, Cockermouth
CA13 9TX
☎ Lorton (0900) 85278
*600-acre hill farming farm.
Traditional farmhouse with
lovely views. 7 miles from
Keswick and 4 miles from
Cockermouth, on the Keswick
to Whinlatter road.*
Bedrooms: 2 double
Bathrooms: 1 public

Bed & breakfast

per night:	£min	£max
Single	15.00	16.00
Double	26.00	28.00

Open March-October
🛁5💷🎖📺🛏❄✗🚲

INGS

Cumbria
Map ref 5A3

Bankfield Country House ⋒

Listed   APPROVED

Ings, Kendal LA8 9PY
☎ Staveley (0539) 821135
*Local turn-of-the-century,
detached house in own
grounds, 2 miles from
Windermere. Meals, licensed
bar and large family rooms.*
Bedrooms: 2 double
Bathrooms: 1 public

Bed & breakfast

per night:	£min	£max
Single	25.00	35.00
Double	30.00	45.50

Half board

per person:	£min	£max
Daily	23.50	38.50
Weekly	140.00	220.00

Lunch available
Evening meal 1700 (last
orders 2000)
Parking for 8
Cards accepted: Access, Visa
🛁🖃🖳🕿🕯§🎖📺🛏
🚲🕾🛁❄🚲 OAP 🚲 T

Bedrooms: 2 twin
Bathrooms: 1 public

Bed & breakfast

per night:	£min	£max
Double	26.00	30.00

Parking for 4
Open March-November
🛁🖃🕯💷§🎖📺🛏🚲✗
🚲🏛

HIGH LORTON

Cumbria
Map ref 5A3

KENDAL

Cumbria
Map ref 5B3

The 'Auld Grey Town' lies
in the valley of the River
Kent with a backcloth of
limestone fells. Situated
just outside the Lake
District National Park, it is
a good centre for touring
the Lakes and
surrounding countryside.
Ruined castle was the
birthplace of Catherine
Parr.
Tourist Information Centre
☎ *(0539) 725758.*

7 Thorny Hills

COMMENDED

Kendal LA9 7AL
☎ (0539) 720207
*Beautiful, unspoilt Georgian
town house. Peaceful, pretty
location close to town centre.
Good home cooking. Self-
catering available. Non-
smokers only please.*
Bedrooms: 2 double, 1 twin
Bathrooms: 1 private,
1 public
Bed & breakfast

per night:	£min	£max
Single	15.00	18.00
Double	27.00	32.00

Half board

per person:	£min	£max
Daily	22.00	24.00

Evening meal from 1800
Parking for 3
Open January-November
🛇🖵🕹🖵ⓢ⅊🅜🕮🛆⚓

Birslack Grange

Cinderbarrow, Levens,
Kendal LA8 8PA
☎ Sedgwick (053 95) 60989
*Converted stone barn with
panoramic views over the
Lyth Valley. Quiet location in
Cumbria's "best kept village",
5 miles south of Kendal. Ideal
stop on route to/from
Scotland.*
Bedrooms: 1 single,
1 double, 3 twin
Bathrooms: 3 public
Bed & breakfast

per night:	£min	£max
Single	13.00	15.00
Double	26.00	30.00

Half board

per person:	£min	£max
Daily	21.00	23.00

Evening meal 1900 (last
orders 2000)
Parking for 8
🛇🕹🖵🅜🅸ⓢ⅊📺🕮🛆🚲∪
⌂✿✕🦽♿📶ⓈᴾⓉ

Cragg Farm 🅼

New Hutton, Kendal
LA8 0BA
☎ (0539) 721760
*17th C farmhouse, tastefully
modernised but retaining its
old world charm. 4 miles
from Kendal, 3 miles from M6
junction 37.*
Bedrooms: 1 double,
1 multiple
Bathrooms: 1 public
Bed & breakfast

per night:	£min	£max
Single	13.50	14.50
Double	27.00	29.00

Evening meal from 1830
Parking for 3
Open March-October
🛇🕹🖵Ⓢᴼ📺🕮🛆✕🦽ᴼᴬᴾ♿

Fairhaven 🅼

Sedgwick Road, Natland,
Kendal LA9 7QQ
☎ Sedgwick (053 95) 60647
*A modern house providing
home cooking, in an
attractive and quiet village 2
miles south of Kendal.*
Bedrooms: 2 double, 1 twin
Bathrooms: 3 private
Bed & breakfast

per night:	£min	£max
Single	18.00	25.00
Double	32.00	35.00

Evening meal from 1830
Parking for 6
🛇🕹12🖵🕹🅜ⓢ⅊🅜📺🕮
🛆✿✕🦽♿

Fairways Guest House

COMMENDED

102 Windermere Road,
Kendal LA9 5EZ
☎ (0539) 725564
*On the main Kendal-
Windermere road. Victorian
guesthouse with en-suite
facilities. TV, tea and coffee
in all rooms. Four-poster
bedrooms. Private parking.*
Bedrooms: 1 single, 3 double
Bathrooms: 4 private,
1 public
Bed & breakfast

per night:	£min	£max
Single	16.00	18.00
Double	30.00	34.00

Parking for 4
🛇🕹3🖵🕅🖵🕹🅜⅊🅜🕮
🅿✕🦽

Garnett House Farm 🅼

Burneside, Kendal LA9 5SF
☎ (0539) 724542
*270-acre mixed farm. Half a
mile down country road from
the A591 Kendal to
Windermere road. Ideal
touring base with ample
parking.*

Gateside Farm

Listed COMMENDED

Burneside, Kendal LA9 5SE
☎ (0539) 722036
*300-acre dairy & livestock
farm. Traditional Lakeland
farm easily accessible from
the motorway and on the
main tourist route through
Lakeland. One night and
short stays are welcomed.*
Bedrooms: 2 double, 2 twin,
1 triple
Bathrooms: 2 public
Bed & breakfast

per night:	£min	£max
Double	28.00	30.00

Half board

per person:	£min	£max
Daily	21.00	22.00

Evening meal (last orders
1700)
Parking for 7
🛇🕹🖵🕹🅜🅜🕮🦽♿Ⓢᴾ

The Glen

Oxenholme, Kendal LA9 7RF
☎ (0539) 726386
*Large, modernised house in
its own grounds. All rooms
have TV, tea-making and
private facilities.*
Bedrooms: 2 double, 1 twin
Bathrooms: 3 private
Bed & breakfast

per night:	£min	£max
Single	18.00	20.00
Double	32.00	36.00

Half board

per person:	£min	£max
Daily	26.00	30.00

Parking for 8
Open April-October
🛇🕹10🖵🕹🅜🅜✕♿

Higher House Farm 🅼

♛♛♛

Oxenholme Lane, Natland,
Kendal LA9 7QH
☎ Sedgwick (053 95) 61177
*17th C beamed farmhouse in
tranquil village south of
Kendal, overlooking Lakeland
fells. Near M6 and Oxenholme
station. Delicious cuisine.
Four poster bed.*

Gateside / right column

Bedrooms: 1 double,
2 multiple
Bathrooms: 1 private,
2 public
Bed & breakfast

per night:	£min	£max
Double	26.00	

Half board

per person:	£min	£max
Daily	39.00	

Evening meal 1830 (last
orders 1730)
Parking for 6
🛇🕹🕹🅜🅜📺🛆✿✕
🦽♿

Bedrooms: 1 double, 1 twin,
1 multiple
Bathrooms: 3 private
Bed & breakfast

per night:	£min	£max
Single	17.50	24.50
Double	35.00	40.00

Half board

per person:	£min	£max
Daily	29.50	36.50

Evening meal 1900 (last
orders 2130)
Parking for 9
🛇🕹🕿🖵🕹🕹🅜🅸ⓢ⅊
🅜📺🕮🛆🅿✿🦽♿Ⓢᴾ♿

Hill Fold Farm

Burneside, Kendal LA8 9AU
☎ (0539) 722574
*500-acre mixed farm. Log
fires and exposed beams.
Overnight storage heaters in
bedrooms. Only 3 miles north
of Kendal and close to the
rolling hills of Potter Fell
with its many quiet walks.*
Bedrooms: 2 double, 1 twin
Bathrooms: 1 public
Bed & breakfast

per night:	£min	£max
Double	24.00	28.00

Half board

per person:	£min	£max
Daily	17.00	19.00

Evening meal 1930 (last
orders 1600)
Parking for 6
🛇🕹🖵🅜📺🛆🛆✿✕
🦽ᴼᴬᴾ

Holmfield 🅼

Listed DE LUXE

41 Kendal Green, Kendal
LA9 5PP
☎ (0539) 720790
*Elegant Edwardian house on
edge of town. Large gardens,
panoramic views, swimming
pool, croquet. Pretty
bedrooms. Renowned
hospitality. Non-smoking
establishment.*
Bedrooms: 2 double, 1 twin
Bathrooms: 2 public
Bed & breakfast

per night:	£min	£max
Double	30.00	35.00

Parking for 7
🌂🕅🕹🖵🅜🅸ⓢ⅊📺🕮
🛆🚲✿✕🦽♿ⓈᴾⓉ

Low Hundhowe Farm 🅼

♛♛♛

Burneside, Kendal LA8 9AB
☎ (0539) 722060
*235-acre mixed farm. This
350-year-old farmhouse,
nestling below Potter Fell, is
a comfortable retreat yet only
minutes from A591. Good*

food and warm welcome await.
Bedrooms: 2 double, 1 twin
Bathrooms: 1 public

Bed & breakfast

per night:	£min	£max
Single	13.00	
Double	25.00	27.00

Half board

per person:	£min	£max
Daily	19.00	
Weekly	126.00	

Evening meal 1830 (last orders 1630)
Parking for 3
Open March-October

Lyndhurst M

8 South Road, Kendal LA9 5QH
☎ (0539) 727281
Terraced house providing comfortable accommodation, in a quiet area with river view. 10 minutes' walk from the town.
Bedrooms: 1 single, 2 double, 1 twin, 1 multiple
Bathrooms: 1 private, 2 public

Bed & breakfast

per night:	£min	£max
Single	13.50	16.50
Double	27.00	33.00

Parking for 4

Riversleigh M

49 Milnthorpe Road, Kendal LA9 5QG
☎ (0539) 726392
Charming Victorian guesthouse 10 minutes' walk from the town centre. Central for the Lakes and Yorkshire Dales.
Bedrooms: 1 single, 1 double, 1 twin, 1 triple
Bathrooms: 1 private, 2 public

Bed & breakfast

per night:	£min	£max
Single	14.00	17.00
Double	30.00	34.00

Half board

per person:	£min	£max
Daily	24.00	27.00

Parking for 6

Stockbridge Farm M
Listed

Kendal Road, Staveley, Kendal LA8 9LP
☎ (0539) 821580
20-acre mixed farm. Comfortable, well-appointed 17th C farmhouse on edge of bypassed village midway between Kendal and Windermere on A591. Central heating. Full English breakfast. Friendly personal attention.
Bedrooms: 1 single, 4 double, 1 triple
Bathrooms: 1 public

Bed & breakfast

per night:	£min	£max
Single	13.00	14.00
Double	26.00	28.00

Parking for 6
Open March-October

Winlea

88 Windermere Road, Kendal LA9
☎ (0539) 723177
Friendly Victorian guesthouse in good location. Well furnished en-suite rooms with colour TV and tea/coffee facilities. Lovely views, private parking. Non-smoking.
Bedrooms: 1 double, 1 triple
Bathrooms: 2 private

> **Please check prices and other details at the time of booking.**

Bed & breakfast

per night:	£min	£max
Double	30.00	32.00

Parking for 4

Winmaur

90 Windermere Road, Kendal LA9 5EZ
☎ (0539) 720253
Victorian guesthouse. All rooms en-suite with colour TV and tea/coffee facilities. Handy for town centre, well situated for touring lakes and dales.
Bedrooms: 2 double, 1 twin
Bathrooms: 3 private

Bed & breakfast

per night:	£min	£max
Double	25.00	32.00

Parking for 3

KESWICK

Cumbria
Map ref 5A3

Beautifully positioned town beside Derwentwater and below the mountains of Skiddaw and Blencathra. Excellent base for walking, climbing, watersports and touring. Motor-launches operate on Derwentwater and motor boats, rowing boats and canoes can be hired. *Tourist Information Centre* ☎ *(076 87) 72645.*

Acorn House Hotel M
HIGHLY COMMENDED

Ambleside Road, Keswick CA12 4DL
☎ (076 87) 72553
Detached Georgian house with newly refurbished rooms, set in own garden. Quiet location close to town centre and 10 minutes from Derwentwater.

Bedrooms: 5 double, 1 twin, 4 triple
Bathrooms: 10 private

Bed & breakfast

per night:	£min	£max
Double	20.00	25.00

Parking for 10
Open February-November
Cards accepted: Access, Visa

Bank Tavern
Listed

47, Main Street, Keswick CA12 5DS
☎ (076 87) 72663
A country pub in the town centre.
Bedrooms: 2 double, 2 twin, 1 triple
Bathrooms: 1 public

Bed & breakfast

per night:	£min	£max
Single	13.00	15.00
Double	26.00	30.00

Lunch available
Evening meal 1800 (last orders 2100)
Parking for 5

The Bay Tree

1 Wordsworth Street, Keswick CA12 4HU
☎ (076 87) 73313
Friendly guesthouse with lovely views over river and Fitz Park to mountains. 3 minutes' walk from town centre. Home-cooked food.
Bedrooms: 3 double, 1 twin, 1 triple
Bathrooms: 1 public

Bed & breakfast

per night:	£min	£max
Double	27.00	

Continued ▶

> **Please mention this guide when making a booking.**

Kings Head Hotel

The Kings Head is situated in Lakelands heart enjoying superb views. It is located on the main A591 5.5 miles from Keswick.

Originally a 17th century inn it retains its features of cosy inglenooks and oak beams whilst having all bedroms with bathrooms, colour TV's and tea and coffee making facilities.

The food is traditionally English with emphasis on fine home cooking featuring local specialities and produce. This allied to a well stocked cellar makes the Kings Head a very popular dining place for locals & visitors alike.

Thirlspot-Keswick The Lake District CA12 4TN
Tel: 07687 72393/72309

KESWICK

Continued

Half board

per person:	£min	£max
Daily	22.00	
Weekly	147.00	

Lunch available
Evening meal 1900 (last orders 1600)

♿5 ♦♠⑤⎗🅜🎚.🅐✕🚬 ⚑ 🆂🅿

Beckstones Farm ⚟

⚄⚄⚄ COMMENDED

Thornthwaite, Keswick
CA12 5SQ
☎ Braithwaite (076 87) 78510
Converted Georgian farmhouse in a typical Lakeland setting, with extensive views of the mountains and Thornthwaite Forest. 3 miles west of Keswick.
Bedrooms: 1 single,
3 double, 1 twin
Bathrooms: 1 public

Bed & breakfast

per night:	£min	£max
Single	16.50	16.50
Double	33.00	36.00

Evening meal 1830 (last orders 1000)
Parking for 8
Open February-November

♿8🔥♦�291⑤⎗🅜🎚.
🌣⚑

Berkeley Guest House ⚟

⚄⚄

The Heads, Keswick
CA12 5ER
☎ (076 87) 74222
On a quiet road overlooking the mini golf-course, with splendid views from each comfortable room. Close to the town centre and lake.
Bedrooms: 3 double, 1 twin,
1 triple
Bathrooms: 2 private,
1 public

Bed & breakfast

per night:	£min	£max
Double	27.00	37.00

Evening meal 1830 (last orders 1400)
Open February-December

♿1🔥♦♠⑤⎗🅜🎚.🅐
✕⚑

Birkrigg Farm

Newlands, Keswick
CA12 5TS
☎ Braithwaite (076 87) 78278
250-acre mixed farm. Pleasantly and peacefully located in the Newlands
valley. 5 miles from Keswick on the Braithwaite to Buttermere road.
Bedrooms: 1 single,
2 double, 1 twin, 1 triple
Bathrooms: 2 public

Bed & breakfast

per night:	£min	£max
Single	13.00	14.00
Double	26.00	28.00

Evening meal from 1900
Parking for 6
Open March-November

♿⎘🅜🅐🎚🅜🎚.🌣✕⚑

Hazeldene Hotel ⚟

⚄⚄⚄

The Heads, Keswick
CA12 5ER
☎ (076 87) 72106
Beautiful and central with open views over Derwentwater to Borrowdale and the Newlands Valley. Close to the town centre and shops.
Bedrooms: 5 single,
9 double, 4 twin, 4 triple
Bathrooms: 18 private,
3 public

Bed & breakfast

per night:	£min	£max
Single	21.00	27.00
Double	42.00	54.00

Half board

per person:	£min	£max
Daily	35.00	41.00
Weekly	238.00	277.00

Evening meal 1830 (last orders 1600)
Parking for 18
Open March-November

♿⎘🅛⎗🖛🍴⑤🅜⎚🎚.🅐
🔍⚑

Heatherlea

26, Blencathra Street,
Keswick CA12 4HP
☎ (076 87) 72430
Traditional Lakeland stone house. All rooms with private facilities, colour TV, kettle etc. Convenient for town centre and all amenities. Non-smoking establishment.
Bedrooms: 1 single,
2 double, 1 triple
Bathrooms: 4 private

Bed & breakfast

per night:	£min	£max
Single	14.50	16.50
Double	29.00	33.00

♿5⎘♦🅛🅜🅐✕🎚.🅐⚑

Keskadale Farm

Newlands Valley, Keswick
CA12 5TS
☎ Braithwaite (076 87) 78544
300-acre livestock farm. Midway between Braithwaite and Buttermere with lovely views over Robinson to
Catbells. Keswick 6 miles, Buttermere 2.5 miles. Bedtime drink and homemade biscuits included in terms.
Bedrooms: 2 double, 1 twin
Bathrooms: 1 public

Bed & breakfast

per night:	£min	£max
Double	26.00	29.00

Parking for 6
Open March-November

♿🅛⎗⑤🅜🎚.🅐⯈⚒✕
⚑🏠

King's Arms Hotel ⚟

⚄⚄⚄

Main Street, Keswick
CA12 5BL
☎ (076 87) 72083
18th C coaching inn. Central. All bedrooms en-suite. Restaurant offers big "help yourself" salad bar, traditional home cooking and speciality dishes. Also Pizzeria and Video Bar.
Bedrooms: 6 double, 5 twin,
2 triple
Bathrooms: 13 private

Bed & breakfast

per night:	£min	£max
Single	30.00	38.50
Double	46.00	55.00

Half board

per person:	£min	£max
Weekly	175.00	234.00

Lunch available
Evening meal 1800 (last orders 2200)
Cards accepted: Access, Visa

♿⎘🅛⎗♦♠⑤🎚.🅐⚑✕
⚲∪⎘✕🆂🅿🏠⛽

Littletown Farm ⚟

Newlands, Keswick
CA12 5TU
☎ Braithwaite (076 87) 78353
150-acre mixed farm. In the beautiful, unspoilt Newlands Valley. En-suite bedrooms. Comfortable residents' lounge, dining room and cosy bar. Traditional 4-course dinner 6 nights a week.
Bedrooms: 1 single,
4 double, 2 twin, 1 triple,
1 multiple
Bathrooms: 7 private,
2 public

Bed & breakfast

per night:	£min	£max
Single	22.00	26.00
Double	44.00	52.00

Half board

per person:	£min	£max
Daily	32.00	36.00
Weekly	200.00	230.00

Evening meal from 1900
Parking for 10
Open March-December

♿⎘♣♦⑤🅜🎚.🅐🌣⚑🏠

Long Close Farm

Underskiddaw, Keswick
CA12 4QD
☎ (076 87) 72581
Peaceful 18th C farmhouse in Underskiddaw facing southwest and overlooking mountains and Bassenthwaite Lake. 3 miles north of Keswick on A591.
Bedrooms: 1 double, 2 twin
Bathrooms: 1 private,
1 public

Bed & breakfast

per night:	£min	£max
Single	20.00	25.00
Double	32.00	42.00

Parking for 6

♿10♦🅛♠⑤🅜⯈◑🎚.🌣
⚑🆂🏠🅣

The Mount ⚟

⚄⚄⚄ COMMENDED

Portinscale, Keswick
CA12 5RD
☎ (076 87) 73070
Small but comfortable guesthouse overlooking Derwentwater in the quiet village of Portinscale.
Bedrooms: 1 single,
2 double, 1 twin
Bathrooms: 3 private,
1 public

Bed & breakfast

per night:	£min	£max
Single	14.50	
Double	34.00	

Half board

per person:	£min	£max
Daily	25.50	
Weekly	150.00	

Evening meal 1830 (last orders 1700)
Parking for 8
Open March-November

♿5⎘♦🅛♠⑤🅜🎚.
🅐⚑

Pitcairn House ⚟

7 Blencathra Street, Keswick
CA12 4HW
☎ (076 87) 72453
Well established, family-run bed and breakfast accommodation in the town. Access to rooms all day. Colour TV in all rooms. Good value.
Bedrooms: 3 double, 2 twin,
2 triple
Bathrooms: 2 public

Bed & breakfast

per night:	£min	£max
Single	13.50	15.00
Double	24.00	29.00

Parking for 2

♿5⎘♦🅛♠⑤✕🅜🎚.
✕⚑

Ravensworth Hotel

♛♛♛ HIGHLY COMMENDED

Station Street, Keswick
CA12 5HH
☎ (076 87) 72476
Pleasant, family-run licensed hotel where you can be at your ease, adjacent to Fitz Park and the town centre.
Bedrooms: 7 double, 1 twin
Bathrooms: 7 private

Bed & breakfast per night:	£min	£max
Single	27.00	29.00
Double	36.00	44.00

Half board per person:	£min	£max
Daily	28.50	33.00
Weekly	190.00	205.00

Evening meal 1900 (last orders 1900)
Parking for 5
Open March-November
Cards accepted: Access, Visa
6 [S] [TV] [SP]

Richmond House

♛♛♛

37-39 Eskin Street, Keswick
CA12 4DG
☎ (076 87) 73965
Family-run guesthouse, home-from-home, easy walking distance to town centre and lake. Vegetarians catered for. Non-smokers only please.
Bedrooms: 3 single, 5 double, 1 twin, 1 triple
Bathrooms: 6 private, 3 public

Bed & breakfast per night:	£min	£max
Single	14.00	16.00
Double	28.00	36.00

Half board per person:	£min	£max
Daily	22.50	26.00
Weekly	170.00	180.00

Evening meal 1900 (last orders 1700)
Cards accepted: Access, Visa
8 [S] [TV] [SP]

Rickerby Grange

♛♛♛ COMMENDED

Portinscale, Keswick
CA12 5RH
☎ (076 87) 72344
Detached country hotel in its own gardens, in a quiet village on the outskirts of Keswick. Provides imaginative cooking, a cosy bar and quiet lounge. Ground floor bedrooms available.
Bedrooms: 2 single, 8 double, 1 twin, 3 triple
Bathrooms: 11 private, 1 public, 1 private shower

Bed & breakfast per night:	£min	£max
Single	21.00	24.00
Double	42.00	48.00

Half board per person:	£min	£max
Daily	32.00	35.00
Weekly	210.00	230.00

Evening meal 1900 (last orders 1800)
Parking for 14
[S] [TV] [SP]

Rowling End

Listed COMMENDED

31 Helvellyn Street, Keswick
CA12 4EP
☎ (076 87) 74108
Small, comfortable, family-run guesthouse. All rooms centrally-heated, with TV, tea and coffee facilities. 5 minutes from town centre. Evening meals available from October to June, excluding school holidays.
Bedrooms: 2 double, 1 triple, 1 multiple
Bathrooms: 2 private, 1 public

Bed & breakfast per night:	£min	£max
Double	29.00	36.00

Half board per person:	£min	£max
Daily	24.00	27.50
Weekly	165.00	190.00

[UL] [SP]

Watendlath Guest House

Listed COMMENDED

15 Acorn Street, Keswick
CA12 4EA
☎ (076 87) 74165
Within easy walking distance of the lake, hills and town centre. We offer a warm and friendly welcome and traditional English breakfast.
Bedrooms: 3 double, 1 twin
Bathrooms: 2 private, 2 public

Bed & breakfast per night:	£min	£max
Double	26.00	30.00

Open March-October
[UL] [S]

Half board prices shown are per person but in some cases may be based on double/twin occupancy.

KIRKBY LONSDALE

Cumbria
Map ref 5B3

Charming old town of narrow streets and Georgian buildings, set in the superb scenery of the Lune Valley. The Devil's Bridge over the River Lune is probably 13th C.

Capernwray House

♛♛

Borrans Lane, Capernwray, Carnforth, Lancashire
LA6 1AE
☎ Carnforth (0524) 732363
Detached house in 5.5 acres. Ideally situated for Lake District and Yorkshire Dales. Located 5-6 miles from Kirkby Lonsdale, M6 junction 35, B6254 Over Kellet, cross roads, turn left. House 2 miles on right. No smoking.
Bedrooms: 2 double, 1 twin
Bathrooms: 3 private, 1 public

Bed & breakfast per night:	£min	£max
Single	15.00	20.00
Double	36.00	45.00

Parking for 8
[UL] [S] [TV] [T]

Pheasant Inn

♛♛♛♛ COMMENDED

Casterton, Kirkby Lonsdale, Carnforth, Lancashire
LA6 2RX
☎ (052 42) 71230
An old world country inn specialising in food and service, ideal for touring the Lakes, dales and coast. Situated amidst the peaceful Lunesdale Fells.
Bedrooms: 2 single, 6 double, 2 twin
Bathrooms: 10 private

Bed & breakfast per night:	£min	£max
Single		37.50
Double		55.00

Half board per person:	£min	£max
Daily		40.00

Evening meal 1830 (last orders 2100)
Parking for 40
Cards accepted: Access, Visa, Switch
[S] [SP]

KIRKBY STEPHEN

Cumbria
Map ref 5B3

Old market town close to the River Eden, with many fine Georgian buildings and an attractive market square. St Stephen's Church is known as the 'Cathedral of the Dales'. Good base for exploring the Eden Valley and the Dales.
Tourist Information Centre ☎ (07683) 71199.

Kings Arms Hotel

Kirkby Stephen CA17 4QN
☎ (076 83) 71378
17th C former posting inn, in the centre of market town, providing home-made food, local game and fresh garden produce. Fully licensed bar and restaurant. Centrally heated throughout.
Bedrooms: 2 single, 4 double, 4 twin, 1 triple
Bathrooms: 3 public

Bed & breakfast per night:	£min	£max
Single	25.00	32.50
Double	45.00	52.50

Half board per person:	£min	£max
Daily	30.00	40.00
Weekly	225.00	250.00

Lunch available
Evening meal 1845 (last orders 2100)
Parking for 12
Cards accepted: Access, Visa
[S] [TV] [DAP] [SP]

Town Head House

♛♛♛♛ HIGHLY COMMENDED

High Street, Kirkby Stephen
CA17 4SH
☎ (076 83) 71044
Georgian/Victorian town house with garden. Spacious en-suite bedrooms with handsome plasterwork, telephone and TV. Four-posters available. 16 miles from junction 38 of M6.
Bedrooms: 1 single, 4 double, 1 twin
Bathrooms: 6 private

Bed & breakfast per night:	£min	£max
Single	37.00	43.00
Double	56.50	67.00

Half board per person:	£min	£max
Daily	48.00	54.00

Continued ►

KIRKBY STEPHEN

Continued

Evening meal 1900 (last orders 2000)
Parking for 8
Cards accepted: Access, Visa

🛇 11 🏦 🎔 📞 🖵 🗗 ♨ 🕯 🛍 S
⅍ 🏲 ▥ 🖴 🗣 ✿ 🖛 🐾 SP T

LAMPLUGH

Cumbria
Map ref 5A3

Near the A5086 between Cockermouth and Cleator Moor, Lamplugh is a scattered village famous for its 'Lamplugh Pudding'. Ideal touring base for the western Lake District.

Briscoe Close

Scalesmoor, Lamplugh, Workington CA14 4TZ
☎ (0946) 861633
Bungalow close to family-run farm. Near Loweswater and Ennerdale, half a mile from A5086. Home cooking using produce grown on farm.
Bedrooms: 2 double
Bathrooms: 1 public

Bed & breakfast

per night:	£min	£max
Single	15.00	
Double	26.00	28.00

Half board

per person:	£min	£max
Daily	19.00	
Weekly	168.00	

Evening meal from 1900
Parking for 2

🛇 🎰 ⅍ ▥ S 🏲 TV ▥ 🖴 ✿
✕ 🖛

LANGDALE

Cumbria
Map ref 5A3

The 2 Langdale valleys (Great Langdale and Little Langdale) lie in the heart of beautiful mountain scenery. The craggy Langdale Pikes are almost 2500 ft high. An ideal walking and climbing area.

Britannia Inn ⋒

😃😃😃 COMMENDED

Elterwater, Ambleside LA22 9HP
☎ (096 67) 210 & 311
A 400-year-old traditional Lake District inn on a village green in the beautiful Langdale Valley. A warm

---

welcome to all. TV available in bedrooms.
Bedrooms: 7 double, 2 twin
Bathrooms: 6 private, 2 public

Bed & breakfast

per night:	£min	£max
Single	17.50	49.50
Double	35.00	61.00

Half board

per person:	£min	£max
Daily	36.50	47.00

Lunch available
Evening meal 1930 (last orders 1930)
Parking for 10
Cards accepted: Access, Visa, Switch

🛇 🕭 🖵 ♨ 🕯 🛍 S 🏲 ▥ 🖴 ✿
🖛 SP 🏠 T

Fell Foot Farm

Little Langdale, Ambleside LA27 9PE
☎ (096 67) 294
431-acre mixed farm. 17th C farmhouse nestling at the foot of the famous Wrynose Pass, offering comfortable accommodation, home cooking and a house full of charm and character.
Bedrooms: 2 double, 1 triple
Bathrooms: 1 private, 1 public

Bed & breakfast

per night:	£min	£max
Double	30.00	

Evening meal (last orders 1830)
Parking for 4
Open March-November

🛇 3 ♨ 🕯 ▮ 🖴 ✓ ✿ ✕ 🖛 🏠

LANGWATHBY

Cumbria
Map ref 5B2

Beck Mill

Langwathby, Penrith CA10 1NY
☎ (0768) 881371
Old mill house and studio/ gallery in tranquil situation amidst wood and farmland including lake. On Kirkland Road 1 mile outside Langthwathby village.
Bedrooms: 1 twin
Bathrooms: 1 private

Bed & breakfast

per night:	£min	£max
Single	15.00	
Double	30.00	

Parking for 6

🛇 1 🖵 🗗 🗣 ▥ 🛍 S ⅍ 🏲 TV
▥ 🖴 🟃 🗣 ✿ 🖛 🏠

LORTON

Cumbria
Map ref 5A3

High and Low Lorton are set in a beautiful vale north of Crummock Water and at the foot of the Whinlatter Pass. Church of St Cuthbert is well worth a visit.

New House Farm ⋒

Lorton, Cockermouth CA13 9UU
☎ (0900) 85404
A beautifully restored 17th C Lakeland farmhouse now offering a homely atmosphere, comfortable accommodation and fine traditional food, in the heart of the lovely Lorton Vale.
Bedrooms: 2 double, 1 twin
Bathrooms: 3 private

Bed & breakfast

per night:	£min	£max
Single	25.00	30.00
Double	50.00	60.00

Half board

per person:	£min	£max
Daily	40.00	50.00

Lunch available
Evening meal 1930 (last orders 1930)
Parking for 20
Open March-November and Christmas

▮ S ⅍ 🏲 ▥ 🖴 ✿ 🖛 🐾 🏠 T

LOWESWATER

Cumbria
Map ref 5A3

This scattered village lies between Loweswater, one of the smaller lakes of the Lake District, and Crummock Water. Several mountains lie beyond the village, giving lovely views.

Brook Farm

😃 COMMENDED

Thackthwaite, Loweswater, Cockermouth CA13 0RP
☎ Lorton (0900) 85606
In quiet surroundings and a good walking area, 5 miles from Cockermouth. Carrying sheep and suckler cows.
Bedrooms: 1 double, 1 twin
Bathrooms: 1 public

Bed & breakfast

per night:	£min	£max
Single	14.00	15.50
Double	28.00	31.00

Half board

per person:	£min	£max
Daily	20.00	21.50
Weekly	140.00	150.50

Evening meal from 1900
Parking for 3
Open May-October

🛇 ♨ ▥ 🛍 ⅍ ✓ 🏲 TV ✿ 🖛

LOWICK

Cumbria
Map ref 5A3

Arthur Ransome, the author of 'Swallows and Amazons', lived in this locality south of Coniston Water at Lowick Hall. The setting of his children's book was based on Windermere and Coniston Water.

Everard Lodge

Lowick, Ulverston LA12 8ER
☎ (022 985) 245
185-acre mixed farm in beautiful surroundings with easy access to Lake District. Non-smoking establishment. Pets and children welcome.
Bedrooms: 1 double, 1 twin, 1 triple
Bathrooms: 1 public

Bed & breakfast

per night:	£min	£max
Double	26.00	28.00

Parking for 3

🛇 🖵 ▥ 🛍 ▮ S ⅍ 🏲 TV 🖴
✿ 🖛

MILNTHORPE

Cumbria
Map ref 5B3

Attractive limestone village with popular market. Good base for touring southern Cumbria and Morecambe Bay.

Eildon

129 Church Street, Milnthorpe LA7 7DZ
☎ (053 95) 63311
Eildon is on the left hand side of the road leading out of Milnthorpe towards Kendal and access is at the back of the house along Kirkgate.
Bedrooms: 1 single, 1 double, 1 twin
Bathrooms: 1 public, 1 private shower

Bed & breakfast

per night:	£min	£max
Single	10.00	12.00
Double	20.00	28.00

Parking for 4
Open February-November

🛇 ♨ ▥ ▮ S 🏲 ▥ 🖴 🖛 SP

MUNGRISDALE

Cumbria
Map ref 5A2

Set in an unspoilt valley the simple, white church in this hamlet has a 3-decker pulpit and box pews.

Low Beckside Farm
Listed   APPROVED

Mungrisdale, Penrith
CA11 0XR
☎ Threkeld (076 87) 79246
1.5 miles from A66. All food freshly prepared on the premises. Special diets catered for.
Bedrooms: 1 double, 1 twin, 1 multiple
Bathrooms: 1 private, 1 public

Bed & breakfast per night:	£min	£max
Single	12.50	14.50
Double	25.00	29.00

Half board per person:	£min	£max
Daily	21.00	23.00

Lunch available
Evening meal 1800 (last orders 2100)
Parking for 4
Open March-December
⛄🔥♦🔥🖭🏠🛍🚲🔥⛵🌊, ▱Ц↑✿🐾 SP

NEWBY BRIDGE

Cumbria
Map ref 5A3

At the southern end of Windermere on the River Leven, this village has an unusual stone bridge with arches of unequal size. The Lakeside and Haverthwaite Railway has a stop here, and steamer cruises on Lake Windermere leave from nearby Lakeside.

Landing Cottage ⋀
⚜⚜

Lakeside, Newby Bridge, Ulverston LA12 8AS
☎ (053 95) 31719
19th C Lakeland-stone cottage, 100 yards from the shores of Lake Windermere, close to the steamer boat terminal and the Lakeside/ Haverthwaite pleasure steam train.
Bedrooms: 3 double, 2 triple
Bathrooms: 2 private, 2 public

Bed & breakfast per night:	£min	£max
Single	15.00	30.00
Double	30.00	36.00

Half board per person:	£min	£max
Daily	24.00	27.00

Evening meal 1900 (last orders 1630)
Parking for 6
⛄🔥♦🏠🛍🖭🏠🛍, ▱✿🐾 SP

PATTERDALE

Cumbria
Map ref 5A3

Amongst the fells at the southern end of the Ullswater Valley, this village is dominated by Helvellyn and St Sunday Crag. Ideal centre for touring and outdoor activities.

Fellside ⋀
Listed   APPROVED

Hartsop, Penrith CA11 0NZ
☎ Glenridding (076 84) 82532
A 17th C Cumbrian farmhouse at the foot of Kirkstone Pass, perfect for fellwalkers; artists also welcome. Magnificent scenery, overlooking Brothers Water.
Bedrooms: 1 single, 1 double, 1 twin
Bathrooms: 2 public

Bed & breakfast per night:	£min	£max
Single	12.00	15.50
Double	24.00	30.00

Parking for 3
⛄🔥🏠🛍🖭🏠🛍, ▱✿🐾 SP🐾T

PENRITH

Cumbria
Map ref 5B2

This ancient and historic market town is the northern gateway to the Lake District. Penrith Castle was built as a defence against the Scots. Its ruins, open to the public, stand in the public park. High above the town is the famous Penrith Beacon.
Tourist Information Centre
☎ (0768) 67466

Brandelhow Guest House

1 Portland Place, Penrith
CA11 7QN
☎ (0768) 64470

Victorian house with spacious, comfortable accommodation and friendly, personal attention. Ideal base for touring Lakes and Border country.
Bedrooms: 2 double, 3 triple
Bathrooms: 2 public

Bed & breakfast per night:	£min	£max
Single	16.00	18.00
Double	26.00	28.00

⛄🔥♦UL🏠🛍⊁🖭🏠🛍, ▱

Bridge End Farm ⋀
⚜⚜ **COMMENDED**

Hutton, Hutton John, Penrith CA11 0LZ
☎ Greystoke (076 84) 83273
14-acre mixed farm. Modernised 17th C farmhouse, with the original oak beams and door, in its own quiet grounds with Lakeland fell views. 5 miles west of M6.
Bedrooms: 2 double, 1 twin, 1 triple
Bathrooms: 3 private, 1 public

Bed & breakfast per night:	£min	£max
Double	28.00	35.00

Half board per person:	£min	£max
Daily	20.50	25.00
Weekly	135.00	160.00

Evening meal 1830 (last orders 1700)
Parking for 6
Open April-October
⛄10🖭🖭🛍, ▱✿✖ 🐾🐟

Glendale ⋀

4 Portland Place, Penrith
CA11 7QN
☎ (0768) 62579
Victorian town house overlooking pleasant gardens. Spacious family rooms. Children and pets welcome.
Bedrooms: 1 single, 1 double, 3 triple
Bathrooms: 1 public

Bed & breakfast per night:	£min	£max
Single	14.00	16.00
Double	26.00	28.00

⛄🔥♦🏠🛍⊁🖭🏠🛍, ▱ SP

Hornby Hall ⋀
⚜⚜ **HIGHLY COMMENDED**

Hornby Hall, Brougham, Penrith CA10 2AR
☎ Culgaith (0768) 891114
800-acre mixed farm. Farmhouse with interesting old hall. Fishing on Eamont available. Within easy reach of Lakes, Pennines and Yorkshire Dales. Home-cooked local produce.
Bedrooms: 2 double, 3 twin
Bathrooms: 2 private, 2 public

Bed & breakfast per night:	£min	£max
Single	22.00	28.00
Double	44.00	56.00

Half board per person:	£min	£max
Daily	34.00	40.00
Weekly	145.00	186.00

Evening meal 1930 (last orders 2000)
Parking for 8
Cards accepted: Access, Visa
⛄🔥♦🔥🏠🛍⊁🖭🏠🛍, ▱🍴✿🐾🐟

Old Victoria Hotel
⚜⚜ **APPROVED**

46 Castlegate, Penrith
CA11 7HY
☎ (0768) 62467
Family-run hotel with public bar. Bar lunches and evening meals. Home-cooked specialities.
Bedrooms: 4 double, 3 twin
Bathrooms: 2 private, 1 public, 5 private showers

Bed & breakfast per night:	£min	£max
Single	20.00	30.00
Double	40.00	44.00

Half board per person:	£min	£max
Daily	27.00	29.00

Lunch available
Evening meal 1900 (last orders 2100)
Parking for 12
⛄🔥♦🏠🛍🖭🏠🛍, ▱🍴🔥✿ GAP 🐾 SP🐾T

Sockbridge Mill Trout Farm

Penrith CA10 2JT
☎ (0768) 65338
8-acre fish farm. Picturesque working trout farm on the River Eamont, off the B5320 between Pooley Bridge and Penrith.
Bedrooms: 1 double, 1 twin
Bathrooms: 1 public

Bed & breakfast per night:	£min	£max
Single	12.00	16.00
Double	24.00	32.00

Half board per person:	£min	£max
Daily	22.00	26.00
Weekly	130.00	175.00

Parking for 6
Open April-October
⛄🔥💷🏠🛍🖭🏠▱Ц♦ ✺✿🐾 SP

PENRITH

Continued

The Sun Inn
Newton Reigny, Penrith
CA11 0AP
☎ (0768) 67055
Small family-owned and run village inn, in pleasant surroundings. Delicious home-made food and local and traditional ales served.
Bedrooms: 1 single, 2 twin, 1 triple
Bathrooms: 2 private, 1 public
Bed & breakfast

per night:	£min	£max
Single	18.00	22.00
Double	36.00	44.00

Lunch available
Evening meal 1830 (last orders 2130)
Parking for 30

PORTINSCALE
Cumbria
Map ref 5A3

Derwentwater Marina ♨
Portinscale, Keswick
CA12 5RF
☎ Keswick (076 87) 72912
Motel accommodation with en-suite rooms and DIY Continental breakfast, on Derwentwater's edge. Magnificent views, sailing, canoeing, windsurfing, hire and instruction, boat park and moorings.
Bedrooms: 2 double, 1 twin
Bathrooms: 3 private, 1 public
Bed & breakfast

per night:	£min	£max
Double	40.00	40.00

Parking for 50
Cards accepted: Access, Visa

There are separate sections in this guide listing groups specialising in farm holidays and accommodation which is especially suitable for young people and organised groups.

RAVENGLASS
Cumbria
Map ref 5A3

An ancient coastal village on the River Esk Estuary. The Romans established a supply base here and a well-preserved bath house can be seen. A miniature railway runs from Ravenglass to Boot in the Eskdale Valley. Muncaster Castle, open to the public, is to the west of the village.
Tourist Information Centre ☎ (0229) 717278

Rosegarth ♨
APPROVED
Main Street, Ravenglass
CA18 1SQ
☎ (0229) 717275
Family-run guesthouse in a rural seaside village with views across the village green to the Irish Sea. BR station in village.
Bedrooms: 1 single, 3 double, 1 twin
Bathrooms: 2 public
Bed & breakfast

per night:	£min	£max
Single	14.50	17.50
Double	29.00	34.00

Parking for 3

RYDAL
Cumbria
Map ref 5A3

Small hamlet next to Rydal Water, a small, beautiful lake sheltered by Rydal Fell. Once the home of William Wordsworth, Rydal Mount is open to the public. It is a good centre for walking and touring.

SANDSIDE
Cumbria
Map ref 5A3

Kingfisher House & Restaurant
COMMENDED
Sandside, Milnthorpe
LA7 7HW
☎ (053 95) 63909
New accommodation overlooking Kent Estuary and Lakeland hills. Perfect for bird-watching, golf, rambling. All food home-cooked using fresh produce.

Bedrooms: 1 single, 2 double, 1 twin, 1 multiple
Bathrooms: 5 private
Bed & breakfast

per night:	£min	£max
Single	25.00	
Double	40.00	

Half board

per person:	£min	£max
Daily	27.25	

Parking for 22
Cards accepted: Access, Visa

SAWREY
Cumbria
Map ref 5A3

Far Sawrey and Near Sawrey lie near Esthwaite Water. Both villages are small but Near Sawrey is famous for Hill Top Farm, home of Beatrix Potter, now owned by the National Trust and open to the public.

The Glen ♨
Far Sawrey, Ambleside
LA22 0LQ
☎ Windermere (053 94) 43370
Comfortable old country house in peaceful surroundings with magnificent views. Ideal for walking and touring. Good home-cooking. Log fire.
Bedrooms: 3 double, 1 twin, 1 triple
Bathrooms: 5 private
Bed & breakfast

per night:	£min	£max
Single	24.00	25.00
Double	34.00	36.00

Half board

per person:	£min	£max
Daily	27.00	28.00
Weekly	160.00	165.00

Evening meal 1930 (last orders 0900)
Parking for 6

Individual proprietors have supplied all details of accommodation. Although we do check for accuracy, we advise you to confirm the information at the time of booking.

SEDBERGH
Cumbria
Map ref 5B3

This busy market town set below the Howgill Fells is an excellent centre for walkers and touring the Dales. The noted boys' school was founded in 1525.

Cross Keys Hotel (Unlicensed)
Cautley, Sedbergh LA10 5NE
☎ (053 96) 20284
Homely, comfortable old National Trust house in magnificent setting. Log fires, well-presented real home cooking (bring your own wine). Guided walking holidays available. Non-smokers only please.
Bedrooms: 1 single, 3 double, 1 twin
Bathrooms: 1 private, 1 public
Bed & breakfast

per night:	£min	£max
Single	23.00	23.00
Double	46.00	53.00

Half board

per person:	£min	£max
Daily	37.00	40.50

Lunch available
Evening meal 2000 (last orders 2000)
Parking for 10
Open April-December

Dalesman Country Inn
COMMENDED
Main Street, Sedbergh
LA10 5BN
☎ (053 96) 21183
On entering Sedbergh from the M6 the Dalesman is the first inn on the left. 17th C but recently refurbished by local craftsmen. 10% discount on weekly bookings.
Bedrooms: 1 double, 2 twin, 3 triple
Bathrooms: 4 private, 1 public
Bed & breakfast

per night:	£min	£max
Double	44.00	48.00

Lunch available
Evening meal 1800 (last orders 2130)
Parking for 10
Cards accepted: Access, Visa

St Marks
Cautley, Sedbergh LA10 5LZ
☎ (053 96) 20287

Elegant Grade II listed Victorian vicarage. Recently refurbished. Three miles from Sedbergh on A683, in outstanding setting in the Rawthey Valley.
Bedrooms: 1 single, 3 twin, 1 multiple
Bathrooms: 4 private, 1 private shower
Bed & breakfast

per night:	£min	£max
Single	16.00	20.00
Double	32.00	40.00

Half board

per person:	£min	£max
Daily	26.00	30.00
Weekly	164.00	189.00

Lunch available
Evening meal 1930 (last orders 2030)
Parking for 10

SHAP
Cumbria
Map ref 5B3

Village lying nearly 1000 ft above sea-level. Shap Abbey, open to the public, is hidden in a valley nearby. Most of the ruins date from the early 13th C, but the tower is 16th C.

Kings Arms Hotel
Main Street, Shap, Penrith CA10 3NU
☎ (0931) 716277
Comfortable friendly accommodation on the fringe of the Lake District near M6 junction 39. Directly on the "Coast to Coast" walk.
Bedrooms: 2 double, 2 twin, 2 triple
Bathrooms: 2 public
Bed & breakfast

per night:	£min	£max
Single	16.00	
Double	32.00	

Lunch available
Evening meal 1900 (last orders 2200)
Parking for 15
Cards accepted: Access

National Crown ratings were correct at the time of going to press but are subject to change. Please check at the time of booking.

SILLOTH
Cumbria
Map ref 5A2

Small port and coastal resort on the Solway Firth with wide cobbled roads and an attractive green leading to the promenade and seashore known for its magnificent sunsets.
Tourist Information Centre
☎ (069 73) 31944.

Nook Farm
Listed APPROVED
Beckfoot, Silloth, Carlisle CA5 4LG
☎ Allonby (0900) 881279
90-acre dairy farm. Within easy reach of all tourist areas, and with views of Lakeland.
Bedrooms: 1 double, 1 triple
Bathrooms: 1 public
Bed & breakfast

per night:	£min	£max
Single	12.00	15.00
Double	22.00	24.00

Half board

per person:	£min	£max
Daily	15.00	

Parking for 3
Open April-October

THRELKELD
Cumbria
Map ref 5A3

This village is a centre for climbing the Saddleback range of mountains, which tower high above it.

The Bungalow
Sunnyside, Threlkeld, Keswick CA12 4SD
☎ (076 87) 79679
Bed and breakfast accommodation, furnished to a high standard, serving full English breakfasts. Excellent views of the surrounding fells. Self-catering also available.
Bedrooms: 1 double, 3 twin, 1 multiple
Bathrooms: 5 private
Bed & breakfast

per night:	£min	£max
Single	24.00	33.00
Double	30.00	

Parking for 15

Scales Farm
COMMENDED
Scales, Threlkeld, Keswick CA12 4SY
☎ (076 87) 79660

Tastefully modernised 17th C farmhouse, conveniently situated for touring the Lakes. All bedrooms en-suite with colour TV and tea/coffee-making facilities. Friendly personal service provided by proprietors.
Bedrooms: 2 double, 2 twin
Bathrooms: 4 private
Bed & breakfast

per night:	£min	£max
Double	34.00	40.00

Parking for 6

TROUTBECK
Cumbria
Map ref 5A3

On the Penrith to Keswick road, Troutbeck was the site of a series of Roman camps. The village now hosts a busy weekly sheep market.

Netherdene Guest House
COMMENDED
Troutbeck, Penrith CA11 0SJ
☎ Greystoke (076 84) 83475
Traditional country house in its own quiet grounds, with extensive mountain views, offering comfortable well-appointed rooms with personal attention. Ideal base for touring Lakeland.
Bedrooms: 2 double, 1 twin, 1 triple
Bathrooms: 2 private, 2 public
Bed & breakfast

per night:	£min	£max
Single	15.00	18.00
Double	28.00	36.00

Half board

per person:	£min	£max
Daily	21.00	25.00
Weekly	140.00	160.00

Evening meal 1830 (last orders 1600)
Parking for 6
Open February-November

Troutbeck Inn
Troutbeck, Penrith CA11 0SJ
☎ Greystoke (076 84) 83635
Small, family-run country inn halfway between Keswick and Penrith. Approximately 10 minutes from the M6, Ullswater and Keswick, and ideal for all Lakeland activities. Bar meals available.
Bedrooms: 2 double, 1 triple
Bathrooms: 1 public

Bed & breakfast

per night:	£min	£max
Single	20.00	20.00
Double	30.00	30.00

Evening meal 1830 (last orders 2100)
Parking for 50

ULLSWATER
Cumbria
Map ref 5A3

This beautiful lake, which is over 7 miles long, runs from Glenridding to Pooley Bridge. Lofty peaks ranging round the lake make an impressive background. A steamer service operates along the lake between Pooley Bridge, Howtown and Glenridding in the summer.
Tourist Information Centre
☎ (07684) 82414.

Cragside Cottage
Thackthwaite, Ullswater, Penrith CA11 0ND
☎ Pooley Bridge (076 84) 86385
Mountainside location, 3 miles north of Ullswater. All rooms have toilet, shower and washbasin, tea making facilities, TV. Reserved parking space. Breakfast served in room. Brochure available.
Bedrooms: 3 double, 2 triple
Bathrooms: 5 private
Bed & breakfast

per night:	£min	£max
Double	31.00	31.00

Parking for 5
Open March-October
Cards accepted: Access, Visa

Low Garth Guest House
Penruddock, Ullswater, Penrith CA11 0QU
☎ (076 84) 83492
Tastefully converted 18th C barn in peaceful surroundings with magnificent views. Easy access to A66.
Bedrooms: 1 twin, 1 triple
Bathrooms: 2 private, 1 public
Bed & breakfast

per night:	£min	£max
Single	14.00	17.00
Double	28.00	34.00

Continued ▶

ULLSWATER

Continued

Half board per person:	£min	£max
Daily	23.00	27.00
Weekly	161.00	189.00

Evening meal 1800 (last orders 2000)
Parking for 8
[S]

Swiss Chalet Inn

APPROVED

Pooley Bridge, Penrith
CA10 2NN
☎ (076 84) 86215
Fax (076 84) 86215
Set in charming village near shores of beautiful Ullswater, 5 miles from M6. All rooms en-suite. Swiss/Continental/ English cuisine.
Bedrooms: 1 single, 6 double, 1 twin, 1 multiple
Bathrooms: 9 private

Bed & breakfast per night:	£min	£max
Single	27.00	32.00
Double	44.00	52.00

Lunch available
Evening meal 1800 (last orders 2145)
Parking for 40
Open February-December
Cards accepted: Access, Visa
[S] [T]

Tymparon Hall

Listed APPROVED

Newbiggin, Stainton, Penrith
CA11 0HS
☎ Greystoke (076 84) 83236
150-acre livestock farm. Excellent base for visiting Hadrian's Wall and touring the Lake District and Yorkshire Dales. Only 3.5 miles from exit 40 of M6.
Bedrooms: 1 double, 1 twin, 1 triple
Bathrooms: 2 private, 1 public

Bed & breakfast per night:	£min	£max
Single	15.00	18.00
Double	30.00	36.00

Half board per person:	£min	£max
Daily	22.50	25.50
Weekly	147.00	175.00

Evening meal 1830 (last orders 1430)
Open April-October
[UL] [S] [TV] [OAP] [SP]

UNDERBARROW

Cumbria
Map ref 5A3

At the foot of limestone escarpment Scout Scar, Underbarrow is close to the National Trust's Brigsteer Woods, west of Kendal. A quiet, spread-out village, overlooking the Lyth Valley.

Kirkby House Farm

Underbarrow, Kendal
LA8 8HH
☎ (053 95) 68310
200-acre mixed farm. Comfortable working farm in small village 6 miles from Windermere. 1 double and 1 twin bedded room with adjoining bathroom.
Bedrooms: 1 double, 1 twin
Bathrooms: 1 public

Bed & breakfast per night:	£min	£max
Single	16.00	17.00
Double	28.00	30.00

Parking for 9
[UL] [TV]

UNDERSKIDDAW

Cumbria
Map ref 5A3

Dancing Beck

Underskiddaw, Keswick
CA12 4PY
☎ Keswick (076 87) 73800
Lakeland house, with views of Lakeland mountains, 2.5 miles from Keswick, just off A591 Keswick-Carlisle road.
Bedrooms: 1 double, 1 twin, 1 triple
Bathrooms: 2 public

Bed & breakfast per night:	£min	£max
Double	34.00	36.00

Parking for 3
Open March-October
3 [UL] [TV]

There are separate sections in this guide listing groups specialising in farm holidays and accommodation which is especially suitable for young people and organised groups.

WASDALE

Cumbria
Map ref 5A3

A very dramatic valley with England's deepest lake, Wastwater; highest mountain, Scafell Pike; smallest church. The eastern shore of Wastwater is dominated by the 1,500 ft screes dropping steeply into the lake. A good centre for walking and climbing.

Church Stile Farm House

COMMENDED

Church Stile, Nether Wasdale, Gosforth, Seascale
CA20 1ET
☎ (094 67) 26252
400-acre hill farm. Traditional Cumbrian farmhouse in the pretty village of Netherwasdale, with superb views, walks and climbing.
Bedrooms: 1 single, 1 double, 1 triple
Bathrooms: 2 private

Bed & breakfast per night:	£min	£max
Single	15.00	16.00
Double	35.00	35.00

Half board per person:	£min	£max
Daily	26.50	27.50
Weekly	178.00	182.00

Evening meal 1800 (last orders 0900)
Parking for 2
[UL] [S] [SP]

WATERMILLOCK

Cumbria
Map ref 5A3

Waterside House

COMMENDED

Watermillock, Penrith
CA11 0JH
☎ Pooley Bridge (076 84) 86038
A Queen Anne house, set amidst gardens and meadows on Ullswater's glorious shores. Peaceful and comfortable, an idyllic retreat from pressures. On A592 to Patterdale, 2 miles south of Pooley Bridge.
Bedrooms: 5 double, 1 twin, 1 triple
Bathrooms: 4 private, 3 public

Bed & breakfast per night:	£min	£max
Single	20.00	30.00
Double	40.00	60.00

Parking for 10
[UL] [S] [TV] [SP]

WHICHAM

Cumbria
Map ref 5A3

Small village consisting mainly of recent buildings. Whicham and Millom Grammar School was founded in 1540 and rebuilt in 1862.

Whicham Hall Farm

Whicham Hall, Silecroft, Millom LA18 5LT
☎ Millom (0229) 772637
300-acre livestock farm. We offer a peaceful holiday and wholesome farm cooking in the unspoilt Whicham Valley. Families are very welcome. 6-berth mobile home also available.
Bedrooms: 1 triple, 1 multiple
Bathrooms: 2 public

Bed & breakfast per night:	£min	£max
Single	15.00	
Double		24.00

Parking for 3
Open April-November
[UL] [TV]

WHITEHAVEN

Cumbria
Map ref 5A3

Historic Georgian port on the west coast. The town was developed in the 17th C and many of the fine buildings of that period have been preserved.
Tourist Information Centre ☎ (0946) 695678.

Glenlea House

Glenlea, Lowca, Whitehaven
CA28 6PS
☎ (0946) 693873
Quiet, Georgian house in its own grounds with panoramic views from all rooms. Home-cooking, vegetarian diets on request. Adjoining a small village and only 1 mile from the centre of Whitehaven.
Bedrooms: 2 single, 3 double, 3 twin, 2 triple
Bathrooms: 11 private, 2 public

Bed & breakfast

per night:	£min	£max
Single	15.00	25.00
Double	30.00	35.00

Half board

per person:	£min	£max
Daily	20.00	24.00

Lunch available
Evening meal 1820 (last orders 1930)
Parking for 10

WINDERMERE

Cumbria
Map ref 5A3

Once a tiny hamlet before the introduction of the railway in 1847, now adjoins Bowness which is on the lakeside. Centre for sailing & boating. A good way to see the lake is a trip on a passenger steamer. Steamboat Museum has fine collection of old boats.
Tourist Information Centre ☎ *(05394) 46499.*

Aaron Slack ₳

48 Ellerthwaite Road, Windermere LA23 2BS
☎ (053 94) 44649
A small friendly guesthouse for non-smokers in a quiet part of Windermere, close to all amenities and concentrating on personal service.
Bedrooms: 2 double, 1 twin
Bathrooms: 3 private

Bed & breakfast

per night:	£min	£max
Single	12.00	20.00
Double	24.00	34.00

Half board

per person:	£min	£max
Daily	19.00	27.00
Weekly	130.00	180.00

Evening meal 1900 (last orders 1900)
Cards accepted: Access, Visa

Almaria House ₳

APPROVED

17 Broad Street, Windermere LA23 2AB
☎ (053 94) 43026
Maria and Alan offer you a warm welcome close to all amenities, public car parking, great breakfast. Ideal holiday base.
Bedrooms: 4 double, 1 triple

Bathrooms: 3 private, 1 public

Bed & breakfast

per night:	£min	£max
Double	24.00	38.00

Open January-November
Cards accepted: Access, Visa

Applegarth Hotel ₳

College Road, Windermere LA23 2AE
☎ (053 94) 43206
Elegant Victorian mansion house with individually designed bedrooms and four-poster suites (extra charge). Lake and fell views.
Bedrooms: 4 single, 6 double, 2 twin, 3 triple, 1 multiple
Bathrooms: 16 private

Bed & breakfast

per night:	£min	£max
Single	25.00	35.00
Double	40.00	50.00

Parking for 25
Cards accepted: Access, Visa, Amex

Ashleigh ₳

Listed COMMENDED

11 College Road, Windermere LA23 1BU
☎ (053 94) 42292
Beautiful, comfortable Victorian home with stunning mountain views. Breakfast choice. Tasty dinners available. Quiet central location. Non-smoking. All rooms en-suite.
Bedrooms: 1 single, 3 double, 1 twin
Bathrooms: 5 private

Bed & breakfast

per night:	£min	£max
Single	18.00	24.00
Double	36.00	48.00

Half board

per person:	£min	£max
Daily	28.00	34.00

Evening meal from 1900
Parking for 2
Cards accepted: Access, Visa

Bannerigg Farm

Windermere LA23 1JL
☎ (053 94) 43362
150-acre mixed farm. Comfortable farmhouse on the A591, 1 mile from Windermere. Separate dining/lounge area. Extensive views. Central position for touring.
Bedrooms: 2 double, 1 twin
Bathrooms: 2 public

Bed & breakfast

per night:	£min	£max
Double	26.00	30.00

Parking for 3
Open March-November

Beckmead House ₳

COMMENDED

5 Park Avenue, Windermere LA23 2AR
☎ (053 94) 42757
Delightful stone-built Victorian house with reputation for high standards, comfort and friendliness. Our a la carte breakfasts are famous. Convenient for lake, shops, restaurants and golf-course.
Bedrooms: 1 single, 2 double, 1 twin, 1 multiple
Bathrooms: 2 private, 1 public, 2 private showers

Bed & breakfast

per night:	£min	£max
Single	13.50	16.00
Double	29.00	38.00

Beckside Cottage ₳

4 Park Road, Windermere LA23 2AW
☎ (053 94) 42069
Small family-run bed and breakfast with 4 en-suite rooms, full central heating. Close to village and all amenities.
Bedrooms: 1 single, 3 double
Bathrooms: 4 private

Bed & breakfast

per night:	£min	£max
Single	13.50	17.00
Double	27.00	34.00

Parking for 3
Open February-December

Beech House ₳

COMMENDED

11 Woodland Terrace, Windermere LA23 2AN
☎ (053 94) 46303
Friendly welcome by local couple to clean and tastefully decorated establishment. Hearty breakfast provided. 5 minutes' walk from station and near all amenities.
Bedrooms: 1 single, 2 double, 2 twin
Bathrooms: 1 private, 2 public

Bed & breakfast

per night:	£min	£max
Double	25.00	36.00

Open April-October

Boston House ₳

4 The Terrace, Windermere LA23 1AJ
☎ (053 94) 43654
Peaceful spacious Victorian listed building within 5 minutes' walk of trains and town centre. Panoramic views, relaxed comfortable atmosphere, private parking.
Bedrooms: 2 double, 2 twin, 1 triple, 1 multiple
Bathrooms: 4 private, 2 public, 1 private shower

Bed & breakfast

per night:	£min	£max
Double	28.00	40.00

Half board

per person:	£min	£max
Daily	22.00	29.00
Weekly	140.00	185.00

Evening meal 1900 (last orders 1930)
Parking for 6

Brook House ₳

3 Craig Walk, Windermere LA23 2ES
☎ (053 94) 43809
Cosy accommodation for non-smokers only. Quiet location. An ideal base from which to explore Lakeland. Good home cooking.
Bedrooms: 2 single, 2 double
Bathrooms: 2 public

Bed & breakfast

per night:	£min	£max
Single	13.50	14.50
Double	26.00	28.00

Parking for 4
Open March-November

Broomhill

Birthwaite Road, Windermere LA23 1BS
☎ (053 94) 43322
Family home in its own large grounds, with wonderful lake and mountain views.
Bedrooms: 2 double, 1 twin
Bathrooms: 2 private, 1 public

Bed & breakfast

per night:	£min	£max
Single	25.00	30.00
Double	30.00	40.00

Parking for 6
Open April-October

The Common Farm

Windermere LA23 1JQ
☎ (053 94) 43433
200-acre dairy farm. Picturesque and homely 17th C farmhouse in peaceful

Continued ▶

WINDERMERE

Continued

surroundings less than 1 mile from Windermere village.
Bedrooms: 2 double, 1 triple
Bathrooms: 1 public
Bed & breakfast

per night:	£min	£max
Double	26.00	30.00

Parking for 4

☎ 5 ⊡ 🅸 🆂 🅼 📺 🈺 ∪ 🗡 🈸
🆂🄿 🏧

Crookleigh ⚄

15 Woodland Terrace,
Windermere LA23 2AE
☎ (053 94) 42557
Ideal for all local amenities, a small friendly guesthouse in the lovely village of Windermere.
Bedrooms: 1 single,
3 double, 1 twin
Bathrooms: 1 private,
2 public
Bed & breakfast

per night:	£min	£max
Single	13.00	18.00
Double	26.00	40.00

Open February-November

☐ 🌢 ⊡ 🅸 🆂 🈺 🈸

Eastbourne Hotel ⚄
🏵🏵

Biskey Howe Road,
Bowness-on-Windermere,
Windermere LA23 2JR
☎ (053 94) 43525
Small family-run hotel offering private facilities and a friendly welcome. Located in a quiet position close to Lake Windermere, an ideal central touring base.
Bedrooms: 2 single,
4 double, 2 triple
Bathrooms: 5 private,
1 public, 1 private shower
Bed & breakfast

per night:	£min	£max
Single	14.50	20.00
Double	29.00	40.00

Parking for 3

☎ 5 ☐ 🌢 🅸 🆂 🗡 🅼 🈺 🚗 ∪
🗡 🈸 🄳🄰🄿 ⛄

Field House Guest House

Kendal Road, Bowness-on-Windermere, Windermere
LA23 3EQ
☎ (053 94) 42476
Central and overlooking the lake at the rear. A comfortable well-established guesthouse with friendly and personal service by the owners.
Bedrooms: 3 double, 2 twin,
2 triple

Bathrooms: 4 private,
2 public
Bed & breakfast

per night:	£min	£max
Double	30.00	45.00

Parking for 7
Cards accepted: Access, Visa

☎ 🌢 ☐ 🌢 ⊡ 🆂 🅼 🈺 🈸

Hazel Bank ⚄
🏵 COMMENDED

Hazel Street, Windermere
LA23 1EL
☎ (053 94) 45486
Quietly situated Victorian residence, with firm beds, log fires, large warm rooms, varied food and guided walks. Non-smokers only please.
Bedrooms: 2 double, 1 twin
Bathrooms: 3 private
Bed & breakfast

per night:	£min	£max
Double	30.00	38.00

Half board

per person:	£min	£max
Daily	23.00	27.00

Evening meal 1800 (last orders 1900)
Parking for 5

☎ 7 🍴 🌢 🅼 🆂 🗡 🅼 📺 🈺
🚗 ⛄ 🗡 🈸 🆂🄿 🆃

Holly Lodge ⚄
🏵 APPROVED

6 College Road, Windermere
LA23 1BX
☎ (053 94) 43873
Traditional Lakeland stone guesthouse, built in 1854. In a quiet area off the main road, close to the village centre, buses, railway station and all amenities.
Bedrooms: 1 single,
5 double, 2 twin, 3 triple
Bathrooms: 4 private,
2 public
Bed & breakfast

per night:	£min	£max
Single	15.00	20.00
Double	30.00	40.00

Half board

per person:	£min	£max
Daily	24.50	29.50

Evening meal from 1900
Parking for 7

☎ ☐ 🌢 🅸 🆂 🅼 🈺 🚗 🗡
🈸 ⛄

Holmlea ⚄
🏵🏵 COMMENDED

Kendal Road, Windermere
LA23 3EW
☎ (053 94) 42597
Very close to both the lake shore and the shops. Private on-site car park. TV in all rooms. A warm welcome awaits you.
Bedrooms: 2 single,
3 double, 1 twin

Bathrooms: 1 public
Bed & breakfast

per night:	£min	£max
Single	14.00	18.00
Double	16.00	19.00

Parking for 6

☎ 🌢 ⊡ 🌢 ⊡ 🅸 🅼 📺 🈺 🚗
🗡 🈸 🄳🄰🄿 🆂🄿

Laurel Cottage ⚄
🏵🏵 COMMENDED

St. Martin's Square,
Bowness-on-Windermere,
Windermere LA23 3EF
☎ (053 94) 45594
Charming early 17th C cottage with front garden, situated in centre of Bowness. Superb selection of restaurants within one minute's stroll.
Bedrooms: 2 single,
10 double, 1 twin, 2 triple
Bathrooms: 10 private,
2 public
Bed & breakfast

per night:	£min	£max
Single	19.00	21.00
Double	34.00	50.00

Parking for 8

☎ 🌢 ⊡ 🅸 🆂 🅼 📺 🈺
🈸 🆂🄿 🏧 🆃

Lingmoor

7 High Street, Windermere
LA23 1AF
☎ (053 94) 44947
Friendly homely accommodation, family-run, close to station, buses, shops and Tourist Information Centre. Good full English breakfast guaranteed.
Bedrooms: 1 single,
2 double, 1 twin, 1 triple
Bathrooms: 1 private,
1 public
Bed & breakfast

per night:	£min	£max
Single	10.00	15.00
Double	20.00	30.00

Half board

per person:	£min	£max
Daily	17.00	25.00
Weekly	100.00	175.00

Evening meal from 1900

🌢 ☐ 🌢 🅼 🅸 📺 🈺 🗡 🈸
⛄ 🆂🄿

Lingwood ⚄

Birkett Hill, Bowness-on-Windermere, Windermere
LA23 3EZ
☎ (053 94) 44680
Comfortable well-positioned guesthouse. Ideal for walking and lake use. Membership available at adjacent country club. Special rates for 3-day breaks.
Bedrooms: 3 double
Bathrooms: 2 public

Bed & breakfast

per night:	£min	£max
Single	15.00	16.00
Double	30.00	32.00

Parking for 6

☎ 🌢 ⊡ 🌢 🅸 🅸 📺 🈺 🚗
🗡 🈸 🆂🄿

Oakthorpe Hotel ⚄

High Street, Windermere
LA23 1AF
☎ (053 94) 43547
Attractive and friendly Lakeland hotel, boasting a reputation for fresh food (especially fish) in the restaurant and the Lamplighter Bar.
Bedrooms: 3 single,
8 double, 1 twin, 2 triple, 3 multiple
Bathrooms: 7 private,
3 public, 3 private showers
Bed & breakfast

per night:	£min	£max
Single	18.00	26.00
Double	52.00	72.00

Half board

per person:	£min	£max
Weekly	168.00	220.00

Lunch available
Evening meal 1900 (last orders 2030)
Parking for 16
Cards accepted: Access, Visa, Switch

☎ 🌢 ☐ 🌢 🅸 🆂 🅼 📺 🈺 🚗
🔍 🆂🄿 🏧

Oakworth ⚄

11 Upper Oak Street,
Windermere LA23 2LB
☎ (053 94) 42782
Small guesthouse in quiet road, yet close to all amenities. Centrally heated, good home cooking with optional evening meal.
Bedrooms: 1 double,
1 multiple
Bathrooms: 1 public
Bed & breakfast

per night:	£min	£max
Single	14.00	16.00
Double	27.00	32.00

Half board

per person:	£min	£max
Daily	21.50	25.00
Weekly	135.00	160.00

Evening meal 1830 (last orders 1930)
Parking for 2

☎ ☐ 🌢 🌢 🅸 🆂 🅼 🈺 🚗 🈸
⛄ 🆂🄿

Oldfield House ⚄
🏵🏵 COMMENDED

Oldfield Road, Windermere
LA23 2BY
☎ (053 94) 88445
Friendly, informal atmosphere within a traditionally-built

Lakeland residence. Quiet central location, free use of swimming and leisure club.
Bedrooms: 2 single,
3 double, 1 triple, 1 multiple
Bathrooms: 5 private,
2 public

Bed & breakfast

per night:	£min	£max
Single	16.00	24.00
Double	32.00	44.00

Parking for 7
Cards accepted: Access, Visa, Switch

Park Beck Guest House ⋒

3 Park Road, Windermere
LA23 2AW
☎ (053 94) 44025
Ideally situated Lakeland-stone guesthouse, close to all facilities. En-suite rooms with colour TV and tea/coffee making facilities.
Bedrooms: 3 double, 1 twin,
1 triple
Bathrooms: 5 private

Bed & breakfast

per night:	£min	£max
Double	28.00	39.00

Lunch available
Parking for 2
Open February-December

The Poplars ⋒

COMMENDED
Lake Road, Windermere
LA23 2EQ
☎ (053 94) 42325 & 446690
Small family-run guesthouse on the main lake road, offering every home comfort. A limited number of non-residents catered for. Advance booking essential for evening meal.
Bedrooms: 1 single,
3 double, 2 twin, 1 triple
Bathrooms: 5 private,
1 public

Bed & breakfast

per night:	£min	£max
Single	20.00	25.00
Double	40.00	50.00

Half board

per person:	£min	£max
Daily	30.00	37.00
Weekly	200.00	249.00

Evening meal 1830 (last orders 1900)
Parking for 7

Sandown ⋒

Lake Road, Bowness-on-Windermere, Windermere
LA23 2JF
☎ (053 94) 45275
Large modern detached house, set in landscaped area with trees and shrubs, 10 minutes' walk from Lake Windermere. Golf, riding, sailing nearby. Safe parking in grounds. SAE or telephone for details.
Bedrooms: 6 double, 1 twin
Bathrooms: 7 private

Bed & breakfast

per night:	£min	£max
Double	25.00	36.00

Parking for 8

South View ⋒

Cross Street, Windermere
LA23 1AE
☎ (053 94) 42951
Small Georgian hotel, family-run for 20 years. Central for all attractions and transport, yet very quiet. Good English food. Heated indoor swimming pool.
Bedrooms: 1 single,
4 double, 2 twin
Bathrooms: 2 public

Bed & breakfast

per night:	£min	£max
Single	18.00	23.00
Double	36.00	50.00

Half board

per person:	£min	£max
Daily	30.00	37.00
Weekly	120.00	150.00

Evening meal 1830 (last orders 1600)
Parking for 6
Cards accepted: Access, Visa, Amex

Thornleigh Guest House

COMMENDED
Thornbarrow Road,
Windermere LA23 2EW
☎ (053 94) 44203
Traditional Lakeland house of character, in quiet, pleasant residential road. Comfortable, well-furnished bedrooms, TV plus tea/coffee making facilities, some private showers. Lake and village a few minutes' drive away.
Bedrooms: 1 single,
2 double, 1 twin, 1 triple
Bathrooms: 1 public,
2 private showers

Bed & breakfast

per night:	£min	£max
Single	15.00	18.00
Double	30.00	36.00

Parking for 5
Open March-November
Cards accepted: Access, Visa

Villa Lodge ⋒

Cross Street, Windermere
LA23 1AE
☎ (053 94) 43318
Friendliness and cleanliness guaranteed. Peacefully situated in quiet cul-de-sac overlooking Windermere village. Splendid views from bedrooms.
Bedrooms: 1 single,
3 double, 2 twin, 1 triple,
1 multiple
Bathrooms: 2 private,
2 public

Bed & breakfast

per night:	£min	£max
Single	16.00	20.00
Double	30.00	46.00

Half board

per person:	£min	£max
Daily	26.00	33.00
Weekly	180.00	200.00

Evening meal 1830 (last orders 1530)
Parking for 8

Westbourne Hotel ⋒

COMMENDED
Biskey Howe Road,
Bowness-on-Windermere,
Windermere LA23 2JR
☎ (053 94) 43625
In a peaceful area of Bowness within a short walk of the lake and shops. Highly recommended by our regular guests for comfort, decor and food.
Bedrooms: 1 single,
3 double, 1 twin, 2 triple
Bathrooms: 3 private,
4 private showers

Bed & breakfast

per night:	£min	£max
Single	25.00	25.00
Double	36.00	50.00

Half board

per person:	£min	£max
Daily	29.00	35.00

Evening meal 1830 (last orders 1900)
Parking for 10
Cards accepted: Access, Visa

White Lodge Hotel ⋒

COMMENDED
Lake Road, Windermere
LA23 2JS
☎ (053 94) 43624
Family-owned hotel with home cooking, only a short walk from Bowness Bay. All bedrooms have private bathrooms, colour TV and tea making facilities. Some with lake views and four posters.
Bedrooms: 2 single,
7 double, 2 twin, 1 triple
Bathrooms: 12 private

Bed & breakfast

per night:	£min	£max
Single	23.00	29.00
Double	46.00	52.00

Half board

per person:	£min	£max
Daily	32.00	36.00
Weekly	225.00	245.00

Lunch available
Evening meal 1900 (last orders 2000)
Parking for 20
Open March-November
Cards accepted: Access, Visa

WINSTER

Cumbria
Map ref 5A3

An unspoilt hamlet of scattered whitewashed stone cottages in wooded seclusion yet close to Lake Windermere and Bowness.

The Wood Farm

Winster, Windermere
LA23 3NY
☎ (053 95) 68790
17th C farmhouse in idyllic rural location, 10 minutes from Lake Windermere, near Masons Arms, offering friendly accommodation for non-smokers in two romantic rooms.
Bedrooms: 2 triple
Bathrooms: 1 public

Bed & breakfast

per night:	£min	£max
Single	13.50	15.00
Double	27.00	30.00

Parking for 6

The colour maps at the back of this guide pinpoint all places with accommodation.

WITHERSLACK

Cumbria
Map ref 5A3

Tranquil village on the east bank of the River Winster, at the south end of the Lyth Valley, famed for its damsons. Good base for touring.

The Old Vicarage Country House Hotel ⋀

HIGHLY COMMENDED

Church Road, Witherslack, Grange-over-Sands
LA11 6RS
☎ (044 852) 381
Fax (044 852) 373
Secluded Georgian country vicarage sheltered by gentle Lakeland fells. Near Lake Windermere and M6 junction 36. Dine by candlelight on fresh local produce.
Bedrooms: 1 single, 9 double, 4 twin
Bathrooms: 14 private

Bed & breakfast

per night:	£min	£max
Single	35.00	78.00
Double	50.00	118.00

Half board

per person:	£min	£max
Daily	44.50	64.50

Evening meal 2000 (last orders 1930)
Parking for 25
Cards accepted: Access, Visa, Amex

Individual proprietors have supplied all details of accommodation. Although we do check for accuracy, we advise you to confirm the information at the time of booking.

WORKINGTON

Cumbria
Map ref 5A2

A deep-water port on the west Cumbrian coast. There are the ruins of the 14th C Workington Hall, where Mary Queen of Scots stayed in 1568.
Tourist Information Centre
☎ (0900) 602923.

Brampton House

29 Parkend Road, Workington CA14 4DE
☎ (0900) 603230
Delightful Victorian building in good location. Park and museum within 100 yards. Town centre 5 minute walk.
Bedrooms: 2 single, 2 double, 3 twin, 1 triple
Bathrooms: 2 public

Bed & breakfast

per night:	£min	£max
Single	15.00	18.00
Double	30.00	36.00

Parking for 5

Morven Guest House ⋀

Siddick road, Siddick, Workington CA14 1LE
☎ (0900) 602118
Detached house north-west of Workington. Ideal base for touring the Lake District and west Cumbria. Large car park.
Bedrooms: 2 single, 1 double, 2 twin, 1 triple
Bathrooms: 4 private, 1 public, 1 private shower

Bed & breakfast

per night:	£min	£max
Single	19.00	30.00
Double	32.00	42.00

Lunch available
Evening meal 1800 (last orders 1600)
Parking for 20

The enquiry coupons at the back will help you when contacting proprietors.

Check the maps

The place you wish to visit may not have accommodation entirely suited to your needs, but there could be somewhere ideal quite close by. Check the colour maps at the back of this guide to identify nearby towns and villages with accommodation listed in the guide, and then use the town index to find page numbers.

Key to symbols

Information about many of the services and facilities at establishments listed in this guide is given in the form of symbols. The key to these symbols is inside the back cover flap. You may find it helpful to keep the flap open when referring to the entry listings.

National Accessible Scheme

◆

If you are a wheelchair user or someone who has difficulty walking, look for the national "Accessible" symbol when choosing where to stay.

All the places that display the symbol have been checked by a Tourist Board inspector against criteria that reflect the practical needs of wheelchair users.

At the moment, the Tourist Boards are concentrating their inspections on hotels, guesthouses, inns, B&Bs, farmhouse acommodation and self-catering holiday homes. There are plans to extend the scheme to holiday caravan parks and visitor attractions in 1994.

◆

There are three categories of accessibility:

Category 1: Accessible to all wheelchair users including those travelling independently

Category 2: Accessible to a wheelchair user with assistance

Category 3: Accessible to a wheelchair user able to walk short distances and up at least three steps

◆

The National Accessible Scheme forms part of the Tourism for All campaign that is being promoted by all three national Tourist Boards.

A leaflet giving more information on the scheme is available free from any Tourist Information Centre, whose staff will also be pleased to help with finding suitable accommodation in the area.

Additional help and guidance can be obtained from the Holiday Care Service, 2 Old Bank Chambers, Station Road, Horley, Surrey RH6 9HW. Tel: (0293) 774535. Fax: (0293) 784647. Minicom: (0293) 776943 (24-hour answering).

◆

Northumbria

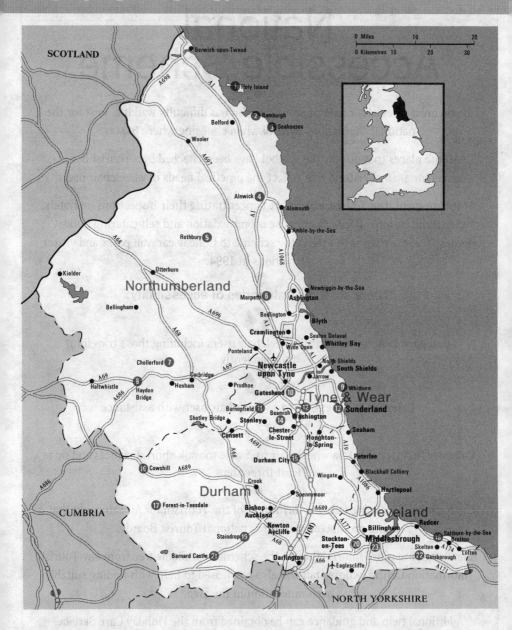

Use the above map to locate places in the "Where to Go, What to See" section opposite.
Use the colour maps at the back of this guide to find places with accommodation.

Land of contrasts, from the lovely river valleys and spectacular waterfalls of Weardale and Teesdale to the sophisticated nightlife of Newcastle upon Tyne, Northumbria has it all. Unspoilt miles of coastline, the wild moorlands of Kielder Forest, the North Pennine hills and dales and Hadrian's Wall country offer endless opportunities for discovering Northumbria's heritage. Visit the island of Lindisfarne and the wildlife sanctuary of the Farne Islands, the 12th century castle at Alnwick, Durham's magnificent Norman cathedral, Stockton, birthplace of the world's railways, and the historic Tees Transporter Bridge. Northumbria is frontier country – yours to explore.

WHERE TO GO, WHAT TO SEE

The number against each name will help you locate it on the map opposite.

❶ Lindisfarne Castle
Holy Island, Berwick-upon-Tweed, Northumberland
Tel: Berwick-upon-Tweed (0289) 89244
Tudor fort converted into a private home in 1903 for Edward Hudson by the architect Sir Edwin Lutyens.

❷ Bamburgh Castle
Bamburgh, Northumberland
NE69 7DE
Tel: Bamburgh (066 84) 208
Coastal castle completely restored in 1900. Collections of china, porcelain, furniture, paintings, arms and armour.

❸ Farne Islands
Seahouses, Northumberland
Bird reserve holding around 55,000 pairs of breeding birds, of 21 species. Home to a large colony of grey seals.

❹ Alnwick Castle
Alnwick, Northumberland
NE66 1NQ
Tel: Alnwick (0665) 510777
Home of the Duke of Northumberland. Magnificent border fortress dating back to the

Rudyard Kipling based three of his stories for children in the book "Puck of Pook's Hill" around Hadrian's Wall, perhaps the most dramatic of Northumbria's many historic attractions

11th C. Main restoration done by Salvin in the 19th C.

❺ Cragside House and Country Park
Cragside, Rothbury, Morpeth, Northumberland
NE65 7PX
Tel: Rothbury (0669) 20333
House built 1864–95 for the first Lord Armstrong, Tyneside industrialist. First house to be lit by electricity generated by water power.

❻ Morpeth Chantry Bagpipe Museum
The Chantry, Bridge Street, Morpeth, Northumberland
NE61 1PJ
Tel: Morpeth (0670) 519466
Craft centre, Tourist Information Centre and museum. Extensive collection of bagpipes, including

Northumberland, Scottish, Irish and Border half-longs.

❼ Chesters Roman Fort
Chollerford, Northumberland
NE46 4EP
Tel: Humshaugh (0434) 681379
Fort built for 500 cavalrymen. Remains include 5 gateways, barrack blocks, commandant's house and headquarters. Finest military bathouse in Britain.

❽ Housesteads Roman Fort
Haydon Bridge, Hexham, Northumberland NE47 6NN

Lindisfarne Castle – a Tudor fort converted into a private home by the architect Sir Edwin Lutyens for the publisher of "Country Life", Edward Hudson, in 1903

Tel: Hexham (0434) 344363
Best preserved and most impressive of the Roman forts. Vercovicium was 5-acre fort for 100 infantry, surrounded by extensive civil settlement.

⑨ Souter Point Lighthouse
Coast Road, Whitburn, South Shields, Tyne & Wear SR6 7NH
Tel: 091-529 3061
The lighthouse and associated buildings were constructed in 1871 and contained the most advanced lighthouse technology of the day.

⑩ MetroCentre
Gateshead, Tyne & Wear
NE11 9XX
Tel: 091-493 2756
Over 300 shops with spacious malls, garden court, children's village. Antique court, Roman forum, over 40 eating outlets, cinema, superbowl and Metroland indoor theme park.

⑪ Gibside Chapel and Grounds
Gibside, Burnopfield, Newcastle upon Tyne, Tyne & Wear
NE16 6BG
Tel: Consett (0207) 542255
Mausoleum of 5 members of the Bowes family, built to a design by James Paine between 1760 and 1812. Restored in 1965. Avenue of Turkey Oak trees.

⑫ The Wildfowl and Wetlands Trust
District 15, Washington, Tyne & Wear NE38 8LE
Tel: 091-416 5454
Collection of 1,250 wildfowl of 108 varieties. Viewing gallery, picnic areas, hides and winter wild bird feeding station. Flamingos. Bird food available.

⑬ Sunderland Illuminations
Sunderland, Tyne & Wear
Tel: 091-512 0444
Over 6 miles of illuminated roads, footpaths and walkways. Over 100 major cross-street features of animated birds, animals and cartoon characters extending into park.

⑭ Beamish – The North of England Open Air Museum
Beamish, Co Durham DH9 0RG
Tel: Stanley (0207) 231811
Open air museum of northern life around the turn of the century. Buildings re-erected to form a town with shops and houses. Colliery village, station and working farm.

⑮ Durham Castle
Palace Green, Durham City, Co Durham DH1 3RW
Tel: 091-374 3863
Castle founded in 1072, Norman chapel dating from 1080, kitchens and great hall dating from 1499 and 1284 respectively.

⑯ Durham Cathedral
Durham City, Co Durham
DH1 3EQ

Tel: 091-386 2367
Widely considered to be the finest example of Norman church architecture in England. Tombs of St. Cuthbert and the Venerable Bede.

⑯ Killhope Leadmining Centre
Cowshill, Upper Weardale, Co Durham DL13 1AR
Tel: Weardale (0388) 537505
Most complete lead mining site in Great Britain. Includes crushing mill with 34ft water wheel, reconstruction of Victorian machinery, railway system and miners' accommodation.

⑰ High Force Waterfall
Forest-in-Teesdale, Co Durham
Tel: (0833) 40209
Most majestic of the waterfalls on the River Tees. The falls are only a short walk from a bus stop and car park and picnic area.

⑱ Saltburn Smugglers
Saltburn-by-the-Sea, Cleveland TS12 1HF
Tel: Guisborough (0287) 625252
Discover the world of smuggling, experience the authentic sights, sounds and smells of Saltburn's smuggling heritage. Listen to tales of John Andrew, "King of the Smugglers".

⑲ Raby Castle
Staindrop, Darlington, Co Durham DL2 3AH
Tel: Staindrop (0833) 60202
Medieval castle in 200-acre park. 600-year-old kitchen and carriage collection. Walled gardens and deer park.

⑳ Green Dragon Museum
Theatre Yard, Stockton-on-Tees, Cleveland TS18 1AT
Tel: Stockton (0642) 674308
Local history museum recording development of Stockton. Dawn of the "railway age" is displayed in an exciting audio-visual show.

⑳ Preston Park Museum
Yarm Road, Stockton-on-Tees, Cleveland TS18 3RH
Tel: Stockton (0642) 781184
Social history museum with period street and rooms, working craftsmen, arms, armour, costume and toys. Set in 116 acres of beautiful parkland. Aviary, pitch and putt.

㉑ The Bowes Museum
Barnard Castle, Co Durham DL12 8NP
Tel: Teesdale (0833) 690606
Fine and decorative 15th and 19th C art collections. Paintings, furniture, ceramics and textiles from Britain and western Europe.

㉒ Gisborough Priory
Guisborough, Cleveland TS14 6HL
Tel: Guisborough (0287) 38301
Remains of 12th C Augustinian priory founded by Robert de Brus, in the grounds of Gisborough Hall. Remains of 12th C gatehouse, 14th C church.

㉓ Ormesby Hall
Ormesby, Middlesbrough, Cleveland TS7 9AS
Tel: Middlesbrough (0642) 324188
Mid-18th C house with fine decorative plasterwork, Jacobean doorway, stable block. Attributed to Carr of York.

FIND OUT MORE

Further information about holidays and attractions in the Northumbria region is available from:
Northumbria Tourist Board
Aykley Heads, Durham DH1 5UX
Tel: 091-384 6905

The following publications are available free from the Northumbria Tourist Board:
Northumbria Holiday Guide 1993
Bed & Breakfast map –
Northumbria and Cumbria
Where to Go map
Caravan and Camping Guide –
Northumbria and Yorkshire
Activity Holidays brochure
Educational brochure
Places to Visit in Winter
Also available is (price includes postage and packing):
Northumbria touring map and guide £5

Heads of mythical beasts at 17th C Wallington, near Cambo, came originally from London's Old Aldersgate

Places to stay

Accommodation entries in this regional section are listed in alphabetical order of place name, and then in alphabetical order of establishment.

The map references refer to the colour maps at the back of the guide. The first figure is the map number; the letter and figure which follow indicate the grid reference on the map.

The symbols at the end of each accommodation entry give information about services and facilities. A 'key' to these symbols is inside the back cover flap, which can be kept open for easy reference.

ALNMOUTH

Northumberland
Map ref 5C1

Quiet village with pleasant old buildings, at the mouth of the River Aln where extensive dunes and sands stretch along Alnmouth Bay. 18th C granaries, some converted to dwellings, still stand.

Blue Dolphins ♠
COMMENDED

Riverside Road, Alnmouth, Alnwick NE66 2SD
☎ (0665) 830893
Beautifully situated Edwardian house with uninterrupted views over mouth of River Aln and North Sea. All rooms en-suite, furnished to high standard.
Bedrooms: 4 double, 1 twin
Bathrooms: 5 private
Bed & breakfast
per night:	£min	£max
Single	20.00	
Double	40.00	

Parking for 5
Open January-November

The Grange ♠
HIGHLY COMMENDED

Northumberland Street, Alnmouth, Alnwick NE66 2RJ
☎ (0665) 830401

Located in the heart of this unspoilt village. 200-year-old former granary in secluded gardens, with views over the River Aln.
Bedrooms: 1 single, 3 double, 1 twin
Bathrooms: 2 private, 1 public
Bed & breakfast
per night:	£min	£max
Single	18.00	19.00
Double	34.00	42.00

Parking for 8

High Buston Hall ♠
HIGHLY COMMENDED

High Buston, Alnmouth, Alnwick NE66 3QH
☎ (0665) 830341
Elegant listed Georgian country house in tranquil village setting, with commanding sea views. Traditional good food and warm hospitality.
Bedrooms: 1 double, 1 triple
Bathrooms: 1 private, 1 public
Bed & breakfast
per night:	£min	£max
Double	37.50	

Half board
per person:	£min	£max
Weekly	125.00	148.00

Evening meal from 1930
Parking for 9
Open March-December

Saddle Hotel ♠

24-25 Northumberland Street, Alnmouth, Alnwick NE66 2RA
☎ (0665) 830476
Personally supervised by owners and offering a high standard of accommodation. Thirteen awards for food in six years.
Bedrooms: 4 double, 4 twin, 1 triple
Bathrooms: 9 private
Bed & breakfast
per night:	£min	£max
Single	34.00	40.00
Double	47.00	53.00

Half board
per person:	£min	£max
Daily	33.00	49.00
Weekly	200.00	300.00

Lunch available
Evening meal 1830 (last orders 2100)
Cards accepted: Access, Visa

National Crown ratings were correct at the time of going to press but are subject to change. Please check at the time of booking.

ALNWICK

Northumberland
Map ref 5C1

Ancient and historic market town, entered through the Hotspur Tower, an original gate in the town walls. The medieval castle, the second biggest in England and still the seat of the Dukes of Northumberland, was restored from ruin in the 18th C.
Tourist Information Centre
☎ (0665) 510665

Cenac ♠

50 Swansfield Park Road, Alnwick NE66 1AR
☎ (0665) 603304
Quietly situated, comfortable house, offering well-appointed accommodation, only 10 minutes' stroll from the centre of Alnwick.
Bedrooms: 1 double, 1 twin
Bathrooms: 1 public, 1 private shower
Bed & breakfast
per night:	£min	£max
Double	32.00	32.00

Half board
per person:	£min	£max
Daily	24.00	24.00
Weekly	161.00	161.00

Evening meal 1900 (last
orders 1600)
Parking for 2
Open April-November
🛇🛏🏧🖵📺▥🅿✕⚲

Clifton House
😊😊 COMMENDED

Clifton Terrace, Alnwick
NE66 1XF
☎ (0665) 510412
*Regency town house in quiet
location 3 minutes from
Alnwick centre and close to
golf-course. Off-street parking.*
Bedrooms: 1 triple
Bathrooms: 1 private,
1 public

Bed & breakfast

per night:	£min	£max
Double	30.00	30.00

Parking for 2
Open March-September
🛇🖿🛏🗇🖵⒮🖵🅼📺▥
🅿✕⚲

"Marae"

13 Bondgate Without,
Alnwick NE66 1PR
☎ (0665) 510334
*Newly modernised Grade II
listed building, conveniently
situated close to town centre.*
Bedrooms: 1 single,
1 double, 1 twin
Bathrooms: 1 public,
1 private shower

Bed & breakfast

per night:	£min	£max
Single	14.00	15.00
Double	28.00	34.00

Open April-October
🛇🛏🖵⒮🗐🖵🅼📺▥⚲🎏

Masons Arms 𝖂
😊😊😊 COMMENDED

Nr Rennington, Alnwick
NE66 3RX
☎ (0665) 577 275
*Country inn offering real ale
and good food. En-suite
bedrooms. 3.5 miles from A1
towards coast and beaches on
B1340.*
Bedrooms: 2 single,
5 double, 1 twin, 1 triple,
1 multiple
Bathrooms: 9 private,
1 public

Bed & breakfast

per night:	£min	£max
Single	20.00	24.50
Double	38.00	49.00

Lunch available
Evening meal 1900 (last
orders 2130)
Parking for 20
Cards accepted: Access, Visa
🛇14🎿🛏🗐🖵🅼📺▥🖵
🅿🎏

Roseworth 𝖂
📧 HIGHLY COMMENDED

Alnmouth Road, Alnwick
NE66 2PR
☎ (0665) 603911
*Mrs Anne Bowden welcomes
you to "Roseworth". Semi-
detached, private home set in
large gaens. Ample parking in
quiet residential area to the
south of Alnwick on
Alnmouth Road. Brochure on
request. Non-smokers
welcome.*
Bedrooms: 1 double, 1 twin
Bathrooms: 1 public

Bed & breakfast

per night:	£min	£max
Double	32.00	32.00

Half board

per person:	£min	£max
Daily	23.00	25.00

Parking for 6
Open April-October
🛇🖿🛏🗐🖵🗜🅼📺▥🔆🎏

Swansfield House 𝖂
😊😊

Alnwick NE66 1EJ
☎ (0665) 602353
*Enjoy this fine country house,
set in 15 acres with hard
tennis court and beautiful
walled gardens. Overlooking
historic Alnwick. Non-smokers
welcome.*
Bedrooms: 1 twin
Bathrooms: 1 private

Bed & breakfast

per night:	£min	£max
Double	35.00	

Parking for 2
🛏🖵🎿🗇📺▥🔍🔎🚶🔆
✕🎏

Windy Gyle
Listed

2 West Acres, Alnwick
NE66 2PU
☎ (0665) 602065
*Facing the A1068 out of
Alnwick towards the coast on
route to Alnmouth and
Warkworth. Spacious 1930s
family home, with gardens to
front and rear which
residents are invited to use.*
Bedrooms: 2 double
Bathrooms: 1 public

Bed & breakfast

per night:	£min	£max
Double	27.00	29.00

Parking for 3
Open June-September
🛇🖿🛏🗇🖵⒮🗜🅼📺▥
🔆✕🎏

**We advise you to
confirm your
booking in writing.**

AMBLE-BY-THE-
SEA

Northumberland
Map ref 5C1

Small fishing town at the
mouth of the River
Coquet, with fine, quiet,
sandy beaches to north
and south. The harbour
and estuary are popular
for sailing and bird-
watching. Coquet Island
lies 1 mile offshore.

Togston Hall
Farmhouse 𝖂
😊😊😊

North Togston, Nr. Amble,
Morpeth NE65 0HR
☎ (0665) 712699
*10-acre mixed farm. Owner-
run establishment, furnished
to a high standard. All
bedrooms with country views.
1 mile from Warkworth Castle
and quiet beaches.*
Bedrooms: 2 double, 1 twin
Bathrooms: 3 private,
1 public

Bed & breakfast

per night:	£min	£max
Single	15.00	17.00
Double	30.00	32.00

Half board

per person:	£min	£max
Daily	24.00	26.00

Evening meal 1900 (last
orders 2030)
Parking for 10
Open March-October
🛇🗇🛏🗐🖵🅼▥🖵🗜
🔆 SP

BAMBURGH

Northumberland
Map ref 5C1

Village with a spectacular
red sandstone castle
standing 150 ft above the
sea. On the village green
the magnificent Norman
church stands opposite a
museum containing
mementoes of the heroine
Grace Darling.

Burton Hall 𝖂
Listed

East Burton, Bamburgh
NE69 7AR
☎ (066 84) 213
*Substantial countryside
farmhouse with spacious
rooms. 1.5 miles from
Bamburgh, 3.5 miles from
Seahouses. Head to Glororum
crossroads, Burton signposted
there.*
Bedrooms: 6 double, 2 twin

Bathrooms: 4 private,
2 public

Bed & breakfast

per night:	£min	£max
Single	16.00	19.00
Double	32.00	52.00

Parking for 10
Open April-November
🛏🖿🛏🖵🅼📺▥🖵🔆
✕🎏

Mizen Head Hotel 𝖂
😊😊😊 APPROVED

Lucker Road, Bamburgh
NE69 7BS
☎ (066 84) 254
*Privately-owned, family-run
hotel in its own grounds, with
accent on good food and
service. Convenient for
beaches, castle and golf.*
Bedrooms: 2 single,
5 double, 5 twin, 3 triple
Bathrooms: 5 private,
3 public

Bed & breakfast

per night:	£min	£max
Single	19.00	30.00
Double	30.00	64.00

Half board

per person:	£min	£max
Daily	29.00	42.00
Weekly	180.00	270.00

Lunch available
Evening meal 1830 (last
orders 2030)
Parking for 30
Cards accepted: Access, Visa
🛇🗆🛏🗐🅼📺🖵🎿🔆🐾 SP

BARNARD CASTLE

Durham
Map ref 5B3

High over the Tees, a
thriving market town with
a busy market square.
Bernard Baliol's 12th C
castle (now ruins) stands
nearby. The Bowes
Museum, housed in a
grand 19th C French
chateau, holds fine
paintings and furniture.
Nearby are some
magnificent buildings.
*Tourist Information Centre
☎ (0833) 690909*

Bowfield Farm

Scargill, Barnard Castle,
County Durham DL12 9SU
☎ Teesdale (0833) 38636
*127-acre mixed farm. 17th C
stone-built farmhouse
overlooking Stang Ridge
Forest, 4 miles from Barnard
Castle off the A66.
Comfortable caravan also
available for holiday letting.*
Continued ▶

BARNARD CASTLE

Continued

Bedrooms: 1 single,
1 double, 1 twin
Bathrooms: 1 public
Bed & breakfast

per night:	£min	£max
Single	10.00	10.00
Double	20.00	20.00

Half board

per person:	£min	£max
Daily	18.00	18.00

Evening meal 1800 (last orders 1600)
Parking for 8
🍳🍴�🆓🖊🕪📺🎬🈁✻✕🎣🏫

George & Dragon Inn
Boldron, Barnard Castle,
County Durham DL12 9RF
☎ Teesdale (0833) 38215
Attractive inn in beautiful Teesdale, offering comfortable accommodation and friendly hospitality.
Bedrooms: 1 double, 1 twin
Bathrooms: 1 public
Bed & breakfast

per night:	£min	£max
Single	13.00	14.00
Double	26.00	28.00

Half board

per person:	£min	£max
Daily	18.00	19.00
Weekly	124.00	131.00

Lunch available
Evening meal 1900 (last orders 1730)
Parking for 20
🍳🖥ⱷ♨🆂🈁📺🎬🈵

Old Well Inn
☺☺ APPROVED
21 The Bank, Barnard Castle, County Durham DL12 8PH
☎ Teesdale (0833) 690130
Historic inn serving home cooking and real ales. Beer garden.
Bedrooms: 1 double, 2 twin
Bathrooms: 1 public
Bed & breakfast

per night:	£min	£max
Single	18.00	18.00
Double	28.00	28.00

Half board

per person:	£min	£max
Daily	28.00	

Lunch available
Evening meal 1900 (last orders 2150)
Cards accepted: Access, Visa
🍳🖥ⱷ🆂🈁🎬🖳🎣🈁🈵

West Roods Tourism ⋀
☺☺☺
West Roods Farm, Boldron,
Barnard Castle, County
Durham DL12 9SW
☎ Teesdale (0833) 690116
Mixed and dairy farm. In Teesdale area, south of Barnard Castle, 2.5 miles east of Bowes on A66. Activities from water divining to table tennis. Home cooking using milk and eggs from our own farm.
Bedrooms: 1 single,
1 double, 1 twin
Bathrooms: 2 private,
2 public
Bed & breakfast

per night:	£min	£max
Single	17.00	20.00
Double	34.00	40.00

Half board

per person:	£min	£max
Daily	27.00	30.00
Weekly	170.00	200.00

Evening meal 1700 (last orders 1830)
Parking for 6
Open March-December
Cards accepted: Visa, Amex
🍳🖊🎬🈁

BARNINGHAM

Durham
Map ref 5B3

Stangfoot Farm
Barningham, Richmond,
North Yorkshire DL11 7EA
☎ Teesdale (0833) 21343
Stangfoot is a working farm on the Scargill to Reeth road at the foot of the Stang Forest.
Bedrooms: 1 single, 1 double
Bathrooms: 1 public
Bed & breakfast

per night:	£min	£max
Single	10.00	12.00
Double	20.00	24.00

Half board

per person:	£min	£max
Daily	16.00	18.00

Evening meal 1800 (last orders 1600)
Parking for 2
Open April-October
🍳4🆄🈁📺🎬🖳🔺✕🎣
🅿🏫

The colour maps at the back of this guide pinpoint all places with accommodation.

BEADNELL

Northumberland
Map ref 5C1

Charming fishing village on Beadnell Bay. Seashore lime kilns (National Trust), dating from the 18th C, recall busier days as a coal and lime port and a pub is built on to a medieval pele tower which survives from days of the border wars.

Low Dover ⋀
☺ HIGHLY COMMENDED
Harbour Road, Beadnell,
Chathill NE67 5BH
☎ (0665) 720291
Quiet, comfortable accommodation in large residence in superb location overlooking Beadnell Bay. 20 yards to beach and 18th C harbour, 3 miles to Farne Islands. No dogs and no smoking. Free brochure.
Bedrooms: 1 double, 1 triple
Bathrooms: 2 private
Bed & breakfast

per night:	£min	£max
Double	34.00	40.00

Parking for 4
🍳6🔥🎬🖥ⱷ♨🆄🆂🖊🈁
📺🖳✕🏫

Shepherd's Cottage
Listed COMMENDED
Beadnell, Chathill NE67 5AD
☎ (0665) 720497
Character cottage, near Beadnell, with spacious garden. Tea and coffee facilities, comfortable sitting room. Ample off-road parking.
Bedrooms: 2 double, 1 twin
Bathrooms: 1 private,
1 public
Bed & breakfast

per night:	£min	£max
Double	30.00	40.00

Parking for 6
🔥🖥🆄🈁📺🎬🖳🖳✕🏫

South Swinhoe Farm ⋀
Listed COMMENDED
Beadnell, Chathill NE67 5AA
☎ (066 589) 226
250-acre mixed farm. South-facing house near sea, within easy reach of many castles, golf-courses, Holy Island and the Farnes. Mainline train to Newcastle and Edinburgh.
Bedrooms: 1 single,
1 double, 1 twin, 1 triple
Bathrooms: 1 public

BEAMISH

Durham
Map ref 5C2

Mount Escob ⋀
Listed COMMENDED
Beamish Woods, Stanley,
County Durham DH9 0SA
☎ 091-370 0289
Country house on picturesque site of former water-powered papermill. Surrounded by wooded hills, 12 acres of grassland where horses are kept. Very close to A1(M), Durham, MetroCentre, half a mile from Beamish Museum.
Bedrooms: 2 double, 1 twin
Bathrooms: 1 public
Bed & breakfast

per night:	£min	£max
Single	15.00	15.00
Double	28.00	30.00

Parking for 7
🍳5🔺🖥ⱷ♨🖊🈁
🖳🅿🖳✕🏫

BELFORD

Northumberland
Map ref 5B1

Small market town on the old coaching road, close to the coast, the Scottish border and the north-east flank of the Cheviots. Built mostly in stone and very peaceful now that the A1 has by-passed the town, Belford makes an ideal centre for excursions to the moors and coast.

Blue Bell Farm House
Listed
West Street, Belford
NE70 7QE
☎ (0668) 213890
Large house in own grounds. 150 yards down West Street to campsite. Private views from all sides.
Bedrooms: 2 double, 1 twin
Bathrooms: 1 private,
2 public
Bed & breakfast

per night:	£min	£max
Single	10.00	12.00
Double	15.00	20.00

Parking for 4
🍳🆄🈁📺🖳🖳🔺✕🎣🏫

Bed & breakfast

per night:	£min	£max
Single	14.00	15.00
Double	28.00	30.00

Parking for 6
Open February-November
🍳ⱷ♨🈁🆄🆂🖊🈁📺🖳🖳
🈁🎣✻🏫

The Cott
COMMENDED

Warenford, Belford
NE70 7HZ
☎ (0668) 213233
On the A1 above Warenford village, 12 miles north of Alnwick and only 4 miles from the beautiful Northumbrian coast.
Bedrooms: 3 double, 2 twin
Bathrooms: 2 public

Bed & breakfast

per night:	£min	£max
Single	15.50	
Double	31.00	

Half board

per person:	£min	£max
Daily	25.00	

Lunch available
Parking for 9
Cards accepted: Amex

Easington Farm
HIGHLY COMMENDED

Belford NE70 7EG
☎ (0668) 213298
Georgian farmhouse with views to Cheviot Hills and Budle Bay. Ideally situated for Holy Island, Farne Islands, Bamburgh Castle, beach and golf-courses.
Bedrooms: 1 double
Bathrooms: 1 private,
1 public

Bed & breakfast

per night:	£min	£max
Single	18.50	
Double	37.00	

Parking for 4

BELLINGHAM

Northumberland
Map ref 5B2

Set in the beautiful valley of the North Tyne close to the Kielder Forest, Kielder Water and lonely moorland below the Cheviots. The church has an ancient stone wagon roof fortified in the 18th C with buttresses.
Tourist Information Centre
☎ *(0434) 220616.*

Mantle Hill ♈

Hesleyside, Bellingham,
Hexham NE48 2LB
☎ (0434) 220428
Fax (0434) 220113
Family home, built as dower house to historic Hesleyside Hall. 200 yards from North

Tyne River with lovely views over unspoilt countryside.
Bedrooms: 1 double, 1 twin
Bathrooms: 2 private

Bed & breakfast

per night:	£min	£max
Double	20.00	22.50

Half board

per person:	£min	£max
Daily	29.00	31.50

Evening meal 1900 (last orders 2100)
Parking for 4

Westfield House ♈
HIGHLY COMMENDED

Bellingham, Hexham
NE48 2DP
☎ (0434) 220340
The guesthouse you always wished to find. Ideal touring spot for Kielder and Hadrian's Wall. Let us spoil you. No smoking.
Bedrooms: 2 double, 2 twin,
1 triple
Bathrooms: 2 private,
2 public

Bed & breakfast

per night:	£min	£max
Double	34.00	50.00

Half board

per person:	£min	£max
Daily	30.00	38.00
Weekly	190.00	240.00

Evening meal from 1930
Parking for 8
Open February-December

BERWICK-UPON-TWEED

Northumberland
Map ref 5B1

Guarding the mouth of the Tweed, England's northernmost town with the best 16th C city walls in Europe. The handsome Guildhall and barracks date from the 18th C. 3 bridges cross to Tweedmouth, the oldest built in 1634.
Tourist Information Centre
☎ *(0289) 330733*

8 Ravensdowne ♈
COMMENDED

Berwick-upon-Tweed
TD15 1HX
☎ (0289) 307883
Small, homely guesthouse, Grade II listed, within easy reach of river, golf, tennis and beaches. Residents' lounge. Access to historic town walls.

Bedrooms: 1 single,
1 double, 3 twin
Bathrooms: 2 private,
2 public

Bed & breakfast

per night:	£min	£max
Single	15.00	
Double	30.00	36.00

The Anchorage
COMMENDED

8 Valley View, Tweedmouth,
Berwick-upon-Tweed
TD15 2ED
☎ (0289) 307060
Modern bungalow in quiet area of town just 2 minutes off the A1, yet close to all amenities.
Bedrooms: 1 double, 1 triple
Bathrooms: 1 private,
1 public

Bed & breakfast

per night:	£min	£max
Double	30.00	36.00

Parking for 6

Dervaig ♈
COMMENDED

1 North Road, Berwick-upon-
Tweed TD15 1PW
☎ (0289) 307378
Beautiful Victorian house, tastefully furnished, with spacious garden. 1 minute from train station, 4 minutes from centre of town. Free covered and outdoor parking.
Bedrooms: 3 double
Bathrooms: 2 private,
1 public

Bed & breakfast

per night:	£min	£max
Double	25.00	40.00

Parking for 8

Drousha
COMMENDED

29 North Road, Berwick-
upon-Tweed TD15 1PW
☎ (0289) 306659
Victorian house with many original features. Sea views, yet close to the centre of town and station.
Bedrooms: 1 double, 1 triple
Bathrooms: 2 public

Bed & breakfast

per night:	£min	£max
Single	15.00	27.00
Double	27.00	30.00

Half board

per person:	£min	£max
Daily	20.00	21.50

Evening meal 1830 (last orders 1900)
Parking for 3

The Estate House ♈
COMMENDED

Ford, Berwick-upon-Tweed
TD15 2QG
☎ Crookham (089 082) 297
changing to (0890) 820297
Edwardian country house with its own grounds, in a peaceful village. Walking, fishing, cycling, gliding, riding by arrangement. Non-smokers only please.
Bedrooms: 2 twin
Bathrooms: 1 public

Bed & breakfast

per night:	£min	£max
Single	14.00	14.00
Double	28.00	28.00

Half board

per person:	£min	£max
Daily	22.00	22.00

Evening meal from 1900
Parking for 2
Open April-October

Ladythorne House
Listed

Cheswick, Berwick-upon-
Tweed TD15 2RW
☎ (0289) 87382
Grade 2 listed building, dated 1721, set in farmland. Only 15 minutes' walk from the beaches.
Bedrooms: 1 single,
1 double, 2 twin, 2 triple
Bathrooms: 3 public

Bed & breakfast

per night:	£min	£max
Single	12.00	15.00
Double	24.00	30.00

Parking for 8

Meadow Hill Guest House ♈
COMMENDED

Duns Road, Berwick-upon-
Tweed TD15 1UB
☎ (0289) 306325
Attractive 150-year-old house with panoramic views of the River Tweed and Cheviot Hills.
Bedrooms: 1 double, 4 triple
Bathrooms: 1 private,
2 public

Continued ▶

Please check prices and other details at the time of booking.

73

BERWICK-UPON-TWEED

Continued

Bed & breakfast

per night:	£min	£max
Single	15.00	20.00
Double	25.00	40.00

Evening meal 1930 (last orders 0900)
Parking for 10

🛇🛆💻🌡☆✂🛏📺🕮🖥 🐕✿🐾🏠

Middle Ord Farm ⚠

☗☗☗ HIGHLY COMMENDED

East Ord, Berwick-upon-Tweed TD15 2XQ
☎ (0289) 306323
320-acre mixed farm. Quality accommodation within Georgian farmhouse. Central for touring the Borders, coast and Holy Island. En-suites and four-poster bed available.
Bedrooms: 2 double, 1 twin
Bathrooms: 2 private, 1 public

Bed & breakfast

per night:	£min	£max
Single	16.00	22.00
Double	31.00	44.00

Parking for 6
Open April-October

🏃🛆🖫🛏✂🛏📺🕮🖥🔲
🕻✿✂🏠 DAP SP 🏠

The Old Vicarage Guest House ⚠

☗☗☗ HIGHLY COMMENDED

24 Church Road, Tweedmouth, Berwick-upon-Tweed TD15 2AN
☎ (0289) 306909
Spacious, detached 19th C vicarage, recently refurbished to a high standard. 10 minutes' walk from town centre and beautiful beaches.
Bedrooms: 1 single, 4 double, 1 twin, 1 triple
Bathrooms: 4 private, 1 public

Bed & breakfast

per night:	£min	£max
Single	13.00	15.00
Double	26.00	40.00

Parking for 4

🛇🛆🖫🌡🖫🛏✂🛏🖥🔲 DAP SP 🕁

National Crown ratings were correct at the time of going to press but are subject to change. Please check at the time of booking.

BISHOP AUCKLAND

Durham
Map ref 5C2

Busy market town on the bank of the Wear. The Palace, a castellated Norman manor house altered in the 18th C, stands in beautiful gardens. Open to the public and entered from the market square by a handsome 18th C gatehouse, the park is a peaceful retreat of trees and streams.

Drive Inn Motel

Manor Road, St. Helens Auckland, Bishop Auckland, County Durham DL14 7ZW
☎ (0388) 663885
Fax (0388) 604497
Situated just off the A68 and ideally placed for exploring the Land of the Prince Bishops and the dales.
Bedrooms: 29 double, 8 twin, 2 triple
Bathrooms: 39 private

Bed & breakfast

per night:	£min	£max
Single	22.95	30.95
Double	30.95	38.95

Lunch available
Evening meal 1900 (last orders 2145)
Parking for 200
Cards accepted: Access, Visa, Amex

🛇🛆🌡📞🖭💻🖫🖫🕮🌡🕮🅣
🕻🖥 DAP ✂ SP

BOWES

Durham
Map ref 5B3

Old stone village high up on a Roman road crossing the Pennines. Settled since Roman times, the town has a sturdy Norman castle keep and an ancient church with a Norman font and Roman inscribed stone.

Ancient Unicorn Inn

☗☗

Bowes, Barnard Castle, County Durham DL12 9HN
☎ Teesdale (0833) 28321 & 28386
16th C inn on the A66 with comfortable bedrooms, extensive bar menu. Ideal base for exploring the Lakes, Northumbria, Yorkshire Dales and Yorkshire Wolds.
Bedrooms: 2 twin, 1 triple

Bathrooms: 3 private

Bed & breakfast

per night:	£min	£max
Single	19.00	19.00
Double	30.00	30.00

Lunch available
Evening meal 1930 (last orders 2130)
Parking for 20

🛇🛆💻🌡🖫🖫🕮🗡🐾🏠

East Mellwaters Farm ⚠

☗☗☗ COMMENDED

Bowes, Barnard Castle, County Durham DL12 9RH
☎ (0833) 28269
350-acre livestock farm. On A66, 1 mile west of Bowes. 17th C farmhouse in attractive setting with views. Sleep in modern comfort, dine by traditional open-fire range. Home-made bread.
Bedrooms: 1 single, 2 double, 1 triple
Bathrooms: 4 private

Bed & breakfast

per night:	£min	£max
Single	15.99	20.00
Double	15.99	36.00

Half board

per person:	£min	£max
Daily	25.00	30.00
Weekly	175.00	210.00

Lunch available
Evening meal 1730 (last orders 1900)
Parking for 6
Cards accepted: Access

🛇🖫🌡🖫🖫🖫✂🛏🖥🔲🛆🕁
🖎🗡✿🐾🏠 DAP SP 🏠

BURNOPFIELD

Tyne and Wear
Map ref 5C2

Lintz Hall Farm

Burnopfield, Newcastle upon Tyne NE16 6AS
☎ (0207) 70233
200-acre mixed farm. Attractive farmhouse in picturesque Derwent Valley. Central for Beamish Museum, MetroCentre, Newcastle and Durham. Close to golf, riding and Derwent walk. Rooms with TV, coffee facilities.
Bedrooms: 1 single, 1 double, 1 triple
Bathrooms: 1 public

Bed & breakfast

per night:	£min	£max
Single	15.00	16.00
Double	30.00	40.00

Parking for 9

🛇🛆💻🌡🖫🛏📺🕮🖥🕁🕨
✿🗡🐾🏠

CAPHEATON

Tyne and Wear
Map ref 5B2

New Houses Farm

Capheaton, Newcastle upon Tyne, Northumberland NE19 2AF
☎ (0830) 30215
Farmhouse situated in quiet country lane, one mile off A696 (Newcastle-Edinburgh), near Hadrian's Wall, historic castles and scenic views.
Bedrooms: 1 single, 1 double, 1 twin
Bathrooms: 1 public

Bed & breakfast

per night:	£min	£max
Single	12.50	15.00
Double	25.00	30.00

Parking for 6
Open April-October

🛇🖫🌡🖫📺🕮🗡🐾🏠

CASTLESIDE

Durham
Map ref 5B2

Village on the edge of the North Pennines on the A68, one of the main routes from England to Scotland.

Castlenook Guest House ⚠

18-20 Front Street, Castleside, Consett, County Durham DH8 9AR
☎ (0207) 506634
On the A68 within easy reach of Durham City, Hadrian's Wall, Beamish Museum and MetroCentre. Excellent village amenities.
Bedrooms: 1 double, 2 twin
Bathrooms: 3 private

Bed & breakfast

per night:	£min	£max
Single	14.00	18.00
Double	28.00	30.00

Half board

per person:	£min	£max
Daily	18.00	20.50
Weekly	130.00	144.00

Evening meal 1700 (last orders 1850)
Parking for 5

🛇🖫🌡🖫🖫🖫🛏📺🕮🖥
🛆🕁✿🐾🖥 SP 🏠

Willerby Grange Farm ⚠

☗☗ COMMENDED

Allensford, Castleside, Consett, County Durham DH8 9BA
☎ (0207) 508752

Self-contained, fully-equipped apartments offering bed and breakfast. In countryside with magnificent views. Horses/ stabling available. Nursery garden on site. Picnic area nearby. 1 kilometre from Allensford on A68.
Bedrooms: 4 double
Bathrooms: 4 private

Bed & breakfast

per night:	£min	£max
Single	25.00	30.00
Double	40.00	50.00

Parking for 100
Cards accepted: Access, Visa, Diners, Amex

CHESTER-LE-STREET
Durham
Map ref 5C2

Originally a Roman military site, town with modern commerce and light industry on the River Wear. The ancient church replaced a wooden sanctuary which sheltered the remains of St. Cuthbert for 113 years. The Anker's house beside the church is now a museum.

Low Urpeth Farm House ₩
Listed COMMENDED
Ouston, Chester-Le-Street, County Durham DH2 1BD
☎ 091-410 2901
Fax 091-410 0081
500-acre arable & livestock farm. Leave A1(M) at Chester-le-Street. Take A693, signpost Beamish. At second roundabout turn right to Ouston. Pass garage, down hill and turn left into farm at "Trees Please" sign.
Bedrooms: 1 double, 2 twin
Bathrooms: 2 private, 1 public

Bed & breakfast

per night:	£min	£max
Single	17.00	
Double	30.00	

Parking for 6

Waldridge Fell House ₩
Listed COMMENDED
Waldridge Lane, Waldridge, Chester-Le-Street, County Durham DH2 3RY
☎ 091-389 1908

Former village chapel, stone-built in 1868. Panoramic views and country walks. Children half price. Winter weekend breaks.
Bedrooms: 4 triple
Bathrooms: 1 public, 1 private shower

Bed & breakfast

per night:	£min	£max
Single	20.00	28.00
Double	30.00	34.00

Parking for 8

Waldridge Hall Farm ₩
Listed HIGHLY COMMENDED
Old Waldridge, Chester-Le-Street, County Durham DH2 3SL
☎ 091-388 4210
40-acre arable farm. Listed 18th C farmhouse in pretty countryside, between Durham City and the Beamish Museum. A warm welcome with homely accommodation. Vegetarians catered for. No smoking in bedrooms.
Bedrooms: 1 double, 1 twin, 1 triple
Bathrooms: 1 public

Bed & breakfast

per night:	£min	£max
Single	21.00	23.00
Double	31.00	35.00

Parking for 8
Open March-October

CHOPPINGTON
Northumberland
Map ref 5C2

Anglers Arms
Sheepwash Bank, Guide Post, Choppington
NE62 5NB
☎ (0670) 822300
Small, friendly residential inn by the River Wansbeck, between Morpeth and Bedlington.
Bedrooms: 1 single, 1 double, 2 twin, 1 triple
Bathrooms: 1 public

Bed & breakfast

per night:	£min	£max
Single	17.00	20.00
Double	30.00	34.00

Half board

per person:	£min	£max
Daily	22.00	25.00

Evening meal 1900 (last orders 2100)
Parking for 25

CONSETT
Durham
Map ref 5B2

Former steel town on the edge of rolling moors. Modern development includes the shopping centre and a handsome Roman Catholic church, designed by a local architect. To the west, the Derwent Reservoir provides water sports and pleasant walks.

Bee Cottage Farm ₩
Listed COMMENDED
Castleside, Consett, County Durham DH8 9HW
☎ (0207) 508224
46-acre livestock farm. 1.5 miles west of the A68, between Castleside and Tow Law. Unspoilt views. Ideally located for Beamish Museum and Durham. No smoking in main farmhouse.
Bedrooms: 3 double, 2 twin, 1 triple, 3 multiple
Bathrooms: 3 private, 5 public

Bed & breakfast

per night:	£min	£max
Single	20.00	30.00
Double	32.00	40.00

Half board

per person:	£min	£max
Daily	26.00	40.00

Lunch available
Evening meal 2015 (last orders 2130)
Parking for 60

CORBRIDGE
Northumberland
Map ref 5B2

Small town on the River Tyne. Close by are extensive remains of the Roman military town Corstopitum, with a museum housing important discoveries from excavations. The town itself is attractive with shady trees, a 17th C bridge and interesting old buildings, notably a 14th C vicarage.

Aydon Grange ₩
DE LUXE
Aydon Road, Corbridge
NE45 5PW
☎ (0434) 632169
Elegant, friendly country manor house set in own grounds with tennis court and

croquet lawn. 5 minutes from centre of Corbridge.
Bedrooms: 1 double, 2 twin
Bathrooms: 3 private

Bed & breakfast

per night:	£min	£max
Single	45.00	50.00
Double	60.00	80.00

Half board

per person:	£min	£max
Daily	52.00	67.00

Evening meal 1930 (last orders 1000)
Parking for 10
Cards accepted: Access, Visa

Fellcroft ₩
COMMENDED
Station Road, Corbridge
NE45 5AY
☎ (0434) 632384
Well-appointed stone-built Edwardian house with full private facilities and colour TV in all bedrooms. Quiet road in country setting, half a mile south of market square. Excellent choice of eating places nearby. Non-smokers only please.
Bedrooms: 2 twin
Bathrooms: 2 private

Bed & breakfast

per night:	£min	£max
Single	18.00	20.00
Double	28.00	32.00

Evening meal 1900 (last orders 1945)
Parking for 2

The Hayes Guest House ₩
Newcastle Road, Corbridge
NE45 5LP
☎ (0434) 632010
Large house set amidst 7.5 acres of woodland and gardens with delightful views. Self-catering flat, caravan and cottages also available.
Bedrooms: 2 single, 1 double, 2 twin, 1 triple
Bathrooms: 2 public, 2 private showers

Bed & breakfast

per night:	£min	£max
Single	15.00	15.00
Double	30.00	30.00

Evening meal 1900 (last orders 1600)
Parking for 14
Open January-November
Cards accepted: Amex

75

COTHERSTONE

Durham
Map ref 5B3

Glendale
☺☺

Cotherstone, Barnard Castle,
County Durham DL12 9UH
☎ (0833) 50384
*Dormer bungalow with
beautiful gardens and large
pond, in quiet, rural
surroundings. Take Briscoe
road from Cotherstone for
200 yards.*
Bedrooms: 3 double
Bathrooms: 3 private,
1 public
Bed & breakfast

per night:	£min	£max
Double	28.00	30.00

Parking for 4
Open February-November
🛴📭➡️🛏️🖥️🔥🛢️🌂⛉💰
📺🍴💈

CRASTER

Northumberland
Map ref 5C1

Small fishing village with a
fine northward view of
Dunstanburgh Castle.
Fishing cobles in the tiny
harbour, stone cottages at
the water's edge and a
kippering shed where
Craster's famous delicacy
is produced give the
village its unspoilt charm.

Keepers Cottage
Craster South Farm, Craster,
Alnwick NE66 3ST
☎ Embleton (0665) 576640
*Within sight of the sea near
the lovely fishing village of
Craster. Holy Island, the
Farne Islands and all of the
beautiful Northumbrian coast
are within easy reach.*
Bedrooms: 1 single, 1 triple
Bathrooms: 1 public,
1 private shower
Bed & breakfast

per night:	£min	£max
Single	14.00	15.00
Double	30.00	34.00

Half board

per person:	£min	£max
Daily	24.00	27.00

Evening meal 1830 (last
orders 1800)
Parking for 2
🛴📭🖥️💈🛢️🌂🍴💰

> **Please mention
> this guide when
> making a booking.**

CRESSWELL

Northumberland
Map ref 5C1

Cresswell House ᴧᴧ
Listed

Cresswell, Morpeth
NE61 5LA
☎ (0670) 861302
*Small seaside village with
beautiful golden beaches. Rear
garden leads to beach. 6.5
miles from Morpeth.*
Bedrooms: 1 single,
1 double, 1 twin
Bathrooms: 1 public
Bed & breakfast

per night:	£min	£max
Single	12.50	15.00
Double	25.00	30.00

🛴📭🖥️💳🛏️🍴📺🛢️🌂💰

CROOK

Durham
Map ref 5C2

Pleasant market town
sometimes referred to as
'the gateway to
Weardale'. The town's
shopping centre
surrounds a large, open
green, attractively laid out
with lawns and flowerbeds
around the Devil's Stone,
a relic from the Ice Age.

Greenhead Country
House Hotel ᴧᴧ
☺☺☺ COMMENDED

Fir Tree, Crook, County
Durham DL15 8BL
☎ Bishop Auckland (0388)
763143
*Superbly located in
countryside, 10 miles from
Durham. Comfortable well
appointed hotel. Overlooks
secluded fields and wooded
area. Lounge with sandstone
arches, log fire and oak
beams.*
Bedrooms: 1 single,
4 double, 1 twin
Bathrooms: 6 private
Bed & breakfast

per night:	£min	£max
Single	30.00	35.00
Double	40.00	45.00

Half board

per person:	£min	£max
Daily	38.00	48.00

Evening meal 1800 (last
orders 1700)
Parking for 15
Cards accepted: Access, Visa
🛴13🛴📭📺📭🛏️🛒📺
🖥️🛢️🌂⛉🍴💰📶🏧

Stockley Farm
Oakenshaw, Crook, County
Durham DL15 0TJ
☎ Bishop Auckland (0388)
746443
*230-acre mixed farm. Family-
run, with pleasant farmland
views. Set in ideal walking
and touring country close to
Brancepeth, Durham and the
dales.*
Bedrooms: 1 single,
1 double, 1 twin, 1 triple
Bathrooms: 1 public
Bed & breakfast

per night:	£min	£max
Single	15.00	17.00
Double	28.00	34.00

Parking for 10
🛴📭➡️🖥️🔥🛢️🌂🛢️🌂⛉
🍴💰

CROOKHAM

Northumberland
Map ref 5B1

Pretty hamlet taking its
name from the winding
course of the River Till
which flows in the shape
of a shepherd's crook. 3
castles - Etal, Duddo and
Ford - can be seen, and
nearby the restored
Heatherslaw Mill is of
great interest.

The Coach House ᴧᴧ
☺☺☺ HIGHLY COMMENDED

Crookham, Cornhill-on-
Tweed TD12 4TD
☎ (089 082) 293 & 373
*Spacious rooms, arranged
around a courtyard, in rolling
country near the Scottish
border. Home-cooked, quality
fresh food. Rooms specially
equipped for disabled guests.*
Bedrooms: 2 single,
2 double, 5 twin
Bathrooms: 7 private,
2 public
Bed & breakfast

per night:	£min	£max
Single	21.00	29.00
Double	42.00	58.00

Half board

per person:	£min	£max
Daily	34.00	42.00

Evening meal 1930 (last
orders 1930)
Parking for 12
Open March-November
Cards accepted: Access, Visa
🛴🛴📭🛏️💈🛏️🛒📺🖥️🛢️🔴🌂
🏧📶

> **We advise you to
> confirm your
> booking in writing.**

CULLERCOATS

Tyne and Wear
Map ref 5C2

15 Wansbeck Avenue
Cullercoats, North Shields
NE30 3DY
☎ 091-252 7095
*Semi-detached house 15
minutes from North Sea
ferries, 2 minutes' walk from
seafront and beach. Close to
Whitley Bay centre, 5 minutes
from Metro station.*
Bedrooms: 1 single, 1 twin
Bathrooms: 1 public
Bed & breakfast

per night:	£min	£max
Single	12.00	15.00
Double	24.00	30.00

Parking for 3
Open June-September
🛴4📭🛴🖥️🛏️📺🖥️🛢️🌂
🍴💰

DARLINGTON

Durham
Map ref 5C3

Industrial town on the
River Skerne, home of
the earliest passenger
railway which first ran to
Stockton in 1825. Now
the home of a railway
museum. Originally a
prosperous market town
occupying the site of an
Anglo-Saxon settlement, it
still holds an open
market.
*Tourist Information Centre
☎ (0325) 382698.*

Alba House
☺

51 Swinburne Road,
Darlington, County Durham
DL3 7TD
☎ (0325) 489690
*Attractively decorated double/
family room, en-suite. Colour
TV, hostess tray. 2 minutes to
art centre and 5 minutes to
town centre. Non smokers
only please.*
Bedrooms: 1 triple
Bathrooms: 1 private
Bed & breakfast

per night:	£min	£max
Single	20.00	20.00
Double	34.00	34.00

Parking for 1
🛴5📭🛴🛏️🛒🍴🖥️🛢️🌂🏧
🌂📶

> **Please check prices
> and other details at
> the time of booking.**

DURHAM
Durham
Map ref 5C2

Ancient city with its
Norman castle and
cathedral set on a bluff
high over the Wear. A
market and university
town and regional centre,
spreading beyond the
market-place on both
banks of the river. July
Miners' Gala is a
celebrated Durham
tradition.
Tourist Information Centre
☎ 091-384 3720

Acorn House ♠
Listed
5 Mowbray Street, Durham,
County Durham DH1 4BH
☎ 091-386 3108
*Built in 1840 and retaining
original character. Town
centre, bus park and rail
station 5 minutes away.
Wooded walks with cathedral
views nearby.*
Bedrooms: 1 single,
1 double, 1 twin
Bathrooms: 1 private,
1 public
Bed & breakfast
per night: £min   £max
Single   15.00   18.00
Double   30.00   45.00
Half board
per person: £min   £max
Daily   25.00   32.00
Weekly   170.00   200.00
Evening meal 1930 (last
orders 1400)
Parking for 1

Bay Horse Inn ♠
APPROVED
Brandon Village, Durham,
County Durham DH7 8ST
☎ 091-378 0498
*3 miles from Durham city
centre. Stone-built chalets all
with shower, toilet, TV, tea
and coffee facilities and
telephone. Ample car parking.*
Bedrooms: 4 twin
Bathrooms: 4 private
Bed & breakfast
per night: £min   £max
Single   26.00   26.00
Double   35.00   35.00
Lunch available
Evening meal 1900 (last
orders 2200)
Parking for 15
Cards accepted: Access

Bees Cottage Guest House ♠
Bridge Street, Durham,
County Durham DH1 4RT
☎ 091-384 5775
*Durham's oldest cottage, a
listed building with modern
interior. City centre, close to
rail and bus stations. All
rooms en-suite, private
parking.*
Bedrooms: 1 double, 2 twin
Bathrooms: 3 private
Bed & breakfast
per night: £min   £max
Single   20.00   25.00
Double   33.00   38.00
Parking for 4

Castledene ♠
Listed COMMENDED
37 Nevilledale Terrace,
Durham, County Durham
DH1 4QG
☎ 091-384 8386
*Edwardian end-of-terrace
house half a mile east of the
market place. Within walking
distance of the riverside,
cathedral and castle.*
Bedrooms: 1 single, 2 twin
Bathrooms: 1 public
Bed & breakfast
per night: £min   £max
Single   16.00
Double   32.00
Parking for 3

Crakemarsh ♠
Listed COMMENDED
Mill Lane, Plawsworth Gate,
Chester-Le-Street, County
Durham DH2 3LG
☎ 091-371 2464
*Comfortable residence with
country views. 10 minutes
from Beamish Museum, 2.5
miles Durham, 30 yards to
A167. Durham to Chester-le-
Street, Leamside/Finchale
Priory turning at Plawsworth
Gate, first house on left.
Evening meals on request.
Strictly no smoking.*
Bedrooms: 1 double, 1 triple
Bathrooms: 1 public
Bed & breakfast
per night: £min   £max
Single   22.00   25.00
Double   34.00   36.00
Half board
per person: £min   £max
Daily   27.00   30.00

Evening meal 1800 (last
orders 1900)
Parking for 4

Grey College
University of Durham, South
Road, Durham DH1 3LG
☎ 091-374 2900
*Overlooking the historic city
of Durham, providing
comfortable accommodation
and good food at modest
prices during vacations.*
Bedrooms: 275 single,
12 twin, 3 triple
Bathrooms: 28 public
Bed & breakfast
per night: £min   £max
Single   15.00
Half board
per person: £min   £max
Daily   23.10
Lunch available
Evening meal from 1900
Parking for 60
Open March-April, June-
October

Lothlorien ♠
COMMENDED
Front Street, Witton Gilbert,
Durham DH7 6SY
☎ 091-371 0067
*Country cottage only 5
minutes by car from Durham
City centre and on a direct
route to Hadrian's Wall. A
good centre for touring.*
Bedrooms: 1 single,
1 double, 1 twin
Bathrooms: 1 public
Bed & breakfast
per night: £min   £max
Single   16.00   16.00
Double   30.00   30.00
Parking for 3

Northolme ♠
21 Hallgarth Street, Durham,
County Durham DH1 3AT
☎ 091-386 9956
*Georgian terraced house 4
minutes' walk from the
cathedral. All rooms with hot
and cold water, tea/coffee
facilities and colour TV.*
Bedrooms: 1 single,
1 double, 1 triple
Bathrooms: 1 private,
1 public
Bed & breakfast
per night: £min   £max
Single   16.00   17.00
Double   32.00   36.00

Parking for 3
Open April-October

St. Aidan's College ♠
Listed
Windmill Hill, Durham,
County Durham DH1 3LJ
☎ 091-374 3269
*Comfortable, modern college
designed by the late Sir Basil
Spence, in beautiful
landscaped gardens
overlooking the cathedral.
Free tennis and croquet.
Adjacent to golf-course.*
Bedrooms: 213 single,
52 twin
Bathrooms: 2 private,
48 public
Bed & breakfast
per night: £min   £max
Single   14.50   16.00
Double   29.00   32.00
Half board
per person: £min   £max
Daily   22.00   23.50
Weekly   150.00   150.00
Lunch available
Evening meal 1830 (last
orders 1900)
Parking for 50
Open January, March-April,
July-September, December

Trevelyan College ♠
Elvet Hill Road, Durham
DH1 3LN
☎ 091-374 3765 & 374
3768
Fax 091-374 3789
*In parkland within 1 mile of
Durham City centre.
Comfortable Cloister Bar and
lounges. Conference facilities.*
Bedrooms: 253 single,
27 twin
Bathrooms: 50 private,
47 public
Bed & breakfast
per night: £min   £max
Single   16.30   24.00
Half board
per person: £min   £max
Daily   24.70   32.40
Lunch available
Evening meal 1830 (last
orders 1930)
Parking for 100
Open March-April, June-
September

77

NORTHUMBRIA

DURHAM

Continued

Victoria Inn ⚊

♛

86 Hallgarth Street, Durham,
County Durham DH1 3AS
☎ 091-386 5269 & 386
0465
*Family-run Victorian public
house with a friendly
atmosphere and bedrooms
with beamed ceilings.*
Bedrooms: 1 double, 1 twin,
1 triple
Bathrooms: 2 private,
2 public
Bed & breakfast

per night:	£min	£max
Single	20.00	25.00
Double	30.00	40.00

Parking for 30
🛇💻♿🛆§⧖🏵📺⬛🔌▰

EDMUNDBYERS

Durham
Map ref 5B2

Small village in hilly
country beneath
Muggleswick Common. A
winding, man-made lake
on the River Derwent just
north complements
smaller reservoirs
southward across the
common, traditionally
offering fishing and picnic
places.

Redwell Hall Farm ⚊
♛

Shotley Bridge, Consett,
County Durham DH8 9TS
☎ (0207) 55216
*Traditional stone-built farm
situated in picturesque valley
and close to beautiful
Derwent Reservoir.
Accommodation is in
farmhouse annexe. Ideal for
visiting Durham, Hexham,
Tynedale and the North
Pennines. Conversational
German.*
Bedrooms: 1 double, 1 twin,
1 multiple
Bathrooms: 1 public
Bed & breakfast

per night:	£min	£max
Single	16.50	18.50
Double	29.00	32.00

Parking for 10
🛇🛆⚊🖤§🏵📺⬛▰🔌§▱

Map references
apply to the colour
maps at the back
of this guide.

EGGLESTON

Durham
Map ref 5B3

Small village between
Barnard Castle and
Middleton-in-Teesdale on
the edge of the moors.
Once a smelting centre
for the North Pennines
lead industry but no trace
of it remains today.

Moorcock Inn
🏵🏵 APPROVED

Hill Top, Gordon Bank,
Eggleston, Barnard Castle,
County Durham DL12 0AU
☎ Teesdale (0833) 50395
*Country inn of character,
with modern amenities and
spectacular views from all
rooms, popular with both
tourists and locals.*
Bedrooms: 1 single,
3 double, 1 twin, 1 triple
Bathrooms: 2 private,
3 public
Bed & breakfast

per night:	£min	£max
Single	20.00	20.00
Double	32.00	37.00

Lunch available
Evening meal 1900 (last
orders 2200)
Parking for 50
🛇💻🖤♿⚊§🏵📺⬛▰
🍴♦🎿 DAP ▱ SP

EMBLETON

Northumberland
Map ref 5C1

Coastal village beside a
golf-course spread along
the edge of Embleton
Bay. The old church was
extensively restored in the
19th C. The vicarage
incorporates a medieval
pele tower.

1 Dunstanburgh
Terrace

Embleton, Alnwick
NE66 3XE
☎ (0665) 576427
*Terraced house on lane to
golf links and beautiful, quiet
beach. Ideal base for touring
historic Northumberland and
Borders.*
Bedrooms: 2 double
Bathrooms: 1 public
Bed & breakfast

per night:	£min	£max
Single	15.00	15.00
Double	25.00	25.00

Parking for 3
Open April-October
🛇12♿⬛§📺⬛🖊🔌

Doxford Farm ⚊
🏵🏵 COMMENDED

Chathill NE67 5DY
☎ Charlton Mires (066 579)
235
*400-acre mixed farm. Listed
Georgian farmhouse set in
wooded grounds 4 miles from
Embleton. Coast and
moorland are within easy
reach. Lake and woodland
nature trail. Home cooking
and home-made bread.*
Bedrooms: 1 double, 1 twin,
1 triple, 1 multiple
Bathrooms: 1 private,
1 public
Bed & breakfast

per night:	£min	£max
Single	15.00	21.00
Double	28.00	36.00

Half board

per person:	£min	£max
Daily	22.00	26.00

Evening meal 1830 (last
orders 1600)
Parking for 8
🛇💻♿⬛§🏵📺⬛,
▰🍴♦🎿♿∪🌙🔌🏵🏰

FALSTONE

Northumberland
Map ref 5B2

Remote village on the
edge of Kielder Forest
where it spreads beneath
the heathery slopes of the
south-west Cheviots along
the valley of the North
Tyne. Just 1 mile west
lies Kielder Water, a vast
man-made lake which
adds boating and fishing
to forest recreations.

Blackcock Inn ⚊
🏵🏵🏵 COMMENDED

Falstone, Hexham NE48 1AA
☎ (0434) 240200
*Traditional old country village
inn close to Kielder Water,
offering cask ale, good food
and comfortable
accommodation. Non-smokers
10% discount.*
Bedrooms: 2 single, 2 double
Bathrooms: 3 private,
1 public
Bed & breakfast

per night:	£min	£max
Double	45.00	50.00

Lunch available
Evening meal 1900 (last
orders 2100)
Parking for 12
🛇💻♿🍗§🏵📺⬛,
▰♦🎿🏵 SP

The Pheasant Inn (by
Kielder Water) ⚊
🏵🏵🏵 COMMENDED

Stannersburn, Falstone,
Hexham NE48 1DD
☎ (0434) 240382
*Historic inn with beamed
ceilings and open fires. Home
cooking. Fishing, riding and
all water sports nearby. Close
to Kielder Water, Hadrian's
Wall and the Scottish border.*
Bedrooms: 4 single,
2 double, 3 twin, 1 multiple
Bathrooms: 5 private,
1 public
Bed & breakfast

per night:	£min	£max
Single	20.00	30.00
Double	38.00	52.00

Half board

per person:	£min	£max
Daily	32.00	43.00

Lunch available
Evening meal 1900 (last
orders 2100)
Parking for 30
🛇🛆♿⚊§🎿🏵▰🆎
🏵 SP 🏰

FOREST-IN-
TEESDALE

Durham
Map ref 5B2

An area in Upper
Teesdale of widely-
dispersed farmsteads set
in wild but beautiful
scenery with High Force
Waterfall and Cauldron
Snout. Once the hunting
park of the Earls of
Darlington.

Langdon Beck Hotel
Listed

Forest-in-Teesdale, Barnard
Castle, County Durham
DL12 0XP
☎ Teesdale (0833) 22267
*A pleasant inn in the
magnificent area of Upper
Teesdale where a friendly
welcome and home cooking
are assured. Ideal for walkers
and nature lovers.*
Bedrooms: 3 single,
1 double, 1 twin, 1 triple
Bathrooms: 2 private,
2 public
Bed & breakfast

per night:	£min	£max
Single	19.00	23.00
Double	38.00	46.00

Half board

per person:	£min	£max
Daily	26.00	30.00
Weekly	180.00	205.00

78

Lunch available
Evening meal 1830 (last
orders 1830)
Parking for 15
Open January-November
🛏 ⓘ Ⓢ Ⓜ ⓉⓋ ▦. ✿ 🕿

HALTWHISTLE

Northumberland
Map ref 5B2

Small market town with
interesting 12th C church,
old inns, and blacksmith's
smithy. North of the town
are several important
sites and interpretation
centres of Hadrian's Wall.
Ideal centre for
archaeology, outdoor
activity or touring
holidays.
*Tourist Information Centre
🕿 (0434) 322002*

Broomhouse Farm ⚠
Listed

Haltwhistle NE49 0JA
🕿 (0434) 321422
*277-acre beef farm.
Traditional 19th C farmhouse
in quiet scenic setting, one
mile from Haltwhistle towards
Alston. Ideal for exploring
Roman Wall and North
Pennines.*
Bedrooms: 1 double,
1 multiple
Bathrooms: 1 public

Bed & breakfast

per night:	£min	£max
Single	16.00	18.00
Double	25.00	27.00

Parking for 2
Open May-October
🛏 ⚴ ♥ ⓤⓛ Ⓢ ⌇ Ⓜ ⓉⓋ ▦. ✿ ✕
🕿 🏠

Broomshaw Hill
Farm ⚠
🏅 HIGHLY COMMENDED

Willia Road, Haltwhistle
NE49 9NP
🕿 (0434) 320866
*5-acre livestock farm.
Attractive modernised 18th C
stone-built farmhouse. On
conjunction of bridleway and
footpath, both leading to
Hadrian's Wall 1 mile away.*
Bedrooms: 2 twin, 1 triple
Bathrooms: 1 public

Bed & breakfast

per night:	£min	£max
Single	15.00	18.00
Double	28.00	32.00

Half board

per person:	£min	£max
Daily	23.00	26.00
Weekly	155.00	168.00

Evening meal 1830 (last
orders 0900)

Parking for 8
Open February-October
🛏 ⌂ ♥ ⓠ ⓤⓛ ⓘ Ⓜ ⓉⓋ ▦. ➿
Ⓤ ᚹ ✿ 🕿 SP

Burnhead Bed &
Breakfast
Listed

Hadrian's Wall, (Near
Cawfields), Haltwhistle
NE49 9PJ
🕿 (0434) 321671
*Family accommodation in
house built on Hadrian's Wall.
Non-smokers only please. No
pets. B6318. Travelling west
turn right at Milecastle Inn.*
Bedrooms: 1 double, 1 twin
Bathrooms: 1 public

Bed & breakfast

per night:	£min	£max
Double	30.00	30.00

Parking for 3
🛏 15 ⌂ ♥ ⌇ ⓤⓛ ♥ ⌇ Ⓜ
ⓉⓋ ◎ ▦. ➹ ✕ 🕿 🏠

Cross Hill House ⚠
APPROVED

Stoneyrigg, Haltwhistle
NE49 9JJ
🕿 (0434) 321568
*Stone-built, 19th C terraced
house on A69, only a few
yards from South Tyne. Ideal
for Hadrian's Wall, North
Pennines, Cumbria.*
Bedrooms: 1 double, 1 triple
Bathrooms: 1 public

Bed & breakfast

per night:	£min	£max
Single	15.00	18.00
Double	24.00	30.00

Half board

per person:	£min	£max
Daily	17.00	23.00

Evening meal from 1930
🛏 ♥ ⓤⓛ ⓘ Ⓢ ⌇ Ⓜ ⓉⓋ ▦. ➹ Ⓤ ✿
✕ 🕿 DAP ♦ SP

Hall Meadows ⚠
🏅

Main Street, Haltwhistle
NE49 0AZ
🕿 (0434) 321021
*Built in 1888, a large family
house with pleasant garden in
the centre of Haltwhistle.
Ideally placed for Hadrian's
Wall.*
Bedrooms: 1 single,
1 double, 1 twin
Bathrooms: 1 public

Bed & breakfast

per night:	£min	£max
Single	14.00	15.00
Double	26.00	28.00

Parking for 3
🛏 ⌂ ♥ ⓤⓛ Ⓢ Ⓜ ⓉⓋ ▦. ➹
✿ 🕿

Oaky Knowe Farm ⚠
Listed   APPROVED

Haltwhistle NE49 0NB
🕿 (0434) 320648
*300-acre livestock farm.
Overlooking the Tyne Valley,
within walking distance of
Haltwhistle and the Roman
wall, this comfortable
farmhouse offers friendly
family holidays.*
Bedrooms: 1 twin, 2 triple
Bathrooms: 1 public

Bed & breakfast

per night:	£min	£max
Single	15.00	16.00
Double	26.00	30.00

Half board

per person:	£min	£max
Daily	19.00	22.00
Weekly	125.00	145.00

Evening meal 1700 (last
orders 1530)
Parking for 8
🛏 ⌂ ⌂ ♥ Ⓜ ⓉⓋ ▦. ➹ 🕿
DAP SP

HAMSTERLEY
FOREST

Durham

*See under Barnard
Castle, Bishop Auckland,
Crook, Tow Law*

HAYDON BRIDGE

Northumberland
Map ref 5B2

Small town on the banks
of the South Tyne with an
ancient church, built of
stone from sites along the
Roman Wall just north.
Ideally situated for
exploring Hadrian's Wall
and the Border country.

Sewing Shields Farm
Hadrian's Wall, Haydon
Bridge, Hexham NE47 6NW
🕿 (0434) 684418
*2000-acre hill farm. 17th C
listed farmhouse, situated on
top of Hadrian's Wall, 1 mile
east of Housesteads, 5 miles
north of Haydon Bridge.
Breathtaking views.*
Bedrooms: 1 double, 1 twin,
1 multiple
Bathrooms: 2 public

Bed & breakfast

per night:	£min	£max
Single	14.00	14.00
Double	26.00	28.00

Half board

per person:	£min	£max
Daily	21.00	21.00
Weekly	140.00	140.00

Evening meal from 1800
Parking for 6
🛏 ⚴ ♥ ⓤⓛ ⓘ Ⓢ ⌇ Ⓜ ⓉⓋ ▦. ➹ 🕿
✿ 🕿 DAP ♦ SP 🏠

HEIGHINGTON

Durham
Map ref 5C3

Eldon House ⚠
🏅🏅 COMMENDED

East Green, Heighington,
Darlington, County Durham
DL5 6PP
🕿 Aycliffe (0325) 312270
*17th C manor house with
large garden overlooking the
village green. Large,
comfortable, well-appointed
rooms.*
Bedrooms: 3 twin
Bathrooms: 1 private,
2 public

Bed & breakfast

per night:	£min	£max
Single	25.00	30.00
Double	35.00	40.00

Parking for 6
🛏 ♥ ⓤⓛ ⓘ Ⓢ Ⓜ ⓉⓋ ▦. ➹ Q ✿
🏠 🏠

HESLEDEN

Durham
Map ref 5C2

A small village south of
the New Town of Peterlee
near the County Durham
coast.

Golden Calf Hotel
Front Street, Hesleden,
Hartlepool, Cleveland
TS27 4PH
🕿 Wellfield (0429) 836493
*Family-run hotel with friendly
service. Only 1 mile from A19
on Castle Eden road. 15
minutes to Teesside, 35
minutes to Newcastle, 12
miles to A1.*
Bedrooms: 1 single, 4 double
Bathrooms: 1 public

Bed & breakfast

per night:	£min	£max
Single	12.00	
Double	24.00	

Half board

per person:	£min	£max
Daily	14.00	18.50

Lunch available
Evening meal 1900 (last
orders 2200)
Parking for 20
🛏 ⌂ ♥ ⌂ ⓘ Ⓜ ▦. ♥ ᚹ 🕿 ⧈ 🏠

**Please mention
this guide when
making a booking.**

79

HEXHAM

Northumberland
Map ref 5B2

Old coaching and market town near Hadrian's Wall. Since pre-Norman times a weekly market has been held in the centre with its market-place and abbey park, and the richly-furnished 12th C abbey church has a superb Anglo-

Anick Grange

⚜⚜ COMMENDED

Hexham NE46 4LP
☎ (0434) 603807
363-acre mixed farm. 17th C farmhouse 1 mile from Hexham. Superb open views. Home cooking and warm welcome.
Bedrooms: 1 single, 1 twin, 1 triple
Bathrooms: 1 private, 1 public

Bed & breakfast

per night:	£min	£max
Single	14.00	14.00
Double	30.00	34.00

Parking for 4
Open April-September
🛠 1 🛏 📺 ⊞ ∪ 🐴

Rye Hill Farm ⋀

⚜⚜⚜ COMMENDED

Slaley, Hexham NE47 0AH
☎ (0434) 673259
30-acre livestock farm. Warm and comfortable barn conversion, 5 miles south of Hexham, where you can enjoy the peace of rural life. Noted for the food and the friendly atmosphere.
Bedrooms: 2 double, 2 twin, 2 triple
Bathrooms: 6 private, 1 public

Bed & breakfast

per night:	£min	£max
Single	18.00	
Double	33.00	

Half board

per person:	£min	£max
Daily	25.50	27.00
Weekly	170.00	

Evening meal 1930 (last orders 1700)
Parking for 6
🛠🖢🗎💧🛏§🗲🖺📺⊞,
🗎🖁🕭🐾🛁🔇

Stotsfold Hall ⋀

⚜⚜

Steel, Hexham NE47 0HP
☎ (0434) 673270
Beautiful house surrounded by 15 acres of gardens and

woodland with streams and flowers. 6 miles south of Hexham.
Bedrooms: 2 single, 1 double, 1 twin
Bathrooms: 3 public

Bed & breakfast

per night:	£min	£max
Single	15.00	15.00
Double	30.00	30.00

Parking for 6
🛠🖺🛏📺⊞,🗎🖢🕭🐾

Thistlerigg Farm

High Warden, Hexham
NE46 4SR
☎ (0434) 602041
630-acre mixed farm. Farmhouse built in 1908 with scenic views, within walking distance of a Roman hill fort and close to Northumberland National Park.
Bedrooms: 2 double, 1 twin
Bathrooms: 1 public

Bed & breakfast

per night:	£min	£max
Double	28.00	30.00

Parking for 4
Open April-October
🛠🖢🛏🖺📺🕭🐾

Topsy Turvy ⋀

Listed COMMENDED

9 Leazes Lane, Hexham
NE46 3BA
☎ (0434) 603152
A cosy home, where you can rest for a while, put your feet up and be thoroughly spoilt.
Bedrooms: 2 double
Bathrooms: 1 private, 1 public

Bed & breakfast

per night:	£min	£max
Double	26.00	30.00

Parking for 3
🛠🖁🖵🖢🛏§⊞,🗎🐾

HOLY ISLAND

Northumberland
Map ref 5B1

Still an idyllic retreat, tiny island and fishing village and cradle of northern Christianity. It is approached from the mainland at low water by a causeway. The clifftop castle (National Trust) was restored by Sir Ed

Britannia

⚜⚜

Holy Island, Berwick-upon-Tweed TD15 2RX
☎ (0289) 89218
Comfortable, friendly bed and breakfast in centre of Holy Island. Hot and cold water,

tea-making facilities in all rooms. TV lounge.
Bedrooms: 1 double, 1 twin, 1 triple
Bathrooms: 1 public

Bed & breakfast

per night:	£min	£max
Single		15.00
Double		28.00

Parking for 4
Open March-November
🛠🖢🛏🖁🖺📺⊞,🕭🐾

Crown & Anchor Hotel ⋀

⚜⚜

Fenkle Street, Holy Island, Berwick-upon-Tweed
TD15 2RX
☎ (0289) 89215
Old fashioned inn with public bar, lounge bar and restaurant. Situated in corner of village green overlooking Lindisfarne Priory and harbour. All bedrooms centrally heated.
Bedrooms: 2 double, 1 twin
Bathrooms: 3 private, 1 public

Bed & breakfast

per night:	£min	£max
Single	18.00	25.00
Double	30.00	40.00

Lunch available
Parking for 5
🖵🖢🖁🗲📺❄🐾🔇

JARROW

Tyne and Wear
Map ref 5C2

St Paul's Monastery was founded in Anglo-Saxon times and later became the home of the Venerable Bede. Jarrow Hall now houses the Bede Monastery Museum. *Tourist Information Centre* ☎ 091-489 2106

The Queens Arms

7-9 Union Street, Jarrow
NE32 3PD
☎ 091-489 7503
Family-run inn with 2 lounge bars and pool room available to guests. Over 100 years old. In the heart of Catherine Cookson Country close to several places of local historic interest.
Bedrooms: 2 single, 1 double, 3 twin, 1 triple
Bathrooms: 2 public

Bed & breakfast

per night:	£min	£max
Single		15.00
Double		30.00

Evening meal 1800 (last orders 1500)
🛠🖵🗎💧🖁🖺📺🕙⊞,🗎🔇
🕭🐾

KIELDER FOREST

Northumberland

See under Bellingham, Falstone, Wark

LOW FELL

Tyne and Wear

"Sakkara" ⋀

⚜⚜⚜ COMMENDED

15 Bude Gardens, Low Fell, Gateshead NE9 6XP
☎ 091-487 5841
Quiet family-run guesthouse. Personal attention guaranteed. Close to A1(M) and convenient for Northumbria, Durham and MetroCentre.
Bedrooms: 1 twin, 1 multiple
Bathrooms: 2 private, 3 public

Bed & breakfast

per night:	£min	£max
Single		20.00
Double		32.00

Half board

per person:	£min	£max
Daily	23.00	27.00

Evening meal 1930 (last orders 1945)
Parking for 2
🛠🖁🖵🛏🖁🗲🖁📺⊞,
🗎❄🕭🐾

LOWICK

Northumberland
Map ref 5B1

Inland from Holy Island and near the A1, Lowick has a long, wide main street with a few shops and inns and is in agricultural land between the foothills of the Cheviots and the coast.

The Old Manse

⚜⚜

5 Cheviot View, Lowick, Berwick-upon-Tweed
TD15 2TY
☎ (0289) 88264
Grade II listed Georgian church manse on the outskirts of Lowick village. 3.5 miles off the A1. In the heart of rural Northumberland.
Bedrooms: 1 double, 2 twin
Bathrooms: 2 private, 1 public

Bed & breakfast per night:	£min	£max
Double	28.00	35.00

Half board per person:	£min	£max
Daily	24.00	27.00
Weekly	168.00	189.00

Evening meal 1830 (last orders 1500)
Parking for 3
Open March-October
☕ [UL] [S] 🚭 🛏 [TV] ▥ ♨ ✿ ✈ 🚌 🏛 [T]

MIDDLESBROUGH

Cleveland
Map ref 5C3

Boom-town of the mid 19th C, today's Teesside industrial and conference town has a modern shopping complex and predominantly modern buildings. An engineering miracle of the early 20th C is the Transporter Bridge which replaced an old ferry.
Tourist Information Centre
☎ (0642) 243425.

Leven Close Farm 👑

👑👑 APPROVED

High Leven, Yarm TS15 9JP
☎ (0642) 750 114
250-acre mixed farm. 18th C farmhouse on working farm. Within easy access of stately homes, coast and market towns.
Bedrooms: 2 double, 1 triple
Bathrooms: 1 public

Bed & breakfast per night:	£min	£max
Single	12.00	15.00
Double	24.00	30.00

Half board per person:	£min	£max
Daily	17.00	20.00

Evening meal 1800 (last orders 1900)
Parking for 14
🐴 ▣ ☎ ▢ ☕ [UL] 🔒 🛏 [TV] ▥ ♨ ⛳ ▤ ▶ ✓ ✿ 🚌

Maltby Farm 👑

👑👑 APPROVED

Maltby, Middlesbrough
TS8 0BP
☎ (0642) 590121
Traditional Yorkshire farmhouse over 200 years old, looking south on to the Cleveland Hills.
Bedrooms: 1 single, 1 twin, 1 triple
Bathrooms: 1 public

Bed & breakfast per night:	£min	£max
Single	13.00	14.00
Double	25.00	26.00

Half board per person:	£min	£max
Daily	18.00	19.00
Weekly	125.00	130.00

Evening meal 1800 (last orders 2000)
Parking for 6
Open April-October
🐴 ☕ [UL] [S] 🛏 [TV] ▥ ♨ ✈ 🚌

MIDDLETON-IN-TEESDALE

Durham
Map ref 5B3

Small stone town of hillside terraces overlooking the river, developed by the London Lead Company in the 18th C. 5 miles up-river is the spectacular 70-ft waterfall, High Force.
Tourist Information Centre
☎ (0833) 40400.

Wythes Hill Farm

👑

Lunedale, Middleton-in-Teesdale, Barnard Castle, County Durham DL12 0NX
☎ Teesdale (0833) 40349
550-acre mixed farm. Farmhouse with panoramic views, on the Pennine Way in lovely walking area. Farmhouse cooking. Peace and quiet, friendliness and comfort guaranteed.
Bedrooms: 1 twin, 1 triple
Bathrooms: 2 public

Bed & breakfast per night:	£min	£max
Single		13.00
Double		26.00

Half board per person:	£min	£max
Daily		20.00
Weekly		125.00

Evening meal 1800 (last orders 1830)
Parking for 3
Open April-October
🐴 ☕ [UL] 🔒 [S] 🛏 [TV] ▥ ♨ ✿ 🚌 [OAP]

National Crown ratings were correct at the time of going to press but are subject to change. Please check at the time of booking.

MORPETH

Northumberland
Map ref 5C2

Market town on the River Wansbeck. There are charming gardens and parks, among them Carlisle Park which lies close to the ancient remains of Morpeth Castle. The chantry building houses the Northumbrian Craft Centre and the bagpipe museum.
Tourist Information Centre
☎ (0670) 511323.

Newminster Cottage

High Stanner, Morpeth
NE61 1QL
☎ (0670) 503195
18th C, double fronted, stone house, overlooking the River Wansbeck. 5 minutes' walk from town centre.
Bedrooms: 1 double, 1 twin, 1 triple
Bathrooms: 3 private

Bed & breakfast per night:	£min	£max
Double	25.00	28.00

Parking for 4
Cards accepted: Access, Visa, C.Bl, Diners, Amex, Switch
🐴 ▢ ☕ ☜ [UL] 🔒 [S] 🚭 🛏 [TV] ▥ ♨ ♪ ✿ 🚌 🏛

The Shieling

2 Manor Farm, Ulgham, Morpeth NE61 3AT
☎ (0670) 790317
Old stone-built farm building converted into a bungalow. In a quiet village 5 miles from Morpeth, on the B1337.
Bedrooms: 3 twin
Bathrooms: 2 public

Bed & breakfast per night:	£min	£max
Single	15.00	17.00
Double	25.00	28.00

Half board per person:	£min	£max
Daily	20.00	22.00

Evening meal 1800 (last orders 2000)
Parking for 3
🐴 ♿ ▢ ☕ ☜ [UL] [S] [TV] ▥ ♨ U ✿ ✈ 🚌

The town index towards the back of this guide gives page numbers of all places with accommodation.

NEWCASTLE UPON TYNE

Tyne and Wear
Map ref 5C2

Commercial and cultural centre of the North East, with a large indoor shopping centre, Quayside market, museums and theatres which offer an annual 6 week season by the Royal Shakespeare Company. Norman castle keep, medieval alleys, old Guildhall.
Tourist Information Centre
☎ 091-261 0691 or 230 0030

Bywell

54, Holly Avenue, Jesmond, Newcastle upon Tyne
NE2 2QA
☎ 091-281 7615
Victorian town house in a quiet residential cul-de-sac, close to city centre and all amenities. No smoking, please.
Bedrooms: 1 double, 1 twin
Bathrooms: 1 public

Bed & breakfast per night:	£min	£max
Single	16.50	16.50
Double	28.00	28.00

🐴 ♿ ▢ ☕ [UL] 🔒 [S] 🚭 ▥ ♨ ✈ 🚌

Colliery Engine Inn

517-519 Shields Road, Walkergate, Newcastle upon Tyne NE6 4NS
☎ 091-265 3082
Very old, cottage-like accommodation, high standard of furnishings. Friendly family inn. Beautiful garden, secure parking.
Bedrooms: 1 double, 1 twin, 1 triple
Bathrooms: 2 public

Bed & breakfast per night:	£min	£max
Single	18.00	
Double	32.00	

Parking for 15
🐴 ▢ ☕ ☜ 🔒 [S] ◐ ▥ ♨ ✿ ✈ 🚌 🏛

George Hotel 👑

👑👑 APPROVED

88 Osborne Road, Jesmond, Newcastle upon Tyne
NE2 2AP
☎ 091-281 4442 & 281 8300
Comfortable town house hotel in a residential area close to the city centre and local shops.

Continued ▶

NEWCASTLE UPON TYNE

Continued

Bedrooms: 5 single,
3 double, 2 twin, 4 triple
Bathrooms: 11 private,
1 public, 3 private showers
Bed & breakfast

per night:	£min	£max
Single	25.00	30.00
Double	35.00	40.00

Half board

per person:	£min	£max
Daily	30.00	35.00

Lunch available
Evening meal 1900 (last
orders 1900)
Parking for 10
Cards accepted: Access, Visa,
Diners, Amex

Grosvenor Hotel ⋒

APPROVED

Grosvenor Road, Jesmond,
Newcastle upon Tyne
NE2 2RR
☎ 091-281 0543
Fax 091-281 9217
*Friendly hotel in quiet
residential suburb, offering a
wide range of facilities. Close
to city centre.*
Bedrooms: 19 single,
11 double, 14 twin
Bathrooms: 21 private,
5 public
Bed & breakfast

per night:	£min	£max
Single	18.00	40.00
Double	36.00	60.00

Half board

per person:	£min	£max
Daily	25.00	50.00

Lunch available
Evening meal 1830 (last
orders 2130)
Parking for 30
Cards accepted: Access, Visa,
Diners, Amex

New Kent Hotel ⋒

COMMENDED

127 Osborne Road, Jesmond,
Newcastle upon Tyne
NE2 2TB
☎ 091-281 1083
Fax 091-281 3369
*A family-run hotel in a quiet
suburban area with accent on
food and warm personal
service. Congenial atmosphere
established 20 years.*
Bedrooms: 16 single,
9 double, 3 twin, 4 triple
Bathrooms: 32 private

Bed & breakfast

per night:	£min	£max
Single	35.00	65.00
Double	56.00	79.00

Half board

per person:	£min	£max
Daily	47.00	77.00

Evening meal 1830 (last
orders 2230)
Parking for 45
Cards accepted: Access, Visa,
Diners, Amex

NEWTON-BY-THE-SEA

Northumberland
Map ref 5C1

Attractive hamlet at the
south end of Beadnell
Bay with a sandy beach
and splendid view of
Dunstanburgh Castle. In a
designated area of
outstanding natural
beauty, Low Newton, part
of the village, is now
owned by the National
Trust.

Newton Hall ⋒

Listed

Newton-by-the-Sea, Alnwick
NE66 3DZ
☎ (0665) 576239
*Country house set in 2 acres
of garden. Ideal for visiting
the historic castles of
Northumberland.*
Bedrooms: 2 double, 1 twin
Bathrooms: 2 public
Bed & breakfast

per night:	£min	£max
Double	28.00	32.00

Parking for 6
Open April-October
Cards accepted: Visa

We advise you to
confirm your
booking in writing.

There are separate
sections in this
guide listing groups
specialising in farm
holidays and
accommodation
which is especially
suitable for young
people and
organised groups.

NORHAM

Northumberland
Map ref 5B1

Border village on the
salmon-rich Tweed,
dominated by its dramatic
castle ruin. Near Castle
Street is the church, like
the castle destroyed after
the Battle of Flodden, but
rebuilt. Norham Station
Railway Museum is just
outside the town.

Dromore House

Listed

12 Pedwell Way, Norham,
Berwick-upon-Tweed
TD15 2LD
☎ (0289) 382313
*Guesthouse in a small village
on the River Tweed, between
the Cheviot and Lammermuir
Hills. Quiet beaches are
within easy reach.*
Bedrooms: 1 double, 1 twin,
1 triple
Bathrooms: 1 private,
1 public, 1 private shower
Bed & breakfast

per night:	£min	£max
Single	12.00	15.00
Double	24.00	30.00

Half board

per person:	£min	£max
Daily	18.00	21.00
Weekly	126.00	147.00

Evening meal 1700 (last
orders 1900)
Parking for 3

OTTERBURN

Northumberland
Map ref 5B1

Small village set at the
meeting of the River
Rede with Otter Burn, the
site of the Battle of
Otterburn in 1388. A
peaceful tradition
continues in the sale of
Otterburn tweeds in this
beautiful region, which is
ideal for exploring the
Border country and the
Cheviots.

The Butterchurn ⋒

APPROVED

Main Street, Otterburn,
Newcastle upon Tyne
NE19 1TP
☎ (0830) 20585
*In village centre, on the River
Rede. Central for Roman Wall
and forts. Within easy reach
of Northumberland coast.
Fishing permits available.*

Bedrooms: 4 double, 1 twin,
3 triple
Bathrooms: 8 private
Bed & breakfast

per night:	£min	£max
Single	18.00	24.00
Double	30.00	35.00

Half board

per person:	£min	£max
Daily	21.00	30.00
Weekly	147.00	210.00

Lunch available
Evening meal 1900 (last
orders 2030)
Parking for 10

OVINGTON

Durham
Map ref 5C3

Ovington Hall Farm

Ovington, Northumberland
NE42 6ED
☎ (0661) 832355
*400-acre mixed farm. 16th C
house, easy access to Roman
Wall area, Beamish Museum,
MetroCentre, Cragside and
Wallington Hall.*
Bedrooms: 1 double, 1 twin
Bathrooms: 1 private,
1 public
Bed & breakfast

per night:	£min	£max
Double	27.00	32.00

Parking for 3

Westgarth Cottage

Ovington, Prudhoe,
Northumberland NE42 6EB
☎
*Atttractive cottage in peaceful
village, one mile south of
A69. Breakfast served at
Stonecroft (30 yards).*
Bedrooms: 1 double, 1 triple
Bathrooms: 1 public
Bed & breakfast

per night:	£min	£max
Single	16.00	16.00
Double	30.00	30.00

Parking for 2

National Crown
ratings were correct
at the time of going
to press but are
subject to change.
Please check at the
time of booking.

PONTELAND

Northumberland
Map ref 5C2

A place of great antiquity,
now a dormitory town for
Newcastle. The fine
Norman church, fortified
rectory, Vicar's Pele and
old inn, formerly a 17th C
manor house, make this
town particularly
interesting.

Blackbird Inn

North Road, Ponteland,
Newcastle upon Tyne
NE20 9UH
☎ (0661) 24949
*14th C inn approximately 1.5
miles from Newcastle Airport.
Restaurant and bar meals
service every day.*
Bedrooms: 2 double, 2 twin
Bathrooms: 4 private

Bed & breakfast

per night:	£min	£max
Single	30.00	
Double	50.00	

Lunch available
Evening meal 1900 (last
orders 2100)
Parking for 60
Cards accepted: Access, Visa

REDCAR

Cleveland
Map ref 5C3

Lively holiday resort near
Teesside with broad
sandy beaches, a fine
racecourse, a large indoor
funfair at Coatham and
other seaside
amusements. Britain's
oldest existing lifeboat
can be seen at the
Zetland Museum.

Sunnyside House

22 Station Road, Redcar
TS10 1AQ
☎ (0642) 477531
*Well situated property close to
town centre and beach.*
Bedrooms: 1 single, 4 triple
Bathrooms: 2 public

Bed & breakfast

per night:	£min	£max
Single	14.00	14.00
Double	25.00	25.00

Half board

per person:	£min	£max
Daily	19.50	19.50

Evening meal 1700 (last
orders 1900)

ROTHBURY

Northumberland
Map ref 5B1

Old market town on the
River Coquet near the
Simonside Hills. It makes
an ideal centre for
walking and fishing or for
exploring all this beautiful
area from the coast to the
Cheviots. Cragside House
and Gardens (National
Trust) are open to the
public.

5 Walby Hill

Rothbury, Morpeth
NE65 7NT
☎ (0669) 20080
*Old country house with large
rooms. 40 yards off road,
through stone gates opposite
Rothbury Motors.*
Bedrooms: 1 single,
1 double, 1 triple
Bathrooms: 2 public

Bed & breakfast

per night:	£min	£max
Single	13.00	13.00
Double	24.00	24.00

Parking for 5

Bickerton Cottage Farm

Listed COMMENDED
Rothbury NE65 7LW
☎ (0669) 40264
*500-acre livestock farm.
Situated in the glorious open
scenery of the
Northumberland National
Park, 10 minutes' drive from
Rothbury. Separate entrance,
staircase, living room and
bathroom.*
Bedrooms: 1 double, 1 twin
Bathrooms: 1 public

Bed & breakfast

per night:	£min	£max
Single	18.00	
Double	25.00	30.00

Parking for 2
Open March-November

Burntlands

Listed
Garleigh Road, Rothbury,
Morpeth NE65 7RB
☎ (0669) 20649
*Bungalow overlooking
Rothbury and Cragside.
Evening meals available if
booked in advance.*
Bedrooms: 1 double, 1 twin
Bathrooms: 1 public

Bed & breakfast

per night:	£min	£max
Double	29.00	31.00

Half board

per person:	£min	£max
Daily	18.50	19.50

Open February-October

Lorbottle West Steads

Thropton, Morpeth
NE65 7JT
☎ (066 574) 672
*310-acre mixed farm. Stone
farmhouse with panoramic
views of the Coquet Valley
and Cheviot Hills. B6341 to
Thropton, turn for
Whittingham, turn at
Lorbottle, first right.*
Bedrooms: 1 single,
1 double, 1 twin
Bathrooms: 1 public

Bed & breakfast

per night:	£min	£max
Single	13.00	15.00
Double	26.00	30.00

Parking for 8
Open May-October

Thropton Demesne

HIGHLY COMMENDED
Thropton, Morpeth
NE65 7LT
☎ (0669) 20196
*24-acre mixed farm. A
traditional farmhouse
peacefully situated in the
picturesque Coquet Valley.
Spectacular views. Ideally
placed for fishing, golf and
walking.*
Bedrooms: 1 double, 1 twin,
1 triple
Bathrooms: 3 private

Bed & breakfast

per night:	£min	£max
Single	15.50	
Double	31.00	

Parking for 6

Tod-le-Moor

Whittingham, Alnwick
NE66 4TW
☎ (066 574) 603
*Comfortable, homely cottage
in beautiful rural
surroundings, near Rothbury.
Ideal for touring, walking or
birdwatching.*
Bedrooms: 1 double, 1 twin
Bathrooms: 2 private,
1 public

Bed & breakfast

per night:	£min	£max
Double	27.00	

Evening meal 1930 (last
orders 1000)
Parking for 2
Open April-September

ROWLANDS GILL

Tyne and Wear
Map ref 5C2

Adjacent to the Derwent
Walk Country Park on the
side of the River Derwent,
opposite the National
Trust Gibside Chapel.

Chopwell Wood House

Chopwell Woods, Rowlands
Gill NE39 1LT
☎ (0207) 542765
*Large, attractive house in 600
acres of woodland in the
Derwent Valley, within easy
reach of Newcastle, Durham
and Hexham. Near
MetroCentre and Beamish
Museum.*
Bedrooms: 1 double, 1 twin,
1 triple
Bathrooms: 1 public

Bed & breakfast

per night:	£min	£max
Single	12.50	18.00
Double	25.00	30.00

Parking for 6

RYTON

Tyne and Wear
Map ref 5C2

Former coal-mining village
west of Tyneside, close to
the eastward limit of
Hadrian's Wall. Since the
mines closed in the early
1960s the village has
been successfully
landscaped to
accommodate light
industries in a leafy,
attractive setting.

Barmoor Old Manse

Listed
The Old Manse, Barmoor,
Ryton NE40 3BD
☎ 091-413 2438
*Large stone Victorian house,
built as Manse for
Congregational Church in
1862.*
Bedrooms: 1 double, 2 twin
Bathrooms: 1 public

Continued ▶

RYTON

Continued

Bed & breakfast

per night:	£min	£max
Single		18.00
Double		35.00

Parking for 2

🏷️🚲🔌📺 S ✕ 🅿️ 📺 🛏️ 🚗 ✻ 🎣 SP

SALTBURN-BY-THE-SEA

Cleveland
Map ref 5C3

Set on fine cliffs just north of the Cleveland Hills, a gracious Victorian resort with later developments and wide, firm sands. A handsome Jacobean mansion at Marske can be reached along the sands.
Tourist Information Centre ☎ (0287) 622422.

Boulby Barns Farm

Easington, Loftus, Saltburn-by-the-Sea TS13 4UT
☎ (0287) 641306
7-acre mixed farm. Traditional stone farmhouse with accommodation on a working smallholding in the national park. Situated half a mile from A174, close to Boulby Cliffs and the Cleveland Way, with views of Moors and sea.
Bedrooms: 2 double, 2 twin
Bathrooms: 2 public

Bed & breakfast

per night:	£min	£max
Single	12.50	16.00
Double	25.00	32.00

Parking for 8
Open May-September

🏷️ 5 🧺 🔌 🚲 ✕ 📺 🛏️ 🚗 🎣

SEAHAM

Durham
Map ref 5C2

Small coalport between Teesside and Wearside. The old village has a clifftop church dating from the Anglo-Saxon period with Roman stones built into its walls.

Adolphus Bed & Breakfast

14 Adolphus Street West,
Seaham, County Durham
SR7 7SE
☎ 091-581 6746
Victorian mid-terrace house with friendly and caring atmosphere. Easy access from

---

A1(M), A19, 3 minutes from train, bus station and shops. Good fishing, golfing and walking, close to uncrowded beaches and lighthouse.
Bedrooms: 1 single, 2 twin
Bathrooms: 1 public

Bed & breakfast

per night:	£min	£max
Single	12.00	12.00
Double	24.00	24.00

Half board

per person:	£min	£max
Daily	17.00	17.00

Parking for 3

🧺 🔌 🚲 S ✕ 🅿️ 📺 🛏️ 🚗 🎣 OAP 🐾 🏠 T

SEAHOUSES

Northumberland
Map ref 5C1

Small modern resort developed around a 19th C herring port. Just offshore, and reached by boat from here, are the rocky Farne Islands (National Trust) where there is an important bird reserve. The bird observatory occupies a medieval pele tower.

"Leeholme" ⋀

Listed

93 Main Street, North Sunderland, Seahouses
NE68 7TS
☎ (0665) 720230
A warm welcome awaits you at this small homely bed and breakfast. 5 minutes' walk to Seahouses harbour and shops. Hearty breakfast assured.
Bedrooms: 1 double, 1 twin
Bathrooms: 1 public

Bed & breakfast

per night:	£min	£max
Single		13.00
Double		26.00

Parking for 2
Open March-October

🏷️🚲📺 🔌 🚲 🅿️ 🍴 ✕ 📺 🚗 ∪ ► 🎣

Malham

🚲

12 King Street, Seahouses
NE68 7XP
☎ (0665) 720201
Small, family-run guesthouse, close to harbour and shops, beaches and golf-course.
Bedrooms: 2 double
Bathrooms: 1 public

Please check prices and other details at the time of booking.

Bed & breakfast

per night:	£min	£max
Double	25.00	27.00

Parking for 2

🏷️🚲📺 🔌 🚲 🅿️ S 🛏️ 📺 🛏️ ✻ 🐾 🎣

Rowena

Listed

99 Main Street, Seahouses
NE68 7TS
☎ (0665) 721309
Comfortable bed and breakfast accommodation, 5 minutes' walk from the harbour where boats leave to visit the Farne Islands.
Bedrooms: 1 single,
1 double, 1 twin, 1 triple
Bathrooms: 1 private,
1 public

Bed & breakfast

per night:	£min	£max
Double	26.00	32.00

Parking for 3

🏷️🚲🚂 🔌 🚲 S 🔌 🚗 🎣

SLALEY

Northumberland
Map ref 5B2

Small hamlet, now a major golfing venue, south of Corbridge near the Derwent Reservoir.

Croft House ⋀

😊 COMMENDED

Slaley, Hexham NE47 0AA
☎ (0434) 673322
Lovely, comfortable old house, pretty gardens, magnificent views. 5 miles south of Hexham. Convenient for Beamish, Durham, Hadrian's Wall, National Trust properties. Sorry, no smoking.
Bedrooms: 1 double, 2 twin
Bathrooms: 2 private,
1 public

Bed & breakfast

per night:	£min	£max
Single	20.00	20.00
Double	35.00	35.00

Parking for 3

🏷️ 14 🚂 🚲 🔍 🔌 S ✕ 🅿️ 📺 🛏️ 🚗 ✕ 🎣

Rose and Crown Inn

Main Street, Slaley, Hexham
NE47 0AA
☎ (0434) 673263
Warm, friendly, family-run business with good wholesome home cooking and a la carte restaurant. Your friendly local.
Bedrooms: 1 single, 3 twin
Bathrooms: 4 private

Bed & breakfast

per night:	£min	£max
Single	17.50	25.00
Double	35.00	45.00

Half board

per person:	£min	£max
Daily	27.50	35.00

Lunch available
Evening meal 1900 (last orders 2000)
Parking for 32
Cards accepted: Access, Visa

🏷️🚲🚂📺 🔌 🚲 S ✕ 🅿️ 📺 🚗 ► ✻ 🎣 🐾 ⤵ SP

SPENNYMOOR

Durham
Map ref 5C2

Booming coal and iron town from the 18th C until early in the present century when traditional industry gave way to lighter manufacturing and trading estates were built. On the moors south of the town there are fine views of the Wear Valley.

Idsley House ⋀

😊 APPROVED

4 Green Lane, Spennymoor, County Durham DL16 6HD
☎ Bishop Auckland (0388) 814237
Long-established Victorian guesthouse on A167/A688 run by local family. Ideal for Durham City. Ample parking on premises. Brochure on request.
Bedrooms: 1 single,
1 double, 2 twin, 1 triple
Bathrooms: 4 private,
1 public

Bed & breakfast

per night:	£min	£max
Single		18.00
Double	30.00	34.00

Parking for 8

🏷️🚲📺 🔌 🚲 S 🛏️ 📺 🛏️ 🚗 ✻

The Misty Blue Inn ⋀

Listed APPROVED

Rock Road, Spennymoor, County Durham DL16 7HJ
☎ (0388) 815351
Former farmhouse, now a select family inn, well located for Durham, Northumberland and the Lakes. Pets' corner, live music weekly, friendly atmosphere.
Bedrooms: 1 double, 1 twin, 1 triple, 1 multiple
Bathrooms: 2 public

Bed & breakfast

per night:	£min	£max
Single	20.00	25.00
Double	30.00	35.00

Half board

per person:	£min	£max
Daily	25.00	30.00
Weekly	175.00	210.00

Lunch available
Evening meal 1900 (last orders 2200)
Parking for 75

🛇🖵📶🖃🔟 🖻🛉♦❄
🏧 DAP 🐾 SP

ST JOHN'S CHAPEL
Durham
Map ref 5B2

Peaceful village in Upper Weardale. Pubs, village shops and cottages are set around a small market square. Nearby Harthope Burn has an attractive waterfall.

"Westwold"
Listed
57 Hood Street, St John's Chapel, Bishop Auckland, County Durham DL13 1QW
☎ (0388) 537288
Bungalow situated in St John's Chapel on main A689 road. Tourist attractions in the Dale easily accessible.
Bedrooms: 1 single, 1 double
Bathrooms: 1 public

Bed & breakfast

per night:	£min	£max
Single	13.00	13.00
Double	26.00	26.00

Parking for 2
Open April-October
🛇4🖳♦🗷🔟⠇🖂🗙🏧

STAINDROP
Durham
Map ref 5B3

Gazebo House
😃😃 HIGHLY COMMENDED
4 North Green, Staindrop, Darlington, County Durham DL2 3JN
☎ (0833) 60222
18th C house with listed gazebo, adjacent to Raby Park and Castle.
Bedrooms: 1 double, 1 twin
Bathrooms: 2 private

Bed & breakfast

per night:	£min	£max
Single	12.50	14.00
Double	30.00	35.00

Evening meal 1900 (last orders 2200)
🛇📞🖵🖻♦🗷🛉🔟⠇
🖂❄🗙🏧🏠

STANLEY
Durham
Map ref 5C2

Small town on the site of a Roman cattle camp. At the Beamish North of England Open Air Museum numerous set-pieces and displays recreate industrial and social conditions prevalent during the area's past.

Bushblades Farm 🚜
Listed
Harperley, Stanley, County Durham DH9 9UA
☎ (0207) 232722
60-acre livestock farm. Comfortable Georgian farmhouse, in rural setting. Within easy reach of Durham City, Beamish Museum, A1M, MetroCentre and Roman Wall.
Bedrooms: 2 double, 1 twin
Bathrooms: 1 private, 1 public

Bed & breakfast

per night:	£min	£max
Single	15.00	25.00
Double	30.00	38.00

Parking for 6
🛇🖵12🖳♦🗷🛉🔟⠇
🗙🏧

STANNINGTON
Northumberland
Map ref 5C2

West House Farm 🚜
Listed
Stannington, Morpeth NE61 6AY
☎ (0670) 789576
200-acre arable farm. Old farmhouse, with oak beams and private drive, half a mile from Stannington village. Just off A1, the first farm on right past the church. Good food available at village pub. Non-smokers only please.
Bedrooms: 1 double, 1 twin
Bathrooms: 1 public

Bed & breakfast

per night:	£min	£max
Single	15.00	20.00
Double	30.00	35.00

Parking for 4
Open April-September
🛇5🗷🛉🔟⠇🖂❄🗙
🏧🏠

Check the introduction to this region for Where to Go, What to See.

SUNDERLAND
Tyne and Wear
Map ref 5C2

Ancient coal and shipbuilding port on Wearside, with important glassworks since the 17th C. Today's industrial complex dates from the 19th C. Modern building includes the Civic Centre.
Tourist Information Centre
☎ *091-565 0960 or 091-565 0990.*

Anthony Lodge
5 Brookside Terrace, Ashbrook, Sunderland, Tyne & Wear SR2 7RN
☎ 091-567 7108
Family-run guesthouse with easy access to town, buses and trains. Parking area to rear.
Bedrooms: 5 single, 1 double, 2 twin, 1 triple
Bathrooms: 1 public

Bed & breakfast

per night:	£min	£max
Single	12.00	12.00
Double	24.00	24.00

Half board

per person:	£min	£max
Daily	17.00	17.00
Weekly	119.00	119.00

Evening meal from 1700
🛇🖾♦🗷🛉🔟⠇🖂
🗙🏧

Bed & Breakfast Stop 🚜
Listed COMMENDED
183 Newcastle Road, Fulwell, Sunderland, Tyne & Wear SR5 1NR
☎ 091-548 2291
Tudor-style semi-detached house on the A1018 Newcastle to Sunderland road, 5 minutes to the railway station and 10 minutes to the seafront.
Bedrooms: 1 single, 1 twin, 1 triple
Bathrooms: 1 public

Bed & breakfast

per night:	£min	£max
Single	13.00	15.00
Double	24.00	26.00

Half board

per person:	£min	£max
Daily	18.00	20.00
Weekly	119.00	126.00

Evening meal 1800 (last orders 1200)
Parking for 3
🛇3♦🗷🛉🔟⠇🖂
🏧 SP

The Chaise Guest House
5 Roker Terrace, Roker, Sunderland, Tyne & Wear SR6 9LY
☎ 091-565 9218
Large Victorian guesthouse facing the sea. 10 minutes from town centre and leisure centre, 30 minutes from Beamish Museum and Gateshead MetroCentre.
Bedrooms: 1 single, 4 double, 3 twin, 4 triple
Bathrooms: 3 public, 1 private shower

Bed & breakfast

per night:	£min	£max
Single	13.00	15.00
Double	22.00	22.00

Half board

per person:	£min	£max
Daily	15.50	17.50
Weekly	95.00	110.00

Evening meal 1730 (last orders 1900)
Parking for 12
🛇🖳📞🖵♦🛉🔟⠇🖂
🏧 SP T

TOW LAW
Durham
Map ref 5B2

Butsfield Abbey Farm
🏡
Satley, Tow Law, Bishop Auckland, County Durham DL13 4JD
☎ Bishop Auckland (0388) 730509
176-acre mixed farm. Farmhouse cottage in a quiet rural setting. 1 mile from A68 and 4 miles from Castleside.
Bedrooms: 1 double
Bathrooms: 1 private, 1 public

Bed & breakfast

per night:	£min	£max
Single	12.00	13.00
Double	24.00	26.00

Parking for 4
🛇🖳🖾🖵♦🗷🔟⠇
🖂🗙🏧🏠

Individual proprietors have supplied all details of accommodation. Although we do check for accuracy, we advise you to confirm the information at the time of booking.

TYNEMOUTH

Tyne and Wear
Map ref 5C2

At the mouth of the Tyne, old Tyneside resort adjoining North Shields with its fish quay and market. The pier is overlooked by the gaunt ruins of a Benedictine priory and a castle. Splendid sands, amusement centre and park.

Hope House ♠

🏯🏯🏯 **HIGHLY COMMENDED**

47 Percy Gardens, Tynemouth, North Shields NE30 4HH
☎ 091-257 1989
Double-fronted Victorian house with superb coastal views from most rooms. Period furnishing and large bedrooms. Fine cuisine.
Bedrooms: 2 double, 1 twin
Bathrooms: 3 private, 1 public

Bed & breakfast per night:	£min	£max
Single	35.00	42.50
Double	37.50	47.50

Half board per person:	£min	£max
Daily	32.25	34.75
Weekly		243.25

Lunch available
Evening meal 1800 (last orders 2100)
Parking for 5
Cards accepted: Access, Visa, Amex

🛇🍴▱♨☎⛵▥🛗🕯🏩
🛏🚶✕🐎 ⓄⒶⓅ ⛷ 🆂🄿 🏮

WALL

Northumberland
Map ref 5B2

Well-kept village with 2 greens in the North Tyne valley, a little to the south of Hadrian's Wall. The historically important Brunton Turret is within walking distance.

St. Oswalds Farm

Wall, Hexham NE46 4HB
☎ (0434) 681307
Stone farmhouse, built on Hadrian's Wall on side of Military Road (B6318). Five miles north of Hexham.
Bedrooms: 1 single, 1 double, 1 twin
Bathrooms: 2 public

Bed & breakfast per night: £min £max
Single	12.00	13.50
Double	24.00	27.00

Parking for 3
Open March-November

🛇♨▱♨▥🕯⛷✕🐎

WARK

Northumberland
Map ref 5B2

Set in the beautiful Tyne Valley amid the Northumbrian fells, old village just above the meeting of Wark Burn with the Tyne. Grey-stone houses surround the green with its shady chestnut trees and an iron bridge spans the stream. The mound of a Norman castle occupies the river bank.

Colt Crag Farmhouse

Colt Crag Farm, Birtley, Wark, Hexham NE48 3JD
☎ (0434) 681419
617-acre hill farm. Northumbrian farmhouse on the shores of a beautiful lake. Excellent centre for Kielder, Hadrian's Wall and the coast on A68.
Bedrooms: 1 double, 1 triple
Bathrooms: 1 public

Bed & breakfast per night:	£min	£max
Single	12.50	15.00
Double		25.00

Half board per person:	£min	£max
Daily	20.50	23.50
Weekly	108.00	138.00

Evening meal 1700 (last orders 2000)
Parking for 10
Cards accepted: Visa

🛇▥🕯🛗♨📺🐎♨ ⓄⒶⓅ 🆂🄿

There are separate sections in this guide listing groups specialising in farm holidays and accommodation which is especially suitable for young people and organised groups.

WARKWORTH

Northumberland
Map ref 5C1

A pretty village overlooked by its medieval castle. A 14th C fortified bridge across the wooded Coquet gives a superb view of 18th C terraces climbing to the castle. Upstream is a curious 14th C Hermitage and in the market square is the Norman church of St Lawrence.

Beck 'N' Call ♠

🏯🏯 **HIGHLY COMMENDED**

Birling West Cottage, Warkworth, Morpeth NE65 0XS
☎ Alnwick (0665) 711653
Country cottage set in half an acre of terraced gardens with stream. First cottage on the right entering Warkworth from Alnwick.
Bedrooms: 2 double, 1 triple
Bathrooms: 1 private, 1 public

Bed & breakfast per night:	£min	£max
Single	14.00	
Double	28.00	

Parking for 4

🛇🍴▱🔌♨▥🕯🛇♨
📺🛗 ♨🐎 🆂🄿

WESTGATE-IN-WEARDALE

Durham
Map ref 5B2

Small Weardale village with an old water-mill and a 19th C church. It is set at the entrance to the Bishops of Durham's former hunting ground, Old Park. Beautiful moorland, river and valley scenery to be explored.

Westgate House ♠

🏯🏯🏯 **HIGHLY COMMENDED**

Westgate-in-Weardale, Bishop Auckland, County Durham DL13 1LW
☎ (0388) 517564
Small Victorian country house with large secluded garden with croquet lawn, bordered by the A689 and the River Wear, situated just outside the village of Westgate.
Bedrooms: 1 double, 2 twin
Bathrooms: 1 private, 2 public

Bed & breakfast per night:	£min	£max
Double	40.00	40.00

Half board per person:	£min	£max
Daily	32.00	32.00

Evening meal from 1900
Parking for 4
Open April-October

🛇♨▱🔌▥🕯🛇♨📺🛗♨🐎♨🍴♨
🐎 Ⓣ

Wingate House Farm ♠

🏯🏯 **COMMENDED**

Westgate-in-Weardale, Bishop Auckland, County Durham DL13 1LP
☎ (0388) 517281
80-acre mixed farm. Victorian farmhouse in own grounds with terraced garden - 100 yards from A689 with level drive. Panoramic views, ideal touring centre.
Bedrooms: 1 twin, 1 triple
Bathrooms: 1 private, 1 public

Bed & breakfast per night:	£min	£max
Double	30.00	32.00

Parking for 4
Open April-October

🛇▱🔌♨▥🕯🛇♨📺🛗♨ ♨
♨🐎

WHITLEY BAY

Tyne and Wear
Map ref 5C2

Seaside resort with a large golf-course, amusement parks and ice-rink. It is edged with wide sands which stretch northward toward a more rugged coastline. St Mary's Island, which can be reached at low tide, has a redundant lighthouse.
Tourist Information Centre
☎ 091-252 4494.

Windsor Hotel ♠

🏯🏯🏯 **COMMENDED**

South Parade, Whitley Bay NE26 2RF
☎ 091-251 8888
Telex 537388
Private hotel close to the seafront and town centre. An excellent base in the north east for business or pleasure.
Bedrooms: 5 single, 16 double, 43 twin
Bathrooms: 64 private, 1 public

Bed & breakfast per night:	£min	£max
Single	35.00	55.00
Double	48.00	65.00

Half board per person:	£min	£max
Daily	45.00	65.00

Lunch available
Evening meal 1800 (last orders 2130)
Parking for 26
Cards accepted: Access, Visa, Diners, Amex

🛏️📞🖥️🗄️♿🐾🏊ⓈⒼⓉⓋ◑
📶🖨️🚲🏇🏋️10-100 ✿ 🅿️ 🅾️ ⓈⒼ🅿️

WOOLER

Northumberland
Map ref 5B1

Old grey-stone town, market-place for foresters and hill farmers, set at the edge of the north-east Cheviots. This makes a good base for excursions to Northumberland's loveliest coastline, or for angling and walking in the Borderlands.

Loreto Guest House M
😊😊
1 Ryecroft Way, Wooler
NE71 6BW
☎ (0668) 81350
Family-run early Georgian house in spacious grounds, in the lovely Cheviot village of

Wooler. Central for touring and walking and close to coastline.
Bedrooms: 1 single, 3 double, 2 twin
Bathrooms: 6 private, 2 public

Bed & breakfast

per night:	£min	£max
Single	15.00	16.00
Double	30.00	34.00

Evening meal 1830 (last orders 1900)
Parking for 12

🛏️♿🐾ⓈⒼ🗄️ⓉⓋ📶📠🍴✿
🚲🅾️🅿️🏇

Saint Hilliers
`Listed` `APPROVED`
6 Church Street, Wooler
NE71 6DA
☎ (0668) 81340
Stone-built family home in the centre of Wooler, opposite police station and car park. Non-smokers only please.
Bedrooms: 1 double, 2 twin
Bathrooms: 1 public

Bed & breakfast

per night:	£min	£max
Single	15.00	20.00
Double	30.00	40.00

🛏️♨️🗄️♿🐾Ⓖ🍴ⓉⓋ🗄️✿
🚲🅾️ⓈⒼ

WYLAM

Northumberland
Map ref 5B2

Well-kept village on the River Tyne, famous as the birthplace of the railway pioneer, George Stephenson. The cottage in which he was born is open to the public, and the Wylam Railway Museum also commemorates William Hedley and Timothy Hackworth.

Wormald House M
😊😊 `HIGHLY COMMENDED`
Main Street, Wylam
NE41 8DN
☎ (0661) 852529 & 852552
Pleasant country home located near centre of Wylam,

George Stephenson's birthplace. House stands on site of Timothy Hackworth's birthplace (Stephenson's contemporary).
Bedrooms: 2 double, 1 twin
Bathrooms: 2 private, 1 public

Bed & breakfast

per night:	£min	£max
Single		16.50
Double		32.00

Parking for 4

🛏️🗄️♿🐾ⓈⒼ🍴🗄️ⓉⓋ📶✿
🏇🚲🏇

Individual proprietors have supplied all details of accommodation. Although we do check for accuracy, we advise you to confirm the information at the time of booking.

Bookings

When enquiring about accommodation you may find it helpful to use the booking enquiry coupons which can be found towards the end of the guide. These should be cut out and mailed direct to the establishments in which you are interested. Do remember to include your name and address.

THIS GREEN & PLEASANT LAND HERE I COME!

Use your *i*'s

Tourist information

There are more than 600 Tourist Information Centres throughout England offering friendly help with accommodation and holiday ideas as well as suggestions of places to visit and things to do. In your home town there may be a centre which can help you before you set out. You'll find the address of your nearest Tourist Information Centre in your local Phone Book.

North West

Use the above map to locate places in the "Where to Go, What to See" section opposite.
Use the colour maps at the back of this guide to find places with accommodation.

North West

Splendid countryside, the biggest and best seaside resorts and a traditional warm welcome make the North West special. Blackpool is more than a fun-filled Golden Mile and a Mecca for family entertainment – it's an ideal base for exploring the rolling landscape of the Fylde and the wild moors of the Forest of Bowland. From the ancient Roman town of Chester, explore the richness of the Cheshire Plain. Visit the new Albert Dock development in Liverpool, sample Manchester's pulsating nightlife, or stroll around Southport's elegant boulevards and shopping arcades. There's a new experience around every corner in England's North West.

WHERE TO GO, WHAT TO SEE

The number against each name will help you locate it on the map opposite.

❶ Steamtown Railway Museum
Warton Road, Carnforth, Lancashire LA5 9HX
Tel: Carnforth (0524) 732100
Former BR-engine shed housing over 30 mainline and industrial locomotives. Signal box, turntable, coaling plant, model railway and gift shop.

❷ Heysham Power Stations and Visitor Centre
Heysham, Morecambe, Lancashire LA3 2YB
Tel: Heysham (0524) 855624
Exhibition centre, tours of nuclear power station and nature reserve.

❸ Wycoller Country Park
Wycoller, Colne, Lancashire
Tel: Colne (0282) 863627
Country park and conservation area enclosing hamlet of Wycoller. Scenic, historic and literary interest. Brontë associations. Information centre.

❹ Blackpool Pleasure Beach
Blackpool, Lancashire FY4 1EZ
Tel: Blackpool (0253) 41033
Europe's greatest amusement

Daresbury in Cheshire was the birthplace of the Reverend Charles Lutwidge Dodgson (better known to us as Lewis Carroll)

park: Space Invader, Big Dipper, Revolution, etc. Funshineland for children. Summer season ice show, illusion show in Horseshoe Bar.

❹ Blackpool Sea Life Centre
Blackpool, Lancashire FY1 5AA
Tel: Blackpool (0253) 22445
Tropical sharks up to 8ft in length housed in 100,000 gallon display with underwater walk-through tunnel.

❹ Tower World
Blackpool, Lancashire
Tel: (0253) 22242
Tower Ballroom, Memory Lane, Jungle Jim's playground, Out of this World, Undersea World, Pool room, Tower Dungeon, Ma Taplow's Restaurant. Children's entertainment daily.

❺ Ribchester Museum of Childhood
Ribchester, Preston, Lancashire PR3 3YE
Tel: Ribchester (0254) 878520
Large building containing childhood toys, dolls, over 50 dolls' houses, 20-piece model fairground, Tom Thumb replica, collectors' toy shop.

❻ Towneley Hall Art Gallery and Museum
Burnley, Lancashire BB11 3RQ
Tel: Burnley (0282) 24213
Country house of Towneley family with period furnishings

The 16th-century Little Moreton Hall at Congleton, Cheshire – as half-timbered as you can get!

and paintings. Museum displays and archaeology.

⑦ Camelot Adventure Theme Park
Park Hall Road, Charnock Richard, Chorley, Nr Preston, Lancashire PR7 5LP
Tel: Eccleston (0257) 453044
A world of thrilling rides, fantastic entertainment and family fun. Over 100 rides and attractions plus medieval entertainment.

⑧ Helmshore Textile Museum
Higher Mill, Holcombe Road, Helmshore, Haslingden, Lancashire BB4 6RE
Tel: Rossendale (0706) 226459
Textile machinery, water wheel and many working exhibits, especially carding engines and cotton spinning mules.

⑨ Hollingworth Lake Country Park
Rakewood Road, Littleborough, Greater Manchester OL15 0AQ
Tel: Littleborough (0706) 73421
Permanent and temporary exhibitions, slide show, 30ft mural by Walter Kershaw.

⑩ East Lancashire Railway
Bury, Lancashire BL9 0EY
Tel: 061-764 7790
Four-mile long preserved railway operated principally by steam traction. Transport museum nearby.

⑪ Butterfly World
Queens Park, Chorley New Road, Bolton, Lancashire
Tel: Bolton (0204) 22311
Butterflies and moths in free flight, goldfish, Koi carp, insects.

⑫ Granada Studios Tour
Quay Street, Manchester M60 9EA
Tel: 061-832 9090
A unique insight into the fascinating world behind the TV screen. Visit three of the most famous streets on TV.

⑫ Manchester Jewish Museum
190 Cheetham Hill Road, Manchester M8 8LW
Tel: 061-834 9879
Restored former Spanish and Portuguese synagogue (1874). Grade II listed building. History of Manchester's Jewish community.

⑫ Museum of Science and Industry in Manchester
Castlefield, Manchester M3 4JP
Tel: 061-832 2244
Europe's largest industrial museum based on the site of the oldest railway station in the world. Exhibitions include the Power Hall and Air and Space Gallery.

⑬ Salford Museum and Art Gallery
The Crescent, Salford, Lancashire M5 4WU

Tel: 061-736 2649
Reconstructed period street: "Lark Hill Place". Largest publicly owned collection of works of L.S. Lowry. Temporary art exhibitions.

⑭ Knowsley Safari Park
Prescot, Merseyside L34 4AN
Tel: 051-430 9009
Five-mile drive through game reserves, set in 400 acres of parkland containing lions, tigers, elephants, rhinos, etc. Large picnic areas and children's amusement park.

⑮ Animation World
Albert Dock, Liverpool L3 4AA
Tel: 051-707 1828
Permanent exhibition of animation featuring the characters and sets of Cosgrove Hall.

⑮ The Beatles Story
Albert Dock, Liverpool L3 4AA
Tel: 051-709 1963
Liverpool's number 1 award-winning visitor attraction. Replica Cavern Club available for private parties.

⑮ Croxteth Hall and Country Park
Off Muirhead Avenue East, Liverpool, Merseyside L12 0HB
Tel: 051-228 5311
500-acre country park and hall with displays and furnished rooms. Walled garden, farm with rare breeds, miniature railway, gift shop, picnic areas, riding centre.

⑯ Port Sunlight Heritage Centre
Greendale Road, Port Sunlight, Wirral, Merseyside L62 4ZP
Tel: 051-644 6466
In listed building, display showing creation of village, with photographs, drawings, models, Victorian model house.

⑰ Alice in Wonderland Tours
Daresbury Village, Cheshire
Tel: Comberbach (0606) 891303
Memorial marking site of parsonage where Lewis Carroll was born. Church with Alice window, Wonderland weather vane, font in which Carroll was christened.

⑱ Lyme Park
Disley, Stockport, Cheshire
SK12 2NX
Tel: Disley (0663) 62023
Nature trails and herds of red and fallow deer in park; state rooms, period furniture, tapestry, Grinling Gibbons carvings in hall, clock collection.

⑲ Tatton Park
Knutsford, Cheshire WA16 6QN
Tel: Knutsford (0565) 654822
Georgian mansion, 60-acre garden, medieval old hall, 1930s farm, shop and restaurant, all set in 1,000-acre deer park with lakes.

⑳ Boat Museum
Ellesmere Port, Cheshire L65 4EF
Tel: 051-355 5017
Over 50 historic craft, largest floating collection in the world, with restored buildings, traditional cottages, workshops, steam engines, boat trips, etc.

㉑ Arley Hall and Gardens
Northwich, Cheshire CW9 6NA
Tel: Arley (0565) 777353
Early Victorian hall set in 12 acres of magnificent gardens. 15th C tithe barn. Unique collection of watercolours of the area. Woodland walk. Shop and craftsmen.

㉒ Capesthorne Hall
Siddington, Macclesfield, Cheshire SK11 9JY
Tel: Chelford (0625) 861221
Sculpture, paintings, furniture, Greek vases, family muniments. Georgian chapel, tea rooms, gardens, lakes, nature walks.

㉓ Jodrell Bank Science Centre
Lower Withington, Cheshire
SK11 9DL
Tel: Lower Withington (0477) 71339
Exhibition and interactive exhibits on astronomy. Planetarium and the Lovell telescope.

㉔ Chester Zoo
Upton-by-Chester, Chester, Cheshire CH2 1LH
Tel: Chester (0244) 380280
Penguin pool with underwater views, tropical house, spectacular displays of spring and summer bedding plants. Chimpanzee house and outdoor enclosure.

FIND OUT MORE

Further information about holidays and attractions in the North West region is available from:
North West Tourist Board
Swan House, Swan Meadow Road, Wigan Pier, Wigan WN3 5BB
Tel: (0942) 821222

These publications are available free from the North West Tourist Board:
North West Welcome Pack
Discover England's North West (map)
Overseas brochure
Group Visits
Bed & Breakfast map
Places to Visit in Winter
Activity Holidays guide
Caravan and Camping Parks guide

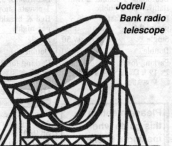

Jodrell Bank radio telescope

91

Places to stay

Accommodation entries in this regional section are listed in alphabetical order of place name, and then in alphabetical order of establishment.

The map references refer to the colour maps at the back of the guide. The first figure is the map number; the letter and figure which follow indicate the grid reference on the map.

The symbols at the end of each accommodation entry give information about services and facilities. A 'key' to these symbols is inside the back cover flap, which can be kept open for easy reference.

ACCRINGTON

Lancashire
Map ref 4A1

Victorian town noted for its red bricks which were extensively used in public buildings throughout Britain. Famous for textiles and general engineering. The Haworth Art Gallery contains collections of Early English watercolours and Tiffany glass.
Tourist Information Centre
☎ (0254) 386807

Corn Mill Cottage
Altham, Accrington BB5 5UP
☎ Padiham (0282) 772208
Charming 18th C country cottage with modern facilities. Situated by the A678 between Clayton Le Moors and Padiham. Close to M65/M66. Personal service.
Bedrooms: 1 double, 2 twin
Bathrooms: 2 public
Bed & breakfast

per night:	£min	£max
Single	17.50	17.50
Double	32.00	34.00

Parking for 3

Please mention this guide when making a booking.

ALDERLEY EDGE

Cheshire
Map ref 4B2

Residential town taking its name from the hill which rises to a height of 600 ft from the Cheshire Plain. The Edge is a well-known beauty spot with superb views. Many historic buildings including Chorley Old Hall (the oldest surviving manor house in Cheshire).

Copper Beech
7 Trafford Road, Alderley Edge SK9 7NT
☎ (0625) 583686
Comfortable, semi-detached, Victorian house, close to the pretty village of Alderley Edge and within easy reach of the station. Convenient for Manchester Airport.
Bedrooms: 2 double, 1 twin
Bathrooms: 1 public,
1 private shower
Bed & breakfast

per night:	£min	£max
Single	17.00	17.00
Double	32.00	32.00

Parking for 2

Dean Green Farm
HIGHLY COMMENDED
Nusery Lane, Nether Alderley, Macclesfield
SK10 4TX
☎ Chelford (0625) 861401

131-acre beef farm. Situated between A34 and A535 at Nether Alderley. Grade II oak-beamed farmhouse surrounded by pastureland looking towards Alderley Edge, convenient for Knutsford, Wilmslow and Macclesfield.
Bedrooms: 1 double
Bathrooms: 1 private
Bed & breakfast

per night:	£min	£max
Double	47.00	

Half board

per person:	£min	£max
Daily	37.68	

Evening meal 1800 (last orders 2100)
Parking for 10

Milverton House Hotel ₳

Wilmslow Road, Alderley Edge SK9 7QL
☎ (0625) 583615 & 585555
Well-appointed Victorian villa on main road with open country views. Home cooking.
Bedrooms: 2 single,
8 double, 3 twin, 1 triple
Bathrooms: 4 private,
4 public, 8 private showers
Bed & breakfast

per night:	£min	£max
Single	30.00	47.00
Double	52.80	60.00

Half board

per person:	£min	£max
Daily	40.00	56.00
Weekly	180.00	240.00

Evening meal from 1830
Parking for 16
Cards accepted: Access, Visa

ALTRINCHAM

Greater Manchester
Map ref 4A2

On the edge of the Cheshire Plain, close to Manchester. Once a thriving textile town, Altrincham is now mainly residential. Good centre for local beauty spots including 18th C Dunham Massey Hall (National Trust) with its deer park.
Tourist Information Centre
☎ 061-941 7337

Ashley Mill ₳
Listed   COMMENDED
Ashley Mill Lane, Ashley, Altrincham, Cheshire
WA14 3PU
☎ 061-928 5751
17th C mill house in delightful Cheshire countryside. A haven of peace and tranquillity yet only 10 minutes from Manchester Airport.
Bedrooms: 1 single,
2 double, 1 twin
Bathrooms: 1 public

Bed & breakfast

per night:	£min	£max
Single	17.00	20.00
Double	34.00	40.00

Evening meal 1930 (last orders 2000)
Parking for 26
☎10 ♦ ⚑ ▥ 🅐 ⚑ ✠ TV ▥ ◨ ✿ ✕ ⚑ ❦ 🏠

Belvedere Guest House

Listed   APPROVED

58 Barrington Road, Altrincham, Cheshire WA14 1HY
☎ 061-941 5996
10 minutes from Manchester Airport; free taxi service. Convenient for buses and trains. All rooms have satellite TV and tea/coffee making facilities.
Bedrooms: 2 double, 1 twin, 1 triple
Bathrooms: 4 private

Bed & breakfast

per night:	£min	£max
Single	20.00	23.00
Double	32.00	38.00

Half board

per person:	£min	£max
Daily	28.00	31.00

Parking for 6
Cards accepted: Access, Visa
☒ ⚑ ▥ ⚑ ▥ 🅐 ▥ ✠ ✠ TV ◐ ▥ ◨ ▶ ❦ SP 🏠 T

BILSBORROW

Lancashire
Map ref 4A1

Guy's Thatched Hamlet ♨

👑👑👑 COMMENDED

Canal-Side, St. Michael's Road, Bilsborrow, Preston PR3 0RS
☎ Brock (0995) 40849 & 40010
Fax (0995) 40141
Thatched, canal-side, pub, restaurant, lodgings, craft shops and cricket pitch. Off junction 32 of M6 then north on A6. Preston 6 miles. Indoor swimming pool due for completion April 1994.
Bedrooms: 28 double, 4 triple
Bathrooms: 32 private

Bed & breakfast

per night:	£min	£max
Single	33.75	36.00
Double	36.50	41.00

Lunch available
Evening meal 1800 (last orders 2330)
Parking for 300

Cards accepted: Access, Visa, Amex, Switch
☒ ⚑ ▥ 🅐 ♦ ▤ 🅢 ◨ ▥ ▪ ▱
☎10-38 ▶ ✠ ▥ DAP SP 🏠

BIRKENHEAD

Merseyside
Map ref 4A2

Shipbuilding, docks and later the Mersey Tunnel turned Birkenhead into a busy town. Good Victorian architecture in Hamilton Square and Town Hall. Williamson Art Gallery contains English watercolours, pottery and porcelain.
Tourist Information Centre
☎ 051-647 6780

Ashgrove

14 Ashville Road, Claughton, Birkenhead L43 8SA
☎ 051-653 3794
Friendly, family-run establishment overlooking Birkenhead Park. 10 minutes' walk to train and 2 stops to Liverpool centre. Excellent shopping facilities nearby, numerous sports facilities. Owner is local guitar vocalist.
Bedrooms: 2 single, 2 double, 3 twin, 1 triple
Bathrooms: 2 private, 3 public

Bed & breakfast

per night:	£min	£max
Single	14.00	18.00
Double	26.00	34.00

Half board

per person:	£min	£max
Daily	18.00	22.00
Weekly	100.00	140.00

Lunch available
Evening meal 1800 (last orders 1600)
Parking for 10
☒ ▥ ♦ ▥ 🅐 🅢 ✠ ✠ TV ▥ ◨ ▪ ◀ ✕ ⚑ DAP ❦ 🏠

We advise you to confirm your booking in writing.

There are separate sections in this guide listing groups specialising in farm holidays and accommodation which is especially suitable for young people and organised groups.

BLACKBURN

Lancashire
Map ref 4A1

Once a thriving cotton town. Models of the old machinery may be seen in Lewis Textile Museum. Relics of the Roman occupation in Blackburn Museum. 19th C cathedral, Victorian landscaped Corporation Park.
Tourist Information Centre
☎ (0254) 53277

Rose Cottage ♨

👑👑👑

Longsight Road, Clayton Le Dale, Blackburn BB1 9EX
☎ Mellor (0254) 813223
100-year-old cottage, on A59, at the gateway to the Ribble Valley, 5 miles from M6 junction 31.
Bedrooms: 1 double, 2 twin
Bathrooms: 2 private, 1 public

Bed & breakfast

per night:	£min	£max
Single	16.50	19.50
Double	25.00	29.00

Parking for 3
☒ ▥ ▥ ♦ ▥ 🅐 🅢 ▥ ▪ ⚑

BLACKPOOL

Lancashire
Map ref 4A1

Largest fun resort in the North with amusement parks, piers, tram rides along the promenade, sandy beaches and the famous Tower. Among its annual events are the Milk Race, the Veteran Car Run and the spectacular autumn illuminations.
Tourist Information Centre
☎ (0253) 21623 or 21891 or (weekdays only) 25212.

Alberts Ramsden Arms Hotel ♨

Listed

204 Talbot Road, Blackpool FY1 3AZ
☎ (0253) 23215
Classic country-style inn close to beach, town centre, theatres, stations. Winner of many awards for inn-keeping and beer.
Bedrooms: 3 twin
Bathrooms: 1 private, 1 public

Bed & breakfast

per night:	£min	£max
Single	17.50	22.50
Double	30.00	40.00

Parking for 10
▥ ▥ ♦ 🅢 ✠ ✠ TV ▥ ▪ ✠ ✕ ⚑ DAP SP 🏠 T

Bel-Royal Private Hotel

7-9 General Street, Blackpool FY1 1RW
☎ (0253) 25127 & 24626
Fax (0253) 23041
Close to town centre, sea and pier, and 200 yards from station. Licensed bar, choice of menu. All rooms en-suite with heaters, teamakers, radio and satellite TV. Some parking available.
Bedrooms: 7 double, 5 twin, 1 triple, 2 multiple
Bathrooms: 15 private, 1 public

Bed & breakfast

per night:	£min	£max
Single	18.00	30.00
Double	35.00	50.00

Half board

per person:	£min	£max
Daily	21.00	28.00
Weekly	130.00	165.00

Evening meal 1800 (last orders 1800)
Parking for 6
Cards accepted: Access, Visa
☒ ▥ ▥ ♦ ▥ 🅐 🅢 ▥ TV ▪ ◨ ✕ ⚑ DAP ❦ SP 🏠 T

Park Lodge

Listed   COMMENDED

98 Park Road, Blackpool FY1 4ES
☎ (0253) 751218
A pleasant, well-equipped bed and breakfast establishment situated on approach road to town centre. Parking to front and rear.
Bedrooms: 1 single, 1 double, 1 triple
Bathrooms: 1 private, 1 public

Bed & breakfast

per night:	£min	£max
Single	16.00	18.00
Double	28.00	32.00

Parking for 4
☒ ▥ 3 ⚑ ▥ ▥ ♦ ▥ 🅐 ▥ 🅢 ▥ ▪ ✕ ⚑ DAP SP T

Sunray Hotel ♨

👑👑👑 COMMENDED

42 Knowle Avenue, Blackpool FY2 9TQ
☎ (0253) 51937
Modern semi in quiet residential part of north Blackpool. Friendly personal service and care.

Continued ▶

BLACKPOOL

Continued

Bedrooms: 3 single,
2 double, 2 twin, 2 triple
Bathrooms: 9 private,
1 public
Bed & breakfast

per night:	£min	£max
Single	22.00	28.00
Double	44.00	56.00

Half board

per person:	£min	£max
Daily	33.00	39.00
Weekly	198.00	234.00

Evening meal 1750 (last
orders 1500)
Parking for 6
Open January-November
Cards accepted: Access, Visa
🛇🌜📞☐💡🅿️⑩⑤🅜📺
🗁🛏️✿🐾 ⒹⒶⓅ ⓈⓅ Ⓣ

BOLTON

Greater Manchester
Map ref 4A1

Once a prosperous cotton
town with Civil War
connections, now has one
of the finest shopping
centres in the region.
Attractions include Hall i'
th' Wood, Smithill's Hall,
Central Museum, Art
Gallery and Octagon
Theatre.
Tourist Information Centre
☎ *(0204) 364333*

Black Dog Inn

2-4 Church Street, Belmont,
Bolton BL7 8AB
☎ Belmont Village (0204)
81218
*Built in 1750, converted to
inn in 1825. Contains old
village court with seats still
in-situ. No juke boxes - only
classical music played. 5
miles north of Bolton.*
Bedrooms: 1 double, 1 twin,
1 triple
Bathrooms: 3 private
Bed & breakfast

per night:	£min	£max
Single	29.50	29.50
Double	38.00	38.00

Lunch available
Evening meal 1900 (last
orders 2100)
Parking for 51
🛇🌜📞☐💡🅜⑤Ⓞ🖂🗁
🔔♪✎✿🐾 ⒹⒶⓅ 🎏

Cheetham Arms ⋒

👑👑👑 COMMENDED
987 Blackburn Road,
Sharples, Bolton BL1 7LG
☎ (0204) 301372

*Recently refurbished stone
cottage. Cosy public house, in
traditional style. Offering en-
suite accommodation and full
menu meals.*
Bedrooms: 1 single,
1 double, 2 triple
Bathrooms: 4 private
Bed & breakfast

per night:	£min	£max
Single	30.00	34.00
Double	40.00	45.00

Half board

per person:	£min	£max
Daily	33.00	40.00

Lunch available
Evening meal 1830 (last
orders 1930)
Parking for 40
Cards accepted: Access, Visa
🛇☐💡⑤🅜🖂🗁✿🐾
🎏 ⓈⓅ

BOLTON-LE-SANDS

Lancashire
Map ref 5A3

The village is on the main
A6 trunk road with the
picturesque Lancaster
Canal passing through it.
An ideal touring base.

Thwaite End Farm ⋒

👑👑
A6 Road, Bolton-le-Sands,
Carnforth LA5 9TN
☎ Carnforth (0524) 732551
*20-acre livestock farm. 17th C
farmhouse in an ideal area
for breaking your journey to
and from Scotland. Well
placed for touring the Lake
District and Lancashire. Self-
catering cottage also
available.*
Bedrooms: 2 double, 1 twin
Bathrooms: 2 private,
2 public
Bed & breakfast

per night:	£min	£max
Single	18.00	20.00
Double	34.00	40.00

Parking for 4
💡🅜📺🖂🗁✿✕🐾

Individual
proprietors have
supplied all details
of accommodation.
Although we do
check for accuracy,
we advise you to
confirm the
information at the
time of booking.

BURNLEY

Lancashire
Map ref 4B1

Once the largest cotton-
weaving centre in the
world but now dominated
by engineering. Towneley
Hall has fine period
rooms and the entrance
hall houses an art gallery
and museum. The Kay-
Shuttleworth collection of
lace and embroidery can
be seen at Gawthorpe
Hall (National Trust).
Tourist Information Centre
☎ *(0282) 55485*

Ormerod Hotel

👑👑 COMMENDED
121-123 Ormerod Road,
Burnley BB11 3QW
☎ (0282) 423255
*Small bed and breakfast hotel
in quiet, pleasant
surroundings facing local
parks. Recently refurbished,
all en-suite facilities. 5
minutes from town centre.*
Bedrooms: 4 single,
2 double, 2 twin, 2 triple
Bathrooms: 10 private
Bed & breakfast

per night:	£min	£max
Single	19.00	23.00
Double	33.00	35.00

Parking for 7
Cards accepted: Access, Visa
🛇🖴☐💡🅜🅸⑤🅜📺🖂
🗁Ⓣ

BURY

Greater Manchester
Map ref 4B1

Birthplace of Sir Robert
Peel, Prime Minister and
founder of police force,
commemorated by statue
in market-place. The East
Lancashire Railway
operates from Bury and
items connected with
steam railways are found
at the Transport Museum.
Tourist Information Centre
☎ *061-705 5111*

Loe Farm Country House

👑👑 COMMENDED
Redisher Lane, Hawkshaw,
Bury, Lancashire BL8 4HX
☎ Tottington (0204) 883668
*19-acre horses farm. Only 5
miles from M62, M61 and
M66. All bedrooms have
private facilities, radio, TV
and tea/coffee making
facilities.*
Bedrooms: 4 double, 2 twin

Bathrooms: 6 private
Bed & breakfast

per night:	£min	£max
Single	25.00	
Double	35.00	

Half board

per person:	£min	£max
Daily	34.50	

Evening meal from 1800
Parking for 18
Cards accepted: Access, Visa
🛇🌜📞☐💡🅜🅸🅹🅜📺🖂🗁
🔔✤✿✕🐾

CARNFORTH

Lancashire
Map ref 5B3

Permanent home of the
'Flying Scotsman' in
Steamtown Railway
Museum. Nearby are
Borwick Hall, an
Elizabethan manor house,
and Leighton Hall which
has good paintings and
early furniture and is open
to the public.

Royal Station Hotel ⋒

👑👑👑 COMMENDED
Market Street, Carnforth
LA5 9BT
☎ (0524) 732033
Fax (0524) 733636
*Refurbished, comfortable,
friendly hotel in centre of this
historic market town
surrounded by the beautiful
countryside of Lonsdale.
English Lakes 20 minutes, 1
mile junction 35 M6. English,
French, Italian cooking.*
Bedrooms: 2 single,
5 double, 4 twin, 1 triple
Bathrooms: 12 private,
4 public
Bed & breakfast

per night:	£min	£max
Single	26.00	
Double	44.00	

Half board

per person:	£min	£max
Daily	36.00	38.00

Lunch available
Evening meal 1800 (last
orders 2030)
Parking for 18
Cards accepted: Access, Visa,
Diners, Amex
🛇🌜📞☐💡🐟⑤🅜📺🖂
🗁Ⓣ120-150 ⒹⒶⓅ ⓈⓅ Ⓣ

The national
Crown scheme is
explained in full
in the information
pages towards the
back of this guide.

CHESTER

Cheshire
Map ref 4A2

Roman and medieval walled city rich in architectural and archaeological treasures. Fine timber-framed and plaster buildings. Shopping in the Rows (galleried arcades reached by steps from the street). 14 C cathedral castle and zoo.
Tourist Information Centre ☎ (0244) 317962 or 351609.

65 Five Ashes Road
Westminster Park, Chester
CH4 7QS
☎ (0244) 678144
Quiet accommodation in sought-after area of city. Approximately one mile from city centre, south of the River Dee.
Bedrooms: 1 double, 1 twin
Bathrooms: 1 public

Bed & breakfast
per night:	£min	£max
Double		26.00

Parking for 2
Open May-October

Cheyney Lodge Hotel
APPROVED
77-79 Cheyney Road, Chester CH1 4BS
☎ (0244) 381925
Small, friendly hotel of unusual design, featuring indoor garden and fish pond. 10 minutes' walk from city centre and on main bus route. Personally supervised with emphasis on good food.
Bedrooms: 5 double, 2 twin, 1 triple
Bathrooms: 7 private, 1 public

Bed & breakfast
per night:	£min	£max
Single	20.00	24.00
Double	30.00	39.00

Half board
per person:	£min	£max
Daily	27.50	31.50

Lunch available
Evening meal 1800 (last orders 2100)
Parking for 12
Cards accepted: Access, Visa

Please check prices and other details at the time of booking.

Curzon Hotel ⋀
52-54 Hough Green, Chester CH4 8JQ
☎ (0244) 678581
Fax (0244) 680866
Large Victorian house set well back in its own grounds. Close to golf, River Dee, racecourse, leisure centre and all amenities.
Bedrooms: 6 single, 7 double, 1 twin, 2 triple
Bathrooms: 16 private

Bed & breakfast
per night:	£min	£max
Single	22.50	35.00
Double		45.00

Evening meal 1900 (last orders 2100)
Parking for 24
Cards accepted: Access, Visa, Diners, Amex

Eaton House
36 Eaton Road, Handbridge, Chester CH4 7EN
☎ (0244) 671346
140-year-old Victorian house with all modern facilities, in pleasant conservation area, near river and town centre.
Bedrooms: 2 double, 1 triple
Bathrooms: 2 private, 3 public

Bed & breakfast
per night:	£min	£max
Double	25.00	30.00

Parking for 5

Gables Guest House ⋀
Listed APPROVED
5 Vicarage Road, Off Hoole Road, Chester CH2 3HZ
☎ (0244) 323969
Guesthouse in quiet road 1 mile from city centre. Park and tennis courts nearby. Easy access to motorways.
Bedrooms: 1 double, 1 twin, 4 triple
Bathrooms: 2 public

Bed & breakfast
per night:	£min	£max
Single	16.00	20.00
Double	26.00	30.00

Parking for 7

Golborne Manor ⋀
Platts Lane, Hatton Heath, Chester CH3 9AN
☎ Tattenhall (0829) 70310
19th C manor house renovated to a high standard, set in 3.5 acres. Lovely rural

setting with fine views. 5 miles south of Chester, off A41 Whitchurch Road, turning right just after DP Motors. Ample parking.
Bedrooms: 1 twin, 1 multiple
Bathrooms: 1 private, 1 public

Bed & breakfast
per night:	£min	£max
Single		25.00
Double		35.00

Parking for 6

Hillsborough
12 Parkgate Road, Chester CH1 4AQ
☎ (0244) 376436
Warm, friendly and comfortable Victorian house in elevated position. 10 minutes' walk into city centre, on the A540. Ample parking. Own keys.
Bedrooms: 1 twin, 1 multiple
Bathrooms: 1 private, 1 public, 1 private shower

Bed & breakfast
per night:	£min	£max
Double	28.00	35.00

Parking for 6

Lloyd's Guest House ⋀
108 Brook Street, Chester CH3 1DU
☎ (0244) 325838
Fax (0244) 317491
Friendly, family-run guesthouse very near rail station, and only 10 minutes' walk from city centre. Good English breakfast is served.
Bedrooms: 2 single, 5 double, 7 triple
Bathrooms: 7 private, 2 public

Bed & breakfast
per night:	£min	£max
Single	15.00	17.00
Double	28.00	36.00

Moorings ⋀
COMMENDED
14 Sandy Lane, Chester CH3 5UL
☎ (0244) 324485
Elegant riverside Victorian house overlooking meadows and having award-winning terraced gardens to River Dee. Within easy walking distance of city centre.
Bedrooms: 1 double, 1 twin
Bathrooms: 1 private, 1 public

Bed & breakfast
per night:	£min	£max
Single	18.00	18.00
Double	28.00	36.00

Open February-December

Tickeridge House ⋀
Whitchurch Road, Milton Green, Chester CH3 9DS
☎ Tattenhall (0829) 70443
Set in 3.5 acres of gardens, 5 miles south of Chester on A41. A warm welcome awaits, with tea and cakes on arrival. Meet our lovable donkey, rabbits and wild birds.
Bedrooms: 1 single, 1 double, 1 twin, 1 triple
Bathrooms: 2 private, 2 public

Bed & breakfast
per night:	£min	£max
Single	15.00	20.00
Double	27.00	35.00

Parking for 6
Cards accepted: Visa

CHIPPING

Lancashire
Map ref 4A1

Hough Clough Farmhouse ⋀
COMMENDED
Hough Clough Lane, Chipping, Preston PR3 2NT
☎ (0995) 61272
Traditional stone-built Victorian farmhouse next to Bleasdale Moors near Chipping and Beacon Fell, one of the nation's first country parks. Ideal for touring.
Bedrooms: 1 triple, 1 multiple
Bathrooms: 2 private, 1 public

Bed & breakfast
per night:	£min	£max
Single		16.50
Double		33.00

Half board
per person:	£min	£max
Daily		24.50
Weekly		161.00

Evening meal 1830 (last orders 1930)
Parking for 5

CHORLEY

Lancashire
Map ref 4A1

Despite its cotton-weaving background, Chorley has a busy market town atmosphere. Jacobean Astley Hall, set in extensive parkland, has fine furniture and long gallery with shovel-board table.

Astley House Hotel

COMMENDED

3 Southport Road, Chorley PR7 1LB
☎ (0257) 272315

An elegant Victorian house with 20th C comforts. Just a few minutes walk from Chorley town centre and park.

Bedrooms: 4 single, 2 twin
Bathrooms: 3 private, 1 public

Bed & breakfast per night:	£min	£max
Single	16.00	20.00
Double	36.00	40.00

Evening meal from 1800
Parking for 6
Cards accepted: Access, Visa, Amex

Farmers Arms

Listed COMMENDED

Towngate, Eccleston, Chorley PR7 5QS
☎ Eccleston (0257) 451594

Village pub with small friendly restaurant offering reasonably priced extensive menu. 2 miles from M6 services.

Bedrooms: 2 double, 2 twin
Bathrooms: 1 private, 1 public

Bed & breakfast per night:	£min	£max
Single	20.00	25.00
Double	30.00	35.00

Lunch available
Evening meal 1730 (last orders 2200)
Parking for 36

National Crown ratings were correct at the time of going to press but are subject to change. Please check at the time of booking.

CLITHEROE

Lancashire
Map ref 4A1

Intriguing town with the castle as its chief attraction. The Edisford Recreation Area with pitch and putt, picnic area and Ribblesdale Pool, and the unique Civic Hall cinema are further attractions. Country market on Tuesdays and Saturdays.
Tourist Information Centre ☎ (0200) 25566

8 Lingfield Avenue

Off Littlemore Road, Clitheroe BB7 1HA
☎ (0200) 22360

Modern, semi-detached house in quiet cul-de-sac on outskirts of town. Suitable for touring and walking in the Ribble Valley.

Bedrooms: 1 single, 1 twin, 1 triple
Bathrooms: 1 public

Bed & breakfast per night:	£min	£max
Single	10.00	
Double	20.00	

Parking for 3

Lower Standen Farm

Whalley Road, Clitheroe BB7 1PP
☎ (0200) 24176

140-acre mixed farm. 17th C farmhouse. Excellent for walking holidays.

Bedrooms: 2 double, 1 twin
Bathrooms: 1 public, 2 private showers

Bed & breakfast per night:	£min	£max
Single	14.00	14.00
Double	28.00	28.00

There are separate sections in this guide listing groups specialising in farm holidays and accommodation which is especially suitable for young people and organised groups.

COLNE

Lancashire
Map ref 4B1

Old market town with mixed industries bordering the moorland Bronte country. Nearby are the ruins of Wycoller House, featured in Charlotte Bronte's 'Jane Eyre' as Ferndean Manor.

148 Keighley Road

Listed HIGHLY COMMENDED

Colne BB8 0PJ
☎ (0282) 862002

Edwardian town house with many original features. Comfortable accommodation with easy access to Pendle, Bronte Country and the Yorkshire Dales. Non-smokers only please.

Bedrooms: 1 single, 1 double
Bathrooms: 1 public

Bed & breakfast per night:	£min	£max
Single	14.00	14.00
Double	28.00	28.00

Parking for 1

Higher Wanless Farm

Red Lane, Barrowford, Nelson BB8 7JP
☎ (0282) 865301

25-acre horses farm. Delightful farmhouse with oak beams and log fires. Tastefully furnished. Convenient for Pendle Witch, Bronte Country and Yorkshire Dales and close to Pendle Way. Evening meal on request.

Bedrooms: 1 twin, 1 triple
Bathrooms: 1 private, 1 public

Bed & breakfast per night:	£min	£max
Single	18.00	22.00
Double	32.00	38.00
Half board per person:	**£min**	**£max**
Daily	27.00	31.00
Weekly	180.00	210.00

Evening meal from 1800
Parking for 4
Open February-November

Middle Beardshaw Head Farm

Burnley Road, Trawden, Colne BB8 8PP
☎ (0282) 865257

17th-18th C Lancashire longhouse with oak beams, panelling, log fires. Panoramic views with pools, woods and stream. Half mile from Trawden. Self-catering cottage nearby also available.

Bedrooms: 2 single, 2 double, 1 triple
Bathrooms: 1 public, 2 private showers

Bed & breakfast per night:	£min	£max
Single	12.50	15.00
Double	25.00	30.00
Half board per person:	**£min**	**£max**
Daily	20.00	22.00
Weekly	140.00	150.00

Lunch available
Evening meal 1900 (last orders 2030)
Parking for 8

CONGLETON

Cheshire
Map ref 4B2

Important cattle market and silk town on the River Dane, now concerned with general textiles. Nearby are Little Moreton Hall, a Tudor house surrounded by a moat, the Bridestones, a chambered tomb, and Mow Cop, topped by a folly.
Tourist Information Centre ☎ (0260) 271095

Sandhole Farm

COMMENDED

Hulme Walfield, Congleton CW12 2JH
☎ Marton Heath (0260) 224419

200-acre arable and mixed farm. Attractive traditional farmhouse well positioned for touring, set in rolling countryside. Two miles north of Congleton on A34.

Bedrooms: 2 double, 7 twin, 1 triple
Bathrooms: 8 private, 2 public

Bed & breakfast per night:	£min	£max
Single	21.00	25.00
Double	35.00	38.00

Parking for 40

Yew Tree Farm

Listed

North Rode, Congleton CW12 2PF
☎ North Rode (0260) 223569

77-acre mixed farm. Peaceful village setting. 20 minutes from M6. Guests are invited to look around the farm and get to know the animals.
Bedrooms: 1 double, 2 twin
Bathrooms: 1 private, 1 public

Bed & breakfast

per night:	£min	£max
Single	15.00	20.00
Double	26.00	35.00

Half board

per person:	£min	£max
Daily	21.00	26.00

Evening meal 1800 (last orders 1900)
Parking for 3

CROSTON

Lancashire
Map ref 4A1

The Mill Hotel ⚊

Moor Road, Croston, Preston PR5 7HP
☎ (0772) 600110
A country family-run hotel providing 2 restaurants, public bar, function rooms and conference facilities, located between Preston and Southport, near Leyland.
Bedrooms: 2 single, 26 double, 7 twin, 1 multiple
Bathrooms: 36 private

Bed & breakfast

per night:	£min	£max
Single	35.00	45.00
Double	55.00	65.00

Half board

per person:	£min	£max
Daily	45.00	60.00

Lunch available
Evening meal 1730 (last orders 2200)
Parking for 130
Cards accepted: Access, Visa

DUTTON

Lancashire
Map ref 4A1

Entirely surrounded by agricultural land, Dutton lies on the south-eastern side of Longridge Fell.

Smithy Farm

Huntingdonhall Lane, Dutton, Longridge, Preston PR3 2ZT
☎ Ribchester (0254) 878250
14-acre mixed farm. Set in the beautiful Ribble Valley, 20 minutes from the M6. Homely

atmosphere, children half price.
Bedrooms: 1 double, 1 twin, 1 triple
Bathrooms: 1 public

Bed & breakfast

per night:	£min	£max
Single	11.00	11.00
Double	22.00	22.00

Half board

per person:	£min	£max
Daily	15.00	15.00
Weekly	105.00	105.00

Evening meal 1900 (last orders 2130)
Parking for 4

FORTON

Lancashire
Map ref 4A1

Middle Holly Cottage ⚊
COMMENDED

Middle Holly, Forton, Preston PR3 1AH
☎ (0524) 792399
Former coaching inn, set in rural surroundings. Adjacent A6 Lancaster road, 7 miles south of city, 3 miles south of M6 junction 33. Convenient for all North Lancashire areas and only 30 minutes' drive to Lakes.
Bedrooms: 1 single, 2 double, 1 twin, 1 triple
Bathrooms: 5 private

Bed & breakfast

per night:	£min	£max
Single	22.50	29.50
Double	34.50	39.50

Parking for 11
Cards accepted: Access, Visa

GARSTANG

Lancashire
Map ref 4A1

Picturesque country market town in the east of the borough. Regarded as the gateway to the fells, it stands on the Lancaster Canal and is popular as a cruising centre. Close by are the remains of Greenhalgh Castle (no public access) and the Bleasdale Circle.
Discovery Centre.
Tourist Information Centre
☎ (0995) 602125

Lucas Farm
Barnacre, Garstang, Preston PR3 1QJ
☎ (0995) 603135

107-acre dairy farm. Breakfast in conservatory with a panoramic view of the countryside. 18th C farmhouse, 2 miles east of Garstang on Calder Vale road.
Bedrooms: 1 double, 1 twin
Bathrooms: 1 public

Bed & breakfast

per night:	£min	£max
Single	13.00	13.00
Double	26.00	26.00

Parking for 4

GREAT ECCLESTON

Lancashire
Map ref 4A1

Cartford Hotel ⚊
⚊⚊⚊
Cartford Lane, Little Eccleston, Preston PR3 0YP
☎ (0995) 70166
A country riverside pub and coaching inn, with 1.5 miles of fishing rights. Within easy reach of Blackpool and the Lake District.
Bedrooms: 6 double
Bathrooms: 6 private

Bed & breakfast

per night:	£min	£max
Single	22.50	26.50
Double	37.00	42.00

Lunch available
Evening meal 1900 (last orders 2130)
Parking for 100
Cards accepted: Access, Visa

HOLMES CHAPEL

Cheshire
Map ref 4A2

Large village with some interesting 18th C buildings and St Luke's Church encased in brick hiding the 15th C original.

Chestnut Farm ⚊
Kermincham, Congleton CW12 2LJ
☎ Lower Withington (0477) 71281
17th C farmhouse set in beautiful Cheshire countryside. Comfortable accommodation with oak furniture and modern facilities.
Bedrooms: 1 single, 2 double, 1 twin, 1 triple
Bathrooms: 2 private, 1 public

Bed & breakfast

per night:	£min	£max
Single	25.00	30.00
Double	40.00	50.00

Half board

per person:	£min	£max
Daily	35.00	

Lunch available
Evening meal 1900 (last orders 2100)
Parking for 12

Tiree ⚊
Listed
5 Middlewich Road, Cranage, Holmes Chapel, Crewe CW4 8HG
☎ (0477) 33716
Modern house set in open country 3 miles from the M6 (junction 18) and close to the A50, 2 miles north of Holmes Chapel.
Bedrooms: 1 single, 1 double, 1 twin
Bathrooms: 1 public

Bed & breakfast

per night:	£min	£max
Single	14.00	14.00
Double	26.00	26.00

Parking for 4

HOOLE

Cheshire
Map ref 4A2

Devonia Guest House
33-35 Hoole Road, Hoole, Chester CH2 3NH
☎ Chester (0244) 322236
Small friendly guesthouse offering good home-cooking and personal attention. Satellite TV.
Bedrooms: 2 single, 2 double, 2 twin, 2 triple
Bathrooms: 3 public

Bed & breakfast

per night:	£min	£max
Single	17.50	22.50
Double	27.50	32.50

Half board

per person:	£min	£max
Daily	24.00	29.00

Evening meal 1800 (last orders 1600)
Parking for 14

The enquiry coupons at the back will help you when contacting proprietors.

HOYLAKE

Merseyside
Map ref 4A2

Once a major port, this residential resort has good beaches, a 4-mile promenade and nearby, the Royal Liverpool Golf Club. Variety of bird life on small offshore Hillbre Islands.

Green Lodge Hotel

👑👑 COMMENDED

2 Stanley Road, Hoylake, Wirral L47 1HW
☎ 051-632 2321
Fax 051-632 6871
Recently renovated public house and restaurant with five bedrooms all offering high standard facilities. Close to Hoylake Village and adjacent to Royal Liverpool Golf Club. Popular for golf holidays. Prices are per room.
Bedrooms: 3 double, 2 triple
Bathrooms: 5 private

Bed & breakfast
per night:	£min	£max
Single	34.50	34.50
Double	34.50	34.50

Lunch available
Evening meal 1730 (last orders 2130)
Parking for 40
Cards accepted: Access, Visa
☎🖭♨⌨ ♦ î S ⊞ 🖵 ※ ✕ 🖚

HYDE

Greater Manchester
Map ref 4B2

Needhams Farm ₥

👑👑 COMMENDED

Uplands Road, Werneth Low, Gee Cross, Hyde, Cheshire SK14 3AQ
☎ 061-368 4610
Fax 061-367 9106
30-acre beef farm. 500-year-old farmhouse with exposed beams in all rooms and an open fire in bar/dining room. Excellent views. Well placed for Manchester city and the airport.
Bedrooms: 1 single, 3 double, 1 twin, 1 triple
Bathrooms: 4 private, 1 public

Bed & breakfast
per night:	£min	£max
Single	18.00	22.00
Double	34.00	38.00

Half board
per person:	£min	£max
Daily	25.00	39.00

Lunch available
Evening meal 1900 (last orders 2130)
Parking for 10
Cards accepted: Access, Visa
☎🖭♨⌨ ♦ î S ※ ✕
🖵🖭 ♨⌨↻ ⇑ ✿ 🖚 OAP ♨ SP
🖚⊞

KNUTSFORD

Cheshire
Map ref 4A2

Derives its name from Canute, King of the Danes, said to have forded the local stream. Ancient and colourful May Day celebrations. Nearby is the Georgian mansion of Tatton Park.
Tourist Information Centre
☎ *(0565) 632611 or 632210*

Laburnum Cottage Guest House ₥

👑👑 HIGHLY COMMENDED

Knutsford Road, Mobberley, Knutsford WA16 7PU
☎ Mobberley (0565) 872464
Small country house set amidst Cheshire countryside on B5085 close to Tatton Park, 6 miles from Manchester Airport, 4 miles from Wilmslow, 4 miles from M6 exit 19 and 2 miles from M56. Pretty garden and log fires, taxi service to airport. Non-smokers only please.
Bedrooms: 2 single, 1 double, 2 twin
Bathrooms: 3 private, 1 public

Bed & breakfast
per night:	£min	£max
Single	25.00	30.00
Double	40.00	46.00

Evening meal from 1830
Parking for 8
☎🖭♨⌨↻ ♎ ⊞ î S ※ ✕
🖭🖵 ♨⌨↺ î ⌀▷✿ 🖚 OAP ▧ SP

Tattondale Farm ₥

Ashley Road, Knutsford WA16 6QJ
☎ (0565) 654692
500-acre arable farm. Farmhouse in the National Trust property of Tatton Park. Near Manchester Airport and junction 19 of M6.
Bedrooms: 1 single, 1 twin, 1 triple
Bathrooms: 1 private, 2 public

> Please mention this guide when making a booking.

Bed & breakfast
per night:	£min	£max
Single	17.50	25.00
Double	32.00	40.00

Parking for 3
☎※🗝⌨ î S ※ 🖚 ✿
🖚⊞

LANCASTER

Lancashire
Map ref 4A1

Interesting old county town on the River Lune with history dating back to Roman times. Norman castle, St Mary's Church, Customs House, City and Maritime Museums, Ashton Memorial and Butterfly House are among places of note. Good centre for touring the Lake District.
Tourist Information Centre
☎ *(0524) 32878.*

Lancaster Town House ₥

👑👑 COMMENDED

11 Newton Terrace, Caton Road, Lancaster LA1 3PB
☎ (0524) 65527
Ideal for touring the area, close to M6 motorway. Colour TV in all rooms. Full menu breakfast.
Bedrooms: 2 single, 3 double, 1 twin
Bathrooms: 6 private

Bed & breakfast
per night:	£min	£max
Single	20.00	22.00
Double	30.00	34.50

☎🖭♨ ⊞ î S ※ ✕ 🖵 ✕
🖚⊞

The Old Mill House

👑👑

Waggon Road, Lower Dolphinholme, Lancaster LA2 9AX
☎ Forton (0524) 791855
17th C mill house with extensive landscaped gardens on River Wyre. Private woodland and ponds, adjacent to Forest of Bowland. 5 minutes from junction 33 of M6.
Bedrooms: 2 double, 1 twin
Bathrooms: 1 private, 1 public

Bed & breakfast
per night:	£min	£max
Single	25.00	36.00
Double	35.00	46.00

Half board
per person:	£min	£max
Daily	35.50	47.50
Weekly	224.00	300.00

Evening meal 1900 (last orders 1200)
Parking for 5
☎🖭🗝♦î S ※ 🖵 🖭🖵.
🖚∪↻✿ 🖚 SP 🖚

LIVERPOOL

Merseyside
Map ref 4A2

Liverpool became a major port in the 18th C. Landmarks include 2 cathedrals, Town Hall, Walker Art Gallery, Merseyside Maritime Museum, excellent shopping centre, entertainment and sports facilities (Aintree Racecourse). Speke Hall (National Trust).
Tourist Information Centre
☎ *051-709 3631 or 708 8854*

Anna's

👑👑

65 Dudlow Lane, Calderstones, Liverpool L18 2EY
☎ 051-722 3708
Fax 051-722 8699
Large family house with friendly atmosphere, in select residential area close to all amenities. Direct transport routes to city centre. 1 mile from end of M62 motorway.
Bedrooms: 1 double, 3 twin
Bathrooms: 1 public

Bed & breakfast
per night:	£min	£max
Single	14.50	17.50
Double	28.00	30.00

Parking for 6
☎🖭♨î⊞ î S ※ 🖵 🖭🖵.
🖚 🖚

Glenavy

76 Beech Lane, Liverpool L18 3ER
☎ 051-724 1717
On A562 between Green Lane and Cromptons Lane. Spacious rooms, cosy and friendly. Non-smoking establishment.
Bedrooms: 1 single, 3 twin
Bathrooms: 1 public

Bed & breakfast
per night:	£min	£max
Single	16.50	
Double	33.00	

Parking for 8
🖵♦î ※ 🖵 🖭🖵. 🖚✕
🖚⊞

The Hollies

24 Sinclair Drive, Allerton, Liverpool L18 OHN
☎ 051-722 1183

Friendly accommodation in pleasant area. Direct route to M62, city and airport. Close to many amenities, Albert Dock, Penny Lane, university halls, colleges and local restaurants.
Bedrooms: 1 single, 1 double, 2 twin
Bathrooms: 1 public

Bed & breakfast

per night:	£min	£max
Single	16.00	18.00
Double	30.00	33.00

Parking for 2

Jamaica House Hotel
142 Upper Parliment Street, Liverpool L8 7LG
☎ 051-708 6881 & 255 0335
Minutes away from Albert Dock, Beatles Museum and cathedrals.
Bedrooms: 3 single, 8 double, 1 twin, 1 triple
Bathrooms: 4 public

Bed & breakfast

per night:	£min	£max
Single	15.00	30.00
Double	30.00	60.00

Half board

per person:	£min	£max
Daily	25.00	49.00
Weekly	105.00	210.00

Lunch available
Evening meal 1700 (last orders 2300)
Cards accepted: Access, Visa

Cheshire
Map ref 4B2

Former silk-manufacturing town with cobbled streets and picturesque cottages overlooking Bollin Valley. West Park Museum and Art Gallery and Gawsworth Hall are places of interest.
Tourist Information Centre
☎ (0625) 504114

The Old Vicarage
58 Blakelow Road, Macclesfield SK11 7ED
☎ (0625) 425575
Former Victorian vicarage, now family home offering guests privacy within a family atmosphere, in interesting surroundings. Plentiful home-cooking. Non-smokers only please.
Bedrooms: 1 twin, 1 multiple
Bathrooms: 1 public

Bed & breakfast

per night:	£min	£max
Single	14.50	14.50
Double	29.00	29.00

Half board

per person:	£min	£max
Daily	22.00	22.00
Weekly	132.00	132.00

Evening meal 1800 (last orders 2000)

Park Vale Guest House
252 Park Lane, Macclesfield SK11 8AA
☎ (0625) 500025
Beautifully appointed large town house convenient for town centre, M6 routes and Peak District National Park. We guarantee you will enjoy your stay.
Bedrooms: 1 single, 2 triple
Bathrooms: 2 public, 1 private shower

Bed & breakfast

per night:	£min	£max
Single	13.50	14.00
Double	27.00	28.00

Parking for 1

Sandpit Farm
Messuage Lane, Marton, Macclesfield SK11 9HS
☎ Marton Heath (0260) 224254
110-acre arable farm. Hot and cold water in single. Twin and double rooms en-suite. Convenient for stately homes and National Trust properties. Easy access to the Peak District, Chester and Manchester Airport. 4 miles north of Congleton and 1 mile west of the A34.
Bedrooms: 1 single, 1 double, 1 twin
Bathrooms: 2 private, 1 public

Bed & breakfast

per night:	£min	£max
Single	13.00	17.00
Double	26.00	34.00

Parking for 4

Cheshire
Map ref 4A2

Millhey Farm
Barton, Malpas SY14 7HY
☎ Tarvin (0829) 782 431

140-acre mixed farm. Typical, lovely Cheshire black and white part-timbered farmhouse in conservation area, 9 miles from Chester, close to Welsh Border country. On A534, just off A41.
Bedrooms: 1 double, 1 triple, 1 multiple
Bathrooms: 1 private, 1 public, 1 private shower

Bed & breakfast

per night:	£min	£max
Single		13.00
Double	24.00	24.00

Parking for 2

The Old Stables
Threapwood, Malpas SY14 7AN
☎ Threapwood (0948) 81249
Walled garden and patio. Rooms with abundant beams. Full-size snooker table. Off B5069 Malpas/Wrexham Road from Malpas (3miles) over Clwyd border. Turn left 100 yards into courtyard.
Bedrooms: 1 double, 1 twin
Bathrooms: 1 public

Bed & breakfast

per night:	£min	£max
Double	28.00	30.00

Parking for 6

Tilston Lodge

HIGHLY COMMENDED

Tilston, Malpas SY14 7DR
☎ Broxton (0829) 250223
12-acre livestock & poultry farm. Comfortable Victorian farmhouse in conservation village. Rare breed farm animals. Spacious, beautifully decorated rooms, friendly service. Ideal for Chester and North Wales.
Bedrooms: 1 single, 1 twin, 1 triple
Bathrooms: 2 private, 2 public, 1 private shower

Bed & breakfast

per night:	£min	£max
Single	15.50	25.00
Double	31.00	42.00

Evening meal from 1830
Parking for 10

National Crown ratings were correct at the time of going to press but are subject to change. Please check at the time of booking.

Greater Manchester
Map ref 4B1

The industrial capital of the North, second only to London as a commercial, financial, banking and newspaper centre. Victorian architecture. 15th C cathedral and the exciting Granada Studios Tour development. Superb shopping centre.
Tourist Information Centre
☎ 061-234 3157/3158 or 061-436 3344.

Ebor Hotel
402 Wilbraham Road, Chorlton-cum-Hardy, Manchester M21 1UH
☎ 061-881 1911 & 881 4855
Hotel offering comfortable accommodation and friendly service, within easy reach of airport, Manchester city centre and motorway network.
Bedrooms: 6 single, 3 double, 3 twin, 3 triple, 1 multiple
Bathrooms: 4 private, 3 public, 3 private showers

Bed & breakfast

per night:	£min	£max
Single	19.00	26.00
Double	31.00	36.00

Half board

per person:	£min	£max
Daily	24.50	31.50
Weekly	171.50	220.50

Lunch available
Evening meal 1830 (last orders 1700)
Parking for 20
Cards accepted: Access, Visa, Amex

Imperial Hotel
157 Hathersage Road, Manchester M13 0HY
☎ 061-225 6500
Fax 061-225 6500
Recently modernised and refurbished hotel. 1.25 miles south of city centre, in the vicinity of university and teaching hospitals.
Bedrooms: 13 single, 5 double, 9 twin
Bathrooms: 21 private, 3 public

Bed & breakfast

per night:	£min	£max
Single	30.00	36.00
Double	44.00	

Continued ▶

MANCHESTER

Continued

Half board
per person:	£min	£max
Daily	40.00	

Lunch available
Evening meal 1830 (last orders 2030)
Parking for 30
Cards accepted: Access, Visa, Diners, Amex

Hotel Montana ▲

59 Palatine Road, West Didsbury, Manchester M20 9LJ
☎ 061-445 6427
Small family hotel with pleasant atmosphere. English and continental food.
Bedrooms: 5 single, 7 double, 14 twin, 1 triple, 1 multiple
Bathrooms: 18 private, 3 public

Bed & breakfast
per night:	£min	£max
Single	20.00	26.00
Double	35.00	41.00

Half board
per person:	£min	£max
Daily	28.00	35.00
Weekly	196.00	245.00

Evening meal 1800 (last orders 2000)
Parking for 22
Cards accepted: Access, Diners

Parkside Guest House ▲

58 Cromwell Road, Off Edge Lane, Stretford, Manchester M32 8QJ
☎ 061-865 2860
Clean, friendly service in a quiet residential area, convenient for Old Trafford football and cricket ground, city centre M63 exit 7. Children over 7 welcome. Family rooms available.
Bedrooms: 3 single, 2 double, 2 twin, 1 multiple
Bathrooms: 6 private, 1 public

Bed & breakfast
per night:	£min	£max
Single	16.00	18.00
Double	29.00	31.00

Parking for 3

248 Upper Chorlton Road

Old Trafford, Manchester M16 0BJ
☎ 061-860 4908
Characteristic turn-of-the-century house. Bus route directly outside. Ideal for city centre and airport (15 minutes).
Bedrooms: 2 double, 2 twin, 1 triple
Bathrooms: 1 public, 1 private shower

Bed & breakfast
per night:	£min	£max
Single	13.00	15.00
Double	26.00	30.00

Half board
per person:	£min	£max
Daily	15.00	17.50
Weekly	90.00	105.00

Lunch available
Evening meal 1830 (last orders 1700)

MANCHESTER AIRPORT

See under Alderley Edge, Altrincham, Hyde, Knutsford, Manchester, Stockport, Wilmslow

MAWDESLEY

Lancashire
Map ref 4A1

Mawdsleys Eating House and Hotel

😊😊😊 COMMENDED

Hall Lane, Mawdesley, Ormskirk L40 2QZ
☎ Rufford (0704) 822552
Fax (0704) 822096
In the picturesque village of Mawdesley, voted "best kept village". Its peaceful setting will be appreciated by business people and pleasure travellers alike.
Bedrooms: 19 double, 1 twin, 5 triple
Bathrooms: 25 private

Bed & breakfast
per night:	£min	£max
Single	30.00	39.50
Double	40.00	49.50

Lunch available
Evening meal 1800 (last orders 2200)
Parking for 100
Cards accepted: Access, Visa, Amex

MIDDLEWICH

Cheshire
Map ref 4A2

Old Cheshire salt town thriving on an industry begun in Roman times. Stone Age tools and weapons and Roman pottery recently found in the area are on display in the town. Was one of the last outposts of bear-baiting in the country.

Forge Mill Farm

Warmingham, Middlewich CW10 OHQ
☎ Warmingham (027 077) 204
140-acre mixed farm. Spacious country house in peaceful location. Friendly welcome, comfort and hospitality assured. Good position for Manchester Airport and touring the North West. Close to exits 17 and 18 on the M6.
Bedrooms: 1 double, 1 twin
Bathrooms: 2 private, 1 public

Bed & breakfast
per night:	£min	£max
Single	15.00	17.00
Double	28.00	30.00

Parking for 9

MOBBERLEY

Cheshire
Map ref 4A2

The Hinton ▲

😊😊😊 COMMENDED

Town Lane, Mobberley, Knutsford WA16 7HH
☎ (0565) 873484
Bed and breakfast for both business and private guests. Within easy reach of M6, M56, Manchester Airport and InterCity rail network. Ideal touring base, on the B5085 between Knutsford and Wilmslow.
Bedrooms: 2 single, 2 double, 1 twin
Bathrooms: 3 private, 1 public

Bed & breakfast
per night:	£min	£max
Single	27.00	30.00
Double	45.00	48.00

Half board
per person:	£min	£max
Daily	35.00	38.00

Evening meal 1900 (last orders 2030)

Parking for 10
Cards accepted: Access, Visa, Diners

NANTWICH

Cheshire
Map ref 4A2

Old market town on the River Weaver made prosperous in Roman times by salt springs. Fire destroyed the town in 1583 and many buildings were rebuilt in Elizabethan style. Churche's Mansion (open to the public) survived the fire.
Tourist Information Centre
☎ *(0270) 623914*

Laburnum House Farm

Hearns Lane, Larden Green, Faddiley, Nantwich CW5 8JL
☎ Faddiley (0270) 74378
19-acre livestock farm. Lovely three-roomed suite with private balcony. Peace, privacy and a warm welcome guaranteed. Central for Chester and the Potteries.
Bedrooms: 1 double
Bathrooms: 1 private

Bed & breakfast
per night:	£min	£max
Single	30.00	33.00
Double	40.00	44.00

Parking for 4

Lea Farm

Wrinehill Road, Wybunbury, Nantwich CW5 7NS
☎ Crewe (0270) 841429
160-acre dairy farm. Charming farmhouse in beautiful gardens where peacocks roam. Comfortable lounge, pool/snooker, fishing pool. Ideal surroundings.
Bedrooms: 2 double, 1 triple
Bathrooms: 1 private, 1 public

Bed & breakfast
per night:	£min	£max
Single	13.00	16.00
Double	25.00	28.00

Half board
per person:	£min	£max
Daily	19.00	22.00
Weekly	130.00	140.00

Evening meal 1800 (last orders 1900)
Parking for 22
🐕🖵♿🎵🅿🛏🆂✂🎯📺🄿 🕛♪✓❄🛵

Poole Bank Farm
⚜⚜ COMMENDED
Poole, Nantwich CW5 6AL
☎ (0270) 625169
260-acre dairy farm. 17th C timbered farmhouse in delightful Cheshire countryside, close to the historic town of Nantwich.
Bedrooms: 2 double, 1 twin
Bathrooms: 1 private, 1 public
Bed & breakfast

per night:	£min	£max
Single	15.00	17.00
Double	25.00	30.00

Parking for 10
Cards accepted:
🐕🖵🛏♿🎵🅿🆂🄿❄✗ 🛵🎯

Red Cow ⚞⚟
Listed
45 Beam Street, Nantwich CW5 7NF
☎ (0270) 628581
Cottage with four letting bedrooms, adjoining 15th C timbered building. Real ale pub with inglenook fireplace.
Bedrooms: 2 single, 1 double, 1 twin
Bathrooms: 1 public
Bed & breakfast

per night:	£min	£max
Single	18.00	
Double	36.00	

Lunch available
Evening meal 1700 (last orders 2145)
Parking for 8
🐕🖵♿🛏🅿🆂🄿🛒❄🛵 🕸🆂🅿🎯

NORTHWICH

Cheshire
Map ref 4A2

An important salt-producing town since Roman times, Northwich has been replanned with a modern shopping centre and a number of black and white buildings. Unique Anderton boat-lift on northern outskirts of town.

Barratwich
Cuddington Lane, Cuddington, Northwich CW8 2SZ
☎ Sandiway (0606) 882412
Attractive cottage set in lovely countryside, yet only 1 mile from A49 and A556. Close to

Delamere Forest, 12 miles from Chester. Comfortable twin rooms.
Bedrooms: 2 twin
Bathrooms: 1 public
Bed & breakfast

per night:	£min	£max
Single	16.00	
Double	28.00	

Half board

per person:	£min	£max
Daily	23.00	

Evening meal 1900 (last orders 1400)
Parking for 4
🐕3🖵🛏♿🅿🆂🄿❄🕛 🛵🎯

Springfield Guest House ⚞⚟
⚜⚜ COMMENDED
Chester Road, Near Delamere, Oakmere, Northwich CW8 2HB
☎ Sandiway (0606) 882538
Family guesthouse erected in 1863. On A556 close to Delamere Forest, midway between Chester and M6 motorway junction 19. Manchester Airport 25 minutes' drive.
Bedrooms: 4 single, 1 double, 1 twin, 1 multiple
Bathrooms: 2 private, 1 public
Bed & breakfast

per night:	£min	£max
Single	19.50	19.50
Double	35.00	35.00

Evening meal 1800 (last orders 2000)
Parking for 12
🐕🖵♿🛏♿🅿🆂🄿📺❄✗ 🛵🎯

OLDHAM

Greater Manchester
Map ref 4B1

Large important textile town, boosted in 19th C by Arkwright's spinning-frame and Watt's steam engine. Outstanding watercolours in Art Gallery and impressive neo-classical Town Hall.
Tourist Information Centre
☎ *061-678 4654*

Boothstead Farm
Listed
Rochdale Road, Denshaw, Oldham OL3 5UE
☎ Saddleworth (0457) 878622 & 874369
200-acre livestock farm. 18th C farmhouse on fringe of Saddleworth (A640) between junctions 21 and 22 of M62 motorway.

Bedrooms: 1 double, 1 twin
Bathrooms: 1 public
Bed & breakfast

per night:	£min	£max
Single	17.00	19.00
Double	34.00	36.00

Parking for 4
🐕4🖵♿📺🛏✗🛵🎯

PRESTON

Lancashire
Map ref 4A1

Scene of decisive Royalist defeat by Cromwell in the Civil War and later of riots in the Industrial Revolution. Local history exhibited in Harris Museum.
Tourist Information Centre
☎ *(0772) 53731*

Brook House Guest House ⚞⚟
COMMENDED
544 Blackpool Road, Ashton, Preston PR2 1HY
☎ (0772) 728684
Detached property 10 minutes from town centre and on bus route. TV lounge, car park, tea/coffee facilities, some en-suite rooms.
Bedrooms: 2 single, 1 double, 1 twin
Bathrooms: 2 private, 1 public
Bed & breakfast

per night:	£min	£max
Single	16.50	27.50
Double	37.50	41.25

Half board

per person:	£min	£max
Daily	24.50	35.50
Weekly	171.50	248.50

Evening meal 1800 (last orders 1800)
Parking for 4
Cards accepted: Access, Visa
🐕🖵🛏♿🅿🆂✂🛵📺🄿🛏 ✗🛵🆂🅿

Olde Duncombe House ⚞⚟
⚜⚜⚜⚜ HIGHLY COMMENDED
Garstang Road, Bilsborrow, Preston PR3 0RE
☎ Brock (0995) 40336
In the beautiful Ribble Valley next to the Lancaster Canal, convenient for canal boat enthusiasts. 4 miles north of the M6 junction 32.
Bedrooms: 1 single, 5 double, 2 twin, 2 triple
Bathrooms: 10 private

Bed & breakfast

per night:	£min	£max
Single	29.50	39.50
Double	39.50	49.50

Lunch available
Evening meal 1800 (last orders 2030)
Parking for 12
Cards accepted: Access, Visa
🐕♿📞🖵🛏♿🆂🄿❄🅿 🛵🎯

Park Head Farm
Listed
Bilsborrow Lane, Inglewhite, Preston PR3 2LN
☎ Brock (0995) 40352
250-acre mixed & dairy farm. Old cottage-style farmhouse on a busy farm, but in a quiet position off the main road. Home-made cheese. Inglewhite is 7 miles north of Preston.
Bedrooms: 1 double, 1 twin, 1 triple
Bathrooms: 1 public
Bed & breakfast

per night:	£min	£max
Single	12.00	
Double	24.00	

Parking for 6
🐕🖵♿📺🛏🄿❄✗🛵

RIBBLE VALLEY

See under Chipping, Clitheroe, Dutton, Slaidburn, Whitewell

ROCHDALE

Greater Manchester
Map ref 4B1

Pennine mill town made prosperous by wool and later cotton- spinning, famous for the Co-operative Movement started in 1844 by a group of Rochdale working men. Birthplace of John Bright (Corn Law opponent) and more recently Gracie Fields. Roman & Bronze Age items in museum.
Tourist Information Centre
☎ *(0706) 356592*

Leaches Farm Bed and Breakfast ⚞⚟
Listed
Ashworth Valley, Rochdale, Lancashire OL11 5UN
☎ (0706) 41116/7 & 228520
140-acre livestock farm. 18th C Pennine hill farmhouse with panoramic views and

Continued ▶

ROCHDALE

Continued

moorland walks. 10 minutes from the M62/M66.
Bedrooms: 1 single, 1 double, 1 twin
Bathrooms: 1 public

Bed & breakfast

per night:	£min	£max
Single	18.00	
Double	32.00	

Parking for 6

SADDLEWORTH

Greater Manchester
Map ref 4B1

Area of outstanding countryside and expanse of moorland.
Tourist Information Centre
☎ *(045 787) 4093 or 0336*

Globe Farm Guest House

Huddersfield Road, Standedge, Delph, Oldham
OL3 5LU
☎ (0457) 873040
18-acre mixed farm. Quarter of a mile from the Pennine Way and high walking country. Bed and breakfast accommodation, 28-bed bunkhouse (self-catering or with meals) and small campsite.
Bedrooms: 2 single, 2 double, 1 twin, 1 triple
Bathrooms: 2 public

Bed & breakfast

per night:	£min	£max
Single	16.00	20.00
Double	32.00	

Half board

per person:	£min	£max
Daily	22.00	26.00

Evening meal 1830 (last orders 2000)
Parking for 7

National Crown ratings were correct at the time of going to press but are subject to change. Please check at the time of booking.

SANDBACH

Cheshire
Map ref 4A2

Small industrial town, originally important for salt production. Contains narrow, winding streets, timbered houses & a cobbled market-place. Town square has 2 Anglo-Saxon crosses to commemorate the conversion to Christianity of the king of Mercia's son.
Tourist Information Centre
☎ *(0270) 760460*

The Village Store

Listed COMMENDED
Hassall Green, Sandbach
CW11 0YB
☎ Crewe (0270) 762266
The house and shop, built circa 1777 at the side of Lock 57 on the Trent and Mersey Canal, have served canal users for over 200 years. Off A533 near Sandbach and junction 17 on M6 - signposted. Small marina, gift shop, tearooms and store.
Bedrooms: 2 single, 1 double, 1 twin
Bathrooms: 1 public

Bed & breakfast

per night:	£min	£max
Single	13.50	15.00
Double	27.00	30.00

Half board

per person:	£min	£max
Daily	21.00	26.00

Parking for 5
Cards accepted: Access, Visa

SHAVINGTON

Cheshire
Map ref 4B2

Oakland House

Listed
252 Newcastle Road, Blakelow, Nantwich
CW5 7ET
☎ Crewe (0270) 67134
Friendly welcome, home comforts, rural views. Superior accommodation at reasonable rates. On A500 (A52) 5 miles from M6 junction 16. Within easy reach of historic Nantwich and Chester, Stapeley Water Gardens and Bridgemere Garden World.
Bedrooms: 2 double, 1 twin
Bathrooms: 1 private, 3 public

Bed & breakfast

per night:	£min	£max
Single	18.00	
Double	30.00	

Parking for 10

SINGLETON

Lancashire
Map ref 4A1

Ancient parish dating from 1175, mentioned in Domesday Book. Chapel and day school dating back to 1865. Mainly rural area to the north of St Anne's.

Old Castle Farm

Listed APPROVED
Garstang Road, Singleton, Blackpool FY6 8ND
☎ Poulton-le-Fylde (0253) 883839
Take junction 3 off M55, follow Fleetwood sign to first traffic lights. Turn right, travel 200 yards on A586 to bungalow.
Bedrooms: 1 double, 1 twin, 1 triple
Bathrooms: 1 public

Bed & breakfast

per night:	£min	£max
Single	15.00	
Double	30.00	

Parking for 20
Open April-October

SLAIDBURN

Lancashire
Map ref 4A1

Picturesque grey-stone village set in moorland region of the Forest of Bowland, with 13th C church, old grammar school, village green and war memorial.

Gold Hill Farmhouse Hotel

COMMENDED
Woodhouse Lane, Slaidburn, Clitheroe BB7 3AH
☎ (020 06) 202
150-acre livestock farm. Family-run licensed 17th C country house with log fires, minstrels' gallery and accent on cooking. Breathtaking views and sporting rights. 1 mile from Slaidburn.
Bedrooms: 1 double, 1 twin, 1 triple
Bathrooms: 3 private

Bed & breakfast

per night:	£min	£max
Single	22.00	22.00
Double	44.00	44.00

Half board

per person:	£min	£max
Daily	32.00	

Lunch available
Evening meal 1900 (last orders 2200)
Parking for 20
Cards accepted: Access, Visa

SOUTHPORT

Merseyside
Map ref 4A1

Pleasant resort noted for its gardens, long sandy beach and many golf-courses, particularly Royal Birkdale. Southport Flower Show is an annual event. Atkinson Art Gallery and Steamport Transport Museum are attractions.
Tourist Information Centre
☎ *(0704) 533333.*

Dukes Folly Hotel

11 Duke Street, Southport
PR8 1LS
☎ (0704) 533355
Fax (0704) 530065
Licensed family-run hotel noted for its high standards and friendly atmosphere. On the corner of Duke Street and Lord Street and within easy reach of all local amenities.
Bedrooms: 5 single, 4 double, 9 twin, 1 triple
Bathrooms: 19 private

Bed & breakfast

per night:	£min	£max
Single	32.50	42.50
Double	50.00	60.00

Half board

per person:	£min	£max
Daily	43.00	53.00
Weekly	250.00	275.00

Evening meal 1800 (last orders 2050)
Parking for 10
Cards accepted: Access, Visa, Amex

Sandy Brook Farm

52 Wyke Cop Road, Scarisbrick, Southport
PR8 5LR
☎ Scarisbrick (0704) 880337
27-acre arable farm. Small comfortable farmhouse in

rural area of Scarisbrick,
offering a friendly welcome.
3.5 miles from seaside town
of Southport.
Bedrooms: 1 double, 3 twin,
1 triple, 1 multiple
Bathrooms: 6 private

Bed & breakfast

per night:	£min	£max
Single	17.50	17.50
Double	28.00	28.00

Parking for 9

🛏🕹🖵💺🖵🆔Ⓢ📺🖩🖴
🐾🖗

ST MICHAEL'S ON WYRE

Lancashire
Map ref 4A1

Village near Blackpool
with interesting 13th C
church of St Michael
containing medieval
stained glass window
depicting sheep shearing,
and clock tower bell
made in 1548.

Compton House ▲▲
☖☖ COMMENDED

Garstang Road, St Michael's
on Wyre, Preston PR3 0TE
☎ (0995) 8378
*Well-furnished country house
in own grounds in a
picturesque village, near M6
and 40 minutes from Lake
District. Fishing in the Wyre.
Antique restoration/
reproduction of furniture
undertaken on the premises.*
Bedrooms: 1 single,
1 double, 2 twin
Bathrooms: 4 private

Bed & breakfast

per night:	£min	£max
Single	15.00	17.50
Double	30.00	35.00

Parking for 6

🛏🕹🖵💺🐾🆔Ⓢ📺
🖩🖴🗝🖗

Individual
proprietors have
supplied all details
of accommodation.
Although we do
check for accuracy,
we advise you to
confirm the
information at the
time of booking.

STOCKPORT

Greater Manchester
Map ref 4B2

Former market town on
the River Mersey, built by
Cheshire gentry, became
an important cotton-
spinning and railway
centre. Town has an
impressive railway viaduct
and shopping precinct
covering the Mersey.
Lyme Hall & Vernon Park
Museum nearby.
*Tourist Information Centre
☎ 061-474 3320/3321.*

35 Corbar Road
Stockport, Cheshire
SK2 6EP
☎ 061-483 4000
*Edwardian house set in a
large garden in a quiet,
residential area close to bus,
rail stations and airport. All
home cooking. Tea/coffee
making. German and some
French spoken. Non-smokers
only please.*
Bedrooms: 1 double, 1 twin
Bathrooms: 1 public

Bed & breakfast

per night:	£min	£max
Single	15.00	18.00
Double	28.00	34.00

Evening meal 1700 (last
orders 1930)
Parking for 3

🛏🕹🖵💺🆔Ⓢ🖦🖴📺🖩🖴
🐾🖗

Shire Cottage ▲▲
☖☖ COMMENDED

Benches Lane, Chisworth,
Broadbottom, Hyde, Cheshire
SK14 6RY
☎ Glossop (0457) 866536
*180-acre mixed farm.
Opposite Woodheys
Restaurant off the A626
Stockport to Glossop road,
close to the Peak District,
Buxton, Derwent Dams and
Kinder Scout. 20 minutes
from the airport, 16 miles
from Manchester city centre.
Swimming, horse riding,
fishing and boating nearby.*
Bedrooms: 1 single,
1 double, 1 twin, 1 triple
Bathrooms: 2 private,
2 public

Bed & breakfast

per night:	£min	£max
Single	16.00	18.00
Double	30.00	34.00

Parking for 7

🛏🖗🐾🖦🆔Ⓢ📺🖩🖴
🖴🗝🖗 OAP 🖴 SP

Waterfall Farm Cottage ▲▲
☖☖ COMMENDED

7 Motcombe Grove, Gatley,
Cheadle, Cheshire SK8 3TL
☎ 061-436 4732
*Large private bungalow in
secluded, gladed setting, 5
minutes from Manchester
Airport. Under personal
supervision of resident
owners.*
Bedrooms: 1 double, 1 twin
Bathrooms: 2 private,
1 public

Bed & breakfast

per night:	£min	£max
Single	25.00	30.00
Double	30.00	35.00

Evening meal 1900 (last
orders 2100)
Parking for 5
Cards accepted: Amex

🛏🖦🖤🖵💺🆔Ⓢ🖦
📺🖴🖴🗝🖗🖗

TATTENHALL

Cheshire
Map ref 4A2

Newton Hall
☖☖

Tattenhall, Chester CH3 9AY
☎ (0829) 70153
*140-acre dairy farm. Bed and
breakfast accommodation in
17th C oak-beamed
farmhouse, 6 miles from
Chester off A41. Lovely
gardens, views of Beeston and
Peckforton castles.*
Bedrooms: 1 double, 1 twin
Bathrooms: 2 private

Bed & breakfast

per night:	£min	£max
Single		20.00
Double	30.00	35.00

Parking for 2

🛏🖗💺🖦🗡🖤📺🖩🖴🗝🖗

WEETON

Lancashire
Map ref 4A1

Agricultural area to the
north-west of Kirkham.
Church dated 1843. Large
army camp in parish.

High Moor Farm
Singleton Road, Weeton,
Preston PR4 3JJ
☎ Blackpool (0253) 836273
*Centrally-heated double and
family rooms, with colour TV
and tea-making facilities.
Reductions for children under
12. 6 miles from Blackpool.*
Bedrooms: 1 double, 1 triple
Bathrooms: 1 public

Bed & breakfast

per night:	£min	£max
Double	24.00	30.00

Parking for 12

🛏🖤🖵💺🆔Ⓢ🖗📺🖩🖴
🖴🗝🖗🖗

Swarbrick Hall Farm
☖☖

Singleton Road, Weeton,
Preston PR4 3JJ
☎ Blackpool (0253) 836465
*200-acre mixed farm.
Georgian farmhouse built in
1802, nestling in beautiful
rural countryside of
Lancashire.*
Bedrooms: 1 multiple
Bathrooms: 1 private

Bed & breakfast

per night:	£min	£max
Single	15.00	20.00
Double	30.00	36.00

Parking for 5

🛏🖵🖗🐾🆔Ⓢ🖦🖴🖴🖤🖵
🗡🖗🖗🖗🖴🖗

WHITEWELL

Lancashire
Map ref 4A1

Locally known as "Little
Switzerland" for the
beauty of the wooded
valley of the River
Hodder.

Inn at Whitewell ▲▲
☖☖☖ COMMENDED

Forest of Bowland,
Whitewell, Clitheroe
BB7 3AT
☎ Dunsop Bridge (020 08)
222
*Property dating back in part
to 14th C in beautiful river
setting. Furnished with
genuine antiques. Log fires.*
Bedrooms: 3 double, 3 twin,
3 triple
Bathrooms: 9 private

Bed & breakfast

per night:	£min	£max
Single	46.00	
Double	60.00	

Lunch available
Evening meal 1930 (last
orders 2130)
Parking for 50
Cards accepted: Access, Visa,
Diners, Amex

🛏🖵🖤🖦🖵🆔Ⓢ🖩🖴
🖴🖤🗡🖤🖗

The colour maps
at the back of this
guide pinpoint all
places with
accommodation.

WILMSLOW

Cheshire
Map ref 4B2

This residential suburb of Manchester is on the River Bollin and bordered on 3 sides by open country.

St. Martins
35 Hawthorn Lane,
Wilmslow SK9 5DD
☎ (0625) 535499
Attractive Victorian family guesthouse, with full modern amenities and comfort. Close to town centre. Airport transport available on request. Car parking facilities.
Bedrooms: 1 single, 1 twin
Bathrooms: 1 public

Bed & breakfast per night:	£min	£max
Single	27.00	34.00
Double	46.00	59.00

Half board per person:	£min	£max
Daily	36.50	43.50
Weekly	201.63	236.67

Evening meal 1900 (last orders 2100)
Parking for 7
🛏 🍴 ⑪ Ⓢ 🅿 📺 ▥ 🐾 ✿ ✈ 🚲

WIRRAL

Merseyside

See under Birkenhead, Hoylake

Use your *i*'s

Tourist information

There are more than 600 Tourist Information Centres throughout England offering friendly help with accommodation and holiday ideas as well as suggestions of places to visit and things to do.

In your home town there may be a centre which can help you before you set out. You'll find the address of your nearest Tourist Information Centre in your local Phone Book.

THE CROWN IS YOUR SURE SIGN OF WHERE TO STAY

HOTELS, GUESTHOUSES, INNS, B&Bs & FARMHOUSES

Throughout Britain, the tourist boards now inspect over 17,000 hotels, guesthouses, inns, B&Bs and farmhouses, every year, to help you find the ones that suit you best.

THE CLASSIFICATIONS: '**Listed**', and then **ONE to FIVE CROWN,** tell you the range of facilities and services you can expect. The more Crowns, the wider the range.

THE GRADES: **APPROVED, COMMENDED, HIGHLY COMMENDED and DE LUXE,** where they appear, indicate the quality standard provided. If no grade is shown, you can still expect a high standard of cleanliness.

Every classified place to stay has a Fire Certificate, where this is required under the Fire Precautions Act, and all carry Public Liability Insurance.

'**Listed**': Clean and comfortable accommodation, but the range of facilities and services may be limited.

ONE CROWN: Accommodation with additional facilities, including washbasins in all bedrooms, a lounge and use of a phone.

TWO CROWN: A wider range of facilities and services, including morning tea and calls, bedside lights, colour TV in lounge or bedrooms, assistance with luggage.

THREE CROWN: At least one-third of the bedrooms with ensuite WC and bath or shower, plus easy chair, full length mirror. Shoe cleaning facilities and hairdryers available. Hot evening meals available.

FOUR CROWN: At least three-quarters of the bedrooms with ensuite WC and bath/shower plus colour TV, radio and phone, 24-hour access and lounge service until midnight. Last orders for meals 8.30 pm or later.

FIVE CROWN: All bedrooms having WC, bath and shower ensuite, plus a wide range of facilities and services, including room service, all-night lounge service and laundry service. Restaurant open for breakfast, lunch and dinner.

Every Crown classified place to stay is likely to provide some of the facilities and services of a higher classification. More information available from any Tourist Information Centre.

We've checked them out before you check in!

Yorkshire & Humberside

Spectacular countryside, a glorious coastline, historic cities, picturesque villages, stately homes and castles add up to a wealth of delights in Yorkshire and Humberside. Sample the bustling resorts of Scarborough and Whitby, where Captain Cook learned to sail, marvel at the glories of York's Gothic Minster and explore the city's many museums, learn about

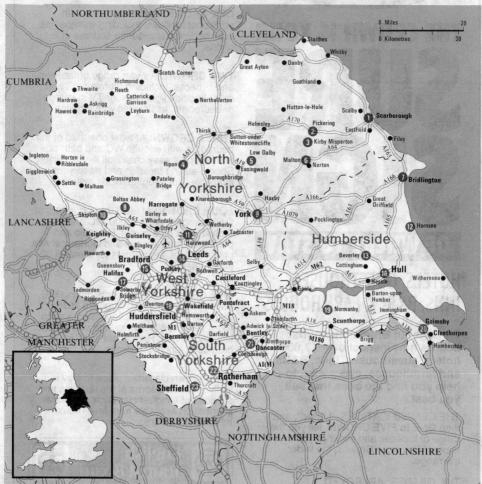

Use the above map to locate places in the "Where to Go, What to See" section opposite.
Use the colour maps at the back of this guide to find places with accommodation.

Grimsby's fishing heritage, be tempted by the sophisticated shopping centres of Leeds, Halifax and Harrogate, with its lovely Valley Gardens. The region's two national parks – Yorkshire Dales and North York Moors – with their lonely, wild scenery, and the gentler, softer countryside of the Wolds add even more variety to this region of riches.

WHERE TO GO, WHAT TO SEE

The number against each name will help you locate it on the map opposite.

❶ Sea Life Centre
Scarborough, North Yorkshire YO12 6RP
Tel: Scarborough (0723) 376125
An opportunity to meet creatures that live in and around the oceans of the British Isles.

❷ North Yorkshire Moors Railway
Pickering Station, Pickering, North Yorkshire YO18 7AJ
Tel: Pickering (0751) 72508
18-mile railway through the national park. Steam and diesel trains.

❸ Flamingo Land Zoo and Funpark
Kirby Misperton, Malton, North Yorkshire YO17 0UX
Tel: Kirby Misperton (065 386) 287
One-price family funpark, with over 100 free attractions including 9 shows and Europe's largest privately-owned zoo. Large lake, children's and thrill rides.

❹ Fountains Abbey and Studley Royal Park
Ripon, North Yorkshire HG4 3DZ
Tel: Sawley (0765) 620333
Largest monastic ruin in Britain, founded by Cistercian monks in 1132. Landscaped garden laid out 1720–40 with lake, formal watergarden and temples, deer park.

❺ Dalby Forest Drive and Visitor Centre
Low Dalby, Pickering, North Yorkshire YO18 7LS
Tel: Pickering (0751) 60295
9-mile scenic drive with car parks, picnic areas, waymarked walks (2–7 miles). Visitor centre with forestry exhibition and audio-visual facility.

❻ Castle Howard
Malton, North Yorkshire YO6 7DA
Tel: Coneysthorpe (065 384) 333
Set in 1,000 acres of parkland with nature walks, scenic lake and stunning rose gardens. Important furniture and works of art.

❻ Eden Camp Modern History Theme Museum
Malton, North Yorkshire YO17 0SD
Tel: Malton (0653) 697777
Modern history theme museum depicting civilian way of life in Britain during World War II. Based in a genuine ex-PoW camp with original buildings.

❼ Bridlington Leisure World
The Promenade, Bridlington, Humberside YO15 2QQ
Tel: Bridlington (0262) 606715
Wave pool, adult and junior pools. Multi-purpose hall with indoor bowling area, entertainment centre, club, disco.

❽ Bolton Priory
Bolton Abbey, Skipton, North Yorkshire BD23 6EX
Tel: Bolton Abbey (0756) 710533
Ruins of 12th C priory in park

Anne, Emily and Charlotte – Yorkshire's own Brontë sisters

setting by River Wharfe. Tea shops, nature trails, fishing, fell walking and picturesque countryside.

❾ Jorvik Viking Centre
Coppergate, York, North Yorkshire YO1 1NT
Tel: York (0904) 643211
Visitors travel in electric cars down a time tunnel to a re-creation of Viking York. Excavated remains of Viking houses and display of objects found.

❾ National Railway Museum
Leeman Road, York, North Yorkshire YO2 4XJ
Tel: York (0904) 621261
Collection of locomotives and carriages with displays depicting the technical, social and economic development of Britain's railway heritage.

Above the town of Whitby in North Yorkshire, on the high headland over the River Esk, stand the ruins of Whitby Abbey, with a history dating from the 7th century, when it was home to Caedmon, the earliest-known English poet

⑭ Tropical World
Canal Gardens, Roundhay Park, Leeds, West Yorkshire LS8 1DF
Tel: Leeds (0532) 661850
Greenhouses, temperate house, butterfly house, tropical house, Jungle Experience, aquaria, insects, fish, streams, waterfalls.

⑨ York Castle Museum
The Eye of York, York, North Yorkshire YO1 1RY
Tel: York (0904) 653611
Museum of everyday life with reconstructed streets and period rooms. Edwardian park, costume and jewellery, arms and armour, craft workshops.

⑩ Skipton Castle
Skipton, North Yorkshire BD23 1AQ
Tel: Skipton (0756) 792442
One of the most complete and best preserved medieval castles in England. Conduit Court with famous yew.

⑪ Harewood House
Harewood, Leeds, West Yorkshire LS17 9LQ
Tel: Harewood (0532) 886225
18th C Carr/Adam house, Capability Brown landscape. Fine Sevres and Chinese porcelain, English and Italian paintings, Chippendale furniture. Exotic bird garden.

⑫ Hornsea Pottery
Hornsea, Humberside HU18 1UD
Tel: Hornsea (0964) 534211
Pottery factory in landscaped parkland. Shops, playground and fort, playbus, birds of prey, butterfly farm, mini dale farm, model village, Yorkshire car collection.

⑬ Museum of Army Transport
Beverley, Humberside HU17 ONG
Tel: Hull (0482) 860445
Army road, rail, sea and air exhibits excitingly displayed in two exhibition halls, plus the huge, last remaining Blackburn Beverley aircraft. Gulf exhibition.

⑭ Leeds City Art Gallery and Henry Moore Centre
The Headrow, Leeds, West Yorkshire LS1 3AA
Tel: Leeds (0532) 462495
19th and 20th C paintings, sculptures, prints and drawings. Permanent collection of 20th C sculpture in Henry Moore Centre.

⑮ National Museum of Photography, Film and Television
Prince's View, Bradford, West Yorkshire BD5 0TR
Tel: Bradford (0274) 727488
The largest cinema screen (Imax) in Britain. Kodak Museum. Fly on a magic carpet, operate TV camera, become a newsreader for a day.

⑯ Hull and East Riding Museum
High Street, Hull, Humberside
Tel: Hull (0482) 593902
Humberside archaeology. Iron Age Hasholme boat and chariot burials, magnificent display of Romano-British mosaics.

⑰ Eureka!
Discovery Road, Halifax, West Yorkshire HX1 2NE
Tel: Halifax (0422) 330069
Eureka! is a new concept in children's museums, designed specifically for children aged 5 to 12 and accompanying adults.

Yorkshire & Humberside

⑰ Piece Hall
Halifax, West Yorkshire HX1 1RE
Tel: Halifax (0422) 358087
Historic colonnaded cloth hall surrounding open-air courtyard, comprising 50 shops, art gallery, museum.

⑱ Yorkshire Mining Museum
Caphouse Colliery, New Road, Overton, Wakefield, West Yorkshire WF4 4RH
Tel: Wakefield (0924) 848806
Exciting award-winning museum of the Yorkshire coalfield, including guided underground tour of authentic old workings.

⑲ Normanby Hall
Normanby, Humberside DN15 9HU
Tel: Scunthorpe (0724) 720588
Regency mansion by Sir Robert Smirke, architect of British Museum. Furnished and decorated in period, with displays of costume.

⑳ National Fishing Heritage Centre
Alexandra Dock, Grimsby, Humberside DN31 1UF
Tel: Grimsby (0472) 344867
Spectacular 1950s steam trawler experience. See, hear, smell and touch a series of re-created environments. Museum displays, aquarium, shop.

㉑ Cusworth Hall Museum of South Yorkshire Life
Cusworth Lane, Doncaster, South Yorkshire DN5 7TU
Tel: Doncaster (0302) 782342
Georgian mansion in landscaped park containing Museum of South Yorkshire Life. Special educational facilities.

㉒ Thrybergh Country Park
Doncaster Road, Thrybergh, Rotherham, South Yorkshire S65 4NU
Tel: Rotherham (0709) 850353
63-acre country park, including 35-acre lake. Fly fishing, sailing, windsurfing, canoeing, picnic area.

㉓ Abbeydale Industrial Hamlet
Abbeydale Road South, Sheffield, South Yorkshire S7 2QW
Tel: Sheffield (0742) 367731
Working museum. Water powered scythe works, steel furnaces and workers' furnished houses.

㉔ Rother Valley Country Park
Mansfield Road, Wales Bar, Sheffield, South Yorkshire S31 8PE
Tel: Sheffield (0742) 471452
Country park with canoes, sailboards, rowing boats and sailing dinghies for hire. Nature reserve, visitor and craft centres, fishing, ski slope.

㉕ Sheffield City Museum
Weston Park, Sheffield, South Yorkshire S10 2TP
Tel: Sheffield (0742) 768588
World-famous cutlery, old Sheffield plate, ceramics, glass, clocks, archaeology, wildlife.

Golcar, West Yorkshire boasts a fine fish & chip shop serving Yorkshire's favourite fare

Places to stay

Accommodation entries in this regional section are listed in alphabetical order of place name, and then in alphabetical order of establishment.

The map references refer to the colour maps at the back of the guide. The first figure is the map number; the letter and figure which follow indicate the grid reference on the map.

The symbols at the end of each accommodation entry give information about services and facilities. A 'key' to these symbols is inside the back cover flap, which can be kept open for easy reference.

ASKRIGG

North Yorkshire
Map ref 5B3

The name of this Dales village means 'ash tree ridge'. It is centred on a steep main street of high, narrow 3-storey houses and thrived on cotton and later wool in 18th C. Once famous for its clock making.

Countersett Hall

👑👑 COMMENDED

Countersett, Askrigg, Leyburn DL8 3DD
☎ Wensleydale (0969) 50373

Peaceful and welcoming 17th C yeoman's farmhouse close to Semerwater, the largest natural lake in Yorkshire. Ideal centre for exploring the Dales. Wonderful scenery. Walk out of our door straight on to the hills. Delicious traditional or vegetarian meals.

Bedrooms: 1 single, 2 double, 1 twin
Bathrooms: 1 private, 2 public

Bed & breakfast per night:	£min	£max
Single	16.00	18.00
Double	32.00	48.00

Half board per person:	£min	£max
Daily	29.00	31.00

Evening meal 1930 (last orders 1700)
Parking for 6
Open March-October
10 [S] [TV] 12 [SP]

Home Farm

[Listed] HIGHLY COMMENDED

Stalling Busk, Askrigg, Leyburn DL8 3DH
☎ Wensleydale (0969) 50360

65-acre mixed farm. Licensed 17th C beamed, dales farmhouse with log fires, beautiful Victorian and antique furnishings, brass bedsteads and patchwork quilts. Traditional cooking and home-made bread.

Bedrooms: 3 double
Bathrooms: 2 public

Bed & breakfast per night:	£min	£max
Single	20.00	20.00
Double	28.00	32.00

Half board per person:	£min	£max
Daily	23.50	25.50

Evening meal 1900 (last orders 2100)
Parking for 4
[S] [TV] [OAP] [SP]

Milton House

👑👑

Askrigg, Leyburn DL8 3HJ
☎ Wensleydale (0969) 50217

Large, comfortable, family house in a beautiful dales village, central for touring or walking. Colour TV lounge and wholesome Yorkshire cooking.

Bedrooms: 1 double, 1 twin, 1 triple
Bathrooms: 2 private, 1 public

Bed & breakfast per night:	£min	£max
Double	28.00	33.00

Evening meal 1900 (last orders 1900)
Parking for 3
[UL] [TV]

Semergarth

[Listed]

Worton, Askrigg, Leyburn DL8 3EU
☎ Wensleydale (0969) 50244

Stone-built house just off the A684. An ideal centre for walking and touring the dales. Warm welcome, comfortable accommodation, log fire and an evening drink.

Bedrooms: 1 single, 1 double, 1 twin
Bathrooms: 1 public

Bed & breakfast per night:	£min	£max
Single	13.50	14.00
Double	27.00	28.00

Parking for 2
[UL] [S] [TV]

Thornsgill Guest House

👑👑 COMMENDED

Moor Road, Askrigg, Leyburn DL8 3HH
☎ Wensleydale (0969) 50617

Spacious, early 20th C family house in the Yorkshire Dales National Park. En-suite bedrooms. Wholesome Yorkshire food. Relaxed friendly atmosphere.

Bedrooms: 2 double, 1 twin
Bathrooms: 3 private

Bed & breakfast per night:	£min	£max
Double	35.00	

Half board per person:	£min	£max
Daily	28.00	

Evening meal from 1830
Parking for 3
8 [S] [TV]

AYSGARTH

North Yorkshire
Map ref 5B3

Famous for its beautiful Falls - a series of 3 cascades extending for half a mile on the River Ure in Wensleydale. There is a coach and carriage museum with a crafts centre at Old Yore Mill and a National Park Centre.

Low Gill Farm

Aysgarth, Leyburn DL8 3AL
☎ Wensledydale (0969) 663554

700-acre dairy & livestock farm. Family farm, with scenic views of Wensleydale. One mile between Aysgarth

and Thornton Rust on a quiet country lane. Ideal for walking and touring.
Bedrooms: 1 double, 1 multiple
Bathrooms: 1 public

Bed & breakfast per night:	£min	£max
Double	24.00	28.00

Lunch available
Parking for 3
Open March-October

Marlbeck
Listed
Aysgarth, Leyburn DL8 3AH
☎ Wensleydale (0969) 663610
Located in Wensleydale in the beautiful Yorkshire Dales National Park, a short walk from Aysgarth's limestone falls. Cafes, post office and public houses in the village.
Bedrooms: 1 twin, 1 triple
Bathrooms: 1 public

Bed & breakfast per night:	£min	£max
Single	15.00	17.00
Double	26.00	26.00

Open April-October

There are separate sections in this guide listing groups specialising in farm holidays and accommodation which is especially suitable for young people and organised groups.

BAINBRIDGE
North Yorkshire
Map ref 5B3

This Wensleydale grey-stone village, with fine views of the River Bain, reputedly England's shortest river, was once a Roman settlement, some of it still visible. Boating and water-skiing on nearby Semerwater. Ancient foresters' custom of hornblowing still continues.

Mrs M Iveson
Listed APPROVED
High Force Farm, Bainbridge, Leyburn DL8 3DL
☎ Wensleydale (0969) 50379
470-acre hill farm. Warm, spacious farmhouse used in the James Herriot TV series, close to Semerwater Lake.
Bedrooms: 2 triple
Bathrooms: 2 public

Bed & breakfast per night:	£min	£max
Single	13.00	14.00
Double	25.00	28.00

Parking for 3

BALK
North Yorkshire
Map ref 5C3

Barley Garth
Listed COMMENDED
Balk, Thirsk YO7 2AJ
☎ Thirsk (0845) 597524
Georgian house in a hamlet between Thirsk and the North York Moors National Park.
Bedrooms: 1 double, 1 twin, 1 triple
Bathrooms: 1 private, 1 public, 1 private shower

Bed & breakfast per night:	£min	£max
Single	15.00	18.00
Double	22.00	35.00

Parking for 3

BARNETBY
Humberside
Map ref 4C1

Holcombe House
APPROVED
34 Victoria Road, Barnetby, South Humberside DN38 6JR
☎ (0652) 680655
Pleasant, homely accommodation in centre of Barnetby village. 5 minutes from M180 and railway station, 3 miles from Humberside Airport, 15-30 minutes from Grimsby, Scunthorpe and Hull.
Bedrooms: 2 single, 1 double, 1 triple
Bathrooms: 1 private, 1 public

Bed & breakfast per night:	£min	£max
Single	15.00	15.00
Double	25.00	30.00

Parking for 4

Individual proprietors have supplied all details of accommodation. Although we do check for accuracy, we advise you to confirm the information at the time of booking.

BEDALE
North Yorkshire
Map ref 5C3

Ancient church of St. Gregory and Georgian Bedale Hall occupy commanding positions over this market town situated in good hunting country. The Hall, which contains interesting architectural features including great ballroom and flying-type staircase, now houses a library and museum.

Elmfield House
Arrathorne, Bedale DL8 1NE
☎ (0677) 50558
Country house in its own grounds with open views of the countryside. Special emphasis on standards and home cooking. Solarium.
Bedrooms: 4 double, 3 twin, 2 triple
Bathrooms: 9 private

Bed & breakfast per night:	£min	£max
Single	25.00	27.00
Double	38.00	44.00

Evening meal from 1900
Parking for 10
Cards accepted: Access, Visa

Southfield
96 Southend, Bedale DL8 2DS
☎ (0677) 423510
House with garden in quiet rural town, 3 minutes' walk to shopping area. Free supper provided.
Bedrooms: 1 single, 1 double, 1 twin, 1 triple
Bathrooms: 1 public

Continued ►

BEDALE
Continued

Bed & breakfast

per night:	£min	£max
Single	14.00	14.00
Double	28.00	28.00

Parking for 4

🐕🖐🔆Ⓤ🅰Ⓢ🅜📺▥.◨ 🐾🦽

BEVERLEY
Humberside
Map ref 4C1

Beverley's most famous landmark is its beautiful medieval Minster with Percy family tomb. Many attractive squares and streets, notably Wednesday and Saturday Market, North Bar Gateway and the Museum of Army Transport, Flemingate. Famous racecourse.
Tourist Information Centre
☎ *(0482) 867430*

Eastgate Guest House ⋀
COMMENDED
7 Eastgate, Beverley, North Humberside HU17 0DR
☎ Hull (0482) 868464
Family-run Victorian guesthouse, established and run by the same proprietor for 25 years. Close to the town centre, Beverley Minster, Museum of Army Transport and railway station.
Bedrooms: 5 single, 5 double, 4 twin, 4 triple
Bathrooms: 5 private, 3 public
Bed & breakfast

per night:	£min	£max
Single	16.50	30.00
Double	26.00	44.00

🐕🖐Ⓤ🅢🔆🅜📺▥.◨
ⒹⒶⓅ 🆂🅿

Northumbria Bed and Breakfast
Listed
13 The Croft, Molescroft, Beverley, North Humberside HU17 7HT
☎ Hull (0482) 872254
Five bedroomed, detached house with large gardens in a quiet residential area, about a mile from town centre.
Bedrooms: 1 double, 1 twin
Bathrooms: 1 private, 1 public

Bed & breakfast

per night:	£min	£max
Single	16.00	18.00
Double	26.00	28.00

Evening meal 1800 (last orders 2100)
Parking for 2
▢🖐Ⓤ🅰Ⓢ🔆▥.◨✿✕
ⒹⒶⓅ

Rudstone Walk Farm, Country House and Conference Centre ⋀
Listed **HIGHLY COMMENDED**
South Cave, Beverley, North Humberside HU15 2AH
☎ North Cave (0430) 422230
303-acre arable farm. Architect-designed en-suite rooms with breakfast in historic farmhouse, mentioned in the Domesday Book. Ideal location for Beverley, York, coast and moors.
Bedrooms: 1 single, 8 double, 8 twin, 1 triple
Bathrooms: 15 private, 2 public
Bed & breakfast

per night:	£min	£max
Single	21.00	35.00
Double	37.00	50.00

Half board

per person:	£min	£max
Daily	30.00	50.00

Evening meal 1900 (last orders 1600)
Parking for 10
Cards accepted: Amex
🐕🖾🐎🖐🅢🅜📺▥.◨🔍
▶✦🐾🦽🎏
[Ad] Display advertisement appears on page 111

BINGLEY
West Yorkshire
Map ref 4B1

Bingley Five-Rise is an impressive group of locks on the Leeds and Liverpool Canal. Town claims to have first bred the Airedale terrier originally used for otter hunting. Among fine Georgian houses is Myrtle Grove where John Wesley stayed. East Riddlesden Hall is nearby.

4 Crosley View
Gilstead, Bingley BD16 4QZ
☎ Bradford (0274) 567270
Private house with letting rooms. TV, shower, central heating.
Bedrooms: 1 single, 1 double
Bathrooms: 1 public

Bed & breakfast

per night:	£min	£max
Single	10.00	12.00
Double	20.00	24.00

🐕5▥🖐🅜📺▥.◨✕🎏

Ashley End
Listed
22 Ashley Road, Off Ashfield Crescent, Bingley BD16 1DZ
☎ Bradford (0274) 569679
Private house just off the main Bradford/Leeds road into Bingley. 5 minutes' walk to Bingley and 10 minutes' walk to the station. Twin room and single room have a wash basin.
Bedrooms: 1 single, 2 twin
Bathrooms: 1 public
Bed & breakfast

per night:	£min	£max
Single	13.50	14.00
Double	27.00	28.00

🐕Ⓤ🅜🔆📺▥.🎏

Oakwood Hall Hotel
Lady Lane, Bingley BD16 4AW
☎ Bradford (0274) 564123 & 563569
Fax (0274) 561477
Impressive listed building with easy access to Leeds, Bradford and Keighley. Small conferences and private parties a speciality.
Bedrooms: 2 single, 10 double, 4 twin
Bathrooms: 16 private
Bed & breakfast

per night:	£min	£max
Single	55.00	75.00
Double	70.00	90.00

Lunch available
Evening meal 1930 (last orders 2130)
Parking for 120
Cards accepted: Access, Visa, Diners, Amex
🐕🖾🐎🖐🆑❑🖐🍴Ⓢ🅜
◉▥.◨🍴10-50✿🆂🅿🎏

BISHOP THORNTON
North Yorkshire
Map ref 5C3

Small village in Nidderdale, near Brimham Rocks.

Hatton House Farm
HIGHLY COMMENDED
Bishop Thornton, Harrogate HG3 3JA
☎ Harrogate (0423) 770315
150-acre dairy & livestock farm. Farmhouse accommodation with special emphasis on well-presented, home-cooked food. Open all year round. No smoking indoors, please.
Bedrooms: 1 single, 2 double, 1 twin
Bathrooms: 1 public
Bed & breakfast

per night:	£min	£max
Single	17.00	18.00
Double	34.00	36.00

Half board

per person:	£min	£max
Daily	25.00	26.00
Weekly	150.00	160.00

Evening meal 1830 (last orders 1800)
Parking for 10
🐕Ⓤ🅰Ⓢ🔆🅜📺▥.◨ꓴ✿
🐾🎏

Raventofts Head House ⋀
🍴🍴🍴
Watergate Road, Bishop Thornton, Harrogate HG3 3JZ
☎ Ripon (0765) 620279
17-acre beef farm. Fully-modernised, stone-built farmhouse providing comfortable and inviting accommodation with a warm welcome. Picturesque countryside near places of historic interest. Evening meal by request only. Tea/coffee available at any time free of charge. Babies welcome.
Bedrooms: 1 single, 1 double, 1 twin
Bathrooms: 1 private, 1 public
Bed & breakfast

per night:	£min	£max
Single	15.00	15.00
Double	24.00	26.00

Half board

per person:	£min	£max
Daily	19.00	20.00
Weekly	129.50	

Evening meal 1900 (last orders 2000)
Parking for 8
🐕8🖐Ⓤ🅜📺▥.◨ꓴ✿
🐾🎏

BISHOP WILTON
Humberside
Map ref 4CI

Fleece Inn
🍴🍴
Bishop Wilton, York YO4 1RU
☎ (075 96) 251
Country inn in an unspoilt village at the foot of the wolds. A free house offering a variety of real ales, traditional meals and fine wines. Most

bedrooms have tea and coffee making facilities.
Bedrooms: 2 single, 3 double, 1 twin, 1 triple
Bathrooms: 4 private, 1 public
Bed & breakfast

per night:	£min	£max
Single	20.00	30.00
Double	40.00	60.00

Evening meal 1900 (last orders 2130)
Parking for 20
🛏🚭🐕📺▥✕

BOLTON ABBEY

North Yorkshire
Map ref 4B1

This hamlet is best known for its priory situated near a bend in the River Wharfe. It was founded in 1151 by Alicia de Romilly and before that was site of Anglo-Saxon manor. Popular with painters, amongst them Landseer.

Howgill Lodge Barn
Howgill Lodge, Barden, Bolton Abbey, Skipton BD23 6DJ
☎ Burnsall (0756) 720655
17th C barn, tastefully converted in 1986. Ideal for a peaceful, relaxing break, away from the crowds. A special corner of Wharfedale.
Bedrooms: 2 double, 1 twin, 1 triple
Bathrooms: 4 private
Bed & breakfast

per night:	£min	£max
Double	44.00	50.00

Parking for 4
🛏🚭🖴🐕▥✕🍴🏠

BOROUGHBRIDGE

North Yorkshire
Map ref 5C3

On the River Ure, Boroughbridge was once an important coaching centre with 22 inns and in the 18th C a port for Knaresborough's linens. It has fine old houses, many trees and a cobbled square with market cross. Nearby stand 3 megaliths known as the Devil's Arrows.

Treble Sykes Farm
Listed
Helperby, York YO6 2SB
☎ (0423) 360667
400-acre arable farm. Peaceful location with panoramic view over the Vale of York.

Centrally situated for visits to all parts of North Yorkshire. 4 miles from A1.
Bedrooms: 2 twin
Bathrooms: 2 public
Bed & breakfast

per night:	£min	£max
Single	14.00	15.00
Double	26.00	28.00

Parking for 10
Open March-October
🛏🚭🖴▥📺▥.🗗∪⊁
❄🏠

Windmill House ⋈
Ripon Road, Kirby Hill, Boroughbridge, York YO5 9DP
☎ (0423) 323255
Country house and windmill set in 2 acres, in rural location only half-a-mile from A1.
Bedrooms: 2 double, 1 twin
Bathrooms: 1 private, 1 public
Bed & breakfast

per night:	£min	£max
Double	32.00	36.00

Parking for 23
🛏🐕▥🖴📺▥.❄⊁🏠
🏠🗂

BRADFORD

West Yorkshire
Map ref 4B1

City founded on wool, with fine Victorian and modern buildings. Attractions include the cathedral, city hall, Cartwright Hall, Lister Park, Moorside Mills Industrial Museum and National Museum of Photography, Film and Television.
Tourist Information Centre ☎ (0274) 753678

Brow Top Farm ⋈
🏵🏵 COMMENDED
Baldwin Lane, Clayton, Bradford BD14 6PS
☎ (0274) 882178
300-acre mixed farm. Newly renovated farmhouse.
Bedrooms: 1 double, 1 twin, 1 triple
Bathrooms: 3 private
Bed & breakfast

per night:	£min	£max
Single	17.00	20.00
Double	28.00	30.00

Parking for 4
🛏🗗🐕🖴▥📺▥.🗗❄
⊁🏠

Carlton House Guest House
Listed APPROVED
Thornton Road, Thornton, Bradford BD13 3QE
☎ (0274) 833397
Detached, Victorian house in open countryside between the Bronte villages of Thornton and Haworth.
Bedrooms: 1 double, 1 twin, 1 triple
Bathrooms: 2 private, 1 public, 1 private shower
Bed & breakfast

per night:	£min	£max
Single	16.00	17.00
Double	26.00	27.00

Parking for 6
🛏🗗🐕▥🛁🗒▥.🗗❄⊁🏠

Carnoustie
🏵
8 Park Grove, Frizinghall, Bradford BD9 4JY
☎ (0274) 490561
Detached Victorian house 1.75 miles from Bradford city centre, close to Lister Park. En-suite rooms.
Bedrooms: 2 twin
Bathrooms: 2 private
Bed & breakfast

per night:	£min	£max
Single	18.00	19.00
Double	29.00	30.00

Parking for 2
🛏🗗🐕▥🗒▥.⊁🏠🗂

Ivy Guest House ⋈
Listed
3 Melbourne Place, Bradford BD5 0HZ
☎ (0274) 727060
Large, detached, listed house built of Bradford stone. Car park and gardens. Close to city centre, National Museum of Photography, Film and Television and Alhambra Theatre.
Bedrooms: 4 single, 2 double, 5 twin, 1 triple
Bathrooms: 3 public
Bed & breakfast

per night:	£min	£max
Single	20.00	20.00
Double	30.00	30.00

Half board

per person:	£min	£max
Daily	20.00	25.00

Lunch available
Evening meal 1800 (last orders 2000)
Parking for 12
Cards accepted: Access, Visa
🛏🗗🖴🐕▥🛁🗒📺▥.
🗗🍴⊁🖴 OAP 🏠🗂

New Beehive Inn ⋈
🏵🏵🏵
171 Westgate, Bradford BD1 3AA
☎ (0274) 721784
Edwardian gaslit oak-panelled inn, full of character, close to centre of Bradford. Antique furniture and individually-furnished bedrooms.
Bedrooms: 2 single, 2 double, 1 twin, 2 multiple
Bathrooms: 7 private
Bed & breakfast

per night:	£min	£max
Single	22.00	28.00
Double	38.00	44.00

Half board

per person:	£min	£max
Daily	30.00	36.00

Lunch available
Evening meal 1900 (last orders 1900)
Parking for 22
Cards accepted: Visa
🛏🗗🐕🖴🗒📺◑🥤⊁
🏠 OAP SP 🏠

BRIGG

Humberside
Map ref 4C1

Small town at an ancient crossing of the River Ancholme, granted a weekly Thursday market and annual horsefair by Henry III in 1235.
Tourist Information Centre ☎ (0652) 57053.

Arties Mill ⋈
🏵🏵 APPROVED
Wressle Road, Castlethorpe, Brigg, South Humberside DN20 9LF
☎ (0652) 652094 & 657107
Situated close to A18 between Brigg and Scunthorpe. Restaurant and bar meals available. Private functions, weddings. Motel and lodge adjacent to the mill.
Bedrooms: 2 single, 3 double, 11 twin, 1 triple
Bathrooms: 12 private, 1 public
Bed & breakfast

per night:	£min	£max
Single	25.00	39.50
Double	39.00	55.00

Half board

per person:	£min	£max
Daily	35.00	49.50

Continued ▶

We advise you to confirm your booking in writing.

BRIGG

Continued

Evening meal 1830 (last orders 2200)
Parking for 100
Cards accepted: Access, Visa, Diners, Amex
🎰🍴🛒🖵♿🅿🕭📺🛁 ♨🍽
✿✕🐾🏨

BROUGH

Humberside
Map ref 4C1

Langtry Lodge ♨
HIGHLY COMMENDED

Mill Lane West, Cave Road, Brough, North Humberside HU15 1HG
☎ Hull (0482) 667337
Country house located in large landscaped gardens, just off the A63 signposted for Brough.
Bedrooms: 2 twin
Bathrooms: 2 private
Bed & breakfast

per night:	£min	£max
Single	30.00	35.00
Double	40.00	50.00

Half board

per person:	£min	£max
Daily	30.00	36.00

Lunch available
Evening meal 1700 (last orders 2100)
Parking for 11
Cards accepted: Access, Visa
🎰📭🛒♿🕯🖎🆂🅼📺🖵
🅿🍴🔍🔍🖰📶✿✕🐾🎖🆂🅿

BULMER

North Yorkshire
Map ref 5C3

Grange Farm
Listed

Bulmer, York YO6 7BN
☎ Whitwell-on-the-Hill (065 381) 376
400-acre arable & dairy farm. Family-run, part of the Castle Howard ("Brideshead") estate. Ideally located for exploring North Yorkshire or just relaxing.
Bedrooms: 1 single, 1 double, 1 twin
Bathrooms: 1 public
Bed & breakfast

per night:	£min	£max
Single	12.50	
Double	25.00	

Open April-October
🎰🐾♿🆄🅻🆂🖎🅼📺🛁♨🍴
🍵🐾

CARLTON

North Yorkshire
Map ref 5B3

Cover Lea ♨
Listed APPROVED

Carlton, Leyburn DL8 4AY
☎ Wensleydale (0969) 40248
30-acre mixed farm. Victorian former farmhouse in a picturesque village in Coverdale. Traditional English breakfast.
Bedrooms: 2 double
Bathrooms: 1 public
Bed & breakfast

per night:	£min	£max
Single	12.00	12.00
Double	23.00	24.00

Parking for 2
Open February-October
🎰🐾5🛁🆄🅻🅼📺🖵🖑∪🐾

CLAPHAM

North Yorkshire
Map ref 5B3

Neat village of grey-stone houses and whitewashed cottages; a pot-holing centre. Upstream are Ingleborough Cave and Gaping Gill with its huge underground chamber. National Park Centre.

Arbutus House ♨
COMMENDED

Riverside, Clapham, Lancaster LA2 8DS
☎ Bentham (052 42) 51240
Family-run guesthouse offering home cooking and a friendly atmosphere. Ideal for touring, walking and relaxing.
Bedrooms: 2 double, 2 twin, 1 triple
Bathrooms: 3 private, 1 public
Bed & breakfast

per night:	£min	£max
Single	19.50	22.50
Double	33.00	39.00

Half board

per person:	£min	£max
Daily	25.50	28.50
Weekly	155.50	176.50

Evening meal 1830 (last orders 1200)
Parking for 6
Open February-November
🎰🐾🖵♿🆄🅻🖎🍴🅼🖵▶✕🐾

The enquiry coupons at the back will help you when contacting proprietors.

CLOUGHTON

North Yorkshire
Map ref 5D3

Village close to the east coast and North York Moors.

Gowland Farm ♨
Listed

Gowland Lane, Cloughton, Scarborough YO13 0DU
☎ Scarborough (0723) 870924
In a quiet, peaceful location with superb views. 2 miles north of Cloughton on the A171 take a sharp left turn on to an unmarked road and house is half a mile down on the left.
Bedrooms: 1 single, 1 double, 1 twin
Bathrooms: 1 public
Bed & breakfast

per night:	£min	£max
Single	13.00	13.00
Double	26.00	26.00

Half board

per person:	£min	£max
Daily	19.00	19.00
Weekly	125.00	125.00

Evening meal 1900 (last orders 2000)
Parking for 8
Open April-October
🎰🐾♿🆄🅼📺🖵♨🍴✿✕
🐾🆂🅿

COXWOLD

North Yorkshire
Map ref 5C3

This well-known beauty spot in Hambleton and Howardian Hills is famous as home of Laurence Sterne, the 18th C country parson and author of 'Tristram Shandy' books who, in 1760, lived at Shandy Hall, now open to the public.

Wakendale House ♨
COMMENDED

Oldstead Grange, Coxwold, York YO6 4BJ
☎ (034 76) 351
160-acre mixed farm. Comfortable accommodation with a friendly family in an attractive farmhouse set in lovely countryside. No smoking in the house.
Bedrooms: 1 double, 1 twin, 1 triple
Bathrooms: 1 public

Bed & breakfast

per night:	£min	£max
Double	28.00	

Parking for 5
Open February-November
🎰🆄🅻🖎📺🖵♨🍴✕🐾

CRAKEHALL

North Yorkshire
Map ref 5C3

Waterside ♨
COMMENDED

Glenaire, Crakehall, Bedale DL8 1HS
☎ Bedale (0677) 422908
Spacious, modern house with 1 acre of mature gardens and a trout stream. Central for the Yorkshire Dales and Moors, the gateway to Herriot country. All rooms have private facilities.
Bedrooms: 2 double, 1 twin, 1 triple
Bathrooms: 4 private, 1 public
Bed & breakfast

per night:	£min	£max
Double	36.00	40.00

Half board

per person:	£min	£max
Daily	48.00	52.00

Evening meal from 1900
Parking for 5
🎰🐾5🖵♿🆄🅻🆂🖎🅼📺🖵 🅿✿✕🐾🖑🅾🆂🅿

DANBY

North Yorkshire
Map ref 5C3

Rowantree Farm

Ainthorpe, Danby, Whitby YO21 2LE
☎ Guisborough (0287) 660396
120-acre mixed farm. Panoramic moorland views and ample car parking facilities, on the outskirts of Danby village. Home cooking.
Bedrooms: 1 single, 1 twin, 1 triple
Bathrooms: 1 public
Bed & breakfast

per night:	£min	£max
Single	11.00	11.00
Double	22.00	22.00

Half board

per person:	£min	£max
Daily	17.50	17.50
Weekly	120.00	120.00

Evening meal 1830 (last orders 1700)
Parking for 6
Open March-November
🎰🐾♿🆄🅻🖎🆂📺🖵♨🍴🐾

DONCASTER

South Yorkshire
Map ref 4C1

Ancient Roman town famous for its heavy industries, butterscotch and race-course (St Leger), also centre of agricultural area. Attractions include 18th C Mansion House, Cusworth Hall Museum, Doncaster Museum, St George's Church, The Dome and Doncaster Leisure Park. *Tourist Information Centre* ☎ *(0302) 734309.*

Canda ⋀
☺☺☺ COMMENDED
Hampole Balk Lane, 5 Lane Ends, Skellow, Doncaster DN6 8LF
☎ (0302) 724028
Charming guesthouse with 6 ground floor bedrooms. Situated close to A1 and ideal for those travelling north/ south. Non-smokers only please.
Bedrooms: 2 single, 3 double, 2 twin, 1 triple
Bathrooms: 4 private, 2 public
Bed & breakfast per night: £min £max
Single 22.00 25.00
Double 32.00 36.00
Parking for 6
Cards accepted: Access, Visa
icons

EASINGWOLD

North Yorkshire
Map ref 5C3

Market town of charm and character with a cobbled square and many fine Georgian buildings.

Alderside
Thirsk Road, Easingwold, York YO6 3HS
☎ (0347) 22132
Comfortable, Edwardian, former school house in large private gardens on the edge of a small market town. Easy access to York and countryside via the A19.
Bedrooms: 2 double
Bathrooms: 2 private
Bed & breakfast per night: £min £max
Double 25.00 32.00
Parking for 6
Open April-October
icons

Station Hotel ⋀
☺☺☺ APPROVED
Knott Lane, Raskelf Road, Easingwold, York YO6 3NT
☎ (0347) 22635
Fax (0347) 23491
Historic Victorian remains of Britain's shortest standard gauge railway. A la carte restaurant. Real ales and foreign beers. Ideal touring base for York, dales and moors.
Bedrooms: 3 double, 3 twin, 1 multiple
Bathrooms: 7 private
Bed & breakfast per night: £min £max
Single 27.00 27.00
Double 44.00 44.00
Lunch available
Evening meal 1800 (last orders 2130)
Parking for 11
Cards accepted: Access, Visa
icons

ELLERBY

North Yorkshire
Map ref 5C3

Ellerby Hotel ⋀
☺☺☺ COMMENDED
Ellerby, Saltburn-by-the-Sea, Cleveland TS13 5LP
☎ Whitby (0947) 840342
Residential country inn within the North York Moors National Park, 9 miles north of Whitby, 1 mile inland from Runswick Bay.
Bedrooms: 7 double, 2 triple
Bathrooms: 9 private
Bed & breakfast per night: £min £max
Single 27.00 32.00
Double 35.00 46.00
Lunch available
Evening meal 1900 (last orders 2200)
Parking for 60
Cards accepted: Access, Visa, Switch
icons

FLAXTON

North Yorkshire
Map ref 5C3

Attractive village with broad greens, just west of the A64 York to Malton highway.

Grange Farm
☺
The Grange, Oak Busk Lane, Flaxton, York YO6 7RL
☎ (090 486) 219

130-acre arable & livestock farm. South-facing, modernised farmhouse in its own gardens. 8 miles from York, off the A64 York to Scarborough road, through Flaxton village and right down Oak Busk Lane.
Bedrooms: 1 double, 1 twin, 1 triple
Bathrooms: 1 private, 2 public
Bed & breakfast per night: £min £max
Single 12.00 15.00
Double 24.00 30.00
Parking for 10
icons

GARGRAVE

North Yorkshire
Map ref 4B1

Unspoilt Dales village in the Aire gap, where the River Aire meanders by the roadside. Interesting church and the most northerly section of the Leeds and Liverpool Canal.

Eshton Grange
Gargrave, Skipton BD23 3QE
☎ Skipton (0756) 749383
20-acre livestock farm. 18th C listed farmhouse and Shetland pony stud, 1 mile from the Pennine Way, close to many beauty spots and James Herriot country. Evening meal by arrangement on Friday, Saturday and Sunday only.
Bedrooms: 1 double, 2 twin, 1 triple
Bathrooms: 4 private
Bed & breakfast per night: £min £max
Single 20.00 22.00
Double 40.00 40.00
Half board per person: £min £max
Daily 28.00 32.00
Evening meal 1900 (last orders 2000)
Parking for 12
icons

National Crown ratings were correct at the time of going to press but are subject to change. Please check at the time of booking.

GIGGLESWICK

North Yorkshire
Map ref 5B3

Picturesque Pennine village of period stone cottages with ancient market cross, stocks and tithe barn. Parish church is dedicated to St Alkeda, an Anglo-Saxon saint. During restoration work the tomb of a 15th C knight with his horse was discovered.

The Old Station ⋀
☺☺☺ COMMENDED
Brackenber Lane, Giggleswick, Settle BD24 OEA
☎ Settle (0729) 823623 & 823623
Traditional dales inn on A65 Settle/Giggleswick bypass. Comfortably furnished en-suite rooms. Ideal touring base for the dales and lakes. Families welcome.
Bedrooms: 4 double, 3 twin, 1 triple
Bathrooms: 8 private
Bed & breakfast per night: £min £max
Single 32.50 35.00
Double 52.00 61.00
Lunch available
Evening meal 1900 (last orders 2130)
Parking for 40
Cards accepted: Access, Visa
icons

GILLAMOOR

North Yorkshire
Map ref 5C3

Village much admired by photographers for its views of Farndale, including 'Surprise View' from the churchyard.

Royal Oak Inn ⋀
☺☺☺ COMMENDED
Gillamoor, York YO6 6HX
☎ Kirkbymoorside (0751) 31414
Old country inn on the edge of the North York Moors. Tastefully renovated, with plenty of character and charm. Open log fires.
Bedrooms: 5 double, 1 twin
Bathrooms: 6 private
Continued ▶

115

GILLAMOOR

Continued

Bed & breakfast

per night:	£min	£max
Single	25.00	27.00
Double	40.00	44.00

Evening meal 1900 (last orders 2130)
Parking for 9
♿🍴🖥♥♨🛏Ⓢ⟋▥☓🛆
🆂 🔥

GLAISDALE

North Yorkshire
Map ref 5C3

Set in a wooded valley with the 350-year-old shingle stone arch 'Beggars Bridge' spanning the River Esk. Often described as the "Queen of the dales", central for the North York Moors National Park and close to Whitby. Numerous lovely walks and bridle paths.

Red House Farm
Glaisdale, Whitby YO21 2PZ
☎ Whitby (0947) 87242
6-acre smallholding. 240-year-old, renovated, listed Georgian farmhouse with lovely views of the dale. Friendly farm animals, duckpond. Half a mile from village and on the Coast-to-Coast walk.
Bedrooms: 1 single, 1 double, 1 triple
Bathrooms: 2 private
Bed & breakfast

per night:	£min	£max
Single	16.50	18.00
Double	33.00	38.00

Parking for 4
🛆6🍴🖥♥♨🛏♥⟋▥🛆
U❄🚲🆂🔥

> There are separate sections in this guide listing groups specialising in farm holidays and accommodation which is especially suitable for young people and organised groups.

GOATHLAND

North Yorkshire
Map ref 5D3

Spacious village has several large greens grazed by sheep and is an ideal centre for walking North York Moors. Nearby are several waterfalls, among them Mallyan Spout. Plough Monday celebrations held in January.

Dale End Farm
Green End, Goathland, Whitby YO22 5LJ
☎ Whitby (0947) 85371
140-acre mixed farm. Moorland farmhouse built in 1720 and retaining much of its character, including oak beams and log fires. Home cooking. We have many repeat bookings. Pets and children welcome.
Bedrooms: 1 double, 2 triple
Bathrooms: 1 public
Bed & breakfast

per night:	£min	£max
Single	12.00	13.00
Double	24.00	26.00

Half board

per person:	£min	£max
Daily	18.00	19.00

Evening meal from 1745
Parking for 4
🛆Ⓜ♨♥♨▥🛏Ⓜ▥🛆U
🚲ⓄⒶⓅ🆂🔥

GOLCAR

West Yorkshire
Map ref 4B1

14 Grandstand
Scapegoat Hill, Golcar, Huddersfield HD7 4NQ
☎ Huddersfield (0484) 658342
Yorkshire stone-built cottage in quiet Pennine village. Panoramic views. Spacious, comfortable rooms with double glazing, central heating and colour TV. Warm welcome assured.
Bedrooms: 2 double
Bathrooms: 2 public
Bed & breakfast

per night:	£min	£max
Single	14.00	
Double	28.00	

Half board

per person:	£min	£max
Daily	20.00	

Evening meal from 1800
Parking for 2
🛆🍴🖥♥🏠♨▥🛏Ⓢ📺▥
🛆🚲

GRASSINGTON

North Yorkshire
Map ref 5B3

Tourists visit this former lead-mining village to see its 'smiddy', antique and craft shops and Upper Wharfedale Museum of Country Trades. Popular with fishermen and walkers. Numerous prehistoric sites. Grassington Feast in October. National Park Centre.

Franor House
👑👑
3 Wharfeside Avenue, Threshfield, Skipton BD23 5BS
☎ (0756) 752115
Large semi-detached house in quiet surroundings. Take B6265 from Skipton, turning right into Grassington. Wharfeside Avenue is half a mile - first turning on left.
Bedrooms: 1 single, 1 twin, 1 triple
Bathrooms: 3 private
Bed & breakfast

per night:	£min	£max
Single	15.00	
Double	30.00	

Parking for 4
🛆🍴♥♨🛏Ⓢ🅟▥🛆U♪
❄☓🚲

Grange Cottage M
👑👑 HIGHLY COMMENDED
Linton, Skipton BD23 5HH
☎ (0756) 752527
Stone-built cottage with open fires and warm hospitality. In a quiet backwater of a picture postcard village, perfect for hiking and car touring in the dales.
Bedrooms: 1 double, 1 twin
Bathrooms: 1 public, 1 private shower
Bed & breakfast

per night:	£min	£max
Single	20.00	
Double	30.00	

Parking for 4
Open March-October
🛆🍴♥♨Ⓢ⟋🅟📺▥
❄🚲

New Laithe House
Wood Lane, Grassington, Skipton BD23 5LU
☎ (0756) 752764
Large detached house, converted from a barn, on the edge of the village. Magnificent views of the River Wharfe.
Bedrooms: 3 double, 2 twin, 2 triple

Bathrooms: 3 private, 1 public, 2 private showers
Bed & breakfast

per night:	£min	£max
Double	34.00	40.00

Parking for 8
🛆♿🖥♥♨🛏Ⓢ▥🛆❄☓
🚲🆂

GREAT AYTON

North Yorkshire
Map ref 5C3

Village famous for its strong connections with Captain Cook. His family are buried in the graveyard and there is the Captain Cook Schoolroom Museum.

Petch's
👑👑 APPROVED
1 Park Rise, Great Ayton, Middlesbrough, Cleveland TS9 6ND
☎ (0642) 722436
Pleasant, modern dormer bungalow, opposite the Captain Cook museum. Tea and home-made cake served on arrival, light supper in the evening.
Bedrooms: 1 twin, 1 triple
Bathrooms: 2 private
Bed & breakfast

per night:	£min	£max
Single	13.00	14.00
Double	22.00	24.00

Parking for 2
🛆3♿🖥Ⓢ🅟📺🛆
☓🚲

GREAT LANGTON

North Yorkshire
Map ref 5C3

Hill House Farm Bed & Breakfast
Little Langton, Northallerton DL7 0PZ
☎ Northallerton (0609) 772605
20-acre mixed farm. Working farm providing afternoon teas. Scenic views, close to the Coast to Coast Walk.
Bedrooms: 1 double, 1 twin
Bathrooms: 1 public
Bed & breakfast

per night:	£min	£max
Single	12.50	15.00
Double	25.00	30.00

Parking for 8
Open March-November
🛆♨♥♨🛏Ⓢ⟋🅟📺🛆
❄☓🚲🆂

GREEN HAMMERTON

North Yorkshire
Map ref 4C1

Bay Horse Inn ⚑
COMMENDED

York Road, Green
Hammerton, York YO5 8BN
☎ Boroughbridge (0423)
330338 & 331113
Fax (0423) 331279
*Village inn 10 miles from
York and Harrogate on the
A59 and 3 miles off the A1.*
Bedrooms: 2 single,
3 double, 4 twin, 1 triple
Bathrooms: 10 private
Bed & breakfast

per night:	£min	£max
Single	30.00	30.00
Double	45.00	45.00

Lunch available
Evening meal 1900 (last
orders 2200)
Parking for 40
Cards accepted: Access, Visa,
Diners

GREWELTHORPE

North Yorkshire
Map ref 5C3

On the edge of
Grewelthorpe Moor,
enhanced by the village
pond, with a well-
established craft industry
using hand-spun wool of
Jacob Sheep reared
locally.

Hackfall Inn
Main Street, Grewelthorpe,
Ripon HG4 3BW
☎ Kirkby Malzeard (0765)
658239
*Wensleydale inn, near
Hackfall Woods, Lightwater
Valley and Fountains Abbey.
Traditional ale, home-cooked
food and friendly atmosphere.*
Bedrooms: 1 double, 2 twin,
2 triple
Bathrooms: 5 private
Bed & breakfast

per night:	£min	£max
Single	25.00	27.50
Double	35.00	45.00

Lunch available
Evening meal 1900 (last
orders 2200)
Parking for 20

> Please check prices
> and other details at
> the time of booking.

HALIFAX

West Yorkshire
Map ref 4B1

Founded on the cloth
trade, and famous for its
building society, textiles,
carpets and toffee. Most
notable landmark is Piece
Hall where wool
merchants traded, now
restored to house shops,
museums and art gallery.
*Tourist Information Centre
☎ (0422) 386725*

Beech Court
Listed

40 Prescott Street, Halifax
HX1 2QW
☎ (0422) 366004
*Late Victorian residence, just
off the town centre. Furnished
and decorated with emphasis
on standards.*
Bedrooms: 1 single,
1 double, 1 triple
Bathrooms: 2 public
Bed & breakfast

per night:	£min	£max
Single	15.00	16.00
Double	30.00	32.00

Parking for 3

The Elms
⚑

Keighley Road, Illingworth,
Halifax HX2 8HT
☎ (0422) 244430
*Victorian residence with
gardens and original ornate
ceilings, within 3 miles of
Halifax.*
Bedrooms: 2 single,
1 double, 1 triple
Bathrooms: 2 private,
1 public
Bed & breakfast

per night:	£min	£max
Single	16.00	18.00
Double	32.00	36.00

Half board

per person:	£min	£max
Daily	23.00	25.00

Evening meal 1800 (last
orders 2000)
Parking for 14

The Hobbit ⚑
COMMENDED

Hob Lane, Norland, Sowerby
Bridge HX6 3QL
☎ (0422) 832202
Fax (0422) 835381
*Country hotel with panoramic
views. Restaurant and Bistro
has reputation for good food
at affordable prices. Friendly
inn-type atmosphere.*

Bedrooms: 3 single,
11 double, 6 twin, 2 triple
Bathrooms: 22 private
Bed & breakfast

per night:	£min	£max
Single	27.00	45.00
Double	40.00	68.00

Half board

per person:	£min	£max
Daily	31.00	45.00

Lunch available
Evening meal 1700 (last
orders 2300)
Parking for 100
Cards accepted: Access, Visa,
Amex, Switch

The Old School ⚑
Deanhead, Barkisland,
Halifax HX4 0EA
☎ (0422) 824117
*Tastefully-converted old
school, in a pleasant Pennine
rural setting overlooking
Scammonden Water. 3 miles
west of Barkisland on the
B6114, turn left opposite
Brown Cow Inn.*
Bedrooms: 1 double, 1 twin
Bathrooms: 2 private,
1 public
Bed & breakfast

per night:	£min	£max
Single	14.00	18.00
Double	24.00	30.00

Parking for 2

HARROGATE

North Yorkshire
Map ref 4B1

A major conference,
exhibition and shopping
centre, renowned for its
spa heritage and award
winning floral displays,
spacious parks and
gardens. Famous for
antiques, toffee, fine
shopping and excellent
tea shops, also its Royal
Pump Rooms and Baths.
*Tourist Information Centre
☎ (0423) 525666*

17 Peckfield Close
Listed APPROVED

Hampsthwaite, Harrogate
HG3 2ES
☎ (0423) 770765
*In picturesque village 4 miles
from Harrogate off A59.
Large, attractive garden. At
start of Nidderdale Walk.*
Bedrooms: 1 single, 2 twin
Bathrooms: 1 public

Bed & breakfast

per night:	£min	£max
Single	14.00	16.00
Double	28.00	32.00

Half board

per person:	£min	£max
Daily	20.00	22.00

Parking for 2

Acacia Lodge
21 Ripon Road, Harrogate
HG1 2JL
☎ (0423) 560752
*Warm, beautifully appointed
and furnished Victorian house
in select area of town centre.
En-suite rooms, pretty
gardens and ample private
parking. Award winning
breakfasts and warm
hospitality.*
Bedrooms: 1 single,
1 double, 2 twin, 1 triple
Bathrooms: 5 private
Bed & breakfast

per night:	£min	£max
Single		27.00
Double		44.00

Parking for 6

The Duchy Hotel ⚑
51 Valley Drive, Harrogate
HG2 0JH
☎ (0423) 565818
*Warm and welcoming small
hotel overlooking Valley
Gardens. Charming bar
lounge, good food the pride
of the house. Wonderful base
for touring the dales.*
Bedrooms: 2 single,
1 double, 3 twin, 3 triple
Bathrooms: 9 private
Bed & breakfast

per night:	£min	£max
Single	23.00	26.00
Double	40.00	50.00

Half board

per person:	£min	£max
Daily	29.00	35.00
Weekly	180.00	210.00

Evening meal 1830 (last
orders 1600)
Cards accepted: Access, Visa

Harrogate Brasserie
Hotel ⚑
COMMENDED

28-30 Cheltenham Parade,
Harrogate HG1 1DB
☎ (0423) 505041
Fax (0423) 530920
*Comfortable, well-appointed,
fully licensed brasserie and
all-day bar. Every room has*

Continued ▶

117

HARROGATE

Continued

been individually designed to reflect a period between 1750-1990.
Bedrooms: 3 single, 6 double, 2 twin, 2 triple
Bathrooms: 13 private
Bed & breakfast

per night:	£min	£max
Single	25.00	35.00
Double	45.00	65.00

Half board

per person:	£min	£max
Daily	35.00	45.00
Weekly	150.00	200.00

Lunch available
Evening meal 1830 (last orders 2300)
Parking for 10
Cards accepted: Access, Visa
⌂ 4 📞 🖃 ☐ ♨ 🛏 S ✗ 🅿 TV 🆑, 🛏 ✗ 🕿 SP

Rose Garth Guest House
Listed
44 Ripon Road, Killinghall, Harrogate HG3 2DF
☎ (0423) 506469
Friendly guesthouse, 2 miles from Harrogate on the A61. Car park, free Sky movies, in-house video, en-suite rooms. Non smokers only, please.
Bedrooms: 1 single, 4 double, 2 twin
Bathrooms: 1 public, 3 private showers
Bed & breakfast

per night:	£min	£max
Single	14.00	17.50
Double	31.00	38.00

Parking for 8
⌂ 🖃 ☐ ♨ ᵁ 🛏 ✗ 🅿 TV 🆑, 🛏 ✿ ✗ 🕿 SP

HARTOFT END

North Yorkshire
Map ref 5C3

In the heart of the North York Moors.

High Farm
Listed
Hartoft End, Pickering YO18 8RP
☎ Lastingham (075 15) 648
16-acre beef farm. Overlooking a wooded valley in an ideal walking and touring area, 3 miles from Rosedale Abbey and 17 miles from the coast.
Bedrooms: 1 single, 1 double
Bathrooms: 1 public

Bed & breakfast

per night:	£min	£max
Single	12.00	12.00
Double	24.00	24.00

Parking for 2
Open April-November
⌂ ♨ ᵁ 🛏 TV 🅿 ✿ ✗ 🆑

HAWES

North Yorkshire
Map ref 5B3

The capital of Upper Wensleydale on the famous Pennine Way, renowned for great cheeses. Popular with walkers. Dales National Park Information Centre and Folk Museum. Nearby is spectacular Hardraw Force Waterfall.

The Bungalow
Spring Bank, Hawes DL8 3NW
☎ (0969) 667209
Large bungalow with panoramic views. In a quiet and restful area, only a short walk to town centre. Private parking. Central heating.
Bedrooms: 2 double, 1 triple
Bathrooms: 2 public
Bed & breakfast

per night:	£min	£max
Single	12.00	14.00
Double	24.00	28.00

Parking for 6
Open March-October
⌂ 3 🖧 ᵁ 🛏 TV 🆑, 🆑

Crosby Guest House ⋀
≝ ≝
Burtersett Road, Hawes DL8 3NP
☎ Wensleydale (0969) 667322
Small guesthouse with spacious rooms and parking at the rear. For quiet relaxation and exploring the dales.
Bedrooms: 1 double, 1 twin, 1 triple
Bathrooms: 1 private, 2 public
Bed & breakfast

per night:	£min	£max
Single	20.00	22.00
Double	26.00	33.00

Parking for 3
Open April-October
⌂ 🖃 ☐ ♨ ᵁ 🛏 S 🛏 TV 🆑, 🛏 🆑

Ebor Guest House ⋀
Listed
Burtersett Road, Hawes DL8 3NT
☎ Wensleydale (0969) 667337
Small, family-run guesthouse, double-glazed and centrally-heated throughout. Walkers are particularly welcome. Clothes washing and drying facilities available.
Bedrooms: 1 single, 2 double, 1 twin
Bathrooms: 1 private, 1 public
Bed & breakfast

per night:	£min	£max
Single	13.00	15.00
Double	26.00	32.00

Parking for 5
⌂ 🖃 ☐ ♨ ᵁ 🛏 S 🛏 TV 🆑, 🛏 🆑 DAP

Rigg House West
Listed — HIGHLY COMMENDED
Appersett, Hawes DL8 3LR
☎ Wensleydale (0969) 667712
Fine house 4 miles west of Hawes on the A684 in an area designated as of outstanding natural beauty. Rivers, waterfalls, fells, the Pennine Way and the historic Settle/Carlisle railway on the doorstep.
Bedrooms: 2 double, 1 twin
Bathrooms: 1 public
Bed & breakfast

per night:	£min	£max
Single	15.00	
Double	30.00	

Half board

per person:	£min	£max
Daily	24.00	
Weekly	161.00	

Evening meal 1900 (last orders 1750)
Parking for 5
⌂ 5 🗻 S 🛏 TV 🆑, 🛏 ✿ ✗ 🆑 🚬 SP 🕿

Springbank House ⋀
≝ COMMENDED
Springbank, Townfoot, Hawes DL8 3NW
☎ Wensleydale (0969) 667376
Delightful Victorian house near the centre of Hawes with superb views over the surrounding fells.
Bedrooms: 1 twin, 1 triple
Bathrooms: 2 private, 1 public
Bed & breakfast

per night:	£min	£max
Double	26.00	32.00

Parking for 3
Open February-November
⌂ 📞 ♨ ᵁ 🛏 S ✗ 🛏 TV 🆑, ✿ ✗ 🆑

White Hart Inn ⋀
≝ ≝
Main Street, Hawes DL8 3QL
☎ Wensleydale (0969) 667259
Small country inn with a friendly welcome, offering home-cooked meals using local produce. An ideal centre for exploring the Yorkshire Dales.
Bedrooms: 1 single, 4 double, 2 twin
Bathrooms: 2 public
Bed & breakfast

per night:	£min	£max
Single	16.50	17.00
Double	31.00	32.00

Lunch available
Evening meal 1900 (last orders 2030)
Parking for 7
Cards accepted: Access
⌂ 🛏 S 🛏 TV SP 🕿

HAWORTH

West Yorkshire
Map ref 4B1

This Pennine town is famous as home of the Bronte family. The parsonage is now a Bronte Museum where furniture and possessions of the family are displayed. Moors and Bronte waterfalls nearby and steam trains on the Keighley & Worth Valley Railway pass through.
Tourist Information Centre
☎ *(0535) 642329*

Ebor House
Lees Lane, Haworth, Keighley BD22 8RA
☎ Keighley (0535) 645869
Yorkshire stone-built house of character, conveniently placed for the main tourist attractions of Haworth, including the Worth Valley Railway and Bronte Parsonage and Museum.
Bedrooms: 2 twin, 1 triple
Bathrooms: 1 public
Bed & breakfast

per night:	£min	£max
Single	13.00	13.00
Double	24.00	24.00

Parking for 2
⌂ 🖃 ♨ ᵁ S 🛏 TV 🆑, ✗ 🆑

Please mention this guide when making a booking.

Hole Farm

Dimples Lane, Haworth, Keighley BD22 8QS
☎ Keighley (0535) 644755
7-acre smallholding. 17th C farmhouse, 5 minutes' walk from Bronte Parsonage and 2 minutes' walk from the moors. Farm has peacocks, geese, cattle and horses. At the top of Haworth take first left after the Sun pub, first left again, then third drive on left.
Bedrooms: 3 double
Bathrooms: 1 public

Bed & breakfast per night:	£min	£max
Double	28.00	28.00

Parking for 4
📺 ☕ [UL] 🔒 [S] 🚭 ♨ 👔 🐎 ✿ ✈ 🚐

Hoyle Farm Cottage

Dimples Lane, Haworth, Keighley BD22 8QS
☎ Keighley (0535) 646809
4-acre livestock farm. Detached stone cottage, dating from 1800s, privately situated with panoramic views. Close to moors yet minutes from Bronte Parsonage.
Bedrooms: 4 double
Bathrooms: 4 private

Bed & breakfast per night:	£min	£max
Single	16.50	
Double	33.00	

Evening meal 1830 (last orders 1830)
Parking for 6
♿ 📺 ☕ [UL] 🔒 [S] ♨ 👔 🐎 ⛳ ✿ ✈ 🚐

The Lee

[Listed]
Lee Lane, Oxenhope, Keighley BD22 9RB
☎ (0535) 646311
Detached 17th C house with 6 acres of land, 1.5 miles from the centre of Haworth. Close to the moors and waterfalls.
Bedrooms: 1 double, 1 triple
Bathrooms: 1 private, 1 public

Bed & breakfast per night:	£min	£max
Double	24.00	27.00

Parking for 4
👶 4 📖 ☕ [UL] 🛏 [TV] 👔 ✿ 🚐 [DAP]

Old White Lion Hotel 🅰

👑👑👑👑 COMMENDED
Haworth, Keighley BD22 8DU
☎ Keighley (0535) 642313
Fax (0535) 646222
Family-run, centuries old coaching inn. Candlelit restaurant using local fresh produce cooked to order and featured in food guides. Old world bars serving extensive range of bar snacks and real ales.
Bedrooms: 3 single, 6 double, 2 twin, 3 triple
Bathrooms: 14 private

Bed & breakfast per night:	£min	£max
Single	34.00	34.00
Double	48.00	48.00

Half board per person:	£min	£max
Daily	24.00	33.00
Weekly	170.00	231.00

Lunch available
Evening meal 1900 (last orders 2200)
Parking for 10
Cards accepted: Access, Visa, Diners, Amex
👶 📞 📖 📺 ☕ 🔒 [S] 🛏 [TV] ♨ 👔 ✈ [SP] 🏠

Three Sisters Hotel

Brow Top Road, Haworth, Keighley BD22 9PH
☎ Keighley (0535) 643458
Fax (0535) 646842
Privately-owned modern hotel in the heart of Bronte country. Picturesque and peaceful, set in its own gardens and only 2 minutes from Haworth.
Bedrooms: 2 single, 3 double, 3 twin, 1 triple, 1 multiple
Bathrooms: 9 private

Bed & breakfast per night:	£min	£max
Single		35.00
Double		45.00

Lunch available
Evening meal 1200 (last orders 2200)
Parking for 100
Cards accepted: Access, Visa, C.Bl, Diners, Amex
👶 📞 📺 ☕ 🔒 [S] 🛏 [TV] ♨ 👔 🔍 🐎 ⛳ ✿ 🚫 [SP] [T]

Mrs V Woodhouse

The Croft, West Lane, Haworth, Keighley BD22 8EL
☎ Keighley (0535) 643389
On edge of moors with beautiful open views, minutes from Bronte Museum, shops and restaurant. All bedrooms with colour TV, tea/coffee facilities, own WC and central heating.
Bedrooms: 2 double, 1 twin
Bathrooms: 3 private, 1 public

Bed & breakfast per night:	£min	£max
Double	28.00	28.00

Parking for 4
👶 📺 ☕ [UL] 🛏 ♨ 🐎 🚐

HEALEY

North Yorkshire
Map ref 5C3

Village to the west of the attractive market town of Masham, on the eastern edge of the Yorkshire Dales.

Leighton Hall Farm

[Listed] APPROVED
Healey, Ripon HG4 4LS
☎ Ripon (0765) 689360
540-acre mixed farm. Farmhouse is a former monastery with beautiful panoramic views.
Bedrooms: 1 double, 1 twin
Bathrooms: 1 private, 1 public

Bed & breakfast per night:	£min	£max
Single	12.00	14.00
Double	24.00	28.00

Half board per person:	£min	£max
Daily	18.00	20.00
Weekly	130.00	140.00

Evening meal from 1830
Parking for 3
Open May-October
👶 📺 ☕ [UL] 🔒 🛏 [TV] ♨ 👔 🐎 ✿ 🚐 [DAP] 🏠

HEBDEN BRIDGE

West Yorkshire
Map ref 4B1

Originally a small town on packhorse route, Hebden Bridge grew into a booming mill town in 18th C with rows of 'up-and-down' houses of several storeys built against hillsides. Ancient 'pace-egg play' custom held on Good Friday.
Tourist Information Centre ☎ *(0422) 843831*

Cherry Tree Cottage 🅰

👑👑👑 COMMENDED
Woodhouse Road, Todmorden, Lancashire OL14 5RJ
☎ Todmorden (0706) 817492
Sympathetically restored, part 17th C country cottage with modern amenities and lovely views. Emphasis on fresh, home-cooked fare.
Bedrooms: 2 twin
Bathrooms: 1 private, 1 public

Bed & breakfast per night:	£min	£max
Double	32.00	36.00

Half board per person:	£min	£max
Daily	22.00	24.00
Weekly	154.00	168.00

Evening meal 1800 (last orders 2000)
Parking for 2
👶 ☕ 🍷 [UL] 🔒 [S] 🚭 🛏 [TV] ♨ 👔 🐎 ✿ ✈ 🚐 [DAP] 🏠

Prospect End

👑👑 COMMENDED
8 Prospect Terrace, Savile Road, Hebden Bridge HX7 6NA
☎ (0422) 843586
Comfortable Victorian house on the edge of town. Self-contained guest accommodation. Convenient for public transport and walking. Close to many Pennine attractions.
Bedrooms: 1 double, 1 twin
Bathrooms: 2 private

Bed & breakfast per night:	£min	£max
Single	17.00	17.00
Double	30.00	30.00

Half board per person:	£min	£max
Daily	22.50	24.50

Evening meal from 1900
Parking for 2
👶 12 ☕ 🍷 [UL] 🔒 [S] 🚭 [TV] ♨ 👔 ✿ ✈ 🚐 🏠

Robin Hood Inn 🅰

[Listed] APPROVED
Pecket Well, Hebden Bridge HX7 8QR
☎ (0422) 842593
Old English inn, with a car park and beer garden, 1 mile from Hebden Bridge. Special emphasis on food and hospitality.
Bedrooms: 1 single, 1 double, 2 triple
Bathrooms: 1 public

Bed & breakfast per night:	£min	£max
Single		16.50
Double	30.00	

Half board per person:	£min	£max
Daily		20.00
Weekly	125.00	

Lunch available
Evening meal 1845 (last orders 2130)
Parking for 28
👶 📺 ☕ 🔒 [S] ♨ 🚐 [SP] 🏠

HEBDEN BRIDGE

Continued

Rogergate

🏠 COMMENDED

Mytholmroyd, Hebden Bridge
HX7 5AP
☎ Halifax (0422) 883355
*Large detached bungalow set
in landscaped gardens, in a
semi-rural location with
panoramic views of the
Calder Valley.*
Bedrooms: 1 double
Bathrooms: 1 private

Bed & breakfast

per night:	£min	£max
Single	20.00	20.00
Double	30.00	30.00

Parking for 2

Shoulder of Mutton Inn

Listed APPROVED

Burnley Road, Blackshaw
Head, Hebden Bridge
HX7 7BF
☎ (0422) 842780 & 844729
*Refurbished inn with
panoramic views, 2.5 miles
from Hebden Bridge, 1.5
miles from historic
Heptonstall and adjacent to
the Pennine and Calderdale
Ways. A multitude of activities
available within the vicinity.*
Bedrooms: 1 single,
3 double, 1 twin
Bathrooms: 2 public

Bed & breakfast

per night:	£min	£max
Single	15.50	
Double	31.00	

Half board

per person:	£min	£max
Daily	21.50	

Lunch available
Evening meal 1900 (last
orders 2230)
Parking for 32
Cards accepted: Access, Visa

Stray Leaves

Listed

Wadsworth, Hebden Bridge
HX7 8TN
☎ (0422) 842353
*Private bungalow in pleasant
rural surroundings
overlooking Hebden Bridge. 1
mile from the centre.*
Bedrooms: 1 double, 1 triple
Bathrooms: 1 private,
1 public

Bed & breakfast

per night:	£min	£max
Single	10.00	10.50
Double	20.00	24.00

Parking for 4

HELLIFIELD

North Yorkshire
Map ref 4B1

Wenningber Farm

🏠 HIGHLY COMMENDED

Airton Road, Hellifield,
Skipton BD23 4JR
☎ (0729) 850856
*80-acre mixed farm. In a
picturesque location between
Hellifield and Otterburn, just
5 miles from Malham in the
Yorkshire Dales National
Park.*
Bedrooms: 1 double, 1 twin
Bathrooms: 1 public

Bed & breakfast

per night:	£min	£max
Single	15.00	17.00
Double	28.00	30.00

Parking for 10
Open March-October

HELMSLEY

North Yorkshire
Map ref 5C3

Pretty town on the River
Rye at the entrance to
Ryedale and the North
York Moors, with large
square and remains of
12th C castle, several
inns, notably the 16th C
'Black Swan', and All
Saints' Church.

Buckingham House

33 Bridge Street, Helmsley,
York YO6 5DX
☎ (0439) 70613
*Comfortable, listed Georgian
house with unrestricted
access. Ideal base for walking,
bird-watching and touring in
this scenic and historic area.*
Bedrooms: 1 single,
1 double, 1 twin
Bathrooms: 1 public

Bed & breakfast

per night:	£min	£max
Single	13.00	14.00
Double	26.00	28.00

Half board

per person:	£min	£max
Daily	21.00	22.00
Weekly	130.00	140.00

Evening meal 1800 (last
orders 2000)
Parking for 2

Lockton House Farm

Bilsdale West, Helmsley,
York YO6 5NE
☎ Bilsdale (043 96) 303
*400-acre mixed farm. Part of
the house is a 16th C cruck
house with oak beams. 7
miles out of Helmsley on the
B1257 Teesside road. Ideal
walking and touring area.
Reduced rates for children.*
Bedrooms: 1 double,
1 multiple
Bathrooms: 1 public

Bed & breakfast

per night:	£min	£max
Single	12.00	13.00
Double	24.00	26.00

Half board

per person:	£min	£max
Daily	20.00	20.00
Weekly	140.00	140.00

Evening meal 1800 (last
orders 1800)
Parking for 6
Open March-October

HOLMFIRTH

West Yorkshire
Map ref 4B1

This village has become
famous as the location for
the filming of the TV
series 'Last of the
Summer Wine'. It has a
postcard museum and is
on the edge of the Peak
District National Park.
*Tourist Information Centre
☎ (0484) 684992*

29 Woodhead Road

🏠 COMMENDED

Holmfirth, Huddersfield
HD7 1JU
☎ (0484) 683962
*200-year-old family home, 5
minutes' walk from Holmfirth.
Full central heating, tea and
coffee available anytime.*
Bedrooms: 1 twin
Bathrooms: 1 private

Bed & breakfast

per night:	£min	£max
Single	12.50	12.50
Double	25.00	25.00

Parking for 2

Melsetter

7 New Road, Holmfirth,
Huddersfield HD7 2XT
☎ (0484) 683212
*Half a mile from the outskirts
of Holmfirth in three quarters
of an acre of ground.
Accommodation is
incorporated in owner's house
but guests have complete
privacy. Children welcome.*
Bedrooms: 1 twin, 1 triple
Bathrooms: 1 public

Bed & breakfast

per night:	£min	£max
Single	18.00	18.00
Double	36.00	36.00

Parking for 2

Shoulder of Mutton

Listed

2 Dunford Road, Holmfirth,
Huddersfield HD7 1DP
☎ (0484) 684414
*In the centre of Holmfirth,
within easy reach of the
Yorkshire Dales.*
Bedrooms: 1 twin, 1 triple
Bathrooms: 1 public

Bed & breakfast

per night:	£min	£max
Single	15.00	20.00
Double	30.00	35.00

Lunch available
Evening meal 1800 (last
orders 2000)
Parking for 6

Spring Head House

15 Holmfirth Road, Shepley,
Huddersfield HD8 8BB
☎ Huddersfield (0484)
606300
Fax (0484) 608030
*Large Georgian house with a
garden, close to Holmfirth
and "Summer Wine" country
and with easy access to the
M1 and M62.*
Bedrooms: 1 single, 1 twin
Bathrooms: 1 private,
1 public

Bed & breakfast

per night:	£min	£max
Single	15.00	20.00
Double	30.00	30.00

Parking for 3

Springfield House

95 Huddersfield Road,
Holmfirth, Huddersfield
HD7 1JA
☎ (0484) 683031
*Elegant early Victorian house
in the "Summer Wine" town
of Holmfirth. Close to shops
and all amenities. Only 2
miles from the Peak District*

National Park and within easy reach of all Pennine Yorkshire attractions. Homely atmosphere with a true Yorkshire welcome.
Bedrooms: 1 double, 1 twin, 1 triple
Bathrooms: 1 private, 1 public
Bed & breakfast

per night:	£min	£max
Single	16.00	18.00
Double	27.00	29.00

Parking for 2
⛽🔧🛏🚲♿🖥♿Ⓢ🖥.🛢✿
🏠 ᴅᴀᴘ SP

HORTON-IN-RIBBLESDALE

North Yorkshire
Map ref 5B3

On the River Ribble and an ideal centre for potholing. The Pennine Way runs eastward over Pen-y-ghent, one of the famous 'Three Peaks'.
Tourist Information Centre
☎ *(072 96) 333*

Crown Hotel ♨
♨♨
Horton-in-Ribblesdale, Settle
BD24 0HF
☎ Settle (0729) 860209
Small family-run country inn offering a warm welcome and friendly hospitality, in the heart of the dales.
Bedrooms: 3 single, 3 double, 4 triple
Bathrooms: 2 private, 2 public, 5 private showers
Bed & breakfast

per night:	£min	£max
Single	16.32	22.41
Double	32.64	44.82

Lunch available
Evening meal 1830 (last orders 2100)
Parking for 15
Cards accepted: Diners
⛽🔥Ⓢ♿🖥🖥.✿🏠♨SP

HUBBERHOLME

North Yorkshire
Map ref 5B3

Ancient Upper Wharfedale village with a charming and interesting church noted for its rood loft dated 1558, a rare survival in England.

The George Inn
Kirk Gill, Hubberholme, Skipton BD23 5JE
☎ Kettlewell (0756) 760223
An ancient inn in the heart of the Yorkshire Dales.

Bedrooms: 2 double, 2 twin
Bathrooms: 1 public
Bed & breakfast

per night:	£min	£max
Double	36.00	36.00

Lunch available
Evening meal 1930 (last orders 2045)
Parking for 20
⛽8♿🖥✿🖥.🌙♿ᴙ🏠

HUDDERSFIELD

West Yorkshire
Map ref 4B1

Founded on wool and cloth, has a famous choral society. Town centre redeveloped, but several good Victorian buildings remain, including railway station, St. Peter's Church, Tolson Memorial Museum, art gallery and nearby Colne Valley Museum.
Tourist Information Centre
☎ *(0484) 430808*

Elm Crest Guest House ♨
♨♨ COMMENDED
2 Queens Road, Edgerton, Huddersfield HD2 2AG
☎ (0484) 530990
Fax (0484) 516227
Victorian residence with Victorian charm and quality, 1 mile from the town centre and 2 miles from the M62.
Bedrooms: 3 single, 1 double, 3 twin, 1 triple
Bathrooms: 5 private, 1 public
Bed & breakfast

per night:	£min	£max
Single	22.00	33.00
Double	42.00	60.00

Half board

per person:	£min	£max
Daily	33.00	50.00
Weekly	210.00	350.00

Lunch available
Evening meal 1800 (last orders 2100)
Parking for 12
Cards accepted: Access, Visa, Amex, Switch
⛽5🖥🕳♿🛏Ⓢ♿🖥🖥.
🛢✿🌙🏠SP♿Ⓣ

Hollies Guest House
♨♨
286 Halifax Old Road, Grimscar, Huddersfield HD2 2SP
☎ (0484) 427097
In woodland on the valley side with wildlife. A beautiful area, renowned for its industrial/historic heritage and music. All rooms with

---

washbasins and colour TV. "Kirklees Way" long distance footpath.
Bedrooms: 1 single, 2 double
Bathrooms: 2 public
Bed & breakfast

per night:	£min	£max
Single	13.00	16.00
Double	26.00	32.00

Lunch available
Evening meal 1800 (last orders 0900)
Parking for 4
⛽3🖥♿🖥♿♿🖥.🛢✿
🌙🏠

HUNTON

North Yorkshire
Map ref 5C3

The Countryman's Inn
♨♨♨
Hunton, Bedale DL8 1PY
☎ Bedale (0677) 50554
Recently modernised village inn and restaurant, retaining its old world charm, with log fires and beamed ceilings. Four-poster room. Just off the A684 between Bedale and Leyburn, convenient for the Yorkshire Dales.
Bedrooms: 5 double, 1 twin
Bathrooms: 6 private
Bed & breakfast

per night:	£min	£max
Single	25.00	30.00
Double	38.00	50.00

Parking for 20
Cards accepted: Access, Visa
🖥🖥♿🗣Ⓢ♿♿🛢🏠♿
Ʊ🌙✿🏠SP

ILKLEY

West Yorkshire
Map ref 4B1

This moorland town is famous for its ballad. The 16th C manor house, now a museum, displays local prehistoric and Roman relics. Popular walk leads up Heber's Ghyll to Ilkley Moor, with the mysterious Swastika Stone and White Wells, 18th C plunge baths.
Tourist Information Centre
☎ *(0943) 602319.*

Beech House
5 St James Road, Ilkley
LS29 9PY
☎ (0943) 601995
Spacious, Victorian house, close to the town centre and public transport. Quiet location within easy walking distance of riverside and moor.

Bedrooms: 1 single, 1 double, 1 twin
Bathrooms: 1 public
Bed & breakfast

per night:	£min	£max
Single	12.00	17.00
Double	24.00	28.00

Parking for 2
⛽♿🖥🛏Ⓢ♿♿🖥🖥.🛢
🏠 ᴅᴀᴘ

Briarwood
♨♨ COMMENDED
Queens Drive, Ilkley
LS29 9QW
☎ (0943) 600870
Victorian ladies' residence with spacious rooms and excellent views. Visitors are entertained as house guests. 5 minutes' walk from Ilkley Moor and Ilkley College.
Bedrooms: 2 twin
Bathrooms: 2 private
Bed & breakfast

per night:	£min	£max
Single	14.00	16.00
Double	28.00	28.00

Parking for 5
⛽🖥Ⓢ♿♿🖥🖥.🌙🏠

INGLEBY CROSS

North Yorkshire
Map ref 5C3

Blue Bell Inn ♨
Ingleby Cross, Northallerton
DL6 3NF
☎ East Harlsey (060 982) 272
On the edge of the North York Moors. Ideal base for walking the Cleveland Way, Coast to Coast or the Lyke Wake Walk.
Bedrooms: 2 double, 3 twin
Bathrooms: 5 private, 1 public
Bed & breakfast

per night:	£min	£max
Single	15.00	
Double	25.00	

Half board

per person:	£min	£max
Daily	17.00	25.00

Lunch available
Evening meal 1900 (last orders 2200)
Parking for 20
⛽🖥Ⓜ♿♿🛏Ⓢ🖥.♿Ʊ✿
🌙🏠

Half board prices shown are per person but in some cases may be based on double/ twin occupancy.

INGLEBY GREENHOW

North Yorkshire
Map ref 5C3

Perched on the edge of Cleveland Hills, the village boasts the Norman church of St Andrew's with well-preserved carving and effigies of a priest and a knight. Ingleby Moor rises 1300 ft above village.

Manor House Farm 🏠

👑👑 COMMENDED

Ingleby Greenhow, Middlesbrough, Cleveland TS9 6RB
☎ Great Ayton (0642) 722384
164-acre mixed farm. In a picture book setting surrounded by hills and forests, in the North York Moors National Park. Ideal for nature lovers, walking, touring, riding and relaxing.
Bedrooms: 1 double, 2 twin
Bathrooms: 3 private

Half board

per person:	£min	£max
Daily	31.00	34.00
Weekly	207.00	228.00

Evening meal 1900 (last orders 1600)
Parking for 66
Cards accepted: Amex
🐴 12 📖 ☕ 🔒 [S] 🚭 🪑 [TV] ♨ 👕 🐎 ⛳ ▶ 🎣 ❀ 🚐 🏛

INGLETON

North Yorkshire
Map ref 5B3

Ingleton is a thriving tourist centre for fell-walkers, climbers and pot-holers. Popular walks up beautiful Twiss Valley to Ingleborough Summit, Whernside, White Scar Caves and waterfalls.

Ingleborough View

👑👑 COMMENDED

Main Street, Ingleton, Carnforth, Lancashire LA6 3HH
☎ (0524) 41523
Family-run guesthouse with a friendly atmosphere. Panoramic views. Ideally situated for all local walks, touring the dales and Lake District.
Bedrooms: 2 double, 1 twin
Bathrooms: 2 public

Bed & breakfast

per night:	£min	£max
Double	26.00	28.00

Parking for 4
🐴 📖 ☕ [UL] 🔒 [S] 🪑 [TV] ♨ 👕 🐕 🚐 [SP]

KEIGHLEY

West Yorkshire
Map ref 4B1

Pleasant Victorian town where Charlotte Bronte used to shop. Cliffe Castle is an art gallery and museum with large collection of Victorian bygones. 17th C East Riddlesden Hall (National Trust) has fine medieval tithe barn. Trips on Keighley and Worth Valley Railway.

Currer Laithe Farm 🏠

Moss Carr Road, Long Lee, Keighley BD21 4SL
☎ (0535) 604387
170-acre beef farm. 16th C farmhouse overlooking pastureland in Bronte country. Panoramic views, a warm welcome and a variety of animals. Popular with disabled persons. Group self-catering winter weekends.
Bedrooms: 1 single, 3 twin, 2 triple
Bathrooms: 2 public

Bed & breakfast

per night:	£min	£max
Single		10.00
Double		20.00

Half board

per person:	£min	£max
Daily		13.50

Evening meal from 1900
Parking for 10
🐴 ♿ [UL] 🔒 🪑 [TV] ♨ 🚐 🏛

Rouselyn Bed & Breakfast 🏠

14 Scott Lane, Riddlesden, Keighley BD20 5BT
☎ (0535) 607705
Guesthouse between Haworth and the Yorkshire Dales on the edge of the picturesque Leeds and Liverpool Canal. Ample parking within large gardens. Evening meal on request.
Bedrooms: 1 single, 1 double, 1 twin
Bathrooms: 2 public

Bed & breakfast

per night:	£min	£max
Single	15.00	15.00
Double	25.00	30.00

Half board

per person:	£min	£max
Daily	21.00	21.00
Weekly	140.00	147.00

Evening meal 1700 (last orders 1900)
Parking for 4
🐴 📺 ☕ [UL] [TV] ♨ 🐕 🚐

KETTLEWELL

North Yorkshire
Map ref 5B3

Set in the spectacular scenery of the Yorkshire Dales National Park in Wharfedale, this former market town is a convenient stopping place for climbers and walkers. Dramatic rock formation of Kilnsey Crag is 3 miles south.

Lynburn Cottage

[Listed]

Langliffe Garth, Kettlewell, Skipton BD23 5RF
☎ (0756) 760803
Cottage with a small, sunny, well-kept garden for guests' use, in a quiet part of Kettlewell with delightful views of the Yorkshire Dales. 100 yards from shops and pubs.
Bedrooms: 1 double, 1 twin
Bathrooms: 1 public

Bed & breakfast

per night:	£min	£max
Double	32.00	

Parking for 2
Open April-October
🐴 10 📺 ☕ [UL] ♨ ❀ 🐕 🚐

KIRBY MISPERTON

North Yorkshire
Map ref 5C3

Halfway between Malton and Pickering and most famous for the Flamingo Land Zoo and Fun Park.

Ashfield Country Manor Hotel

Kirby Misperton, Malton YO17 0UU
☎ (065 386) 221
Small, family-run hotel in the heart of Ryedale. Close to Malton, Pickering and North York Moors.
Bedrooms: 1 single, 3 double, 2 triple
Bathrooms: 6 private, 1 public

Bed & breakfast

per night:	£min	£max
Single	26.00	30.00
Double	45.00	52.00

Half board

per person:	£min	£max
Daily	35.00	45.00
Weekly	245.00	300.00

Evening meal 1900 (last orders 2130)
Parking for 50
Cards accepted: Visa
🐴 📺 ☕ 🔒 [S] 🪑 [TV] ♨ 👕 🔍 🎣 ⛳ ❀ 🐕 🚐 🚭 [SP]

KIRKBYMOORSIDE

North Yorkshire
Map ref 5C3

Attractive market town with remains of Norman castle. Good centre for exploring moors. Nearby are wild daffodils of Farndale.

Low Northolme Farm 🏠

👑👑 COMMENDED

Salton, York YO6 6RP
☎ (0751) 32321
250-acre mixed farm. 18th C farmhouse set in peaceful area of Ryedale, 6 miles from Helmsley, just two miles south of A170.
Bedrooms: 1 twin, 1 multiple
Bathrooms: 2 private

Bed & breakfast

per night:	£min	£max
Single	14.00	14.00
Double	32.00	35.00

Half board

per person:	£min	£max
Daily	24.50	26.00

Evening meal 1830 (last orders 1930)
Parking for 15
🐴 5 [UL] 🚭 🪑 [TV] ♨ 👕 🐎 🎣 ❀ 🐕 🚐

KNARESBOROUGH

North Yorkshire
Map ref 4B1

Picturesque market town on the River Nidd, famous for its 11th C castle ruins, overlooking town and river gorge. Attractions include oldest chemist's shop in country, prophetess Mother Shipton's cave, Dropping Well and Court House Museum. Boating on river.

Ebor Mount 🏠

👑👑

18 York Place, Knaresborough HG5 0AA
☎ Harrogate (0423) 863315
Charming 18th C town-house with private car park, providing bed and breakfast

*accommodation in recently
refurbished rooms. Ideal
touring centre.*
Bedrooms: 1 single,
3 double, 2 twin, 2 triple
Bathrooms: 8 private,
1 public
**Bed & breakfast
per night:** £min £max
Single 18.00 20.00
Double 36.00 40.00
Parking for 10
Cards accepted: Access, Visa

West Yorkshire
Map ref 4B1

Large city with excellent
modern shopping centre
and much splendid
Victorian architecture.
Museums and galleries
including Temple Newsam
House (the Hampton
Court of the North). Home
of Opera North and a new
playhouse.
Tourist Information Centre
☎ (0532) 478301

Eagle Tavern ⚔
Listed
North Street, Leeds LS7 1AF
☎ (0532) 457146
*Traditional pub in a
commercial district of Leeds,
offering friendly service at
reasonable prices. Close to
the city centre. Colour TV in
all rooms. Voted CAMRA pub
of the year 1989 and 1990.*
Bedrooms: 1 single, 6 twin,
2 triple
Bathrooms: 2 public
**Bed & breakfast
per night:** £min £max
Single 18.00 20.00
Double 36.00 40.00
Evening meal 1730 (last
orders 1900)
Parking for 12

Harewood Arms Hotel ⚔
HIGHLY COMMENDED
Harrogate Road, Harewood,
Leeds LS17 9LH
☎ (0532) 886566
Fax (0532) 886064
*Stone-built hotel and
restaurant of character with a
rural aspect, 8 miles from
Harrogate and Leeds.
Opposite Harewood House
and close to all amenities,
including golf and racing.*
Bedrooms: 2 single,
11 double, 10 twin, 1 triple
Bathrooms: 24 private

**Bed & breakfast
per night:** £min £max
Single 48.00 65.00
Double 63.00 78.00
**Half board
per person:** £min £max
Daily 62.50 79.50
Lunch available
Evening meal 1900 (last
orders 2200)
Parking for 60
Cards accepted: Access, Visa,
Diners, Amex, Switch

St Michael's Tower Hotel ⚔
5 St Michael's Villas,
Cardigan Road, Headingley,
Leeds LS6 3AF
☎ (0532) 755557
*Licensed, private hotel with
easy access to Leeds city
centre (2 miles) and close to
both the university and
Yorkshire Cricket Ground.*
Bedrooms: 7 single,
5 double, 8 twin, 1 triple
Bathrooms: 10 private,
4 public
**Bed & breakfast
per night:** £min £max
Single 18.00 25.00
Double 30.00 35.00
**Half board
per person:** £min £max
Daily 25.50 32.50
Weekly 118.00 160.00
Evening meal 1830 (last
orders 2000)
Parking for 26

The White House ⚔
157 Middleton Park Road,
Leeds LS10 4LZ
☎ (0532) 711231
*Detached spacious house.
Convenient for local
transport, West Riding towns,
M1 and M62, and ideal for
North/South travellers. Non-
smokers only please.*
Bedrooms: 2 twin
Bathrooms: 1 public
**Bed & breakfast
per night:** £min £max
Single 14.00
Double 26.00
Parking for 2

*See under Bingley,
Bradford, Leeds, Otley*

North Yorkshire
Map ref 5B3

Attractive dales market
town where Mary Queen
of Scots was reputedly
captured after her escape
from Bolton Castle. Fine
views over Wensleydale
from nearby.
Tourist Information Centre
☎ (0969) 23069 or 22773

Eastfield Lodge Private Hotel ⚔
APPROVED
St Matthews Terrace,
Leyburn DL8 5EL
☎ Wensleydale (0969) 23196
*Family-run, private hotel,
central for touring the dales.
En-suite facilities, good car
parking, garden, residential
licence.*
Bedrooms: 4 double, 2 twin,
2 triple
Bathrooms: 5 private,
2 public
**Bed & breakfast
per night:** £min £max
Single 19.00 21.00
Double 32.00 38.00
Parking for 10
Cards accepted: Access, Visa

Greystone
Preston-under-Scar, Leyburn
DL8 4AQ
☎ Wensleydale (0969)
22042
*Stone-built guesthouse in
peaceful village, between
Wensley and Castle Bolton.
Extensive views over
Wensleydale, excellent
walking and touring centre.*
Bedrooms: 1 double, 1 twin
Bathrooms: 1 public,
1 private shower
**Bed & breakfast
per night:** £min £max
Double 23.00 25.00
**Half board
per person:** £min £max
Daily 18.00 19.00
Weekly 120.00 124.00
Evening meal 1830 (last
orders 2030)
Parking for 2
Open March-October

North Yorkshire
Map ref 4C1

Close to the site of the
Battle of Marston Moor, a
decisive Civil War battle
of 1644. A monument
commemorates the event.

Gill House Farm ⚔
COMMENDED
Tockwith Road, Long
Marston, York YO5 8PJ
☎ Rufforth (090 483) 379
*500-acre mixed farm. Peaceful
period farmhouse set in
glorious countryside
overlooking the Vale of York.
Warm welcome.*
Bedrooms: 3 double
Bathrooms: 3 private
**Bed & breakfast
per night:** £min £max
Double 38.00
Parking for 5

North Yorkshire
Map ref 4B1

Village surrounded by
limestone country and
overlooking Ribblesdale.

Maypole Inn ⚔
APPROVED
Maypole Green, Main Street,
Long Preston, Skipton
BD23 4PH
☎ (0729) 840219
*17th C inn, with open fires,
on the village green. Easy
access to many attractive
walks in the surrounding
dales.*
Bedrooms: 1 single,
3 double, 1 triple, 1 multiple
Bathrooms: 6 private
**Bed & breakfast
per night:** £min £max
Single 24.00 24.00
Double 33.00 37.00
Lunch available
Evening meal 1830 (last
orders 2100)
Parking for 25
Cards accepted: Access, Visa,
Amex

The colour maps
at the back of this
guide pinpoint all
places with
accommodation.

The enquiry
coupons at the
back will help you
when contacting
proprietors.

123

LUND

Humberside
Map ref 4C1

Clematis House, Farmhouse Bed & Breakfast ⋈

1 Eastgate, Lund, Driffield,
North Humberside
YO25 9TQ
☎ Driffield (0377) 217204
*389-acre arable & livestock
farm. Family establishment in
a quiet village 7 miles north
of Beverley, on the B1248 at
the Eastgate/Lockington road
corner.*
Bedrooms: 1 double, 1 twin
Bathrooms: 2 private

Bed & breakfast

per night:	£min	£max
Single	17.00	
Double	34.00	

Half board

per person:	£min	£max
Daily	24.50	
Weekly	160.00	

Evening meal 1800 (last
orders 2000)
Parking for 4

MALHAM

North Yorkshire
Map ref 5B3

Hamlet of stone cottages
amid magnificent rugged
limestone scenery in the
Yorkshire Dales National
Park. Malham Cove is a
curving, sheer white cliff
240 ft high. Malham Tarn,
one of Yorkshire's few
natural lakes, belongs to
the National Trust.
National Park Centre.

Beck Hall Guest House

Malham, Skipton BD23 4DJ
☎ Airton (0729) 830332
*Family-run guesthouse set in
a spacious riverside garden.
Homely atmosphere, four-
poster beds, log fires and
home cooking.*
Bedrooms: 1 single,
8 double, 3 twin, 3 triple
Bathrooms: 15 private,
3 public

Bed & breakfast

per night:	£min	£max
Single	16.50	24.00
Double	30.00	40.00

Half board

per person:	£min	£max
Daily	22.00	27.00

Lunch available
Evening meal 1900 (last
orders 2000)
Parking for 30
Open January-November

Miresfield Farm ⋈

Malham, Skipton BD23 4DA
☎ Airton (0729) 830414
*In a beautiful garden
bordering the village green
and a tumbling stream. Ideal
base for touring the national
park.*
Bedrooms: 6 double, 3 twin,
4 triple
Bathrooms: 11 private,
2 public

Bed & breakfast

per night:	£min	£max
Single	20.00	22.00
Double	36.00	40.00

Half board

per person:	£min	£max
Daily	26.00	28.00
Weekly	182.00	196.00

Evening meal 1830 (last
orders 1200)
Parking for 16

MALTON

North Yorkshire
Map ref 5D3

A thriving farming town on
the River Derwent with
large livestock market.
Famous for race horse
training. The local
museum has Roman
remains and many World
War II relics from the
'Eden' prisoner of war
camp on site in the town.
Castle Howard within
easy reach.

The Brow

25 York Road, Malton
YO17 OAX
☎ (0653) 693402
*Large Georgian residence in
its own grounds on the main
approach road to Malton from
York. Superb views over the
River Derwent extending
across to the Yorkshire Wolds.
18 miles to York, 22 miles to
Scarborough.*
Bedrooms: 2 double, 1 twin
Bathrooms: 1 private,
1 public

Bed & breakfast

per night:	£min	£max
Single	10.00	25.00
Double	22.00	

Evening meal 1830 (last
orders 1900)
Parking for 5

Leonard House

🏅 COMMENDED

45 Old Maltongate, Malton
YO17 0EH
☎ (0653) 697242
*Comfortable Georgian house
in market town, central for
touring Ryedale, the moors
and coast. Easy access by car,
train or bus. Non-smokers
only please.*
Bedrooms: 1 double, 1 twin
Bathrooms: 1 public

Bed & breakfast

per night:	£min	£max
Single	14.00	14.00
Double	28.00	28.00

Parking for 3

Manor Farm

Listed

Little Barugh, Malton
YO17 0UY
☎ Kirby Misperton (065 386)
262
*Georgian farmhouse with
extensive garden and tennis
court, close to Castle Howard,
Flamingo Land and North
York Moors.*
Bedrooms: 1 single, 2 twin
Bathrooms: 1 private,
1 public

Bed & breakfast

per night:	£min	£max
Single	17.00	19.00
Double	34.00	38.00

Half board

per person:	£min	£max
Daily	26.00	28.00
Weekly	170.00	

Evening meal 1800 (last
orders 1200)
Parking for 5
Open April-October

Individual
proprietors have
supplied all details
of accommodation.
Although we do
check for accuracy,
we advise you to
confirm the
information at the
time of booking.

MARKET WEIGHTON

Humberside
Map ref 4C1

Small town on the
western side of the
Yorkshire Wolds. A tablet
in the parish church
records the death of
William Bradley in 1820 at
which time he was 7ft 9in
tall and weighed 27
stone!

Arras Farmhouse ⋈

Listed

Arras Farm, Market
Weighton, York YO4 3RN
☎ (0430) 872404
*460-acre arable farm.
Traditional family farmhouse
on the Wolds Way, secluded
with lots of space and a
peaceful atmosphere, but
close to the main road.*
Bedrooms: 2 double, 1 twin
Bathrooms: 2 private,
1 public

Bed & breakfast

per night:	£min	£max
Single	16.00	18.00
Double	28.00	32.00

Parking for 5

MASHAM

North Yorkshire
Map ref 5C3

Famous market town on
the River Ure, with a large
market square. St Mary's
Church has Norman tower
and 13th C spire.
Theakston's 'Old Peculier'
ale is brewed here.

Lamb Hill Farm

Listed COMMENDED

Masham, Ripon HG4 4DJ
☎ Ripon (0765) 89274
*390-acre mixed farm.
Spacious and comfortable old
farmhouse on a working farm
with views of the dales.
Ideally situated for walking,
exploring abbeys, castles and
towns. Masham 2 miles, A1 5
miles. York 45 minutes.*
Bedrooms: 1 single, 2 double
Bathrooms: 1 public

Bed & breakfast

per night:	£min	£max
Single	13.50	14.00
Double	28.00	36.00

Evening meal from 1900
Parking for 5

Pasture House ⚑
☕ COMMENDED
Healey, Ripon HG4 4LJ
☎ Ripon (0765) 689149
*100-year-old detached house
in 3.5 acres at the foot of
Colsterdale, a beautiful, small
and quiet dale leading to
grouse moors. Fishing and
golf available by arrangement.*
Bedrooms: 1 double, 1 twin,
1 triple
Bathrooms: 2 public
Bed & breakfast

per night:	£min	£max
Single	12.00	
Double	24.00	

Half board

per person:	£min	£max
Daily	25.00	
Weekly	125.00	

Lunch available
Evening meal from 1900
Parking for 6
🛇🖵🕭🚷♿🛉🅟❄

MICKLETHWAITE
West Yorkshire
Map ref 4B1

Small hamlet close to
Rombald's Moor and the
Leeds Liverpool Canal.

Holroyd House
Beck Road, Micklethwaite,
Bingley BD16 3JN
☎ Bradford (0274) 562464
*Former mill owner's house
overlooking the mill pond, set
in the small conservation
village of Micklethwaite on
the edge of the Yorkshire
Dales.*
Bedrooms: 2 single,
1 double, 2 twin
Bathrooms: 3 private,
1 public
Bed & breakfast

per night:	£min	£max
Single	15.00	15.00
Double	30.00	30.00

Half board

per person:	£min	£max
Daily	23.50	23.50

Evening meal 1800 (last
orders 1900)
Parking for 12
🛇8🖵♿🛉🕭🚷❄

> The town index
> towards the back
> of this guide gives
> page numbers of
> all places with
> accommodation.

MIDDLEHAM
North Yorkshire
Map ref 5C3

Town famous for
racehorse training, with
cobbled squares and
houses of local stone.
Norman castle, once
principal residence of
Warwick the Kingmaker
and later Richard III.
Ruins of Jervaulx Abbey
nearby.

Black Swan Hotel ⚑
☕☕ APPROVED
Market Place, Middleham,
Leyburn DL8 4NP
☎ Wensleydale (0969)
22221
*Unspoilt 17th C inn, with
open fires and beamed
ceilings, allied to 20th C
comforts. Emphasis on food.*
Bedrooms: 1 single,
4 double, 1 twin, 1 triple
Bathrooms: 7 private
Bed & breakfast

per night:	£min	£max
Single	24.50	25.00
Double	38.50	54.00

Half board

per person:	£min	£max
Daily	28.25	36.00

Lunch available
Evening meal 1900 (last
orders 2100)
Parking for 3
Cards accepted: Access, Visa
🛇🖵🕭🛉🅂🏮♿♨❄
🚷🖩 SP 🏮

Waterford House ⚑
☕☕☕ HIGHLY COMMENDED
19 Kirkgate, Middleham,
Leyburn DL8 4PG
☎ Wensleydale (0969)
22090
Fax (0969) 24020
*Fine food and wine and a
warm, friendly and
comfortable stay in beautiful
surroundings are assured.
Lunch and full English
afternoon tea available.*
Bedrooms: 4 double, 1 triple
Bathrooms: 4 private,
1 public
Bed & breakfast

per night:	£min	£max
Single	39.00	49.00
Double	49.00	69.00

Half board

per person:	£min	£max
Daily	54.00	64.00
Weekly	339.00	399.00

Lunch available
Evening meal 1900 (last
orders 2200)

Parking for 8
Cards accepted: Access, Visa
🛇🖵🕭🏮♿🅂🖩♨🛉🅟🏮
🖩🏮🕭♿♨🥛🏮

MYTON-ON-SWALE
North Yorkshire
Map ref 5C3

Small village on the
mighty River Swale.

Plump House Farm ⚑
☕
Myton-on-Swale, York
YO6 2RA
☎ Boroughbridge (0423)
360650
*160-acre mixed farm. A warm
welcome with comfortable
accommodation on a working
family farm. Easy access to
York and Harrogate and an
ideal centre for the coast,
dales and moors. Reductions
for children.*
Bedrooms: 1 double, 1 triple
Bathrooms: 2 private,
1 public
Bed & breakfast

per night:	£min	£max
Single	12.00	
Double	24.00	

Half board

per person:	£min	£max
Daily	17.00	

Evening meal 1800 (last
orders 2000)
Parking for 4
🛇🖵♿♿🛉🕭📺🕮🖩♨🥛❄
🚷🏮

OSMOTHERLEY
North Yorkshire
Map ref 5C3

The famous 'Lyke Wake
Walk', across the
Cleveland Hills to
Ravenscar 40 miles away,
starts here in this ancient
village. Attached to the
village cross is a large
stone table used as a
'pulpit' by John Wesley.

Quintana House ⚑
Listed COMMENDED
Back Lane, Osmotherley,
Northallerton DL6 3BJ
☎ (060 983) 258 &
Northallerton (0609) 883258
*Detached, stone-built house
near the village centre, within
90 metres of the Cleveland
Way, affording panoramic
views of Black Hambleton.
Non-smokers only please.*
Bedrooms: 1 double, 1 twin
Bathrooms: 1 public

Bed & breakfast

per night:	£min	£max
Double	25.00	27.00

Half board

per person:	£min	£max
Daily	17.50	29.00
Weekly	122.00	205.00

Evening meal 1830 (last
orders 2000)
Parking for 4
🛇🖵♿🕭♨🛉🅂🖩📺
🕮🏮🥛♨🚷🏮

OSWALDKIRK
North Yorkshire
Map ref 5C3

Village on the hillside
overlooking the valley
which separates the
Howardian and
Hambleton Hills. In the
Domesday Book as
'Oswaldeschurcha'
meaning the church of
Oswald.

Thirklewood House
Oswaldkirk, York YO6 5YB
☎ Ampleforth (043 93) 229
*Large country house in 2
acres of gardens on the
B1257 between Helmsley and
Malton. All rooms have
central heating and tea/coffee
making facilities. Friendly
atmosphere.*
Bedrooms: 3 double, 1 twin,
1 triple
Bathrooms: 2 private,
3 public
Bed & breakfast

per night:	£min	£max
Double	30.00	34.00

Parking for 6
Cards accepted: Visa
♿♿♨🕮🛉🕭📺🕮🖩♨
🚷🏮

OTLEY
West Yorkshire
Map ref 4B1

Market and manufacturing
town in Lower
Wharfedale, the birthplace
of Thomas Chippendale.
Has a Maypole, several
old inns, rebuilt medieval
bridge and a local history
museum. All Saints
Church dates from
Norman times.
*Tourist Information Centre
☎ (0532) 477707*

Paddock Hill
☕ APPROVED
Norwood, Otley LS21 2QU
☎ (0943) 465977

Continued ▶

OTLEY

Continued

Converted farmhouse on the B6451 with open fires and lovely views. Within easy reach of Herriot, Bronte and Emmerdale country, the dales, Skipton, Harrogate and Leeds. Reservoir fishing nearby.
Bedrooms: 1 double, 2 twin
Bathrooms: 1 public,
1 private shower

Bed & breakfast

per night:	£min	£max
Single	13.50	14.50
Double	27.00	29.00

Parking for 3

Spring House ♠
Listed
101 Cross Green, Otley
LS21 1HE
☎ (0943) 462281
18th C house of character encompassing the old school room. On the edge of town within easy reach of the dales and A1 (20 minutes).
Bedrooms: 1 single,
1 double, 1 twin
Bathrooms: 1 public

Bed & breakfast

per night:	£min	£max
Single	14.00	15.00
Double	28.00	30.00

Half board

per person:	£min	£max
Daily	19.00	20.00
Weekly	130.00	137.00

Evening meal from 1800
Parking for 6

PATELEY BRIDGE

North Yorkshire
Map ref 5C3

Small market town at centre of Upper Nidderdale. Flax and linen industries once flourished in this remote and beautiful setting.

Bewerley Hall Farm ♠
Bewerley, Harrogate
HG3 5JA
☎ Harrogate (0423) 711636
87-acre mixed farm. Grade II listed building dating from 1870, in a secluded location near the River Nidd. Through Glasshouses village, over the river, turn right and the farm is first on the right.
Bedrooms: 3 double, 1 twin,
1 triple

Bathrooms: 2 private,
1 public

Bed & breakfast

per night:	£min	£max
Single	18.50	18.50
Double	27.00	27.00

Half board

per person:	£min	£max
Daily	22.75	22.75

Lunch available
Evening meal from 1800
Parking for 10
Open March-December

Nidderdale Lodge
Felbeck, Pateley Bridge,
Harrogate HG3 5DR
☎ Harrogate (0423) 711677
30-acre mixed farm. Spacious bungalow in Nidderdale. Guests have a private sitting room and a kitchen equipped with facilities for their own use. Choice of breakfast.
Bedrooms: 2 double, 1 triple
Bathrooms: 2 private,
2 public

Bed & breakfast

per night:	£min	£max
Single		15.00
Double		28.00

Parking for 6
Open March-October
Cards accepted: Visa

North Pasture Farm
Brimham Rocks, Summer Bridge, Harrogate HG3 4DW
☎ Harrogate (0423) 711470
135-acre dairy farm. The house dates back to 1400 and 1657. John Wesley preached in what is now the lounge.
Bedrooms: 1 single, 2 triple
Bathrooms: 3 private,
1 public

Bed & breakfast

per night:	£min	£max
Single		17.50
Double		38.00

Evening meal from 1830
Parking for 6
Open April-October

The Woodlands ♠
Bewerley, Pateley Bridge,
Harrogate HG3 5HS
☎ Harrogate (0423) 711175
Tastefully furnished Edwardian house in beautiful Nidderdale. All rooms en-suite. 14 miles from

Harrogate, and central for varied and interesting walks.
Bedrooms: 1 double, 1 twin
Bathrooms: 2 private

Bed & breakfast

per night:	£min	£max
Single	25.00	28.00
Double	30.00	40.00

Parking for 3

PICKERING

North Yorkshire
Map ref 5D3

Market town and tourist centre on edge of North York Moors. Parish church has complete set of 15th C wall paintings depicting lives of saints. Part of 12th C castle still stands. Beck Isle Museum. The North Yorkshire Moors Railway begins here.
Tourist Information Centre
☎ (0751) 73791.

Grindale House ♠
123 Eastgate, Pickering
YO18 7DW
☎ (0751) 76636
Beautiful 18th C stone/ pantile townhouse. Lovely rooms with antique furniture, private facilities, TVs. Car park. Friendly informal atmosphere. Non-smokers only please.
Bedrooms: 2 double, 1 twin
Bathrooms: 3 private

Bed & breakfast

per night:	£min	£max
Single	18.00	24.00
Double	15.00	45.00

Parking for 8

Marton Hill ♠
Marton, Sinnington, York
YO6 6RG
☎ Kirkbymoorside (0751) 31418
18-acre livestock farm. 300-year-old country house with spectacular views. 3 miles from Kirkbymoorside on the Malton road, with good easy access.
Bedrooms: 1 double, 1 twin
Bathrooms: 1 public

Bed & breakfast

per night:	£min	£max
Double	20.00	24.00

Parking for 2
Open April-October

Mrs R Metcalf
Listed
103 Westgate, Pickering
YO18 8BB
☎ (0751) 72500
18th C town centre farmhouse, tastefully modernised.
Bedrooms: 2 double, 1 twin
Bathrooms: 1 public

Bed & breakfast

per night:	£min	£max
Double		26.00

Parking for 3

Rains Farm
Allerston, Pickering
YO18 7PQ
☎ Scarborough (0723) 859333
120-acre arable & livestock farm. Renovated farmhouse, peaceful, picturesque location in the Vale of Pickering. Ideal touring base for moors and coast. Good food, warm welcome.
Bedrooms: 2 double, 2 twin,
1 triple
Bathrooms: 5 private

Bed & breakfast

per night:	£min	£max
Double		30.00

Half board

per person:	£min	£max
Daily		24.00

Evening meal 1800 (last orders 1400)
Parking for 6
Open April-October

Station Hotel
11 Park Street, Pickering
YO18 7AJ
☎ (0751) 72171
Country inn opposite the North Yorkshire Moors Steam Railway. Fine ales, home-cooked food and an a la carte restaurant.
Bedrooms: 3 double, 1 twin,
1 triple, 1 multiple
Bathrooms: 1 public

Bed & breakfast

per night:	£min	£max
Single		18.00
Double		35.00

Half board

per person:	£min	£max
Daily	23.00	29.00
Weekly	145.00	185.00

Lunch available
Evening meal 1900 (last orders 2145)
Parking for 10
Cards accepted: Access, Visa

RAVENSCAR

North Yorkshire
Map ref 5D3

Splendidly-positioned small coastal resort with magnificent views over Robin Hood's Bay. Its Old Peak is the end of the famous Lyke Wake Walk or 'corpse way'.

Foxcliffe Tea Rooms ⋒
Station Square, Ravenscar, Scarborough YO13 OLU
☎ Scarborough (0723) 871028
Family-run bed and breakfast accommodation in a Victorian house with sea views from every room, set amongst beautiful countryside in the North York Moors National Park.
Bedrooms: 2 double, 2 twin
Bathrooms: 1 public, 1 private shower

Bed & breakfast

per night:	£min	£max
Single	13.00	13.00
Double	26.00	26.00

Half board

per person:	£min	£max
Daily	20.00	20.00
Weekly	140.00	140.00

Lunch available
Evening meal 1830 (last orders 1600)
Open March-October

Smugglers Rock Country Guest House ⋒
Ravenscar, Scarborough YO13 OER
☎ Scarborough (0723) 870044
Georgian country house, reputedly a former smugglers' haunt, with panoramic views over the surrounding national park and sea. Half a mile from the village, an ideal centre for touring, walking and pony trekking.
Bedrooms: 2 single, 4 double, 2 twin, 2 multiple
Bathrooms: 10 private, 1 public

Bed & breakfast

per night:	£min	£max
Single	19.00	19.50
Double	38.00	39.00

Half board

per person:	£min	£max
Daily	26.50	27.00
Weekly	169.00	175.00

Evening meal 1830 (last orders 1600)
Parking for 12
Open March-November

REDMIRE

North Yorkshire
Map ref 5B3

Peaceful and little-known dales village at east end of Wensleydale. Pale stone cottages scattered around a large green with ancient oak tree and pinfold where stray animals were penned.

Elm House ⋒
HIGHLY COMMENDED
Elm House Estate, Redmire, Leyburn DL8 4EW
☎ Wensleydale (0969) 22313
Stone-built, 17th C manor house, fully modernised to provide every comfort. In a peaceful garden setting, overlooking beautiful Wensleydale. Personal service by resident owners.
Bedrooms: 1 double, 1 twin, 1 triple
Bathrooms: 3 private

Bed & breakfast

per night:	£min	£max
Double	19.00	21.00

Parking for 10

REETH

North Yorkshire
Map ref 5B3

Once a market town and lead-mining centre, Reeth today serves holiday-makers in Swaledale with its folk museum and 18th C shops and inns lining the green at High Row.

Kings Arms Hotel
Listed APPROVED
High Row, Reeth, Richmond DL11 6SY
☎ Richmond (0748) 84259
Family-run hotel dating from 1736, in a pleasant setting overlooking the village green with wonderful views of Swaledale.
Bedrooms: 1 double, 1 twin, 2 triple
Bathrooms: 4 private showers

Bed & breakfast

per night:	£min	£max
Single	14.00	22.00
Double	25.00	36.00

Lunch available
Evening meal 1830 (last orders 2130)

RICHMOND

North Yorkshire
Map ref 5C3

Market town on edge of Swaledale with 11th C castle, Georgian and Victorian buildings surrounding cobbled market-place. Green Howards' Museum is in the former Holy Trinity Church. Attractions include the Georgian Theatre, Richmondshire Museum and Easby Abbey.
Tourist Information Centre ☎ (0748) 850252

47 Maison Dieu
Richmond DL10 7AU
☎ (0748) 825982
Large stone-built family house with pleasant aspect and gardens. Excellent views of the castle and falls and Richmond old town. On main road to Richmond from Brompton-on-Swale.
Bedrooms: 1 single, 2 twin, 1 triple
Bathrooms: 1 private, 1 public

Bed & breakfast

per night:	£min	£max
Single	14.00	15.00
Double	28.00	34.00

Parking for 5

Browson Bank
Dalton, Richmond DL11 7HE
☎ Darlington (0325) 718504 & 718246
16th C converted barn, full of character, in beautiful farmland near Richmond and 6 miles west of Scotch Corner.
Bedrooms: 2 double
Bathrooms: 2 private, 1 public

Bed & breakfast

per night:	£min	£max
Single	15.00	18.00
Double	25.00	25.00

Parking for 4

Dalton Grange
Listed
Dalton, Richmond DL11 7HP
☎ Teesdale (0833) 21235
90-acre dairy farm. Situated between Barnard Castle and Richmond, with easy access to A1 south or A66 Lake District. A working farm with beautiful views and lots to see.
Bedrooms: 1 single, 1 twin, 1 triple
Bathrooms: 1 public

Bed & breakfast

per night:	£min	£max
Single	12.00	15.00
Double	24.00	30.00

Half board

per person:	£min	£max
Daily	18.00	25.00

Lunch available
Evening meal 1900 (last orders 2000)
Parking for 5

Mrs L Brooks
Holmedale, Dalton, Richmond DL11 7HX
☎ Teesdale (0833) 21236
Georgian house in a quiet village, midway between Richmond and Barnard Castle. Ideal for the dales and Lakes.
Bedrooms: 1 double, 1 triple
Bathrooms: 1 public

Bed & breakfast

per night:	£min	£max
Single		13.00
Double		24.00

Half board

per person:	£min	£max
Daily		17.00
Weekly		105.00

Evening meal 1800 (last orders 1200)
Parking for 2

Mount Pleasant Farm ⋒
COMMENDED
Whashton, Richmond DL11 7JP
☎ (0748) 822784
280-acre mixed farm. En-suite rooms in a converted stable, 1 suitable for disabled. Ideal for a family holiday and a pleasant place to stay. Good home cooking. Lots to see and do on the farm. Please ring for brochure and menus.
Bedrooms: 2 double, 2 triple
Bathrooms: 4 private
Continued ▶

RICHMOND

Continued

Bed & breakfast

per night:	£min	£max
Single	16.00	17.00
Double	30.00	32.00

Half board

per person:	£min	£max
Daily	46.00	48.00
Weekly	160.50	164.50

Evening meal 1830 (last orders 1200)
Parking for 6

The Restaurant On The Green

Listed COMMENDED

5-7 Bridge Street, Richmond
DL10 4RW
☎ (0748) 826229
Imposing William and Mary property with Georgian sundials. At corner of green at foot of castle bluff, near River Swale and countryside, yet 250 yards from Market Place.
Bedrooms: 1 double, 1 twin
Bathrooms: 1 private, 1 public

Bed & breakfast

per night:	£min	£max
Single	18.50	23.00
Double	29.00	37.00

Evening meal 1900 (last orders 2130)
Cards accepted: Access, Visa

RIPON

North Yorkshire
Map ref 5C3

Small, ancient city with impressive cathedral containing Saxon crypt which houses church treasures from all over Yorkshire. 'Setting the Watch' tradition kept nightly by horn-blower in Market Square. Fountains Abbey nearby.

The Coopers ▲

36 College Road, Ripon
HG4 2HA
☎ (0765) 603708
Spacious, comfortable Victorian house overlooking countryside in quiet area. En-suite facilities available. Special rates for children. Cyclists welcome, storage for bicycles. Take-away meals acceptable in rooms.

Bedrooms: 1 single, 1 twin, 1 triple
Bathrooms: 1 private, 1 public

Bed & breakfast

per night:	£min	£max
Single	14.00	15.00
Double	24.00	32.00

Parking for 3

Heatherlands

Grantley, Ripon HG4 3PL
☎ Sawley (0765) 620634
Between Ripon and Pateley Bridge in a beautiful situation offering peaceful, comfortable accommodation. Large, award-winning garden. Ideal base for walking/touring.
Bedrooms: 2 double, 1 twin
Bathrooms: 3 private

Bed & breakfast

per night:	£min	£max
Double	28.00	32.00

Parking for 5
Open April-October

Marrick House ▲

21 Iddesleigh Terrace, Bondgate Green, Ripon HG4 1QW
☎ (0765) 602707
Comfortable, Victorian terraced house facing the canal basin, on the B6265, approximately 300 yards from Ripon Cathedral and 6 minutes' walk from the market square. Evening meal by arrangement.
Bedrooms: 1 single, 1 twin, 1 triple
Bathrooms: 1 private, 1 public

Bed & breakfast

per night:	£min	£max
Single	14.00	16.00
Double	28.00	32.00

Half board

per person:	£min	£max
Daily	20.00	22.00
Weekly	125.00	

Evening meal 1830 (last orders 1600)
Parking for 2

Moor End Farm ▲

Knaresborough Road, Littlethorpe, Ripon HG4 3LU
☎ (0765) 677419
57-acre livestock farm. 2.5 miles south of Ripon, between Bishop Monkton and Ripon on the Knaresborough Road. Ideal centre for the dales and

Herriot country. Home cooking and a warm Yorkshire welcome. Non-smokers only please.
Bedrooms: 2 double, 1 triple
Bathrooms: 1 public

Bed & breakfast

per night:	£min	£max
Double	27.00	32.00

Half board

per person:	£min	£max
Daily	22.00	24.50
Weekly	147.00	164.00

Evening meal 1830 (last orders 1600)
Parking for 7
Open March-November

St George's Court ▲

Listed COMMENDED

Old Home Farm, Grantley, Ripon HG4 3EU
☎ Sawley (0765) 620618
5 miles from Ripon, beautifully situated accommodation in renovated farm buildings. Comfortable rooms with colour TV. Breakfast served in the 17th C farmhouse.
Bedrooms: 3 double, 1 twin, 1 triple
Bathrooms: 5 private

Bed & breakfast

per night:	£min	£max
Single	22.50	
Double	38.00	

Half board

per person:	£min	£max
Daily	28.50	

Evening meal 1900 (last orders 2000)
Parking for 12

ROSEDALE ABBEY

North Yorkshire
Map ref 5C3

Sturdy hamlet built around Cistercian nunnery in the reign of Henry II, in the middle of Rosedale, largest of the moorland valleys.

Low Bell End Farm

Rosedale Abbey, Pickering YO18 8RE
☎ Lastingham (075 15) 451
173-acre mixed farm. Farmhouse set in North York Moors National Park.
Bedrooms: 1 double, 1 twin, 1 triple
Bathrooms: 1 public

Bed & breakfast

per night:	£min	£max
Single	14.00	
Double	28.00	

Half board

per person:	£min	£max
Daily	19.00	

Evening meal from 1900
Parking for 3
Open January-November

RUFFORTH

North Yorkshire
Map ref 4C1

Village west of York. There is a small airfield, and it is also the home of the York Gliding Centre.

Rosedale Guest House ▲

COMMENDED

Wetherby Road, Rufforth, York YO2 3QB
☎ (0904) 83297
Small, family-run guesthouse with a homely atmosphere and all facilities, in a delightful, unspoilt village 4 miles west of York on the B1224. Private parking available.
Bedrooms: 1 single, 2 double, 1 twin, 1 triple
Bathrooms: 1 private, 2 public, 2 private showers

Bed & breakfast

per night:	£min	£max
Single	15.00	16.00
Double	28.00	34.00

Parking for 5

Wellgarth House ▲

Wetherby Road, Rufforth, York YO2 3QB
☎ (0904) 738592 & 738595
Individual and attractive country guesthouse in the delightful village of Rufforth. Ideal touring base for York and the Yorkshire Dales.
Bedrooms: 1 single, 3 double, 2 twin, 1 triple
Bathrooms: 1 private, 2 public

Bed & breakfast

per night:	£min	£max
Single	16.00	18.00
Double	28.00	40.00

Parking for 10
Cards accepted: Access, Visa

SCARBOROUGH

North Yorkshire
Map ref 5D3

Large, popular east coast
seaside resort, formerly a
spa town. Beautiful
gardens and splendid
sandy beaches in North
and South Bays. Castle
ruins date from 1100, fine
Georgian and Victorian
houses in old town.
Angling, theatres, cricket
festivals and seasonal
entertainment.
Tourist Information Centre
☎ *(0723) 373333*

Falcon Inn ⚫⚫
Whitby Road, Cloughton,
Scarborough YO13 0DY
☎ (0723) 870717
*Select freehouse, 9 miles from
Scarborough, 12 miles from
Whitby. Open all year. Bar
meals and restaurant.*
Bedrooms: 3 double, 3 twin
Bathrooms: 6 private

Bed & breakfast

per night:	£min	£max
Single	37.50	37.50
Double	45.00	45.00

Lunch available
Evening meal 1900 (last
orders 2130)
Parking for 30

Wrea Head House ⚫⚫
HIGHLY COMMENDED
Wrea Head Farm, Barmoor
Lane, Scalby, Scarborough
YO13 0PB
☎ (0723) 375844
*Country house in a beautiful
location with panoramic
coastal and country views.
Scalby village is only 3 miles
from Scarborough on the
edge of the North York Moors.
Non smoking establishment.*
Bedrooms: 2 double, 1 twin
Bathrooms: 3 private

Bed & breakfast

per night:	£min	£max
Double	37.00	48.00

Parking for 50
Cards accepted: Access, Visa

The national
Crown scheme is
explained in full
in the information
pages towards the
back of this guide.

SCRUTON

North Yorkshire
Map ref 5C3

Little village east of the
A1 and west of the River
Swale. The church is 1 of
only 5 in the country
dedicated to St
Radegund.

Richmond House
6 Beech Close, Scruton,
Northallerton DL7 0TU
☎ Northallerton (0609)
748369
*Pleasant surroundings, 3
miles from A1. Ideal stop-over
for north/south travellers.
Central for touring dales,
moors and coast.*
Bedrooms: 1 double
Bathrooms: 1 public

Bed & breakfast

per night:	£min	£max
Double	25.00	28.00

Parking for 1
Open April-October

SELBY

North Yorkshire
Map ref 4C1

Small market town on the
River Ouse, believed to
have been birthplace of
Henry I, with a
magnificent abbey
containing much fine
Norman and Early English
architecture.
Tourist Information Centre
☎ *(0757) 703263*

Hazeldene Guest House
34 Brook Street, Doncaster
Road, Selby YO8 0AR
☎ (0757) 704809
*Victorian town house, on the
A19 and close to town centre.
12 miles from York, 7 miles
from A1 and 6 miles from
M52. Non-smokers only
please.*
Bedrooms: 2 single,
2 double, 3 triple
Bathrooms: 2 public

Bed & breakfast

per night:	£min	£max
Single	15.00	17.00
Double	30.00	34.00

Parking for 6

Villa Nurseries ⚫⚫
33 York Road, Riccall, York
YO4 6QG
☎ (0757) 248257

*Family-run house in a quiet
village 9 miles south of York,
offering comfortable, friendly
accommodation. Some en-
suite rooms.*
Bedrooms: 7 single,
2 double, 6 twin, 1 triple,
1 multiple
Bathrooms: 9 private,
1 public

Bed & breakfast

per night:	£min	£max
Single	13.00	17.00
Double	24.00	30.00

Parking for 10

SETTLE

North Yorkshire
Map ref 5B3

Town of narrow streets
and Georgian houses in
an area of great
limestone hills and crags.
Panoramic view from
Castleberg Crag which
stands 300 ft above town.
Tourist Information Centre
☎ *(0729) 825192*

Accerhill Hall Farm
Giggleswick, Settle
BD24 0DX
☎ (0729) 823152
*100-acre livestock farm.
Peaceful with friendly
atmosphere, 4 miles from
Settle and with lovely views of
Ingleborough and Pen-y-
ghent. Ideal centre for
Yorkshire Dales and the
Lakes.*
Bedrooms: 1 single, 1 triple,
1 multiple
Bathrooms: 2 public

Bed & breakfast

per night:	£min	£max
Single	15.00	15.00
Double	28.00	28.00

Parking for 6

Chalimbana Cottage
3 Ribble Terrace, Settle
BD24 9DE
☎ (0729) 823988
*Homely accommodation in a
Victorian stone terraced
house, 7 to 8 minutes' walk
from the town centre. In a
beautiful setting overlooking
River Ribble with Pen-y-ghent
in the distance.*
Bedrooms: 1 double, 1 triple
Bathrooms: 1 public

Bed & breakfast

per night:	£min	£max
Double	29.00	29.00

Halsteads ⚫⚫
COMMENDED
3 Halsteads Terrace, Duke
Street, Settle BD24 9AP
☎ (0729) 822823
*With magnificent views and
ideally situated near the town
centre, this elegant Victorian
house is the perfect base for
exploring the dales or the
Settle-Carlisle Railway.
Generous discounts for longer
holidays or off-peak breaks.
Tourist information available.*
Bedrooms: 2 double, 2 twin
Bathrooms: 2 private,
1 public

Bed & breakfast

per night:	£min	£max
Single	16.50	27.50
Double	33.00	40.00

Parking for 4

Penmar Court ⚫⚫
Listed
Duke Street, Settle
BD24 9AS
☎ (0729) 823258
*Large Victorian house with
excellent views, near to A65
and railway station. TV and
tea/coffee-making facilities.*
Bedrooms: 2 single,
3 double, 1 twin
Bathrooms: 3 private,
2 public

Bed & breakfast

per night:	£min	£max
Single	14.00	16.00
Double	28.00	32.00

Parking for 14
Cards accepted: Access, Visa

The Riddings ⚫⚫
COMMENDED
Long Preston, Skipton
BD23 4QN
☎ Long Preston (0729) 840
231
*Grade II listed country house
with extensive formal and
walled gardens, private
woodland and landscaped
waterfalls. Superb views over
the Ribble Valley.*
Bedrooms: 2 double, 1 twin,
1 triple
Bathrooms: 2 private,
1 public

Bed & breakfast

per night:	£min	£max
Single	25.00	35.00
Double	39.00	55.00

SETTLE

Continued

Half board

per person:	£min	£max
Daily	31.00	39.00
Weekly	195.00	245.00

Evening meal 1830 (last orders 1000)
Parking for 14

☼ 10 ♐ ♨ ⬚ UL ▯ S ✂ ♨
TV ▥, ♫ ♣ ✕ ♠ ❧ SP ⚑

Scar Close Farm ♈

⚱ ⚱ ⚱ COMMENDED

Feizor, Austwick, Lancaster
LA2 8DF
☎ (0729) 823496
*185-acre dairy & livestock
farm. High standard en-suite
farmhouse accommodation
and food in a picturesque
hamlet near Settle. A tourist
centre for the dales, Lakes
and seaside.*
Bedrooms: 1 double, 1 twin,
1 triple
Bathrooms: 3 private

Bed & breakfast

per night:	£min	£max
Double	32.00	34.00

Half board

per person:	£min	£max
Daily	24.00	26.00
Weekly	168.00	180.00

Evening meal 1800 (last orders 1830)
Parking for 5

☼ ♣ ♨ ♐ UL ▯ S ♨ TV ▥, ♫
U ✿ ✕ ♠ ❧ SP

SHEFFIELD

South Yorkshire
Map ref 4B2

Local iron ore and coal
gave Sheffield its
prosperous steel and
cutlery industries. The
modern city centre has
many interesting buildings
- cathedral, Cutlers' Hall,
Crucible Theatre, Graves
and Mappin Art Galleries -
and has an excellent
shopping centre.
Tourist Information Centre
☎ *(0742) 734671 or
795901*

Greensleeves Cottage

183 Foxhill Road, Birley
Carr, Sheffield S6 1HF
☎ (0742) 321107
*Detached stone cottage 4.5
miles north-west of city
centre. Take A61 Penistone
road north to Wadsley Bridge,
turn left at traffic lights and
follow signs for Foxhill.*
Bedrooms: 1 single, 1 double
Bathrooms: 1 public

Bed & breakfast

per night:	£min	£max
Single	16.00	18.00
Double	30.00	32.00

Parking for 2
Open January-April, July-
December

☼ ▯ ♣ UL TV ▥. ♫ ❧

SINNINGTON

North Yorkshire
Map ref 5C3

Delightful village with
broad greens and dried
river beds. A tall maypole
and the spired school
overlook a curious
packhorse bridge.

Fox & Hounds Hotel ♈

⚱ ⚱ ⚱ COMMENDED

Main Street, Sinnington,
York YO6 6SQ
☎ Pickering (0751) 31577
*Old coaching inn, newly
refurbished, with open fires
and period furniture. In a
rural setting. Fishing, riding
and riverside walks close by.
Private parking.*
Bedrooms: 1 single,
5 double, 1 twin, 1 triple
Bathrooms: 8 private

Bed & breakfast

per night:	£min	£max
Single	35.00	
Double	55.00	

Lunch available
Evening meal 1830 (last orders 2130)
Parking for 30
Cards accepted: Access, Visa

☼ ♣ ✆ ▯ ♐ ♨ ♨ S ▯ ▥.
♫ ◗ U ♪ ✿ ♠ ✎ SP

SKIPTON

North Yorkshire
Map ref 4B1

Pleasant market town with
farming community
atmosphere, at gateway
to Dales with a Palladian
Town Hall, parish church
and fully roofed castle at
the top of High Street.
Tourist Information Centre
☎ *(0756) 792809*

Fox & Hounds Inn

Starbotton, Skipton
BD23 5HY
☎ (0756) 760269
*150-year-old unspoilt inn,
offering a happy atmosphere,
real ale and home-cooked
food. In beautiful scenery,
ideal for unwinding.*
Bedrooms: 1 double, 1 twin
Bathrooms: 2 private

Bed & breakfast

per night:	£min	£max
Double	40.00	40.00

Lunch available
Evening meal 1900 (last orders 2100)
Parking for 25
Open March-December

☐ ♣ S ✂ ▥. ✕ ❧ ♠

SLEIGHTS

North Yorkshire
Map ref 5D3

Village close to Whitby at
the bottom of Blue Bank
and on the broad, deep
point of the River Esk.

Ryedale House ♈

♨

154-158 Coach Road,
Sleights, Whitby YO22 5EQ
☎ Whitby (0947) 810534
*Friendly cottage-style house
with a large garden and
beautiful views, at the foot of
the moors and 4 miles from
the coast. Traditional and
vegetarian cooking with
plenty of choice. No pets.
Non-smokers only please.
Minimum stay 2 nights in
summer.*
Bedrooms: 2 double, 1 twin
Bathrooms: 2 public

Bed & breakfast

per night:	£min	£max
Double	28.00	31.00

Parking for 3
Open March-November

☼ ♣ 5 ♣ UL ♨ S ✂ TV ▥. ♫ ✿
✕ ❧ OAP

SLINGSBY

North Yorkshire
Map ref 5C3

Large, attractive village
with a green, a ruined
mansion and Wyville Hall,
all steeped in history.

Lowry's Restaurant and Guest House

Malton Road, Slingsby, York
YO6 7AF
☎ Hovingham (0653)
628417
*At the foot of the Howardian
Hills on the main Malton to
Helmsley road. 3 miles from
Castle Howard. 1.5 miles from
Centenary Walk.*
Bedrooms: 1 single,
1 double, 1 twin, 1 triple
Bathrooms: 2 private,
3 private showers

Bed & breakfast

per night:	£min	£max
Single	16.00	18.00
Double	32.00	36.00

Lunch available
Evening meal 1930 (last orders 2130)
Parking for 7

☼ ♣ ♨ S ✂ ♨ TV ▥. ♫ U ✿
✕ ❧ SP

SPENNITHORNE

North Yorkshire
Map ref 5C3

Quiet, rural village with
small fragments remaining
of a castle and an
interesting church.

Old Horn Inn ♈

⚱ ⚱

Spennithorne, Leyburn
DL8 5PR
☎ Wensleydale (0969) 22370
*17th C country inn in
beautiful Lower Wensleydale,
with a warm, friendly
welcome and emphasis on
food. Children 10 years and
over welcome. Special rates
available for winter breaks.*
Bedrooms: 2 double
Bathrooms: 2 private

Bed & breakfast

per night:	£min	£max
Double	37.00	40.00

Lunch available
Evening meal 1900 (last orders 2100)
Parking for 6

☼ 10 ▯ ♐ ♣ S ▥. ♫ ◗
❧ SP

STARBOTTON

North Yorkshire
Map ref 5B3

Quiet, picturesque village
midway between
Kettlewell and Buckden in
Wharfedale. Many
buildings belong to the
17th C and several have
dated lintels.

Calfhalls Farm

Starbotton, Skipton
BD23 5HY
☎ Kettlewell (0756) 760370
*350-acre mixed farm. In a
quiet unspoilt dales village,
easily accessible for walking
or touring.*
Bedrooms: 2 double, 1 twin
Bathrooms: 2 public

Bed & breakfast

per night:	£min	£max
Single	18.00	
Double	28.00	30.00

Half board

per person:	£min	£max
Daily	24.00	25.00
Weekly	98.00	98.00

Evening meal 1900 (last orders 1900)
Parking for 4
🛇 ♥ 👪 ▮ § ⨂ 🖵 ⬛, ⬚ 🥢
✓ ✿ ✕ 🐾 SP

STOKESLEY

North Yorkshire
Map ref 5C3

Handsome market town midway between the North York Moors and the Cleveland border. Famous for its annual show in September.

Busby House
Listed   HIGHLY COMMENDED

Stokesley, Middlesbrough,
Cleveland TS9 5LB
☎ (0642) 710425
250-acre mixed farm. Beautiful old farmhouse overlooking garden and Cleveland Hills. Warm and friendly atmosphere. Central location for moors, dales, coast and places of historic interest. Easy access A1.
Bedrooms: 2 twin
Bathrooms: 1 private,
1 public

Bed & breakfast

per night:	£min	£max
Single	30.00	35.00
Double	47.00	52.00

Evening meal from 1930
Parking for 4
Open February-November
📺 🛇 🖵 ✕ ⨂ ⬛, ⬚ ✿
✕ 🐾

SUTTON BANK

North Yorkshire
Map ref 5C3

Cotefaw

Hambleton Cottages, Sutton
Bank, Thirsk YO7 2EZ
☎ Thirsk (0845) 597363
Stone-built country cottage on the Cleveland Way, within the North York Moors National Park and close to York, Herriot country, the Yorkshire Gliding Club and the East Coast.
Bedrooms: 1 single,
1 double, 1 triple
Bathrooms: 1 public

Bed & breakfast

per night:	£min	£max
Single	12.00	14.00
Double	24.00	28.00

Parking for 4
Open April-October
🛇 ⚹ 🖵 ▮ § ⨂ 🖵 ⬛, ⬚ 🥢
✕ 🐾

TERRINGTON

North Yorkshire
Map ref 5C3

In the Howardian Hills, the name of this picturesque village is said to refer in Old English to the practice of sorcery. There is a church and an old rectory now known as Terrington Hall.

Gate Farm
Listed

Ganthorpe, Terrington, York
YO6 4QD
☎ Coneysthorpe (065 384)
269
150-acre dairy farm. Stone-built farmhouse offering traditional Yorkshire hospitality in a quiet village near Castle Howard. Convenient for the moors, wolds and the East Coast.
Bedrooms: 1 double, 1 twin,
1 triple
Bathrooms: 1 public

Bed & breakfast

per night:	£min	£max
Single	15.00	
Double	25.00	

Half board

per person:	£min	£max
Daily	21.00	

Evening meal 1830 (last orders 1600)
Parking for 3
Open March-October
🛇 📺 🛇 🖵 ▮ § ⨂ 🖵 ⬛, ⬚
🖵 🥢 ✿ 🐾

THIRSK

North Yorkshire
Map ref 5C3

Thriving market town with cobbled square surrounded by old shops and inns and also with a local museum. St. Mary's Church is probably the best example of Perpendicular work in Yorkshire.

Doxford House 🏔
🔱🔱

Front Street, Sowerby,
Thirsk YO7 1JP
☎ (0845) 523238
Handsome, Georgian house with attractive gardens and paddock with animals, overlooking the greens of

Sowerby. Comfortable rooms - all en-suite.
Bedrooms: 1 double, 1 twin,
2 triple
Bathrooms: 4 private

Bed & breakfast

per night:	£min	£max
Single	18.00	19.00
Double	28.00	30.00

Half board

per person:	£min	£max
Daily	21.00	22.50

Evening meal from 1830
Parking for 4
Cards accepted:
🛇 ♿ 🛇 🖵 § ✕ 🖵 🖵 ⬛, ⬚
✿ 🐾 🏧

Eldmire Hill 🏔
Listed

Dalton, Thirsk YO7 3JH
☎ (0845) 577252
360-acre arable farm. Farmhouse in open countryside with magnificent views. 4 miles south of Thirsk and 5 minutes from A1 and A19. York, dales and moors close by.
Bedrooms: 1 double, 1 twin
Bathrooms: 1 public

Bed & breakfast

per night:	£min	£max
Single	13.00	14.00
Double	26.00	28.00

Parking for 5
Open March-October
🛇 ♥ 🖵 🖵 ⨂ 🖵 ⬛, ⬚ ✿ ⟲ ∪ ✿
🥢 🖵 OAP

Firtree Farmhouse

Easingwold, York YO6 3NN
☎ (0845) 401201 & 401220
650-acre arable farm. 18th C farmhouse with attractive gardens set in beautiful countryside 5 miles south of Thirsk. Traditionally decorated bedrooms. Tennis and horse riding. Dales and moors nearby.
Bedrooms: 1 double, 1 twin,
1 triple
Bathrooms: 2 private,
1 public

Bed & breakfast

per night:	£min	£max
Single	15.00	17.00
Double	26.00	30.00

Half board

per person:	£min	£max
Daily	20.00	24.00
Weekly	110.00	130.00

Evening meal 1900 (last orders 2100)
Parking for 5
🛇 ♿ 🛇 🖵 ▮ § ✕ ✕ ⨂ 🖵 ⬛,
⟲ ∪ ⟲ 🖵 ✿ 🖵 OAP 🖵 SP

Garth House 🏔
Listed

Dalton, Thirsk YO7 3HY
☎ (0845) 577310
50-acre livestock farm. Farmhouse set in a country village. Central for York, Harrogate and many historic, interesting places. Friendly welcome awaiting guests.
Bedrooms: 1 double, 1 twin,
1 triple
Bathrooms: 2 public

Bed & breakfast

per night:	£min	£max
Single	11.00	
Double	22.00	

Parking for 6
🛇 ♥ 🖵 🖵 ⨂ 🖵 ⬛, ⬚ ✿ 🖵

High House Farm 🏔
🔱🔱   APPROVED

Sutton Bank, Thirsk
YO7 2HA
☎ (0845) 597557
113-acre mixed farm. Family-run stone-built farmhouse and courtyard. Magnificent views. Splendid walking country. Home-produced food and emphasis on comfort and warm hospitality. 5 miles east of Thirsk.
Bedrooms: 1 double, 1 triple
Bathrooms: 1 public

Bed & breakfast

per night:	£min	£max
Double	28.00	30.00

Parking for 2
Open April-November
🛇 ♥ 🖵 ▮ ▮ ⨂ 🖵 ⬛, ⬚ ✿ ∪ ✿ ✕
🖵 OAP

Lavender House

27 Kirkgate, Thirsk YO7 1PL
☎ (0845) 522224
Small, friendly guesthouse in an ideal location from which to tour Yorkshire. Two minutes from Town Square on the Northallerton road.
Bedrooms: 1 double, 1 triple
Bathrooms: 2 public

Bed & breakfast

per night:	£min	£max
Single	11.50	
Double	23.00	

Parking for 3
🛇 ♥ 🖵 ▮ § ⨂ 🖵 ⬛, ⬚ ✿ ✕
🖵 OAP

Otterington Shorthorn Inn
▣

South Otterington,
Northallerton DL7 9HP
☎ Northallerton (0609)
773816
Early 19th C inn with an open fire and oak beams, serving traditional ales and

Continued ▶

THIRSK

Continued

offering a warm welcome. Bar
meals, pool table and private
entrance. In village north of
Thirsk.
Bedrooms: 1 single,
3 double, 1 twin
Bathrooms: 1 public

Bed & breakfast

per night:	£min	£max
Single	15.00	17.00
Double	30.00	34.00

Half board

per person:	£min	£max
Daily	20.00	28.00
Weekly	140.00	196.00

Lunch available
Evening meal 1900 (last
orders 2130)
Parking for 12

Plump Bank
COMMENDED

Felixkirk Road, Thirsk
YO7 2EW
☎ (0845) 522406
From Thirsk take the A170
Scarborough road. After 1
mile turn left for Felixkirk
and Boltby and house is on
the left after 100 yards.
Bedrooms: 2 double, 1 twin
Bathrooms: 3 private

Bed & breakfast

per night:	£min	£max
Double	25.00	

Parking for 9

Station House

Station Road, Thirsk
YO7 4LS
☎ (0845) 522063
Spacious detached house with
private parking and garden.
Convenient for railway
station, 23 minutes to York.
Ideal base for touring dales
and moors.
Bedrooms: 1 single,
1 double, 1 triple
Bathrooms: 1 public

Bed & breakfast

per night:	£min	£max
Single	13.00	13.00
Double	26.00	26.00

Parking for 3
Open April-October

Thornborough House Farm

South Kilvington, Thirsk
YO7 2NP
☎ (0845) 522103

206-acre mixed farm. 200-
year-old farmhouse in an
ideal position for walking and
touring in the North York
Moors and Yorkshire Dales.
Bedrooms: 2 double,
1 multiple
Bathrooms: 2 private,
2 public

Bed & breakfast

per night:	£min	£max
Single	12.00	17.00
Double	24.00	34.00

Half board

per person:	£min	£max
Daily	19.00	24.00
Weekly	130.00	145.00

Evening meal from 1830
Parking for 6

THORALBY

North Yorkshire
Map ref 5B3

Small village south of
Aysgarth in Wensleydale.

High Green House
HIGHLY COMMENDED

Thoralby, Leyburn DL8 3SU
☎ Wensleydale (0969)
663420
Listed Georgian house with
fine views, period furniture,
beams, log fires. Walled
garden to rear. Good
traditional food. Excellent
centre for touring and
walking.
Bedrooms: 2 double, 1 twin
Bathrooms: 3 private

Bed & breakfast

per night:	£min	£max
Double	18.00	

Half board

per person:	£min	£max
Daily	30.00	

Evening meal from 1900
Parking for 4
Open April-October
Cards accepted: Access, Visa

There are separate
sections in this
guide listing groups
specialising in farm
holidays and
accommodation
which is especially
suitable for young
people and
organised groups.

THORNTON RUST

North Yorkshire
Map ref 5B3

A peaceful Wensleydale
village in the heart of the
Yorkshire Dales. 2 miles
west of Aysgarth Falls on
a quiet loop road just off
the A684, between
Bainbridge and Aysgarth.
An excellent centre for
walking and touring.

Penny Acre

Thornton Rust, Leyburn
DL8 3AN
☎ Wensleydale (0969)
663293
Detached house in a
picturesque village two miles
from Aysgarth. Superb views
from the garden. Every
comfort and interesting meals.
Bedrooms: 1 double, 2 twin
Bathrooms: 3 private

Bed & breakfast

per night:	£min	£max
Double	33.00	36.00

Half board

per person:	£min	£max
Daily	27.00	28.50

Evening meal 1830 (last
orders 2000)
Parking for 5
Open March-October

THORNTON WATLASS

North Yorkshire
Map ref 5C3

The Buck Inn
COMMENDED

Thornton Watlass, Ripon
HG4 4AH
☎ Bedale (0677) 422461
Friendly village inn
overlooking the delightful
cricket green in a small
village, 3 miles from Bedale
on the Masham road, and
close to the A1. In James
Herriot country. Ideal for
walking.
Bedrooms: 1 single,
2 double, 1 twin, 1 triple
Bathrooms: 5 private

Bed & breakfast

per night:	£min	£max
Single	25.00	28.00
Double	40.00	45.00

Lunch available
Evening meal 1830 (last
orders 2130)
Parking for 40

Cards accepted: Access, Visa,
Amex

The Old Rectory
Listed DE LUXE

Thornton Watlass, Ripon
HG4 4AH
☎ Bedale (0677) 423456
Welcoming Georgian rectory
in the centre of a peaceful
Wensleydale village. An ideal
base for exploring the
Yorkshire Dales. Winner of
Yorkshire and Humberside
Tourist Board's "White Rose"
award for best B & B of the
year 1992.
Bedrooms: 2 double, 1 twin
Bathrooms: 1 private,
2 public

Bed & breakfast

per night:	£min	£max
Single	30.00	35.00
Double	46.00	60.00

Parking for 10

THURLSTONE

South Yorkshire
Map ref 4B1

On the River Don and
close to the Peak District
National Park. Has some
19th C weavers' cottages
with long upper windows.

Weaver's Cottages

3-5 Tenter Hill, Thurlstone,
Sheffield S30 6RG
☎ Barnsley (0226) 763350
18th C weavers' cottages in
conservation area and listed
Grade II. Original workrooms
converted into private suites
with authentic furnishings.
Bedrooms: 1 single,
1 double, 1 twin
Bathrooms: 2 private,
1 public

Bed & breakfast

per night:	£min	£max
Single	18.00	22.00
Double	36.00	44.00

Parking for 2

National Crown
ratings were correct
at the time of going
to press but are
subject to change.
Please check at the
time of booking.

TODMORDEN

West Yorkshire
Map ref 4B1

In beautiful scenery on the edge of the Pennines at junction of 3 sweeping valleys. Until 1888 the county boundary between Yorkshire and Lancashire cut this old cotton town in half, running through the middle of the Town Hall.
Tourist Information Centre
☎ *(0706) 818181*

Black Swan Hotel
31 Burnley Road,
Todmorden, Lancashire
OL14 7BU
☎ (0706) 813507
Inn purpose-built in the 1930s and furnished in period. In town centre, opposite the market place, at the gateway to the Yorkshire Dales. Lunchtime bar meals.
Bedrooms: 1 single,
1 double, 3 twin, 1 triple
Bathrooms: 1 public,
5 private showers
Bed & breakfast

per night:	£min	£max
Single	17.50	20.00
Double	35.00	40.00

Lunch available
Cards accepted: Visa
🛇🍴♿🛈⑤♂🖾📺🛁
🍷 🐾

WARTER

Humberside
Map ref 4C1

Rickman House ⋀
Listed COMMENDED
Huggate Road, Warter, York
YO4 2SY
☎ Pocklington (0759)
304303
Secluded 17th C wolds farmhouse in picturesque village of Warter. Log fires. Central for touring, 20 miles from York, Hull, and the east coast.
Bedrooms: 1 double, 2 twin
Bathrooms: 1 private,
1 public
Bed & breakfast

per night:	£min	£max
Single	15.00	16.50
Double	30.00	32.00

Parking for 4
🛇10🎿🍴♿🖵🛈⑤📺🖾
🌻🐾

> We advise you to confirm your booking in writing.

WEAVERTHORPE

North Yorkshire
Map ref 5D3

Star Inn ⋀
🎖🎖🎖
Main Street, Weaverthorpe,
Malton YO17 8EY
☎ West Lutton (094 43) 273
Charming wolds village inn renowned for local game and traditional beers. Ideally situated for York, East Coast and North York Moors.
Bedrooms: 1 single,
2 double, 1 twin, 1 triple,
1 multiple
Bathrooms: 3 private,
2 public
Bed & breakfast

per night:	£min	£max
Single	16.00	16.00
Double	30.00	34.00

Evening meal 1930 (last orders 2145)
Parking for 30
Cards accepted: Access, Visa
🛇🖵♿🛈⑤♂🖾♦◖∪►
🍴🐾

WELTON

Humberside
Map ref 4C1

Wolds village has old houses with red pantiles and a delightful green with an old stone carved fountain. The church stands to one side with a stream and a pool by the churchyard wall.

Green Dragon ⋀
🎖🎖🎖 COMMENDED
Cowgate, Welton, Brough,
North Humberside
HU15 1NB
☎ Hull (0482) 666700
Fax (0482) 667808
Delightful 16th C inn on the edge of the Yorkshire Wolds in the picturesque conservation village of Welton, 5 miles west of Hull.
Bedrooms: 3 single,
4 double, 3 twin, 1 multiple
Bathrooms: 11 private
Bed & breakfast

per night:	£min	£max
Single	40.00	
Double	55.00	

Lunch available
Evening meal 1700 (last orders 2200)
Parking for 24
Cards accepted: Access, Visa
🛇♿🍲📠🍴🖵♿🛈⑤♂
🖾♦∪►🍴🌻SP🏛T

WEST BURTON

North Yorkshire
Map ref 5B3

Fox & Hounds Inn ⋀
🎖🎖🎖
West Burton, Leyburn
DL8 4JY
☎ Wensleydale (0969)
663279
Fax (0969) 663279
Inn on the green of an unspoilt village in Herriot country, an excellent walking area. Rooms are situated around a cobbled courtyard.
Bedrooms: 2 double, 3 twin
Bathrooms: 5 private
Bed & breakfast

per night:	£min	£max
Single	30.00	35.00
Double	41.00	51.00

Lunch available
Evening meal 1900 (last orders 2100)
Parking for 11
♿🍴🖵🛈♂🖾🛁
📠🍲◖∪🍴🌻SP🏛T

WETHERBY

West Yorkshire
Map ref 4B1

Prosperous market town on the River Wharfe noted for horse-racing.
Tourist Information Centre
☎ *(0937) 582706*

14 Woodhill View ⋀
Wetherby LS22 4PP
☎ (0937) 581200
Semi-detached house in a quiet residential area near the town centre.
Bedrooms: 1 double, 1 twin
Bathrooms: 1 public
Bed & breakfast

per night:	£min	£max
Single	15.00	
Double	25.00	

Parking for 1
Cards accepted: Access, Visa
🛇♿♿🖵⑤🖾📺📠🐾

Number Fifty ⋀
Listed HIGHLY COMMENDED
50 Westgate, Wetherby
LS22 4NJ
☎ (0937) 583106
Elegant early Victorian town house with a large garden and within easy walking distance of market square, restaurants and pleasant riverside.
Bedrooms: 1 double, 2 twin
Bathrooms: 1 public

Bed & breakfast

per night:	£min	£max
Single	20.00	21.00
Double	30.00	32.00

Parking for 4
🛇🖵♿🖵⑤🖾📺🛁🖇
🍴🐾

Prospect House ⋀
Listed
8 Caxton Street, Wetherby
LS22 4RU
☎ (0937) 582428
Established for over 30 years, with easy access to Harrogate, York, the dales and James Herriot country. Colour TV. Pets welcome.
Bedrooms: 1 single,
2 double, 2 twin, 1 triple
Bathrooms: 1 public
Bed & breakfast

per night:	£min	£max
Single	15.00	15.50
Double	30.00	31.00

Parking for 6
🛇🖾🛈⑤🖾📺🛁🖇✿

WHITBY

North Yorkshire
Map ref 5D3

Quaint holiday town with narrow streets and steep alleys at the mouth of the River Esk. Captain James Cook, the famous navigator, lived in Grape Lane. 199 steps lead to St Mary's Church and St Hilda's Abbey overlooking harbour. Dracula connections. Sandy beach.
Tourist Information Centre
☎ *(0947) 602674.*

Ashford ⋀
8 Royal Crescent, Whitby
YO21 3EJ
☎ (0947) 602138
Family-run guesthouse providing a relaxed, informal and friendly service. Magnificent views overlooking Crescent Gardens and the sea.
Bedrooms: 1 single,
3 double, 5 triple
Bathrooms: 5 private,
1 public
Bed & breakfast

per night:	£min	£max
Single	14.00	18.00
Double	28.00	36.00

Continued ►

> The symbols are explained on the flap inside the back cover.

133

WHITBY

Continued

Half board

per person:	£min	£max
Daily	22.00	26.00
Weekly	140.00	170.00

Evening meal 1800 (last orders 1600)
Cards accepted: Access, Visa

🛏🗣🗂🖭🛋🍴🖼🖵⚫ ✦ ⛽ 🏧

Cote Bank Farm
⊟

Aislaby, Whitby YO21 1UQ
☎ (0947) 85314
300-acre mixed farm. In national park, 18th C house with mullioned windows, spacious rooms, period furniture, log fires, home cooking. Many local places of interest, including Goathland (location for TV programme Heartbeat).
Bedrooms: 1 double, 1 triple
Bathrooms: 1 public

Bed & breakfast

per night:	£min	£max
Double	32.00	

Half board

per person:	£min	£max
Daily	25.00	30.00

Evening meal from 1745
Parking for 3
Cards accepted: Amex

🛏🗣🖭🛋🗂✂🖭🛀🌸🍴
🔲🏧

Falcon Guest House

29 Falcon Terrace, Whitby
YO21 1EH
☎ (0947) 603507
Quiet area, 7 minutes' walk from harbour and town centre. Good street parking. Full breakfast, catering for all diets. Lounge available.
Bedrooms: 1 double, 1 twin, 1 triple
Bathrooms: 1 public

Bed & breakfast

per night:	£min	£max
Single	12.00	12.00
Double	24.00	24.00

🛏🗣🖭⚫🗂🛋🍴✂🖼✦
🗑🔲

Newholm Green Farm

Newholm, Whitby YO21 3QY
☎ (0947) 603871
Period farmhouse, all rooms having a southerly outlook over farmland. 1 mile from the beach, and close to Whitby.
Bedrooms: 1 double, 2 twin
Bathrooms: 1 private, 1 public

Bed & breakfast

per night:	£min	£max
Double	23.00	27.00

Parking for 2
Open April-October

🛏🗣🗂🖭🛋🍴🖵. ⚫✦
✂🏧

Prospect Villa ♨

13 Prospect Hill, Whitby
YO21 1QE
☎ (0947) 603118
Victorian town house with cosy bar and separate lounge, ideal for fishing, walking, touring and seaside holiday. Convenient for town, beaches and moors.
Bedrooms: 2 single, 2 double, 1 twin, 1 triple, 1 multiple
Bathrooms: 1 public, 1 private shower

Bed & breakfast

per night:	£min	£max
Single	12.50	15.50
Double	25.00	31.00

Half board

per person:	£min	£max
Daily	19.50	22.50
Weekly	123.75	148.75

Lunch available
Evening meal 1830 (last orders 2000)
Parking for 5

🛏🗣⚫🛋🗂🖭🛀🍴⚫💷✂
🏧🗑

White House Hotel ♨

🏵🏵🏵 `COMMENDED`

Upgang Lane, West Cliff, Whitby YO21 3JJ
☎ (0947) 600469
Family-run hotel in a unique position with panoramic views, overlooking Sandsend Bay, adjoining a golf course. Emphasis on food.
Bedrooms: 3 single, 4 double, 2 twin, 2 triple
Bathrooms: 10 private, 1 public

Bed & breakfast

per night:	£min	£max
Single	18.50	25.50
Double	37.00	50.00

Half board

per person:	£min	£max
Daily	28.50	35.50
Weekly	200.00	240.00

Lunch available
Evening meal 1830 (last orders 2130)
Parking for 50
Cards accepted: Access, Visa

🛏🗣☎💷🖭⚫🗂🛀🖭🖵.
⚫✦🌸🏧

YORK

North Yorkshire
Map ref 4C1

Ancient walled city nearly 2000 years old containing many well-preserved medieval buildings. Its Minster has over 100 stained glass windows. Attractions include Castle Museum, National Railway Museum, Jorvik Viking Centre and York Dungeon.
Tourist Information Centre
☎ *(0904) 621756 or 643700 or 620557*

The Abbingdon ♨
🏵🏵

60 Bootham Crescent, Bootham, York YO3 7AH
☎ (0904) 621761
Centrally located and well-appointed. All bedrooms have TV and hair dryer and five have private facilities.
Bedrooms: 1 single, 3 double, 1 twin, 3 triple
Bathrooms: 5 private, 1 public

Bed & breakfast

per night:	£min	£max
Single	16.00	18.00
Double	30.00	36.00

🛏🗣⚫🛋🗂🛀🖭🖵. ⚫
✂🏧🔲

Ardsley House

`Listed` `APPROVED`

92 Main Street, Askham Bryan, York YO2 3QS
☎ (0904) 707521
Large detached house within rural village, 3 miles from York. Peaceful gardens. Easy access to racecourse, golf and Herriot country
Bedrooms: 1 double, 1 twin
Bathrooms: 1 public

Bed & breakfast

per night:	£min	£max
Single	14.00	14.00
Double	28.00	28.00

Half board

per person:	£min	£max
Daily	19.00	19.00

Parking for 7
Cards accepted: Access, Visa

🛏🗣⚫🖭⚫🗂🛀🖭. ⚫✦
🏧🔲

Arnot House ♨
🏵🏵

17 Grosvenor Terrace, Bootham, York YO3 7AG
☎ (0904) 641966
Beautifully preserved Victorian town house with original cornices, fireplaces and staircase. Large rooms,

---

tastefully decorated and well appointed. 5 minutes' walk from York Minster. Brochure available.
Bedrooms: 1 single, 4 double, 1 triple
Bathrooms: 2 public

Bed & breakfast

per night:	£min	£max
Single	12.50	15.00
Double	25.00	30.00

Half board

per person:	£min	£max
Daily	22.25	24.75

Evening meal from 1830
Parking for 2
Open February-November

🛏🗣🕯⚫🛀⚫🗂🛀🖭🖵.⚫
✂🌸🔲

Avimore House Hotel ♨
🏵🏵🏵

78 Stockton Lane, York
YO3 0BS
☎ (0904) 425556
Edwardian house, now a family-run hotel in a pleasant residential area on the east side of the city.
Bedrooms: 2 single, 1 double, 2 twin, 1 triple
Bathrooms: 6 private

Bed & breakfast

per night:	£min	£max
Single	18.00	22.00
Double	32.00	40.00

Evening meal 1800 (last orders 1200)
Parking for 6

🛏🗣🖭💷⚫🗂✂🖭🖵.
⚫✂🌸🏧🔲

Barbican Hotel ♨
🏵🏵🏵 `COMMENDED`

20 Barbican Road, York
YO1 5AA
☎ (0904) 627617
Small, friendly family-run Victorian residence of charm and character. Lovingly restored. Overlooking medieval bar walls. 7 minutes' walk to tourist attractions.
Bedrooms: 4 double, 1 twin, 1 triple
Bathrooms: 6 private, 1 public

Bed & breakfast

per night:	£min	£max
Single	20.00	35.00
Double	36.00	48.00

Half board

per person:	£min	£max
Daily	29.00	35.00

Evening meal 1830 (last orders 1900)
Parking for 7
Cards accepted: Access, Visa

🛏🗣🕯🖭💷⚫🖭🗂🖭.
⚫✂🌸🔲

Beech House ▲
🏠🏠

6-7 Longfield Terrace,
Bootham, York YO3 7DJ
☎ (0904) 634581
*Small, family-run guesthouse
with a warm welcome and a
relaxing atmosphere only 5
minutes' walk from York
Minster.*
Bedrooms: 1 single,
6 double, 1 twin
Bathrooms: 8 private
Bed & breakfast

per night:	£min	£max
Single	17.00	23.00
Double	34.00	42.00

Evening meal from 1800
Parking for 5

Blue Bridge Hotel ▲
🏠🏠🏠

Fishergate, York YO1 4AP
☎ (0904) 621193
*Friendly, private hotel,
reputation for food, relaxed
atmosphere and a warm
welcome. Short riverside walk
to city. Private car park.*
Bedrooms: 2 single,
6 double, 3 twin, 5 triple
Bathrooms: 14 private,
1 public
Bed & breakfast

per night:	£min	£max
Single	40.00	48.00
Double	50.00	58.00

Half board

per person:	£min	£max
Daily	39.50	72.00

Evening meal 1830 (last
orders 2130)
Parking for 20
Cards accepted: Access, Visa

Bowen House ▲
🏠🏠

4 Gladstone Street,
Huntington Road, York
YO3 7RF
☎ (0904) 636881
*Victorian townhouse, carefully
restored using antique and
period furniture. Very close to
city centre, restaurants and
tourist attractions. Private
parking. No smoking
throughout.*
Bedrooms: 1 single,
2 double, 2 multiple
Bathrooms: 2 private,
1 public, 1 private shower

**Please check prices
and other details at
the time of booking.**

Bed & breakfast per night:	£min	£max
Single	16.00	20.00
Double	24.00	40.00

Parking for 4

Briar Lea Guest House ▲
🏠🏠

8 Longfield Terrace,
Bootham, York YO3 7DJ
☎ (0904) 635061
*Victorian house with some
rooms en-suite, 5 minutes'
walk from the city centre and
railway station.*
Bedrooms: 1 single,
2 double, 1 twin, 1 multiple
Bathrooms: 2 private,
1 public
Bed & breakfast

per night:	£min	£max
Single	15.00	18.00
Double	28.00	36.00

Parking for 1

Brookside Guest House
🏠 APPROVED

73 Huntington Road, York
YO3 7RL
☎ (0904) 633575
*Victorian house overlooking
the River Foss, close to the
Roman walls, minster and the
city centre.*
Bedrooms: 3 double, 1 twin,
1 triple
Bathrooms: 3 private,
1 public
Bed & breakfast

per night:	£min	£max
Double	27.00	36.00

Parking for 5

Bull Lodge Guest House ▲
🏠🏠

37 Bull Lane, Lawrence
Street, York YO1 3EN
☎ (0904) 415522
*Modern detached residence in
quiet tree-lined street three-
quarters of a mile from city
centre, Barbican Centre and
university. Private enclosed
parking. Optional dinner.*
Bedrooms: 1 single,
5 double, 2 twin
Bathrooms: 3 private,
2 public
Bed & breakfast

per night:	£min	£max
Single	16.00	18.00
Double	28.00	36.00

Half board per person:	£min	£max
Daily	22.00	26.00
Weekly	146.00	173.00

Evening meal 1830 (last
orders 1830)
Parking for 7
Open February-November

City Guest House ▲
🏠🏠

68 Monkgate, York YO3 7PF
☎ (0904) 622483
*Cosy guesthouse 3 minutes
from York Minster. En-suite
rooms and car parking. Non-
smokers only please.*
Bedrooms: 1 single,
2 double, 2 twin, 2 multiple
Bathrooms: 6 private,
1 private shower
Bed & breakfast

per night:	£min	£max
Single	15.00	22.00
Double	30.00	40.00

Parking for 5
Cards accepted: Access, Visa

Claremont Guest House ▲
Listed COMMENDED

18 Claremont Terrace,
Gillygate, York YO3 7EJ
☎ (0904) 625158
*Small, city centre guesthouse
quietly located in a cul-de-sac
of Victorian terraced
properties, close to the city
walls and 5 minutes' walk
from York Minster.*
Bedrooms: 2 double, 1 twin
Bathrooms: 1 private,
1 public
Bed & breakfast

per night:	£min	£max
Single	15.00	30.00
Double	24.00	40.00

Half board

per person:	£min	£max
Daily	17.00	25.00
Weekly	110.00	160.00

Evening meal 1800 (last
orders 1600)
Parking for 1

Clifton Bridge Hotel ▲
🏠🏠 COMMENDED

Water End, Clifton, York
YO3 6LL
☎ (0904) 610510
Fax (0904) 640208
*On the north side of the city
between the A19 and A59.
Adjacent to a delightful*

---

*riverside walk into the city
centre and opposite a very
pleasant park.*
Bedrooms: 2 single,
2 double, 9 twin, 1 triple
Bathrooms: 14 private
Bed & breakfast

per night:	£min	£max
Single	35.00	43.00
Double	50.00	60.00

Half board

per person:	£min	£max
Daily	35.50	39.00

Lunch available
Evening meal 1830 (last
orders 2000)
Parking for 14
Cards accepted: Access, Visa,
Amex

Clifton Guest House ▲
🏠🏠🏠

127 Clifton, York YO3 6BL
☎ (0904) 634031
*Splendid Victorian family-run
guesthouse with bedrooms on
the ground and first floors.
Less than a mile from York
Minster and city centre.*
Bedrooms: 1 single,
3 double, 2 twin, 1 triple,
1 multiple
Bathrooms: 8 private,
2 public
Bed & breakfast

per night:	£min	£max
Single	15.00	18.00
Double	30.00	36.00

Half board

per person:	£min	£max
Daily	23.50	26.50

Evening meal 1800 (last
orders 0900)
Parking for 14

Cornerways Guest House
🏠🏠

16 Murton Way, Osbaldwick,
York YO1 3UN
☎ (0904) 621888 & 413366
*Detached house in a village
location, yet only five minutes
from the city and close to
York's outer ring road,
convenient for the coast.*
Bedrooms: 1 single,
1 double, 1 twin
Bathrooms: 2 private,
1 public

Continued ►

**Map references
apply to the colour
maps at the back
of this guide.**

135

YORK

Continued

Bed & breakfast

per night:	£min	£max
Single	12.00	16.00
Double	30.00	34.00

Parking for 4

Cumbria House ♠

Listed

2 Vyner Street, Haxby Road,
York YO3 7HS
☎ (0904) 636817
*Friendly, family-run
guesthouse, 10 minutes' walk
from York Minster. En-suites
available. Easily located from
ring road. Private car park.*
Bedrooms: 1 single,
1 double, 1 twin, 2 triple
Bathrooms: 3 private,
1 public

Bed & breakfast

per night:	£min	£max
Single	15.00	18.00
Double	30.00	36.00

Parking for 5

Curzon Lodge and Stable Cottages ♠

COMMENDED

23 Tadcaster Road,
Dringhouses, York YO2 2QG
☎ (0904) 703157
*Delightful 17th C listed house
and former stables in pretty
conservation area overlooking
racecourse, once a home of
the Terry "chocolate" family .
All en-suite, some four
posters. Many antiques. Large
enclosed car park.*
Bedrooms: 1 single,
4 double, 3 twin, 2 triple
Bathrooms: 10 private

Bed & breakfast

per night:	£min	£max
Single	29.50	38.00
Double	42.00	56.00

Parking for 16
Cards accepted: Access, Visa

Eastons

COMMENDED

90 Bishopthorpe Road, York
YO2 1JS
☎ (0904) 626646
*Restored Victorian wine
merchant's residence. William
Morris decor, open fires,
period furniture, original
paintings. Just 300 yards from
city walls and near
racecourse. Car park.*

Bedrooms: 1 single,
3 double, 1 twin, 1 triple
Bathrooms: 3 private,
1 public

Bed & breakfast

per night:	£min	£max
Single	15.00	18.00
Double	27.00	38.00

Parking for 4

Hotel Fairmount ♠

APPROVED

230 Tadcaster Road, Mount
Vale, York YO2 2ES
☎ (0904) 638298
Fax (0904) 627626
Telex 557720 APO/G
*Large, tastefully furnished,
Victorian villa dated 1881,
with open views over the
racecourse and within
walking distance of medieval
York. All rooms have colour
TV, tea-making facilities and
hairdryer.*
Bedrooms: 2 single,
6 double, 1 twin, 3 triple
Bathrooms: 10 private

Bed & breakfast

per night:	£min	£max
Single	15.00	27.00
Double	35.00	65.00

Half board

per person:	£min	£max
Daily	38.00	42.00

Lunch available
Evening meal 1900 (last
orders 2100)
Parking for 10
Cards accepted: Access, Visa

Farthings Hotel ♠

5 Nunthorpe Avenue, York
YO2 1PF
☎ (0904) 653545
*Lovingly renovated Victorian
residence with a friendly,
informal atmosphere. In a
quiet cul-de-sac approximately
10 minutes' walk from the
city centre.*
Bedrooms: 6 double, 1 twin,
2 triple
Bathrooms: 3 private,
2 public

Bed & breakfast

per night:	£min	£max
Double	36.00	38.00

Foss Bank Guest House

16 Huntington Road,
YO3 7RB
☎ (0904) 635548

*Small Victorian family-run
guesthouse opposite the River
Foss on the north-east side of
the city. 5 minutes' walk from
the city wall.*
Bedrooms: 2 single,
2 double, 1 twin
Bathrooms: 1 public,
1 private shower

Bed & breakfast

per night:	£min	£max
Single	12.00	15.00
Double	24.00	30.00

Parking for 4
Open February-December

Four Seasons Hotel ♠

COMMENDED

7 St Peter's Grove, Clifton,
York YO3 6AQ
☎ (0904) 622621
Fax (0904) 430565
*Licensed Victorian hotel with
modern facilities, in a quiet
area. Private car park,
English breakfast. Easy
walking distance from all
places of interest.*
Bedrooms: 2 double, 1 twin,
1 triple, 1 multiple
Bathrooms: 5 private,
1 public

Bed & breakfast

per night:	£min	£max
Single	24.00	27.00
Double	38.00	44.00

Parking for 6
Cards accepted: Access, Visa

Fourposter Lodge Hotel ♠

COMMENDED

68-70 Heslington Road,
Barbican Road, York
YO1 5AU
☎ (0904) 651170
*Victorian villa, lovingly
restored and furnished for
your comfort. Just 10 minutes'
walk from historic York with
all its fascinations.*
Bedrooms: 7 double, 1 twin,
2 triple
Bathrooms: 3 private,
1 public, 1 private shower

Bed & breakfast

per night:	£min	£max
Single	26.00	32.00
Double	40.00	58.00

Half board

per person:	£min	£max
Daily	31.00	40.00

Evening meal 1830 (last
orders 0800)
Parking for 8
Cards accepted: Access, Visa

Hedley House ♠

APPROVED

3-4 Bootham Terrace, York
YO3 7DH
☎ (0904) 637404
*Family-run hotel close to the
city centre. 1 ground floor
bedroom. All rooms en-suite.
Home cooking, special diets
catered for.*
Bedrooms: 2 single,
5 double, 5 twin, 2 triple,
1 multiple
Bathrooms: 15 private

Bed & breakfast

per night:	£min	£max
Single	20.00	30.00
Double	36.00	50.00

Half board

per person:	£min	£max
Daily	29.00	40.00

Lunch available
Evening meal 1830 (last
orders 1830)
Parking for 12
Cards accepted: Access, Visa,
Amex

Heworth Guest House ♠

Listed

126 East Parade, Heworth,
York YO3 7YG
☎ (0904) 426384
*Family-run hotel in a quiet
conservation area, with easy
parking, 15 minutes' walk
from city centre. Excitingly
different menus are the house
speciality - vegetarian and
vegan dishes always available.*
Bedrooms: 3 single,
1 double, 2 twin
Bathrooms: 2 public

Bed & breakfast

per night:	£min	£max
Single	13.50	16.00
Double	27.00	32.00

Half board

per person:	£min	£max
Daily	21.50	24.00

Evening meal 1800 (last
orders 0900)
Parking for 1

Hobbits Hotel ♠

COMMENDED

9 St Peter's Grove, York
YO3 6AQ
☎ (0904) 624538
*Edwardian-style small hotel in
a quiet cul-de-sac, within easy
walking distance of the city
centre.*
Bedrooms: 2 single, 2 twin,
2 triple
Bathrooms: 6 private

Bed & breakfast

per night:	£min	£max
Single	25.00	27.00
Double	50.00	54.00

Parking for 5
Cards accepted: Visa

🐕🎣🖵🕴Ⓢ🗲🕅📺🎛 📻
📷 OAP SP 🏠

Holgate Hill Hotel ⋀⋀

👑👑👑👑 APPROVED
124 Holgate Road, York
YO2 4BB
☎ (0904) 653786
Fax (0904) 643223
*Family hotel where home
cooking is a speciality. Close
to the city centre, points of
historic interest and the
racecourse.*
Bedrooms: 6 single,
15 double, 7 twin, 4 triple,
1 multiple
Bathrooms: 27 private,
2 public

Bed & breakfast

per night:	£min	£max
Single	30.00	
Double	48.00	

Half board

per person:	£min	£max
Daily	34.00	

Lunch available
Evening meal 1900 (last
orders 2030)
Parking for 14
Cards accepted: Access, Visa,
Diners, Amex

🐕🎣🖵🖵🕴🍴Ⓢ🕅
📺🎛 📻🗲🍴🎣 OAP 🏠 SP 🏠

Holly Lodge ⋀⋀

👑👑 APPROVED
206 Fulford Road, York
YO1 4DD
☎ (0904) 646005
*Listed Georgian building on
the A19, convenient for both
the north and south and
within walking distance of the
city centre. Quiet rooms and
private car park.*
Bedrooms: 3 double, 1 twin,
1 multiple
Bathrooms: 5 private

Bed & breakfast

per night:	£min	£max
Single	25.00	30.00
Double	30.00	45.00

Parking for 5
Open January-November
Cards accepted: Access, Visa

🐕🎣🖵🕴🖵🍴🛁🕅🎛🗲🍴
📻 SP 🏠

Horseshoe House

👑👑 COMMENDED
York Road, Dunnington,
York YO1 5QJ
☎ (0904) 489369
*Well-appointed
accommodation in a country*

*setting, half a mile from the
A1079 and 4 miles from York
city centre. Easy access to the
racecourse and golf-course.
Restaurants close by.*
Bedrooms: 2 double, 1 twin
Bathrooms: 2 private,
1 public, 1 private shower

Bed & breakfast

per night:	£min	£max
Double	24.00	30.00

Parking for 4

🐕🎣🖵🕴🖵🕅🗲🕅📺🎛 🗲
🌸 📻 SP

Jacobean Lodge Hotel ⋀⋀

🖵👑
Plainville Lane, Wigginton,
York YO3 8RG
☎ (0904) 762749
Fax (0904) 762749
*Converted 17th C farmhouse,
4 miles north of York. Set in
picturesque gardens with
ample parking. Open log fire,
warm, friendly atmosphere
and traditional cuisine.*
Bedrooms: 1 single,
3 double, 1 twin, 1 triple,
1 multiple
Bathrooms: 2 private,
2 public

Bed & breakfast

per night:	£min	£max
Single	25.00	35.00
Double	30.00	55.00

Lunch available
Evening meal 1900 (last
orders 2200)
Parking for 70
Cards accepted: Access, Visa

🐕🎣🖵🕴🖵Ⓢ🕅🗲🍴
🕐🗲🌸🍴📻 SP 🏠

The Limes ⋀⋀

👑👑 APPROVED
135 Fulford Road, York
YO1 4HE
☎ (0904) 624548
*Small, family-run hotel, 10
minutes from the city centre.
Licensed bar, colour TV, all
rooms en-suite. Family rooms
available. Private car park.
Close to university and golf-
course.*
Bedrooms: 7 double, 3 twin,
2 triple
Bathrooms: 12 private,
1 public

Bed & breakfast

per night:	£min	£max
Single	16.00	46.00
Double	30.00	46.00

Half board

per person:	£min	£max
Daily	22.00	52.00

Evening meal 1900 (last
orders 1830)

Parking for 14
Cards accepted: Access, Visa

🐕🎣🖵🕴Ⓢ🗲🕅🎛 🗲🍴
SP 🎛

The Lodge

🖵
Earswick Grange, Old
Earswick, York YO3 9SW
☎ (0904) 761387
*Modern family house in its
own grounds. Large
comfortable rooms ideal for
families. No smoking
establishment. Easy access to
York.*
Bedrooms: 1 double,
1 multiple
Bathrooms: 2 public

Bed & breakfast

per night:	£min	£max
Single	15.00	24.00
Double	28.00	

Parking for 3

🐕🎣🖵🕴🖵Ⓢ🕅🗲🕅📺🎛
🗲🌸🍴📻

Maxwell's Hotel ⋀⋀

Listed
54 Walmgate, York YO1 2TJ
☎ (0904) 624048
Telex 57877
*Quiet, city centre guesthouse
offering a warm welcome.
Lunches available on request.*
Bedrooms: 3 single,
2 double, 3 twin, 5 triple,
2 multiple
Bathrooms: 5 private,
3 public

Bed & breakfast

per night:	£min	£max
Single	12.00	18.00
Double	24.00	36.00

Half board

per person:	£min	£max
Daily	18.00	24.00
Weekly	126.00	168.00

Lunch available
Evening meal 1800 (last
orders 1830)
Parking for 15
Cards accepted: Access, Visa

🐕1🖵🕴🖵Ⓢ🕅📺🎛 🗲
🍷 OAP SP 🏠 🎛

Monkgate Lodge ⋀⋀

👑👑
51 Monkgate, York YO3 7PB
☎ (0904) 631501
*Listed Georgian city-centre
house. 300 yards from York
Minster and close to all
amenities. En-suite house
with colour TV and tea/coffee
trays. Non-smokers welcome.*
Bedrooms: 1 double, 1 triple
Bathrooms: 1 private,
1 public, 1 private shower

Bed & breakfast

per night:	£min	£max
Double	38.00	40.00

Open March-December

🐕5🖵🕴🖵🕅Ⓢ🕅🎛 🗲🍴
OAP 🏠

Mont-Clare Guest House ⋀⋀

🖵🖵
32 Claremont Terrace,
Gillygate, York YO3 7EJ
☎ (0904) 627054 & 651011
Fax (0904) 627054
*City centre guesthouse in a
quiet cul-de-sac. All historic
attractions are within a few
minutes' walk. Priorities are
cleanliness, good food,
pleasant surroundings and
friendliness. Reduced rates for
weekly stay.*
Bedrooms: 4 double, 1 twin,
1 triple
Bathrooms: 4 private,
2 public

Bed & breakfast

per night:	£min	£max
Single	16.00	30.00
Double	26.00	40.00

Parking for 6

🐕2🕻🖵🕴🖵🍷🕅Ⓢ🗲🕅
🎛 🗲🍴📻 OAP 🎣 SP

Mulberry Guest House ⋀⋀

👑👑 COMMENDED
124 East Parade, Heworth,
York YO3 7YG
☎ (0904) 423468
*Beautifully appointed
Victorian town house, a short
walk from the city centre.
Lovingly furnished
throughout. Warm welcome
assured. Non-smokers
preferred. Easy parking.*
Bedrooms: 1 single,
1 double, 1 twin
Bathrooms: 3 private

Bed & breakfast

per night:	£min	£max
Single	14.50	17.00
Double	29.00	34.00

Parking for 2

🐕🖵🖵🕴🖵Ⓢ🗲🕅🎛
🗲🍴📻 OAP SP

Oaklands

🖵🖵
351 Strensall Road, Old
Earswick, York YO3 9SW
☎ (0904) 768443
*Friendly, well-furnished
house, 3 miles from the city
and within easy reach of the
A64 and A1237.*
Bedrooms: 1 double, 1 twin,
1 triple
Bathrooms: 1 private,
1 public

Continued ▶

YORK

Continued

Bed & breakfast

per night:	£min	£max
Single	10.50	20.00
Double	24.00	32.00

Parking for 5

Pauleda House Hotel **

123 Clifton, York YO3 6BL
☎ (0904) 634745
Fax (0904) 621327
Family-run hotel with well-decorated, spacious rooms. Less than 1 mile from the city centre on the A19 north. Managed by the owners.
Bedrooms: 1 single,
4 double, 3 triple
Bathrooms: 8 private,
1 public

Bed & breakfast

per night:	£min	£max
Single	15.00	25.00
Double	30.00	50.00

Half board

per person:	£min	£max
Daily	25.00	35.00

Evening meal 1830 (last orders 2100)
Parking for 16
Cards accepted: Access, Visa, Diners, Switch

Primrose Lodge **

Listed
Hull Road, Dunnington, York YO1 5LR
☎ (0904) 489140
Spacious, modern rooms to which guests have their own private entrance. Colour TV, tea and coffee making facilities in every room. 5 minutes from York on the A1079.
Bedrooms: 2 double, 1 twin
Bathrooms: 3 private

Bed & breakfast

per night:	£min	£max
Double	28.00	32.00

Parking for 6

Ship Inn **

Listed COMMENDED
Acaster Malbis, York
YO2 1UH
☎ (0904) 705609 & 703888
Fax (0532) 439693
17th C coaching inn on the banks of the River Ouse 3.5 miles from York city centre. A la carte restaurant.
Bedrooms: 5 double, 2 twin,
1 triple
Bathrooms: 8 private

Bed & breakfast

per night:	£min	£max
Single	37.50	37.50
Double	40.00	65.00

Lunch available
Evening meal 1900 (last orders 2130)
Parking for 60
Cards accepted: Access, Visa

Stanley Guest House **

⬛⬛ COMMENDED
Stanley Street, Haxby Road, York YO3 7NW
☎ (0904) 637111
Friendly, comfortable guesthouse close to the many attractions of York. 10 minutes' walk to York Minster and city.
Bedrooms: 2 single,
2 double, 1 twin, 1 triple
Bathrooms: 3 private,
2 public, 2 private showers

Bed & breakfast

per night:	£min	£max
Single	15.00	17.50
Double	28.00	35.00

Parking for 5
Cards accepted: Access, Visa

Tower Guest House

⬛⬛⬛ COMMENDED
2 Feversham Crescent, Wigginton Road, York YO3 7HQ
☎ (0904) 655571 & 635924
Within easy walking distance of York Minster and the city centre. All en-suite, colour satellite TV and car park.
Bedrooms: 1 single,
1 double, 1 twin, 3 triple
Bathrooms: 6 private

Bed & breakfast

per night:	£min	£max
Single	18.00	20.00
Double	32.00	38.00

Half board

per person:	£min	£max
Daily	28.00	30.00
Weekly	175.00	190.00

Evening meal 1830 (last orders 1900)
Parking for 6
Open February-December
Cards accepted: Access, Visa

Victoria Villa **

Listed
72 Heslington Road, York
YO1 5AU
☎ (0904) 631647
Victorian town house, close to city centre. Offering clean and friendly accommodation and a full English breakfast.
Bedrooms: 1 single,
2 double, 1 twin, 2 triple
Bathrooms: 2 public

Bed & breakfast

per night:	£min	£max
Single	15.00	20.00
Double	28.00	34.00

Parking for 4

Winston House **

⬛⬛
4 Nunthorpe Drive, Bishopthorpe Road, York YO2 1DY
☎ (0904) 653171
Close to racecourse and 10 minutes' walk to city centre, railway station. Character en-suite room with all facilities. Private car park.
Bedrooms: 1 double
Bathrooms: 1 private

Bed & breakfast

per night:	£min	£max
Double	26.00	30.00

Parking for 6

Key to symbols

Information about many of the services and facilities at establishments listed in this guide is given in the form of symbols. The key to these symbols is inside the back cover flap. You may find it helpful to keep the flap open when referring to the entry listings.

I WANT TO GETAWAY FROM CYMBALS!

WHERE TO STAY

National
Accessible Scheme

◆

If you are a wheelchair user or someone who has difficulty walking, look for the national "Accessible" symbol when choosing where to stay.

All the places that display the symbol have been checked by a Tourist Board inspector against criteria that reflect the practical needs of wheelchair users.

At the moment, the Tourist Boards are concentrating their inspections on hotels, guesthouses, inns, B&Bs, farmhouse acommodation and self-catering holiday homes. There are plans to extend the scheme to holiday caravan parks and visitor attractions in 1994.

◆

There are three categories of accessibility:

Category 1: Accessible to all wheelchair users including those travelling independently

Category 2: Accessible to a wheelchair user with assistance

Category 3: Accessible to a wheelchair user able to walk short distances and up at least three steps

◆

The National Accessible Scheme forms part of the Tourism for All campaign that is being promoted by all three national Tourist Boards.

A leaflet giving more information on the scheme is available free from any Tourist Information Centre, whose staff will also be pleased to help with finding suitable accommodation in the area.

Additional help and guidance can be obtained from the Holiday Care Service, 2 Old Bank Chambers, Station Road, Horley, Surrey RH6 9HW.
Tel: (0293) 774535. Fax: (0293) 784647.
Minicom: (0293) 776943 (24-hour answering).

◆

Heart of England

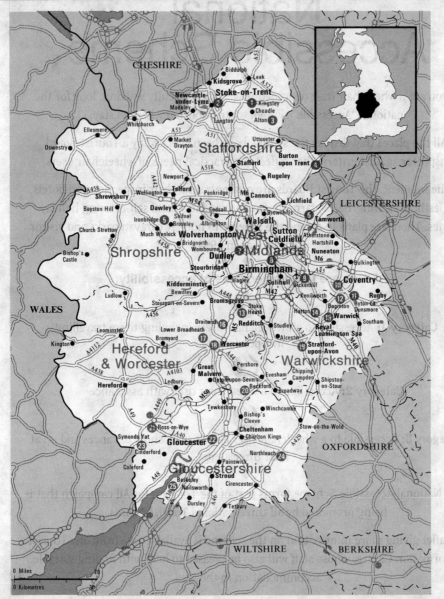

Use the above map to locate places in the "Where to Go, What to See" section opposite.

Use the colour maps at the back of this guide to find places with accommodation.

Heart of England

From the peaceful countryside of Herefordshire, land of the cider apple, to the bustling city of Birmingham and Coventry's remarkable modern architecture, there's a lot to enjoy in this big-hearted region. Succumb to the mellow charm of honey-coloured Cotswold villages, walk in the dramatic Wye Valley and the Forest of Dean, visit the world-famous bone china factories of the Potteries, trace Shakespeare's life in Stratford-upon-Avon, visit Ironbridge Gorge, cradle of the Industrial Revolution and a UNESCO World Heritage Site. Browse around Cheltenham, England's most stylish spa town, and wonder at the glories of the region's cathedrals and churches. The pleasures are many and diverse in the great Heart of England.

WHERE TO GO, WHAT TO SEE

The number against each name will help you locate it on the map opposite.

Stratford-upon-Avon's most famous resident, William Shakespeare

❶ The Falconry, Otter and Wildlife Sanctuary
Shrinks Lane, Kingsley, Stoke on Trent, Staffordshire ST10 2BX
Tel: Cheadle (0538) 754784
Educational and guided tours of the sanctuary, close encounters with many species of wild birds and animals, both native and exotic.

❷ Chatterley Whitfield Mining Museum
Tunstall, Stoke on Trent, Staffordshire ST6 8UN
Tel: Stoke on Trent (0782) 813337
Underground guided tour, British Coal Collection, energy hall, winding engine, pit ponies, underground and surface locomotives.

❸ Alton Towers Theme Park
Alton, Staffordshire ST10 4DB
Tel: Oakamoor (0538) 702200
Over 125 rides and attractions including Haunted House, Runaway Mine Train, Congo Train, Congo River Rapids, Log Flume, New Beast, Corkscrew and Thunderlooper.

❹ Bass Museum, Visitor Centre and Shire Horse Stables
Horninglow Street, Burton upon Trent, Staffordshire DE14 1JZ
Tel: Burton upon Trent (0283) 42031
First major museum of brewing industry. Story of different methods of transporting beer since the early 1800s.

❺ Ironbridge Gorge Museum
Ironbridge, Shropshire TF8 7AW
Tel: Ironbridge (0952) 433522
World's first cast iron bridge, Museum of the River and visitor centre, tar tunnel, Jackfield Tile Museum, Coalport China Museum, Rosehill House and Blists Hill Museum.

❻ Tamworth Castle and Museum Service
Tamworth, Staffordshire B79 7LR
Tel: Tamworth (0827) 63563
Norman motte and bailey castle, shell keep and Norman tower. Late medieval great hall, Tudor

stairs, Jacobean state apartments. Local history museum.

❼ Black Country Museum
Dudley, West Midlands DY1 4SQ
Tel: 021-557 9643
26-acre open-air museum with shops, chapel, chainmaker's house, canal. Underground mining display and electrical tramway.

❼ Dudley Zoo and Castle
Dudley, West Midlands DY1 4QB
Tel: Dudley (0384) 252401
Set in 40-acre wooded grounds of Dudley Castle. Visitors can enjoy

141

Beacon Tower, which stands on the top of Broadway Hill in Worcestershire, was built by Lady Coventry in 1797

⑦ Avoncroft Museum of Buildings
Stoke Heath, Worcestershire B60 4JR
Tel: Bromsgrove (0527) 31363
Re-erected buildings saved from destruction, including a working windmill, a cockpit, 1946 prefab and a dovecote.

a varied day combining zoology, history and geology.

⑧ Birmingham Museum of Science and Industry
Birmingham B3 1RZ
Tel: 021-235 1661
Steam engines, aircraft, veteran cars and motorcycles. Steam locomotives and other items of industrial or scientific interest.

⑧ Patrick Collection
180 Lifford Lane, Birmingham B30 3NT
Tel: 021-459 9111
Features include 3 exhibition halls, housing cars from 1904–1990 in period settings. Terraced gardens, wildlife lake, children's play area, shop.

⑧ Selly Manor
Maple Road, Bourneville, Birmingham
Tel: 021-472 0199
13th C cruck house and 14th C/16th C half-timbered house with period furniture and fittings. Exhibitions, herbs and plants.

⑨ National Motorcycle Museum
Bickenhill, West Midlands B92 OEJ

Tel: Solihull (067 55) 3311
Museum with a collection of 550 British machines from 1898–1980.

⑩ Museum of British Road Transport
Hales Street, Coventry CV1 1NN
Tel: Coventry (0203) 832425
Commercial vehicles dating from 1800s to date. "Thrust 2" holder of land speed record. Coventry Blitz experience.

⑪ Ryton Gardens
National Centre for Organic Gardening, Ryton-on-Dunsmore, Coventry CV8 3LG
Tel: Coventry (0203) 303517
Exhibition gardens where no pesticides or artificial fertilisers are used. Wildlife and bee garden, shrub borders, native tree walk.

⑫ Midland Air Museum
Baginton, West Midlands CV8 3AZ
Tel: Coventry (0203) 301033
Collection of over 20 historic aeroplanes. Recently completed Sir Frank Whittle Jet Heritage Centre includes early jet aircraft and aero engines.

⑬ Hatton Country World
Hatton, Warwickshire CV35 0XA
Tel: Claverdon (0926) 842436
100-acre haven of rural attractions including over 40 breeds of rare farm animals.

⑮ Ashorne Hall
Ashorne Hill, Nr Warwick, Warwickshire CV33 9QN
Tel: Barford (0926) 651444
Britain's only "nickelodeon" with unique presentation of automatic musical instruments. Vintage cinema showing silent films with organ accompaniment.

⑮ Warwick Castle
Warwick, Warwickshire CV34 4QU
Tel: Warwick (0926) 495421
Set in 60 acres of grounds and gardens. State rooms, armoury, dungeon, torture chamber, clock tower. "A Royal Weekend Party 1898" by Madame Tussauds. Medieval banquets.

⑯ Droitwich Spa Brine Baths
Droitwich, Worcestershire WR9 8EA
Tel: Droitwich (0905) 79489
Unique experience of floating weightless in natural Droitwich

Heart of England

brine. *Other fitness and health facilities also available.*

⑰ Elgar's Birthplace Museum
Crown East Lane, Lower
Broadheath, Worcestershire
WR2 6RH
Tel: Cotheridge (0905) 333224
Cottage in which Edward Elgar was born, now housing a museum of photographs, musical scores, letters and records associated with the composer.

⑱ The Commandery
Sidbury, Worcester,
Worcestershire WR1 2HU
Tel: Worcester (0905) 355071
15th C timber-framed building with great hall and panelled rooms. Civil War audio-visual show and exhibition. Displays on Worcester's working past.

⑲ Shakespeare's Birthplace
Stratford-upon-Avon,
Warwickshire CV37 6QW
Tel: Stratford-upon-Avon (0789) 204016
Half-timbered building furnished in period style, containing many fascinating books, manuscripts and objects. BBC TV Shakespeare costume exhibition.

⑳ Beckford Silk
Ashton Road, Beckford,
Gloucestershire GL20 7AD
Tel: Evesham (0386) 881507
Visitors can watch the hand printing of silk and other processes in the making of silk scarves and silk ties.

㉑ The Lost Street Museum
27 Brookend Street, Ross-on-Wye, Herefordshire HR9 7EE
Tel: Ross-on-Wye (0989) 62752
Complete Edwardian street of shops including tobacconist, glassware, grocer's, chemist, clothes store, pub and many others.

㉒ National Waterways Museum
Gloucester Docks, Gloucester
GL1 2EH
Tel: Gloucester (0452) 307009
Three floors of dockside warehouse with lively displays telling the story of Britain's canals. Outside craft area with demonstrations, cafe and shop.

㉒ Robert Opie Collection
Gloucester Docks, Gloucester
GL1 2EH
Tel: Gloucester (0452) 302309
Steeped in nostalgia, the Robert Opie Collection of packaging and advertising brings over 100 years of shopping basket history vividly to life.

㉓ Jubilee Maze and Museum of Mazes
Symonds Yat, Herefordshire
HR9 6DA
Tel: Symonds Yat (0600) 890 360
A traditional hedge maze with carved stone temple centrepiece, created to celebrate Queen Elizabeth's Jubilee in 1977. World's only "hands-on" interactive" Museum of Mazes.

㉔ Keith Harding's World of Mechanical Music
Northleach, Gloucestershire
GL54 3EU
Tel: Cotswold (0451) 60181
17th C wool merchant's house, antique clocks, musical boxes, automata and mechanical musical instruments presented as an entertainment. A unique experience of sound.

㉕ Berkeley Castle
Berkeley, Gloucestershire
GL13 9BQ
Tel: Dursley (0453) 810332
Perfectly preserved 800-year-old castle, scene of Edward II's murder. 14th C great hall, keep, dungeon, kitchen, tapestries, furniture. Ornamental gardens.

The north Staffordshire towns of Tunstall, Burslem, Hanley, Stoke, Fenton and Longton are the traditional workshop of English potters. This mermaid plate by Thomas Toft dates from 1670.

Places to stay

Accommodation entries in this regional section are listed in alphabetical order of place name, and then in alphabetical order of establishment.

The map references refer to the colour maps at the back of the guide. The first figure is the map number; the letter and figure which follow indicate the grid reference on the map.

The symbols at the end of each accommodation entry give information about services and facilities. A 'key' to these symbols is inside the back cover flap, which can be kept open for easy reference.

ALCESTER

Warwickshire
Map ref 2B1

Town has Roman origins and many old buildings around the High Street. It is close to Ragley Hall, the 18th C Palladian mansion with its magnificent baroque Great Hall.

Orchard Lawns ⋀⋀
HIGHLY COMMENDED

Wixford, Alcester B49 6DA
☎ Bidford upon Avon (0789) 772668
Bed and breakfast accommodation in a small village on B4085, 7 miles from Stratford-upon-Avon. TV lounge. Garden.
Bedrooms: 1 single, 1 double, 1 twin
Bathrooms: 1 private, 1 public
Bed & breakfast

per night:	£min	£max
Single	15.50	17.00
Double	31.00	34.00

Parking for 6
Cards accepted: Access, Visa
⛲ 5 🖥️ S ⊬ 🗘 📺 ▥ 🗲 🕾
🖰 🌣 ✗ 🚲 🛏

> **Please mention this guide when making a booking.**

Sambourne Hall Farm ⋀⋀
COMMENDED

Wike Lane, Sambourne
B96 6NZ
☎ Studley (0527) 852151
315-acre arable & livestock farm. Mid 17th C farmhouse in a peaceful village, close to local pub. Just off the A435 between Alcester and Studley and 9 miles from Stratford.
Bedrooms: 1 double, 1 triple
Bathrooms: 2 private
Bed & breakfast

per night:	£min	£max
Single	18.00	20.00
Double	35.00	35.00

Parking for 6
⛲ 🖵 🗘 🖥️ S ⊬ 🗘 📺 ▥ 🗲
🌣 🚲 🛏 🖵

ALSTONEFIELD

Staffordshire
Map ref 4B2

Peaceful village well situated for exploring the pleasant countryside of Dovedale, much of which is owned by the National Trust.

Valley View

Milldale, Alstonefield, Ashbourne, Derbyshire
DE6 2GB
☎ (0335) 27442
On a hillside overlooking the Dove Valley in the hamlet of Milldale. A stone-built, family

---

residence with comfortable accommodation.
Bedrooms: 2 double, 1 twin
Bathrooms: 1 public
Bed & breakfast

per night:	£min	£max
Single	13.50	17.50
Double	27.00	35.00

Parking for 4
Cards accepted: Visa
⛲ 🗘 🖥️ ⊬ 🗘 📺 ▥ 🗲 🌣 ✗
🚲 SP

ALTON

Staffordshire
Map ref 4B2

Alton Castle, an impressive 19th C building, dominates the village which is set in spectacular scenery. Nearby is Alton Towers, a romantic 19th C ruin with innumerable tourist attractions in its 800 acres of magnificent gardens.

Bee Cottage Bed & Breakfast ⋀⋀
Listed

Saltersford Lane, Alton,
Stoke-on-Trent ST10 4AU
☎ Oakamoor (0538) 702802
Traditional stone-built cottage, extended over a period of 200 years. In countryside, 2 miles from Alton Towers. Adjoining paddock and orchard extending to 2 acres.
Bedrooms: 3 double

Bathrooms: 1 public
Bed & breakfast

per night:	£min	£max
Single	15.00	30.00
Double	25.00	30.00

Parking for 5
Open March-November
⛲ 🗘 💧 ▥ ⊬ 🗘 📺 ▥ 🚲

Bradley Elms Farm ⋀⋀
⚜⚜⚜

Threapwood, Cheadle, Stoke-on-Trent ST10 4RA
☎ (0538) 753135 & 750202
Well-appointed farm accommodation providing a comfortable and relaxing atmosphere for that well-earned break. On the edge of the Staffordshire Moorlands. 3 miles from Alton Towers, close to the Potteries and the Peak District National Park.
Bedrooms: 2 double, 1 twin, 1 triple, 1 multiple
Bathrooms: 5 private
Bed & breakfast

per night:	£min	£max
Double	33.00	36.00

Half board		
per person:	£min	£max
Daily	25.50	31.00

Lunch available
Evening meal 1900 (last orders 2100)
Parking for 10
⛲ 🖧 🖵 🗘 💧 🖥️ ▥ 🗲 🍴 🌣
✗ SP 🖵

Hillside Farm
Denstone, Uttoxeter
ST14 5HG
☎ Rocester (0889) 590760
Victorian farmhouse with extensive views to the Weaver Hills and Churnet Valley. Situated 2 miles south of Alton Towers on the B5032.
Bedrooms: 3 triple
Bathrooms: 2 public
Bed & breakfast

per night:	£min	£max
Single	12.00	15.00
Double	22.00	28.00

Parking for 7

Meallmore
High Street, Alton, Stoke-on-Trent ST10 4AQ
☎ Oakamoor (0538) 702344 & 703037
Comfortable accommodation and a friendly atmosphere. Located in the centre of Alton village, 1 mile from Alton Towers.
Bedrooms: 2 single, 1 double, 1 twin
Bathrooms: 3 public
Bed & breakfast

per night:	£min	£max
Single	14.00	16.00
Double	28.00	30.00

Open April-October

Talbot Inn ₥
Listed
Alton, Stoke-on-Trent
ST10 4BX
☎ Oakamoor (0538) 702767
Charming country inn, delightful setting within view of Alton Towers, offering varied, interesting home-cooked food, real ale and comfortable accommodation.
Bedrooms: 1 twin, 1 triple
Bathrooms: 1 public
Bed & breakfast

per night:	£min	£max
Single	23.00	
Double	35.00	

Lunch available
Evening meal 1830 (last orders 2100)
Parking for 20

Wild Duck Inn
Listed
New Road, Alton, Stoke-on-Trent ST10 4AF
☎ Oakamoor (0538) 702218
Large country inn, near Alton Towers Leisure Park. Comfortable bedrooms, restaurant, bar and family lounge.
Bedrooms: 7 triple

Bathrooms: 2 public
Bed & breakfast

per night:	£min	£max
Double	33.00	50.00

Evening meal 1900 (last orders 2030)
Parking for 50
Open March-November
Cards accepted: Access, Visa

AMPNEY CRUCIS
Gloucestershire
Map ref 2B1

This is one of the 4 Ampney villages and is situated in pleasant countryside. Its church has Saxon features. The very attractive gardens at nearby Barnsley House are open Monday to Friday and offer plants for sale.

Waterton Garden Cottage ₥
HIGHLY COMMENDED
Ampney Crucis, Cirencester
GL7 5RX
☎ (0285) 851303
Sympathetically converted part of Victorian stable block, retaining many original features. Walled garden, heated pool, croquet lawn. Tranquil situation, not too far from Cirencester.
Bedrooms: 1 single, 2 double
Bathrooms: 3 private
Bed & breakfast

per night:	£min	£max
Single	20.00	30.00
Double	35.00	40.00

Half board

per person:	£min	£max
Daily	35.00	45.00

Lunch available
Parking for 6

AMPNEY ST. PETER
Gloucestershire
Map ref 2B1

Iveson House ₥
Listed
Ampney St. Peter, Cirencester GL7 5SH
☎ (0285) 851217
Fax (0285) 850359
Grade II listed Cotswold country house in very pretty village, quiet location 4 miles Cirencester. Each bedroom has private bathroom with bath/shower. Large garden, tennis, heated pool.

Bedrooms: 1 double, 1 twin
Bathrooms: 2 private
Bed & breakfast

per night:	£min	£max
Double	30.00	38.00

Parking for 2
Open March-November

The Manor House
Listed
Ampney St. Peter, Cirencester GL7 5SH
☎ (0285) 851425
Very comfortable small manor house in delightful unspoilt Cotswold village off A417. Between Cirencester and Fairford. You will be welcomed as house guests.
Bedrooms: 2 twin
Bathrooms: 1 private
Bed & breakfast

per night:	£min	£max
Single	20.00	25.00
Double	35.00	40.00

Parking for 2

AVON DASSETT
Warwickshire
Map ref 2C1

Village on the slopes of the Dasset Hills, with good views. The church, with its impressive tower and spire, dates from 1868 though it incorporates a 14th C window with 15th C glass.

Crandon House ₥
HIGHLY COMMENDED
Avon Dassett, Leamington Spa CV33 0AA
☎ Fenny Compton (0295) 770652
20-acre mixed farm. Farmhouse offering a high standard of accommodation with superb views over unspoilt countryside. Quiet and peaceful. Easy access to Warwick, Stratford and Cotswolds. 4 miles from junctions 11 and 12 of M40.
Bedrooms: 1 double, 2 twin
Bathrooms: 3 private
Bed & breakfast

per night:	£min	£max
Single	22.00	25.00
Double	34.00	39.00

Half board

per person:	£min	£max
Daily	28.00	34.00
Weekly	196.00	238.00

Evening meal 1900 (last orders 1200)

Parking for 22
Cards accepted: Access, Visa

BALTERLEY
Staffordshire
Map ref 4A2

Hamlet on the Staffordshire/Cheshire border with an interesting modern church and a black and white Tudor hall.

Pear Tree Lake Farm ₥
Balterley, Crewe CW2 5QE
☎ Crewe (0270) 820307
115-acre mixed farm. Lovely old farmhouse enhanced by impressive hall, oak beams and open fires. An inglenook and antique furnishings create an atmosphere of yesteryear. Riding from own stables.
Bedrooms: 2 double, 1 twin, 1 triple
Bathrooms: 3 private, 1 public
Bed & breakfast

per night:	£min	£max
Single	15.00	30.00
Double	25.00	35.00

Lunch available
Evening meal 1800 (last orders 1800)
Parking for 16
Cards accepted: Access, Visa

BASCHURCH
Shropshire
Map ref 4A3

The older part of this village forms a compact group around the church and inn, with some black and white buildings. Thomas Telford, the great engineer, was responsible for major work on the church in 1790.

Frankbrook ₥
Listed COMMENDED
Yeaton Lane, Baschurch, Shrewsbury SY4 2HZ
☎ (0939) 260778
Peaceful, secluded family home in lovely countryside, 1 mile from Baschurch. Attractive garden. Fine views. Good base for touring Wales,
Continued ▶

145

BASCHURCH

Continued

Shrewsbury, Chester and Ironbridge. Warm welcome.
Bedrooms: 2 double, 1 twin
Bathrooms: 2 public

Bed & breakfast

per night:	£min	£max
Single	12.50	13.50
Double	24.00	26.00

Half board

per person:	£min	£max
Daily	18.50	20.00
Weekly	125.00	127.00

Evening meal 1830 (last orders 1930)
Parking for 5

BERKELEY

Gloucestershire
Map ref 2B1

Town dominated by the castle where Edward II was murdered. Dating from Norman times, it is still the home of the Berkeley family and is open to the public. Slimbridge Wildfowl Trust is nearby.

Green Acres Farm Guest House ⚅

COMMENDED

Breadstone, Berkeley
GL13 9HF
☎ Dursley (0453) 810348
45-acre livestock & horses farm. Rural position in beautiful Berkeley Vale. Tastefully furnished, warm welcome. Excellent for touring Cotswolds, Wales, Bath and Bristol. Short break specials. Sauna and fitness room.
Bedrooms: 2 single,
1 double, 1 twin
Bathrooms: 4 private

Bed & breakfast

per night:	£min	£max
Single	16.00	18.50
Double	30.00	35.00

Parking for 6

Pickwick Farm

Listed

Berkeley GL13 9EU
☎ Dursley (0453) 810241
120-acre dairy farm. Easily located family farm, formerly a coaching inn used by Charles Dickens. Close to Berkeley Castle and Slimbridge Wildfowl Trust. Non-smoking establishment.

Bedrooms: 1 single,
1 double, 1 twin
Bathrooms: 1 public,
1 private shower

Bed & breakfast

per night:	£min	£max
Single	15.00	
Double	30.00	

Parking for 3
Open April-October

BERKSWELL

West Midlands
Map ref 4B3

Windmill open to the public every Sunday afternoon from May until the end of September. The Norman church is one of the finest in the area, with many interesting features.

Lower Barn House ⚅

HIGHLY COMMENDED

Spencers Lane, Berkswell,
Coventry CV7 7BB
☎ (0676) 535020 & 32877
Beautifully converted barn set in pretty Warwickshire village, convenient for National Exhibition Centre and historic towns of Stratford-upon-Avon, Warwick and Kenilworth.
Bedrooms: 1 single, 2 twin
Bathrooms: 3 private

Bed & breakfast

per night:	£min	£max
Single	15.00	25.00
Double	30.00	45.00

Evening meal 2000 (last orders 2000)
Parking for 8

BETLEY

Staffordshire
Map ref 4A2

Once a market town, now a village with many whitewashed and timber-framed houses. Much of the 17th C church was paid for by the Egerton family, whose monuments may be seen inside. Noteworthy is the unusual use of wood in the interior of the church.

Betley Court Farm ⚅

Betley, Crewe, Cheshire
CW3 9BH
☎ (0270) 820229

220-acre mixed farm. In village 6 miles west of Newcastle under Lyme. Betley Mere is on the farm, ideal for walking, fishing and country pursuits.
Bedrooms: 1 double, 1 triple
Bathrooms: 2 private

Bed & breakfast

per night:	£min	£max
Single	18.00	22.00
Double	34.00	40.00

BIBURY

Gloucestershire
Map ref 2B1

Village on the River Coln with stone houses and the famous 17th C Arlington Row, former weavers' cottages. Arlington Mill is now a folk museum with a trout farm nearby which is open to the public.

Bibury Court Hotel ⚅

COMMENDED

Bibury, Cirencester GL7 5NT
☎ (0285) 740337
Fax (0285) 740660
Beautiful Cotswold Jacobean manor house in 6 acres of grounds by River Coln. Family-run with informal country house atmosphere.
Bedrooms: 3 single,
12 double, 5 twin
Bathrooms: 18 private

Bed & breakfast

per night:	£min	£max
Single	46.00	55.00
Double	70.00	74.00

Half board

per person:	£min	£max
Daily	59.00	69.00

Lunch available
Evening meal 1900 (last orders 2100)
Parking for 100
Cards accepted: Access, Visa, Diners, Amex

Cotteswold House ⚅

Arlington, Bibury,
Cirencester GL7 5ND
☎ (0285) 740609
Extensively refurbished Regency-style house in the Cotswold village of Bibury, offers purpose-built facilities in a friendly family atmosphere.
Bedrooms: 2 double, 1 twin
Bathrooms: 3 private

Bed & breakfast

per night:		£min £max
Single		22.00
Double		38.00

Parking for 4

Manor Farm ⚅

Ablington, Bibury,
Cirencester GL7 5NY
☎ (0285) 740266
700-acre arable and mixed farm. Cotswolds farmhouse in beautiful hamlet of Ablington. Good pubs/restaurants in Bibury (1 mile). Ideal base for touring Cotswolds. Evening meal by arrangement.
Bedrooms: 1 double, 1 twin,
1 triple
Bathrooms: 1 private,
2 public

Bed & breakfast

per night:	£min	£max
Single	15.00	20.00
Double	28.00	32.00

Half board

per person:	£min	£max
Daily	20.00	25.00

Evening meal 1830 (last orders 1930)
Parking for 10

BIDDULPH

Staffordshire
Map ref 4B2

Village set in the heart of moorlands and high hills in the north-west corner of Staffordshire near the Cheshire border. The River Trent has its source near here. In the parish church are some Crusader monuments, and the remains of Biddulph Old Hall stand as a memorial to civil strife.

Badger Hill Guest House ⚅

Rock End, Knypersley,
Biddulph, Stoke-on-Trent
ST8 7NR
☎ (0782) 519203
Picturesque country guesthouse and smallholding in unique rural setting, 1.5 miles off A527, east of Biddulph in Staffordshire Moorlands.
Bedrooms: 2 single,
1 double, 1 twin
Bathrooms: 2 private,
1 public

Bed & breakfast

per night:	£min	£max
Single	16.00	30.00
Double	40.00	

Half board

per person:	£min	£max
Daily	26.00	40.00

Evening meal 1800 (last orders 2000)
Parking for 5
🛇🚲📞🖵♿ⓦ🅰Ⓢ✗♨
📺🖵🛥∪🌣🅿🚲

Warwickshire
Map ref 2B1

Attractive village with an ancient 8-arched bridge and a main street with some interesting 15th C houses.

Huit Barn
Listed
Tower Croft, Tower Hill, Bidford-on-Avon, Alcester B50 4DY
☎ Stratford-upon-Avon (0789) 778516
Victorian barn conversion in the riverside village of Bidford-on-Avon, overlooking outstanding open countryside, the Avon Valley and the Cotswolds. Situated close to the B439 Evesham to Stratford-upon-Avon road.
Bedrooms: 1 double
Bathrooms: 1 private
Bed & breakfast

per night:	£min	£max
Double	32.00	34.00

Parking for 3
🖵♿🔥♨🅰✗🖵🌣✗
🚲🏠

Gloucestershire
Map ref 2B1

Hamlet at the top of a very steep descent down to the Gloucester Vale and close to the Crickley Hill Country Park.

Beechmount
😊😊 COMMENDED
Birdlip, Gloucester GL4 8JH
☎ Gloucester (0452) 862262
A small family-run guesthouse with personal attention. Ideal centre for the Cotswolds.
Bedrooms: 2 double, 2 twin, 2 triple
Bathrooms: 2 private, 1 public

Bed & breakfast

per night:	£min	£max
Single	14.00	28.00
Double	28.00	42.00

Evening meal (last orders 1900)
Parking for 7
🛇🖵📞ⓦ🅰Ⓢ✗♨🖵
🛥🌣🚲

West Midlands
Map ref 4B3

Britain's second city, with many attractions including the City Art Gallery, Barber Institute of Fine Arts, 17th C Aston Hall, science museum, railway museum, 2 cathedrals and 10-acre Botanical Gardens. It is well placed for exploring Shakespeare country.
Tourist Information Centre
☎ 021-643 2514.

Prince Hotel
4 Stanmore Road, Edgbaston, Birmingham B16 9TA
☎ 021-434 3123
Ideally situated accommodation, with homely and friendly atmosphere. All rooms with satellite TV and tea-making. Money-back guarantee.
Bedrooms: 3 single, 3 double, 3 twin, 1 triple
Bathrooms: 1 private, 2 public, 3 private showers
Bed & breakfast

per night:	£min	£max
Single	15.00	20.00
Double	30.00	40.00

Parking for 6
Cards accepted: Access, Visa, Amex
🛇🚲🏠🖵📞ⓦ♿🅰📺◐
🖵🛥✗Ⓢ🅿

West Midlands

See under Berkswell, Birmingham, Coleshill, Coventry, Hampton in Arden, Meriden, Solihull

National Crown ratings were correct at the time of going to press but are subject to change. Please check at the time of booking.

Gloucestershire
Map ref 2B1

Village close to the Oxfordshire border, with a pleasant green and a beautiful church.

Kings Head Inn & Restaurant ♨
😊😊😊 COMMENDED
The Green, Bledington, Oxford OX7 6HD
☎ Kingham (0608) 658365
Fax (0608) 658365
15th C inn located in the heart of the Cotswolds, facing the village green. Main building has 2 bars, one with inglenook fireplace.
Bedrooms: 5 double, 1 twin
Bathrooms: 6 private
Bed & breakfast

per night:	£min	£max
Single	28.00	32.00
Double	49.00	55.00

Lunch available
Evening meal 1900 (last orders 2200)
Parking for 60
Cards accepted: Access, Visa
🛇📞🖵📞ⓦ♿🅰Ⓢ✗♨📺
🖵🛥∪🅿🌣✗🚲🅿🅰
🏠Ⓣ

Gloucestershire
Map ref 2B1

This village's prosperity was founded in silk mills and other factories but now it is a quiet, unspoilt place. An excellent centre for exploring pretty Cotswold villages, especially Chipping Campden and Broadway.

21 Station Rd. ♨
😊😊 COMMENDED
Blockley, Moreton-in-Marsh GL56 9ED
☎ (0386) 700402
Attractive Cotswold-stone house on the edge of a peaceful village.
Bedrooms: 1 double, 2 twin
Bathrooms: 2 public
Bed & breakfast

per night:	£min	£max
Single	17.00	17.00
Double	29.00	29.00

Parking for 9
🛇5🖵🖵♿ⓦⓈ✗♨📺
🖵🛥🌣✗🚲

Hereford and Worcester
Map ref 2A1

An attractive village with old timbered cottages and stone houses and an interesting church. Here the River Lugg makes a loop and flows under an ancient bridge at the end of the village.

Maund Court
😊😊 HIGHLY COMMENDED
Bodenham, Hereford HR1 3JA
☎ (056 884) 282
150-acre mixed farm. Attractive 15th C farmhouse with a large garden, swimming pool and croquet. Riding, golf and pleasant walks nearby. Ideal centre for touring.
Bedrooms: 1 single, 2 double, 1 twin
Bathrooms: 4 private
Bed & breakfast

per night:	£min	£max
Single	15.00	16.00
Double	30.00	32.00

Parking for 8
Open March-November
🛇🖵🖵ⓦ🅿📺🖵🛥🚲
∪🌣🚲🏠

Gloucestershire
Map ref 2B1

The River Windrush flows through this famous Cotswold village which has a green, and cottages and houses of Cotswold stone. Its many attractions include a model village, Birdland and a Motor Museum.

Berkeley Guesthouse ♨
😊😊 COMMENDED
Moore Road, Bourton-on-the-Water, Cheltenham GL54 2AZ
☎ Cotswold (0451) 810388
Detached house with a homely, relaxed atmosphere, furnished to a high standard. Personal attention. Attractive gardens, sun lounge, car park. No smoking.
Bedrooms: 1 double, 1 twin, 1 triple
Bathrooms: 3 private
Continued ▶

147

BOURTON-ON-THE-WATER

Continued

Bed & breakfast

per night:	£min	£max
Single	17.50	20.00
Double	30.00	35.00

Parking for 4

🌊🚴🍴🖥🐾ⓘⓈ✗🏵 📺🌙🛁🚪↑🐾🚐 DAP ⊠ SP

Coombe House ₩

HIGHLY COMMENDED

Rissington Road, Bourton-on-the-Water, Cheltenham GL54 2DT

☎ Cotswold (0451) 821966

Bright, fresh, comfortable, family-run home. All en-suite facilities. Pretty garden, ample parking. Restaurants within walking distance. No smoking in house please.

Bedrooms: 3 double, 2 twin, 2 triple

Bathrooms: 7 private

Bed & breakfast

per night:	£min	£max
Single	33.00	42.00
Double	49.00	58.00

Parking for 10

🌊🚴🍴🖥♨Ⓢ✗🏵🏠 🏵✕🐾🚐 SP

Duke of Wellington Inn

₩₩

Sherborne Street, Bourton-on-the-Water, Cheltenham GL54 2BY

☎ Cotswold (0451) 820539

16th C Cotswolds inn in the centre of the village, bordered by the River Windrush. Real ales and a beer garden.

Bedrooms: 2 double, 1 twin

Bathrooms: 3 private

Bed & breakfast

per night:	£min	£max
Single	23.00	27.00
Double	36.00	40.00

Half board

per person:	£min	£max
Daily	25.50	29.00
Weekly	170.00	200.00

Lunch available

Evening meal 1800 (last orders 2200)

Parking for 16

🌊🍴🖥♨ⓘⓈ🏠✕🐾 SP 🍺

Farncombe ₩

₩₩

Clapton, Bourton-on-the-Water, Cheltenham GL54 2LG

☎ Cotswold (0451) 820120

Quiet comfortable accommodation with superb views of the Windrush Valley. In the hamlet of Clapton, 2.5 miles from Bourton-on-the-Water. No-smoking house.

Bedrooms: 2 double, 1 twin

Bathrooms: 2 public, 1 private shower

Bed & breakfast

per night:	£min	£max
Single	14.50	18.50
Double	29.00	34.00

Parking for 3

🌊🍴♨ⓘⓈ✗🏵📺🏠 ∪🏵✕🐾

Folly Court ₩

Bourton-on-the-Water, Cheltenham GL54 3BY

☎ Cotswold (0451) 821007

Cotswold stone built house, next to Folly Farm Domestic Waterfowl and with direct access to extensive bridleway system - horses welcome, too.

Bedrooms: 1 double, 2 twin

Bathrooms: 1 public

Bed & breakfast

per night:	£min	£max
Single	12.50	15.00
Double	25.00	30.00

Half board

per person:	£min	£max
Daily	25.00	

Evening meal 1830 (last orders 2100)

Parking for 4

Open January-November

Cards accepted: Visa

🌊♨ⓘⓈ✗📺🏠🏠∪ 🐾Ⓣ

Hill Farm ₩

₩₩

Little Rissington, Bourton-on-the-Water, Cheltenham GL54 2ND

☎ Cotswold (0451) 820330

10-acre market garden. Large farmhouse in a quiet position in the heart of the Cotswolds. Centrally situated for Oxford, Stratford-upon-Avon, and Gloucester. Home-made bread.

Bedrooms: 1 twin, 1 triple, 1 multiple

Bathrooms: 1 private, 2 public

Bed & breakfast

per night:	£min	£max
Single	16.00	20.00
Double	26.00	34.00

Parking for 6

🌊♨ⓘⓈ✗🏵📺🏠🏵 🐾Ⓣ

We advise you to confirm your booking in writing.

Lamb Inn ₩

₩₩₩ COMMENDED

Great Rissington, Bourton-on-the-Water, Cheltenham GL54 2LP

☎ Cotswold (0451) 820388 & 820724

Country inn in rural setting, with home-cooked food, including steaks and local trout, served in attractive restaurant. Beer garden and real ale. Honeymoon suite also available.

Bedrooms: 10 double, 2 twin

Bathrooms: 10 private, 3 public

Bed & breakfast

per night:	£min	£max
Single	30.00	45.00
Double	36.00	70.00

Half board

per person:	£min	£max
Daily	40.00	55.00

Lunch available

Evening meal 1900 (last orders 2130)

Parking for 10

Cards accepted: Access, Visa

🌊🚴🏪ⓘⓈ🏵📺🏠🏠🔱🏵 🐾🍺

Lansdowne House

₩ COMMENDED

Lansdowne, Bourton-on-the-Water, Cheltenham GL54 2AT

☎ Cotswold (0451) 820812

Large, period, stone family house, 2 minutes' level walk from the centre of this much visited and delightful Cotswold village.

Bedrooms: 2 double, 1 twin

Bathrooms: 3 private

Bed & breakfast

per night:	£min	£max
Single	18.00	28.00
Double	28.00	33.00

Parking for 4

🌊🚴🍴♨ⓘⓈ✗📺 🏠🏠🏵✕🐾🚐

The Ridge ₩

₩₩

Whiteshoots Hill, Bourton-on-the-Water, Cheltenham GL54 2LE

☎ Cotswold (0451) 820660

Large country house surrounded by beautiful grounds. Central for visiting many places of interest and close to all amenities. Ground floor en-suite bedroom available.

Bedrooms: 3 double, 1 twin, 1 triple

Bathrooms: 4 private, 1 public

Bed & breakfast

per night:	£min	£max
Single	20.00	25.00
Double	28.00	36.00

Parking for 12

🌊6🚴🏠♨ⓤ✗📺🏠🏠 🏵✕🐾🚐

Rooftrees Guesthouse ₩

₩₩

Rissington Road, Bourton-on-the-Water, Cheltenham GL54 2EB

☎ Cotswold (0451) 821943

Detached Cotswold-stone family house, all rooms individually decorated, 8 minutes' level walk from village centre. Home cooking with fresh local produce. 2 four-poster en-suite rooms, 2 ground floor en-suite rooms. No smoking.

Bedrooms: 3 double

Bathrooms: 3 private, 1 public

Bed & breakfast

per night:	£min	£max
Single	18.00	22.00
Double	28.00	38.00

Half board

per person:	£min	£max
Daily	24.00	29.00

Evening meal 1830 (last orders 1200)

Parking for 8

Cards accepted: Access, Visa

🌊6🚴🏪🍴🏠ⓤⓘⓈ ✗📺🏠🚐✕🐾

Stepping Stone

₩₩

Rectory Lane, Great Rissington, Cheltenham

☎ Cotswold (0451) 821385

Large detached house in country village lane with private grounds and views across the Windrush Valley.

Bedrooms: 1 single, 1 double, 1 twin, 1 triple

Bathrooms: 2 private, 1 public

Bed & breakfast

per night:	£min	£max
Single	16.00	36.00
Double	30.00	36.00

Parking for 6

🌊10🚴🏠✗🐝ⓤⓘⒶⒽ🏠 🏠🏵✕🐾🚐

Strathspey ₩

Listed   APPROVED

Lansdown, Bourton-on-the-Water, Cheltenham GL54 2AR

☎ Cotswold (0451) 820694

Character, Cotswold-stone house 400 yards' walk from village centre. Quiet location with pretty riverside walk.

Bedrooms: 3 double, 1 twin
Bathrooms: 2 private,
1 public
Bed & breakfast

per night:	£min	£max
Double	28.00	32.00

Parking for 6

⚒🕻⌨🏠♿🆙🛎🅂✂️🛏🅿✳
✕🚭 ᴅᴀᴘ 🆂🅿

Upper Farm
⚒⚒

Clapton on the Hill,
Bourton-on-the-Water,
Cheltenham GL54 2LG
☎ Cotswold (0451) 820453
*130-acre mixed farm. 17th C
Cotswold farmhouse in a
quiet, unspoilt village 2.5
miles from Bourton-on-the-
Water. Magnificent views.
Fresh farm produce.*
Bedrooms: 1 single,
2 double, 2 twin
Bathrooms: 2 private,
2 public
Bed & breakfast

per night:	£min	£max
Single	16.00	18.00
Double	27.00	36.00

Parking for 6
Open March-November
🖤5⚒🕻⌨🛎✂️🛏🆃🖤🏠
🖊✳✕🚭🁢

Windrush Farm
⚒⚒ COMMENDED

Bourton-on-the-Water,
Cheltenham GL54 3BY
☎ Cotswold (0451) 820419
*150-acre arable farm.
Beautiful Cotswold-stone
house on a family-run farm,
in a peaceful setting 1.5 miles
from Bourton-on-the-Water.*
Bedrooms: 1 double, 1 twin
Bathrooms: 2 private
Bed & breakfast

per night:	£min	£max
Single	20.00	
Double	35.00	

Parking for 8
♿🍷🆙🆂✂️🆃🖤🏠🖊
✳🚭

BREDENBURY

Hereford and Worcester
Map ref 2A1

Redhill Farm
Listed

Bredenbury, Bromyard,
Herefordshire HR7 4SY
☎ Bromyard (0885) 483255
& 4835355
*86-acre mixed farm.
Farmhouse bed and breakfast
in peaceful Herefordshire
countryside. Children and
pets welcome. Golf, tennis,
fishing, leisure centre and*

*riding nearby. On the A44
road. Ample parking.*
Bedrooms: 1 double, 1 twin,
1 triple
Bathrooms: 1 public
Bed & breakfast

per night:	£min	£max
Single	13.00	14.00
Double	22.00	24.00

Parking for 23
🖤🕻⌨♿🆙🛎🆂🅿🆃
🏠🖊🚭🁢

BREDON'S NORTON

Hereford and Worcester
Map ref 2B1

Hamlet at the foot of
Bredon Hill with a
substantial Victorian
mansion in Tudor style.

Lampitt House ⚔
⚒⚒ COMMENDED

Lampitt Lane, Bredon's
Norton, Tewkesbury,
Gloucestershire GL20 7HB
☎ Bredon (0684) 72295
*Large house set in 1.5 acre
garden in picturesque
Cotswold village at the foot of
Bredon Hill. Extensive views.
Tewkesbury 4 miles. Beautiful
hill and riverside walks.*
Bedrooms: 2 double, 1 twin
Bathrooms: 3 private
Bed & breakfast

per night:	£min	£max
Single	18.00	26.00
Double	30.00	34.00

Half board

per person:	£min	£max
Daily	28.00	54.00

Evening meal 1800 (last
orders 2000)
Parking for 6
🖤♿🕻⌨♿🆙🛎🆂✂️🖤
🏠🖊✳🁢

Check the
introduction to this
region for Where to
Go, What to See.

Individual
proprietors have
supplied all details
of accommodation.
Although we do
check for accuracy,
we advise you to
confirm the
information at the
time of booking.

BRIDGNORTH

Shropshire
Map ref 4A3

Interesting red sandstone
town in 2 parts - High and
Low - linked by a cliff
railway. It has much of
interest including a ruined
Norman keep, half-
timbered 16th C houses,
Midland Motor Museum
and Severn Valley
Railway.
Tourist Information Centre
☎ *(0746) 763358*

The Albynes
⚒⚒

Nordley, Bridgnorth
WV16 4SX
☎ (0746) 762261
*263-acre arable and mixed
farm. Large country house,
peacefully set in parkland
with spectacular views of
Shropshire countryside. On
B4373 - Bridgnorth 3 miles,
Ironbridge 4 miles.*
Bedrooms: 2 twin
Bathrooms: 1 private,
2 public
Bed & breakfast

per night:	£min	£max
Single	15.00	
Double	30.00	

Parking for 8
🖤♿🛎🆂🅿🆃🏠🖊✕
🚭🁢

Aldenham Weir ⚔
⚒⚒ COMMENDED

Muckley Cross, Bridgnorth
WV16 4RR
☎ Morville (074 631) 352
*Superb country house, set in
11.5 acres, with working mill
race, weir and trout stream
for fishing. All rooms en-suite.
Close to Ironbridge Gorge
Museum. Quietly located off
the A458, central between
Much Wenlock and
Bridgnorth.*
Bedrooms: 2 double, 2 twin,
1 triple
Bathrooms: 5 private
Bed & breakfast

per night:	£min	£max
Single	22.00	
Double	34.00	36.00

Parking for 5
🖤♿🕻⌨♿🛎🆂🅿
🆃🏠🖊🖊✳🚭🆂🅿

Bear Inn ⚔
⚒⚒

Northgate, Bridgnorth
WV16 4ET
☎ (0746) 763250
*A personal welcome awaits
you at the Bear Inn, along*

*with freshly prepared food,
two characterful bars and
comfortable en suite
accommodation.*
Bedrooms: 1 single,
1 double, 1 twin
Bathrooms: 3 private
Bed & breakfast

per night:	£min	£max
Single	25.00	30.00
Double	40.00	45.00

Lunch available
Parking for 20
🖤🕻⌨♿🆂🏠🖊🁢🆃

Charlcotte Farm ⚔
⚒⚒ APPROVED

Cleobury North, Bridgnorth
WV16 6RR
☎ Burwarton (074 633) 238
*300-acre mixed farm.
Spacious, Georgian farmhouse
set in pleasant grounds at the
foot of the Clee Hills.*
Bedrooms: 1 double, 1 twin,
1 triple
Bathrooms: 1 private,
1 public
Bed & breakfast

per night:	£min	£max
Single	15.00	18.00
Double	28.00	32.00

Parking for 6
🖤🆙🛎🆃🏠✳✕🚭

Church House ⚔
⚒⚒

Aston Eyre, Bridgnorth
WV16 6XD
☎ Morville (074 631) 248
*A peaceful holiday in sleepy
hamlet. Modernised oak-
beamed cottage with log fire.
Summer house in 1 acre of
gardens (next to Norman
church). Evening meals by
arrangement.*
Bedrooms: 1 double, 1 twin
Bathrooms: 2 private
Bed & breakfast

per night:	£min	£max
Double	28.00	32.00

Half board

per person:	£min	£max
Daily		24.00
Weekly		154.00

Evening meal 1800 (last
orders 2000)
Parking for 4
Open April-October
🖤♿🆙🛎🆂✂️🖤🆃🏠🖊
✳🚭

Court House ⚔
⚒⚒

South Road, Ditton Priors,
Bridgnorth WV16 6SJ
☎ Ditton Priors (074 634)
554
*Friendly accommodation in a
tastefully converted barn set*
Continued ▶

HEART OF ENGLAND

BRIDGNORTH
Continued

*under the Clee Hills.
Conservation area. Non-
smoking. Off B4304. Ludlow
12 miles, Bridgnorth 7.5
miles. Evening meals served
on request.*
Bedrooms: 2 double, 1 triple
Bathrooms: 3 private
Bed & breakfast

per night:	£min	£max
Single	15.00	20.00
Double	30.00	40.00

Half board

per person:	£min	£max
Daily	24.50	29.50

Evening meal from 1800
Parking for 7

Haven Pasture ⚑
HIGHLY COMMENDED — COMMENDED
Underton, Bridgnorth
WV16 6TY
☎ Middleton Scriven (074
635) 632
Fax (074 635) 632
*Large country bungalow, set
in 1 acre of gardens, with
panoramic views. Outdoor
heated swimming pool.
Evening meals on request.
Trout pools 400 yards.*
Bedrooms: 1 single, 1 twin,
1 triple
Bathrooms: 1 private,
1 public
Bed & breakfast

per night:	£min	£max
Single	18.50	18.50
Double	30.00	35.00

Evening meal 1830 (last
orders 2100)

Middleton Lodge
HIGHLY COMMENDED
Middleton Priors, Bridgnorth
WV16 6UR
☎ Ditton Priors (074 634)
228
*Imposing stone building in its
own grounds, in a quiet
hamlet in the Shropshire
hills, 6 miles from
Bridgnorth.*
Bedrooms: 2 double, 1 twin
Bathrooms: 3 private
Bed & breakfast

per night:	£min	£max
Single	20.00	25.00
Double	35.00	40.00

Parking for 4

The Old Forge House ⚑
Hampton Loade, Bridgnorth
WV15 6HD
☎ Quatt (0746) 780338
*200-year-old house in
woodland setting, peaceful
and homely. Pub and River
Severn within 100 yards.
Near Severn Valley railway
station. 1 mile from A442.*
Bedrooms: 2 double, 1 twin
Bathrooms: 2 private,
1 public
Bed & breakfast

per night:	£min	£max
Single	16.00	22.00
Double	24.00	34.00

Parking for 6

Park Grange ⚑
Morville, Bridgnorth
WV16 4RN
☎ Morville (074 631) 285
*Spacious, beamed family
house set in 12 acres, with
goats, poultry and pony.
Children's play area.
Panoramic views of the
Shropshire hills. Fishing.
Quiet location midway
between Bridgnorth and Much
Wenlock just off A458, ideal
for Ironbridge Gorge.*
Bedrooms: 1 multiple
Bathrooms: 1 private
Bed & breakfast

per night:	£min	£max
Double	32.00	34.00

Parking for 10
Open March-October

BROAD CAMPDEN
Gloucestershire
Map ref 2B1

Holly Bush Barns
Listed
Broad Campden, Chipping
Campden GL55 6UZ
☎ Evesham (0386) 840051
*Grade II converted stone barn
in private courtyard and
gardens, on the edge of the
village and overlooking a
cherry orchard.*
Bedrooms: 1 multiple
Bathrooms: 1 private
Bed & breakfast

per night:	£min	£max
Single	17.00	
Double	34.00	

Parking for 2

BROADWAY
Hereford and Worcester
Map ref 2B1

*Beautiful Cotswold village
called the 'Show village of
England', with 16th C
stone houses and
cottages. Near the village
is Broadway Tower with
magnificent views over 12
counties and a country
park with nature trails and
adventure playground.*

Cinnibar Cottage ⚑
Listed   HIGHLY COMMENDED
45 Bury End, (Snowshill
Rd.,), Broadway,
Worcestershire WR12 7AF
☎ (0386) 858 623
*150-year-old Cotswold-stone
cottage. Quiet situation with
open country views, half a
mile from Broadway village
green, along Snowshill road.
Non-smoking establishment.*
Bedrooms: 1 double, 1 twin
Bathrooms: 1 public
Bed & breakfast

per night:	£min	£max
Double	28.00	31.00

Parking for 1

Crown and Trumpet Inn ⚑
Listed
Church Street, Broadway,
Worcestershire WR12 7AE
☎ (0386) 853202
*Traditional English inn with
log fires and oak beams,
quietly located just off the
village green. Home-cooked
local and seasonal English
food.*
Bedrooms: 3 double, 1 twin
Bathrooms: 3 private,
1 public
Bed & breakfast

per night:	£min	£max
Double	37.00	50.00

Lunch available
Evening meal 1830 (last
orders 2130)
Parking for 6

Eastbank ⚑
Station Drive, Broadway,
Worcestershire WR12 7DF
☎ (0386) 852659
*Quiet location, half a mile
from village. All rooms fully
en-suite (bath/shower), with
colour TV and beverage
facilities. Homely atmosphere.
Free brochure.*

Bedrooms: 2 double, 2 twin,
2 triple
Bathrooms: 6 private
Bed & breakfast

per night:	£min	£max
Single	15.00	
Double	30.00	45.00

Evening meal 1900 (last
orders 1000)
Parking for 6

Leasow House ⚑
HIGHLY COMMENDED
Laverton Meadow, Broadway,
Worcestershire WR12 7NA
☎ Stanton (038 673) 526
Fax (038 673) 596
*17th C Cotswold stone
farmhouse tranquilly set in
open countryside close to
Broadway village.*
Bedrooms: 3 double, 2 twin,
2 triple
Bathrooms: 7 private
Bed & breakfast

per night:	£min	£max
Double	43.00	60.00

Parking for 14
Cards accepted: Access, Visa,
Amex

Milestone House Hotel ⚑
COMMENDED
122 High Street, Broadway,
Worcestershire WR12 7AJ
☎ (0386) 853432
*17th C listed building in
beautiful area, run by Luigi
and Pauline Bellorini.
Victorian-style conservatory,
Luigi's Backyard Restaurant,
overlooking quiet garden.
Licensed bar.*
Bedrooms: 3 double, 1 twin
Bathrooms: 4 private
Bed & breakfast

per night:	£min	£max
Double	49.50	55.00

Half board

per person:	£min	£max
Daily	42.25	45.00

Evening meal 1930 (last
orders 2130)
Parking for 6
Open February-December
Cards accepted: Access, Visa

Millhay Cottage
Listed
Bury End, Broadway,
Worcestershire WR12 7JS
☎ (0386) 858241
*House set in a superb garden
off the Snowshill road and
adjacent to Cotswold Way.*

The suite of two bedrooms, bathroom and WC is let as one family unit (1-4 persons).
Bedrooms: 1 double, 1 twin
Bathrooms: 2 private, 1 public
Bed & breakfast

per night:	£min	£max
Single	18.00	20.00
Double	36.00	40.00

Parking for 12

Mount Pleasant Farm ⋀

HIGHLY COMMENDED

Childswickham, Broadway, Worcestershire WR12 7HZ
☎ (0386) 853424
250-acre mixed farm. Large Victorian farmhouse with excellent views. Very quiet accommodation with all modern amenities. Approximately 3 miles from Broadway.
Bedrooms: 2 double, 1 twin
Bathrooms: 3 private
Bed & breakfast

per night:	£min	£max
Single		22.00
Double	34.00	38.00

Parking for 8

Olive Branch Guest House ⋀

78 High Street, Broadway, Worcestershire WR12 7AJ
☎ (0386) 853440
Old house with modern amenities close to centre of village. Traditional English breakfast served. Reduced rates for 3 nights or more.
Bedrooms: 3 single, 2 double, 2 twin, 2 triple
Bathrooms: 5 private, 2 public
Bed & breakfast

per night:	£min	£max
Single	16.50	18.50
Double	35.00	40.00

Half board

per person:	£min	£max
Daily	24.50	26.50

Evening meal 1900 (last orders 2000)
Parking for 8
Cards accepted: Amex

Please check prices and other details at the time of booking.

The Orchard Bed and Breakfast

Listed

The Orchard, Leamington Road, Broadway, Worcestershire WR12 7EB
☎ (0386) 852534
Modern house in the Cotswold style, in a large garden with magnificent views. On the main Stratford road between Broadway and Willersey.
Bedrooms: 1 single, 1 double, 1 twin
Bathrooms: 1 public
Bed & breakfast

per night:	£min	£max
Single	14.00	16.00
Double	28.00	30.00

Parking for 4

Orchard Grove ⋀

HIGHLY COMMENDED

Station Road, Broadway, Worcestershire WR12 7DE
☎ Evesham (0386) 853834
Attractive detached Cotswold house, just minutes from village centre, tastefully appointed for guests' every comfort. Warm welcome assured. Non-smokers only please.
Bedrooms: 1 double, 1 triple
Bathrooms: 2 private, 1 public
Bed & breakfast

per night:	£min	£max
Single	18.00	
Double	40.00	40.00

Parking for 3

Southwold House ⋀

COMMENDED

Station Road, Broadway, Worcestershire WR12 7DE
☎ (0386) 853681
Warm welcome, friendly service, good cooking at this large Edwardian house, only 4 minutes' walk from village centre. Reductions for 2 or more nights.
Bedrooms: 1 single, 5 double, 2 twin
Bathrooms: 5 private, 2 public
Bed & breakfast

per night:	£min	£max
Single	16.50	
Double	33.00	45.00

Parking for 8
Open February-December
Cards accepted: Access, Visa

White Acres Guesthouse ⋀

COMMENDED

Station Road, Broadway, Worcestershire WR12 7DE
☎ (0386) 852320
Spacious Victorian house providing a variety of en-suite bedrooms, 3 with 4-poster beds. Ample off-the-road parking. Only 4 minutes' walk from the village centre. Brochure available.
Bedrooms: 5 double, 1 twin
Bathrooms: 6 private
Bed & breakfast

per night:	£min	£max
Single	24.00	24.00
Double	36.00	42.00

Parking for 6
Open March-November

BROMSGROVE

Hereford and Worcester
Map ref 4B3

This market town near the Lickey Hills has an interesting 14th C church with fine tombs and a Carillon tower. The Avoncroft Museum of Buildings is nearby where many old buildings have been re-assembled, having been saved from destruction.
Tourist Information Centre
☎ *(0527) 31809*

95 Old Station Rd.

Listed

Bromsgrove, Worcestershire B60 2AF
☎ (0527) 74463
Modern house in quiet pleasant location close to the A38, 3 miles from the M5 and 1.5 miles from the M42. Within easy reach of National Exhibition Centre, Worcester and Stratford. Car parking. TV lounge.
Bedrooms: 2 single, 1 twin
Bathrooms: 1 public
Bed & breakfast

per night:	£min	£max
Single	15.00	15.00
Double	30.00	30.00

Half board

per person:	£min	£max
Daily	20.00	20.00
Weekly	120.00	120.00

Evening meal 1800 (last orders 0900)
Parking for 2

Crofton Lodge

Listed   COMMENDED

80 New Road, Bromsgrove, Worcestershire B60 2LA
☎ (0527) 74136
Attractive Victorian town house with a walled garden. Sitting room with TV.
Bedrooms: 1 double, 1 twin
Bathrooms: 1 public
Bed & breakfast

per night:	£min	£max
Single	17.00	17.00
Double	29.00	29.00

Parking for 2

Victoria Guest House

31 Victoria Road, Bromsgrove, Worcestershire B61 0DW
☎ (0527) 75777
Homely, family-run guesthouse near Bromsgrove town centre, M5 and M42. Convenient for the NEC/ICC and touring the Cotswolds and Midlands. Interest holidays and courses.
Bedrooms: 3 single, 1 triple
Bathrooms: 1 public
Bed & breakfast

per night:	£min	£max
Single	14.50	20.50
Double	26.00	26.00

Half board

per person:	£min	£max
Daily	18.50	24.50
Weekly	125.50	167.50

Evening meal 1800 (last orders 1700)
Parking for 3

BROMYARD

Hereford and Worcester
Map ref 2B1

Market town on the River Frome surrounded by orchards, with black and white houses and a Norman church. Nearby at Lower Brockhampton is a 14th C half-timbered moated manor house owned by the National Trust.
Tourist Information Centre
☎ *(0885) 482038 (summer)*

Park House ⋀

28 Sherford Street, Bromyard, Herefordshire HR7 4DL
☎ (0885) 482294

Continued ►

BROMYARD

Continued

Close to town centre, restaurant and shops, and a desirable location for touring. Ample parking.
Bedrooms: 1 single,
1 double, 1 twin, 2 triple
Bathrooms: 3 private,
1 public
Bed & breakfast

per night:	£min	£max
Single	14.00	15.00
Double	28.00	30.00

Parking for 6
🚭 ♿ ⅏ 🅰 🅂 ♨ 📺 ▥ ✿ ✗ ⋙

BROSELEY

Shropshire
Map ref 4A3

Lord Hill Guest House
`Listed`

Duke Street, Broseley
TF12 5LU
☎ (0952) 884270
Former public house renovated to a high standard. Easy access to Ironbridge, Bridgnorth, Shrewsbury and Telford town centre.
Bedrooms: 1 single,
1 double, 5 twin
Bathrooms: 2 private,
2 public, 1 private shower
Bed & breakfast

per night:	£min	£max
Single	13.00	18.00
Double	25.00	32.00

Parking for 9
🚭 8 ⅍ ♿ ▯ 🅰 📺 ▥ ✿ ✗
🅾🅰🅿 🆂🅿

BUCKNELL

Shropshire
Map ref 4A3

Village by the River Redlake with thatched black and white cottages, a Norman church and the remains of an Iron Age fort on a nearby hill. It is a designated Area of Outstanding Natural Beauty.

The Hall ♠
`COMMENDED`

Bucknell SY7 0AA
☎ (054 74) 249
225-acre mixed farm. Georgian farmhouse in the picturesque village of Bucknell, with a peaceful and relaxed atmosphere.
Bedrooms: 2 double, 1 twin
Bathrooms: 1 public

Bed & breakfast

per night:	£min	£max
Single	15.00	16.00
Double	30.00	32.00

Half board

per person:	£min	£max
Daily	23.00	24.00
Weekly	155.00	

Evening meal 1800 (last orders 1200)
Parking for 4
Open March-November
🚭 7 ▯ ♿ ⅏ ✗ 🅰 📺 ✿
⋙ ⋙

BURTON UPON TRENT

Staffordshire
Map ref 4B3

An important brewing town with the Bass Museum of Brewing, where the Bass shire horses are stabled. There are 3 bridges with views over the river and some interesting public buildings including the 18th C St Modwen's Church.
Tourist Information Centre
☎ (0283) 516609

Hayfield House
`Listed`

13 Ashby Road, Woodville,
Swadlincote, Derbyshire
DE11 7BZ
☎ Swadlincote (0283)
225620
Victorian villa on the A50 in South Derbyshire, close to the Leicestershire/Staffordshire/Derbyshireshire border.
Bedrooms: 1 triple,
1 multiple
Bathrooms: 1 private,
1 public
Bed & breakfast

per night:	£min	£max
Single	12.50	15.00
Double	25.00	28.00

Half board

per person:	£min	£max
Daily	17.50	21.00
Weekly	115.00	125.00

Evening meal 1800 (last orders 1900)
Parking for 3
🚭 ⅏ 🅰 🅂 ✗ 📺 ▥ 🖃 ✿ ⋙

New Inn Farm
`Listed`

Needwood, Burton upon
Trent DE13 9PB
☎ (0283) 75435
122-acre mixed & dairy farm. In the heart of Needwood Forest on the main B5234 Newborough to Burton upon Trent road. Central for

Uttoxeter, Lichfield, Derby and A38 eastern access to Burton upon Trent.
Bedrooms: 1 single,
1 double, 1 triple
Bathrooms: 1 public
Bed & breakfast

per night:	£min	£max
Single	14.00	15.00
Double	28.00	30.00

Parking for 6
🚭 ⅏ ⅏ 🅰 📺 ▥ ▰ ✿ ✗ ⋙

CHELMARSH

Shropshire
Map ref 4A3

An unspoilt village near the River Severn, with old timbered cottages and an imposing 14th C church.

Bulls Head Inn ♠
`COMMENDED`

Chelmarsh, Bridgnorth
WV16 6BA
☎ Highley (0746) 861469
17th C village inn with warm friendly atmosphere. All rooms en-suite. TV lounge, jacuzzi, solarium. Magnificent views.
Bedrooms: 1 single,
3 double, 1 twin, 1 triple
Bathrooms: 6 private,
1 public
Bed & breakfast

per night:	£min	£max
Single	25.00	25.00
Double	39.00	39.00

Lunch available
Evening meal 1900 (last orders 2130)
Parking for 50
🚭 ⅏ 🅂 🅰 📺 ⊙ ▥ ▰ ●
⋙ 🆂🅿

CHELTENHAM

Gloucestershire
Map ref 2B1

Cheltenham was developed as a spa town in the 18th C and has some beautiful Regency architecture, in particular the Pittville Pump Room. It holds international music and literature festivals and is also famous for its race meetings and cricket.
Tourist Information Centre
☎ (0242) 522878

Central Hotel ♠
`⚜ ⚜`

7-9 Portland Street,
Cheltenham GL52 2NZ
☎ (0242) 582172 & 524789
Family-run hotel close to town centre, shops, coach

station, racecourse, cinema and theatre. Fully-licensed bar and restaurant.
Bedrooms: 3 single,
5 double, 7 twin, 2 triple
Bathrooms: 8 private,
2 public
Bed & breakfast

per night:	£min	£max
Single	23.00	32.00
Double	40.00	50.00

Half board

per person:	£min	£max
Daily	33.00	42.00

Lunch available
Evening meal 1800 (last orders 2100)
Parking for 5
Cards accepted: Access, Visa, Diners, Amex
🚭 ♿ ⅏ ▯ 🅰 🅂 🅰 🖃
⋙ 🅾🅰🅿 🆂🅿 🕮 🆃

Cleyne Hage ♠
`⚜ ⚜` `APPROVED`

Southam Lane, Southam,
Cheltenham GL52 3NY
☎ (0242) 518569
Cotswold-stone house in secluded setting between B4632 and A435, 3 miles north of Cheltenham. Open view of hills and racecourse. Pets welcome. Parking. Non-smokers only please.
Bedrooms: 2 single,
1 double, 1 twin
Bathrooms: 2 public
Bed & breakfast

per night:	£min	£max
Single	15.00	20.00
Double	25.00	35.00

Parking for 8
Cards accepted: Access, Visa
🚭 ▯ ♨ ⅏ ✗ 📺 ⊙ ▥ 🖃
∪ ┏ ✿ ⋙ 🅾🅰🅿 🆂🅿 🆃

Grovelands ♠
`⚜` `APPROVED`

12 Montpellier Grove,
Cheltenham GL50 2XB
☎ (0242) 525311 & 231462
Small family guesthouse in the centre of town has spacious bedrooms, all with TV, radio and telephone.
Bedrooms: 1 double, 3 twin,
2 triple
Bathrooms: 2 public
Bed & breakfast

per night:	£min	£max
Single	16.00	18.00
Double	32.00	34.00

Parking for 6
🚭 ⅏ ▯ ♨ 🅰 🅂 🅰 📺
▥ 🖃

Ham Hill Farm ♠
`⚜ ⚜` `COMMENDED`

Whittington, Cheltenham
GL54 4EZ
☎ (0242) 584415

152

160-acre mixed farm. Farmhouse, built in 1983 to a high standard, with good views of the Cotswolds. 2 miles from Cheltenham, on the Cotswold Way.
Bedrooms: 1 single, 5 double
Bathrooms: 4 private,
1 public
Bed & breakfast

per night:	£min	£max
Single	17.00	20.00
Double	28.00	34.00

Parking for 7
☒7🖧🖵♿️🅿️🛏🅂🕯📺🎜. 🖴✗🐾

Hamilton
Listed
46 All Saints Road,
Cheltenham GL52 2HA
☎ (0242) 582845
Early Victorian town house, with spacious accommodation, near town centre. Ideal for visitors to Stratford-upon-Avon, the Cotswolds and Forest of Dean.
Bedrooms: 1 twin
Bathrooms: 1 public
Bed & breakfast

per night:	£min	£max
Double	26.00	44.00

Open January-November
🖵♿️🅿️🅂📺🎜. 🖴✗🐾

Kielder ♠
COMMENDED
222 London Road, Charlton
Kings, Cheltenham
GL52 6HW
☎ (0242) 237138
Comfortable family house on A40, near junction with A435. One and a quarter miles from town centre. Stair chairlift available.
Bedrooms: 1 double, 2 twin
Bathrooms: 1 private,
1 public
Bed & breakfast

per night:	£min	£max
Single	16.00	17.00
Double	30.00	32.00

Parking for 5
Open March-October
☒🖵♿️🅿️🎜. 🖴🐾

Lawn House
COMMENDED
11 London Road,
Cheltenham GL52 6EX
☎ (0242) 578486
Elegant Grade II listed house. Good parking and close to town centre. Friendly atmosphere. Family-run.
Bedrooms: 1 single,
3 double, 2 twin, 2 triple
Bathrooms: 2 private,
2 public

Bed & breakfast

per night:	£min	£max
Single	18.00	22.00
Double	36.00	44.00

Parking for 8
Cards accepted: Access, Visa
☒🖵♿️🅿️🛏🅂✗📺🎜. 🖴🐾🕯🏵

Lonsdale House ♠
COMMENDED
Montpellier Drive,
Cheltenham GL50 1TX
☎ (0242) 232379
Regency house situated 5 minutes' walk from the town hall, promenade, shopping centre, parks and theatre. Easy access to all main routes.
Bedrooms: 5 single,
2 double, 1 twin, 2 triple,
1 multiple
Bathrooms: 3 private,
4 public

Bed & breakfast

per night:	£min	£max
Single	17.00	25.00
Double	34.00	45.00

Parking for 6
Cards accepted: Access, Visa, Amex
☒3🖵♿️🅿️🛏🅂📺🎜. 🖴🕯✗🐾🅂🏵

North Hall Hotel ♠
COMMENDED
Pittville Circus Road,
Cheltenham GL52 2PZ
☎ (0242) 520589
Fax (0242) 261953
Early Victorian town house situated in a wide tree lined road near Pittville Park.
Bedrooms: 8 single,
6 double, 5 twin, 1 triple
Bathrooms: 13 private,
5 public

Bed & breakfast

per night:	£min	£max
Single	19.75	29.75
Double	33.00	46.00

Half board

per person:	£min	£max
Daily	30.25	33.50
Weekly	181.00	201.00

Lunch available
Evening meal 1830 (last orders 1930)
Parking for 20
Cards accepted: Access, Visa
☒🖵♿️🅿️🛏🅂📺🎜. 🖴🕯 🏵🅂🏵🇹

Old Rectory ♠
COMMENDED
Woolstone, Cheltenham
GL52 4RG
☎ Bishops Cleeve (024 267)
3766
Beautiful Victorian rectory in peaceful hamlet, 4 miles

north of the Regency town of Cheltenham. Tranquil spot with lovely views.
Bedrooms: 1 double, 1 twin,
1 triple
Bathrooms: 3 private
Bed & breakfast

per night:	£min	£max
Single	20.00	25.00
Double	35.00	40.00

Parking for 6
Open March-November
☒🖧♿️🅿️🛏✗🅂📺🖴U
🎜🐾🏵

St. Michaels ♠
COMMENDED
4 Montpellier Drive,
Cheltenham GL50 1TX
☎ (0242) 513587
Elegant, Edwardian guesthouse, 5 minutes' walk from shops, town hall, theatres and restaurants. All rooms offer central heating, tea/coffee facilities, colour TV, clock/radio and hairdryer. Friendly relaxed atmosphere.
Bedrooms: 2 double, 1 twin,
1 triple
Bathrooms: 1 private,
1 public
Bed & breakfast

per night:	£min	£max
Single	17.00	25.00
Double	29.00	36.50

Parking for 3
Cards accepted: Access, Visa
☒5🖵♿️🅿️🖁🅂✗🎜.
🖴🐾📇🅂

The Wynyards ♠
COMMENDED
Butts Lane, Woodmancote,
Cheltenham GL52 4QH
☎ Bishops Cleeve (024 267)
3876
Secluded old Cotswolds house with panoramic views. Ideal touring centre. Cheltenham, 4 miles away, offers many leisure activities.
Bedrooms: 1 double, 1 twin
Bathrooms: 2 public
Bed & breakfast

per night:	£min	£max
Single	15.00	18.00
Double	27.00	30.00

Parking for 6
☒🕯♿️🅿️🅂✗🛏📺🖌🎜.
🖴🕂U🎿✗🐾🅂

Half board prices shown are per person but in some cases may be based on double/twin occupancy.

CHIPPING CAMPDEN

Gloucestershire
Map ref 2B1

Outstanding Cotswold wool town with many old stone gabled houses, a splendid church and 17th C almshouses. Nearby are Kiftsgate Court Gardens and Hidcote Manor Gardens (National Trust).

Brymbo ♠
Listed
Honeybourne Lane,
Mickleton, Chipping
Campden GL55 6PU
☎ Mickleton (0386) 438876
Fax (0386) 438113
Comfortable, spacious farm building conversion with large garden in beautiful Cotswold countryside. 3 miles Chipping Campden, close to Stratford and Broadway. Free "4 wheel drive tour" offer.
Bedrooms: 1 double, 1 twin
Bathrooms: 2 private
Bed & breakfast

per night:	£min	£max
Single	14.00	16.50
Double	28.00	34.00

Parking for 4
☒🛝🖧📇🖵♿️🅿️🛏🅂
📺🎜. 🖴🕯🐾🅂🇹

Lower High Street
Listed
Chipping Campden
GL55 6DZ
☎ Evesham (0386) 840163
Cotswold-stone house in the Lower High Street, conveniently situated for tours and walks in the Cotswolds, shops and restaurants.
Bedrooms: 1 double, 1 twin
Bathrooms: 1 private,
1 public
Bed & breakfast

per night:	£min	£max
Double	30.00	35.00

Open April-October
☒📇♿️🅿️🛏🅂🎜. 🐾

Manor Farm ♠
APPROVED
Weston Subedge, Chipping
Campden GL55 6QT
☎ Evesham (0386) 840390
Traditional 17th C farmhouse in the heart of the Cotswolds, completely refurbished and restored. All rooms en-suite. 1.5 miles from Chipping Campden.
Bedrooms: 2 double, 1 twin
Bathrooms: 3 private
Continued ▶

CHIPPING CAMPDEN

Continued

Bed & breakfast

per night:	£min	£max
Single	18.00	20.00
Double	36.00	40.00

Parking for 8

Norton Grounds Farm

Aston Subedge, Chipping Campden GL55 6PY
☎ Mickleton (0386) 438482
900-acre arable farm. Cotswold farmhouse in rural setting. One and a half miles from Mickleton to Broadway on B4632. Ideal for exploring Cotwolds and Shakespeare country.
Bedrooms: 1 double, 1 twin
Bathrooms: 2 public

Bed & breakfast

per night:	£min	£max
Single	18.00	18.00
Double	30.00	30.00

Parking for 10

Sparlings

COMMENDED

Leysbourne, High Street, Chipping Campden GL55 6HL
☎ Evesham (0386) 840505
Fully centrally heated, comfortable, attractive 18th C Cotswold house in Chipping Campden High Street. Walled garden. Easy parking.
Bedrooms: 1 double, 1 twin
Bathrooms: 2 private

Bed & breakfast

per night:	£min	£max
Single	24.00	24.00
Double	40.00	42.00

Weston Park Farm ♠

Dovers Hill, Chipping Campden GL55 6WW
☎ (0386) 840835
20-acre mixed farm. Self-contained wing of secluded, magnificently situated farmhouse, 1 mile from Chipping Campden, adjacent to National Trust land.
Bedrooms: 1 triple
Bathrooms: 1 private

Please mention this guide when making a booking.

Bed & breakfast

per night:	£min	£max
Double	35.00	35.00

Parking for 10

Wyldlands

Listed COMMENDED

Broad Campden, Chipping Campden GL55 6UR
☎ Evesham (0386) 840478
Non-smoking accommodation in quiet scenic village. Extensive views. Good food at traditional pub nearby.
Bedrooms: 2 double, 1 twin
Bathrooms: 1 private, 2 public

Bed & breakfast

per night:	£min	£max
Single	18.00	
Double	32.00	

Parking for 4

CHURCH LENCH

Hereford and Worcester
Map ref 2B1

Hill Barn Orchard ♠

Listed

Church Lench, Evesham, Worcestershire WR11 4UB
☎ Evesham (0386) 871035
50-acre arable farm. North of Evesham overlooking Church Lench and lakes in orchard setting. Close to Cotswolds and Stratford-upon-Avon. Fishing, good pub food locally.
Bedrooms: 1 double, 4 twin
Bathrooms: 3 private, 1 public

Bed & breakfast

per night:	£min	£max
Single	20.00	20.00
Double	30.00	30.00

Parking for 12

There are separate sections in this guide listing groups specialising in farm holidays and accommodation which is especially suitable for young people and organised groups.

CHURCH STRETTON

Shropshire
Map ref 4A3

Church Stretton lies under the eastern slope of the Longmynd surrounded by hills. It is ideal for walkers, with marvellous views, golf and gliding. The town has a small puppet theatre and Wenlock Edge is not far away.
Tourist Information Centre
☎ *(0694) 723133*

Acton Scott Farm ♠

Listed APPROVED

Acton Scott, Church Stretton SY6 6QN
☎ Marshbrook (0694) 781260
320-acre mixed farm. Conveniently situated 17th C farmhouse of character with comfortable, spacious rooms and log fires. Beautiful countryside.
Bedrooms: 1 double, 1 twin, 1 triple
Bathrooms: 1 public

Bed & breakfast

per night:	£min	£max
Single	12.00	15.00
Double	24.00	30.00

Parking for 6
Open February-November

The Elms

Little Stretton, Church Stretton SY6 6RD
☎ (0694) 723084
Victorian country house in spacious grounds, decorated and furnished in Victorian style.
Bedrooms: 2 double, 1 twin
Bathrooms: 2 public

Bed & breakfast

per night:	£min	£max
Single	17.00	
Double	29.00	

Parking for 3

Gilberries Cottage ♠

COMMENDED

Wall-under-Heywood, Church Stretton SY6 7HZ
☎ Longville (0694) 771400
Country cottage adjoining family farm, in peaceful and beautiful countryside. Ideal for walking. Numerous places of interest nearby.
Bedrooms: 1 twin, 1 triple
Bathrooms: 1 public

Bed & breakfast

per night:	£min	£max
Double	30.00	34.00

Parking for 8
Open February-November

Travellers Rest Inn ♠

APPROVED

Upper Affcot, Church Stretton SY6 6RL
☎ Marshbrook (0694) 781275
Traditional inn between Craven Arms and Church Stretton in beautiful countryside, with real ale, good food and accommodation and good company.
Bedrooms: 2 single, 2 double, 3 twin, 3 triple
Bathrooms: 4 private, 1 public

Bed & breakfast

per night:	£min	£max
Single	18.50	30.00
Double	37.00	45.00

Lunch available
Evening meal 1730 (last orders 2130)
Parking for 80
Cards accepted: Access, Visa, Amex

Woolston Farm ♠

Church Stretton SY6 6QD
☎ Marshbrook (0694) 781201
312-acre mixed farm. Victorian farmhouse in the small hamlet of Woolston, off A49. Good centre for touring Shropshire. Children most welcome.
Bedrooms: 1 double, 1 triple
Bathrooms: 1 public

Bed & breakfast

per night:	£min	£max
Single	13.50	14.50
Double	27.00	27.00

Half board

per person:	£min	£max
Daily	21.00	21.00
Weekly	136.50	136.50

Evening meal 1850 (last orders 2000)
Open January-November

The symbols are explained on the flap inside the back cover.

CIRENCESTER

Gloucestershire
Map ref 2B1

'Capital of the Cotswolds', Cirencester was Britain's second most important Roman town with many finds housed in the Corinium Museum. It has a very fine Perpendicular church and old houses around the market place. *Tourist Information Centre* ☎ (0285) 654180.

The Coach House ⋀
Listed | APPROVED

Middle Duntisbourne, Cirencester GL7 7AR
☎ (0285) 653058
400-acre arable & livestock farm. Set in 400 acres of farmland in the beautiful Duntisbourne Valley. Always a good choice of breakfast, special diets welcome.
Bedrooms: 1 double, 1 twin
Bathrooms: 2 private

Bed & breakfast
per night:	£min	£max
Single	16.00	20.00
Double	27.00	32.00

Parking for 8

The Leauses
APPROVED

101 Victoria Road, Cirencester GL7 1EU
☎ (0285) 653643
Guesthouse with spacious rooms and pretty gardens, close to town centre. Ideal touring base. Large secure car park. Non-smokers only please.
Bedrooms: 1 double, 1 twin, 1 triple
Bathrooms: 2 public

Bed & breakfast
per night:	£min	£max
Single	17.00	
Double	28.00	

Parking for 6

Royal Agricultural College ⋀

Stroud Road, Cirencester GL7 6JS
☎ (0285) 652531 & Direct Line 640644
Fax (0285) 640644
Set majestically on a 30-acre private Cotswold estate, bordering the Roman town of Cirencester.

Bedrooms: 50 single, 190 twin
Bathrooms: 48 private, 53 public

Bed & breakfast
per night:	£min	£max
Single	23.70	33.90
Double	40.00	50.20

Half board
per person:	£min	£max
Daily	32.20	42.40
Weekly	198.00	270.00

Lunch available
Evening meal 1800 (last orders 1900)
Parking for 700
Open January, March-April, July-September, December

Sunset

Baunton Lane, Cirencester GL7 2NQ
☎ (0285) 654822
Small friendly detached house pleasantly situated close to Cirencester. Within easy access of Cheltenham, Gloucester and Swindon.
Bedrooms: 1 single, 1 twin
Bathrooms: 1 public

Bed & breakfast
per night:	£min	£max
Single	11.50	12.00
Double	23.00	24.00

Parking for 4
Open May-October

The Village Pub
Listed | APPROVED

Barnsley, Cirencester GL7 5EF
☎ (0285) 740421
The Village Pub has 6 rooms, 4 with showers en-suite, and is situated in a pretty Cotswold village.
Bedrooms: 4 double, 2 twin
Bathrooms: 4 private, 1 public

Bed & breakfast
per night:	£min	£max
Single	30.00	
Double	45.00	

Lunch available
Evening meal 1900 (last orders 2130)
Parking for 40
Cards accepted: Access, Visa

Warwick Cottage Guest House ⋀
COMMENDED

75 Victoria Road, Cirencester GL7 1ES
☎ (0285) 656279
Attractive Victorian townhouse, 5 minutes from the town centre. Good base

for touring the Cotswolds. Family rooms available as doubles or twins.
Bedrooms: 2 double, 1 triple, 1 multiple
Bathrooms: 4 private, 1 public

Bed & breakfast
per night:	£min	£max
Double	29.00	33.00

Half board
per person:	£min	£max
Daily	21.50	23.50
Weekly	132.00	152.00

Evening meal from 1830
Parking for 4

Wimborne House ⋀
APPROVED

91 Victoria Road, Cirencester GL7 1ES
☎ (0285) 653890
Cotswold-stone house, built in 1886, with a warm and friendly atmosphere and spacious rooms. Non-smokers only please.
Bedrooms: 4 double, 1 twin
Bathrooms: 5 private

Bed & breakfast
per night:	£min	£max
Single	20.00	25.00
Double	25.00	35.00

Evening meal 1830 (last orders 1730)
Parking for 6

CLEARWELL

Gloucestershire
Map ref 2A1

Attractive village in the Forest of Dean, noted for its castle, built in 1735 and one of the oldest Georgian Gothic houses in England. The old mines in Clearwell Caves are open to the public.

Tudor Farmhouse Hotel

Clearwell, Coleford GL16 8JS
☎ Dean (0594) 833046
Fax (0594) 837093
Charming 13th C listed house with original oak panelling and unique spiral staircase. Well appointed bedrooms and restaurant.
Bedrooms: 6 double, 2 twin, 1 triple
Bathrooms: 9 private

Bed & breakfast
per night:	£min	£max
Single	42.50	47.00
Double	49.00	65.00

Half board
per person:	£min	£max
Daily	30.00	36.25

Evening meal 1830 (last orders 2130)
Parking for 42
Cards accepted: Access, Visa, Amex

CLEOBURY MORTIMER

Shropshire
Map ref 4A3

Village with attractive timbered and Georgian houses and a church with a wooden spire. It is close to the Clee Hills with marvellous views and Clee Hill Garden with over 400 birds and animals.

Cleeton Court
Listed | APPROVED

Cleeton St Mary, Kidderminster, Worcestershire DY14 0QZ
☎ Stoke St Milborough (0584) 75379
Substantial stone farmhouse on Clee Hill, with medieval hall, Tudor and Georgian rooms.
Bedrooms: 1 double, 1 twin
Bathrooms: 2 private

Bed & breakfast
per night:	£min	£max
Double	30.00	40.00

Parking for 6

CLIFTON UPON TEME

Hereford and Worcester
Map ref 2B1

Village standing 600 ft above the River Teme in beautiful countryside with a mixture of red-brick and black and white houses.

The Lion Inn

Clifton upon Teme, Worcester WR6 6DH
☎ Shelsley Beauchamp (088 65) 617 & 235
One of Worcestershire's oldest coaching inns. Enjoy the hospitality, the cooking, and the taste of real ale from an 800-year-old cellar.
Bedrooms: 1 double, 1 twin
Bathrooms: 2 private
Continued ▶

CLIFTON UPON TEME

Continued

Bed & breakfast

per night:	£min	£max
Single	30.00	38.00
Double		55.00

Half board

per person:	£min	£max
Daily	35.00	52.00
Weekly	240.00	305.00

Lunch available
Evening meal 1900 (last orders 2200)
Parking for 23
Cards accepted: Access, Visa, Switch
🛇🗠💷🖵♿🅂🕮🖳🍴➤✕ 🖦🅿

CLUN

Shropshire
Map ref 4A3

Small, ancient town on the Welsh border with flint and stone tools in its museum and Iron Age forts nearby. The impressive ruins of a Norman castle lie beside the River Clun and there are some interesting 17th C houses.

Hurst Mill Farm 🏡
🚭🚭

Clunton, Craven Arms
SY7 0JA
☎ (058 84) 224
100-acre mixed farm. Attractive farmhouse and old mill in the lovely Clun Valley. River and woodland trails, 2 riding ponies, pets welcome. Winners of "Great Shropshire Breakfast" challenge.
Bedrooms: 1 double, 1 triple
Bathrooms: 2 public

Bed & breakfast

per night:	£min	£max
Single	12.00	14.00
Double	24.00	28.00

Half board

per person:	£min	£max
Daily	19.00	22.00
Weekly	133.00	150.00

Evening meal 1800 (last orders 2000)
Parking for 8
🛇♿🖳🅂🕮🅂📺🕮🖳♿🅿🚗✓ ✿🖦🅿

Lower Duffryn Farm 🏡
Listed COMMENDED

Newcastle-on-Clun, Craven Arms SY7 8PQ
☎ (0588) 640239

130-acre mixed & livestock farm. Situated 5 miles west of Clun on the B4368, in unspoilt countryside and enjoying lovely views of the Shropshire borders' environmentally sensitive area.
Bedrooms: 3 double
Bathrooms: 1 public

Bed & breakfast

per night:	£min	£max
Single	13.00	
Double	24.00	26.00

Half board

per person:	£min	£max
Daily	18.00	19.00
Weekly	120.00	126.00

Evening meal 1830 (last orders 1200)
Parking for 2
Open March-October
🛇🗠10♿🖳🅰🅂🕮📺🕮🖳♿ ✕🖦

CLUNGUNFORD

Shropshire
Map ref 4A3

Village near the River Clun and Stokesay Castle, a 13th C fortified manor house with an Elizabethan gatehouse.

Broadward Hall 🏡
Listed

Clungunford, Craven Arms SY7 0QA
☎ Bucknell (054 74) 357
176-acre mixed farm. Grade II listed, castellated. 9 miles west of Ludlow in rural Clun Valley surroundings.
Bedrooms: 2 twin, 1 triple
Bathrooms: 2 public

Bed & breakfast

per night:	£min	£max
Single	13.00	
Double	26.00	

Half board

per person:	£min	£max
Daily	20.00	
Weekly	133.00	

Evening meal 1900 (last orders 0900)
Parking for 15
Open March-November
🛇🗠🖳🅂🕮📺🖳♿🚗✿✕ 🖦🅿

National Crown ratings were correct at the time of going to press but are subject to change. Please check at the time of booking.

CODDINGTON

Hereford and Worcester
Map ref 2B1

Village in charming countryside close to the wooded slopes of Combe and Oyster Hills, with a cluster of black and white houses and a 700-year-old church.

Church Farm
Listed

Coddington, Ledbury, Herefordshire HR8 1JJ
☎ Bosbury (0531) 640271
100-acre mixed farm. Black and white 16th C listed farmhouse in a quiet location, on working farm. Warm welcome, log fires and home cooking.
Bedrooms: 2 double, 1 twin
Bathrooms: 1 public

Bed & breakfast

per night:	£min	£max
Double	33.00	

Half board

per person:	£min	£max
Daily	25.00	

Evening meal from 1830
Parking for 3
Open February-November
🛇🖳🅰🅂🕮📺🖳♿✓✿🖦 🅂🅿🖦

CODSALL

Staffordshire
Map ref 4B3

Expanding residential village a few miles from Wolverhampton.

Moors Farm and Country Restaurant 🏡

Chillington Lane, Codsall, Wolverhampton WV8 1QF
☎ (0902) 842330
100-acre mixed farm. 200-year-old farmhouse, 1 mile from pretty village. All home produce used. Many local walks and places of interest.
Bedrooms: 2 double, 2 twin, 1 triple, 1 multiple
Bathrooms: 2 private, 2 public

Bed & breakfast

per night:	£min	£max
Single	23.00	28.00
Double	38.00	46.00

Half board

per person:	£min	£max
Daily	28.00	37.00

Evening meal 1830 (last orders 1900)
Parking for 20
🛇🗠4🗠🖵♿🅂🕮🖳♿🚗✓ ✿✕🖦🖦🅿🅣

COLEFORD

Gloucestershire
Map ref 2A1

Small town in the Forest of Dean with the ancient iron mines at Clearwell Caves nearby, where mining equipment and geological samples are displayed. There are several forest trails in the area.
Tourist Information Centre
☎ *(0594) 836307*

Forest House Hotel 🏡
🚭🚭

Cinder Hill, Coleford GL16 8HQ
☎ Dean (0594) 832424
Gracious listed building with spacious, well-furnished rooms, 2 minutes' walk from town centre.
Bedrooms: 2 single, 3 double, 2 twin
Bathrooms: 1 private, 2 public

Bed & breakfast

per night:	£min	£max
Single	16.00	16.00
Double	32.00	38.00

Half board

per person:	£min	£max
Daily	25.00	28.00

Evening meal 1900 (last orders 1900)
Parking for 10
🛇🗠3♿🖵✕🖳♿🕮🖳✕🖦🖦

Marefold 🏡

Gorsty Knoll, Milkwall, Coleford GL16 7LR
☎ Dean (0594) 833969
200-year-old stone cottage surrounded by woodland of the Forest of Dean, and 5 minutes' walk from nature reserve.
Bedrooms: 1 single, 1 twin
Bathrooms: 1 private, 2 public

Bed & breakfast

per night:	£min	£max
Single	13.50	15.00
Double	27.00	30.00

Parking for 2
🛇♿🖳✕📺🖳♿🅿➤✿ 🖦🅂🅿🅣

We advise you to confirm your booking in writing.

COLESHILL

Warwickshire
Map ref 4B3

Close to Birmingham's many attractions including the 17th C Aston Hall with its plasterwork and furnishings, the Railway Museum and Sarehole Mill, an 18th C water-powered mill restored to working order.

Maxstoke Hall Farm

🕮 🕮 COMMENDED

Maxstoke, Coleshill, Birmingham B46 2QT
☎ (0675) 463237
230-acre arable farm. Elegant farmhouse, 1634, with en-suite rooms. 10 minutes from M42 and M6, 15 minutes from National Exhibition Centre and Birmingham Airport.
Bedrooms: 1 single, 1 twin
Bathrooms: 2 private
Bed & breakfast

per night:	£min	£max
Single	22.50	
Double	39.00	

Half board

per person:	£min	£max
Daily	29.15	

Evening meal 1830 (last orders 2000)
Parking for 30
Cards accepted: Access
🕭 🖵 🕴 🕮 🕮 🟦 🛇 🗡 🅜 🕮. 🖃
🍴 🕽 🎋 ✿ 🕮 T

Maxstoke Priory ♉

🕮 🕮 COMMENDED

Maxstoke, Coleshill, Birmingham B46 2QW
☎ (0675) 462117
500-acre mixed farm. Historic farmhouse with unique dining room, in peaceful surroundings. Easy access to National Exhibition Centre, airport and motorways.
Bedrooms: 2 twin
Bathrooms: 2 private, 2 public
Bed & breakfast

per night:	£min	£max
Single	24.00	30.00
Double	36.00	40.00

Parking for 10
🕭 🖵 🕴 🟦 🕮 🟦 🅜 🕮.
🖃 🕽 🕽 ✿ 🎋 🕮

The colour maps at the back of this guide pinpoint all places with accommodation.

CORSE HARTPURY

Gloucestershire
Map ref 2B1

Kilmorie Guest House

🕮 🕮

Gloucester Road, Corse, Snigs End, Staunton, Gloucester GL19 3RQ
☎ Gloucester (0452) 840224
7-acre livestock & fruit farm. Grade II listed Chartist smallholding, built in 1848 in conservation area. Comfortable, homely accommodation. Ideally situated for touring Cotswolds, Forest of Dean and Malvern Hills. Pony riding.
Bedrooms: 1 single, 3 double, 1 twin, 1 multiple
Bathrooms: 2 public, 2 private showers
Bed & breakfast

per night:	£min	£max
Single	10.00	
Double	20.00	

Half board

per person:	£min	£max
Daily	15.50	
Weekly	108.50	

Lunch available
Evening meal from 1800
Parking for 8
🕭 5 🖧 🕴 🕮 🟦 🛇 🗡 🅜 🕮 🖃
🕛 ✿ 🎋 SP 🕮

COTSWOLDS

See under Ampney Crucis, Ampney St. Peter, Berkeley, Bibury, Birdlip, Bledington, Blockley, Bourton-on-the-Water, Broad Campden, Broadway, Cheltenham, Chipping Campden, Cirencester, Cowley, Donnington, Dursley, Ewen, Fairford, Frocester, Gloucester, Great Rissington, Guiting Power, Lower Swell, Mickleton, Minchinhampton, Moreton-in-Marsh, Nailsworth, Naunton, Northleach, Nympsfield, Painswick, Slimbridge, Stonehouse, Stow-on-the-Wold, Stratton, Stroud, Teddington, Temple Guiting, Tetbury, Tewkesbury, Upton St Leonards, Winchcombe, Winstone

---

Please check prices and other details at the time of booking.

COVENTRY

West Midlands
Map ref 4B3

Modern city with a long history. It has many places of interest including the post-war and ruined medieval cathedrals, art gallery and museums, some 16th C almshouses, St Mary's Guildhall, Lunt Roman fort and the Belgrade Theatre.
Tourist Information Centre ☎ (0203) 832303

Acorn Lodge Private Guest House, Pond Farm ♉

🕮 🕮

Upper Eastern Green Lane, Coventry CV5 7DP
☎ (0203) 465182
300-year-old beamed house of character in secluded position 100 yards off the road, with fields at the rear. Free tea or coffee always available.
Bedrooms: 2 single, 1 double, 1 twin
Bathrooms: 1 private, 2 public
Bed & breakfast

per night:	£min	£max
Single	15.00	20.00
Double	30.00	34.00

Parking for 6
🕭 10 🕴 🕮 🟦 🅜 🕮. 🖃 ✿
✕ 🎋 🕮

Mill Farmhouse ♉

🕮 🕮

Mill Lane, Fillongley, Coventry CV7 8EE
☎ Fillongley (0676) 41898
Beautiful farmhouse set in rolling countryside, offering peace and tranquillity. Detached apartments and home cooking. Convenient for Coventry, Birmingham, Warwick and Stratford-upon-Avon.
Bedrooms: 1 single, 1 double
Bathrooms: 1 public
Bed & breakfast

per night:	£min	£max
Single	30.00	35.00
Double	40.00	45.00

Half board

per person:	£min	£max
Daily	38.00	52.00

Lunch available
Evening meal 1800 (last orders 2000)
Parking for 8
🖧 🖵 🖵 🕴 🕮 🟦 🛇 🗡 🅜 🕮
🕮. 🖃 ✿ ✕ 🎋 🕮 OAP 🔆 SP

Northanger House ♉

🕮 🕮

35 Westminster Road, Coventry CV1 3GB
☎ (0203) 226780
Friendly home 5 minutes from the city centre. Close to railway and bus stations. Convenient for all amenities.
Bedrooms: 2 single, 2 double, 3 twin, 2 triple
Bathrooms: 3 public
Bed & breakfast

per night:	£min	£max
Single	16.00	17.00
Double	28.00	30.00

Parking for 1
🕭 🖧 🖵 🕴 🕮 🟦 🅜 🕮. 🖃

Spire View Guest House

Listed

36 Park Rd., (Nr. Railway Station), Coventry CV1 2LD
☎ (0203) 251602
Centrally situated in quiet tree-lined cul-de-sac, within walking distance of cathedral and sports centre. Easy access to National Exhibition Centre and National Agricultural Centre.
Bedrooms: 3 single, 2 twin, 3 triple
Bathrooms: 2 public, 4 private showers
Bed & breakfast

per night:	£min	£max
Single	13.00	18.00
Double	26.00	32.00

Parking for 3
🕭 🖧 🖵 🕴 🕮 🟦 S 🕮. 🖃
✕ 🎋

Westwood Cottage

🕮 🕮

79 Westwood Heath Road, Westwood Heath, Coventry CV4 8GN
☎ (0203) 471084
One of 4 sandstone farm cottages, circa 1834, in rural surroundings. Recently converted but with character maintained and offering comfortable accommodation for a small number of guests.
Bedrooms: 2 single, 1 double, 1 twin
Bathrooms: 2 private, 4 public, 2 private showers
Bed & breakfast

per night:	£min	£max
Single	16.00	17.00
Double	30.00	32.00

Parking for 5
🕭 🖧 🖵 🕴 🕮 🟦 S 🗡 🕮 🕮. 🖃 ✿
✕ 🕮

COVENTRY

Continued

Woodlands

Oak Lane, Allesley, Coventry
CV5 9BX
☎ Meriden (0676) 22688
*Comfortable, detached and
privately situated in a
beautiful country lane only
150 yards from the A45. 7
minutes from NEC and
Birmingham Airport, ideal for
Coventry, Stratford-upon-Avon
and Warwick.*
Bedrooms: 3 twin
Bathrooms: 1 public
Bed & breakfast

per night:	£min	£max
Single	17.00	19.00
Double	34.00	36.00

Parking for 6
🏠7⛱📺🛁🅂✕🔼📺🎅.
🛏️🅿️↻↑✕🍴

COWLEY

Gloucestershire
Map ref 2B1

Butlers Hill Farm

APPROVED

Cockleford, Cowley,
Cheltenham GL53 9NW
☎ Coberley (0242) 870455
*130-acre livestock farm. A
spacious, modern farmhouse
on a working stock farm in a
quiet unspoilt river valley
with attractive walks.*
Bedrooms: 1 double, 1 twin
Bathrooms: 2 public
Bed & breakfast

per night:	£min	£max
Double	30.00	

Half board		
per person:	£min	£max
Daily	37.00	

Evening meal from 1900
Parking for 6
Open March-September
🏠10⛱🔼📺🎅.🛏️🅿️↻
✕🍴🐾

Individual
proprietors have
supplied all details
of accommodation.
Although we do
check for accuracy,
we advise you to
confirm the
information at the
time of booking.

CRAVEN ARMS

Shropshire
Map ref 4A3

Village close to Wenlock
Edge and the Longmynd
and an ideal centre for
walking with many fine
views. It is close to
Stokesay Castle, a 13th C
fortified manor house, the
ruins of Hopton Castle
and Ludlow.

The Castle Farm 🅜

Cheyney Longville, Craven
Arms SY7 8DR
☎ (0588) 673255
*300-acre mixed farm. 13th C
farmhouse standing in its
own grounds. Private
courtyard, many interesting
features.*
Bedrooms: 1 double, 1 triple
Bathrooms: 1 public
Bed & breakfast

per night:	£min	£max
Double	26.00	28.00

Parking for 4
Open March-October
🏠3🔼📺🌸🐾🍴

DARLINGSCOTT

Warwickshire
Map ref 2B1

Lower Farm 🅜

Listed HIGHLY COMMENDED

Darlingscott, Shipston-on-
Stour CV36 4PN
☎ Ilmington (060 882) 750
*18th C farmhouse offering a
high level of class and
comfort, just off the Fosse
Way between Shipston and
Ilmington. Chipping Campden
5 miles, Stratford 9 miles.*
Bedrooms: 2 double
Bathrooms: 2 private
Bed & breakfast

per night:	£min	£max
Single	23.00	25.00
Double	40.00	45.00

Parking for 4
📼🛏️🔼🅂✕🎅.🛏️🅿️↻
✕🍴🐾

DONNINGTON

Gloucestershire
Map ref 2B1

Holmleigh

Listed

Donnington, Moreton-in-
Marsh GL56 0XX
☎ (0451) 830792
*15-acre dairy farm.
Farmhouse accommodation
with friendly welcome. In a
peaceful setting with own
private lane from the village*

*of Donnington, 1 mile from
Stow-on-the-Wold.*
Bedrooms: 1 double, 1 twin
Bathrooms: 2 private,
1 public
Bed & breakfast

per night:	£min	£max
Single	12.00	12.00
Double	24.00	24.00

Parking for 3
Open April-October
🏠5🛁🔼🔼🃏🅂✕🅼📺🎅.
🌸✕🐾

DROITWICH

Hereford and Worcester
Map ref 2B1

Old town with natural
brine springs, developed
as a spa town at the
beginning of the 19th C. It
has some interesting
churches, in particular the
Church of the Sacred
Heart with splendid
mosaics. There are
several fine parks and a
Heritage Centre.
*Tourist Information Centre
☎ (0905) 774312*

Astwood Court Farm 🅜

Listed

Astwood Lane, Stoke Prior,
Bromsgrove, Worcestershire
B60 4BB
☎ Hanbury (0527) 821362
*16th C farmhouse, within
easy reach of Stratford-upon-
Avon, Warwick and the
Cotswolds. Exit 5 of the M5 to
Stoke Works. After 1.5 miles,
take first right after Bowling
Green Inn.*
Bedrooms: 1 double, 2 twin
Bathrooms: 1 private,
1 public
Bed & breakfast

per night:	£min	£max
Single	17.00	25.00
Double	30.00	35.00

Parking for 20
🏠10🔼📼🔼🎅.↻🌸
✕🐾🍴

Richmond Guest House 🅜

Listed

3 Ombersley St. West,
Droitwich, Worcestershire
WR9 8HZ
☎ (0905) 775722
*Victorian-built guesthouse in
the town centre, 5 minutes
from railway station and bus
route. English breakfast. 30
minutes from National
Exhibition Centre via M5/
M42.*

Bedrooms: 6 single,
1 double, 4 twin, 3 triple
Bathrooms: 3 public
Bed & breakfast

per night:	£min	£max
Single	15.00	16.00
Double	26.00	28.00

Parking for 12
🏠🔼🔼🅂🅼📺🎅.

DURSLEY

Gloucestershire
Map ref 2B1

Market town with some
Georgian houses and an
18th C arched market hall
with a statue of Queen
Anne. Nearby is the
weaving village of Uley
with 17th C houses.

Claremont House 🅜

66 Kingshill Road, Dursley
GL11 4EG
☎ (0453) 542018
*In beautiful location on the
edge of the Cotswolds on
scenic route and within easy
reach of Slimbridge Wildfowl
Trust, Berkeley Castle and
Westonbirt Arboretum. Fresh
farm produce. Evening meal
by arrangement.*
Bedrooms: 1 single,
1 double, 1 twin, 1 triple
Bathrooms: 2 private,
1 public
Bed & breakfast

per night:	£min	£max
Single	13.50	15.00
Double	30.00	

Evening meal from 1800
Parking for 8
🏠🔼🔼🃏🅂🅼📺🎅.🛏️🌸
🐾🍴

The Old Crown Inn

17 The Green, Uley, Dursley
GL11 5SN
☎ (0453) 860502
*17th C village inn situated on
Uley Village green, between
Stroud and Dursley on the
B4066 in Gloucestershire. On
Cotswold Way route.*
Bedrooms: 2 double,
1 multiple
Bathrooms: 3 private
Bed & breakfast

per night:	£min	£max
Single	28.00	28.00
Double	40.00	40.00

Lunch available
Evening meal 1900 (last
orders 2100)
Parking for 18
🏠🔼🔼🅂🎅.🛏️🌸🐾🍴

EARLSWOOD

West Midlands
Map ref 4B3

Johalin
120 Shutt Lane, Earlswood,
Solihull B94 6BZ
☎ (056 46) 2652
*Earlswood is a rural village,
car essential. Beautiful
country walks at Earlswood
Lakes.*
Bedrooms: 1 single, 2 double
Bathrooms: 1 public
Bed & breakfast

per night:	£min	£max
Single	15.00	17.00
Double	28.00	30.00

Half board

per person:	£min	£max
Daily	20.00	

Evening meal 1900 (last
orders 2100)
Parking for 2
🌣🏠🕿🐾🛆🅿🆂📺🛏🖵🍴
🎿🛴

ECCLESHALL

Staffordshire
Map ref 4B3

Small market town has
long associations with the
Bishops of Lichfield, 6 of
whom are buried in the
large 12th C parish
church. The ruined castle
was formerly the
residence of these
bishops.

Glenwood ♠♠
≝ ≝ **COMMENDED**
Croxton, Eccleshall, Stafford
ST21 6PF
☎ Wetwood (063 082) 238
*16th C timber-framed cottage
in an ideal position for
visiting the many attractions
of Staffordshire and
Shropshire.*
Bedrooms: 1 double, 1 twin,
1 triple
Bathrooms: 1 private,
1 public
Bed & breakfast

per night:	£min	£max
Single	15.00	17.00
Double	26.00	34.00

Parking for 6
Cards accepted: Access, Visa
🌣🔔📞🐾🛆🅿🆂🖂🔆📺
🖵🍴🗘🎿🛴🅿🆂🏵🆃

King's Arms Hotel
Stafford Street, Eccleshall,
Stafford ST21 6BL
☎ Stafford (0785) 850294
*Town's original 16th C
coaching inn, renowned for*

*its food and relaxing
atmosphere.*
Bedrooms: 2 double, 1 twin,
1 triple
Bathrooms: 2 public
Bed & breakfast

per night:	£min	£max
Single	21.00	24.00
Double	39.00	42.00

Lunch available
Evening meal 1900 (last
orders 2200)
Parking for 50
Cards accepted: Access, Visa
🌣🖵🔆🛆🆂🖵🛆🍴🐾🏵🆃

EDGE

Gloucestershire
Map ref 2B1

Near the picturesque wool
town of Painswick. The
village church is of rock-
faced stone with
freestone dressings.

The Orchard
Listed **HIGHLY COMMENDED**
Edge, Stroud GL6 6NE
☎ (0452) 813581
Fax (0452) 813581
*Attractive cottage in
picturesque valley close to
Cotswold Way. Take Edge
road from Painswick, 100
yards past bridge at bottom of
valley.*
Bedrooms: 1 single, 1 double
Bathrooms: 1 public
Bed & breakfast

per night:	£min	£max
Single	20.00	25.00
Double	28.00	35.00

Parking for 4
🌣🖵🔆🐾🛆🆂🔆🖂📺🖵
🛆🏵🐾

ELLESMERE

Shropshire
Map ref 4A2

Small market town with
old streets and houses
and situated close to 9
lakes. The largest, The
Mere, has many
recreational facilities and
some of the other meres
have sailing and fishing.

Hordley Hall ♠♠
Listed
Hordley, Ellesmere
SY12 9BB
☎ (0691) 622772
Fax (0691) 622772
*A Georgian house with large
garden, in a quiet village.
Ideal for visiting the
Shropshire lakelands, the
Welsh Marches and Offa's
Dyke.*

Bedrooms: 2 triple
Bathrooms: 1 public
Bed & breakfast

per night:	£min	£max
Single		15.00
Double		30.00

Parking for 6
🌣🖵🔆🐾🛆🆂🔆🖂📺🖵🛆
🏵🎿🐾

ELMLEY CASTLE

Hereford and Worcester
Map ref 2B1

The Cloisters
≝ ≝ **HIGHLY COMMENDED**
Main Street, Elmley Castle,
Pershore, Worcestershire
WR10 3HS
☎ (0386) 710241
*A stone and half-timbered
Tudor house, part of which
dates back to the 14th C.
Located towards the end of
the main street, on the left-
hand corner of Ashton-under-
Hill Lane. Elmley Castle, at
the foot of Bredon Hill, is one
of the most attractive villages
in the Vale of Evesham.*
Bedrooms: 1 double, 1 triple
Bathrooms: 2 private
Bed & breakfast

per night:	£min	£max
Double	36.00	38.00

Parking for 3
🖵🔆🛆🆂🖵🛆🎿🐾

ENDON

Staffordshire
Map ref 4B2

Village between Stoke-on-
Trent and Leek, noted for
its well-dressing ceremony
on Spring Bank Holiday.

Hollinhurst Farm
Park Lane, Endon, Stoke-on-
Trent ST9 9JB
☎ Stoke-on-Trent (0782)
502633
*116-acre dairy farm. 17th C
farmhouse within easy reach
of Potteries, Peak District and
Alton Towers. Panoramic
views, walking and touring.*
Bedrooms: 2 double, 1 triple
Bathrooms: 3 private,
2 public
Bed & breakfast

per night:	£min	£max
Double	28.00	32.00

Evening meal 1800 (last
orders 1600)
Parking for 10
Open May-December
🌣🔆🛆🆂🖂📺🖵🛆🗘🍴
🎿🐾🆎

ENGLISH BICKNOR

Gloucestershire
Map ref 2A1

Village with views of the
River Wye and the Forest
of Dean. The 13th-15th C
sandstone church is built
on the foundations of a
Norman castle and boasts
the original Norman nave.

Bicknor Court
Listed
English Bicknor, Coleford
GL16 7PD
☎ Dean (0594) 860210
*Period country house set in
its own grounds in beautiful
countryside, close to the
beauty spot of Symonds Yat.*
Bedrooms: 1 double,
1 multiple
Bathrooms: 1 private,
1 public
Bed & breakfast

per night:	£min	£max
Double	30.00	35.00

Parking for 4
Open March-October
🌣🐾🔆🆂📺🖵🏵🐾🆂🅿
🏵🆃

Lower Tump Farm ♠♠
🕿
Eastbach, English Bicknor,
Coleford GL16 7EU
☎ Dean (0594) 860253
*150-acre mixed farm.
Attractive 16th C farmhouse.
Spectacular views. Take
turning signposted English
Bicknor from A4136
Monmouth to Gloucester road,
or take turning signposted
Eastbach from B4234 Ross to
Coleford road.*
Bedrooms: 1 double, 1 triple
Bathrooms: 2 private
Bed & breakfast

per night:	£min	£max
Single	16.00	20.00
Double	25.00	30.00

Parking for 6
🌣🖵🐾🔆🛆🆂🖵🛆🏵
🐾🏵

There are separate
sections in this
guide listing groups
specialising in farm
holidays and
accommodation
which is especially
suitable for young
people and
organised groups.

EVESHAM

Hereford and Worcester
Map ref 2B1

Evesham is a market town in the centre of a fruit-growing area. There are pleasant walks along the River Avon and many old houses and inns. A fine 16th C bell tower stands between 2 churches.
Tourist Information Centre
☎ *(0386) 446944*

Chequers Inn ⚜
☺☺☺ COMMENDED
Fladbury, Pershore,
Worcestershire WR10 2PZ
☎ (0386) 860276 & 860527
14th C inn between Evesham and Pershore, on the edge of the Cotswolds. Off B4084 and A44, in a quiet village location, 17 miles from Stratford-upon-Avon.
Bedrooms: 3 double, 4 twin,
1 triple
Bathrooms: 8 private

Bed & breakfast
per night:	£min	£max
Single	41.00	45.00
Double	61.00	65.00

Lunch available
Evening meal 1830 (last orders 2130)
Parking for 30
Cards accepted: Access, Visa, Amex
🛇 🕭 🖳 🖵 🍴 ♿ 🛆 🖸 S 🎠 ⬛ 🛢 🗩 ♪
❄ ✗ 🖼 DAP 🗟 SP 🐾

The Croft ⚜
☺☺ COMMENDED
54 Greenhill, Evesham,
Worcestershire WR11 4NF
☎ (0386) 446035
Splendid Georgian home offering comfortable overnight and holiday accommodation. Large private garden and ample parking.
Bedrooms: 1 double, 1 twin,
1 triple
Bathrooms: 2 private,
1 public

Bed & breakfast
per night:	£min	£max
Single	25.00	35.00
Double	35.00	42.00

Parking for 6
🛇 🖵 🛆 ♿ 🖸 UL S 🎠 TV ⬛
❄ 🖼

Far Horizon ⚜
☺☺ COMMENDED
Long Hyde Road, South
Littleton, Evesham,
Worcestershire WR11 5TH
☎ (0386) 831691

Elegant family home of character, with fine views over surrounding Cotswolds and Malvern Hills. Rural location 4 miles from Evesham.
Bedrooms: 1 single,
1 double, 1 twin
Bathrooms: 1 private,
2 public

Bed & breakfast
per night:	£min	£max
Single	15.00	16.50
Double	30.00	33.00

Parking for 3
Open March-November
🛇 10 🖵 🛆 ♿ UL 🎠 ⬛ 🛆 ❄
✗ 🖼

Park View Hotel ⚜
☺☺☺
Waterside, Evesham,
Worcestershire WR11 6BS
☎ (0386) 442639
Riverside hotel offering personal attention. Traditional English breakfast included, evening meal available. Base for touring Cotswolds and Shakespeare Country.
Bedrooms: 11 single,
4 double, 10 twin, 1 triple,
1 multiple
Bathrooms: 7 public

Bed & breakfast
per night:	£min	£max
Single	18.50	20.50
Double	34.50	38.00

Half board
per person:	£min	£max
Daily	27.50	29.50

Lunch available
Evening meal 1800 (last orders 1900)
Parking for 50
Cards accepted: Access, Visa, Amex
🛇 🖸 S 🎠 TV 🛆 🍴 20-30 SP 🔳

Riverside Hotel ⚜
☺☺☺ HIGHLY COMMENDED
The Parks, Offenham Road,
Evesham, Worcestershire
WR11 5JP
☎ (0386) 446200
Fax (0386) 40021
Small country house hotel offering panoramic views across the Avon.
Bedrooms: 3 double, 4 twin
Bathrooms: 7 private

Bed & breakfast
per night:	£min	£max
Single	25.00	55.00
Double	50.00	75.00

Half board
per person:	£min	£max
Daily	46.00	75.00

Lunch available
Evening meal 1930 (last orders 2100)

Parking for 45
Cards accepted: Access, Visa
🛇 🕭 🖵 🛆 ♿ 🖸 S 🎠 ⬛ 🛆 🗩
❄ ✗ 🖼 SP 🐾 🔳

The Waterside Hotel ⚜
☺☺☺ COMMENDED
56 Waterside, Evesham,
Worcestershire WR11 6JZ
☎ (0386) 442420
Warm and friendly owner-run hotel, in exceptional position overlooking river and parks. Designer interior, themed restaurant, extensive menu with affordable wines.
Bedrooms: 16 double,
2 twin, 2 triple
Bathrooms: 17 private,
1 public

Bed & breakfast
per night:	£min	£max
Single	34.00	48.00
Double	48.00	58.00

Half board
per person:	£min	£max
Daily	34.00	58.00
Weekly	230.00	390.00

Lunch available
Evening meal 1830 (last orders 2130)
Parking for 30
Cards accepted: Access, Visa, Amex
🛇 🖸 🕭 🖳 🖵 🛆 ♿ S 🎠 🗲 ⚜
TV ⬛ 🛆 🗩 ❄ 🖼 DAP SP 🔳

EWEN

Gloucestershire
Map ref 2B1

Village in the South Cotswolds of attractive stone cottages and houses.

Wild Duck Inn ⚜
☺☺☺ APPROVED
Drakes Island, Ewen,
Cirencester GL7 6BY
☎ (0285) 770310 & 770364
Fax (0285) 770169
15th C Cotswold stone inn, set in a rural position in the village. Two four-poster rooms in the oldest part of the building. All rooms with private facilities. Delightful garden.
Bedrooms: 5 double, 4 twin
Bathrooms: 9 private

Bed & breakfast
per night:	£min	£max
Single	48.00	
Double	65.00	

Lunch available
Evening meal 1900 (last orders 2145)

Parking for 50
Cards accepted: Access, Visa
🛇 🖁 🕭 🖳 🖵 🛆 ♿ S 🎠
TV ⬛ 🛆 🗩 ♿ ❄ SP 🐾

FAIRFORD

Gloucestershire
Map ref 2B1

Small town with a 15th C wool church famous for its complete 15th C stained glass windows, interesting carvings and original wall paintings. It is an excellent touring centre and the Cotswold Wildlife Park is nearby.

Lady Lamb Farm
Fairford, Cirencester
GL7 5LH
☎ Cirencester (0285)
712206
200-acre arable farm. Traditional Cotswold farmhouse in open countryside. Three-quarters of a mile from Fairford, 6 miles from Cirencester.
Bedrooms: 1 single, 3 twin
Bathrooms: 2 public

Bed & breakfast
per night:	£min	£max
Single	17.00	
Double	35.00	

Parking for 4
Open April-October
🛇 🛆 ♿ UL 🗲 ⬛ 🛆 ♿ ✔ ⚜
❄ 🖼 ⬛

FOREST OF DEAN

See under Clearwell, Coleford, Corse Hartpury, English Bicknor, Newent, Newland, Parkend, St Briavels, Upper Lydbrook

FOWNHOPE

Hereford and Worcester
Map ref 2A1

Attractive village close to the River Wye with black and white cottages and other interesting houses. It has a large church with a Norman tower and a 14th C spire.

Green Man Inn ⚜
☺☺☺☺ COMMENDED
Fownhope, Hereford
HR1 4PE
☎ (0432) 860243
Fax (0432) 860207
15th C black and white coaching inn, mid-way between Ross-on-Wye and Hereford, in the picturesque village of Fownhope. On the B4224, close to the River

Wye, and set in the beautiful Wye Valley. Self-catering cottage also available.
Bedrooms: 1 single,
13 double, 1 twin, 4 triple
Bathrooms: 19 private

Bed & breakfast

per night:	£min	£max
Single	31.00	31.00
Double	47.50	48.50

Half board

per person:	£min	£max
Daily	33.50	34.50
Weekly	223.00	223.00

Lunch available
Evening meal 1900 (last orders 2100)
Parking for 80
Cards accepted: Access, Visa, Amex

FROCESTER

Gloucestershire
Map ref 2B1

Village at the foot of Frocester Hill with one of the oldest and best-preserved of the country's tithe barns.

Elmtree Farm ♠

♛ COMMENDED

Frocester, Stonehouse
GL10 3TG
☎ Stonehouse (0453) 823274
201-acre dairy farm. 200-year-old farmhouse with inglenooks and beams. Ideal for visiting Slimbridge Wildfowl Trust, Berkeley Castle and for touring the Cotswolds.
Bedrooms: 1 single,
1 double, 1 twin
Bathrooms: 1 public

Bed & breakfast

per night:	£min	£max
Single	15.00	17.00
Double	25.00	27.00

Parking for 5
Open April-October

GLOUCESTER

Gloucestershire
Map ref 2B1

A Roman city and inland port on the Severn, its cathedral is one of the most beautiful in Britain. Gloucester's many attractions include museums, old buildings and inns and the house of Beatrix Potter's 'Tailor of Gloucester'.
Tourist Information Centre
☎ *(0452) 421188*

Hill Farm ♠

♛♛♛

Wainlodes Lane, Bishops Norton, Gloucester GL2 9LN
☎ (0452) 730351
14th C thatched farmhouse in rural setting, close to River Severn, offering facilities for "get away from it all" breaks.
Bedrooms: 4 double, 1 twin
Bathrooms: 2 private,
1 public

Bed & breakfast

per night:	£min	£max
Single	16.00	22.50
Double	32.00	45.00

Half board

per person:	£min	£max
Daily	26.00	32.50
Weekly	180.00	225.00

Evening meal 1845 (last orders 2100)
Parking for 12

Merrivale ♠

♛ COMMENDED

Tewkesbury Road, Norton, Gloucester GL2 9LQ
☎ (0452) 730412
Large private house with a pleasant garden, 3 miles from Gloucester. TV and tea/coffee-making facilities in all bedrooms.
Bedrooms: 2 double, 3 twin,
1 triple
Bathrooms: 1 public,
2 private showers

Bed & breakfast

per night:	£min	£max
Single	13.50	15.50
Double	27.00	31.00

Parking for 8

Notley House and Coach House ♠

♛♛♛ COMMENDED

93 Hucclecote Road,
Hucclecote, Gloucester
GL3 3TR
☎ (0452) 611584
Affordable quality accommodation. Ideal for historic Gloucester and the Cotswolds. Tastefully furnished en-suite rooms, suite with four-poster bed.
Bedrooms: 1 single,
2 double, 2 twin, 2 triple
Bathrooms: 5 private,
2 private showers

Bed & breakfast

per night:	£min	£max
Single	20.00	25.00
Double	33.00	37.00

Half board

per person:	£min	£max
Daily	29.00	33.00
Weekly	203.00	231.00

Lunch available
Evening meal 1800 (last orders 2030)
Parking for 8

GREAT RISSINGTON

Gloucestershire
Map ref 2B1

The Malthouse

♛♛

Great Rissington,
Cheltenham GL54 2LH
☎ Cotswolds (0451) 820582
Cotswold-stone malthouse built in 1648, in sought after, quiet Cotswold village. Accommodation is private suite with gallery bedroom. Non-smokers only please.
Bedrooms: 1 double
Bathrooms: 1 private

Bed & breakfast

per night:	£min	£max
Double	35.00	40.00

Parking for 2

GUITING POWER

Gloucestershire
Map ref 2B1

Unspoilt village with stone cottages and a green. The Cotswold Farm Park, with a collection of rare breeds, an adventure playground and farm trail, is nearby.

Farmers Arms

Guiting Power, Cheltenham
GL54 5TZ
☎ (0451) 850358
Country pub in lovely Cotswold village 13 miles from Cheltenham. Good access to local places of interest.
Bedrooms: 1 double, 1 triple
Bathrooms: 1 public,
1 private shower

Bed & breakfast

per night:	£min	£max
Double	33.00	35.00

Lunch available
Evening meal 1900 (last orders 2115)
Parking for 24

Guiting Guesthouse ♠

♛♛ COMMENDED

Post Office Lane, Guiting Power, Cheltenham
GL54 5TZ
☎ (0451) 850470
Cotswold-stone farmhouse with inglenooks and four-posters. In centre of delightful village, convenient for Stratford-upon-Avon, Cheltenham, Oxford, Stow, etc.
Bedrooms: 3 double
Bathrooms: 3 private

Bed & breakfast

per night:	£min	£max
Single	22.00	24.00
Double	35.00	40.00

Evening meal 1845 (last orders 1845)
Parking for 6

161

HALFORD

Warwickshire
Map ref 2B1

Village in attractive
countryside near Hidcote
Manor Gardens (National
Trust) and Stratford.

Halford Bridge Inn
APPROVED
Fosseway, Halford, Shipston-
on-Stour CV36 5BN
☎ Stratford-upon-Avon
(0789) 740382
*16th C coaching inn/
restaurant with 200-year-old
bowling green in the grounds.
River walks.*
Bedrooms: 1 single,
2 double, 2 twin, 1 multiple
Bathrooms: 2 public,
3 private showers
Bed & breakfast

per night:	£min	£max
Single	17.50	25.00
Double	35.00	46.00

Lunch available
Evening meal 1830 (last
orders 2130)
Parking for 50
Cards accepted: Access, Visa
☎🖬⌂♨💷🅂🅟🖭🗗🍴👥 🍴 🆂🅿️ 🏧

HAMPTON IN ARDEN

West Midlands
Map ref 4B3

The Cottage
Listed COMMENDED
Kenilworth Road, On A452
to Balsall Common,
Hampton in Arden, Solihull
B92 0LW
☎ (0675) 442323
*Charming cottage 2.5 miles
from National Exhibition
Centre and Birmingham
Airport. All bedrooms have
TV, radio alarms, tea and
coffee facilities.*
Bedrooms: 2 single,
3 double, 2 twin, 2 triple
Bathrooms: 4 private,
2 public
Bed & breakfast

per night:	£min	£max
Single	18.00	25.00
Double	34.00	40.00

Parking for 15
☎🖬⌂♨💷🅂🅟🖭🗗🆔 🗗🍴🏧🅾️

The Hollies
Listed
Kenilworth Road, Hampton
in Arden, Solihull B92 0LW
☎ (0675) 442941 & 442681

On the A452, ideally located
for many major attractions of
the Midlands, including the
National Agricultural Centre,
Warwick Castle and Stratford-
upon-Avon. Only 5 minutes to
National Motorcycle Museum
and the National Exhibition
Centre.
Bedrooms: 1 single,
2 double, 4 twin
Bathrooms: 5 private,
1 public
Bed & breakfast

per night:	£min	£max
Single	20.00	20.00
Double	34.00	38.00

Half board

per person:	£min	£max
Weekly	140.00	140.00

Parking for 10
☎🖬⌂♨💷🅂🅟🖭🗗🍴👥

HARLEY

Shropshire
Map ref 4A3

Rowley Farm
Listed
Harley, Shrewsbury SY5 6LX
☎ Much Wenlock (0952)
727348
*290-acre arable & livestock
farm. 18th C Georgian
farmhouse in secluded rural
area with views of Wrekin
and Wenlock Edge.
Convenient for Ironbridge,
Bridgnorth, Severn Railway,
Much Wenlock and
Shrewsbury. Footpath to
Wenlock Edge. Two inns
nearby for evening meals.*
Bedrooms: 1 double, 1 twin
Bathrooms: 1 public
Bed & breakfast

per night:	£min	£max
Double	28.00	28.00

Parking for 10
☎🖬⌂💷🅂🅟🖭🗗🍴👥🏧

HASELEY

Warwickshire
Map ref 4B3

Village which has an
interesting church with
many original features
including box pews and
candles.

Shrewley Pools Farm
Listed COMMENDED
Haseley, Warwick CV35 7HB
☎ (0926) 484315
*260-acre mixed farm.
Traditional mid 17th C
beamed farmhouse set in 1*

acre of gardens. 5 miles north
of Warwick on the A4177.
Bedrooms: 1 twin, 1 triple
Bathrooms: 2 private,
1 public
Bed & breakfast

per night:	£min	£max
Single	18.00	21.00
Double	35.00	42.00

Half board

per person:	£min	£max
Daily	24.00	28.00
Weekly	150.00	180.00

Evening meal 1800 (last
orders 2100)
Parking for 10
☎🖬⌂♨💷🅂🅟🖭🗗🍴👥🆂🅿️

HENLEY-IN-ARDEN

Warwickshire
Map ref 2B1

Old market town which in
Tudor times stood in the
Forest of Arden. It has
many ancient inns, a 15th
C Guildhall and parish
church. Coughton Court
with its Gunpowder Plot
connections is nearby.

Irelands Farm
COMMENDED
Irelands Lane, Henley-in-
Arden, Solihull, West
Midlands B95 5SA
☎ (0564) 792476
*220-acre arable & livestock
farm. Secluded farmhouse in
peaceful countryside. Close to
Stratford, Warwick, National
Exhibition Centre and the
Cotswolds. 1 mile off A34
between Henley and M42.*
Bedrooms: 2 double, 1 twin
Bathrooms: 2 private,
1 public
Bed & breakfast

per night:	£min	£max
Single	18.00	22.00
Double	32.00	40.00

Parking for 6
💷🖬⌂♨🅂🅟🖭🗗🍴👥

Individual
proprietors have
supplied all details
of accommodation.
Although we do
check for accuracy,
we advise you to
confirm the
information at the
time of booking.

HEREFORD

Hereford and Worcester
Map ref 2A1

Agricultural county town,
its cathedral containing
much Norman work and a
large chained library. The
city's varied attractions
include the Bulmer
Railway Centre and
several museums
including a cider museum.
Tourist Information Centre
☎ (0432) 268430

The Ancient Camp Inn
COMMENDED
Ruckhall, Eaton Bishop,
Hereford HR2 9QX
☎ Golden Valley (0981)
250449
*This inn is on the site of an
Iron Age fort dating from the
4th-5th C BC. Spectacular
views of the River Wye.
Restaurant and bar food a
speciality.*
Bedrooms: 4 double, 1 twin
Bathrooms: 5 private
Bed & breakfast

per night:	£min	£max
Single	35.00	45.00
Double	48.00	58.00

Lunch available
Evening meal 1900 (last
orders 2130)
Parking for 45
Cards accepted: Access, Visa
☎10💷🖬⌂♨🅂🖭🗗🍴👥🆔

Broughton House Guest House
Listed
32 Ledbury Road, Hereford
HR1 1ZY
☎ (0432) 277984
Bed and breakfast guesthouse.
Bedrooms: 2 twin
Bathrooms: 2 public
Bed & breakfast

per night:	£min	£max
Single	11.00	
Double	22.00	

Evening meal from 1730
Parking for 6
🖬⌂♨💷🅂🖭🗗🍴👥🏧🅾️

Cwm Craig Farm
COMMENDED
Little Dewchurch, Hereford
HR2 6PS
☎ Carey (0432) 840250
*190-acre arable & livestock
farm. Spacious Georgian
farmhouse on edge of Wye
Valley, surrounded by superb,
unspoilt countryside. 5 miles*

south of Hereford. Easy access from M50.
Bedrooms: 1 double, 1 twin, 1 triple
Bathrooms: 2 public
Bed & breakfast

per night:	£min	£max
Single	14.00	14.00
Double	26.00	28.00

Parking for 6
🐕🚲♿🅿️Ⅲ📺Ⅲ.🖥️🍴✿
💈🎁

Felton House
♛♛

Felton, Hereford HR1 3PH
☎ (0432) 820366
Tranquil stone-built rectory with period furnishings, in extensive landscaped gardens with small church. Felton hamlet is 8 miles from Hereford, Leominster and Bromyard in the heart of old rural England.
Bedrooms: 1 single, 2 double, 1 twin
Bathrooms: 2 public
Bed & breakfast

per night:	£min	£max
Single	14.50	
Double	26.00	30.00

Parking for 6
Open January-November
🐕🚲♿UL⌧✶♿📺Ⅲ.🖥️✿
🎁🚬

Grafton Villa Farm House
♛♛ COMMENDED

Grafton, Hereford HR2 8ED
☎ (0432) 268689
180-acre mixed farm. Family farmhouse of great character and warmth. Set back from the main Hereford to Ross-on-Wye road, surrounded by peaceful countryside. Ideal for touring the Wye Valley.
Bedrooms: 1 double, 1 twin, 1 triple
Bathrooms: 2 private, 3 public
Bed & breakfast

per night:	£min	£max
Single	18.00	20.00
Double	28.00	32.00

Half board

per person:	£min	£max
Daily	28.00	30.00

Evening meal 1900 (last orders 1600)
Parking for 10
🐕🚲♿UL🛈⌧♿📺Ⅲ.🖥️
💈✿🎁🚬

> **Please mention this guide when making a booking.**

Lower Bartestree Farm
♛♛

Bartestree, Hereford HR1 4DT
☎ (0432) 851005
Comfortable accommodation in a peaceful setting with splendid views. Home-made bread, preserves and crafts available. Off A438, 4 miles from city centre.
Bedrooms: 1 twin, 1 triple
Bathrooms: 1 public
Bed & breakfast

per night:	£min	£max
Single		15.00
Double		28.00

Evening meal 1800 (last orders 1700)
Parking for 5
🐕🚲♿UL🛈⌧♿📺Ⅲ.🖥️
♿✿🎁

Lyston Smithy ♨
♛♛ COMMENDED

Wormelow, Hereford HR2 8EL
☎ Golden Valley (0981) 540625
14-acre fruit farm. 6 miles south of Hereford on A466 Hereford/Monmouth road. Wonderful views. Residents' dining room and lounge with library.
Bedrooms: 2 twin, 1 triple
Bathrooms: 3 private
Bed & breakfast

per night:	£min	£max
Double	31.00	33.00

Parking for 8
Open March-December
🐕4🚲♿🛈⌧♿📺Ⅲ.
🖥️✿🎁 SP

Sink Green Farm
♛♛

Rotherwas, Hereford HR2 6LE
☎ Holme Lacy (0432) 870223
170-acre livestock farm. 16th C farmhouse on family-run farm. Overlooking River Wye and 3 miles from Hereford city centre. Establishment is non-smoking.
Bedrooms: 2 double, 1 twin
Bathrooms: 3 private
Bed & breakfast

per night:	£min	£max
Single	18.00	22.00
Double	32.00	40.00

Parking for 10
🐕🚲🍴♿UL⌧⌧♿📺
Ⅲ.🖥️✎✿🎁 SP

INKBERROW

Hereford and Worcester Map ref 2B1

Attractive village with a green surrounded by black and white half-timbered houses. Nearby is Ragley Hall, a 17th C Palladian house with beautiful plasterwork, furniture and paintings.

Bulls Head Inn ♨

High Street, Inkberrow, Worcester WR7 4DY
☎ (0386) 792233 & 793090
15th C main building, an old coaching inn, with Georgian facade. Imaginative food.
Bedrooms: 3 double, 1 twin, 1 triple
Bathrooms: 5 private
Bed & breakfast

per night:	£min	£max
Single	30.00	
Double	40.00	

Lunch available
Evening meal 1800 (last orders 2100)
Parking for 45
Cards accepted: Access, Visa
🐕🚲♿🍷🛈⌧✶🖥️Ⅲ.🖥️🍴
🎁✿✂🎁 DAP ◪🏠

IRONBRIDGE

Shropshire Map ref 4A3

Small town on the Severn where the Industrial Revolution began. It has the world's first iron bridge built in 1774. The Ironbridge Gorge Museum contains several industrial sites and museums spread over 2 miles and is exceptionally interesting.
Tourist Information Centre
☎ *(0952) 432166*

46 Wigmore
Listed

Woodside, Telford TF7 5NB
☎ (0952) 583748
Privately-owned house with garden and garage at rear. TV in all rooms.
Bedrooms: 1 single, 1 twin
Bathrooms: 1 public
Bed & breakfast

per night:	£min	£max
Single	10.00	12.00
Double	20.00	24.00

Half board

per person:	£min	£max
Daily	13.00	15.00
Weekly	70.00	84.00

Evening meal from 1700
Parking for 2
🚗🖥️UL🛈⌧♿📺Ⅲ.🖥️🎁

Hundred House Hotel ♨
♛♛♛♛ HIGHLY COMMENDED

Bridgnorth Rd., A442, Norton, Shifnal TF11 9EE
☎ (095 271) 353
Fax (095 271) 355
Homely, family-run hotel, with atmospheric historic bars, interesting bar food and intimate restaurant. Antique patchwork themed bedrooms with all facilities. Beautiful, relaxing cottage gardens.
Bedrooms: 1 single, 2 double, 1 twin, 5 triple
Bathrooms: 9 private
Bed & breakfast

per night:	£min	£max
Single	59.00	69.00
Double	69.00	79.00

Half board

per person:	£min	£max
Daily	45.00	49.00
Weekly	284.00	315.00

Lunch available
Evening meal 1800 (last orders 2200)
Parking for 30
Cards accepted: Access, Visa
🐕🚲🍴♿🍷🛈⌧🖥️Ⅲ.🖥️
♿▶🖥️✿🎁 SP 🏠 T

Orchard House
♛♛

40 King Street, Broseley TF12 5NA
☎ Telford (0952) 882684
3-storey Georgian family house with large garden, in small historic town, 1 mile from Ironbridge Gorge and River Severn.
Bedrooms: 1 double, 1 twin, 1 triple, 1 multiple
Bathrooms: 1 private, 2 public
Bed & breakfast

per night:	£min	£max
Single	15.00	18.00
Double	28.00	30.00

Parking for 3
🐕🚲♿UL🛈⌧♿📺Ⅲ.🖥️✿
🎁🏠

Paradise House ♨
Listed APPROVED

Coalbrookdale, Telford TF8 7NR
☎ (095 243) 3379
Georgian family home with large airy rooms, overlooking
Continued ▶

IRONBRIDGE

Continued

the valley. Central for museums and adjacent to the Shropshire Way footpath.
Bedrooms: 1 double,
1 multiple
Bathrooms: 1 private,
1 public

Bed & breakfast

per night:	£min	£max
Single	18.00	24.00
Double	32.00	38.00

Parking for 2
Open February-November
🛇🏕📭♨️🅿️🚬🅢📺🏧🖕
❋✕🎣🏠

Post Office House ⚹
🏵️
6 The Square, Ironbridge,
Telford TF8 7AQ
☎ (0952) 433201
Elegant residence, centrally situated, overlooking Ironbridge. Ideal for visiting museums, Shropshire countryside and hills.
Bedrooms: 2 double, 1 triple
Bathrooms: 1 private,
1 public, 1 private shower

Bed & breakfast

per night:	£min	£max
Double	29.00	35.00

🛇📭♨️🅿️♨️🅢🏧🖕✕
🎣🏠

KENILWORTH

Warwickshire
Map ref 4B3

The main feature of the town is the ruined 12th C castle. It has many royal associations but was damaged by Cromwell. A good base for visiting Coventry, Leamington Spa and Warwick.
Tourist Information Centre
☎ *(0926) 52595*

Banner Hill Farmhouse
🏵️
Rouncil Lane, Kenilworth
CV8 1NN
☎ (0926) 52850
250-acre mixed farm. Farmhouse set in Warwickshire countryside with local walks - bicycles available. Also a 30-foot residential van with 2 bedrooms, bathroom and kitchen.
Bedrooms: 1 double, 1 twin,
1 triple
Bathrooms: 2 private,
1 public

Bed & breakfast

per night:	£min	£max
Single	12.50	18.50
Double	28.00	34.00

Half board

per person:	£min	£max
Daily	16.00	22.50
Weekly	70.00	110.00

Lunch available
Parking for 8
🛇📭♨️🅿️♨️🅢🏧🖕🏧
🅰️🍃🖕

Oldwych House Farm ⚹
👑👑 COMMENDED
Oldwych Lane, Fen End,
Kenilworth CV8 1NR
☎ Berkswell (0676) 33552
35-acre mixed farm. 14th C half-timbered farmhouse in open countryside. 2 pools, sheep, horses, abundant wildlife. Resident artist's gallery. 6 miles from NEC and NAC, 8 miles Warwick, 12 miles Stratford-upon-Avon, 4 miles junction 5 of M42.
Bedrooms: 2 double
Bathrooms: 2 private

Bed & breakfast

per night:	£min	£max
Single	30.00	30.00
Double	38.00	40.00

Parking for 6
Open January-November
🛇7📭📭♨️🅿️♨️🅢🏧🖕
❋✕🎣🏠🅣

KIDDERMINSTER

Hereford and Worcester
Map ref 4B3

The town is the centre for carpet manufacturing. It has a medieval church with good monuments and a statue of Sir Rowland Hill, a native of the town and founder of the penny post. West Midlands Safari Park is nearby.

Cedars Hotel ⚹
👑👑👑 APPROVED
Mason Road, Kidderminster,
Worcestershire DY11 6AL
☎ (0562) 515595
Fax (0562) 751103
Charming conversion of a Georgian building close to the River Severn, Severn Valley Railway and Worcestershire countryside. 15 minutes from the M5.
Bedrooms: 1 single,
7 double, 7 twin, 1 triple,
4 multiple
Bathrooms: 20 private

Bed & breakfast

per night:	£min	£max
Single	33.70	44.60
Double	40.50	49.00

Half board

per person:	£min	£max
Daily	37.50	44.70

Evening meal 1900 (last orders 2030)
Parking for 21
Cards accepted: Access, Visa, Diners, Amex
🛇🏕♨️📭♨️🅿️🍴🅢🖕
🏧🅰️💷8-26❋🅿️🅣

Clay Farm ⚹
👑👑 COMMENDED
Clows Top, Kidderminster,
Worcestershire DY14 9NN
☎ (0299) 832421
98-acre mixed farm. Modern farmhouse with grass and woodlands. Trout and coarse fishing pools. Brochures on request. On the B4202 Clows Top to Cleobury Mortimer road.
Bedrooms: 2 double, 1 twin
Bathrooms: 2 private,
1 public

Bed & breakfast

per night:	£min	£max
Single	15.00	18.00
Double		30.00

Parking for 10
Open April-October
🛇3♨️🅿️🍴📺🏧🅰️🖍❋
🖕🍃

KINETON

Warwickshire
Map ref 2C1

Attractive old village in rolling countryside. 1 mile from site of famous battle of Edgehill. Medieval church of St Peter.

Willowbrook House ⚹
👑👑
Lighthorne Road, Kineton,
Warwick CV35 0JL
☎ (0926) 640475
Fax (0926) 641747
4-acre smallholding. Very comfortable house and small farm surrounded by lovely countryside, 3 miles to M40 (junction 12) and B4100, half a mile from Kineton village. Handy for Stratford-upon-Avon, Warwick and Cotswolds. Tea trays, antiques and friendly service.
Bedrooms: 2 double, 1 twin
Bathrooms: 1 private,
2 public

Bed & breakfast

per night:	£min	£max
Double	28.00	34.00

Parking for 6
🛇🍃♨️🅢🖕📺🏧🅰️🖕
❋🏵️🅿️

KINGSTONE

Hereford and Worcester
Map ref 2A1

Village near the Golden Valley.

Webton Court Farmhouse
Kingstone, Hereford
HR2 9NF
☎ Golden Valley (0981)
250220
280-acre mixed farm. Large black and white Georgian farmhouse in a quiet and peaceful part of Herefordshire. Lunch provided upon request.
Bedrooms: 1 single,
2 double, 2 twin, 1 triple,
2 multiple
Bathrooms: 2 private,
3 public

Bed & breakfast

per night:	£min	£max
Single	15.00	15.00
Double	24.00	30.00

Lunch available
Evening meal 1900 (last orders 2000)
Parking for 10
🛇📭♨️🅿️♨️🅢🏧📺🖕🍴❋
🖕 DAP 🖕

KINVER

Staffordshire
Map ref 4B3

Interesting village, once a flourishing town, at the foot of Kinver Edge, a sandstone ridge with fine views. There are cave dwellings carved into the sandstone at Holy Austin Rock and pleasant walks along the River Stour.
Tourist Information Centre
☎ *(0384) 872940*

Ashdown House ⚹
👑👑 HIGHLY COMMENDED
Forest Drive, Kinver DY7
☎ (0384) 873603
Colonial-style house in two acres of woodland ground, with swimming pool and jacuzzi. Backing on to Kinver Edge, close to A449.
Bedrooms: 2 double
Bathrooms: 2 private

Bed & breakfast

per night:	£min	£max
Single	20.00	22.00
Double	35.00	38.00

Parking for 5
Cards accepted: Access, Visa
🖃⌂📞📶 ㉿ 🛁 📺 🖼 📠
🎿 ❊ ✗ 🖧 OAP SP ⊤

LEAMINGTON SPA

Warwickshire
Map ref 4B3

18th C spa town with
many fine Georgian and
Regency houses. Tea can
be taken in the 19th C
Pump Room. The
attractive Jephson
Gardens are laid out
alongside the river and
there is a museum and
art gallery.
Tourist Information Centre
☎ *(0926) 311470*

Agape ⋀
Listed
26 St. Mary's Road,
Leamington Spa CV31 1JW
☎ (0926) 882896
*A private house to refresh the
visitor to Regency Royal
Leamington Spa. Close to
historic Warwick and
Stratford-upon-Avon.*
Bedrooms: 1 single,
1 double, 1 twin
Bathrooms: 1 public,
1 private shower
Bed & breakfast

per night:	£min	£max
Single	18.50	
Double	36.00	

Parking for 2
🎿5🖃⌂❖📶 ㉿ 📠 ㉿ 📺
🖼 🍴✗🖧 OAP SP

Charnwood Guest House ⋀
APPROVED
47 Avenue Road,
Leamington Spa CV31 3PF
☎ (0926) 831074
*Attractive Victorian house
near railway station and town
centre. All rooms have colour
TV and tea/coffee.*
Bedrooms: 1 single,
2 double, 2 twin, 1 triple
Bathrooms: 2 private,
2 public, 1 private shower
Bed & breakfast

per night:	£min	£max
Single	14.00	15.00
Double	27.00	36.00

Half board

per person:	£min	£max
Daily	20.00	24.50

Evening meal 1800 (last
orders 1600)
Parking for 5
Cards accepted: Access, Visa
🎿⌂❖📶 ㉿ 📠 ⓢ ✗ 📺 🖼 📠 ⊤

Hill Farm ⋀
APPROVED
Lewis Road, Radford Semele,
Leamington Spa CV31 1UX
☎ (0926) 337571
*350-acre mixed farm.
Farmhouse set in large
attractive garden, 2 miles
from Leamington town centre
and close to Warwick Castle
and Stratford-upon-Avon.*
Bedrooms: 3 double, 2 twin
Bathrooms: 3 private,
2 public
Bed & breakfast

per night:	£min	£max
Single	15.00	18.00
Double	26.00	34.00

Parking for 4
🎿❖📶 ㉿ ⓢ 📠 📺 🖼 📠 ⌴ ❊
✗ 🖧

Northton
COMMENDED
77 Telford Avenue,
Lillington, Leamington Spa
CV32 7HQ
☎ (0926) 425609
*Detached family home with
large garden in quiet
residential area off A445, 2.5
miles from National
Agricultural Centre. No
smoking and no pets please.*
Bedrooms: 1 single, 1 twin
Bathrooms: 2 private
Bed & breakfast

per night:	£min	£max
Single	15.00	20.00
Double	25.00	35.00

Parking for 4
Open February-October
🎿⌂❖📶 ㉿ 🖼 ✗ 🖧

The Orchard
Listed
3 Sherbourne Terrace,
Leamington Spa CV32 5SP
☎ (0926) 428198
*Victorian double-fronted
terrace with walled garden. 5
minutes' walk to town centre.
Overseas visitors welcome.*
Bedrooms: 1 single, 1 twin,
1 triple
Bathrooms: 2 public
Bed & breakfast

per night:	£min	£max
Single	14.00	18.00
Double	26.00	30.00

Half board

per person:	£min	£max
Daily	19.00	23.00
Weekly	100.00	120.00

Lunch available
Evening meal from 1800
🎿📶 ㉿ 🛁 ✗ ㉿ 📺 🖼 📠 ❊
✗ 🖧

Sharmer Farm ⋀
COMMENDED
Fosse Way, Radford Semele,
Leamington Spa CV31 1XH
☎ Harbury (0926) 612448
*120-acre arable farm.
Comfortable, modern
farmhouse set in fields in
peaceful countryside just off
the Fosse Way, 4 miles from
Leamington Spa.*
Bedrooms: 2 single,
1 double, 1 twin, 1 triple
Bathrooms: 1 private,
1 public
Bed & breakfast

per night:	£min	£max
Single	15.00	20.00
Double	30.00	35.00

Parking for 5
🎿📶 ㉿ 🛁 ⓢ 📺 🖼 ❊ ✗ 🖧

Snowford Hall Farmhouse Bed & Breakfast ⋀
COMMENDED
Snowford Hall Farm,
Hunningham, Leamington
Spa CV33 9ES
☎ Marton (0926) 632297
*250-acre arable and mixed
farm. 18th C farmhouse off
the Fosse Way, on the edge of
Hunningham village. On
elevated ground overlooking
quiet surrounding
countryside.*
Bedrooms: 1 double, 2 twin
Bathrooms: 1 private,
1 public, 1 private shower
Bed & breakfast

per night:	£min	£max
Single	20.00	25.00
Double	30.00	38.00

Half board

per person:	£min	£max
Daily	27.00	

Evening meal from 1800
Parking for 4
🎿📶 ㉿ 🛁 ✗ 📺 🖼 📠 ❊
✗ 🖧

The Willis ⋀
♛♛
11 Eastnor Grove,
Leamington Spa CV31 1LD
☎ (0926) 425820
*Spacious Victorian family
house with large garden, in
quiet cul-de-sac near town
centre. Supper and diets by
arrangement. Summer meals
in conservatory. Non-smokers
only please.*
Bedrooms: 1 single,
1 double, 1 twin

Bathrooms: 1 private,
2 public
Bed & breakfast

per night:	£min	£max
Single	22.00	25.00
Double	40.00	45.00

Evening meal 1830 (last
orders 0830)
Parking for 2
🎿⌂❖📶 ㉿ ⓢ ✗ ㉿ 📺 🖼 📠
❊ 🖧 🏢

LEDBURY

Hereford and Worcester
Map ref 2B1

Town with cobbled streets
and many black and white
timbered houses,
including the 17th C
market house and old
inns. Nearby is Eastnor
Castle with an interesting
collection of tapestries
and armour.
Tourist Information Centre
☎ *(0531) 6147*

The Barn House ⋀
♛♛ HIGHLY COMMENDED
New Street, Ledbury,
Herefordshire HR8 2DX
☎ (0531) 2825
*17th C house of great
character in the centre of the
old market town of Ledbury,
close to the Malverns and the
Wye Valley.*
Bedrooms: 2 double, 1 twin
Bathrooms: 1 private,
1 public
Bed & breakfast

per night:	£min	£max
Double	36.00	41.00

Parking for 4
Open March-December
🖃❖🐾📶 ⓢ ✗ 📺 🖼 📠 🍴 ❊
✗ 🖧 🏢

Birchcroft
Listed COMMENDED
72 Bank Crescent, Ledbury,
Herefordshire HR8 1AF
☎ (0531) 2485
*Four-bedroomed detached
house in an elevated
residential area, with central
heating and double glazing
throughout. Guests are
welcomed as one of the
family. Panoramic views.
Easy access to M50/M5
motorways.*
Bedrooms: 2 double
Bathrooms: 1 private,
1 public
Half board

per person:	£min	£max
Daily	15.00	17.50

Parking for 3
🎿⌂❖📶 ㉿ ⓢ 🖼 📠 ✗ 🖧

165

LEEK

Staffordshire
Map ref 4B2

Old silk and textile town, with some interesting buildings and a number of inns dating from the 17th C. Its art gallery has displays of embroidery. Brindley Mill, designed by James Brindley, has been restored as a museum.
Tourist Information Centre
☎ *(0538) 381000*

Abbey Inn
APPROVED

Abbey Green Road, Leek
ST13 8SA
☎ (0538) 382865
17th C inn with accommodation in a separate annexe, set in beautiful countryside. 1 mile from the town and just off the main A523.
Bedrooms: 2 single, 5 double
Bathrooms: 7 private
Bed & breakfast

per night:	£min	£max
Single	26.00	28.00
Double	42.00	46.00

Lunch available
Evening meal 1830 (last orders 2100)
Parking for 60
Cards accepted: Access, Visa, Amex

Bank End Farm Motel
COMMENDED

Old Leek Road, Longsdon, Stoke-on-Trent ST9 9QJ
☎ (0538) 383638
62-acre mixed farm. Pleasant motel in converted dairy and old stone barn, in a quiet lane close to Leek, Peak District National Park and Alton Towers.
Bedrooms: 1 single, 3 double, 3 twin, 1 triple, 2 multiple
Bathrooms: 8 private, 1 public
Bed & breakfast

per night:	£min	£max
Single	23.50	26.50
Double	42.00	46.00

Half board

per person:	£min	£max
Daily	33.50	36.50

Evening meal from 1830
Parking for 10

Micklea Farm
Listed

Micklea Lane, Longsdon, Stoke-on-Trent ST9 9QA
☎ (0538) 385006
Fax (0538) 382882
17th C stone-built house in quiet village, off A53, 9 miles from motorway, within easy access of the Peak District, the Potteries and Alton Towers. Evening meals by arrangement.
Bedrooms: 2 single, 2 twin
Bathrooms: 2 public
Bed & breakfast

per night:	£min	£max
Single	14.00	15.00
Double	28.00	30.00

Half board

per person:	£min	£max
Daily	25.00	25.00
Weekly		135.00

Evening meal 1830 (last orders 2000)
Parking for 4

Three Horseshoes Inn
APPROVED

Blackshaw Moor, Leek
ST13 8TW
☎ Blackshaw (0538) 300296
Fax (0538) 300320
Log fire, slate floor, oak and pine beams, good food and wines. Cottage-style rooms. Convenient for Peak District National Park and Alton Towers.
Bedrooms: 1 single, 4 double, 1 twin
Bathrooms: 6 private
Bed & breakfast

per night:	£min	£max
Single	40.00	
Double	40.00	52.00

Half board

per person:	£min	£max
Daily	41.50	45.00

Lunch available
Evening meal 1900 (last orders 2130)
Parking for 100
Cards accepted: Access, Visa

National Crown ratings were correct at the time of going to press but are subject to change. Please check at the time of booking.

LEOMINSTER

Hereford and Worcester
Map ref 2A1

The town owed its prosperity to wool and has many interesting buildings, notably the timber-framed Grange Court, a former town hall. The impressive Norman priory church has 3 naves and a ducking stool. Berrington Hall (National Trust) is nearby.
Tourist Information Centre
☎ *(0568) 616460*

Bank Farm
Listed COMMENDED

Kingsland, Leominster, Herefordshire HR6 9PY
☎ Kingsland (0568) 708638
30-acre mixed farm. Secluded farmhouse with half-timbered Tudor-style interior, in area noted for black and white villages. Situated on Kingsland to Yarpole road, half a mile from Kingsland and 5 miles from Leominster.
Bedrooms: 1 single, 1 double, 1 triple
Bathrooms: 2 public
Bed & breakfast

per night:	£min	£max
Single	14.00	18.00
Double	26.00	30.00

Parking for 10

Heath House

Humber, Stoke Prior, Leominster, Herefordshire HR6 0NF
☎ Steens Bridge (056 882) 385
Old oak framed stone farmhouse now used as comfortable family home. 4 miles from Leominster. Phone for directions. Evening meal on request.
Bedrooms: 1 double, 2 twin
Bathrooms: 3 private
Bed & breakfast

per night:	£min	£max
Single	15.00	18.50
Double	30.00	37.00

Half board

per person:	£min	£max
Daily	25.00	33.50
Weekly	161.00	220.00

Evening meal 1900 (last orders 2100)
Parking for 6
Open March-December

Home Farm

Bircher, Leominster, Herefordshire HR6 0AX
☎ Yarpole (056 885) 525
150-acre mixed farm. Traditional farmhouse accommodation with tea room on Welsh border, 4 miles north of Leominster and 7 miles south of Ludlow. On B4362. Paradise for walkers and country-lovers.
Bedrooms: 1 double, 1 twin, 1 triple
Bathrooms: 2 public, 1 private shower
Bed & breakfast

per night:	£min	£max
Single	16.00	20.00
Double	30.00	35.00

Parking for 6
Open February-November

Lower Bache
HIGHLY COMMENDED

Kimbolton, Leominster, Herefordshire HR6 0ER
☎ Leysters (056 887) 304
17th C farmhouse in tranquil valley, with annexe comprising 3 suites, each with bedroom, bath/shower and sitting room. Period country furniture. Organic food. Wildlife, walking, ideal for touring base. Please ring for brochure.
Bedrooms: 2 double, 1 twin
Bathrooms: 3 private
Bed & breakfast

per night:	£min	£max
Single	19.50	
Double	39.00	

Half board

per person:	£min	£max
Daily	29.25	36.00

Evening meal 1950 (last orders 1230)
Parking for 10

Withenfield
HIGHLY COMMENDED

South Street, Leominster, Herefordshire HR6 8JN
☎ (0568) 612011
Elegantly furnished Georgian house with modern facilities and conservatory overlooking garden. Conveniently situated for touring countryside, castles, black and white villages.
Bedrooms: 2 double, 2 twin
Bathrooms: 4 private

Bed & breakfast

per night:	£min	£max
Single	39.00	49.00
Double	56.00	68.00

Half board

per person:	£min	£max
Daily	47.50	68.50
Weekly	325.50	402.50

Lunch available
Evening meal from 1830
Parking for 5
Cards accepted: Access, Visa

LICHFIELD

Staffordshire
Map ref 4B3

Lichfield is Dr Samuel Johnson's birthplace and commemorates him with a museum and statue. The 13th C cathedral has 3 spires and the west front is full of statues. There is a regimental museum and Heritage Centre.
Tourist Information Centre
☎ (0543) 252109

20 Beacon St.
Lichfield WS13 7AD
☎ (0543) 262338
Spacious and elegant Georgian town house with a welcoming atmosphere, conveniently situated near Lichfield Cathedral and all amenities.
Bedrooms: 1 single, 1 double
Bathrooms: 2 private, 1 public

Bed & breakfast

per night:	£min	£max
Single		15.00
Double	27.00	32.00

Parking for 5

Main View
APPROVED
18 Burton Road, Alrewas, Burton upon Trent
DE13 7BB
☎ (0283) 790725
Detached house on the main A38 northbound. Country village convenient for Birmingham and the North. Pleasant views.
Bedrooms: 1 single, 1 double, 1 twin
Bathrooms: 1 public

Bed & breakfast

per night:	£min	£max
Single	15.00	17.00
Double	29.00	32.00

Half board

per person:	£min	£max
Daily	19.00	25.00
Weekly	120.00	140.00

Evening meal 1700 (last orders 1800)
Parking for 6

LLANWARNE

Hereford and Worcester
Map ref 2A1

Village close to Kilpeck which has a well-known church with Norman carved doorway.

The Lawns
Listed
Llanwarne, Hereford
HR2 8EN
☎ Golden Valley (0981) 540351
On A466 Hereford - Monmouth Road, this secluded homely farmhouse is centrally situated for touring Herefordshire, Welsh Borders and Forest of Dean. Evening meals available by prior arrangement.
Bedrooms: 1 twin
Bathrooms: 2 public

Bed & breakfast

per night:	£min	£max
Single	15.00	20.00
Double	30.00	40.00

Half board

per person:	£min	£max
Daily	23.00	30.00
Weekly	150.00	210.00

Lunch available
Parking for 17

LONG COMPTON

Warwickshire
Map ref 2B1

Village with a restored church displaying Norman doorways and a thatched room above the lych gate. Several interesting old houses exist in the area.

Ascott House Farm
Whichford, Long Compton, Shipston-on-Stour CV36 5PP
☎ (060 884) 655
500-acre arable & livestock farm. Old stone farmhouse in beautiful countryside on edge of Cotswolds. 3 miles off A3400 between Stratford-upon-Avon and Oxford. 10 miles from M40 at Banbury. Swimming pool, games room

---

and walks. Riding and golf within 3 miles.
Bedrooms: 2 double, 1 twin
Bathrooms: 2 private, 2 public

Bed & breakfast

per night:	£min	£max
Single	15.00	17.00
Double	27.00	33.00

Parking for 12

LOWER BENTLEY

Hereford and Worcester
Map ref 4B3

Lower Bentley Farm
Lower Bentley Lane, Lower Bentley, Bromsgrove, Worcestershire B60 4JB
☎ Bromsgrove (0527) 821286
300-acre dairy & livestock farm. Victorian farmhouse 5 miles from Redditch, Bromsgrove, Droitwich, M5 and M42, in open countryside with picturesque views and walks.
Bedrooms: 1 double, 1 multiple
Bathrooms: 2 private

Bed & breakfast

per night:	£min	£max
Single	17.50	20.00
Double	30.00	32.00

Parking for 6

LOWER SWELL

Gloucestershire
Map ref 2B1

Attractive village in the Cotswolds, on the River Dikler, with stone houses, some dating from the 17th C. There is a large house and gardens designed by Lutyens.

Golden Ball Inn
Lower Swell, Cheltenham
GL54 1LF
☎ Cotswold (0451) 30247
17th C Cotswold inn providing accommodation, real ale and food. No children under the age of 14 and no dogs allowed in the accommodation or bar. Also, no-smoking accommodation.
Bedrooms: 2 double
Bathrooms: 2 public

Bed & breakfast

per night:	£min	£max
Single	12.00	16.00
Double	32.00	36.00

Lunch available
Evening meal 1900 (last orders 2045)
Parking for 20

LUDLOW

Shropshire
Map ref 4A3

Outstandingly interesting border town with a magnificent castle high above the River Teme, 2 half-timbered old inns and an impressive 15th C church. The Reader's House, with its 3-storey Jacobean porch, should also be seen.
Tourist Information Centre
☎ (0584) 875053

28 Lower Broad St.
COMMENDED
Ludlow SY8 1PQ
☎ (0584) 876996
Listed town house of charm and character. Secluded walled garden. Emphasis on good food and wines, warm hospitality and quiet relaxed atmosphere.
Bedrooms: 1 double, 1 twin
Bathrooms: 2 private, 1 public

Bed & breakfast

per night:	£min	£max
Single	30.00	35.00
Double	40.00	46.00

Half board

per person:	£min	£max
Daily	32.00	38.00
Weekly	195.00	250.00

Evening meal 1930 (last orders 2030)

Blue Boar Inn
Mill Street, Ludlow SY8 1BB
☎ (0584) 872630 & 872429
16th C coaching inn, home to Ludlow Festival.
Bedrooms: 3 double, 2 twin, 1 triple
Bathrooms: 2 public

Bed & breakfast

per night:	£min	£max
Single	17.00	
Double	30.00	34.00

Continued ▶

LUDLOW

Continued

Half board per person:	£min	£max
Daily	20.00	28.00

Lunch available
Evening meal 1830 (last orders 2100)
Cards accepted: Access, Visa
🐴🔒[S]👔🐎⛳✈[SP]🏛

The Church Inn 🔑

♕♕♕

Butter Cross, Ludlow SY8 1AW
☎ (0584) 872174
Centrally located on one of the most ancient sites in Ludlow, going back at least seven centuries.
Bedrooms: 6 double, 2 twin, 1 triple
Bathrooms: 9 private

Bed & breakfast per night:	£min	£max
Single	25.00	28.00
Double	40.00	40.00

Lunch available
Evening meal 1900 (last orders 2130)
Cards accepted: Access, Visa
🐴🖥☕🔒[S]🚭♨👔🐕🏛

Corndene 🔑

♕♕♕

Coreley, Ludlow SY8 3AW
☎ (0584) 890324
18th C country house set in 2-acre garden in South Shropshire Hills. Seven miles east of Ludlow. Non-smoking establishment.
Bedrooms: 3 twin
Bathrooms: 3 private

Bed & breakfast per night:	£min	£max
Single	18.00	21.00
Double	32.00	37.00

Half board per person:	£min	£max
Daily	24.00	27.00
Weekly	150.00	168.00

Evening meal 1830 (last orders 2000)
Parking for 5
🐴🛏☕[UL]🔒[S]🚭🪑[TV]♨👔
✿✈🐕

Haynall Villa 🔑

♕♕ COMMENDED

Haynall Lane, Little Hereford, Ludlow SY8 4BG
☎ Brimfield (0584) 711589
72-acre mixed & livestock farm. Early 19th C farmhouse set in the peaceful Teme Valley, 6 miles from historic Ludlow. Friendly atmosphere, comfortable rooms, lounge with log fires. Tasty home cooking. Holiday makers and business people welcome. Fishing available.
Bedrooms: 1 double, 1 twin, 1 multiple
Bathrooms: 1 private, 2 public

Bed & breakfast per night:	£min	£max
Single	15.00	
Double	30.00	

Half board per person:	£min	£max
Daily	26.00	
Weekly	175.00	

Evening meal 1900 (last orders 1600)
Parking for 6
🐴6☕[UL]🔒[S]🪑[TV]♨👔🐟
🏌✿🐕

Longlands

[Listed]

Woodhouse Lane, Richards Castle, Ludlow SY8 4EU
☎ Richards Castle (058 474) 636
35-acre livestock farm. Bradstone farmhouse, centrally located. Home-grown produce. Lovely country views from every window. Close to Mortimer Forest and Croft Castle.
Bedrooms: 1 double, 1 twin
Bathrooms: 2 private, 1 public

Bed & breakfast per night:	£min	£max
Single	14.00	
Double	28.00	

Half board per person:	£min	£max
Daily	20.00	

Evening meal 1830 (last orders 1930)
Parking for 2
🐴🛏🍴☕[UL]🔒[S]🪑[TV]♨
👔🐎✿🐕

Lower Hayton Grange

Lower Hayton, Ludlow SY8 2AQ
☎ Seifton (058 473) 371 & 296
Magnificent house of architectural interest, beautifully furnished. 4 miles from Ludlow in the picturesque Corve Dale Valley. All weather tennis court, swimming pool, good walking.
Bedrooms: 2 double
Bathrooms: 2 private

Bed & breakfast per night:	£min	£max
Double	34.00	50.00

Parking for 4
🐴5🍴🖥☕☎[UL][S]🚭♨
👔🏊🎾✿✈🐕[OAP]🏛[T]

Marlbrook Hall

♕

Elton, Ludlow SY8 2HR
☎ Wigmore (056 886) 230
440-acre mixed farm. Comfortable 18th C farmhouse on a family-run farm. Close to Mortimer Forest and Ludlow. Ideal for walking.
Bedrooms: 1 double, 1 twin
Bathrooms: 1 public

Bed & breakfast per night:	£min	£max
Double	28.00	

Parking for 3
Open April-October
🐴5☕[UL][S][TV]✿🐕🏛

Seifton Court 🔑

♕♕ COMMENDED

Culmington, Ludlow SY8 2DG
☎ Seifton (058 473) 214
50-acre mixed farm. Period farmhouse, 5 miles from Ludlow on the B4365 road. Set in the beautiful Corve Dale valley. Near Longmynd, Ironbridge. Ideal for walking and visiting National Trust properties. Farmhouse fare using home-grown produce.
Bedrooms: 1 single, 2 double, 1 twin
Bathrooms: 2 private, 1 public

Bed & breakfast per night:	£min	£max
Single	18.00	25.00
Double	30.00	36.00

Half board per person:	£min	£max
Daily	28.00	35.00
Weekly	165.00	

Lunch available
Evening meal 1800 (last orders 1900)
Parking for 7
🐴🍴🖥☕☎🔒[S]🪑[TV]♨
👔🏌✿✈🐕🎯[SP]

We advise you to confirm your booking in writing.

There are separate sections in this guide listing groups specialising in farm holidays and accommodation which is especially suitable for young people and organised groups.

MALVERN

Hereford and Worcester
Map ref 2B1

Spa town in Victorian times, its water is today bottled and sold worldwide. 6 resorts, set on the slopes of the Hills, form part of Malvern. Great Malvern Priory has splendid 15th C windows. It is an excellent walking centre.
Tourist Information Centre ☎ (0684) 892289.

Cowleigh Park Farm

♕♕ HIGHLY COMMENDED

Cowleigh Road, Malvern, Worcestershire WR13 5HJ
☎ (0684) 566750
2-acre mixed farm. Beautifully restored, Grade II listed timbered farmhouse, in a tranquil setting at the foot of the Malvern Hills. Lovely gardens, ample secure parking.
Bedrooms: 1 double, 2 twin
Bathrooms: 2 private, 1 public

Bed & breakfast per night:	£min	£max
Single	28.00	
Double	40.00	

Evening meal 1830 (last orders 1000)
Parking for 6
🐴4🖥☕[UL]🔒[S]🚭♨👔🐎
✿🐕[SP]🏛

The Dell House

♕♕

2 Green Lane, Malvern Wells, Malvern, Worcestershire WR14 4HU
☎ (0684) 564448
Elegant Regency period home, once a rectory and spa hotel. Peaceful seclusion and superb views, set in two private acres of wooded grounds.
Bedrooms: 2 double, 1 twin
Bathrooms: 1 private, 1 public

Bed & breakfast per night:	£min	£max
Single	21.00	35.00
Double	42.00	

Parking for 6
🐴☕[UL]🔒[S]🚭🪑[TV]♨👔✿
🐕[OAP][SP]🏛

Grove House Farm 🔑

♕♕ COMMENDED

Guarlford, Malvern, Worcestershire WR14 3QZ
☎ (0684) 574256
370-acre mixed farm. Large farmhouse at the foot of the

Malvern Hills, in peaceful surroundings. Close to the Three Counties Showground.
Bedrooms: 1 double, 1 twin, 1 triple
Bathrooms: 2 public

Bed & breakfast

per night:	£min	£max
Single	18.00	20.00
Double	30.00	32.00

Half board

per person:	£min	£max
Daily	23.50	27.50

Evening meal 1830 (last orders 2100)
Parking for 8
Open February-November

🛇 🌢 🗑 🛋 S ⊱ 🛏 TV Ⅲ. 🖉 ✿ 🛍

Mayalls Farm
`Listed` `APPROVED`
Upper Welland, Malvern, Worcestershire WR14 4JX
☎ (0684) 573917
100-acre mixed farm. Late 17th C farmhouse at the foot of the Malvern Hills, close to the Gloucestershire/ Herefordshire borders. Ideal for walking, touring, or just relaxing.
Bedrooms: 2 double, 1 twin
Bathrooms: 1 public

Bed & breakfast

per night:	£min	£max
Single	15.00	16.00
Double	25.00	26.00

Parking for 5
Open March-October

🛇 🌢 🗑 🛋 🛏 TV 🖉 U ⏰ ✿ 🛍

Mellbreak
🛏🛏
177 Wells Road, Malvern Wells, Malvern, Worcestershire WR14 4HE
☎ (0684) 561287
Comfortable Regency house with garden and views, near Three Counties Showground. English cooking of old-world style and substance. Extensive wine list.
Bedrooms: 1 single, 1 double, 1 twin, 1 triple
Bathrooms: 1 public, 3 private showers

Bed & breakfast

per night:	£min	£max
Single	17.00	19.00
Double	34.00	38.00

Half board

per person:	£min	£max
Daily	27.00	29.50

Evening meal from 1800
Parking for 4

🛇 🎺 🗑 🌢 🛋 S 🛏 TV Ⅲ. 🖉 ✿ 🕱 🛍 ⏰ SP 🛍

The Nupend ⋀
🛏🛏🛏
Cradley, Malvern, Worcestershire WR13 5NP
☎ Ridgeway Cross (0886) 880881
Elegant Georgian farmhouse set in grounds of 2 acres and enjoying glorious views of Malvern Hills. Ideal for walkers, bird-watchers, painters or as a touring base. Peacefully situated off A4103. French/German spoken. Non-smokers only please.
Bedrooms: 2 double, 2 twin
Bathrooms: 4 private

Bed & breakfast

per night:	£min	£max
Single	26.00	30.00
Double	40.00	48.00

Evening meal 1800 (last orders 1930)
Parking for 10

⛶ 🌢 🗑 🛋 S ⊱ 🛏 🖉 ✿ 🛍 OAP SP 🛍

Priory Holme
🛏🛏
18 Avenue Road, Malvern, Worcestershire WR14 3AR
☎ (0684) 568455
Elegantly furnished large Victorian house in a tree-lined avenue. Well situated for all local amenities.
Bedrooms: 1 single, 1 double, 1 twin, 1 triple
Bathrooms: 1 private, 2 public

Bed & breakfast

per night:	£min	£max
Single	17.00	20.00
Double	34.00	40.00

Half board

per person:	£min	£max
Daily	27.00	30.00

Evening meal 1800 (last orders 1900)
Parking for 5

🛇 🌢 🗑 🛋 S ⊱ 🛏 TV Ⅲ. 🖉 ✿ 🛍

Rock House ⋀
😊 `COMMENDED`
144 West Malvern Road, Malvern, Worcestershire WR14 4NJ
☎ (0684) 574536
Late Georgian house on Malvern Hills with large garden and wonderful views. Ideal for rambling and touring. Comfortable bedrooms, fine cuisine, licensed. Special mid-week prices available.
Bedrooms: 5 double, 4 twin, 2 triple
Bathrooms: 1 private, 3 public

Bed & breakfast

per night:	£min	£max
Single	20.00	24.00
Double	32.00	38.00

Half board

per person:	£min	£max
Daily	26.00	30.00

Evening meal 1830 (last orders 1700)
Parking for 10

🛇 🌢 3 🗑 🛋 S ⊱ 🛏 TV Ⅲ. ✿ 🛍 🛍 SP

Sidney House ⋀
😊 😊 `COMMENDED`
40 Worcester Road, Malvern, Worcestershire WR14 4AA
☎ (0684) 574994
Small, attractive Georgian hotel with personal and friendly service. Magnificent views over the Worcestershire countryside. Close to town centre and hills. Dinner by arrangement only. Stay for 8 nights bed and breakfast - pay for 7.
Bedrooms: 1 single, 4 double, 2 twin, 1 triple
Bathrooms: 5 private, 1 public

Bed & breakfast

per night:	£min	£max
Single	20.00	35.00
Double	39.00	49.00

Half board

per person:	£min	£max
Daily	35.00	64.00
Weekly	245.00	463.00

Evening meal 1900 (last orders 1500)
Parking for 10
Cards accepted: Access, Visa, Amex

🛇 🎺 🖳 🗑 🛋 S ⊱ 🛏 TV Ⅲ. 🖉 U 🖊 ✿ 🛍 SP 🛍 T

The Wyche Inn ⋀
`Listed`
74 Wyche Road, Malvern, Worcestershire WR14 4EQ
☎ (0684) 575396
The highest inn in Worcestershire, nestling on top of the Malvern Hills and with spectacular views across the Severn Valley.
Bedrooms: 2 double, 2 twin, 1 triple
Bathrooms: 5 private

Bed & breakfast

per night:	£min	£max
Single	24.00	
Double	34.00	

Lunch available
Evening meal 1900 (last orders 2200)
Parking for 12

🛇 🖳 🗑 🌢 🛋 S 🛏 TV Ⅲ. 🔍 🛍

Warwickshire
Map ref 4B3

Bright little village on the road from Banbury to Coventry, with an ancient stone bridge across the River Leam.

Elms Farm ⋀
`Listed`
Oxford Road, Marton, Rugby CV23 9RQ
☎ (0926) 632770
800-acre mixed farm. Listed farmhouse set next to River Leam, just north of Marton on A423.
Bedrooms: 2 double, 1 twin
Bathrooms: 1 private, 1 public

Bed & breakfast

per night:	£min	£max
Double	30.00	40.00

Parking for 6
Open January-November

🛇 🌢 🖳 🛏 Ⅲ. 🖊 ⏰ ✿ 🕱 🛍 🛍

West Midlands
Map ref 4B3

Village halfway between Coventry and Birmingham. Said to be the centre of England, marked by a cross on the green.

Cooperage Farm Bed and Breakfast ⋀
`Listed` `APPROVED`
Old Road, Meriden, Coventry CV7 7JP
☎ (0676) 23493
Fax (0676) 23922
6-acre mixed farm. 300-year-old red brick, Grade II listed farmhouse, set in beautiful countryside. Ideally situated for the National Exhibition Centre, airport and touring the centre of England.
Bedrooms: 1 double, 4 twin, 1 triple
Bathrooms: 4 private, 2 public

Bed & breakfast

per night:	£min	£max
Single	22.00	27.00
Double	44.00	48.00

Half board

per person:	£min	£max
Daily	25.00	30.00
Weekly	120.00	135.00

Continued ▶

169

MERIDEN

Continued

Lunch available
Evening meal 1800 (last
orders 1900)
Parking for 4

🏅1🛁🍴📺♦🔍⬛ⓘⓈ
🏧📺◑⬛�️💷🚗❄🦽[OAP]
[SP]🏠[T]

Grange Farm

Fillongley Road, Meriden,
Coventry CV7 7HU
☎ (0676) 22312
*3-acre smallholding. Georgian
farmhouse convenient for
Birmingham Airport, N.E.C,
Warwick and Stratford-upon-
Avon. Converted stable block,
en-suite facilities. Floodlit
tennis court. Ideal touring-
business base.*
Bedrooms: 2 twin, 1 triple
Bathrooms: 1 public
Bed & breakfast

per night:	£min	£max
Single	18.00	27.00
Double	35.00	45.00

Parking for 13

🅿🔥🍴♦📺⬛ⓘⓈ✂🦽
📺💷🚗🔍U🄿❄🦽

MICKLETON

Gloucestershire
Map ref 2B1

Mickleton lies in the Vale
of Evesham and is close
to Hidcote Manor
Gardens (National Trust)
and to the beautiful
Cotswold town of
Chipping Campden.

Bank House

♨♨ APPROVED

Mickleton, Chipping
Campden GL55 6RX
☎ (0386) 438302
*Period house with a tranquil
old world garden. Excellent
restaurant and inns within 2
minutes' walk. Hidcote
Gardens 1 mile, Broadway 6
miles.*
Bedrooms: 1 double, 2 twin
Bathrooms: 1 private,
2 public
Bed & breakfast

per night:	£min	£max
Single	23.00	25.00
Double	32.00	36.00

Parking for 4
Open April-October

🅿🍴♦🔍💷🚗❄✂🦽🛁

📦 **Please check prices
and other details at
the time of booking.**

MINCHINHAMPTON

Gloucestershire
Map ref 2B1

A stone-built town, with
many 17th/18th C
buildings, owing its
existence to the wool and
cloth trades. A 17th C
pillared market house may
be found in the town
square, near which is the
Norman and 14th C
church.

Hope Cottage Guesthouse

♨♨

Box, Stroud GL6 9HD
☎ (0453) 832076
Fax (0453) 835941
*Comfortable family-run
Cotswold country guesthouse
with extensive landscaped
gardens, woodlands and
pastures. Stunning views in
an area of outstanding
natural beauty.*
Bedrooms: 2 double
Bathrooms: 2 private,
1 public
Bed & breakfast

per night:	£min	£max
Single	20.00	25.00
Double	35.00	40.00

Parking for 5

🅿🔥🍴♦🔍Ⓢ✂📺💷
🄿U🄿❄🦽🛁

Hunters Lodge

♨♨

Dr Brown's Road,
Minchinhampton, Stroud
GL6 9BT
☎ Brimscombe (0453)
883588
*Cotswold stone house
adjoining Minchinhampton
common and golf-course.
Ideal centre for Bath,
Gloucester, Cheltenham and
Bristol. Located 2 miles from
A419 Stroud-Cirencester road
(first house on right going
into Minchinhampton).*
Bedrooms: 1 twin, 1 triple
Bathrooms: 2 private,
1 public
Bed & breakfast

per night:	£min	£max
Single	22.00	24.00
Double	32.00	36.00

Parking for 8

🅿🍴♦🔍📺💷🚗❄🦽

Saint Giles

Listed

Box, Minchinhampton,
Stroud GL6 9HE
☎ Stroud (0453) 832283
*Quiet 250-year-old cottage in
delightful Cotswold village,*

---

*adjacent to National Trust
common, woods and golf-
course. Ideal walking and
touring centre.*
Bedrooms: 1 single, 1 double
Bathrooms: 2 public
Bed & breakfast

per night:	£min	£max
Single	15.00	18.00
Double	30.00	36.00

Parking for 2

🅿🛁🔥🍴♦🔍ⓘⓈ✂📺
◑💷🚗❄🦽🛁

Sunnycroft

Listed

Chapel Lane,
Minchinhampton, Stroud
GL6 2NP
☎ (0453) 883159
*Bungalow overlooking
Gatcombe woods. From
Minchinhampton Post Office
take next turning left then
half a mile down country
lane.*
Bedrooms: 1 single, 1 double
Bathrooms: 1 public
Bed & breakfast

per night:	£min	£max
Single	14.00	16.00
Double	28.00	32.00

Parking for 3

🅿🦽♦🔍🔍✂📺💷🚗U🄿
❄🦽

MINSTERLEY

Shropshire
Map ref 4A3

Village with a curious little
church of 1692 and a fine
old black and white hall.
The lofty ridge known as
the Stiperstones is 4
miles to the south.

Cricklewood Cottage

♨♨ HIGHLY COMMENDED

Plox Green, Minsterley,
Shrewsbury SY5 0HT
☎ Shrewsbury (0743)
791229
*Delightful 18th C cottage with
countryside views, at foot of
Stiperstones Hills. Exposed
beams, inglenook fireplace,
traditional furnishings. Lovely
cottage garden. Wholesome
food.*
Bedrooms: 1 double, 2 twin
Bathrooms: 3 private
Bed & breakfast

per night:	£min	£max
Double	32.40	36.00

Half board

per person:	£min	£max
Daily	24.70	26.50
Weekly	172.90	172.90

Evening meal 1900 (last
orders 1000)
Parking for 6

🅿8💷♦🔍⬛ⓘⓈ✂📺📺💷
🄿U🄿❄🦽🚗🦽[SP]🏠

Village Farm

♨♨ HIGHLY COMMENDED

Bromlow, Minsterley,
Shrewsbury SY5 0DX
☎ (0743) 891398
*80-acre mixed farm. Attractive
stone-built house with beams,
set in the Shropshire Hills, 14
miles south west of
Shrewsbury.*
Bedrooms: 1 double
Bathrooms: 1 private
Bed & breakfast

per night:	£min	£max
Double	17.00	17.00

Half board

per person:	£min	£max
Daily	27.00	27.00
Weekly	177.10	177.10

Evening meal 1900 (last
orders 1700)
Parking for 1
Open April-October

🅿🔥♦🔍⬛ⓘⓈ✂📺💷
🄿❄🦽🚗🦽[SP]🏠

MORETON-IN-MARSH

Gloucestershire
Map ref 2B1

Attractive town of
Cotswold stone with 17th
C houses, an ideal base
for touring the Cotswolds.
Some of the local
attractions include
Batsford Park Arboretum,
the Jacobean Chastleton
House and Sezincote
Garden.

Blue Cedar House

♨♨

Stow Road, Moreton-in-
Marsh GL56 0DW
☎ (0608) 50299
*Attractive detached residence
set in half-acre garden in the
Cotswolds, with pleasantly
decorated, well-equipped
accommodation and garden
room. Close to village centre.*
Bedrooms: 2 double, 1 twin,
1 triple
Bathrooms: 2 private,
2 public
Bed & breakfast

per night:	£min	£max
Single	15.50	30.00
Double	31.00	39.00

Half board

per person:	£min	£max
Daily	22.50	27.00
Weekly	149.50	179.50

Evening meal 1800 (last orders 1800)
Parking for 7
Open February-November
☎🖳🖵🚲🕆Ⓤ🅸Ⓢ🅼📺
🍴◿✿✕🐾

Dorn Priory
👑

Dorn, Moreton-in-Marsh
☎ (0608) 50152
17th C Cotswold house in peaceful surroundings. Set in a small hamlet on edge of Cotswolds, within easy reach of Stratford and Oxford.
Bedrooms: 1 twin, 1 multiple
Bathrooms: 1 public

Bed & breakfast

per night:	£min	£max
Double	28.00	30.00

Parking for 10
☎🕆Ⓤ🅸Ⓢ✕📺🍴◿✿🐾🏠

Lines Farm ᐱᐱ
👑👑

Chastleton Road, Little Compton, Moreton-in-Marsh GL56 OSL
☎ Barton on the Heath (060 874) 343
27-acre livestock farm. Detached Cotswold-stone house with good facilities and beautiful views. Easily accessible from A44 between Chipping Norton and Moreton-in-Marsh.
Bedrooms: 1 double, 1 twin, 1 triple
Bathrooms: 1 private, 1 public

Bed & breakfast

per night:	£min	£max
Double	30.00	32.00

Parking for 10
☎🕆Ⓤ🅸📺🍴◿✿ OAP SP

Lower Farm Barn ᐱᐱ
👑👑

Great Wolford, Shipston-on-Stour, Warwickshire CV36 5NQ
☎ Barton on the Heath (060 874) 435
900-acre arable farm. 18th C converted barn combines modern comforts with exposed beams and ancient stonework. Use of attractive drawing room. Quiet village between A34, A44 and A429.
Bedrooms: 1 twin, 1 triple
Bathrooms: 1 private, 1 public

Check the introduction to this region for Where to Go, What to See.

Bed & breakfast

per night:	£min	£max
Single	16.00	16.00
Double	27.00	30.00

Parking for 10
☎🕆Ⓤ Ⓢ📺🍴◿🔾Ս
✿🐾🏠

Manor Farm ᐱᐱ
Listed

Great Wolford, Shipston-on-Stour, Warwickshire CV36 5NQ
☎ Barton-on-the-Heath (060 874) 247
270-acre mixed farm. Comfortable listed farmhouse in a small village close to Moreton-in-Marsh. Open fire, TV lounge, lovely views. Ideal for Cotswolds and Stratford.
Bedrooms: 1 double, 1 twin
Bathrooms: 1 public

Bed & breakfast

per night:	£min	£max
Single	16.00	18.00
Double	26.00	30.00

Parking for 12
Open March-November
☎🖳🕆Ⓤ🅸Ⓢ🅼📺🍴Ս✿
✕🐾🏠

Moreton House ᐱᐱ
👑👑 APPROVED

Moreton-in-Marsh GL56 0LQ
☎ (0608) 50747
Family-run guesthouse providing full English breakfast and optional evening meal. Tea shop, open 6 days a week, lounge bar with restaurant. Ideal for touring the Cotswolds. Children and dogs welcome.
Bedrooms: 3 single, 6 double, 3 twin
Bathrooms: 5 private, 2 public

Bed & breakfast

per night:	£min	£max
Single	22.50	22.50
Double	42.00	55.00

Half board

per person:	£min	£max
Daily	31.00	39.00

Lunch available
Evening meal 1800 (last orders 2030)
Parking for 5
Cards accepted: Access, Visa
☎🖵🕆🕯Ⓢ✕🅼Ⓥ🍴◿
🐾 OAP ✕ SP

New Farm ᐱᐱ
👑👑 COMMENDED

Dorn, Moreton-in-Marsh GL56 9NS
☎ (0608) 50782
250-acre dairy farm. Old farmhouse in hamlet of Dorn. Full English breakfast with hot, crispy bread. Large,

spacious bedrooms, dining room with impressive Cotswolds stone fireplace. Ideal for touring Cotswolds.
Bedrooms: 1 double, 1 twin, 1 triple
Bathrooms: 2 private, 1 public

Bed & breakfast

per night:	£min	£max
Single	14.00	16.00
Double	28.00	30.00

Parking for 10
☎3🖵🕆Ⓤ Ⓢ🅼📺🍴◿
✿🐾🏠

Old Farm ᐱᐱ
👑👑 COMMENDED

Dorn, Moreton-in-Marsh GL56 9NS
☎ (0608) 50394
250-acre mixed farm. Enjoy the delights of a 15th C farmhouse - a comfortable family home. Spacious bedrooms. Tennis and croquet. Children welcome.
Bedrooms: 1 double, 1 twin, 1 triple
Bathrooms: 1 private, 1 public

Bed & breakfast

per night:	£min	£max
Single	15.00	20.00
Double	28.00	32.00

Parking for 8
Open March-October
☎🖾🕆Ⓤ🅸Ⓢ🅼📺◿🔾
✿🐾 OAP 🏠

Red Lion Inn ᐱᐱ
👑 APPROVED

Little Compton, Moreton-in-Marsh GL56 0RT
☎ Barton-on-the-Heath (060 874) 397
Fax (060 874) 521
16th C village inn with large garden, offering comfortable accommodation, bar meals, home-made dishes and quality rump steaks. 4 miles from Moreton-in-Marsh off A44.
Bedrooms: 2 double, 1 twin
Bathrooms: 1 public

Bed & breakfast

per night:	£min	£max
Single		22.00
Double		34.00

Lunch available
Evening meal 1900 (last orders 2045)
Parking for 20
Cards accepted: Access, Visa, Switch
☎🕆8🕆🅸Ⓢ🍴◿✿✕🐾🏠

Rest Harrow ᐱᐱ
Listed

Evenlode Road, Moreton-in-Marsh GL56 0NJ
☎ (0608) 50653

Large four-bedroomed house in rural location. Take Evenlode turning by Wellington public house on main Oxford-London road, then half a mile on left.
Bedrooms: 1 double, 1 triple
Bathrooms: 1 public

Bed & breakfast

per night:	£min	£max
Single	12.00	12.00
Double	24.00	24.00

Parking for 3
☎🕆Ⓤ🅸Ⓢ🅼📺🍴◿
✕🐾 OAP

Treetops ᐱᐱ
👑👑 COMMENDED

London Road, Moreton-in-Marsh GL56 0HE
☎ (0608) 51036
Family guesthouse on the A44, set in half an acre of secluded gardens. 5 minutes' walk from the village centre.
Bedrooms: 3 double, 2 twin, 1 triple
Bathrooms: 4 private, 1 public

Bed & breakfast

per night:	£min	£max
Single	18.00	26.00
Double	28.00	35.00

Evening meal 1830 (last orders 1200)
Parking for 8
Open February-December
Cards accepted: Access, Visa
☎🖾🖳🖵🕆Ⓢ✕🅼📺🍴
◿✿🐾 OAP ⅋

Twostones

Evenlode, Moreton-in-Marsh GL56 0NY
☎ (0608) 51104
16th C priest cottage, on smallholding, in quiet village, 3 miles from Stow-on-the-Wold and 2.5 miles from Moreton-in-Marsh. Ideal for Stratford and Cotswolds.
Bedrooms: 1 double, 2 twin
Bathrooms: 3 private

Bed & breakfast

per night:	£min	£max
Double	32.00	34.00

Parking for 6
☎10🕆Ⓤ✕🅼📺🍴✿✕
🐾🏠

National Crown ratings were correct at the time of going to press but are subject to change. Please check at the time of booking.

171

MUCH WENLOCK

Shropshire
Map ref 4A3

Small town close to Wenlock Edge in beautiful scenery and full of interest. In particular there are the remains of an 11th C priory with fine carving and the black and white 16th C Guildhall.

The Longville Arms
Listed

Longville in the Dale, Much Wenlock TF13 6DT
☎ Longville (0694) 771206
18th C rural pub, home-cooked food, friendly atmosphere, good walking. National Trust buildings nearby. Garden. Children welcome. Self-catering accommodation available.
Bedrooms: 1 multiple
Bathrooms: 1 public
Bed & breakfast

per night:	£min	£max
Single	20.00	20.00
Double	30.00	30.00

Half board

per person:	£min	£max
Daily	25.00	30.00

Lunch available
Evening meal 1900 (last orders 2100)
Parking for 24

The Old Barn ♨
COMMENDED · APPROVED

45 Sheinton Street, Much Wenlock TF13 6HR
☎ Telford (0952) 728191
18th C barn, converted to cottage-style accommodation, in the beautiful town of Much Wenlock.
Bedrooms: 2 double, 2 twin
Bathrooms: 4 private

Bed & breakfast per night:	£min	£max
Single	25.00	28.00
Double	34.00	38.00

Parking for 4

Perkley House
COMMENDED

5 Bourton Westwood, Much Wenlock TF13 6QB
☎ (0952) 727252
Comfortable, traditional stone house quietly situated in 2 acres with spectacular views. 1 mile from Much Wenlock on B4378.
Bedrooms: 2 double
Bathrooms: 2 private

Bed & breakfast per night:	£min	£max
Single	25.00	
Double	34.00	38.00

Parking for 6
Open February-November

Walton House ♨
Listed · COMMENDED

35 Barrow Street, Much Wenlock TF13 6EP
☎ (0952) 727139
Two minutes' walk from town centre. 5 miles from Ironbridge Gorge, 13 miles from Shrewsbury, 8 miles from Bridgnorth and 10 miles from Telford town centre. Lawns and patio.
Bedrooms: 1 single, 2 twin
Bathrooms: 1 public

Bed & breakfast per night:	£min	£max
Single	12.00	14.00
Double	28.00	32.00

Parking for 2
Open April-October
Cards accepted: Visa

NAILSWORTH

Gloucestershire
Map ref 2B1

Ancient wool town with several elegant Jacobean and Georgian houses, surrounded by wooded hillsides with fine views.

Apple Orchard House
COMMENDED

Orchard Close, Springhill, Nailsworth, Stroud GL6 0LX
☎ (0453) 832503 & 833544
Fax (0453) 836213
Elegant and spacious Cotswold house in pretty 1 acre garden. Panoramic views from bedrooms and sitting room of picturesque Cotswold hills. Excellent touring centre.
Bedrooms: 1 double, 2 twin
Bathrooms: 3 private

Bed & breakfast per night:	£min	£max
Single	18.00	22.00
Double	28.00	30.00

Half board

per person:	£min	£max
Daily	46.00	48.00
Weekly	151.00	158.00

Evening meal 1900 (last orders 2030)
Parking for 3
Cards accepted: Access, Visa

Ad Display advertisement appears on this page

North Farm ♨
COMMENDED

Nympsfield Road, Nailsworth, Stroud GL6 0ET
☎ (045 383) 3598
Modernised former farmhouse, 3 large bedrooms, all with bathroom en-suite. Panoramic views of surrounding countryside.

Convenient for touring.
Brochure on request.
Bedrooms: 1 double, 2 twin
Bathrooms: 3 private

Bed & breakfast per night:	£min	£max
Single	15.00	18.00
Double	30.00	30.00

Half board

per person:	£min	£max
Daily	24.00	27.00

Evening meal 1800 (last orders 2000)
Parking for 4

The Vicarage

Avening Road, Nailsworth, Stroud GL6 0BS
☎ (0453) 832181
Secluded country vicarage on the edge of Cotswolds town. Two minutes' walk from restaurants, delicatessen. Good access to M4 and M5.
Bedrooms: 2 single, 1 twin
Bathrooms: 1 public

Bed & breakfast per night:	£min	£max
Single	20.00	
Double	40.00	

Parking for 4

Windsoredge House
COMMENDED

Windsoredge, Nailsworth, Stroud GL6 0NP
☎ Stroud (0453) 833626
Substantial Cotswold-stone house, circa 1650, in a designated area of outstanding natural beauty. Prominent yet secluded location with panoramic hillside and woodland views.
Bedrooms: 1 double, 1 twin, 1 triple
Bathrooms: 3 private

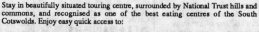

Bed & breakfast per night:	£min	£max
Single	16.00	25.00
Double	25.00	40.00

Half board per person:	£min	£max
Daily	25.00	34.00
Weekly	165.00	220.00

Evening meal from 1830
Parking for 5

🛇⛺🏠♿⚓🅱✗📶📺🛏,
🚗✿✗🐾🚲 SP T

NAUNTON

Gloucestershire
Map ref 2B1

A high place on the Windrush, renowned for its wild flowers and with an attractive dovecote.

Eastern Hill Farm ⚴

Listed

Naunton, Cheltenham
GL54 3AF
☎ Guiting Power (0451) 850716
77-acre arable and mixed farm. Traditional-style Cotswolds farmhouse, within walking distance of Bourton-on-the-Water and the Slaughters.
Bedrooms: 1 double, 1 twin, 1 triple
Bathrooms: 3 public

Bed & breakfast per night:	£min	£max
Single	17.00	18.00
Double	34.00	36.00

Evening meal from 1900
Parking for 6

🛇5🏠♿🆄🅱📺🛏,✿🐾

NEWENT

Gloucestershire
Map ref 2B1

Small town with the largest collection of birds of prey in Europe at the Falconry Centre where there are flying demonstrations daily. There is also a glass workshop where visitors can watch glass being blown and there is a 'seconds' shop.
Tourist Information Centre
☎ *(0531) 822145*

Ford House Farm

Tewkesbury Road, Newent
GL18 1LQ
☎ (0531) 820594
Mellow Georgian farmhouse in beautiful lakeside setting surrounded by apple orchards. Ideal base for

touring, walking or just relaxing.
Bedrooms: 1 twin, 1 triple
Bathrooms: 1 public

Bed & breakfast per night:	£min	£max
Single	13.00	13.00
Double	26.00	26.00

Parking for 8
Open April-October

🛇♿🆄S🅱📺🚗🛏✗🐾🏠

Orchard House ⚴

Listed | HIGHLY COMMENDED

Aston Ingham Road, Kilcot,
Newent GL18 1NP
☎ Gorsley (0989) 82417
In 5 acres of lawns, paddocks and woodlands. Relaxed and friendly. Delicious food. TV lounge, conservatory, delightful bedrooms. Non-smoking. Licensed.
Bedrooms: 2 double, 1 twin
Bathrooms: 1 private, 1 public

Bed & breakfast per night:	£min	£max
Single	27.00	31.00
Double	39.00	47.00

Half board per person:	£min	£max
Daily	32.00	36.00
Weekly	210.00	238.00

Evening meal 1930 (last orders 2030)
Parking for 10
Cards accepted: Access, Visa

🛇12🏠▸✿🆄S✗📺🛏,
🚗▸✿✗🐾 SP

NEWLAND

Gloucestershire
Map ref 2A1

Probably the most attractive of the villages of the Forest of Dean. The church is often referred to as 'the Cathedral of the Forest'; it contains a number of interesting monuments and the Forest Miner's Brass. Almshouses nearby were endowed by William Jones, founder of Monmouth School.

Tan House Farm

Listed

Newland, Coleford GL16 8NP
☎ (059 48) 32222
14-acre livestock farm. Queen Anne house dating from 1709, situated in one of the most beautiful villages in the Forest of Dean. Walking distance of 16th C pub.
Bedrooms: 2 double
Bathrooms: 2 private

Bed & breakfast per night:	£min	£max
Single	17.50	
Double	35.00	

Parking for 20

🛇🆄✗🅱✿🐾🏠

NEWPORT

Shropshire
Map ref 4A3

Small market town on the Shropshire Union Canal has a wide High Street and a church with some interesting monuments. Newport is close to Aqualate Mere which is the largest lake in Staffordshire.

Sambrook Manor

Listed

Sambrook, Newport
TF10 8AL
☎ Sambrook (0952) 550256
260-acre mixed farm. Old manor farmhouse built in 1702. Close to Stoke Potteries, Shrewsbury, Ironbridge, Wolverhampton and many places of historic interest.
Bedrooms: 1 single, 1 double, 1 twin
Bathrooms: 2 public

Bed & breakfast per night:	£min	£max
Single	14.00	15.00
Double	28.00	30.00

Parking for 10

🛇♿🆄🅱♿✗🅱📺🚗🎣✿
✗🐾🏠

NORTHLEACH

Gloucestershire
Map ref 2B1

Village famous for its beautiful 15th C wool church with its lovely porch and interesting interior. There are also some fine houses including 16th C almshouses, a 17th C manor house and a collection of agricultural instruments in the former prison.

Cotteswold House ⚴

Listed | COMMENDED

Market Place, Northleach,
Cheltenham GL54 3EG
☎ Cotswold (0451) 860493
A traditional Cotswold-stone house with many interesting architectural features and modernised to a high standard. Ideal base from which to tour, or rest.

Bedrooms: 1 double, 1 twin, 1 triple
Bathrooms: 3 public

Bed & breakfast per night:	£min	£max
Double	31.00	34.00

🛇10🆄🅱📺🛏,🚗✗🐾🏠

Northfield Bed & Breakfast ⚴

👑👑👑 COMMENDED

Cirencester Road (A429),
Northleach, Cheltenham
GL54 3JL
☎ Cotswold (0451) 860427
Detached family house in the country with large gardens and home-grown produce. Excellent centre for visiting the Cotswolds and close to local services.
Bedrooms: 1 double, 1 twin, 1 triple
Bathrooms: 3 private

Bed & breakfast per night:	£min	£max
Single	20.00	20.00
Double	30.00	36.00

Half board per person:	£min	£max
Daily	30.00	40.00

Lunch available
Evening meal 1900 (last orders 2000)
Parking for 10

🛇🏠⛺🖵♿🅱♿✗🅱
📺🛏,🚗✿✗🐾 SP

The Old House

👑

Turkdean, Northleach,
Cheltenham GL54 3NS
☎ Cotswold (0451) 860226
Charming and comfortable listed 500-year-old Cotswold house in quiet and beautiful valley. Good breakfasts. 2 miles from Northleach.
Bedrooms: 1 single, 1 double, 1 triple
Bathrooms: 2 private

Bed & breakfast per night:	£min	£max
Single	18.00	20.00
Double	36.00	40.00

Parking for 6
Open February-November

🛇3🆄S✗🅱📺🛏,✿✗
🐾🏠

> National Crown ratings were correct at the time of going to press but are subject to change. Please check at the time of booking.

NUNEATON

Warwickshire
Map ref 4B3

Busy town with an art gallery and museum which has a permanent exhibition of the work of George Eliot. The library also has an interesting collection of material. Arbury Hall, a fine example of Gothic architecture, is nearby.
Tourist Information Centre
☎ *(0203) 384027*

Triple 'A' Lodge Guest House
Listed
94-96 Coleshill Road, Chapel End, Nuneaton CV10 0PH
☎ Coventry (0203) 394515
Family-run guesthouse on the outskirts of Nuneaton, in the pleasant village of Chapel End. Tea/coffee facilities and colour TV all rooms. Evening meals available.
Bedrooms: 3 double, 3 twin
Bathrooms: 2 public

Bed & breakfast per night:	£min	£max
Single	15.00	18.00
Double	24.00	30.00

Evening meal 1800 (last orders 2130)
Parking for 12
Cards accepted: Diners, Amex

☎ 2 🏊 🖵 🌢 🍵 ⓤ 🛆 🎈 �📺 🛏 ✕ 🛡 ᴰᴬᴾ

NYMPSFIELD

Gloucestershire
Map ref 2B1

Pretty village high up in the Cotswolds, with a simple mid-Victorian church and a prehistoric long barrow nearby.

Rose and Crown Inn 🍴
Listed APPROVED
Nympsfield, Stonehouse GL10 3TU
☎ Dursley (0453) 860240
Fax (0453) 860700
300-year-old inn, in quiet Cotswold village, close to Cotswold Way and Nympsfield Gliding Club. Easy access to M4/M5.
Bedrooms: 1 double, 3 triple
Bathrooms: 1 private, 1 public

Bed & breakfast per night:	£min	£max
Single	25.00	29.00
Double	34.00	44.00

Half board per person:	£min	£max
Daily	29.00	40.00

Lunch available
Evening meal 1830 (last orders 2130)
Parking for 30
Cards accepted: Access, Visa, Amex

🛇 🖵 🌢 🍵 🛆 ⓢ 🛏, 🛆 🎈 ❀ ✕ 🛡 ᴰᴬᴾ 🛡 ˢᴾ ⊤

OMBERSLEY

Hereford and Worcester
Map ref 2B1

A particularly fine village full of black and white houses including the 17th C Dower House and some old inns. The church contains the original box pews.

The Crown and Sandys Arms 🍴
🏅🏅 COMMENDED
Ombersley, Droitwich, Worcestershire WR9 0EW
☎ Worcester (0905) 620252
Fax (0905) 620767
Freehouse with comfortable bedrooms, draught beers and open fires. Home-cooked meals available lunch and evenings, 7 days a week.
Bedrooms: 1 single, 5 double, 1 twin
Bathrooms: 5 private, 1 public

Bed & breakfast per night:	£min	£max
Single	20.00	25.00
Double	40.00	45.00

Lunch available
Evening meal 1800 (last orders 2200)
Parking for 100
Cards accepted: Access, Visa, Switch

🛇 🖵 🌢 🍵 🛆 ✕ 🛏 �📺 🛏, 🛆 🔺 ❀ ✕ 🛡

Individual proprietors have supplied all details of accommodation. Although we do check for accuracy, we advise you to confirm the information at the time of booking.

ONIBURY

Shropshire
Map ref 4A3

Pleasant village of red-brick and half-timbered buildings has a plain but interesting church with unusual turn of the century carving.

Fairview
🏅🏅 HIGHLY COMMENDED
Green Lane, Onibury, Ludlow SY7 9BL
☎ Bromfield (058 477) 505
5-acre smallholding. 300-year-old cottage 6 miles north of Ludlow. Panoramic views of Wenlock Edge, Long Mynd and Clee Hills.
Bedrooms: 2 double, 1 twin
Bathrooms: 1 private, 1 public

Bed & breakfast per night:	£min	£max
Single	15.40	16.40
Double	26.40	28.40

Half board per person:	£min	£max
Daily	24.50	25.50
Weekly	154.00	161.00

Evening meal 1930 (last orders 1930)
Parking for 8
Open April-October

🛇 10 🌢 🍵 ⓤ 🛆 ⓢ ✕ 🛏 �📺 🛏, 🛆 ❀ ✕ 🛡

ONNELEY

Staffordshire
Map ref 4A2

The Wheatsheaf Inn at Onneley 🍴
🏅 COMMENDED
Bar Hill Road, Onneley CW3 9QF
☎ Stoke-on-Trent (0782) 751581
Fax (0782) 751499
18th C country inn with bars, restaurant, conference and function facilities. On the A525, 3 miles from Bridgemere and Keele University, 7 miles from Newcastle-under-Lyme.
Bedrooms: 4 double, 1 twin
Bathrooms: 5 private

Bed & breakfast per night:	£min	£max
Single	40.00	45.00
Double	45.00	55.00

Lunch available
Evening meal 1800 (last orders 2200)
Parking for 150

Cards accepted: Access, Visa, Amex

🛇 🏊 🖵 🌢 🍵 🛆 ⓢ 🛏, 🛆 🎈 ᴰᴬᴾ ˢᴾ ⊤

OSWESTRY

Shropshire
Map ref 4A3

Town close to the Welsh border, the scene of many battles. To the north are the remains of a large Iron Age hill fort. An excellent centre for exploring Shropshire and Offa's Dyke.
Tourist Information Centre
☎ *(0691) 662488.*

April Spring Cottage
🏅
Nantmawr, Oswestry SY10 9HL
☎ Llansantffraid (0691) 828802
Cottage in pretty garden in rural hamlet. Beautiful, unspoilt countryside. Comfortable bedrooms. Good walking, including Offa's Dyke.
Bedrooms: 1 double, 1 twin
Bathrooms: 1 private, 1 public

Bed & breakfast per night:	£min	£max
Single	15.00	15.00
Double	30.00	30.00

Half board per person:	£min	£max
Daily	22.00	22.00
Weekly	154.00	

Evening meal 1830 (last orders 2000)
Parking for 6

🛇 8 🖵 🌢 🍵 ⓤ 🛆 ✕ 🛏 �📺 🛏, 🛆 ꂅ 🔺 ❀ ✕ 🛡

Frankton Manor 🍴
🏅 HIGHLY COMMENDED
Welsh Frankton, Whittington, Oswestry SY11 4NX
☎ Ellesmere (0691) 622454
Charming Victorian country house in small village near Oswestry. Beautifully decorated and furnished, spacious bedrooms. Large landscaped garden with lovely south-facing views.
Bedrooms: 1 single, 1 double, 1 multiple
Bathrooms: 1 public

Bed & breakfast per night:	£min	£max
Single	17.00	19.50
Double	34.00	39.00

Half board per person:	£min	£max
Daily	26.00	29.00
Weekly	169.00	189.00

Evening meal 1900 (last orders 1100)
Parking for 20
Open March-October
🚭 3 ♨ UL 🅰 Ⓢ ⅋ 🏢 ◢ ✻ 🛏 ⊗ SP 🏮

Rhoswiel Lodge ⚑

Listed

Weston Rhyn, Oswestry
SY10 7TG
☎ Chirk (0691) 777609
Victorian country house with modern annexe in pleasant surroundings beside Llangollen Canal, 4 miles north of Oswestry. 300 yards from the A5.
Bedrooms: 2 single, 2 double, 2 twin
Bathrooms: 3 public
Bed & breakfast

per night:	£min	£max
Single	12.00	15.00
Double	24.00	28.00

Parking for 6
🚭 ⚒ ♨ ♨ UL Ⓢ TV ◢ ✻ 🛏

PAINSWICK

Gloucestershire
Map ref 2B1

Picturesque wool town with inns and houses dating from the 14th C. Painswick House is a Palladian mansion with Chinese wallpaper. The churchyard is famous for its yew trees.

Upper Doreys Mill ⚑
⊗

Edge, Painswick, Stroud
GL6 6NF
☎ (0452) 812459
18th C cloth mill with log fires and old beams. By a stream and in a rural setting. Half a mile from Painswick, down Edge Lane.
Bedrooms: 2 double, 1 twin
Bathrooms: 3 private
Bed & breakfast

per night:	£min	£max
Double	35.00	

Parking for 6
🚭 ♨ ⚒ UL Ⓢ ⅋ 🐾 TV ◢ ∪ ⊳ ✻ 🛏 🏮

The enquiry coupons at the back will help you when contacting proprietors.

PARKEND

Gloucestershire
Map ref 2A1

Village in the Forest of Dean, once an important industrial and railway centre, but now quiet and peaceful and a good base for exploring the forest.

The Fountain Inn ⚑
⊗⊗⊗

Fountain Way, Parkend, Lydney GL15 4JD
☎ Dean (0594) 562189
Fax (0594) 564438
Beautifully renovated country pub in the heart of the Royal Forest of Dean, 3.5 miles from Lydney on A48 Gloucester to Chepstow road. Ideally situated for touring.
Bedrooms: 2 single, 4 double, 2 twin
Bathrooms: 8 private
Bed & breakfast

per night:	£min	£max
Single	26.00	
Double	44.00	

Half board

per person:	£min	£max
Daily	27.00	

Lunch available
Evening meal 1800 (last orders 2130)
Parking for 30
Cards accepted: Access, Visa, Diners, Amex
🚭 ⚒ ♨ 🆎 🅰 Ⓢ TV 🏢 ◢ ⅋ ✻ SP 🏮

PENKRIDGE

Staffordshire
Map ref 4B3

Small town south of Stafford in the wide valley of the Penk has a stately church with many monuments to the Littleton family.

Littleton Arms Hotel
St. Michael's Square, Penkridge, Stafford
ST19 5AL
☎ (0785) 712287
Historic coaching inn with restaurant, bars, large bedrooms all en-suite. Easy access from M6.
Bedrooms: 2 single, 4 double, 4 twin, 3 triple
Bathrooms: 13 private
Bed & breakfast

per night:	£min	£max
Single	27.00	35.00
Double	38.00	44.00

Half board per person:	£min	£max
Daily	37.00	64.00
Weekly	225.00	600.00

Lunch available
Evening meal 1900 (last orders 2200)
Parking for 50
Cards accepted: Access, Visa
🚭 ⚒ 🖵 ♨ 🅰 Ⓢ 🏢 ◢ 🖭 ⊗ SP 🏮

PERSHORE

Hereford and Worcester
Map ref 2B1

Attractive Georgian town on the River Avon close to the Vale of Evesham, with fine houses and old inns. The remains of the beautiful Pershore Abbey form the parish church.

Oaklands ⚑

APPROVED

Main Evesham Rd., (A44), Pershore, Worcestershire WR10 3JT
☎ Evesham (0386) 860323
5-acre nursery. In the beautiful Vale of Evesham, close to Worcester, the Cotswolds, Stratford-upon-Avon, Cheltenham and Broadway. Georgian-style country house, with large garden, situated in rural area.
Bedrooms: 2 twin, 1 triple
Bathrooms: 1 public
Bed & breakfast

per night:	£min	£max
Single	20.00	20.00
Double	30.00	35.00

Evening meal from 1930
Parking for 20
🚭 ♨ UL 🅰 Ⓢ 🖭 TV ✻ ✻ 🛏 SP

PUTLEY

Hereford and Worcester
Map ref 2B1

The Coach House

Listed

Putley, Ledbury, Herefordshire HR8 2QP
☎ (0531) 670684
18th C coach house and stables with cobbled courtyard, originally part of the nearby Putley Court.
Bedrooms: 2 double
Bathrooms: 2 private
Bed & breakfast

per night:	£min	£max
Double	25.00	30.00

Parking for 6
⚒ 📞 🖵 ♨ 🏢 ◢ ✻ 🛏

REDDITCH

Hereford and Worcester
Map ref 4B3

Town has remains of a Cistercian Abbey which have been excavated to reveal the Abbey's history. Forge Mill is close by with a restored water wheel and Wynyates Craft Centre.
Tourist Information Centre
☎ *(0527) 60806*

Cherrypit

Cherrypit Lane, Beoley, Redditch, Worcestershire B98 9DH
☎ (0527) 62454
Quiet secluded country guesthouse. Near junction 3 of M42, off the A435. Standing in 6 acres. Non-smoking establishment.
Bedrooms: 2 single, 2 twin
Bathrooms: 1 private, 2 public
Bed & breakfast

per night:	£min	£max
Single	17.00	25.00
Double	34.00	50.00

Half board

per person:	£min	£max
Daily	27.00	35.00

Evening meal 1800 (last orders 1900)
Parking for 8
🚭 ♨ UL 🅰 ⅋ 🖭 TV 🏢 ◢ ✻ 🛏 🏮 Ⓣ

ROCESTER

Staffordshire
Map ref 4B2

The Leeze Guest House ⚑
⊗⊗

63 High Street, Rocester, Uttoxeter ST14 5JU
☎ (0889) 591146
Just off the B5030 Uttoxeter to Ashbourne road. Traditional country cooking, handy for Peak District, Potteries, Alton Towers and Churnet Valley.
Bedrooms: 1 double, 2 twin, 1 triple
Bathrooms: 2 public
Bed & breakfast

per night:	£min	£max
Single	16.00	
Double	28.00	

Continued ►

Please mention this guide when making a booking.

ROCESTER
Continued

Half board
per person:	£min	£max
Daily		24.00

Evening meal 1800 (last orders 1600)
Parking for 6

🐕🛇🖵🔌💰🛎️S♨️🚿🆔📺💻,🖨️
📶 OAP SP

Monks Clownholme Farm ⋀

Rocester, Uttoxeter
ST14 5BP
☎ (0889) 590347
89-acre livestock farm. 16th C farmhouse with views over the River Dove. Beautiful four-poster beds, jacuzzi, sauna, games room, play areas.
Bedrooms: 1 double, 1 multiple
Bathrooms: 1 public
Bed & breakfast
per night:	£min	£max
Single	17.00	20.00
Double	30.00	32.00

Parking for 8
Open April-October

🐕🛇🔌🖵💰🛎️🆔📺💻♨️🖨️🛎️♪
✆❀📶

Red Lion

High Street, Rocester,
Uttoxeter ST14 5JU
☎ (0889) 590337
Old coaching inn in the centre of the village. Ideal for visiting Alton Towers and the Derbyshire Peak District.
Bedrooms: 1 double, 2 twin, 1 triple
Bathrooms: 1 public
Bed & breakfast
per night:	£min	£max
Single		15.00
Double		28.00

Lunch available
Evening meal 1930 (last orders 2145)
Parking for 2

🐕🛇🖵🔌💰🛎️S💻,🖨️❦∪✗
📶 OAP 📶

ROCK
Hereford and Worcester
Map ref 4A3

The Old Forge
Listed

Gorst Hill, Rock,
Kidderminster,
Worcestershire DY14 9YG
☎ (0299) 266745
Recently renovated country cottage, near the Wyre Forest. Ideal for country walks and

---

visiting local places of interest.
Bedrooms: 2 twin
Bathrooms: 1 public, 1 private shower
Bed & breakfast
per night:	£min	£max
Single	13.50	15.00
Double	25.00	30.00

Parking for 5

🐕🛇🖵🔌💰🛎️S🆔📺💻,🖨️
✗📶

ROSS-ON-WYE
Hereford and Worcester
Map ref 2A1

Attractive market town with a 17th C market hall, set above the River Wye. There are lovely views over the surrounding countryside from the Prospect and the town is close to Goodrich Castle and the Welsh border.
*Tourist Information Centre
☎ (0989) 62768*

The Arches Country House ⋀

Walford Road, Ross-on-Wye,
Herefordshire HR9 5TP
☎ (0989) 63348
Family-run hotel set in half an acre of lawns, half a mile from the town centre. All bedrooms are furnished to a high standard and have views of the lawned garden. Warm, friendly atmosphere and personal service.
Bedrooms: 1 single, 4 double, 2 twin, 1 triple
Bathrooms: 4 private, 2 public
Bed & breakfast
per night:	£min	£max
Single	18.00	21.00
Double	30.00	42.00

Parking for 8

🐕🛇🖵💰🛎️S🚿🆔📺💻
🖨️❀📶 OAP SP

Brook House ⋀
👑👑

Lea, Ross-on-Wye,
Herefordshire HR9 7JZ
☎ (0989) 750710
Fine Queen Anne Grade II listed house offering a warm welcome, comfortable rooms and open fires. Home-cooked and produced fare. Home-made muffins a speciality.
Bedrooms: 2 double, 1 twin
Bathrooms: 1 private, 1 public, 2 private showers

Bed & breakfast
per night:	£min	£max
Single	16.00	18.00
Double	30.00	34.00

Evening meal 1900 (last orders 1800)
Parking for 2

🐕🛇8🖵🔌💰🛎️S♨️🚿🆔📺💻,
🖨️📶❧SP📶

Brookfield House ⋀
👑👑

Over Ross, Ross-on-Wye,
Herefordshire HR9 7AT
☎ (0989) 62188
Queen Anne/Georgian listed building close to the town centre. Private car park.
Bedrooms: 2 single, 3 double, 3 twin
Bathrooms: 3 private, 3 public
Bed & breakfast
per night:	£min	£max
Single	15.00	16.00
Double	30.00	36.00

Parking for 11
Cards accepted: Access, Visa

🐕🛇🖵🔌💰S🆔💻,🖨️❀📶
SP📶 T

Edde Cross House ⋀
👑👑 HIGHLY COMMENDED

Edde Cross Street, Ross-on-Wye, Herefordshire HR9 7BZ
☎ (0989) 65088
Delightful Georgian town house overlooking river, with the atmosphere and character of a comfortable private home. Close to town centre. Bedrooms with colour TV and beverage tray, some en-suite. No smoking house.
Bedrooms: 1 single, 3 double, 1 twin
Bathrooms: 2 private, 1 public
Bed & breakfast
per night:	£min	£max
Single	18.00	28.00
Double	34.00	44.00

Open February-November

🐕🛇10🖵🔌🍷🛎️🆔S🚿🆔💻,
🖨️❀✗📶 OAP SP📶

Lavender Cottage
Listed

Bridstow, Ross-on-Wye,
Herefordshire HR9 6QB
☎ (0989) 62836
Part 17th C character property, 1 mile from Ross-on-Wye. Take Hereford road, turn right to Foy and then first turning on left.
Bedrooms: 1 double, 1 twin
Bathrooms: 2 private, 1 public

Bed & breakfast
per night:	£min	£max
Single	18.00	20.00
Double	25.00	27.00

Half board
per person:	£min	£max
Daily	20.00	24.00
Weekly	140.00	154.00

Evening meal from 1830
Parking for 3

🐕🛇5🖵🔌💻,🖨️❀
✗📶

Merrivale Place ⋀
👑👑 APPROVED

The Avenue, Ross-on-Wye,
Herefordshire HR9 5AW
☎ (0989) 64929
Fine Victorian house in quiet tree-lined avenue. Large comfortable rooms and lovely views. Home cooking. Near town and river.
Bedrooms: 1 double, 1 twin, 1 triple
Bathrooms: 2 public
Bed & breakfast
per night:	£min	£max
Single	18.00	19.00
Double	32.00	34.00

Half board
per person:	£min	£max
Daily	25.00	26.00
Weekly	170.00	175.00

Evening meal 1830 (last orders 1600)
Parking for 6
Open March-October

🐕🛇🔌💻,🖨️❀✗📶
📶

Rudhall Farm ⋀
👑👑 HIGHLY COMMENDED

Ross-on-Wye, Herefordshire HR9 7TL
☎ Upton Bishop (098 985) 240
Savour the tranquillity of this elegant and superior farmhouse accommodation. Millstream flowing nearby. Panoramic views across rolling countryside. Friendly and homely atmosphere, home cooking. Ideal for exploring the Wye Valley.
Bedrooms: 1 single, 1 double
Bathrooms: 1 private, 1 public
Bed & breakfast
per night:	£min	£max
Single	17.00	18.50
Double	32.00	35.00

Parking for 10
Open March-November

🛇🖵🔌🍷🛎️S🚿🆔📺💻,
🖨️❀✗📶📶

Ryefield House Hotel ⋀

😟 😟 APPROVED

Gloucester Road, Ross-on-Wye, Herefordshire HR9 5NA
☎ (0989) 63030
Informal yet quietly efficient family-run hotel. All bedrooms have telephone, colour TV, fresh flowers and fudge!
Bedrooms: 1 single, 2 double, 1 twin, 4 triple
Bathrooms: 5 private, 1 public

Bed & breakfast

per night:	£min	£max
Single	22.00	35.00
Double	44.00	55.00

Evening meal 1900 (last orders 1700)
Parking for 10
🐕☎⌂♦🛏🄂🅂🄼📺 🖲,🚗✿ 🚲 🐾 SP

The Skakes ⋀

Glewstone, Ross-on-Wye, Herefordshire HR9 6AZ
☎ (0989) 770456
18th C farmhouse, offering peace and quiet, comfortable rooms, varied home cooking, and parking. On A4137 near Glewstone.
Bedrooms: 2 single, 4 double, 2 twin
Bathrooms: 4 public

Bed & breakfast

per night:	£min	£max
Single	20.00	
Double	28.00	

Half board

per person:	£min	£max
Daily	24.50	
Weekly	154.35	

Evening meal 1900 (last orders 2000)
Parking for 8
🐕 10 🛏 ⌂ 🆒 🆓 🛏 🄂 🅂 🄼 📺 🖲. 🚗 🎇 ✿ 🚲 🐾 SP 🅃

Sunnymount Hotel ⋀

😟 😟 COMMENDED

Ryefield Road, Ross-on-Wye, Herefordshire HR9 5LU
☎ (0989) 63880
Warm, comfortable hotel in quiet location on edge of town, offering French and English cooking with home-grown and local produce freshly cooked for each meal.
Bedrooms: 2 single, 3 double, 4 twin
Bathrooms: 6 private, 1 public

Bed & breakfast

per night:	£min	£max
Single	17.50	29.00
Double	44.00	48.00

Half board

per person:	£min	£max
Daily	33.00	41.00
Weekly	215.00	250.00

Evening meal 1900 (last orders 1730)
Parking for 7
Cards accepted: Access, Visa, Amex
🐕☎♦🆓🅂✂🄼📺🖲,🚗✿🦮 🚲 SP 🐾 🅃

Thatch Close ⋀

😟 😟 APPROVED

Llangrove, Ross-on-Wye, Herefordshire HR9 6EL
☎ Llangarron (098 984) 300
13-acre mixed farm. Secluded Georgian country farmhouse midway between Ross-on-Wye and Monmouth. Home-produced vegetables and meat. Ideal for country lovers of any age. Map sent on request. Ordnance Survey: 51535196.
Bedrooms: 1 double, 1 twin, 1 triple
Bathrooms: 3 private

Bed & breakfast

per night:	£min	£max
Double	26.00	34.00

Half board

per person:	£min	£max
Daily	23.00	27.00
Weekly	155.00	185.00

Lunch available
Evening meal 1830 (last orders 1800)
Parking for 7
Open March-November
🐕♦🆓🅂🄼📺🖲.✿🚗🦮 SP

RUDYARD

Staffordshire
Map ref 4B2

Village close to the attractive Rudyard Reservoir where there are facilities for fishing, boating and pleasant walks. Rudyard gave its name to the famous writer, Kipling, whose parents are said to have often visited it.

Fairboroughs Farm

😟 😟

Rudyard, Leek ST13 8PR
☎ Rushton Spencer (0260) 226341
150-acre livestock farm. Comfortable oak-beamed 17th C stone house, with log fires and splendid views. The Potteries, Peak District, Cheshire and Alton Towers within easy reach.
Bedrooms: 1 double, 1 triple
Bathrooms: 1 public

Bed & breakfast

per night:	£min	£max
Single	14.00	15.00
Double	25.00	28.00

Parking for 4
Open March-November
🐕🦮🆓🅂🄼📺 🖲.🚗✿ 🚲 🐾

RUGBY

Warwickshire
Map ref 4C3

Town famous for its public school which gave its name to Rugby Union football and which featured in 'Tom Brown's Schooldays'.
Tourist Information Centre
☎ (0788) 535348

Avondale Guest House ⋀

😟 😟

16 Elsee Road, Rugby CV21 3BA
☎ (0788) 578639
Victorian town residence close to Rugby School, convenient for Warwick Castle, Coventry Cathedral, Leamington Spa, National Exhibition Centre and Birmingham.
Bedrooms: 3 twin, 1 triple
Bathrooms: 1 private, 2 public, 1 private shower

Bed & breakfast

per night:	£min	£max
Single		19.00
Double		34.00

Parking for 8
🐕🦮🆓🄼📺🖲.🚗🚲

White Lion Inn ⋀

Listed APPROVED

Coventry Road, Pailton, Rugby CV23 0QD
☎ (0788) 832359
Former 17th C coaching inn, recently refurbished but maintaining all old world features. Close to Rugby, Coventry and Stratford. Within 2 miles of motorways.
Bedrooms: 6 twin
Bathrooms: 6 private, 2 public

Bed & breakfast

per night:	£min	£max
Single	17.50	17.50
Double	30.00	35.00

Lunch available
Evening meal 1830 (last orders 2200)
Parking for 60
Cards accepted: Access, Visa
🐕☎🆒🆓🅂🄼📺🖲.🚗🅃20-30 DAP

RUSHTON SPENCER

Staffordshire
Map ref 4B2

Village with an interesting church built in the 14th C of wood, some of which still remains. It is close to the pleasant Rudyard Reservoir.

Barnswood Farm

Listed

Rushton Spencer, Macclesfield, Cheshire SK11 0RA
☎ (0260) 226261
100-acre dairy farm. In a lovely setting overlooking Rudyard Lake 400 yards down the field. Alton Towers, Peak District and the Potteries all within a 15 mile radius. Homely welcome, English breakfast.
Bedrooms: 1 double, 2 triple
Bathrooms: 1 public

Bed & breakfast

per night:	£min	£max
Single	14.00	14.00
Double	24.00	25.00

Parking for 5
🐕🦮🆓🄼📺🖲.✿🦮🚲

RUYTON-XI-TOWNS

Shropshire
Map ref 4A3

Town got its name from the time when, at the beginning of the 14th C, it was one of 11 towns 'joined' into 1 manor. It is situated above the River Perry and has the remains of a castle in the churchyard.

Brownhill House ⋀

😟 😟 COMMENDED

Ruyton-XI-Towns, Shrewsbury SY4 1LR
☎ Baschurch (0939) 260626
Comfortable accommodation, relaxed atmosphere, good food and home-grown produce. Extensive breakfast menu. Unique garden bordering River Perry, as seen on TV. Fishing, canoeing, walks, local pubs. Golf and horseriding nearby.
Bedrooms: 1 single, 1 double, 1 twin
Bathrooms: 1 private, 1 public

Continued ▶

RUYTON-XI-TOWNS

Continued

Bed & breakfast

per night:	£min	£max
Single	13.50	
Double	27.00	

Half board

per person:	£min	£max
Daily	20.50	

Lunch available
Evening meal 1800 (last orders 1600)
Parking for 5

♻ ♿ ✿ 🖥 📶 🅸 § ⚲ 📺 🎵 ▦. ♨ ∪
♪ ▶ ❀ ✕ 🏸 OAP SP 🏵

SEVERN STOKE

Hereford and Worcester
Map ref 2B1

Village to the south of Worcester with a picturesque group of houses surrounding the church and magnificent views across the Severn to the Malvern Hills.

Madge Hill House
Listed

Severn Stoke, Worcester
WR8 9JN
☎ (0905) 371362
Georgian house in peaceful country setting, between Tewkesbury and Worcester on A38. En-suite bedrooms with TV.
Bedrooms: 1 double, 1 twin
Bathrooms: 1 public

Bed & breakfast

per night:	£min	£max
Double	34.00	

Parking for 2

♻ ♿ 🖥 ✿ ✿ 🅸 📺 ▦. ✿
🏵 🏸

The colour maps at the back of this guide pinpoint all places with accommodation.

There are separate sections in this guide listing groups specialising in farm holidays and accommodation which is especially suitable for young people and organised groups.

SHREWSBURY

Shropshire
Map ref 4A3

Beautiful historic town on the River Severn retaining many fine old timber-framed houses. Its attractions include Rowley's Museum with Roman finds, remains of a castle, Clive House Museum, St. Chad's 18th C round church and rowing on the river.
Tourist Information Centre
☎ *(0743) 350761.*

Ashton Lees
♛♛ **COMMENDED**

Dorrington, Shrewsbury
SY5 7JW
☎ (074 373) 378
6 miles south of Shrewsbury on the A49. Well placed for exploring the south Shropshire area.
Bedrooms: 1 double, 1 twin, 1 triple
Bathrooms: 1 private, 1 public

Bed & breakfast

per night:	£min	£max
Single	14.75	17.50
Double	29.50	35.00

Parking for 6

♻ ♿ 🖥 ✿ ✿ 🅸 § 📺 ♨
✿ ✕ 🏸 OAP SP

Cardeston Park Farm
♛ **COMMENDED**

Ford, Shrewsbury SY5 9NH
☎ (0743) 884265
150-acre mixed farm. Spacious farmhouse set in countryside on the English/ Welsh border. On A458 Shrewsbury to Welshpool road, 7 miles from Shrewsbury, 13 miles from Welshpool.
Bedrooms: 1 single, 1 double, 1 twin
Bathrooms: 2 private, 1 public

Bed & breakfast

per night:	£min	£max
Single	14.00	18.00
Double	28.00	30.00

Parking for 4

♻ 🖥 ✿ 🖥 ▦. ✿ ✕ 🏸

The Castle Vaults Inn
Listed

16 Castle Gates, Shrewsbury
SY1 2AB
☎ (0743) 358807
Public house/inn with an open Mexican eating house, situated in the shadows of Shrewsbury Castle. Roof garden. Fully automatic fire alarm system throughout the building.
Bedrooms: 3 single, 2 double, 1 twin, 1 triple
Bathrooms: 4 private, 1 public

Bed & breakfast

per night:	£min	£max
Single	19.00	25.00
Double	30.00	39.00

Lunch available
Evening meal 1800 (last orders 2200)

♻ ✕ 🖥 ✿ 🅸 § ⚲ ▦. ✿ 🏸 SP

Chatford House ♙
♛

Bayston Hill, Shrewsbury
SY3 0AY
☎ (0743) 718301
5-acre mixed farm. Comfortable farmhouse built in 1776, 5.5 miles south of Shrewsbury off A49. Turn right at the bottom of the hill by the golf-course, then right to Chatford.
Bedrooms: 3 twin
Bathrooms: 1 public

Bed & breakfast

per night:	£min	£max
Double	24.00	

Parking for 2
Open April-October

♻ 🖥 ✿ 🖥 📺 ▦. ♨ ∪ ▶ ✿
🏸 🏵

Haughmond Cottage
Listed

Haughmond Villa, Ebrey Wood, Astley, Shrewsbury
SY4 4DD
☎ (0939) 250689
Country location, 4 miles north of Shrewsbury on the A49 and 1 mile off A53 towards Haughton.
Bedrooms: 1 single, 1 double, 1 triple
Bathrooms: 2 public

Bed & breakfast

per night:	£min	£max
Single	14.00	16.00
Double	28.00	32.00

Parking for 8
Open February-December

♻ ♿ ✿ 🖥 📺 ▦. ♨ ✿
✕ 🏸

Hillsboro
Listed

1 Port Hill Gardens, Shrewsbury SY3 8SH
☎ (0743) 231033
Charming Edwardian private house in quiet residential area, near park, river and Shrewsbury School. 5 minutes from town centre. Traditional breakfast a speciality. Parking.
Bedrooms: 1 double, 1 twin
Bathrooms: 1 public

Bed & breakfast

per night:	£min	£max
Single	13.50	13.50
Double	27.00	27.00

Half board

per person:	£min	£max
Daily	21.00	21.00
Weekly	140.00	140.00

Evening meal 1900 (last orders 2100)
Parking for 2

♻ ✿ 8 🖥 ✿ ✿ 🅸 § ⚲ ▦. ♨
🏸 🏵 🆃

Merevale House
♛ **COMMENDED**

66 Ellesmere Road, Shrewsbury SY1 2QP
☎ (0743) 243677
Comfortable and attractive detached Victorian house, 10 minutes' walk from town and railway station. On bus route. Private car parking.
Bedrooms: 2 double
Bathrooms: 1 public

Bed & breakfast

per night:	£min	£max
Single	12.00	12.00
Double	27.00	30.00

Parking for 8

♻ ✿ 🖥 ✿ 🖥 § ✿ ▦.
♨ ✕ 🏸 SP

Mytton Farmhouse

Mytton, Montford Bridge, Shrewsbury SY4 1EU
☎ (0743) 850994
Converted farmhouse in quiet location 5 miles from Shrewsbury, offering homely accommodation. Oak-panelled dining room. Breakfast with home-made bread.
Bedrooms: 1 double
Bathrooms: 1 private

Bed & breakfast

per night:	£min	£max
Double	32.00	34.00

Half board

per person:	£min	£max
Daily	23.00	24.00

Parking for 8
Open March-October

✿ ✿ 🖥 📺 ✕ 🏸 🏵

The Old House

Ryton, Dorrington, Shrewsbury SY5 7LY
☎ (0743) 718585
17 C manor house in peaceful hamlet with beautiful 2-acre garden and fine views. 6 miles from Shrewsbury, 12 miles from Ironbridge, 1 mile from A49.
Bedrooms: 1 double, 2 twin
Bathrooms: 3 private

Bed & breakfast

per night:	£min	£max
Double	37.00	

Parking for 10

🏠 8 📺 ♨ ⬛ 🅱 📶 🔒 📺 🖥 🍴
🛏 ✿ 🚾 SP 🏧

The Old School House
🛏 **COMMENDED**

Hanwood, Shrewsbury
SY5 8LJ
☎ (0743) 860694
*Old school house, built in
1863, in pleasant village 5
minutes' drive from the town
centre. Adjacent to beautiful
Shropshire hills and
countryside.*
Bedrooms: 1 double, 1 twin,
1 triple
Bathrooms: 1 public

Bed & breakfast

per night:	£min	£max
Single	15.00	
Double	28.00	

Parking for 10

🏠 🚾 ⬛ ♨ ⬛ 🅱 📶 🔒
📺 🖥 🛏 🍴 ✿ 🍴 🏧 SP 🏧

The Old Vicarage M
🛏 **COMMENDED**

Bicton Lane, Bicton,
Shrewsbury SY3 8EU
☎ (0743) 850288
Fax (0743) 850189
*Early Victorian house, set in
an acre and a half of mature
gardens in a peaceful village
location just off A5, two and a
half miles from Shrewsbury.*
Bedrooms: 3 double, 2 twin
Bathrooms: 3 private,
2 private showers

Bed & breakfast

per night:	£min	£max
Single	22.00	25.00
Double	36.00	38.00

Evening meal 1900 (last
orders 1800)
Parking for 8

🏠 🚾 ⬛ ♨ ⬛ 🅱 📶 🔒 📺
🖥 🛏 ✿ 🍴 🍴 OAP 🚾 SP 🏧

Restawhile M
🛏 **APPROVED**

36 Coton Crescent, Coton
Hill, Shrewsbury SY1 2NZ
☎ (0743) 240969
*In quiet one-way street at
junction of A528/B5067,
north of town. 10 minutes'
walk to town centre, railway
station, and bus station.*
Bedrooms: 1 single,
2 double, 1 twin
Bathrooms: 4 private

Bed & breakfast

per night:	£min	£max
Single	16.00	20.00
Double	30.00	40.00

Half board

per person:	£min	£max
Daily	23.00	28.00
Weekly	145.00	176.50

Evening meal 1730 (last
orders 1800)
Cards accepted: Visa

🏠 14 🚾 ⬛ 🅱 📶 🔒
📺 🖥 🛏 🍴 🍴 OAP 🍴

Roseville M
🛏 **HIGHLY COMMENDED**

12 Berwick Road,
Shrewsbury SY1 2LN
☎ (0743) 236470
*Late Victorian detached town
house, close to town centre.
Comfortable, relaxed
atmosphere, imaginative food.
No-smoking establishment.*
Bedrooms: 1 single,
1 double, 1 twin
Bathrooms: 2 private,
1 public

Bed & breakfast

per night:	£min	£max
Single	15.50	17.00
Double	34.00	39.00

Parking for 3
Open February-December

🏠 12 ⬛ 🔒 🛏 📺 🖥 🍴
🍴 🏧

The Stiperstones
Guest House

18 Coton Crescent, Coton
Hill, Shrewsbury SY1 2NZ
☎ (0743) 246720
*100-year-old half-timbered
property a short stroll from
the River Severn and town
centre, located near beautiful
countryside.*
Bedrooms: 1 single,
1 double, 1 triple
Bathrooms: 2 public

Bed & breakfast

per night:	£min	£max
Single	16.00	16.00
Double	30.00	30.00

Half board

per person:	£min	£max
Daily	22.00	24.00
Weekly	140.00	154.00

Evening meal 1900 (last
orders 1200)
Parking for 8

🏠 🍴 ⬛ ♨ ⬛ 🅱 📶 🔒 📺 🖥
🛏 ✿ 🍴 🍴 OAP 🚾 SP

Sydney House
Hotel M
🛏 **APPROVED**

Coton Cres, Coton Hill,
Shrewsbury SY1 2LJ
☎ (0743) 354681
*Edwardian town house with
period features, 10 minutes'
walk from town centre and
railway station. Some rooms
en-suite. All with direct dial*

---

*telephone, colour TV, hot
drink facilities and hairdryer.*
Bedrooms: 2 single,
2 double, 2 twin, 1 triple
Bathrooms: 4 private,
2 public

Bed & breakfast

per night:	£min	£max
Single	32.00	42.00
Double	40.00	58.00

Half board

per person:	£min	£max
Daily	29.00	50.00
Weekly	193.00	325.00

Evening meal 1930 (last
orders 2100)
Parking for 7
Cards accepted: Access, Visa,
Amex

🏠 🚾 ⬛ ♨ ⬛ 🅱 📶 🔒 📺 🖥
🛏 🍴 ✿ 🍴 SP 🏧

Upper Brompton Farm
Listed

Brompton, Cross Houses,
Shrewsbury SY5 6LE
☎ Cross Houses (0743)
761629
*316-acre arable & livestock
farm. Georgian farmhouse,
close to the River, views of
Shropshire Hills. Medieval
Shrewsbury nearby, short
drive to historic Ironbridge. 1
mile from Atcham (A5) and
half a mile from Cross
Houses (A458).*
Bedrooms: 1 double, 1 twin,
1 triple
Bathrooms: 1 public

Bed & breakfast

per night:	£min	£max
Single	15.00	20.00
Double	30.00	35.00

Parking for 10

🏠 ⬛ ♨ ⬛ 🅱 🔒 🛏 🍴 🚾 🍴 ✿
🍴 OAP

SLIMBRIDGE

Gloucestershire
Map ref 2B1

The Wildfowl and
Wetlands Trust was
founded by Sir Peter
Scott and has the world's
largest collection of
wildfowl. Of special
interest are the wild
swans and the geese
which wander around the
grounds.

Tudor Arms Lodge
🛏🛏

Shepherds Patch, Slimbridge,
Gloucester GL2 7BP
☎ Dursley (0453) 890306
*Newly-built lodge adjoining an
18th C freehouse, alongside
Gloucester and Sharpness
Canal. Renowned Slimbridge*

---

*Wildfowl Trust only 800 yards
away.*
Bedrooms: 4 double, 5 twin,
2 triple, 1 multiple
Bathrooms: 12 private

Bed & breakfast

per night:	£min	£max
Single	29.50	32.50
Double	39.50	44.50

Half board

per person:	£min	£max
Daily	28.25	38.00
Weekly	182.00	234.50

Lunch available
Evening meal 1900 (last
orders 2200)
Parking for 70
Cards accepted: Access, Visa

🏠 🚾 🍴 ⬛ ♨ 🍴 🅱 🔒 📶 🖥
🍴 ▶ 🍴

SOLIHULL

West Midlands
Map ref 4B3

On the outskirts of
Birmingham. Some Tudor
houses and a 13th C
church remain amongst
the new public buildings
and shopping centre. The
16th C Malvern Hall is
now a school and the
15th C Chester House at
Knowle is now a library.
Tourist Information Centre
☎ *021-704 6130*

The Gate House

Barston Lane, Barston,
Solihull B92 0JN
☎ (0675) 443274
*Early Victorian mansion
house set in beautiful
countryside. Close to the
National Exhibition Centre,
International Convention
Centre, airport and motorway.*
Bedrooms: 1 single,
1 double, 1 twin
Bathrooms: 3 private,
1 public

Bed & breakfast

per night:	£min	£max
Single	20.00	25.00
Double	36.00	40.00

Parking for 20

🏠 🚾 ⬛ ♨ ⬛ 🅱 🔒 🖥 📺 🖥
🛏 ✿ 🍴 🍴

Rivendell

64 Dorchester Road, Solihull
B91 1LJ
☎ 021-7050502
*Detached family residence in
quiet, central location, close
to rail and bus station, shops
and leisure centre. Non-
smokers only please.*
Bedrooms: 1 single, 2 twin
Bathrooms: 1 public

Continued ▶

SOLIHULL

Continued

Bed & breakfast

per night:	£min	£max
Single	17.00	19.00
Double	34.00	36.00

Parking for 3

🗪7🚗💆🖵👗📺🎿⬛🚗❋ 🛠️🎣

Silica Country Guest House

Bakers Lane, Knowle,
Solihull B93 0DZ
☎ Knowle (0564) 773712
Guesthouse with exposed beams located alongside the canal. 2 miles south of Knowle, Solihull. A quarter of a mile off the A4141, 15 minutes from the National Exhibition Centre.
Bedrooms: 2 single,
1 double, 1 twin
Bathrooms: 2 private,
2 public

Bed & breakfast

per night:	£min	£max
Single	18.00	25.00
Double	36.00	45.00

Parking for 8

🗪🚗💆🖵🎴📶⬛🚗🎣❋🛠️🎣

ST BRIAVELS

Gloucestershire
Map ref 2A1

Village with remains of a
13th C castle, set above
the Wye Valley in the
Forest of Dean. Tintern,
with its magnificent abbey
ruins, is nearby.

Ivydene Cottage

High Street, St Briavels,
Lydney GL15 6TD
☎ Dean (0594) 530699
18th C ivy-covered stone cottage in centre of historic village. Ideally situated for Wye Valley and Forest of Dean. Accommodation available for children.
Bedrooms: 1 double, 1 triple
Bathrooms: 1 private,
1 public

Bed & breakfast

per night:	£min	£max
Double	27.00	31.00

Parking for 2

🗪🚗💆🖵🎴📶🎿⬛❋🎣

> The enquiry coupons at the back will help you when contacting proprietors.

STAUNTON

Gloucestershire
Map ref 2B1

Village near the
Worcestershire border,
with picturesque grouping
of church, farm and pond.
Nearby are cottages built
by the Chartists in 1849
as a land settlement for
industrial workers.

Mayfield Cottage ⚑

🛏️🛏️

Moat Lane, Staunton,
Gloucester GL19 3QA
☎ (0452) 840673
Sympathetically extended 18th C cottage in rural location. Easy access for M50/M5, Gloucester, Tewkesbury, Malverns, Cheltenham and the Cotswolds. Good walking and touring area.
Bedrooms: 1 single,
1 double, 1 twin
Bathrooms: 3 private

Bed & breakfast

per night:	£min	£max
Single	18.00	20.00
Double	36.00	40.00

Half board

per person:	£min	£max
Daily		26.00	28.00

Parking for 3

🚗💆🖵🎴🅸📶📺⬛🚗🎣 🎣 SP

STIPERSTONES

Shropshire
Map ref 4A3

Below the spectacular
ridge of the same name,
from which superb views
over moorland, forest and
hills may be enjoyed.

Tankerville Lodge ⚑

🛏️🛏️ COMMENDED

Stiperstones, Minsterley,
Shrewsbury SY5 0NB
☎ Shrewsbury (0743)
791401
Country house noted for warm hospitality, set in superb landscape which offers breathtaking views. Ideal touring base for Shropshire and Welsh borderland. Adjacent to Stiperstones Nature Reserve.
Bedrooms: 1 double, 3 twin
Bathrooms: 2 public

Bed & breakfast

per night:	£min	£max
Single	14.00	16.00
Double	28.00	28.00

Half board

per person:	£min	£max
Daily	21.50	23.50
Weekly	140.70	154.70

Evening meal 1900 (last
orders 1600)
Parking for 5

🗪💆🖵🅸📶📺⬛🚗🕛❋ 🎣 SP

STOKE LACY

Hereford and Worcester
Map ref 2A1

Small village by the River
Leadon, a few miles from
Bromyard. Lower
Brockhampton Manor
House is nearby.

Nether Court

🛏️🛏️ COMMENDED

Stoke Lacy, Bromyard,
Herefordshire HR7 4HJ
☎ Hereford (0432) 820247
*260-acre mixed farm.
Victorian farmhouse in peaceful village surroundings. Tennis court. Small lake for wildlife. Good restaurant within walking distance. Near Hereford, Ludlow, Malvern, Leominster and Worcester.*
Bedrooms: 1 single,
1 double, 1 triple
Bathrooms: 2 private

Bed & breakfast

per night:	£min	£max
Single	15.00	18.00
Double		30.00

Evening meal from 1800

🗪🚗💆🖵🎴📶📺⬛🚗🔍🕛 ✓❋🎣🎣🏛️

STOKE-ON-TRENT

Staffordshire
Map ref 4B2

Famous for its pottery.
Factories of several
famous makers, including
Josiah Wedgwood, can
be visited. The City
Museum has one of the
finest pottery and
porcelain collections in
the world.
Tourist Information Centre
☎ *(0782) 411222 or
284600.*

The Hollies

🛏️🛏️

Clay Lake, Endon, Stoke-on-
Trent ST9 9DD
☎ (0782) 503252
Delightful Victorian house in a quiet country setting off B5051. Convenient for M6, the Potteries and Alton Towers. Non-smokers only, please.

Bedrooms: 2 double, 1 twin,
2 triple
Bathrooms: 3 private,
1 public

Bed & breakfast

per night:	£min	£max
Single	18.00	24.00
Double	28.00	34.00

Parking for 5

🗪🚗💆🖵🅸🎿📺⬛🚗 ❋🎣

The Limes ⚑

🛏️🛏️

Cheadle Road, Blythe
Bridge, Stoke-on-Trent
ST11 9PW
☎ (0782) 393278
Victorian residence of character in large, landscaped gardens, near Alton Towers, Wedgwood, the Potteries and Staffordshire Moorlands.
Bedrooms: 1 single,
1 double, 1 triple
Bathrooms: 1 public,
2 private showers

Bed & breakfast

per night:	£min	£max
Single	18.00	20.00
Double	32.00	35.00

Parking for 8

🗪🚗4🅸🎴📺⬛❋🎣🎣🏛️

Old Vicarage

Leek Road, Endon, Stoke-on-
Trent ST9 9BH
☎ (0782) 503686
In quiet setting off main A53 road, 6 miles northeast of Stoke-on-Trent. World famous pottery firms within easy reach. Convenient for M6 travellers. Non-smoking establishment.
Bedrooms: 1 double, 2 twin
Bathrooms: 2 public

Bed & breakfast

per night:	£min	£max
Single	20.00	20.00
Double	30.00	30.00

Parking for 6

🗪🚗💆🖵🅸🎿📺⬛🚗🎣

Tenement Farm ⚑

🛏️🛏️

Three Lows, Ribden,
Oakamoor, Stoke-on-Trent
ST10 3BW
☎ Oakamoor (0538) 702333
*100-acre livestock farm.
Traditional farmhouse bed and breakfast in the heart of the Midlands. Alton Towers 2 miles. Close to Manifold Valley and Dovedale.*
Bedrooms: 2 double, 1 triple,
1 multiple
Bathrooms: 2 private

Bed & breakfast

per night:	£min	£max
Double	30.00	35.00

Parking for 10
Open April-November

STONE

Staffordshire
Map ref 4B2

Town on the River Trent with the remains of a 12th C Augustinian priory. It is surrounded by pleasant countryside. Trentham Gardens with 500 acres of parklands and recreational facilities is within easy reach.

The Boat House ⋀

71 Newcastle Road, Stone
ST15 8LD
☎ (0785) 815389
Renovated 18th C former inn adjacent to Trent and Mersey Canal. Convenient for M6, Wedgwood, the Potteries and Stafford.
Bedrooms: 1 double, 1 twin
Bathrooms: 1 public
Bed & breakfast

per night:	£min	£max
Single	15.50	22.00
Double	34.00	34.00

Parking for 3

Couldreys ⋀
COMMENDED
8 Airdale Road, Stone
ST15 8DW
☎ (0785) 812500
Large house and garden, quietly situated on the outskirts of a small market town and convenient for visiting the Wedgwood factory and The Potteries. Non-smokers only please.
Bedrooms: 1 twin
Bathrooms: 1 private
Bed & breakfast

per night:	£min	£max
Single		18.00
Double		28.00

Parking for 2

Half board prices shown are per person but in some cases may be based on double/twin occupancy.

STONEHOUSE

Gloucestershire
Map ref 2B1

Village in the Stroud Valley with an Elizabethan Court, later restored and altered by Lutyens.

Merton Lodge
Listed
Ebley Road, Stonehouse
GL10 2LQ
☎ (0453) 822018
Former gentleman's residence offering a warm welcome. Non-smokers only please. 3 miles from junction 13 of M5. Take A419 to Stroud, over 3 roundabouts, under footbridge - located opposite garden centre.
Bedrooms: 3 double
Bathrooms: 2 public
Bed & breakfast

per night:	£min	£max
Single	12.00	12.00
Double	24.00	24.00

Parking for 6

STOURBRIDGE

West Midlands
Map ref 4B3

Town on the River Stour, famous for its glassworks. Several of the factories can be visited and glassware purchased at the factory shops.

St. Elizabeth's Cottage ⋀
COMMENDED
Woodman Lane, Clent, Stourbridge DY9 9PX
☎ Hagley (0562) 883883
Beautiful country cottage with lovely gardens and interior professionally decorated throughout. 20 minutes from Birmingham, and close to all motorway links.
Bedrooms: 1 twin
Bathrooms: 1 public
Bed & breakfast

per night:	£min	£max
Double	36.00	40.00

Parking for 2

The symbols are explained on the flap inside the back cover.

STOURPORT-ON-SEVERN

Hereford and Worcester
Map ref 4B3

Town standing at the confluence of the Rivers Stour and Severn and on the Staffordshire and Worcestershire Canal which was built in the 18th C and is now a popular place for pleasure boats. Some fine Georgian houses remain.

Worrall's Farm
Listed
Netherton Lane, Dunley, Stourport-on-Severn, Worcestershire DY13 0UL
☎ Great Witley (0299) 896245
5-acre smallholding. Early 18th C mill house near the Severn Valley. A millstream setting amid rolling Worcestershire countryside.
Bedrooms: 1 twin, 1 triple
Bathrooms: 1 public, 1 private shower
Bed & breakfast

per night:	£min	£max
Single	16.00	20.00
Double	26.00	30.00

Parking for 2
Open April-October

STOW-ON-THE-WOLD

Gloucestershire
Map ref 2B1

Attractive Cotswold wool town with a large market-place and some fine houses, especially the old grammar school. There is an interesting church dating from Norman times. Stow-on-the-Wold is surrounded by lovely countryside and Cotswold villages.
Tourist Information Centre ☎ (0451) 31082

Bretton House ⋀
HIGHLY COMMENDED
Fosseway, Stow-on-the-Wold, Cheltenham GL54 1JU
☎ Cotswold (0451) 830388
Fine Victorian house in own grounds with glorious views of the Cotswolds. Tastefully refurbished, providing accommodation of a good standard and friendly atmosphere.
Bedrooms: 2 double, 1 twin

Bathrooms: 3 private
Bed & breakfast

per night:	£min	£max
Double	36.00	40.00

Half board

per person:	£min	£max
Daily		32.50
Weekly		190.00

Evening meal 1900 (last orders 2100)
Parking for 10

Corsham Field Farmhouse ⋀
Listed
Bledington Road, Stow-on-the-Wold, Cheltenham GL54 1JH
☎ Cotswold (0451) 831750
100-acre mixed farm. Homely farmhouse with breathtaking views. Heating, TVs, washbasins, tea and coffee making facilities in all bedrooms. Good pub food 5 minutes' walk away.
Bedrooms: 1 double, 1 twin, 1 triple
Bathrooms: 1 private, 2 public
Bed & breakfast

per night:	£min	£max
Single	12.00	18.00
Double	24.00	35.00

Parking for 10

Horse and Groom Inn ⋀
COMMENDED
Upper Oddington, Moreton-in-Marsh GL56 0XH
☎ Cotswold (0451) 830584
16th C old world character inn serving lunchtime and evening meals all year round. Families welcome. En-suite rooms.
Bedrooms: 4 double, 2 twin, 2 triple
Bathrooms: 8 private
Bed & breakfast

per night:	£min	£max
Single		29.00
Double	42.00	47.00

Lunch available
Evening meal 1900 (last orders 2130)
Parking for 40
Cards accepted: Access, Visa

Journeys End ⋀
Listed
Evenlode, Moreton-in-Marsh GL56 0NN
☎ (0608) 50786
Continued ▶

181

STOW-ON-THE-WOLD

Continued

20-acre mixed farm. Peaceful, comfortable, modernised 18th C farmhouse in quiet village. Approximately 3 miles from Moreton-in-Marsh and Stow-on-the-Wold. One ground floor bedroom.
Bedrooms: 1 double, 1 triple
Bathrooms: 2 private

Bed & breakfast

per night:	£min	£max
Single	16.00	18.00
Double	32.00	36.00

Parking for 5

Old Farmhouse Hotel ⋀

APPROVED

Lower Swell, Stow-on-the-Wold, Cheltenham GL54 1LF
☎ Cotswold (0451) 830232
Sympathetically converted 16th C Cotswold stone farmhouse in a quiet hamlet, 1 mile west of Stow-on-the-Wold. Offers warm and informal hospitality.
Bedrooms: 9 double, 4 twin, 1 multiple
Bathrooms: 12 private, 1 public

Bed & breakfast

per night:	£min	£max
Single	25.00	55.00
Double	50.00	95.00

Half board

per person:	£min	£max
Daily	39.95	69.95

Lunch available
Evening meal 1900 (last orders 2100)
Parking for 25
Cards accepted: Access, Visa

Orchard Cottage ⋀

HIGHLY COMMENDED

Back Lane, Upper Oddington, Moreton-in-Marsh GL56 0XL
☎ Cotswold (0451) 830785
Traditional stone cottage in quiet location, 2 miles from Stow-on-the-Wold. Sitting room with open fire, evening meal, home cooking and warm welcome.
Bedrooms: 1 double, 1 twin
Bathrooms: 1 private, 1 public

Bed & breakfast

per night:	£min	£max
Double	33.00	35.00

Half board

per person:	£min	£max
Daily	19.50	21.50

Evening meal 1900 (last orders 2000)
Parking for 3
Open February-November

Royalist Hotel ⋀

Digbeth Street, Stow-on-the-Wold, Cheltenham GL54 1BN
☎ Cotswold (0451) 830670
The oldest inn in England (947 AD) with all the inherent charm and character of the past, yet every modern day facility as well.
Bedrooms: 2 single, 5 double, 3 twin, 1 triple
Bathrooms: 13 private

Bed & breakfast

per night:	£min	£max
Single	30.00	49.00
Double	45.00	75.00

Lunch available
Parking for 12
Cards accepted: Access, Visa, Amex

South Hill Farmhouse ⋀

Fosseway, Stow-on-the-Wold, Cheltenham GL54 1JU
☎ Cotswold (0451) 831219
Fax (0451) 831219
Base your touring holiday in this Victorian farmhouse. Individually furnished and spacious rooms, a hearty breakfast, lounge with open fires.
Bedrooms: 2 double, 1 twin, 1 triple
Bathrooms: 4 private, 1 public

Bed & breakfast

per night:	£min	£max
Single	15.00	25.00
Double	30.00	36.00

Parking for 8

South Hill Lodge ⋀

Fosseway, Stow-on-the-Wold, Cheltenham GL54 1JU
☎ Cotswold (0451) 831083
Homely, family-run Victorian lodge house with superb views over the Cotswold Hills.
Bedrooms: 2 double, 1 twin
Bathrooms: 1 private, 1 public

Bed & breakfast

per night:	£min	£max
Double	30.00	36.00

Parking for 6

STRATFORD-UPON-AVON

Warwickshire
Map ref 2B1

Famous as Shakespeare's home town, Stratford's many attractions include his birthplace, New Place where he died, the Royal Shakespeare Theatre and Gallery, 'The World of Shakespeare' audio-visual theatre and Hall's Croft (his daughter's house).
Tourist Information Centre ☎ *(0789) 293127.*

34 Banbury Rd. ⋀

Listed   APPROVED

Stratford-upon-Avon CV37 7HY
☎ (0789) 269714
Homely accommodation offering good value in a warm, clean, friendly environment. Very convenient for theatre and town centre.
Bedrooms: 1 twin
Bathrooms: 1 public

Bed & breakfast

per night:	£min	£max
Single	12.00	13.00
Double	24.00	26.00

Parking for 4

Abberley

COMMENDED

12 Albany Road, Stratford-upon-Avon CV37 6PG
☎ (0789) 295934
Comfortable home set in a quiet residential area yet within easy walking distance of theatres and town centre. Non-smokers only please.
Bedrooms: 1 twin
Bathrooms: 1 private

Bed & breakfast

per night:	£min	£max
Double	38.00	42.00

Parking for 2

Amelia Linhill Guesthouse ⋀

Listed

35 Evesham Place, Stratford-upon-Avon CV37 6HT
☎ (0789) 292879
Fax (0789) 414478
Comfortable Victorian guesthouse offering warm welcome and good food. 5 minutes' walk from town centre and theatres. Convenient for racecourse, NEC and Cotswolds.
Bedrooms: 1 single, 1 double, 3 twin, 3 triple
Bathrooms: 1 private, 2 public

Bed & breakfast

per night:	£min	£max
Single	11.00	18.00
Double	22.00	39.00

Half board

per person:	£min	£max
Daily	16.00	25.00
Weekly	100.00	160.00

Evening meal 1700 (last orders 1930)

Bronhill House ⋀

Listed

260 Alcester Road, Stratford-upon-Avon CV37 9JQ
☎ (0789) 299169
Detached family house in elevated position, 1 mile from Stratford-upon-Avon.
Bedrooms: 2 double
Bathrooms: 2 public

Bed & breakfast

per night:	£min	£max
Single	24.00	28.00

Parking for 5
Open April-October

Carlton Guest House ⋀

COMMENDED

22 Evesham Place, Stratford-upon-Avon CV37 6HT
☎ (0789) 293548
Tasteful decor, elegantly furnished, combining Victorian origins with modern facilities. A peaceful home, happily shared with guests.
Bedrooms: 1 single, 2 double, 1 twin, 1 multiple
Bathrooms: 3 private, 1 public

Bed & breakfast

per night:	£min	£max
Double	34.00	42.00

Parking for 3

Cherangani ⋀

COMMENDED

61 Maidenhead Road, Stratford-upon-Avon CV37 6XU
☎ (0789) 292655
Pleasant detached house in a quiet, residential area, offering warm, attractive accommodation. Within

walking distance of the town and theatre.
Bedrooms: 1 twin
Bathrooms: 1 public
Bed & breakfast

per night:	£min	£max
Double	30.00	34.00

Parking for 3

Church Farm ⋀

⛤⛤ COMMENDED

Dorsington, Stratford-upon-Avon CV37 8AX
☎ (0789) 720471 & (0831) 504194
127-acre mixed farm. Situated in beautiful countryside, some rooms en-suite, TV, tea and coffee facilities. Close to Stratford-upon-Avon, Warwick, the Cotswolds and Evesham.
Bedrooms: 3 double, 2 twin, 2 triple
Bathrooms: 2 public
Bed & breakfast

per night:	£min	£max
Double	26.00	33.00

Parking for 12

Church Farm ⋀

⛤⛤ COMMENDED

Long Marston, Stratford-upon-Avon CV37 8RH
☎ (0789) 720275
A very friendly welcome at this old family farmhouse in quiet village. Close to Stratford-upon-Avon, Warwick Castle and the Cotswolds.
Bedrooms: 1 twin, 1 triple
Bathrooms: 2 private, 1 public
Bed & breakfast

per night:	£min	£max
Double	30.00	36.00

Parking for 4

Clomendy Guest House ⋀

157 Evesham Road, Stratford-upon-Avon CV37 9BP
☎ (0789) 266957
Small, detached, mock-Tudor family-run guesthouse, convenient for town centre, Anne Hathaway's cottage and theatres. Stratford-in-Bloom commendation winner. Rail/coach guests met and returned.

Bedrooms: 1 single, 1 double, 1 twin
Bathrooms: 1 public, 1 private shower
Bed & breakfast

per night:	£min	£max
Single	14.00	18.00
Double	24.00	34.00

Parking for 4

East Bank House ⋀

⛤⛤

19 Warwick Road, Stratford-upon-Avon CV37 6YW
☎ (0789) 292758
Fine Victorian house set in well-tended grounds just 3 minutes' walk from town centre. Friendly, good food and good value.
Bedrooms: 1 single, 6 double, 3 twin, 1 triple
Bathrooms: 6 private, 2 public
Bed & breakfast

per night:	£min	£max
Single	19.50	35.00
Double	31.00	50.00

Evening meal 1800 (last orders 2000)

Parking for 5
Cards accepted: Access, Visa

Field View ⋀

⛤ APPROVED

35 Banbury Road, Stratford-upon-Avon CV37 7HW
☎ (0789) 292694
10 minutes' walk from Stratford town centre, offering comfortable, family-type accommodation.
Bedrooms: 1 double
Bathrooms: 1 public
Bed & breakfast

per night:	£min	£max
Single	13.00	16.00
Double	26.00	30.00

Parking for 3

Gravelside Barn ⋀

⛤⛤ HIGHLY COMMENDED

Binton, Stratford-upon-Avon CV37 9TU
☎ (0789) 750502 & 297000
Fax (0789) 298056
A peaceful converted barn, set on a hill in farmland. Magnificent views, great breakfasts. Easy access to motorways and Stratford-upon-Avon.

Continued ▶

STRATFORD-UPON-AVON

Continued

Bedrooms: 2 double, 1 twin
Bathrooms: 3 private
Bed & breakfast

per night:	£min	£max
Single	35.00	40.00
Double	50.00	70.00

Parking for 6
Cards accepted: Access, Visa
🛁🚻🖳🖵📶🖵📵🅂✕🏧
🏛🛏🍴🐾🛢🛉✕🚬🐾🆂🅿
🏤🅣

Green Gables 🏍
🎖🎖 COMMENDED
47 Banbury Road, Stratford-upon-Avon CV37 7HW
☎ (0789) 205557
Edwardian house in a residential area, within 10 minutes' walk of the town centre and theatre.
Bedrooms: 1 double
Bathrooms: 1 public
Bed & breakfast

per night:	£min	£max
Double	30.00	36.00

Parking for 3
🐾🛉🖵🖳🍴📶🖵📵🅂✕🅿
🛢✕🐾

Green Haven
217 Evesham Road,
Stratford-upon-Avon
CV37 9AS
☎ (0789) 297874
Situated within walking distance of theatre and town centre amenities. Off-street parking. Homely atmosphere.
Bedrooms: 1 single, 4 double
Bathrooms: 2 private,
3 public
Bed & breakfast

per night:	£min	£max
Single	18.00	18.00
Double	32.00	32.00

Half board

per person:	£min	£max
Weekly	105.00	

Parking for 5
Open February–November
🐾🛉🛢🖵🖳🖵📵🅃🖵🛢🛉
🅾🅿

Highcroft 🏍
🎖 APPROVED
Banbury Road, Stratford-upon-Avon CV37 7NF
☎ (0789) 296293
Beautifully converted barn and country residence. Rural location 2 miles from Stratford-upon-Avon on A422.
Bedrooms: 1 double,
1 multiple
Bathrooms: 2 private

Bed & breakfast

per night:	£min	£max
Single	12.50	17.50
Double	30.00	35.00

Parking for 3
🐾🛉🖵📶🖵📵🐾✳🐾

Houndshill House 🏍
🎖🎖 APPROVED
Banbury Road, Ettington,
Stratford-upon-Avon
CV37 7NS
☎ (0789) 740267
Family-run pub with restaurant. 4 miles from Stratford-upon-Avon. Informal and friendly atmosphere.
Bedrooms: 2 single,
3 double, 2 twin, 1 triple
Bathrooms: 8 private

Bed & breakfast

per night:	£min	£max
Single	29.00	
Double	48.00	

Lunch available
Evening meal 1900 (last orders 2200)
Parking for 50
Cards accepted: Access, Visa
🐾🛡🖵🛉🍴📶🛢🛉✳🅿

Moonraker House 🏍
🎖🎖 COMMENDED
40 Alcester Road, Stratford-upon-Avon CV37 9DB
☎ (0789) 299346 & 267115
Fax (0789) 295504
Family-run, near town centre. Beautifully co-ordinated decor throughout. Some rooms with four-poster beds and garden terrace available for non-smokers.
Bedrooms: 19 double,
3 twin, 2 triple
Bathrooms: 24 private
Bed & breakfast

per night:	£min	£max
Single	25.00	32.00
Double	37.00	55.00

Parking for 24
Cards accepted: Access, Visa
🐾🛉🛡🖵🖳📶🖳📵🅂✕
📵🖵🛢🅾🆙🅿🅣

Moss Cottage 🏍
🎖🎖 COMMENDED
61 Evesham Road, Stratford-upon-Avon CV37 9BA
☎ (0789) 294770
Detached cottage. Attractive full en-suite accommodation. Traditional breakfast, tea tray, TV. Reduction for 2 or more nights.
Bedrooms: 2 double
Bathrooms: 2 private
Bed & breakfast

per night:	£min	£max
Single	25.00	28.00
Double	32.00	36.00

Parking for 3
Open March–December
🐾9🛉🖳🖳🅂📵🅃🖵📵✕
🐾🆂🅿

Newlands 🏍
🎖🎖 COMMENDED
7 Broad Walk, Stratford-upon-Avon CV37 6HS
☎ (0789) 298449
Park your car at Sue Boston's home and walk to the Royal Shakespeare Theatre, town centre and Shakespeare properties.
Bedrooms: 1 single,
1 double, 1 twin
Bathrooms: 2 private,
1 public
Bed & breakfast

per night:	£min	£max
Single	16.00	17.50
Double	32.00	40.00

Parking for 2
🐾10🖵🛡🖳🛉🅂✕
📵🖵🛢✕🐾

One Acre Guest House 🏍
🎖🎖🎖
One Acre, Barton Road, Welford-on-Avon, Stratford-upon-Avon CV37 8EZ
☎ (0789) 750477
Family house in Shakespearean village with countryside views and a warm friendly atmosphere. 4 miles from Stratford-upon-Avon, off A439.
Bedrooms: 1 double, 1 twin,
1 triple
Bathrooms: 3 private
Bed & breakfast

per night:	£min	£max
Single	18.00	20.00
Double	30.00	45.00

Half board

per person:	£min	£max
Daily	22.50	27.50

Evening meal 1800 (last orders 2100)
Parking for 6
🐾🛉🛢📶🖵🅂📵🅃🖵🛢🛢🛉
🐾✕🐾🐾

Oxstalls Farm 🏍
🎖🎖 COMMENDED
Warwick Road, Stratford-upon-Avon CV37 0NS
☎ (0789) 205277
Beautifully situated 60-acre stud farm overlooking the Welcome Hills and golf course. 1 mile from Stratford-upon-Avon town centre and the Royal Shakespeare Theatre.
Bedrooms: 1 single,
7 double, 4 twin, 7 triple
Bathrooms: 11 private,
2 public, 3 private showers

Bed & breakfast

per night:	£min	£max
Single	14.00	25.00
Double	28.00	50.00

Parking for 20
🐾🛉🖵🛉🖳🖳🅂✕📵🅃🖵
🛢🛡🖊✳🅇🏤
Ad Display advertisement appears on page 183

Peartree Cottage 🏍
🎖🎖 HIGHLY COMMENDED
7 Church Road, Wilmcote, Stratford-upon-Avon CV37 9UX
☎ (0789) 205889
Elizabethan house, furnished with antiques, set in beautiful garden overlooking Mary Arden's house. Pub and restaurant within walking distance.
Bedrooms: 4 double, 2 twin,
1 triple
Bathrooms: 7 private
Bed & breakfast

per night:	£min	£max
Single	28.00	30.00
Double	38.00	40.00

Parking for 8
🐾2🛉🛉🖵🛉🅂📵🅃
🖵🛢🛡✳🐾🏤

Penshurst Guesthouse
Listed
34 Evesham Place, Stratford-upon-Avon CV37 6HT
☎ (0789) 205259 & 298936
Victorian town house with character, ideally located for theatres and for touring the Cotswolds. Children and vegetarians especially welcome.
Bedrooms: 1 single,
1 double, 1 twin, 3 triple
Bathrooms: 2 public
Bed & breakfast

per night:	£min	£max
Single	17.00	25.00
Double	34.00	50.00

Half board

per person:	£min	£max
Daily	26.00	37.00
Weekly	170.00	220.00

Evening meal 1700 (last orders 1600)
Cards accepted: Access, Visa, Diners
🐾🛉🖵🛉🖳🅂🖵🅾🐾🆂

Quilt and Croissants 🏍
Listed
33 Evesham Place, Stratford-upon-Avon CV37 6HT
☎ (0789) 267629 & 267671
Young, family-run business in Victorian premises in the heart of Stratford-upon-Avon.

Bedrooms: 1 single,
3 double, 2 twin, 2 triple
Bathrooms: 4 private,
1 public
Bed & breakfast

per night:	£min	£max
Single	15.00	20.00
Double	30.00	45.00

Parking for 2

Ravenhurst ♠♠

2 Broad Walk, Stratford-
upon-Avon CV37 6HS
☎ (0789) 292515
*Quietly situated, a few
minutes' walk from the town
centre and places of historic
interest. Comfortable home,
with substantial breakfast
provided.*
Bedrooms: 4 double, 1 twin,
1 triple
Bathrooms: 5 private,
1 public
Bed & breakfast

per night:	£min	£max
Single	19.00	30.00
Double	32.00	43.00

Parking for 4
Cards accepted: Access, Visa,
Diners, Amex

Rookery Farm

Ettington, Stratford-upon-
Avon CV37 7TN
☎ (0789) 740474
*Family dairy farm pleasantly
situated at the edge of village,
6 miles from Stratford-upon-
Avon. Warwick and the
Cotswolds within easy reach.
Good home cooking, friendly
atmosphere.*
Bedrooms: 1 double, 1 twin,
1 triple
Bathrooms: 2 public
Bed & breakfast

per night:	£min	£max
Single	11.00	14.00
Double	22.00	28.00

Half board

per person:	£min	£max
Daily	18.00	20.00

Evening meal 1800 (last
orders 1600)
Parking for 4

Sequoia House ♠♠

51-53 Shipston Road,
Stratford-upon-Avon
CV37 7LN
☎ (0789) 268852 & 294940
Fax (0789) 414559
*Beautifully-appointed private
hotel with large car park and
delightful garden walk to the*

theatre, riverside gardens and
*Shakespeare properties. Fully
air-conditioned dining room.*
Bedrooms: 2 single,
10 double, 12 twin
Bathrooms: 20 private,
3 public, 1 private shower
Bed & breakfast

per night:	£min	£max
Single	25.00	55.00
Double	39.00	72.00

Lunch available
Evening meal 1800 (last
orders 1930)
Parking for 33
Cards accepted: Access, Visa,
Diners, Amex

Thirkleby

60 Evesham Road, Stratford-
upon-Avon CV37 9BA
☎ (0789) 298640
*Elegant town house, tastefully
furnished, within walking
distance of town and theatre.
Parking. En-suite rooms
overlooking delightful
secluded gardens.*
Bedrooms: 1 single,
1 double, 1 twin
Bathrooms: 1 public
Bed & breakfast

per night:	£min	£max
Single	16.00	18.00
Double	28.00	34.00

Parking for 3

Twelfth Night ♠♠
♠♠ COMMENDED

Evesham Place, Stratford-
upon-Avon CV37 6HT
☎ (0789) 414595
*Elegant Victorian villa once
owned for almost a quarter of
a century by the governors of
the Royal Shakespeare
Company. Delightfully
refurbished for the
connoisseur. Non-smokers
only please.*
Bedrooms: 1 single,
3 double, 3 twin
Bathrooms: 6 private,
1 private shower
Bed & breakfast

per night:	£min	£max
Single	19.00	32.00
Double	38.00	52.00

Parking for 7

Whitchurch Farm ♠♠
Listed

Wimpstone, Stratford-upon-
Avon CV37 8NS
☎ Alderminster (0789)
450275

260-acre mixed farm. Listed
*Georgian farmhouse set in
park-like surroundings on the
edge of the Cotswolds. Ideal
for a touring holiday. Small
village 4 miles south of
Stratford-upon-Avon.*
Bedrooms: 2 double, 1 twin
Bathrooms: 2 private,
2 public
Bed & breakfast

per night:	£min	£max
Single	14.00	17.00
Double	28.00	34.00

Half board

per person:	£min	£max
Daily	22.00	25.00

Evening meal from 1830
Parking for 3

The White House ♠♠
♠♠ HIGHLY COMMENDED

Kings Lane, Bishopton,
Stratford-upon-Avon
CV37 0RD
☎ (0789) 294296
Fax (0789) 45090
*Elegant Edwardian house in
rural setting, only one and a
half miles from centre of
Stratford-upon-Avon, close to
A46 and A3400. Ideal
location for Cotswolds,
Warwick, NEC and NAC.*
Bedrooms: 1 twin
Bathrooms: 1 private
Bed & breakfast

per night:	£min	£max
Double	37.00	40.00

Parking for 6

Wood View ♠♠
♠♠ HIGHLY COMMENDED

Pathlow, Stratford-upon-
Avon CV37 0RQ
☎ (0789) 295778
*Beautifully situated
comfortable home, with fine
views over fields and woods.
Ideal for touring Stratford-
upon-Avon and the Cotswolds.*
Bedrooms: 2 twin
Bathrooms: 2 private
Bed & breakfast

per night:	£min	£max
Single	20.00	25.00
Double	36.00	50.00

Parking for 6

The town index
towards the back
of this guide gives
page numbers of
all places with
accommodation.

STRATTON
Gloucestershire
Map ref 2B1

Chesil Rocks
Listed

Baunton Lane, Stratton,
Cirencester GL7 2LL
☎ (0285) 655031
*Pleasant and friendly home
in a quiet lane, with easy
access to town and country
walks.*
Bedrooms: 2 single, 1 twin
Bathrooms: 1 public,
1 private shower
Bed & breakfast

per night:	£min	£max
Single	15.00	
Double	30.00	

Parking for 3

STRETTON
Staffordshire
Map ref 4B3

Road Farm

Watling Street, (A5),
Stretton, Stafford ST18 9LL
☎ (0902) 850294
*200-acre mixed farm. Homely
and comfortable 18th C
farmhouse, conveniently
located on Roman Watling
Street (A5), approximately 2
miles from exit 12 of the M6
or exit 2 of M54. Full English
breakfast.*
Bedrooms: 1 single,
1 double, 1 twin, 1 triple
Bathrooms: 2 public
Bed & breakfast

per night:	£min	£max
Single	15.00	
Double	30.00	

Parking for 6

We advise you to
confirm your
booking in writing.

Individual
proprietors have
supplied all details
of accommodation.
Although we do
check for accuracy,
we advise you to
confirm the
information at the
time of booking.

STRETTON ON FOSSE

Warwickshire
Map ref 2B1

Village on the Warwickshire/ Gloucestershire border, through which the Roman Fosse Way passes, and with a mixture of stone and brick houses.

Ditchford Farmhouse ⋒

APPROVED

Stretton on Fosse, Moreton-in-Marsh, Gloucestershire GL56 9RD
☎ Shipston-on-Stour (0608) 663307
Secluded Georgian farmhouse in lovely north Cotswold countryside. Large garden with children's corner. Home-grown produce and country cooking. Winter breaks with log fires. Private facilities available.
Bedrooms: 3 double, 1 twin, 1 multiple
Bathrooms: 3 private, 2 public

Bed & breakfast

per night:	£min	£max
Single	17.00	18.50
Double	33.00	35.00

Half board

per person:	£min	£max
Daily	26.50	28.00
Weekly	156.50	175.00

Evening meal from 1830
Parking for 8

STROUD

Gloucestershire
Map ref 2B1

This old town has been producing broadcloth for centuries and the local museum has an interesting display on the subject. It is surrounded by attractive hilly country.
Tourist Information Centre
☎ *(0453) 765768*

Cairngall Guest House

APPROVED

65 Bisley Old Road, Stroud GL5 1NF
☎ (0453) 764595
Unique, Bath-stone house in French style with porticoed west front, furnished to complement the architectural design.
Bedrooms: 1 double, 1 triple

Bathrooms: 1 public

Bed & breakfast

per night:	£min	£max
Single	12.00	14.00
Double	28.00	32.00

Parking for 3
Open February-December

The Frith ⋒

COMMENDED

Slad, Stroud GL6 7QD
☎ Painswick (0452) 814117
Country house set in one and a half acres, on B4070 Stroud to Birdlip road. Panoramic views of the Slad Valley, in an area of outstanding natural beauty near the Cotswold Way. Golf and riding nearby.
Bedrooms: 3 double
Bathrooms: 1 private, 1 public

Bed & breakfast

per night:	£min	£max
Single	19.00	25.00
Double	28.00	35.00

Parking for 6

Hawthorns

APPROVED

Lower Littleworth, Amberley, Stroud GL5 5AW
☎ Amberley (0453) 873535
Early 18th C house in National Trust setting. Glorious 20-mile views. Walking. Half a mile west of Bear Inn, Rodborough, along lane signposted "Houndscroft". Wild badgers feed on floodlit terrace at nightfall.
Bedrooms: 2 double, 1 twin
Bathrooms: 3 private

Bed & breakfast

per night:	£min	£max
Single	20.00	30.00
Double	28.00	40.00

Parking for 3

New Inn House ⋒

Listed APPROVED

The Camp, Stroud GL6 7HL
☎ Cirencester (0285) 821336
In a small hamlet amid unspoilt Cotswold countryside, convenient for Severn Wildfowl Trust and Prinknash Abbey. Guests have own door key. Separate tables. Non-smokers preferred.
Bedrooms: 1 single, 1 twin
Bathrooms: 1 public

Bed & breakfast

per night:	£min	£max
Single	13.00	15.00
Double	26.00	30.00

Parking for 3
Open April-October

The Yew Tree Tea Rooms ⋒

Walls Quarry, Brimscombe, Stroud GL5 2PA
☎ Brimscombe (0453) 883428
Built c1669 of Cotswold stone. Once a fine brewhouse, entrance through ex-barley door. Picturesque views across valleys to Stroud and the surrounding hills. Amidst National Trust common land.
Bedrooms: 1 twin
Bathrooms: 1 private

Bed & breakfast

per night:	£min	£max
Single	15.00	18.00
Double	30.00	36.00

Lunch available
Open February-December

SWINSCOE

Staffordshire
Map ref 4B2

Hamlet close to Alton Towers with its many attractions and to beautiful scenery of Dovedale.

Dog & Partridge Inn ⋒

Swinscoe, Ashbourne, Derbyshire DE6 2HS
☎ Ashbourne (0335) 43183
A warm welcome from Mary and Martin at this 17th C inn. Close to the Peak District, Ashbourne and Alton Towers. Vegetarian and special diets catered for. Children and pets welcome.
Bedrooms: 7 double, 2 twin, 2 triple, 17 multiple
Bathrooms: 28 private

Bed & breakfast

per night:	£min	£max
Single	41.00	51.00
Double	51.00	65.00

Half board

per person:	£min	£max
Daily	35.00	40.00
Weekly	225.00	300.00

Lunch available
Evening meal 1730 (last orders 2230)
Parking for 82
Cards accepted: Access, Visa, Diners, Amex

SYMONDS YAT WEST

Hereford and Worcester
Map ref 2A1

Jubilee Maze and Exhibition was created here in 1977 to commemorate Queen Elizabeth II's Jubilee. The area of Symonds Yat is a world-renowned beauty spot.

Riversdale Lodge Hotel

COMMENDED

Symonds Yat West, Ross-on-Wye, Herefordshire HR9 6BL
☎ (0600) 890445
High standard accommodation, set in 2 acres on the banks of the River Wye. Spectacular views of the rapids and gorge. Traditional food.
Bedrooms: 5 double
Bathrooms: 5 private, 1 public

Bed & breakfast

per night:	£min	£max
Single	22.00	25.00
Double	44.00	50.00

Half board

per person:	£min	£max
Daily	33.00	35.00
Weekly	231.00	245.00

Evening meal 1900 (last orders 1300)
Parking for 11

TEDDINGTON

Gloucestershire
Map ref 2B1

Village a few miles east of Tewkesbury and north of Cheltenham, with just a few farms and houses, but an interesting church.

Bengrove Farm

APPROVED

Bengrove, Teddington, Tewkesbury GL20 8JB
☎ Cheltenham (0242) 620332
10-acre mixed farm. Large, interesting 14th C farmhouse

with attractive rooms, timbered and beamed. 2 twin rooms, lounge and guests' bathroom. Comfortably furnished.
Bedrooms: 2 twin
Bathrooms: 1 public

Bed & breakfast

per night:	£min	£max
Single	13.00	13.00
Double	26.00	26.00

Parking for 10

🐕🖈🕯🖳📠⑤✕🕮📺🎞️◿ ❋🎠🏤

TELFORD

Shropshire
Map ref 4A3

New Town named after Thomas Telford, the famous engineer who designed many of the country's canals, bridges and viaducts. It is close to Ironbridge with its monuments and museums to the Industrial Revolution, including restored 18th C buildings.
Tourist Information Centre
☎ (0952) 291370

Allscott Inn

❦❦❦ APPROVED
Walcot, Wellington, Telford TF6 5EQ
☎ (0952) 248484
Homely country inn offering delicious food and comfortable accommodation. Beer garden. Easy access Shrewsbury, Ironbridge and Telford.
Bedrooms: 2 double, 2 twin
Bathrooms: 2 private, 1 public

Bed & breakfast

per night:	£min	£max
Single	22.00	30.00
Double	36.00	40.00

Lunch available
Evening meal 1900 (last orders 2200)
Parking for 50

🐕🖐🖳♦⑤✕🕮🎞️◿ ●❋🎠

Old Rectory

❦❦
Stirchley Village, Telford TF3 1DY
☎ (0952) 596308
Large, comfortable guesthouse dating from 1734. Set in an acre of secluded gardens, on edge of town park. Convenient for town centre and Ironbridge museums.
Bedrooms: 2 single, 1 twin, 1 multiple
Bathrooms: 2 public

Bed & breakfast

per night:	£min	£max
Single		17.50
Double		30.00

Half board

per person:	£min	£max
Daily		24.00
Weekly		168.00

Evening meal 1800 (last orders 2100)
Parking for 6

🐕🕯🖳♦🖳⑤✕🕮📺 🎞️◿❍🖈❋🎠 SP 🏤 Ⓣ

TEMPLE GUITING

Gloucestershire
Map ref 2B1

Delightful village in the Windrush valley with the church on one side of a wooded ravine and Temple Guiting House on the other. Cotswolds Farm Park Rare Breeds Farm is nearby.

New Barn Farmhouse

Listed
Temple Guiting, Cheltenham GL54 5RW
☎ Guiting Power (0451) 850367
563-acre arable farm. Cotswold farmhouse, spacious drawing room, dining and TV rooms. Pleasant garden. Situated between Broadway, Stow-on-the-Wold and Bourton-on-the-Water, off B4070.
Bedrooms: 1 double, 2 twin
Bathrooms: 2 public

Bed & breakfast

per night:	£min	£max
Double	29.00	36.00

Parking for 6
Open January-September

🐕2🖳🖳✕🕮📺🎞️◿ 🖈🎠

TETBURY

Gloucestershire
Map ref 2B2

Small market town with 18th C houses and an attractive 17th C Town Hall. It is a good touring centre with many places of interest nearby including Badminton House and Westonbirt Arboretum.

Tavern House ⋀

❦❦ HIGHLY COMMENDED
Willesley, Tetbury GL8 8QU
☎ (0666) 880444
A Grade II listed Cotswold stone house (formerly a

staging post) on the A433 Bath road, 1 mile from the Westonbirt Arboretum and 4 miles from Tetbury.
Bedrooms: 3 double, 1 twin
Bathrooms: 4 private

Bed & breakfast

per night:	£min	£max
Single	32.00	38.00
Double	45.00	55.00

Parking for 4
Cards accepted: Access, Visa

🐕10🕾🖳♦🖳⑤🕮 🎞️◿❍🖈❋✕🎠 SP 🏤 Ⓣ

TEWKESBURY

Gloucestershire
Map ref 2B1

Tewkesbury's outstanding possession is its magnificent church, built as an abbey, with a great Norman tower and beautiful 14th C interior. The town stands at the confluence of the Severn and Avon and has many old houses, inns and several museums.
Tourist Information Centre
☎ (0684) 295027

Abbots Court Farm ⋀

❦❦ APPROVED
Church End, Twyning, Tewkesbury GL20 6DA
☎ (0684) 292515
450-acre arable & dairy farm. Large, comfortable farmhouse in excellent touring area. Most rooms en-suite, 3 games rooms, grass tennis court. Fishing available.
Bedrooms: 1 single, 1 double, 2 twin, 1 triple, 2 multiple
Bathrooms: 3 private, 1 public

Bed & breakfast

per night:	£min	£max
Single	16.00	18.00
Double	26.00	30.00

Half board

per person:	£min	£max
Daily	21.00	23.00
Weekly	132.00	148.00

Evening meal 1830 (last orders 1830)
Parking for 20

🐕🕯🖳♦🕿⑤🕮📺🎞️ ◿●🕾🖈❍♪❋🎠 DAP SP🏤

Newton Farm ⋀

❦
Ashchurch, Tewkesbury GL20 7BE
☎ (0684) 295903
10-acre smallholding. Easy to find accommodation, half a mile off the M5 at junction 9, then on the A438 heading

towards Stow. All rooms en-suite with TV and tea-making facilities.
Bedrooms: 3 multiple
Bathrooms: 3 private

Bed & breakfast

per night:	£min	£max
Single	15.00	15.00
Double	28.00	28.00

Half board

per person:	£min	£max
Daily	21.00	21.00
Weekly	140.00	140.00

Parking for 10

🐕🕯🖳♦🖳⑤🕮📺🎞️ ◿❍🖈❋✕🎠 DAP 🏤

Personal Touch ⋀

Listed
37 Tirle Bank Way, Tewkesbury GL20 8ES
☎ (0684) 297692
Semi-detached overlooking farmland. Leave M5 at junction 9, Tewkesbury. Second left past traffic lights, then left and immediately right, follow road round to right.
Bedrooms: 2 twin
Bathrooms: 1 public

Bed & breakfast

per night:	£min	£max
Single		13.50
Double		27.00

Half board

per person:	£min	£max
Daily		18.00

Lunch available
Evening meal from 1830
Parking for 2
Open February-October

🐕3🖳♦🖳⑤🕮📺🎞️◿ ✕🎠 DAP

Town Street Farm ⋀

❦❦ APPROVED
Tirley, Gloucester GL19 4HG
☎ Gloucester (0452) 780442
500-acre mixed farm. 18th C farmhouse set in beautiful surroundings and within half a mile of the River Severn.
Bedrooms: 1 twin, 1 triple
Bathrooms: 1 private, 1 public

Bed & breakfast

per night:	£min	£max
Single		20.00
Double	28.00	30.00

Parking for 4

🐕🖳♦🖳⑤🕮📺🎞️◿ 🕿❍❋🎠

Walton Cardiff Manor ⋀

Listed
Tewkesbury GL20 7BL
☎ (0684) 292600
Fax (0684) 850308

Continued ▶

187

TEWKESBURY
Continued

17th C manor house set in a large garden, 1 mile from Tewkesbury.
Bedrooms: 1 double, 1 twin
Bathrooms: 1 private, 2 public
Bed & breakfast

per night:	£min	£max
Single	18.00	
Double	32.00	36.00

Parking for 4
Open April-October

TODDINGTON
Gloucestershire
Map ref 2B1

Noted for its huge, picturesque Gothic revival house of 1820-35, set in a park of 150 acres with a splendid Victorian church, golden brown outside and white within.

Stanway Grounds ♠
APPROVED
Toddington, Cheltenham
GL54 5DR
☎ Cheltenham (0242) 620079
Late Victorian farmhouse in quiet location surrounded by open countryside. Beautiful, unspoilt views. Ideally situated for all the Cotswolds have to offer.
Bedrooms: 3 double
Bathrooms: 2 private, 1 public
Bed & breakfast

per night:	£min	£max
Single	15.00	16.50
Double	30.00	33.00

TREDINGTON
Gloucestershire
Map ref 2B1

Gothic Farm
Listed
Woolstone Lane, Tredington, Tewkesbury GL20 7BS
☎ Tewkesbury (0684) 293360
Arable and livestock farm. Rural farmhouse midway between Tewkesbury and Cheltenham. Peaceful setting 10 minutes from M5 junction 9. Good centre for discovering historic Tewkesbury, the Cotswolds and Shakespeare country, with fine shopping in Cheltenham.

Bedrooms: 1 double, 1 twin
Bathrooms: 2 public
Bed & breakfast

per night:	£min	£max
Double	26.00	30.00

Parking for 8

TYSOE
Warwickshire
Map ref 2C1

Parish of 3 small villages, close to where the Battle of Edgehill was fought. The church at Middle Tysoe is of considerable interest.

Laurel House
Shipston Road, Tysoe, Warwick CV35 0TR
☎ (0295) 680285
Stone house standing in lawns and gardens, 2 miles off A422 Banbury to Stratford road, below Edgehill.
Bedrooms: 1 double, 1 triple
Bathrooms: 1 public
Bed & breakfast

per night:	£min	£max
Single	15.00	15.00
Double	25.00	25.00

Parking for 4

UPPER HULME
Staffordshire
Map ref 4B2

Picturesque hamlet in the Manifold Valley where a former narrow gauge railway line, which ran between Hulme End and Waterhouses, is now a macadamised walkers' path.

Keekorok Lodge Farm Guest House ♠
Upper Hulme, Leek
ST13 8UA
☎ Blackshaw (0538) 300218
15-acre mixed farm. Old world farmhouse with panoramic views, rocks to the rear, lake to the front. Very peaceful. Near Chatsworth, Alton Towers, and the Potteries.
Bedrooms: 1 double, 1 twin
Bathrooms: 1 public
Bed & breakfast

per night:	£min	£max
Single	21.00	21.00
Double	27.00	31.00

Evening meal from 1800
Parking for 10
Open April-October

UPPER LYDBROOK
Gloucestershire
Map ref 2A1

The Old Vicarage
Listed
Upper Lydbrook, Lydbrook
GL17 9LJ
☎ Dean (0594) 860521
Attractive Victorian vicarage in Forest of Dean, near Wye Valley. Ideal for walking, riding, biking, fishing and sight-seeing. Home cooking, log fires, children welcome.
Bedrooms: 1 double, 2 twin
Bathrooms: 1 public
Bed & breakfast

per night:	£min	£max
Single	15.00	19.00
Double	30.00	38.00

Half board

per person:	£min	£max
Daily	25.00	29.00
Weekly	158.00	183.00

Evening meal 1830 (last orders 2030)
Parking for 6

UPTON ST LEONARDS
Gloucestershire
Map ref 2B1

Village in a lovely setting below hills, with many old houses and a part-Norman church.

Bullen Manor Farm
Listed HIGHLY COMMENDED
Portway, Upton St Leonards, Gloucester GL4 8DL
☎ (0452) 616463
Fax (0452) 371695
Half-timbered black and white farmhouse newly fitted out for bed and breakfast, with beautiful views towards Painswick. From Gloucester, B4073, signposted to Upton St Leonards, from Cheltenham A46 Stroud to Painswick road.
Bedrooms: 1 double, 2 triple
Bathrooms: 3 private
Bed & breakfast

per night:	£min	£max
Single	20.00	22.00
Double	32.00	35.00

Parking for 10

UPTON-UPON-SEVERN
Hereford and Worcester
Map ref 2B1

Attractive country town on the banks of the Severn and a good river cruising centre. It has many pleasant old houses and inns.
Tourist Information Centre
☎ (0684) 64200

Jessamine Cottage ♠
1 Laburnum Walk, Upton-upon-Severn, Worcester WR8 0LW
☎ (0684) 593179
Modernised 19th C cottage, set in 1 acre of market garden, within walking distance of town centre. Fresh garden produce available. Reduced tariff for 3 or more nights.
Bedrooms: 1 single, 1 double, 1 twin
Bathrooms: 2 public
Bed & breakfast

per night:	£min	£max
Single		15.00
Double		30.00

Parking for 6

Pool House Riverside Country House Hotel ♠
COMMENDED
Hanley Road, Upton-upon-Severn, Worcester WR8 0PA
☎ (0684) 592151
Fine Queen Anne country house in large picturesque garden running down to the River Severn. Quiet, comfortable accommodation.
Bedrooms: 3 double, 4 twin, 2 triple
Bathrooms: 6 private, 1 public
Bed & breakfast

per night:	£min	£max
Single	22.00	34.50
Double	35.00	50.00

Parking for 20
Open February-November
Cards accepted: Access, Visa

Tiltridge Farm ♠
COMMENDED
Upper Hook Road, Upton-upon-Severn, Worcester WR8 0SA
☎ (0684) 592906

188

Comfortable old farmhouse close to Upton with views of the Malverns. Fully renovated with own vineyard and wine for sale. Home-cooked meals.
Bedrooms: 1 double, 1 triple
Bathrooms: 1 public

Bed & breakfast

per night:	£min	£max
Single	17.00	19.00
Double	30.00	34.00

Half board

per person:	£min	£max
Daily	25.50	27.50

Evening meal 1800 (last orders 2000)
Parking for 5
🏕 ♨ ＵＬ Ｓ ✂ Ｍ ＴＶ 🎛, ♨ ✿ 🐾 DAP 🏵

UTTOXETER

Staffordshire
Map ref 4B2

Small market town which is famous for its racecourse. There are half-timbered buildings round the Market Square.

Stramshall Farm ♠
Listed COMMENDED
Stramshall, Uttoxeter
ST14 5AG
☎ (0889) 562363
140-acre dairy & livestock farm. A large late-Victorian house of typical architecture. Set in attractive garden and in the centre of Stramshall village, 2 miles north of Uttoxeter.
Bedrooms: 2 triple
Bathrooms: 1 public

Bed & breakfast

per night:	£min	£max
Single	16.00	20.00
Double	26.00	30.00

Parking for 4
Open March-October
🏕 ♨ ＵＬ Ｓ Ｍ ＴＶ 🎛 ♨ ✂ 🐾

West Lodge ♠
Listed HIGHLY COMMENDED
Bramshall, Uttoxeter
ST14 5BG
☎ (0889) 566000
Detached residence in 1 acre of attractive garden, on the B5027, 2 miles from Uttoxeter. Easy access to the Derbyshire Dales and Alton Towers.
Bedrooms: 2 double, 1 twin
Bathrooms: 2 public

Map references apply to the colour maps at the back of this guide.

Bed & breakfast

per night:	£min	£max
Single	18.50	20.00
Double	27.00	30.00

Parking for 8
🏕 🍽 🖧 □ ♨ ＵＬ Ｓ 🎛, ♨ ✿ 🍴 🐾

VOWCHURCH

Hereford and Worcester
Map ref 2A1

Village in the Golden Valley by the River Dore and set in beautiful countryside. It has an interesting 14th C church and is close to Abbey Dore with its famous Cistercian church.

Sefton Cottage
Vowchurch Common,
Vowchurch, Hereford
HR2 0RL
☎ Peterchurch (0981) 550319
Small house in glorious countryside. Ideal for a peaceful holiday and for touring. Superb views. Open all year with picnics and lunch available.
Bedrooms: 1 double, 1 twin
Bathrooms: 1 public

Bed & breakfast

per night:	£min	£max
Single	15.00	15.00
Double	25.00	30.00

Half board

per person:	£min	£max
Daily	25.00	25.00
Weekly	175.00	175.00

Lunch available
Evening meal 1900 (last orders 2000)
Parking for 2
🖧 ♨ ＵＬ 🔒 Ｓ ✂ 🎛, ♨ ✿ 🍴 🐾 📺

Upper Gilvach Farm
♛♛
St. Margarets, Vowchurch,
Hereford HR2 0QY
☎ Michaelchurch (098 123) 618
90-acre dairy farm. Between Golden Valley and Black Mountains. Very quiet with much historic interest.
Bedrooms: 1 double, 1 triple, 1 multiple
Bathrooms: 3 private, 1 public

Bed & breakfast

per night:	£min	£max
Double	25.00	33.00

Half board

per person:	£min	£max
Daily	21.00	24.00

Parking for 20
🏕 🍽 ＵＬ 🔒 Ｍ ＴＶ 🎛, ✿ 🐾

WARMINGTON

Warwickshire
Map ref 2C1

Harbages Farmhouse ♠
Listed
Warmington, Banbury,
Oxfordshire OX17 1BU
☎ (0295) 89770 & 250318
Historic 15th C farmhouse overlooking village green and duck pond, flag floors, beams, five open fires. Also self-contained character stable conversions. 3-4 or 7-day breaks.
Bedrooms: 1 double, 1 twin
Bathrooms: 2 private

Bed & breakfast

per night:	£min	£max
Single	17.50	22.50
Double	35.00	45.00

Parking for 12
Cards accepted: Access, Visa, Diners, Amex
🏕 □ ＵＬ ✂ ＴＶ 🎛, ♨ ✿ 🐾 📺

WARWICK

Warwickshire
Map ref 2B1

Warwick is outstanding for its castle rising above the River Avon and for the 15th C Beauchamp Chapel attached to St Mary's Church. The medieval Lord Leycester's Hospital almshouses and several museums are amongst the other attractions.
Tourist Information Centre
☎ (0926) 492212

30 Eastley Crescent ♠
HIGHLY COMMENDED
Warwick CV34 5RX
☎ (0926) 496480
Next to A46 and 5 minutes from the M40. Own dining tables, use of garden. Hair-dryer, shoe cleaning, trouser press. Non-smoking establishment.
Bedrooms: 1 single, 1 double
Bathrooms: 1 public, 1 private shower

Please check prices and other details at the time of booking.

Bed & breakfast

per night:	£min	£max
Single	15.00	15.00
Double	30.00	30.00

Parking for 2
🏕 8 □ ♨ ♒ ＵＬ Ｓ ✂ ＴＶ 🎛,
♨ ✿ 🍴 🐾 DAP

The Croft ♠
♛♛♛ COMMENDED
Haseley Knob, Warwick
CV35 7NL
☎ Haseley Knob (0926) 484447
With friendly family atmosphere in picturesque rural setting. On A4177 between Balsall Common and Warwick, convenient for the NEC, National Agricultural Centre, Stratford and Coventry. 15 minutes from Birmingham Airport.
Bedrooms: 1 single,
1 double, 2 twin, 1 triple
Bathrooms: 3 private, 2 public

Bed & breakfast

per night:	£min	£max
Single	18.50	25.00
Double	35.00	39.00

Half board

per person:	£min	£max
Daily	27.00	35.00

Evening meal 1800 (last orders 2000)
Parking for 10
🏕 ♨ ♒ ♨ ＶＬ ♨ ＵＬ 🔒 Ｓ ✂
ＴＶ 🎛, ♨ ✿ 🐾 SP Ｔ

Forth House ♠
♛♛ HIGHLY COMMENDED
44 High Street, Warwick
CV34 4AX
☎ (0926) 401512
Ground floor and first floor guest suites with sitting room and bathroom at the back of the house. Overlooking peaceful garden, in town centre.
Bedrooms: 1 twin, 1 triple
Bathrooms: 2 private

Bed & breakfast

per night:	£min	£max
Single	25.00	35.00
Double	38.00	48.00

Parking for 2
🏕 ♨ 🛎 ♨ 🖧 □ ♨ ♒ ＵＬ 🔒 ✂ Ｍ
ＴＶ 🎛, ♨ ✿ 🐾 📺

Fulbrook Edge ♠
♛ COMMENDED
Sherbourne Hill, Warwick
CV35 8AG
☎ (0926) 624242
Bed and breakfast in spectacular panoramic surroundings. All rooms at ground level. Croquet lawn. Midway Stratford/Warwick on
Continued ▶

WARWICK
Continued

the A46, 2 miles from the
M40, junction 15.
Bedrooms: 1 double, 2 twin
Bathrooms: 1 public
Bed & breakfast

per night:	£min	£max
Double	34.00	40.00

Parking for 12

Merrywood
Listed HIGHLY COMMENDED
Hampton on the Hill,
Warwick CV35 8QR
☎ (0926) 492766
Family house in small village
2 miles from Warwick, with
open views from 2 of the
rooms.
Bedrooms: 1 single, 1 twin
Bathrooms: 2 public
Bed & breakfast

per night:	£min	£max
Single	13.50	13.50
Double	25.00	25.00

Parking for 3

Northleigh House ⚕
⚜⚜ HIGHLY COMMENDED
Five Ways Road, Hatton,
Warwick CV35 7HZ
☎ (0926) 484203
Comfortable, peaceful country
house where the elegant
rooms are individually
designed and have en-suite
bathroom, fridge, kettle and
remote-control TV.
Bedrooms: 1 single,
4 double, 1 twin
Bathrooms: 6 private
Bed & breakfast

per night:	£min	£max
Single	29.00	37.00
Double	42.00	54.00

Parking for 8
Open February-November

Old Rectory
⚜⚜ APPROVED
Vicarage Lane, Sherbourne,
Warwick CV35 8AB
☎ Barford (0926) 624562
Georgian country house with
beams and inglenook
fireplaces, furnished with
antiques. Well-appointed
bedrooms, many with brass
beds, all with en-suite
facilities and colour TV.
Hearty breakfast. Situated half
a mile from M40 junction 15.

Bedrooms: 4 single,
6 double, 2 twin, 1 triple,
1 multiple
Bathrooms: 14 private
Bed & breakfast

per night:	£min	£max
Single	30.00	35.00
Double	39.00	48.00

Evening meal 1800 (last
orders 2200)
Parking for 14
Cards accepted: Access, Visa

Redlands Farm House
⚜⚜
Banbury Road, Lighthorne,
Warwick CV35 0AH
☎ Leamington Spa (0926)
651241
Built in local stone, mainly
17th C, tastefully restored and
with a wealth of timber
beams. Centrally located for
Warwick and Stratford-upon-
Avon, 2 miles from M40
junction 12.
Bedrooms: 1 single,
1 double, 1 triple
Bathrooms: 2 private,
2 public
Bed & breakfast

per night:	£min	£max
Single	14.00	15.00
Double	29.00	34.00

Parking for 6

Shrewley House ⚕
⚜⚜ HIGHLY COMMENDED
Hockley Road, Shrewley,
Warwick CV35 7AT
☎ Claverdon (092 684) 2549
Grade II listed Georgian
farmhouse and home dating
back to 17th C, set amidst
beautiful gardens. 4 miles
from Warwick.
Bedrooms: 2 double,
1 multiple
Bathrooms: 3 private
Bed & breakfast

per night:	£min	£max
Single	30.00	35.00
Double	43.00	58.00

Half board

per person:	£min	£max
Daily	35.00	50.00

Evening meal 1830 (last
orders 1930)
Parking for 22
Cards accepted: Access, Visa

Tudor House Inn ⚕
⚜⚜
90-92 West Street, Warwick
CV34 6AW
☎ (0926) 495447
Fax (0926) 492948
Inn of character dating from
1472, with a wealth of beams.
One of the few buildings to
survive the great fire of
Warwick in 1694. Opposite
Warwick Castle and close to
Warwick racecourse.
Bedrooms: 3 single,
5 double, 2 twin, 1 multiple
Bathrooms: 1 public, 2 private showers
Bed & breakfast

per night:	£min	£max
Single	24.00	40.00
Double	54.00	60.00

Lunch available
Evening meal 1800 (last
orders 2300)
Parking for 6
Cards accepted: Access, Visa,
Diners, Amex, Switch
12-15

Woodside ⚕
⚜ APPROVED
Langley Road, Claverdon,
Warwick CV35 8PJ
☎ (092 684) 2446
Quiet, warm and comfortable,
in acres of English garden
and woodland nature reserve.
Near Warwick, Shakespeare
country and National
Exhibition Centre. Excellent
touring centre.
Bedrooms: 1 double, 1 twin,
1 triple
Bathrooms: 2 public
Bed & breakfast

per night:	£min	£max
Single	14.00	20.00
Double	28.00	34.00

Half board

per person:	£min	£max
Daily	26.50	32.50
Weekly	181.00	222.00

Evening meal 2000 (last
orders 1400)
Parking for 13

National Crown
ratings were correct
at the time of going
to press but are
subject to change.
Please check at the
time of booking.

WATERHOUSES
Staffordshire
Map ref 4B2

Village in the valley of the
River Hamps, once the
terminus of the Leek and
Manifold Light Railway, 8
miles of which is now a
macadamised walkers'
path.

Ye Olde Crown ⚕
⚜⚜ APPROVED
Leek Road, Waterhouses,
Stoke-on-Trent ST10 3HL
☎ (0538) 308204
On the edge of the Peak
District National Park and at
the start of the beautiful
Manifold Valley. It is built of
natural stone and has a
wealth of original oak beams.
Bedrooms: 2 single,
3 double, 1 twin, 1 multiple
Bathrooms: 5 private,
1 public
Bed & breakfast

per night:	£min	£max
Single	15.00	21.50
Double	33.00	33.00

Half board

per person:	£min	£max
Daily	21.00	35.00

Lunch available
Evening meal 1900 (last
orders 2200)
Parking for 50

WEM
Shropshire
Map ref 4A3

Small town connected
with Judge Jeffreys who
lived in Lowe Hall. Well
known for its ales.

Forncet
Listed COMMENDED
Soulton Road, Wem,
Shrewsbury SY4 5HR
☎ (0939) 232996
Spacious, centrally heated
Victorian house on the edge
of this small market town,
200 yards from British Rail
station.
Bedrooms: 1 single, 1 twin,
1 triple
Bathrooms: 2 public
Bed & breakfast

per night:	£min	£max
Single	11.00	14.00
Double	22.00	28.00

Half board

per person:	£min	£max
Daily	20.00	20.00

Evening meal 1830 (last orders 1930)
Parking for 4
🐾🖵♨🛁ⓢ📺💻🖩🅿
♣✿✕🚲

Lowe Hall Farm M
🏠

Wem, Shrewsbury SY4 5UE
☎ (0939) 232236
134-acre dairy farm. Historically famous Grade II listed farmhouse, once the country residence of Judge Jeffreys, 1648-1689. High standard of food, decor and accommodation is guaranteed.
Bedrooms: 1 double, 1 twin, 1 triple
Bathrooms: 1 private, 1 public
Bed & breakfast

per night:	£min	£max
Single	17.00	17.00
Double	32.00	32.00

Half board

per person:	£min	£max
Daily	23.00	23.00
Weekly	140.00	140.00

Evening meal 1830 (last orders 1930)
Parking for 8
🐾🖵♨🛁ⓢ📺💻🖩🅿
♣♪✿✕🚲🏠

Soulton Hall M
🏠🏠🏠 COMMENDED

Wem, Shrewsbury SY4 5RS
☎ (0939) 232786
Fax (0939) 232786
560-acre mixed farm. Tudor manor house with moated Domesday site in grounds, offering relaxing holiday. Private riverside and woodland walks.
Bedrooms: 1 single, 1 double, 1 twin, 2 triple
Bathrooms: 4 private, 1 public
Bed & breakfast

per night:	£min	£max
Single	21.50	31.50
Double	43.00	51.00

Half board

per person:	£min	£max
Daily	35.00	45.00
Weekly	220.00	283.00

Evening meal 1900 (last orders 2030)
Parking for 23
Cards accepted: Access, Visa
🐾🛁🍴💷🖵♨🛁ⓢ📺💻
🖩♣🚻∪♪✕✿🚲🅿
🏠ⓣ

Check the introduction to this region for Where to Go, What to See.

WEOBLEY
Hereford and Worcester
Map ref 2A1

One of the most beautiful Herefordshire villages and full of attractive black and white timber-framed houses. It is dominated by the church which has a fine spire.

Ye Olde Salutation Inn M
🏠🏠🏠 COMMENDED

Market Pitch, Weobley, Hereford HR4 8SJ
☎ (0544) 318443
Traditional black and white country inn overlooking the main Broad Street. Quality home-cooked bar meals and a la carte menu. Inglenook fireplace. Homely atmosphere.
Bedrooms: 4 double, 1 twin
Bathrooms: 3 private, 1 public
Bed & breakfast

per night:	£min	£max
Single	21.00	31.50
Double	32.00	53.00

Lunch available
Evening meal 1900 (last orders 2130)
Parking for 20
Cards accepted: Access, Visa
🐾12🖵♨🛁ⓢ💷🖩
📺💻🖩♣∪✿🚲🅿🏠

WESTBURY-ON-SEVERN
Gloucestershire
Map ref 2B1

Cowleys Elm Farm
Rodley, Westbury-on-Severn GL14 1QZ
☎ (0452) 760284
166-acre dairy & livestock farm. Character farmhouse, c1670, short walk from River Severn. 2 miles left into Rodley from A48 Gloucester/Chepstow road.
Bedrooms: 1 double, 1 twin, 1 triple
Bathrooms: 2 private, 1 public
Bed & breakfast

per night:	£min	£max
Single	11.00	15.00
Double	22.00	28.00

Parking for 10
🐾♨🖩ⓢ🛁🖵📺💻🖩♣✿🚲

Please mention this guide when making a booking.

WHITNEY-ON-WYE
Hereford and Worcester
Map ref 2A1

Here the main Hereford to Brecon road crosses into Wales and nearby the Wye is spanned by its only surviving toll bridge, the owners of which are exempt, by the terms of an Act of George III, from payments of taxes.

The Rhydspence Inn M
🏠🏠🏠 HIGHLY COMMENDED

Whitney-on-Wye, Hereford HR3 6EU
☎ Clifford (049 73) 262
16th C black and white country inn offering food and hospitality, in superb Wye Valley and Black Mountains countryside.
Bedrooms: 1 single, 3 double, 1 twin
Bathrooms: 5 private
Bed & breakfast

per night:	£min	£max
Single	27.50	35.00
Double	55.00	75.00

Lunch available
Evening meal 1900 (last orders 2130)
Parking for 60
Cards accepted: Access, Visa, Amex
🐾🖵♨ⓢ🖩💻🖩♣✿✕
🚲🅿🏠

WINCHCOMBE
Gloucestershire
Map ref 2B1

Ancient town with a folk museum and railway museum. To the south lies Sudeley Castle with its fine collection of paintings and toys and an Elizabethan garden.
Tourist Information Centre
☎ (0242) 602925

Ireley Grounds Farm
🏠🏠 COMMENDED

Broadway Road, Winchcombe, Cheltenham GL54 5NY
☎ Cheltenham (0242) 603582 & 603928
Fax (0242) 603443
Impressive farmhouse, offering comfortable accommodation, standing in 6 acres with fine views, 1 mile from Winchcombe.
Bedrooms: 1 single, 1 double, 1 twin
Bathrooms: 3 private

Bed & breakfast

per night:	£min	£max
Single	20.00	22.00
Double	45.00	50.00

Parking for 15
Open January-November
🐾8🖵💷🖵♨🛁💻🖩✕🛁📺
💻🖩♣✿🚲🅿

Isbourne House M
🏠🏠 COMMENDED

Castle Street, Winchcombe, Cheltenham GL54 5JA
☎ Cheltenham (0242) 602281
Listed part-Georgian part-Elizabethan house overlooking the grounds of Sudeley Castle, situated within attractive gardens bordered by the River Isbourne. 2 minutes from both open countryside and town centre. Spacious rooms with en-suite facilities.
Bedrooms: 1 single, 1 double, 1 triple
Bathrooms: 3 private
Bed & breakfast

per night:	£min	£max
Single	25.00	30.00
Double	45.00	55.00

Parking for 2
♨🖩📺💻🖩♣∪✿
🏠ⓣ

Manor Farm
Listed

Greet, Winchcombe, Cheltenham GL54 5BJ
☎ Cheltenham (0242) 602423
400-acre mixed farm. Modernised Cotswolds manor in quiet hamlet. Good views of Cotswold Escarpment and GWR steam railway. Near racecourse. Picturesque well-equipped holiday cottages also available.
Bedrooms: 2 double
Bathrooms: 1 private, 2 public
Bed & breakfast

per night:	£min	£max
Single	20.00	22.00
Double	40.00	42.00

Parking for 10
Open January-November
🐾5🖵♨🛁🖩📺💻🖩♣✿
∪✿✕🚲🏠ⓣ

The Plaisterers Arms
🏠🏠

Abbey Terrace, Winchcombe, Cheltenham GL54 5LL
☎ (0242) 602358
17th C inn with en-suite bed and breakfast accommodation, close to Sudeley Castle and town centre. Extensive menu,
Continued ►

WINCHCOMBE
Continued

evening meal and lunches.
Large garden and patio.
Bedrooms: 1 single,
1 double, 1 triple
Bathrooms: 2 private,
1 public

Bed & breakfast
per night:	£min	£max
Single	18.00	22.00
Double	30.00	35.00

Lunch available
Evening meal 1830 (last
orders 2130)
Cards accepted: Access, Visa,
Amex

Postlip Hall Farm ₳
COMMENDED
Winchcombe, Cheltenham
GL54 5AQ
☎ Cheltenham (0242)
603351
300-acre mixed farm. Family
farm, 1 mile from
Winchcombe on Cleeve Hill.
Perfect location for touring
the Cotswolds, Bath, Warwick,
etc. Superb scenery.
Bedrooms: 1 double, 1 triple
Bathrooms: 2 private

Bed & breakfast
per night:	£min	£max
Single	16.00	18.00
Double	28.00	30.00

Parking for 6

WINSTONE
Gloucestershire
Map ref 2B1

Winstone Glebe ₳
COMMENDED
Winstone, Cirencester
GL7 7JU
☎ Cirencester (0285)
821451
Small Georgian rectory in
Domesday listed village,
overlooking Saxon church.
Spectacular rural views. Six
miles north west of
Cirencester.
Bedrooms: 2 twin
Bathrooms: 2 private

Bed & breakfast
per night:	£min	£max
Single	22.50	
Double	40.00	

Half board
per person:	£min	£max
Daily	30.00	37.50

Parking for 6

WOODCHESTER
Gloucestershire
Map ref 2B1

Southfield House
Listed
Woodchester, Stroud
GL5 5PA
☎ Amberley (045 387) 3437
Fax (045 387) 2049
Beautiful old Cotswold house
dating from 1560, with
swimming pool and pleasant
gardens and paddock. Very
accessible to beautiful
countryside, activities, walks.
Good shopping nearby. Close
to Minchinhampton Golf Club.
Bedrooms: 1 single, 2 twin
Bathrooms: 1 private,
2 public

Bed & breakfast
per night:	£min	£max
Single	18.00	20.00
Double	35.00	36.00

Parking for 20

WOOTTON WAWEN
Warwickshire
Map ref 2B1

Attractive village which
has an unspoilt church
with an Anglo-Saxon
tower, the only chained
library in Warwickshire
and some good brasses
and monuments.

Wootton Park Farm
APPROVED
Alcester Road, Wootton
Wawen, Solihull, West
Midlands B95 6HJ
☎ Henley-in-Arden (0564)
792673
340-acre arable & dairy farm.
Delightful 16th C half-
timbered farmhouse with a
wealth of oak beams. 5 miles
north of Stratford-upon-Avon
in quiet countryside.
Conveniently situated for the
National Agricultural Centre
and the National Exhibition
Centre.
Bedrooms: 1 double, 1 twin,
1 triple
Bathrooms: 1 private,
1 public

Bed & breakfast
per night:	£min	£max
Single	20.00	22.00
Double	34.00	40.00

Parking for 6

WORCESTER
Hereford and Worcester
Map ref 2B1

Lovely city which is
dominated by its Norman
and Early English
cathedral, King John's
burial place. The city has
many old buildings
including the 15th C
Commandery and the
18th C Guildhall. There
are several museums and
the Royal Worcester
porcelain factory.
Tourist Information Centre
☎ *(0905) 726311*

14 Shrubbery Rd. ₳
Listed
Worcester WR1 1QR
☎ (0905) 24502
Victorian house backing on to
canal. Food is home cooked
and interesting. Atmosphere
relaxed and informal. Suite of
one double, one twin
bedroom and bathroom.
Bedrooms: 1 double, 1 twin
Bathrooms: 1 private

Bed & breakfast
per night:	£min	£max
Double	26.00	30.00

Half board
per person:	£min	£max
Daily	18.00	20.00
Weekly	115.00	125.00

Evening meal 1800 (last
orders 2100)
Parking for 1

40 Britannia Square ₳
COMMENDED
Worcester WR1 3DN
☎ (0905) 611920
Beautiful listed Georgian
house in quiet conservation
square, close to city centre
and M5. Featured by interior
design magazines and the
BBC. Lovely garden and
courtyard.
Bedrooms: 1 double, 2 twin
Bathrooms: 3 private

Bed & breakfast
per night:	£min	£max
Single	22.00	28.00
Double	36.00	45.00

Parking for 2

49 Britannia Sq. ₳
Listed **COMMENDED**
Worcester WR1 3HP
☎ (0905) 22756
An attractive Grade II listed
Georgian house with
comfortable accommodation,
in a quiet and pleasant
square near the city centre.
Bedrooms: 1 single,
1 double, 1 twin
Bathrooms: 1 private,
1 public

Bed & breakfast
per night:	£min	£max
Single	21.00	25.00
Double	38.00	40.00

Parking for 2

Burgage House
Listed
4 College Precincts,
Worcester WR1 2LG
☎ (0905) 25396
Comfortable accommodation
in elegant Georgian mews
house in quiet cobbled street
next to cathedral. Close to
River Severn and cricket
ground.
Bedrooms: 1 single,
1 double, 1 twin, 1 triple
Bathrooms: 2 public

Bed & breakfast
per night:	£min	£max
Single	18.00	20.00
Double	30.00	32.00

Hazelholm
13 Droitwich Road,
Worcester WR3 7LG
☎ (0905) 25858
Large double-fronted Victorian
house with character. Car
park at rear.
Bedrooms: 1 single, 3 twin,
2 triple
Bathrooms: 1 public

Bed & breakfast
per night:	£min	£max
Single	14.00	
Double	28.00	28.00

Parking for 7

Ivy Cottage ₳
Sinton Green, Hallow,
Worcester WR2 6NP
☎ (0905) 641123

We advise you to confirm your booking in writing.

Please check prices and other details at the time of booking.

Cottage-style house in small village, 4 miles north of Worcester, half a mile off A443 Worcester to Tenbury road.
Bedrooms: 1 double, 1 triple
Bathrooms: 2 private

Bed & breakfast per night:	£min	£max
Single	16.00	
Double	32.00	35.00

Parking for 4
[UL] [S]

Little Lightwood Farm

COMMENDED
Lightwood Lane, Cotheridge, Worcester WR6 5LT
☎ Cotheridge (0905) 333236
56-acre dairy farm. Farmhouse accommodation with en-suite rooms, tea-making facilities and heating in all bedrooms. Delightful views of the Malvern Hills. Just off the A44 from Worcester to Leominster, 3.5 miles from Worcester.
Bedrooms: 2 double, 1 twin
Bathrooms: 3 private

Bed & breakfast per night:	£min	£max
Single	18.00	22.00
Double	32.00	40.00

Half board per person:	£min	£max
Daily	24.00	29.00
Weekly	165.00	168.00

Evening meal from 1800
Parking for 6
Open February-November
1 [UL] [TV]

The Old Smithy

Listed HIGHLY COMMENDED
Pirton, Worcester WR8 9EJ
☎ (0905) 820482
Half-timbered 16th C country house of character. Relaxed and homely atmosphere. Farmhouse breakfast. Craft workshop. 4.5 miles from M5 junction 7.
Bedrooms: 1 double, 1 twin
Bathrooms: 1 public

Bed & breakfast per night:	£min	£max
Double	28.00	35.00

Half board per person:	£min	£max
Daily	21.00	26.00

Evening meal from 1830
Parking for 6
[UL] [TV]

Osborne House

COMMENDED
17 Chestnut Walk, Worcester WR1 1PR
☎ (0905) 22296
Comfortable accommodation in restored Victorian house in a quiet position near station, city centre, swimming baths and antique shops.
Bedrooms: 1 single, 1 double, 2 twin, 1 triple
Bathrooms: 5 private showers

Bed & breakfast per night:	£min	£max
Single	15.00	15.00
Double	30.00	30.00

Parking for 4
[UL] [S] [TV]

WORMBRIDGE

Hereford and Worcester
Map ref 2A1

Village in the Golden Valley close to the very beautiful churches at Kilpeck and Abbey Dore.

The Upper House

DE LUXE
Didley, Wormbridge, Hereford HR2 9DA
☎ (098 121) 212
400-acre arable farm. Listed part 17th C farmhouse with inglenook fireplaces, beams, lounge, dining room. Large garden. Off A465 Hereford-Abergavenny road, 7 miles from Hereford.
Bedrooms: 1 double, 1 twin
Bathrooms: 2 private

Bed & breakfast per night:	£min	£max
Double		49.00

Half board per person:	£min	£max
Daily		40.00

Lunch available
Evening meal 1930 (last orders 1700)
Parking for 12
Open April-October
[UL] [S]
[SP]

WYE VALLEY

See under Fownhope, Hereford, Ross-on-Wye, Symonds Yat West

YOXALL

Staffordshire
Map ref 4B3

The Moat

COMMENDED
Town Hill, Yoxall, Burton upon Trent DE13 8NN
☎ (0543) 472210
Country house sited in 2.5 acres of garden, dry moated, of historic interest. Grounds listed Grade II.
Bedrooms: 3 twin
Bathrooms: 3 private, 1 public

Bed & breakfast per night:	£min	£max
Single	25.00	30.00
Double	45.00	55.00

Parking for 6
[UL] [TV]

Country Code

- Enjoy the countryside and respect its life and work
- Guard against all risk of fire
- Fasten all gates
- Keep your dogs under close control
- Keep to public paths across farmland
- Use gates and stiles to cross fences, hedges and walls
- Leave livestock, crops and machinery alone
- Take your litter home
- Help to keep all water clean
- Protect wildlife, plants and trees
- Take special care on country roads
- Make no unnecessary noise

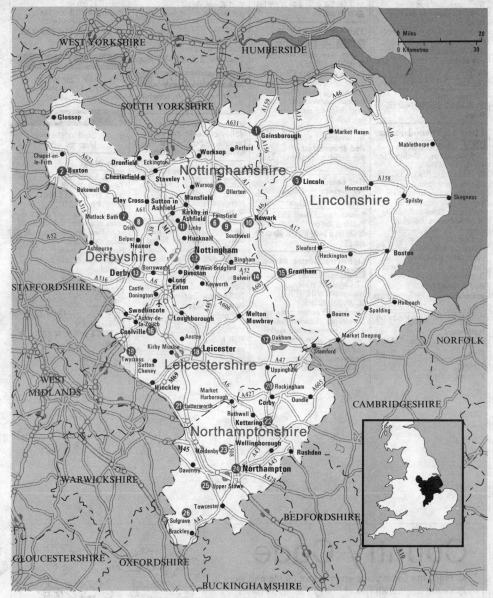

Use the above map to locate places in the "Where to Go, What to See" section opposite.
Use the colour maps at the back of this guide to find places with accommodation.

Middle England

Rich in character and widely varied, Middle England has something for everyone. The undulating hills of the Peak District, the brooding heaths of Charnwood Forest, Rutland's rich pasture and thatched cottages and the riot of springtime colour in the Fenland bulbfields give a landscape of many moods. Visit Lincoln's magnificent cathedral, Chesterfield with its twisted spire and the ancient town of Stamford. For seaside fun, take a trip to one of the region's fine resorts – Mablethorpe with its golden sands or Skegness with its lovely seafront gardens and wide range of entertainments. Whatever your mood, you'll find something to fit.

WHERE TO GO, WHAT TO SEE

The number against each name will help you locate it on the map opposite.

❶ Gainsborough Old Hall
Parnell Street, Gainsborough,
Lincolnshire DN21 2NB
Tel: Gainsborough (0427) 612669
Late medieval timber-framed manor house built c1460, with fine medieval kitchen. Displays on the building and its restoration.

❷ Buxton Micrarium
Buxton, Derbyshire SK17 6BQ
Tel: Buxton (0298) 78662

Unique exhibition of the natural world under the microscope, using special push-button projection microscopes operated by visitors.

❸ Lincoln Cathedral
Lincoln, Lincolnshire LN2 1PZ
Tel: Lincoln (0522) 544544
Triple-towered cathedral founded 1072, with Norman west front, 12th C work, Angel Choir of 1280. Wren library of 1674. Treasury. Regular services.

❸ Museum of Lincolnshire Life
Burton Road, Lincoln,
Lincolnshire LN1 3LY
Tel: Lincoln (0522) 528448
Agricultural, industrial and social history of Lincolnshire from 1800. Edwardian room setting. Display of craftwork in progress. First World War tank on display.

D.H. Lawrence was born in the Nottinghamshire mining community of Eastwood, though he was deeply influenced by the quiet rural beauty close to the town

❹ Chatsworth House
Bakewell, Derbyshire DE4 1PP
Tel: Baslow (0246) 582204
Built 1687–1707. Collection of fine pictures, books, drawings, furniture. Garden laid out by Capability Brown with fountains, cascade. Farmyard and adventure playground.

❺ Rufford Country Park and Craft Centre
Ollerton, Nottinghamshire NG22 9DF
Tel: Mansfield (0623) 824153
Parkland and 25-acre lake with ruins of Cistercian abbey. Woodland walks, formal gardens, sculpture garden. Craft centre with exhibitions of British craftsmanship.

❻ White Post Modern Farm Centre
Farnsfield, Nr Newark,
Nottinghamshire NG22 8HL
Tel: Mansfield (0623) 882977
Working farm with llama, ostriches, egg incubator, free-range hens, lakes, picnic areas, tea gardens.

❼ The Heights of Abraham
Matlock Bath, Derbyshire DE4 3PD
Tel: Matlock (0629) 582365
Cable car ride across Derwent

Valley gives access to Alpine Centre with refreshments, superb views, woodland, prospect tower and two show caves.

8 The National Tramway Museum
Crich, Matlock, Derbyshire
DE4 5DP
Tel: Ambergate (0773) 852565
Collection of 50 tramcars from Britain and overseas built 1873–1953. Tram rides on one-mile route, period street scene, depots, power station, workshops.

9 Southwell Minster
Southwell, Nottinghamshire
Tel: Southwell (0636) 812649
Building started c1108. Saxon tympanum, Norman nave and crossing, Early English choir. Oustanding foliage carving in chapter house. Archbishop's palace ruins.

"Skegness is so bracing" – an image from a famous 1930's railway poster

10 Millgate Museum of Social and Folk Life
Newark, Nottinghamshire
NG24 4TS
Tel: Newark (0636) 79403
Museum portraying local social and folk life. Series of street scenes with period shops. Mezzanine gallery with regular programme of temporary exhibitions.

11 Newstead Abbey
Linby, Nottinghamshire
NG15 8GE
Tel: Mansfield (0623) 793557
800-year old remains of priory church, converted into country house in 16th C. Home of Lord Byron with possessions and manuscripts. Parkland, lake, gardens.

12 Nottingham Industrial Museum
Woolaton Park, Nottingham
NG8 2AE
Tel: Nottingham (0602) 284602
18th C stables presenting history of Nottingham's industries: printing, pharmacy, hosiery and lace. Victorian beam engine, horse gin, transport.

12 The Tales of Robin Hood
Nottingham, Nottinghamshire
NG1 6GF
Tel: Nottingham (0602) 414414
Join the world's greatest medieval adventure and hide out in the Sheriff's eerie cave. Ride through the magical greenwood and play the Silver Arrow game.

13 Derby Industrial Museum
Full Street, Derby DE1 3AR
Tel: Derby (0332) 255308
Displays on industries of Derbyshire, including Rolls-Royce aero engines. New railway engineering gallery. Museum is in former silk mill.

14 Belvoir Castle
Belvoir, Lincolnshire NG32 1PD
Tel: Grantham (0476) 870262
Seat of Dukes of Rutland since Henry VIII. Rebuilt in 1816. Museum of 17th/21st Lancers, picture gallery, magnificent state rooms.

15 Belton House, Park and Gardens
Grantham, Lincolnshire
NG32 2LS
Tel: Grantham (0476) 66116
The crowning achievement of Restoration country house architecture, built in 1685–88 for Sir John Brownlow. Alterations by James Wyatt in 1777.

16 Snibston Discovery Park
Coalville, Leicestershire
Tel: Coalville (0530) 510851
Former coal mine site with new museum building, nature trail.

17 Oakham Castle
Oakham, Leicestershire
Tel: Oakham (0572) 723654
Part of late 12th C manor house of which only Norman hall

remains. Collection of horseshoes left as a "toll" by peers of the realm and royalty visiting Oakham.

⑰ Rutland Water
Sykes Lane, Empingham, Oakham, Leicestershire LE15 8PX
Tel: Empingham (078 086) 321
Largest man-made lake in western Europe, 3,100 acres. Water and land based recreational facilities, pleasure cruiser, museum.

⑱ Newarke Houses Museum
The Newarke, Leicester, Leicestershire LE2 7BY
Tel: Leicester (0533) 554100
Local history and crafts from 1485. Toys and games, clocks, mechanical instruments. 19th C street scene, early 20th C shop. Furniture by Gimson/ Waals/Barnsley Brothers.

⑱ Wygston's House Museum of Costume
Applegate, Leicester, Leicestershire
Tel: Leicester (0533) 554100
Late medieval building with later additions. Displays on costume and accessories. 1920s draper's and shoe shops. Symington corsetry collection.

⑲ Twycross Zoo
Twycross, Warwickshire CV9 3PX
Tel: Tamworth (0827) 880250
Gorillas, orang-utans, chimpanzees, modern gibbon complex, elephants, lions, cheetahs, giraffes, reptile house, pets' corner, rides.

⑳ Rockingham Castle
Rockingham, Leicestershire LE16 8TH
Tel: Rockingham (0536) 770240
Elizabethan house within walls of Norman castle. Fine pictures. Extensive views and gardens with roses and ancient yew hedge.

㉑ Stanford Hall and Motor Cycle Museum
Lutterworth, Leicestershire LE17 6DH
Tel: Rugby (0788) 860250
William and Mary house on River Avon. Family costumes, furniture, pictures. Replica 1898 flying machine, motorcycle museum, rose garden, nature trail, craft centre.

Nottingham is famous as the "City of Lace" and traditional patterns still live on, though production methods have radically changed

㉒ Manor House Museum
Sheep Street, Kettering, Northamptonshire
Tel: Kettering (0536) 410333
Showing Kettering's past, with collections of agricultural equipment, shoe-making machinery and the Kettering-made Robinson car of 1907.

㉓ Holdenby House Gardens
Holdenby, Northampton NN6 8DJ
Tel: Northampton (0604) 770074
Remains of Elizabethan gardens. Original entrance, arches and terraces. King Charles Walk. Museum. Craft shop. Rare breeds of farm animals. Falconry centre.

㉔ Central Museum and Art Gallery
Guildhall Road, Northampton, Northamptonshire NN1 1DP
Tel: Northampton (0604) 39415
Displays on Northampton's history from earliest times to present, using objects, sound and film. Footwear through the ages, ceramics.

㉕ Old Dairy Farm Centre
Upper Stowe, Northampton, Northamptonshire NN7 4SH
Tel: Weedon (0327) 40525
Wood turning, picture framing and various craft workshops.

㉖ Sulgrave Manor
Sulgrave, Nr Banbury, Oxfordshire OX17 2SD
Tel: Sulgrave (029 576) 205
Early English home of ancestors of George Washington. Small manor house of Shakespeare's time, with furniture of period. Fine kitchen.

FIND OUT MORE

Further information about holidays and attractions in Middle England is available from: **East Midlands Tourist Board** Exchequergate, Lincoln LN2 1PZ
Tel: (0522) 531521

These publications are available free from the East Midlands Tourist Board:
Middle England '93 (general brochure including accommodation)
The Peak District 1993
Events list (please send large stamped and addressed envelope)
Also available is (price includes postage and packing):
Shires of Middle England Leisure Map £3.50

Places to stay

Accommodation entries in this regional section are listed in alphabetical order of place name, and then in alphabetical order of establishment.

The map references refer to the colour maps at the back of the guide. The first figure is the map number; the letter and figure which follow indicate the grid reference on the map.

The symbols at the end of each accommodation entry give information about services and facilities. A 'key' to these symbols is inside the back cover flap, which can be kept open for easy reference.

ABTHORPE

Northamptonshire
Map ref 2C1

Stone Cottage

Main Street, Abthorpe,
Towcester NN12 8QN
☎ Silverstone (0327) 857544
Grade II listed cottage in delightful secluded position on edge of conservation village. Convenient for Silverstone, Cotswolds and Oxford.
Bedrooms: 1 single, 2 twin
Bathrooms: 2 public

Bed & breakfast per night:	£min	£max
Single	15.00	15.00
Double	30.00	30.00

Parking for 7
… [UL] … [S] … [TV] …

ALDWINCLE

Northamptonshire
Map ref 3A2

Pear Tree Farm

COMMENDED
Aldwincle, Kettering
NN14 3EL
☎ Clopton (080 15) 614
400-acre mixed farm. Located in the picturesque Nene Valley, within easy reach of Oundle and Thrapston.
Bedrooms: 3 double
Bathrooms: 1 private, 1 public

Bed & breakfast per night:	£min	£max
Single	15.00	17.00
Double	29.00	33.00

Half board per person:	£min	£max
Daily	24.00	26.00

Lunch available
Evening meal 1830 (last orders 2000)
Parking for 6
… 10 … [UL] … [S] … [TV] …

ALFORD

Lincolnshire
Map ref 4D2

Busy market town with attractive Georgian houses and shops and a Folk Museum in the thatched manor house. A craft market is held on Fridays in the summer months and there is a working 5-sailed tower mill.

Halton House

50 East Street, Alford
LN13 9EH
☎ Louth (0507) 462058
Detached house in own gardens in the rural setting of a small market town on the edge of the Lincolnshire Wolds. Non-smokers preferred.
Bedrooms: 1 double, 1 twin
Bathrooms: 2 public

Bed & breakfast per night:	£min	£max
Single		14.00
Double		28.00

Parking for 3
… 3 … [UL] … [TV] …

ALKMONTON

Derbyshire
Map ref 4B2

Dairy House Farm

COMMENDED
Alkmonton, Longford,
Ashbourne DE6 3DG
☎ Ashbourne (0335) 330359
82-acre livestock farm. Old red brick farmhouse with oak beams, an inglenook fireplace and a comfortable atmosphere. Guests have their own lounge and dining room. Non-smokers only and no pets please.
Bedrooms: 3 single, 2 double, 1 twin, 1 triple
Bathrooms: 3 private, 1 public

Bed & breakfast per night:	£min	£max
Single	16.00	22.00
Double	32.00	38.00

Half board per person:	£min	£max
Daily	26.00	32.00
Weekly	175.00	217.00

Lunch available
Evening meal 1830 (last orders 2030)
Parking for 8
… 5 … [S] … [TV] …

ANCASTER

Lincolnshire
Map ref 3A1

Large village on the Roman Ermine Street, within easy drive of Belton House, Grantham and the cathedral city of Lincoln.

Woodlands

[Listed]
West Willoughby, Ancaster,
Grantham NG32 3SH
☎ Loveden (0400) 30340
12-acre mixed farm. Quiet farmhouse on the A153. 1 mile west of Ancaster, 4 miles from Belton House, 9 miles from the A1 and 20 miles from Lincoln. Farmhouse breakfasts and home-cooked food with vegetables from own garden where possible.
Bedrooms: 1 twin, 1 triple
Bathrooms: 1 public

Bed & breakfast per night:	£min	£max
Single	14.00	16.00
Double	25.00	30.00

Half board per person:	£min	£max
Daily	21.00	22.00

Evening meal 1700 (last orders 2000)
Parking for 6
Open April-October
🐾📺♦️Ⓦ▲📺🅿️☀️🚗

ASHBOURNE

Derbyshire
Map ref 4B2

Market town on the edge of the Peak District National Park and an excellent centre for walking. Its impressive church with 212-ft spire stands in an unspoilt old street. Ashbourne is well-known for gingerbread and its Shrovetide football match.
Tourist Information Centre
☎ *(0335) 43666*

Anacre Hill
♛♛

Snelston, Ashbourne
DE6 2DN
☎ Ellastone (0335) 324326
Guesthouse in a quiet and lovely part of Derbyshire, offering home cooking using fresh local produce. Within easy reach of Alton Towers. Non-smokers only please.
Bedrooms: 1 twin, 1 triple
Bathrooms: 2 public

Bed & breakfast

per night:	£min	£max
Single	15.00	17.00
Double	28.00	32.00

Parking for 2
Open April-October
🐾📺♦️Ⓦ⊁📺📺🅿️☀️

Collycroft Farm
Clifton, Ashbourne DE6 2GN
☎ (0335) 42187
260-acre mixed farm. Located south of Ashbourne on the A515 in lovely countryside. Within easy reach of Alton Towers, the Peak District and Carsington water sports.
Bedrooms: 1 double, 1 twin, 1 triple
Bathrooms: 1 public

Bed & breakfast

per night:	£min	£max
Single	13.00	14.00
Double	26.00	28.00

Parking for 8
🐾📺📺♦️Ⓦ▲📺📺🅿️☀️🚗
☀️🚗🆂🅿️

Henmore Cottage
Clifton, Ashbourne DE6 2GL
☎ (0335) 44492
An 18th C cottage in a delightful area of Ashbourne, near Alton Towers, Chatsworth, Dovedale and Carsington Water.

Bedrooms: 2 double
Bathrooms: 1 public
Bed & breakfast

per night:	£min	£max
Double	27.00	30.00

Parking for 7
Open March-November
🐾3❄️📺Ⓦ▲🆂⊁📺📺
🅿️☀️🚗🚗🏠

Little Park Farm
🏠 COMMENDED

Mappleton, Ashbourne
DE6 2BR
☎ Thorpe Cloud (033 529) 341
123-acre mixed farm. 300-year-old listed oak-beamed farmhouse, tastefully furnished. In the peaceful Dove Valley, 3 miles from Ashbourne. Superb views.
Bedrooms: 2 double, 1 twin
Bathrooms: 1 public

Bed & breakfast

per night:	£min	£max
Single	14.00	15.00
Double	25.00	28.00

Half board

per person:	£min	£max
Daily	20.00	22.00

Evening meal from 1830
Parking for 3
Open March-October
🐾12Ⓦ⊁📺📺🚗🏠

Mercaston Hall ♙
♛♛

Mercaston, Ashbourne
DE6 3BL
☎ (0335) 60263
55-acre mixed farm. Listed buildings in attractive, quiet countryside. Hard tennis court. Kedleston Hall (NT) 1 mile, Carsington Reservoir 5 minutes away.
Bedrooms: 1 double, 1 twin
Bathrooms: 2 private, 1 public

Bed & breakfast

per night:	£min	£max
Single	19.50	
Double	29.00	36.00

Parking for 16
🐾📺📺♦️Ⓦ🆂⊁📺📺
📺🚗🔍🚗☀️🚗🏠

Shirley Hall Farm
🏠 COMMENDED

Shirley, Ashbourne DE6 3AS
☎ (0335) 60346
200-acre mixed farm. This peaceful timbered manor house, complete with part of its moat, is adjacent to superb woodland walks and makes an excellent centre for Sudbury and Kedleston Hall, Chatsworth and Alton Towers.
Bedrooms: 2 double, 1 twin

Bathrooms: 2 private, 1 public
Bed & breakfast

per night:	£min	£max
Single	17.00	22.00
Double	26.00	36.00

Parking for 5
🐾3♦️Ⓦ▲🆂📺📺🚗🚗☀️
⊁🚗🏠

Water Keepers Cottage
Mappleton, Ashbourne
DE6 2AB
☎ Thorpe Cloud (033 529) 444
A cosy cottage in a quiet village midway between Ashbourne and Thorpe, on the border of Staffordshire and Derbyshire.
Bedrooms: 1 double, 1 twin
Bathrooms: 1 public

Bed & breakfast

per night:	£min	£max
Double	25.00	30.00

Parking for 2
🐾📺Ⓦ▲🆂⊁📺📺🚗🚗🏠

ASHBY-DE-LA-ZOUCH

Leicestershire
Map ref 4B3

Lovely market town with late 15th C church, impressive ruined 15th C castle, an interesting small museum and a wide, sloping main street with Georgian buildings. Twycross Zoo is nearby.
Tourist Information Centre
☎ *(0530) 411767*

The Laurels Guesthouse
🏠 APPROVED

17 Ashby Road, Measham, Swadlincote, Derbyshire
DE12 7JR
☎ Measham (0530) 272567
A warm welcome awaits you at this modern guesthouse on the B5006 convenient for the M42/M1. Rural location.
Bedrooms: 1 single, 1 double, 1 twin
Bathrooms: 2 private, 1 public

Bed & breakfast

per night:	£min	£max
Single	16.50	16.50
Double	33.00	33.00

Parking for 7
🐾📺♦️Ⓦ▲🆂⊁📺📺
🚗☀️🚗🆂🅿️

Measham House Farm
🏠🏠 HIGHLY COMMENDED

Gallows Lane, Measham, Swadlincote DE12 7HD
☎ Measham (0530) 270465

500-acre mixed farm. 200-year-old Grade II listed Georgian farmhouse. 2 miles from the M42 junction 11, 8 miles from the M1 junction 22.
Bedrooms: 2 twin, 1 triple
Bathrooms: 1 private, 2 public

Bed & breakfast

per night:	£min	£max
Single	16.00	19.00
Double	35.00	38.00

Parking for 10
🐾📺♦️Ⓦ🆂⊁📺📺
🚗☀️🚗🏠Ⓣ

Talbot House Farm
Talbot Lane, Whitwick, Leicester LE6 4NQ
☎ Coalville (0530) 222233
150-acre dairy farm. The farm was once a stagecoach stop and retains its old world charm. It is an ideal touring centre and is only 4.5 miles west of the M1 junction 23 on road to Ashby-de-la-Zouch.
Bedrooms: 2 double, 2 triple
Bathrooms: 2 public

Bed & breakfast

per night:	£min	£max
Single	18.00	
Double	30.00	

Half board

per person:	£min	£max
Daily	28.00	
Weekly	186.20	

Evening meal 1830 (last orders 1200)
Parking for 8
🐾📺♦️Ⓦ▲📺📺🚗🚗🅿️
🚗☀️🚗🔍🏠

ASHFORD IN THE WATER

Derbyshire
Map ref 4B2

Limestone village in attractive surroundings of the Peak District approached by 3 bridges over the River Wye. There is an annual well-dressing ceremony and the village was well-known in the 18th C for its black marble quarries.

Gritstone House ♙
♛♛ HIGHLY COMMENDED

Greaves Lane, Ashford in the Water, Bakewell DE4 1QH
☎ Bakewell (0629) 813563
Charming 18th C Georgian house offering friendly service and accommodation designed with comfort and style in mind. Ideal centre for exploring the Peak District's
Continued ▶

199

ASHFORD IN THE WATER

Continued

scenery and country houses, and close to an extensive range of dining-out facilities.
Bedrooms: 2 double, 1 twin
Bathrooms: 1 private, 1 public

Bed & breakfast per night:	£min	£max
Double	32.00	

Open March-October
📰 ☕ 🚰 [UL] [S] 🚭 🛏 [TV] ♨ 🧺
✈ 🚐 🏛

ASHOVER

Derbyshire
Map ref 4B2

Unspoilt village with a 13th C church.

Fairhaven 🏛

Stone Rows Lane, Ashover, Chesterfield S45 0HE
☎ Chesterfield (0246) 590405
A secluded, stone-built, oak beamed cottage with log fires in winter and a friendly atmosphere. Close to Peak District and Matlock.
Bedrooms: 1 single, 1 double, 1 triple
Bathrooms: 1 public

Bed & breakfast per night:	£min	£max
Single	12.00	15.00
Double	26.00	30.00
Half board per person:	**£min**	**£max**
Daily	20.00	22.00
Weekly	140.00	142.00

Evening meal 1800 (last orders 2100)
Parking for 8
🐴 📰 ☕ 🚰 [UL] [S] 🚭 🛏 [TV] ♨
🧺 U ⛳ ✿ 🚐 🏛

Old School Farm

[Listed]

Uppertown, Ashover, Chesterfield S45 0JF
☎ Chesterfield (0246) 590813
25-acre mixed farm. A working farm welcoming children but not pets, suitable for visitors with their own transport. In a small hamlet bordering the Peak District, ideal for Chatsworth, Chesterfield and Matlock Bath.
Bedrooms: 1 single, 1 double, 2 triple
Bathrooms: 1 public

Bed & breakfast per night:	£min	£max
Single	12.00	14.00
Double	24.00	28.00
Half board per person:	**£min**	**£max**
Daily	18.00	20.00
Weekly	126.00	140.00

Evening meal 1900 (last orders 0930)
Parking for 10
Open March-November
🐴 🛁 📰 📺 [UL] [S] 🛏 [TV] ♨ ✿
✈ 🚐

BAKEWELL

Derbyshire
Map ref 4B2

Pleasant market town, famous for its pudding. It is set in beautiful countryside on the River Wye and is an excellent centre for exploring the Derbyshire Dales, the Peak District National Park, Chatsworth and Haddon Hall.
Tourist Information Centre
☎ *(0629) 813227*

Bourne House

The Park, Haddon Road, Bakewell DE4 1AW
☎ (0629) 813274
Former manse on the corner of the park. Short riverside stroll into town centre. Chatsworth and Haddon Hall nearby. En-suite rooms available.
Bedrooms: 2 double, 1 twin
Bathrooms: 3 private, 1 public

Bed & breakfast per night:	£min	£max
Double	30.00	40.00

Parking for 4
☕ 🚰 [UL] 🔒 [S] 🚭 🛏 [TV] ♨ 🧺 ✿
✈ 🚐 ➘

Everton

Haddon Road, Bakewell DE4 1AW
☎ (0629) 813725
Located near the park. Offers home comforts and makes an excellent base for visiting the stately homes and dales of the Peak District.
Bedrooms: 2 double, 1 twin
Bathrooms: 1 public

Bed & breakfast per night:	£min	£max
Double	27.00	

Parking for 3
Open April-October
🐴 📺 ☕ [UL] 🔒 [S] ♨ 🧺 U ⛳
✈ 🚐

Merlin House

Monsal Head, Bakewell DE45 1NL
☎ Great Longstone (0629) 640475
Comfortable, well-appointed bed and breakfast accommodation with en-suite facilities. Quiet rural location amid outstanding scenery, in the heart of the Peak District National Park, close to Chatsworth and Haddon Hall.
Bedrooms: 1 single, 4 double, 1 twin
Bathrooms: 6 private

Bed & breakfast per night:	£min	£max
Single	22.00	24.00
Double	40.00	44.00

Parking for 6
Open March-October
🛁 ☕ [UL] 🚭 🛏 [TV] ♨ ✿ ✈ 🚐

BAMFORD

Derbyshire
Map ref 4B2

Village in the Peak District near the Upper Derwent Reservoirs of Ladybower, Derwent and Howden. An excellent centre for walking.

Welburn

Shatton Lane, Shatton, Bamford, Sheffield S30 2BG
☎ Hope Valley (0433) 51278
Halfway between Hathersage and Hope near Derwent Valley reservoirs, Chatsworth and Castleton's caverns. Ideal centre for walking and touring.
Bedrooms: 1 double, 1 twin
Bathrooms: 2 public

Bed & breakfast per night:	£min	£max
Double	26.00	26.00

Parking for 3
🐴 📰 ☕ [UL] 🔒 [S] 🛏 [TV] ♨ ✿ 🚐

BARKSTON

Lincolnshire
Map ref 3A1

Barkston House 🏛

👑👑 COMMENDED

Barkston, Grantham NG32 2NH
☎ Loveden (0400) 50555
Small Georgian country house, with fine lawns and mature cedar trees to the front and open countryside to rear; furnished as a private home, with antiques.
Bedrooms: 2 twin
Bathrooms: 2 private

Bed & breakfast per night:	£min	£max
Single	25.00	
Double	45.00	
Half board per person:	**£min**	**£max**
Daily	37.50	40.00

Evening meal 1930 (last orders 2030)
Parking for 15
Cards accepted: Access, Visa, Diners, Amex
🐴 ☎ 📰 📺 🚰 🔒 [S] 🛏 ♨ 🧺
🐕 🚐 [SP] 🏛 [T]

BASLOW

Derbyshire
Map ref 4B2

Small village on the River Derwent with a stone-built toll-house and a packhorse bridge. Chatsworth, home of the Duke of Devonshire, is nearby.

Bubnell Cliff Farm

Wheatlands Lane, Baslow, Bakewell DE4 1RH
☎ (0246) 582454
300-acre mixed farm. Ideal for touring the Peak District. The farm has magnificent views of Chatsworth and surrounding area.
Bedrooms: 1 double, 1 triple
Bathrooms: 1 public

Bed & breakfast per night:	£min	£max
Single	13.00	20.00
Double		26.00

Parking for 6
🐴 ☕ [UL] 🔒 [S] [TV] 🧺 🚐

The Rutland Arms Hotel

Calver Road, Baslow, Bakewell DE4 1RP
☎ Chesterfield (0256) 582276
A delightful English pub serving home-made fare. Overlooking River Derwent in the picturesque Peak District National Park, close to many places of interest.
Bedrooms: 1 double, 2 triple, 1 multiple
Bathrooms: 2 public

Bed & breakfast per night:	£min	£max
Single	20.00	
Double	30.00	

Lunch available
Evening meal 1830 (last orders 2130)
Parking for 30
🐴 📺 ☕ 🔒 [S] ♨ 🧺 ✿ 🚐 ➘
[SP] 🏛 [T]

Wheatsheaf Hotel

Netherend, Baslow, Bakewell
DE4 1SR
☎ (0246) 582240
*A traditional stone-built inn
in the heart of the Peak
District. Oak beams, home-
cooked food and an open fire
in winter.*
Bedrooms: 3 double, 1 twin,
2 triple
Bathrooms: 1 private,
1 public
Bed & breakfast

per night:	£min	£max
Single	20.00	
Double	30.00	

Lunch available
Evening meal 1900 (last
orders 2130)
Parking for 100
🛇🖵♨🛍S⅊▥ 🗕●✻ ✕🏛

Derbyshire
Map ref 4B2

Chevin Green Farm ⋀

APPROVED
Chevin Road, Belper, Derby
DE5 2UN
☎ (0773) 822328
*38-acre mixed farm. Extended
and improved 300-year-old
beamed farmhouse
accommodation with all
bedrooms en-suite, an ideal
base to explore Derbyshire.*
Bedrooms: 2 single,
2 double, 1 twin, 1 triple
Bathrooms: 6 private
Bed & breakfast

per night:	£min	£max
Single	15.00	19.00
Double	26.00	34.00

Parking for 6
🛇🚲♨▥⅃TV▥ 🗕U ✕🐴

Nottinghamshire
Map ref 4C2

Village on the old Great
North Road. A busy
staging post in Georgian
times with many examples
of Georgian Gothic
architecture. The remains
of a Norman Benedictine
priory survive as the
parish church.

Priory Farm Guesthouse ⋀

Hodsock Priory Estate,
Blyth, Worksop S81 OTY
☎ (0909) 591768 & 474299

*1000-acre mixed farm.
Farmhouse in peaceful
surroundings on a private
country estate. Easy access
from the A1(M).*
Bedrooms: 2 single,
1 double, 1 twin
Bathrooms: 2 private,
1 public
Bed & breakfast

per night:	£min	£max
Single	14.50	16.00
Double	29.00	32.00

Half board

per person:	£min	£max
Daily	21.00	22.50
Weekly	118.50	130.00

Evening meal 1800 (last
orders 2000)
Parking for 6
🛇🚲♨▥⅃S⅊🐴TV🗕 🐴🏛

Lincolnshire
Map ref 3A1

Historic town famous for
its church tower, the
Boston Stump, 272 ft
high. Still a busy port, the
town is full of interest and
has links with Boston
Massachusetts through
the Pilgrim Fathers. The
cells where they were
imprisoned can be seen
in the medieval Guildhall.
*Tourist Information Centre
☎ (0205) 356656*

Bramley House

Listed COMMENDED
267 Sleaford Road, Boston
PE21 7PQ
☎ (0205) 354538
*Small, family-run bed and
breakfast establishment with a
warm and friendly, old world
atmosphere. Completely
refurbished in late 1990.*
Bedrooms: 2 single,
1 double, 1 twin
Bathrooms: 1 public
Bed & breakfast

per night:	£min	£max
Single	17.50	19.50
Double	30.00	40.00

Half board

per person:	£min	£max
Daily	21.00	25.50
Weekly	145.00	175.00

Evening meal 1700 (last
orders 1900)
Parking for 10
🖵♨▥S▥ 🗕✻🐴

Northamptonshire
Map ref 2C1

Historic market town of
mellow stone, with many
fine buildings lining the
wide High Street and
Market Place. Sulgrave
Manor (George
Washington's ancestral
home) and Silverstone
Circuit are nearby.
*Tourist Information Centre
☎ (0280) 700111.*

Walltree House Farm ⋀

🛏🛏
Steane, Brackley NN13 5NS
☎ Banbury (0295) 811235
*200-acre arable farm. Warm,
comfortable farmhouse offers
high standards and attention
to detail. Further
accommodation available in
adjoining courtyard. Mostly
private bathrooms. Ideal base
for touring and relaxation.*
Bedrooms: 2 double, 3 twin,
3 triple
Bathrooms: 7 private,
1 public
Bed & breakfast

per night:	£min	£max
Single	18.00	30.00
Double	36.00	40.00

Half board

per person:	£min	£max
Daily		28.00

Evening meal from 1900
Parking for 10
Cards accepted: Access, Visa
🛇🚲🖵♨S🐴TV▥ 🗕
⅃✻✕🐴 OAP T

Welbeck House ⋀

🛏
Pebble Lane, Brackley
NN13 5DA
☎ (0280) 702364
*A large house in a quiet,
attractive area of Brackley,
close to the A43, M40 and
many places of interest. We
pride ourselves on our full-
scale breakfasts and a warm
welcome to all.*
Bedrooms: 2 double, 1 twin
Bathrooms: 2 public
Bed & breakfast

per night:	£min	£max
Single		14.00
Double		25.00

Parking for 4
✕🖵♨▥S TV▥ 🗕✻
✕🐴

Northamptonshire
Map ref 3A2

The Olde Three Cocks

Listed
14 High Street, Brigstock,
Kettering NN14 3HA
☎ (0536) 373214
*A 300-year-old, old world type
pub with a restaurant and
carvery.*
Bedrooms: 4 single,
4 double, 2 twin
Bathrooms: 2 public
Bed & breakfast

per night:	£min	£max
Single	20.00	25.00
Double	35.00	40.00

Lunch available
Evening meal 1800 (last
orders 2200)
Parking for 30
Cards accepted: Access, Visa,
Diners, Amex
🛇🖵♨S⅊🐴TV▥ SP

Leicestershire
Map ref 4C3

The Old Farm House

Old Mill Road, Broughton
Astley, Leicester LE9 6PQ
☎ Sutton in the Elms (0455)
282254
*Recently converted farmhouse
overlooking grass fields.
Quietly situated behind the
church, 1 minute from village
centre. Near junctions 20/21
of M1, junction 1 of M69.*
Bedrooms: 1 double, 2 twin
Bathrooms: 2 public
Bed & breakfast

per night:	£min	£max
Single	16.00	16.00
Double	32.00	32.00

Parking for 4
🛇♨▥S⅊▥ 🗕🔍U✕
🐴🏛

There are separate
sections in this
guide listing groups
specialising in farm
holidays and
accommodation
which is especially
suitable for young
people and
organised groups.

201

BUXTON

Derbyshire
Map ref 4B2

The highest market town in England and one of the oldest spas, with an elegant Crescent, Micrarium, Poole's Cavern, Opera House and attractive Pavilion Gardens. An excellent centre for exploring the Peak District.
Tourist Information Centre
☎ *(0298) 25106*

Candlemas Cottage
Damside Lane, Peak Forest, Buxton SK17 8EH
☎ (0298) 24853
Peacefully situated, with a large garden and pleasant country views. Sumptuous breakfasts, excellent evening meals locally, beautiful walks in National Park.
Bedrooms: 2 double, 1 triple
Bathrooms: 2 public

Bed & breakfast

per night:	£min	£max
Single	18.50	22.50
Double	27.00	29.00

Parking for 3

Cotesfield Farm
Parsley Hay, Buxton SK17 0BD
☎ Longnor (029 883) 256
300-acre mixed farm. In the Peak District National Park on the Tissington Trail, this farmhouse offers peace and quiet. Access from the A515 Buxton to Ashbourne road.
Bedrooms: 2 double, 1 twin
Bathrooms: 1 public

Bed & breakfast

per night:	£min	£max
Double	28.00	30.00

Parking for 6

Fairhaven ⋀
Listed APPROVED
1 Dale Terrace, Buxton SK17 6LU
☎ (0298) 24481
Centrally placed with ample roadside parking, offering English home cooking in a warm and friendly atmosphere.
Bedrooms: 1 single, 1 double, 1 twin, 3 triple
Bathrooms: 1 public

Bed & breakfast

per night:	£min	£max
Single	15.50	
Double	26.00	

Half board

per person:	£min	£max
Daily	17.75	20.25
Weekly	117.25	134.25

Evening meal 1800 (last orders 1600)
Cards accepted: Access, Visa

Hawthorn Farm Guesthouse
⬜⬜ COMMENDED
Fairfield Road, Buxton SK17 7ED
☎ (0298) 23230
A 400-year-old ex-farmhouse which has been in the family for 10 generations. Full English breakfast.
Bedrooms: 3 single, 2 double, 2 twin, 4 triple
Bathrooms: 4 private, 2 public

Bed & breakfast

per night:	£min	£max
Single	17.00	18.00
Double	34.00	36.00

Parking for 15
Open April-October

Lynstone Guesthouse
⬜⬜
3 Grange Road, Buxton SK17 6NH
☎ (0298) 77043
A spacious, welcoming and homely Victorian house, recently modernised and centrally, yet quietly, located. Both family rooms can be used as doubles or twins. Non-smokers only please.
Bedrooms: 2 double, 2 twin, 1 triple, 1 multiple
Bathrooms: 2 public

Bed & breakfast

per night:	£min	£max
Double	28.00	

Half board

per person:	£min	£max
Daily	21.00	
Weekly	140.00	

Evening meal 1800 (last orders 1800)
Parking for 3
Open March-December

Oldfield House ⋀
⬜⬜⬜ COMMENDED
8 Macclesfield Road, Buxton SK17 9AH
☎ (0298) 24371

Attractive detached Victorian guesthouse with gardens, close to the town centre and Pavilion Gardens. Spacious bedrooms. Non-smoking.
Bedrooms: 2 double, 1 triple
Bathrooms: 3 private, 1 public

Bed & breakfast

per night:	£min	£max
Single	20.00	20.00
Double	32.00	32.00

Half board

per person:	£min	£max
Daily	24.00	25.00
Weekly	161.00	161.00

Parking for 8

Pedlicote Farm
Peak Forest, Buxton SK17 8EG
☎ (0298) 22241
Old farmhouse conversion in the Peak District National Park, full of character, with a charming atmosphere and magnificent views.
Bedrooms: 1 double, 1 twin
Bathrooms: 1 public

Bed & breakfast

per night:	£min	£max
Single	18.00	18.00
Double	28.00	28.00

Half board

per person:	£min	£max
Daily	21.00	25.00
Weekly	130.00	165.00

Lunch available
Parking for 9

Portland Hotel and Park Restaurant ⋀
⬜⬜⬜
32 St. John's Road, Buxton SK17 6XQ
☎ (0298) 71493 & 22462
Fax (0298) 27464
Comfortable, family-run, Peak District hotel, with conservatory restaurant. Opposite Buxton's Pavilion Gardens and swimming pool.
Bedrooms: 5 single, 9 double, 11 twin
Bathrooms: 25 private

Bed & breakfast

per night:	£min	£max
Single	48.00	52.00
Double	56.00	65.00

Half board

per person:	£min	£max
Daily	64.50	68.50
Weekly	387.00	408.00

Lunch available
Evening meal 1845 (last orders 2100)

Parking for 17
Cards accepted: Access, Visa, Diners, Amex

CASTLE DONINGTON

Leicestershire
Map ref 4C3

A Norman castle once stood here. The world's largest collection of single-seater racing cars is displayed at Donington Park alongside the racing circuit, and an Aeropark Visitor Centre can be seen at nearby East Midlands International Airport.

The Bumble Hole
9 Borough Street, Castle Donington, Derby DE7 2LA
☎ Derby (0332) 810775
A row of converted 17th C cottages, part of which was once a basket weaving factory. It has immense character.
Bedrooms: 2 double, 1 twin
Bathrooms: 2 private, 1 public

Bed & breakfast

per night:	£min	£max
Single	25.00	25.00
Double	35.00	35.00

Half board

per person:	£min	£max
Daily	32.50	32.50

Evening meal 1930 (last orders 1200)
Parking for 3

High Barn Farm ⋀
Listed
Isley Walton, Castle Donington, Derby DE7 2RL
☎ Derby (0332) 810360
84-acre mixed farm. Accommodation is in a self-contained cottage, farmhouse and the barn. Small, friendly and peacefully rural.
Bedrooms: 2 single, 1 double, 6 twin
Bathrooms: 3 private, 3 public

Bed & breakfast

per night:	£min	£max
Single	15.00	22.00
Double	38.00	40.00

Parking for 16

CASTLETON

Derbyshire
Map ref 4B2

Large village in a spectacular Peak District setting with ruined Peveril Castle and 4 great show caverns, where the Blue John stone and lead were mined. One cavern offers a mile-long underground boat journey.

Bargate Cottage

⊜ ⊜ ⊜ COMMENDED

Bargate, Pindale Road, Castleton, Sheffield S30 2WG
☎ Hope Valley (0433) 620201
Unspoilt, renovated 17th C cottage adjacent to Peveril Castle in the centre of the village. An ideal base for relaxing, walking or touring. Many recreational facilities available locally.
Bedrooms: 3 double, 1 twin
Bathrooms: 4 private
Bed & breakfast

per night:	£min	£max
Single	17.50	

Evening meal from 1830
Parking for 6
⌂ 3 ♨ ⚑ ▭ ◆ ⊠ ⑾ ⓐ ⑤ ⨊
⑩. ⌸ ∪ ⚘ 🐾 ⚒ 🏠

Peak Hotel ⚐

How Lane, Castleton, Sheffield S30 2WJ
☎ Hope Valley (0433) 620247
Small, friendly, family-run hotel-cum-pub providing food and accommodation at reasonable prices.
Bedrooms: 2 double, 1 twin
Bathrooms: 2 public
Bed & breakfast

per night:	£min	£max
Single	20.00	20.00
Double	32.00	32.00

Lunch available
Evening meal 1800 (last orders 2200)
Parking for 60
Cards accepted: Access, Visa
⌂ ▭ ◆ ⓐ ⑤ ⑩. ⌸ ⌕ ⚘ ⚒ 🐾

Ye Olde Cheshire Cheese Inn

How Lane, Castleton, Sheffield S30 2WJ
☎ Hope Valley (0433) 620330
17th C inn providing home-cooked food, set in the heart of the Peak District. 30 home-cooked dishes, including roast wild boar and guinea fowl. No pool table, no jukebox, no machines!

Bedrooms: 1 single, 3 double, 2 twin
Bathrooms: 6 private
Bed & breakfast

per night:	£min	£max
Single	22.50	25.00
Double	43.00	45.00

Lunch available
Evening meal 1800 (last orders 2250)
Parking for 100
Cards accepted: Access, Visa
⌖ ▭ ◄ ⓐ ⑤ ⌕ ⑩. ⌸ ∪ ↑
∕ ⚒ 🐾 🏠

CHESTERFIELD

Derbyshire
Map ref 4B2

Famous for the twisted spire of its parish church, Chesterfield has some fine modern buildings and excellent shopping facilities, including a large, traditional open-air market. Hardwick Hall and Bolsover Castle are nearby.
Tourist Information Centre
☎ *(0246) 207777/8*

34 Gladstone Road

 Listed

Chesterfield S40 4TE
☎ (0246) 209060
Private detached house built in 1982 in an old, quiet part of town and within walking distance of town centre. Car parking space available.
Bedrooms: 1 single, 1 double
Bathrooms: 1 public
Bed & breakfast

per night:	£min	£max
Single	13.00	13.00
Double	26.00	26.00

Parking for 1
⌂ 5 ⑩ ⓐ ⚑ ⑩ ⑩. ⌸ ⚒ 🐾

Wilday Meadow

⊜ ⊜

Barlow, Sheffield S18 5SH
☎ Sheffield (0742) 890541
10-acre mixed farm. A large, old stone-built bungalow with a lovely garden and open views. A large conservatory is available. Non-smokers only please.
Bedrooms: 2 twin
Bathrooms: 2 private
Bed & breakfast

per night:	£min	£max
Single	18.50	25.00
Double	30.00	37.50

Half board

per person:	£min	£max
Daily	26.50	30.00
Weekly	150.00	175.00

Evening meal 1830 (last orders 1930)
Parking for 9
⌂ 2 ♨ ⚑ ▭ ◆ ⑩ ⓐ ⑤ ⌕ ⊠
⑩ ⑩. ⌸ ∪ ⚘ ⚒ 🐾

CHINLEY

Derbyshire
Map ref 4B2

The Squirrels

1 Green Lane, Chinley, Stockport, Cheshire SK12 6AA
☎ New Mills (0663) 750001
Fax (0663) 750830
A comfortable, family-run country hotel offering substantial home-cooked meals and real ales. Many varied activities and attractions are within easy reach.
Bedrooms: 6 double, 1 triple
Bathrooms: 5 private, 1 public, 1 private shower
Bed & breakfast

per night:	£min	£max
Single	17.50	
Double	25.50	

Half board

per person:	£min	£max
Daily	15.00	

Lunch available
Evening meal 1800 (last orders 2230)
Parking for 17
Cards accepted: Access, Visa, Diners
⌂ ◆ ⓐ ⑤ ⑩. ⌸ ⚘ ⚒ 🐾

CLAYBROOKE PARVA

Leicestershire
Map ref 4C3

Claybrooke Rectory

 Listed

Claybrooke Parva, Lutterworth LE17 5AE
☎ Leire (0455) 209277
Fax (0455) 290277
Telex 311754 CHACOM G
A Queen Anne rectory with high Gothic extension, in spacious grounds. Stands next to the church. A5, M1, M69 and M6 are all nearby.
Bedrooms: 2 single, 1 double, 1 twin, 1 triple
Bathrooms: 1 public
Bed & breakfast

per night:	£min	£max
Single	15.00	20.00
Double	25.00	30.00

Evening meal 1830 (last orders 2300)
Parking for 10
⌂ ⚑ ◆ ⑩ ⓐ ⑤ ⌕ ⊠ ⑩.
⌸ ∪ ⚘ ⑩ ⑩ 🏠 ⑦

COALVILLE

Leicestershire
Map ref 4B3

Home of new Snibston Discovery Park and close to Twycross Zoo and the Charnwood Forest area.
Tourist Information Centre
☎ *(0530) 510851/473000*

Church Lane Farm

⊜

Ravenstone LE6 2AE
☎ (0530) 810536
Traditional Leicestershire, 18th C beamed farmhouse, furnished with antiques. Non-smokers only please. Evening meals by arrangement.
Bedrooms: 2 double, 1 twin
Bathrooms: 3 private
Bed & breakfast

per night:	£min	£max
Single	19.00	
Double	30.00	

Half board

per person:	£min	£max
Daily	24.50	

Evening meal 1845 (last orders 1930)
Parking for 10
Cards accepted: Access, Visa
⊟ ◆ ⑩ ⓐ ⑤ ⌕ ⊠ ⑩ ⑩. ⌸
∪ ↑ ⚘ 🐾 ⏚ 🏠

Saint Josephs

Abbey Road, Coalville, Leicester LE67 4UA
☎ Shepshed (0509) 503943
Country cottage of character in the heart of Charnwood Forest, 2 miles from M1 junction 23. A car is essential.
Bedrooms: 2 single, 1 double, 2 twin
Bathrooms: 2 public
Bed & breakfast

per night:	£min	£max
Single	15.00	19.00
Double	30.00	38.00

Parking for 3
Open April-October
⌂ ⚘ ⚑ ◆ ⑩ ⓐ ⑤ ⊠ ⑩ ⑩. ⌸ ⚘
⚒ 🐾

CONINGSBY

Lincolnshire
Map ref 4D2

White Bull Inn

55 High Street, Coningsby, Lincoln LN4 4RB
☎ (0526) 42439
A warm welcome awaits at this friendly pub with real ale, riverside beer garden and large children's playground. Traditional home-made meals are available every day, lunch
Continued ▶

CONINGSBY

Continued

time and evening. Half a mile from RAF Coningsby.
Bedrooms: 2 single,
1 double, 1 twin
Bathrooms: 2 public

Bed & breakfast

per night:	£min	£max
Single	12.00	14.00
Double	22.00	25.00

Half board

per person:	£min	£max
Daily	14.00	18.00
Weekly	70.00	100.00

Lunch available
Evening meal 1900 (last orders 2200)
Parking for 60
Cards accepted: Access, Visa

COTGRAVE

Nottinghamshire
Map ref 4C2

Jerico Farm

COMMENDED

Fosse Way, Cotgrave,
Nottingham NG12 3HG
☎ Kinoulton (0949) 81733
*120-acre mixed farm.
Attractive, warm, comfortable accommodation with views over the Nottinghamshire Wolds. Only 8 miles from Nottingham off the Fosse Way between Newark and Leicester. A warm welcome assured. Family-run.*
Bedrooms: 1 double, 2 twin
Bathrooms: 1 private,
1 public

Bed & breakfast

per night:	£min	£max
Single	16.00	
Double	30.00	

Parking for 3

CRANFORD ST ANDREW

Northamptonshire
Map ref 3A1

Dairy Farm

COMMENDED

Cranford St Andrew,
Kettering NN14 4AQ
☎ (053 678) 273
350-acre mixed farm. 17th C thatched house with inglenook fireplaces and a garden with an ancient circular dovecote and mature trees. Good food.
Bedrooms: 1 double, 2 twin

Bathrooms: 2 private,
1 public

Bed & breakfast

per night:	£min	£max
Single	18.00	25.00
Double	36.00	40.00

Half board

per person:	£min	£max
Daily	28.00	35.00

Evening meal 1900 (last orders 1200)
Parking for 5

CRICK

Northamptonshire
Map ref 4C3

The Hall

Crick, Northampton
NN6 7TP
☎ Rugby (0788) 822393
Comfortable and spacious, late Georgian house with a walled garden. Located at the end of Church Street on the road to Yelvertoft in a village setting.
Bedrooms: 1 double, 1 twin
Bathrooms: 2 private

Bed & breakfast

per night:	£min	£max
Single	22.00	
Double	38.00	

Parking for 4
Open February-October

CROMFORD

Derbyshire
Map ref 4B2

Sir Richard Arkwright built the world's first mechanized cotton spinning mill here in 1771, together with cottages for his workers and a church. The mill can still be visited.

Tinsmiths Workshop ⋀

Collectors Corner, 43 Market Place, Cromford, Matlock DE4 3RE
☎ Wirksworth (0629) 822659
Fax (0629) 826132
Bedrooms are in a recently converted tinsmith's workshop annexe building. Part of Cromford conservation area. Group facilities and discounts. Activity holidays a speciality.
Bedrooms: 1 single,
2 multiple
Bathrooms: 2 public

Bed & breakfast

per night:	£min	£max
Single		11.25

Half board

per person:	£min	£max
Daily		15.00

Lunch available
Evening meal 1800 (last orders 2030)

CROPWELL BISHOP

Nottinghamshire
Map ref 4C2

Home Farm

Listed

Fern Road, Cropwell Bishop, Nottingham NG12 3BU
☎ Nottingham (0602) 892598
280-acre arable & livestock farm. Family-run, opposite the church in Cropwell Bishop. Approximately 10 miles south-east of Nottingham in the Vale of Belvoir.
Bedrooms: 1 double, 1 twin
Bathrooms: 1 public

Bed & breakfast

per night:	£min	£max
Single	14.00	15.00
Double	28.00	30.00

Parking for 6

CURBAR

Derbyshire
Map ref 4B2

Breeze Hill

The Green, Curbar, Calver, Sheffield S30 1YH
☎ Hope Valley (0433) 630046
Comfortable accommodation within an extended and improved cottage which has retained its old fashioned charm, in a peaceful village. Elevated views of Calver, Curbar and Froggatt Edge.
Bedrooms: 1 single, 1 triple
Bathrooms: 2 public,
1 private shower

Bed & breakfast

per night:	£min	£max
Single	16.00	17.00
Double	32.00	34.00

Half board

per person:	£min	£max
Daily	25.00	27.00
Weekly	175.00	195.00

Lunch available
Evening meal from 1800
Parking for 1

DERBY

Derbyshire
Map ref 4B2

Modern industrial city but with ancient origins. There is a wide range of attractions including several museums (notably Royal Crown Derby), a theatre, a concert hall, and the cathedral with fine ironwork and Bess of Hardwick's tomb.
Tourist Information Centre
☎ *(0332) 255802*

189 Main Road

Morley, Derby DE7 6DG
☎ (0332) 780349
Friendly family bungalow in the country, facing the Rose & Crown public house on the Smalley crossroads, 6 miles from Derby.
Bedrooms: 1 double, 1 twin
Bathrooms: 1 private,
1 public

Bed & breakfast

per night:	£min	£max
Double		24.00

Half board

per person:	£min	£max
Daily		18.00

Parking for 2

Bonehill Farm

Listed

Etwall Road, Mickleover, Derby DE3 5DN
☎ (0332) 513553
120-acre mixed farm. A traditional farmhouse in a rural setting, 3 miles from Derby. Alton Towers, the Peak District, historic houses and the Potteries are all within easy reach.
Bedrooms: 1 double, 1 twin,
1 triple
Bathrooms: 1 public

Bed & breakfast

per night:	£min	£max
Single	13.00	16.00
Double	26.00	32.00

Parking for 6

Braemar Guesthouse ⋀

1061 London Road, Alvaston, Derby DE2 8PZ
☎ (0332) 572522
Family-run guesthouse near the city centre, Donington Park, M1, airport, Alton Towers, BMX track and Moor Ways Sports Centre.
Bedrooms: 6 single,
2 double, 3 twin, 4 triple

Bathrooms: 3 private,
5 public, 4 private showers
Bed & breakfast

per night:	£min	£max
Single	15.00	16.00
Double	26.00	30.00

Evening meal 1830 (last
orders 1730)
Parking for 10
Cards accepted: Access, Visa

Rangemoor Hotel
67 Macklin Street, Derby
DE1 1LF
☎ (0332) 47252
*Family-run city centre hotel
within walking distance of all
amenities and with a large
lock-up car park.*
Bedrooms: 12 single,
5 double, 4 twin, 3 triple
Bathrooms: 6 public
Bed & breakfast

per night:	£min	£max
Single	22.00	30.00
Double	34.00	42.00

Parking for 28

DESBOROUGH
Northamptonshire
Map ref 4C3

West Lodge Farm ♠♠
COMMENDED
Pipewell Road, Desborough,
Kettering NN14 2SH
☎ Kettering (0536) 760552
*570-acre arable farm. Late
Georgian farmhouse on a
farm which includes 60 acres
of woodland, farm walks and
site of an old Cistercian
abbey.*
Bedrooms: 1 double, 1 twin
Bathrooms: 1 private,
1 public, 1 private shower

Bed & breakfast

per night:	£min	£max
Single	18.00	22.00
Double	38.00	42.00

Evening meal 1730 (last
orders 1930)
Parking for 5
Open January-July,
September-December

DONINGTON ON BAIN
Lincolnshire
Map ref 4D2

Black Horse Inn
Main Road, Donington on
Bain, Louth LN11 9TJ
☎ Louth (0507) 343640
*On the Viking Way with many
market towns within a 10-20
mile radius. Near to Lincoln,
the coast, Grimsby and
Boston. 4 family rooms can
be made available.*
Bedrooms: 8 twin
Bathrooms: 8 private
Bed & breakfast

per night:	£min	£max
Single	25.00	30.00
Double	40.00	50.00

Lunch available
Evening meal 1900 (last
orders 2200)
Parking for 100

Individual
proprietors have
supplied all details
of accommodation.
Although we do
check for accuracy,
we advise you to
confirm the
information at the
time of booking.

DOVEDALE
Derbyshire
Map ref 4B2

Very popular beauty spot
best seen from the
footpath bordering the
River Dove. It runs in a
narrow valley between
high wooded banks with
rocky outcrops and caves.

St. Leonards Cottage
Dovedale, Thorpe,
Ashbourne DE6 2AW
☎ Thorpe Cloud (033 529)
224
*Country cottage on Thorpe
village green, ideal for
touring. 4 bedrooms en-suite,
central heating, tea/coffee
facilities. Sorry no pets in the
house.*
Bedrooms: 3 double, 1 twin
Bathrooms: 4 private,
1 public
Bed & breakfast

per night:	£min	£max
Single	16.50	
Double	33.00	

Half board

per person:	£min	£max
Daily	25.00	

Evening meal from 1830
Parking for 5

DOVERIDGE
Derbyshire
Map ref 4B2

The Beeches Farmhouse ♠♠
HIGHLY COMMENDED
The Beeches, Waldley,
Doveridge, Derby DE6 5LR
☎ Rocester (0889) 590288
Fax (0889) 590288
*160-acre dairy farm. 18th C
farmhouse with licensed
restaurant in beautiful
Derbyshire, close to Alton*

*Towers and Dovedale. Won
top national award for farm-
based catering service in
1992.*
Bedrooms: 2 double, 4 twin,
6 multiple
Bathrooms: 8 private,
2 public
Bed & breakfast

per night:	£min	£max
Single	21.00	35.00
Double	30.00	52.00

Half board

per person:	£min	£max
Daily	25.50	39.50

Evening meal 1830 (last
orders 2030)
Parking for 15
Cards accepted: Access, Visa,
Amex

Ad Display advertisement
appears on this page

EARL STERNDALE
Derbyshire
Map ref 4B2

Dowall Hall Farm ♠♠
Glutton Bridge, Earl
Sterndale, Buxton
SK17 0RW
☎ Longnor (029 883) 297
Fax (0298) 83297
*300-acre dairy & livestock
farm. A 17th C farmhouse,
ideal for touring the Peak
District.*
Bedrooms: 1 double, 1 triple
Bathrooms: 1 public
Bed & breakfast

per night:	£min	£max
Single		13.00
Double		24.00

Parking for 3
Open May-November

205

EARLS BARTON

Northamptonshire
Map ref 2C1

The church of All Saints is particularly noted for its fine Anglo-Saxon tower.

Glebe House
Sunny Side, Earls Barton, Northampton NN6 0EX
☎ Northampton (0604) 811312
200-year-old stone, 3-storey, former rectory in a quiet location with views across the Nene Valley.
Bedrooms: 1 double, 2 twin, 1 triple
Bathrooms: 1 private, 1 public

Bed & breakfast

per night:	£min	£max
Single	16.00	17.50
Double	32.00	35.00

Parking for 2

EDALE

Derbyshire
Map ref 4B2

Rambler Inn ♨

Edale, Sheffield S30 2ZA
☎ Hope Valley (0433) 670268
Small, stone-built hotel in its own grounds in Edale village at the start of the Pennine Way. Walkers are very welcome.
Bedrooms: 2 double, 3 twin, 3 triple
Bathrooms: 3 public

Bed & breakfast

per night:	£min	£max
Single	18.75	21.75
Double	37.50	43.50

Half board

per person:	£min	£max
Daily	25.00	28.00

Lunch available
Evening meal 1830 (last orders 2100)
Parking for 20
Cards accepted: Access, Visa, Amex

EDWINSTOWE

Nottinghamshire
Map ref 4C2

Village close to Sherwood Forest, famous for the legend of Robin Hood. The Visitor Centre and Country Park includes a Robin Hood exhibition, and there are guided walks and many special events.
Tourist Information Centre
☎ (0623) 824490

Duncan Wood Lodge
Carburton, Worksop S80 3BP
☎ Worksop (0909) 483614
Countryside lodge in the heart of the Dukeries in woodland surroundings. 3 miles from the Major Oak on the B6034. Adjacent to Clumber Park.
Bedrooms: 1 single, 3 double, 3 twin, 1 multiple
Bathrooms: 4 private, 2 public

Bed & breakfast

per night:	£min	£max
Single	25.00	30.00
Double	30.00	35.00

Lunch available
Evening meal 1830 (last orders 2030)
Parking for 12
Cards accepted:

ELMESTHORPE

Leicestershire
Map ref 4C3

Water Meadows Farm
22 Billington Road East, Elmesthorpe, Leicester LE9 7SB
☎ Earl Shilton (0455) 843417
15-acre beef farm. Tudor-style, oak-beamed farmhouse with extensive gardens, including private woodland and stream. Own produce, home cooking. Located along a private road. Central for visiting many places of scenic and historic interest.
Bedrooms: 1 double, 1 twin, 1 multiple
Bathrooms: 1 public

Bed & breakfast

per night:	£min	£max
Single	16.00	16.00
Double	26.00	26.00

Half board

per person:	£min	£max
Daily	23.00	23.00
Weekly	120.00	120.00

Evening meal from 1900
Parking for 10

GAINSBOROUGH

Lincolnshire
Map ref 4C2

Laundry Cottage
Knaith Hill, Knaith, Gainsborough DN21 5PF
☎ (0427) 613248
Attractive family cottage with character, converted from an old laundry, 3 miles south of Gainsborough. Local inns serve good food.
Bedrooms: 1 double, 2 twin
Bathrooms: 2 public

Bed & breakfast

per night:	£min	£max
Single	13.00	13.00
Double	26.00	26.00

Parking for 6

GONALSTON

Nottinghamshire
Map ref 4C2

Hall Farm House ♨
👑 COMMENDED
Gonalston, Nottingham NG14 7JA
☎ Nottingham (0602) 663112
Fax (0602) 664844
30-acre mixed farm. Beautiful 18th C farmhouse in quiet, pretty village off the A612. Comfortable rooms overlook lovely garden with swimming pool and tennis court. Games room, table tennis, piano.
Bedrooms: 2 double, 1 triple
Bathrooms: 1 private, 2 public

Bed & breakfast

per night:	£min	£max
Single	20.00	25.00
Double	35.00	40.00

Half board

per person:	£min	£max
Daily	32.50	

Parking for 4

GRANTHAM

Lincolnshire
Map ref 3A1

On the old Great North Road (A1), Grantham's splendid parish church has a fine spire and chained library. Sir Isaac Newton was educated here and his statue stands in front of the museum which includes displays on Newton and other famous local people.
Tourist Information Centre
☎ (0476) 66444.

Green Hill House
55 Barrowby Road, Grantham NG31 8AA
☎ (0476) 73104
Georgian Grade II listed town house with a large, private garden and enclosed patio. Close to town centre.
Bedrooms: 1 double, 1 twin
Bathrooms: 2 private, 1 public

Bed & breakfast

per night:	£min	£max
Single	22.50	27.50
Double	35.00	40.00

Half board

per person:	£min	£max
Daily	31.50	36.50

Evening meal from 1830
Parking for 2

GREAT CASTERTON

Leicestershire
Map ref 3A1

Plough Inn
Main Street, Great Casterton, Stamford, Lincolnshire PE9 4AA
☎ Stamford (0780) 62178
A village pub, 500 yards from the A1, north of Stamford on the B1081. Close to Stamford and Rutland Water.
Bedrooms: 2 double
Bathrooms: 2 private

Bed & breakfast

per night:	£min	£max
Single	25.00	
Double	45.00	

Lunch available
Evening meal 1900 (last orders 2130)
Parking for 16
Cards accepted: Access, Visa

GREAT LONGSTONE

Derbyshire
Map ref 4B2

Willow Croft
Station Road, Great Longstone, Bakewell DE4 1TS
☎ Bakewell (0629) 640576
Lovely bungalow with private garden. Short, level walk to village, which has good meal facilities. Within easy reach of stately homes. Looking forward to welcoming you.
Bedrooms: 1 double, 1 twin, 1 triple
Bathrooms: 3 private

Bed & breakfast

per night:	£min	£max
Single	15.00	25.00
Double	30.00	36.00

Parking for 4
Open February-December

GUNTHORPE

Nottinghamshire
Map ref 4C2

The Unicorn Hotel and Restaurant
COMMENDED
Gunthorpe Bridge, Gunthorpe NG14 7FB
☎ Nottingham (0602) 663612
Fax (0602) 664801
A fully residential riverside inn with private fishing and moorings. Ideal for small fishing parties and for exploring Nottinghamshire.
Bedrooms: 7 double, 5 twin, 4 multiple
Bathrooms: 16 private

Bed & breakfast

per night:	£min	£max
Single	40.00	
Double	55.00	

Lunch available
Evening meal 1815 (last orders 2145)
Parking for 200
Cards accepted: Access, Visa, Amex

National Crown ratings were correct at the time of going to press but are subject to change. Please check at the time of booking.

HAINTON

Lincolnshire
Map ref 4D2

Old Vicarage
School Lane, Hainton, Lincoln LN3 6LW
☎ Burgh on Bain (0507) 313660
Quiet country household in the Wolds, in 1 acre of secluded gardens. We offer home baking and produce, and are convenient for the Viking Way, the coast and Lincoln. Evening meals by arrangement. Non-smokers only please.
Bedrooms: 1 double, 2 twin
Bathrooms: 2 public

Bed & breakfast

per night:	£min	£max
Single	15.00	
Double	30.00	

Half board

per person:	£min	£max
Daily	22.50	
Weekly	145.00	

Evening meal from 1900
Parking for 6

HALLATON

Leicestershire
Map ref 4C3

The Bewicke Arms
Listed COMMENDED
1 Eastgate, Hallaton, Market Harborough LE16 8UB
☎ (085 889) 217
400-year-old thatched pub offering the best in pub meals and real ale. A great place to stay. Telephone for brochure.
Bedrooms: 1 double, 2 twin
Bathrooms: 2 public

Bed & breakfast

per night:	£min	£max
Single	32.50	
Double	39.50	

Lunch available
Evening meal 1930 (last orders 2145)
Parking for 20
Cards accepted: Access, Visa

Half board prices shown are per person but in some cases may be based on double/twin occupancy.

HARTINGTON

Derbyshire
Map ref 4B2

Village with a large market-place set in fine surroundings near the River Dove, well-known for its fishing and Izaak Walton, author of 'The Compleat Angler'.

Ivy House
Biggin by Hartington, Newhaven, Buxton SK17 0DT
☎ (0298) 84709
19th C house near the High Peak and Tissington Trails at Newhaven. Panoramic views of the Staffordshire hills can be found at this establishment. Dogs welcome. No smoking.
Bedrooms: 1 double, 1 twin, 1 triple
Bathrooms: 1 private, 1 public

Bed & breakfast

per night:	£min	£max
Double	32.00	50.00

Half board

per person:	£min	£max
Daily	26.00	35.00
Weekly	154.00	190.00

Evening meal from 1900
Parking for 3

HATHERSAGE

Derbyshire
Map ref 4B2

Hillside village in the Peak District, dominated by the church with many good brasses and monuments to the Eyre family which provide a link with Charlotte Bronte. Little John, friend of Robin Hood, is said to be buried here.

Hillfoot Farm
Castleton Road, Hathersage, Sheffield S30 1AH
☎ Hope Valley (0433) 51673
Newly built accommodation on the existing farmhouse. Ground floor rooms. All rooms are en-suite with colour TV, tea/coffee facilities. Large car park.
Bedrooms: 1 double, 2 twin, 1 multiple
Bathrooms: 4 private

Bed & breakfast

per night:	£min	£max
Single	20.00	30.00
Double	30.00	36.00

Half board

per person:	£min	£max
Daily	24.50	

Lunch available
Evening meal 1800 (last orders 1900)
Parking for 13

The Mount
Castleton Road, Hathersage, Sheffield S30 1AH
☎ Hope Valley (0433) 50388
A recently renovated Victorian family house on the A625 Hathersage to Castleton road. There is a bathroom for the sole use of guests.
Bedrooms: 1 double, 2 twin
Bathrooms: 1 public

Bed & breakfast

per night:	£min	£max
Single	15.00	18.00
Double	30.00	32.00

Parking for 6

The Old Vicarage
Church Bank, Hathersage, Sheffield S30 1AB
☎ Hope Valley (0433) 651099
In 1845 Charlotte Bronte stayed in this listed building which is beside Little John's grave overlooking the Hope Valley. Central for Chatsworth, the caves, fishing and walking.
Bedrooms: 2 double, 1 twin
Bathrooms: 1 private, 2 public, 1 private shower

Bed & breakfast

per night:	£min	£max
Single	17.50	18.00
Double	30.00	36.00

Parking for 3

Windrush
6 Park Edge, Hathersage, Sheffield S30 1BS
☎ Hope Valley (0433) 50531
An Edwardian house overlooking the village and grazing sheep in superb scenery. Large rooms, a comfortable atmosphere, a warm welcome and English country cooking.
Bedrooms: 1 triple
Bathrooms: 1 public

Bed & breakfast

per night:	£min	£max
Single	15.00	15.00
Double	30.00	30.00

Continued ▶

207

HATHERSAGE

Continued

Half board

per person:	£min	£max
Daily	22.00	22.00
Weekly	154.00	154.00

Evening meal from 1900
Parking for 2

🛇🗗♨⬚Ⓤ🛆Ⓢ✕📺🖿🛆

HAYFIELD

Derbyshire
Map ref 4B2

Village set in spectacular scenery at the highest point of the Peak District with the best approach to the Kinder Scout plateau via the Kinder Downfall. An excellent centre for walking. Three reservoirs close by.

Bridge End Guesthouse and Restaurant

7 Church Street, Hayfield, Stockport, Cheshire
SK12 5JE
☎ New Mills (0663) 747321
In the picturesque conservation area of Hayfield, adjoining Kinder Scout and extensive moorlands. Accessible to all parts of the Peak District National Park.
Bedrooms: 4 double, 1 twin, 1 triple
Bathrooms: 6 private

Bed & breakfast

per night:	£min	£max
Single		28.00
Double		40.00

Half board

per person:	£min	£max
Daily		43.00
Weekly		250.00

Lunch available
Evening meal 1900 (last orders 2200)
Parking for 6
Cards accepted: Access, Visa

🛇🗗🖿⬚🐕🛆Ⓢ🗗📺◐
🖿🛆🍴🛥🗗OAP🝔SP

Stet Barn Farm

Lane Head Road, Little Hayfield, Stockport, Cheshire
SK12 5NS
☎ New Mills (0663) 745970
Stone farmhouse in a peaceful rural setting with views of Kinder Scout. 1.5 miles from Hayfield and Kinder Reservoir.
Bedrooms: 1 double, 1 twin
Bathrooms: 2 private

Bed & breakfast

per night:	£min	£max
Single		15.00
Double		30.00

Parking for 4
Open February-December

🛇🗗🖿⬚Ⓤ🛆Ⓢ✕🖿🛆✿🖿🏛

The Waltzing Weasel Inn

New Mills Road, Birch Vale, Hayfield, Stockport, Cheshire
SK12 5BT
☎ New Mills (0663) 743402
Peak District inn. Stunning views of Kinder Scout. Fine restaurant, music and machine-free bar with open fire and country antiques. Owner-run.
Bedrooms: 1 single, 5 double, 2 twin
Bathrooms: 8 private

Bed & breakfast

per night:	£min	£max
Single	40.00	75.00
Double	55.00	90.00

Half board

per person:	£min	£max
Daily	61.50	96.50

Lunch available
Evening meal 1900 (last orders 2100)
Parking for 35
Cards accepted: Access, Visa

🛇12🗗🖿Ⓔ🗗⬚♨🝔🛡
Ⓢ🖿🛆🍴✿🖿SP🏛

HINCKLEY

Leicestershire
Map ref 4B3

The town has an excellent leisure centre. Bosworth Battlefield, with its Visitor Centre and Battle Trail, is 5 miles away.
Tourist Information Centre
☎ *(0455) 635106*

Hoults of Hollygrange ∧∧

🝔🝔
101 Hollycroft, Hinckley
LE10 0HF
☎ (0455) 230154
Family residence built in 1930, with a friendly and homely atmosphere.
Bedrooms: 1 single, 1 twin, 2 triple
Bathrooms: 1 public, 4 private showers

> Map references apply to the colour maps at the back of this guide.

Bed & breakfast

per night:	£min	£max
Single		14.00	16.00
Double		28.00	32.00

Parking for 6

🛇🗗🖿⬚Ⓤ🝔🛡📺🖿,
🛆🖿

Woodside Farm Guesthouse ∧∧

🝔🝔🝔 COMMENDED
Ashby Road, Stapleton, Leicester LE9 8JE
☎ Market Bosworth (0455) 291929
16-acre arable & horse farm. Close to the Battle of Bosworth site and Kirkby Mallory race track. 3 miles to North Hinckley on A447.
Bedrooms: 1 single, 3 double, 1 twin, 1 triple
Bathrooms: 3 private, 2 public, 1 private shower

Bed & breakfast

per night:	£min	£max
Single	18.00	22.50
Double	32.50	48.00

Half board

per person:	£min	£max
Daily	25.00	40.00

Lunch available
Evening meal 1830 (last orders 2130)
Parking for 17
Cards accepted: Access, Visa

🛇🗗🖿⬚Ⓢ✕🖿📺🖿🛆
Ⓤ🍴✿🛥🖿OAP🝔SP

HOLCOT

Northamptonshire
Map ref 4C3

The White Swan Inn

Main Street, Holcot, Northampton NN6 9SP
☎ Northampton (0604) 781263
250-year-old, part-thatched inn, in village 1 mile from Pitsford Reservoir where there are facilities for fishing, sailing and bird-watching.
Bedrooms: 1 single, 1 double, 1 twin
Bathrooms: 1 public

Bed & breakfast

per night:	£min	£max
Single	18.00	18.00
Double	35.00	35.00

Lunch available
Evening meal 1800 (last orders 2030)
Parking for 24
Cards accepted: Access, Visa

🛇🗗🖿⬚🛡🖿🛆❊✿🛥🖿

HOPE

Derbyshire
Map ref 4B2

Village in the Hope Valley which is an excellent base for walking in the Peak District and for fishing and shooting. There is a well-dressing ceremony each June and its August sheep dog trials are well-known. Castleton Caves are nearby.

Underleigh House ∧∧

🝔🝔🝔 HIGHLY COMMENDED
Off Edale Road, Hope, Sheffield S30 2RG
☎ (0433) 621372
Secluded farmhouse-style home 1.5 miles from village. Magnificent countryside views from all rooms. En-suite facilities, colour TV and resident teddy bear. Gourmet dinners by owner chef.
Bedrooms: 3 double, 2 twin
Bathrooms: 5 private

Bed & breakfast

per night:	£min	£max
Single	26.00	29.00
Double	40.00	44.00

Half board

per person:	£min	£max
Daily	33.00	35.00

Evening meal from 1930
Parking for 5
Cards accepted: Access, Visa

🛇12🗗Ⓔ🗗⬚♨⬚Ⓤ🛆Ⓢ
✕🖿🛆✿🖿🝔SP

HORSLEY

Derbyshire
Map ref 4B2

Horsley Lodge ∧∧

🝔🝔🝔 COMMENDED
Smalley Mill Road, Horsley, Derby DE2 5BL
☎ Derby (0332) 780838
Fax (0332) 781118
Magnificent stone country house, 5 miles from Derby. Easy access to M1. 18 hole golf-course, private fishing, free golf.
Bedrooms: 2 double, 2 twin, 2 triple
Bathrooms: 6 private

Bed & breakfast

per night:	£min	£max
Single	30.00	40.00
Double	40.00	60.00

Half board

per person:	£min	£max
Daily	40.00	50.00

Lunch available
Evening meal 1900 (last orders 2100)
Parking for 200
Cards accepted: Access, Visa

🎅👤🛐🖵♦🏧📶⒮♨📺
🏠, 🗲↑1-180 ⚘🔍🕯↺♪↿
❀🐾🅿️🏠

HUSBANDS BOSWORTH

Leicestershire
Map ref 4C3

Mrs J. Armitage

🖼 APPROVED

31-33 High Street, Husbands Bosworth, Lutterworth LE17 6LJ
☎ Market Harborough (0858) 880066
Village centre home of character on A427, with wholesome cooking and warm welcome. Good choice of reasonably-priced evening meals at nearby inn.
Bedrooms: 2 twin
Bathrooms: 1 public
Bed & breakfast

per night:	£min	£max
Single	12.00	14.00
Double	24.00	28.00

Parking for 6

🎅🐴Ⓜ♦🔲🛐⒮♨📺🏠, ✈
🐾🅃

KEYWORTH

Nottinghamshire
Map ref 4C2

Laurel Farm

Browns Lane, Stanton-on-the-Wolds, Keyworth, Nottingham NG12 5BL
☎ Plumtree (060 77) 3488
An old farmhouse adjacent to village church with easy access from the A46 and 20 minutes from M1. Large garden, children welcome. Non-smokers only please.
Bedrooms: 3 twin, 1 triple
Bathrooms: 1 private, 1 public
Bed & breakfast

per night:	£min	£max
Single	15.00	16.50
Double	30.00	33.00

Half board

per person:	£min	£max
Daily	22.50	25.00

Evening meal 1900 (last orders 1900)
Parking for 8

🎅🖵♦🔲🛐⒮♨🏠, 🚗↺
❀🐾

KIRBY MUXLOE

Leicestershire
Map ref 4C3

Faith Cottage

Listed

400 Ratby Lane, Kirby Muxloe, Leicester LE9 9AQ
☎ Leicester (0533) 387435
Old world cottage, convenient for Leicester and surrounding places of interest.
Bedrooms: 1 single, 1 twin
Bathrooms: 1 private, 1 public
Bed & breakfast

per night:	£min	£max
Single	15.00	15.00
Double	30.00	30.00

Parking for 3

🎅🐴7🖵♦🔲♨🐾❀🐾

LANEHAM

Nottinghamshire
Map ref 4C2

The Old Cottage

Main Street, Laneham, Retford DN22 0NA
☎ Dunham-on-Trent (0777) 228555
Small family-run licensed hotel quietly situated in centre of village near River Trent. Convenient for Lincoln, Newark and Sherwood Forest.
Bedrooms: 2 single, 1 twin, 1 triple
Bathrooms: 3 private, 1 public
Bed & breakfast

per night:	£min	£max
Single	22.00	25.00
Double	32.00	35.00

Lunch available
Evening meal 1900 (last orders 1930)
Parking for 18
Cards accepted: Access, Visa

🎅🐴5🖵♦🛐♨↺🏠, 🚗↺❀
✈🐾🅿️🏠

LANGHAM

Leicestershire
Map ref 4C3

Village with a fine church, whose tower and spire are a local landmark, and a 17th C hall and manor. Sailing and fishing facilities are available at Rutland Water 2 miles away.

The Old Hall

Langham, Oakham LE15 7JE
☎ Oakham (0572) 722923 & 757338

17th C country home in Langham village opposite the church. Three pubs in village, convenient for A1. Large garden and billiard room.
Bedrooms: 1 single, 1 double, 1 triple
Bathrooms: 1 private, 1 public
Bed & breakfast

per night:	£min	£max
Single	17.00	17.00
Double	25.00	28.00

Parking for 12

🎅♦🔲⒮♨📺🏠, 🚗🔍❀
🐾🅿️🏠

LEICESTER

Leicestershire
Map ref 4C3

Modern industrial city with a wide variety of attractions including Roman remains, ancient churches, Georgian houses and a Victorian clock tower. Excellent shopping precincts, arcades and market, museums, theatres, concert hall and sports and leisure centres.
Tourist Information Centre ☎ (0533) 511300 or 511301

David House

17-21 Saxby Street, Highfields, Leicester LE2 0ND
☎ (0533) 545139
Family-run bed and breakfast, near train station and city centre. Children welcome. Parking places. TV in all rooms.
Bedrooms: 10 single, 3 double, 6 twin, 5 triple, 1 multiple
Bathrooms: 6 public
Bed & breakfast

per night:	£min	£max
Single	11.00	11.00
Double	22.00	22.00

Parking for 6

🎅🛐♿🔲♨📺🏠, ✈✈

Richards Backpackers Hostel.

157 Wanlip Lane, Birstall, Leicester LE4 4GL
☎ (0533) 673107
Small establishment catering mainly for backpackers, and other young tourists. Tent space. Home-made bread. Non-smokers only please.
Bedrooms: 1 twin, 1 triple
Bathrooms: 1 public
Bed & breakfast

per night:	£min	£max
Single	7.00	10.00

Half board

per person:	£min	£max
Daily	11.00	14.00

Evening meal 1800 (last orders 2000)
Parking for 1

🎅🐴6🔲🛐⒮♨🏠, 🚗❀
✈🐾

LINCOLN

Lincolnshire
Map ref 4C2

Ancient city dominated by the magnificent 11th C cathedral with its triple towers. A Roman gateway is still used and medieval houses line narrow, cobbled streets. Other attractions include the Norman castle, several museums and the Usher Gallery.
Tourist Information Centre ☎ (0522) 529828 or 512971.

Garden House ♨

Burton-By-Lincoln, Lincoln LN1 2RD
☎ (0522) 526120
Fully restored 300-year old house with oak beams. A stair lift and wheelchair ramp are available. 1 mile north of Lincoln off the B1398.
Bedrooms: 1 double, 2 twin
Bathrooms: 2 private, 1 public
Bed & breakfast

per night:	£min	£max
Single	15.00	19.00
Double	30.00	34.00

Evening meal 1800 (last orders 1930)
Parking for 4
Open March-October

🔲♿♨📺🏠, 🚗❀✈🐾
🏠🅃

Mayfield Guesthouse

🖼 APPROVED

213 Yarborough Road, Lincoln LN1 3NQ
☎ (0522) 533732
Small homely guesthouse with views of the Trent Valley, a short level walk from the cathedral. Private enclosed car park.
Bedrooms: 1 single, 1 double, 1 twin, 2 triple
Bathrooms: 4 private, 1 public, 1 private shower
Continued ▶

Check the introduction to this region for Where to Go, What to See.

209

LINCOLN

Continued

Bed & breakfast

per night:	£min	£max
Single	14.00	15.00
Double	28.00	30.00

Parking for 4
Cards accepted: Access, Visa

New Farm

Burton, Lincoln LN1 2RD
☎ (0522) 527326
360-acre arable & dairy farm. Twin-bedded room with private bathroom. Use of lounge with colour TV. 2 miles north of Lincoln. Evening meal by prior arrangement.
Bedrooms: 1 twin
Bathrooms: 1 private

Bed & breakfast

per night:	£min	£max
Single		20.00
Double	28.00	28.00

Half board

per person:	£min	£max
Daily		21.00

Parking for 3
Open March-November

Newport Guesthouse ⋀

26-28 Newport, Lincoln LN1 3DF
☎ (0522) 528590
Part of a Victorian terrace only 4 minutes' walk from cathedral and castle.
Bedrooms: 1 single, 1 double, 4 twin, 1 triple
Bathrooms: 2 public

Bed & breakfast

per night:	£min	£max
Single	16.00	16.00
Double	32.00	32.00

Parking for 6

Winnowsty House

Winnowsty Lane, Lincoln LN2 5RZ
☎ (0522) 528600
A pretty, Victorian family house in the shadow of the cathedral, 2 minutes' walk from the historic city centre.
Bedrooms: 1 triple
Bathrooms: 1 public

Bed & breakfast

per night:	£min	£max
Single		18.00
Double		28.00

Parking for 2

LONG BUCKBY

Northamptonshire
Map ref 4C3

Murcott Mill

COMMENDED

Murcott, Long Buckby, Northampton NN6 7QR
☎ (0327) 842236
100-acre livestock farm. A recently renovated Georgian farmhouse adjoining an old mill. In a rural setting overlooking fields yet only 2 miles from M1.
Bedrooms: 1 double, 2 twin
Bathrooms: 3 private, 1 public

Bed & breakfast

per night:	£min	£max
Single	15.00	20.00
Double	30.00	30.00

Half board

per person:	£min	£max
Daily		22.50

Lunch available
Evening meal 1900 (last orders 2100)
Parking for 9

LOUGHBOROUGH

Leicestershire
Map ref 4C3

Industrial town famous for its bell foundry and 47-bell Carillon Tower. The Great Central Railway operates steam railway rides of over 7 miles through the attractive scenery of Charnwood Forest.
Tourist Information Centre
☎ *(0509) 230131*

Moat House

Bramcote Road, Loughborough LE11 2SH
☎ (0509) 214154
17th C farmhouse in mature gardens with small woodland. Direct access for walkers to footpaths. A non-smoking establishment.
Bedrooms: 1 single, 1 double, 2 twin
Bathrooms: 2 public

Bed & breakfast

per night:	£min	£max
Single	15.00	17.00
Double	30.00	30.00

Half board

per person:	£min	£max
Daily	20.00	20.00

Evening meal 1830 (last orders 2100)
Parking for 15

LOUTH

Lincolnshire
Map ref 4D2

Attractive old market town set on the eastern edge of the Lincolnshire Wolds. St James's Church has an impressive tower and spire and there are the remains of a Cistercian abbey. The museum contains an interesting collection of local material.
Tourist Information Centre
☎ *(0507) 609289*

Wickham House

HIGHLY COMMENDED

Church Lane, Conisholme, Louth LN11 7LX
☎ North Somercotes (0507) 358 465
Attractive 18th C cottage, in country setting. En-suite bedrooms, separate tables, home cooking. Convenient for coast, bird reserves, Cadwell Park and Wolds. Non smokers only please.
Bedrooms: 1 single, 1 double, 1 twin
Bathrooms: 3 private

Bed & breakfast

per night:	£min	£max
Double		17.50

Evening meal 1900 (last orders 1300)
Parking for 4
Open January-November

LUDFORD

Lincolnshire
Map ref 4D2

Walk Farm

Listed COMMENDED

Ludford, Lincoln LN3 6AP
☎ Burgh on Bain (0507) 313242
Very peaceful and beautiful area on Lincolnshire Wolds. Outstanding views. Good food and homely atmosphere. Small pets welcome.
Bedrooms: 1 single, 1 double, 1 triple
Bathrooms: 1 public

Bed & breakfast

per night:	£min	£max
Single		13.00
Double		26.00

Half board

per person:	£min	£max
Daily	20.50	21.50
Weekly	123.00	130.00

Evening meal 1900 (last orders 2130)
Parking for 6

MANSFIELD

Nottinghamshire
Map ref 4C2

Ancient town, now an industrial and shopping centre, with a popular market, in the heart of Robin Hood country. There is an impressive 19th C railway viaduct, 2 interesting churches, an 18th C Moot Hall and a museum and art gallery.

Blue Barn Farm ⋀

APPROVED

Nether Langwith, Mansfield NG20 9JD
☎ (0623) 742248
450-acre arable and mixed farm off the A616 north of Mansfield, near Cuckney. Close to Sherwood Forest, Robin Hood country, the Dukeries and the Peak District; many places of interest are only a short car journey away. Easy access from the M1 and A1.
Bedrooms: 1 double, 1 twin, 1 triple
Bathrooms: 1 public

Bed & breakfast

per night:	£min	£max
Single	15.00	17.00
Double	30.00	34.00

Parking for 8

Bridleways ⋀

Newlands Farm Lane, Forest Town, Mansfield NG19 0HU
☎ (0623) 635725
Quietly situated in pretty rural setting east of Mansfield. Set in 3 acres, away from traffic. Play area. Bridlepaths and fishing nearby. Self-catering accommodation also available.
Bedrooms: 1 double, 2 twin
Bathrooms: 1 private, 2 public

Bed & breakfast

per night:	£min	£max
Single	13.00	15.00
Double	26.00	30.00

Half board

per person:	£min	£max
Daily	16.50	20.00
Weekly	122.50	140.00

Parking for 20

🕭♿👪🛌⬛S✂🅜📺🕐🖩,🚗
🚶❄🍴

Holly Lodge
♨♨

Rickett Lane, Blidworth,
Mansfield NG21 0NQ
☎ (0623) 793853
*19th C hunting lodge, with
attractive ground floor en-
suite accommodation, offering
comfort and friendly service
in a delightful country setting.
Located 10 miles north of
Nottingham, off the A60. No
smoking in bedrooms.*
Bedrooms: 1 single,
2 double, 1 twin
Bathrooms: 4 private

Bed & breakfast

per night:	£min	£max
Single	26.00	29.00
Double	32.00	38.00

Parking for 7

🕭♿🖩🛌⬛🅜S✂📺🖩,
🚗⚲◷↑❄✗🍴

Barn Croft

Main Street, Mareham le
Fen, Boston PE22 7QJ
☎ Louth (0507) 568264
*Modern accommodation in
rural setting, central for
Lincoln, Boston, the Wolds
and coast. TV lounge. Meals
available in village. Non-
smoking.*
Bedrooms: 2 double, 1 twin
Bathrooms: 3 private

Bed & breakfast

per night:	£min	£max
Single	17.50	
Double	30.00	

Parking for 6

🛌⬛S✂🅜📺🖩,✗🍴

National Crown
ratings were correct
at the time of going
to press but are
subject to change.
Please check at the
time of booking.

There have been markets
here since the early 13th
C, and the town was also
an important coaching
centre, with several
ancient hostelries. The
early 17th C grammar
school was once the
butter market.
*Tourist Information Centre
☎ (0858) 462649 or
462699*

The Fox Inn
Listed

Church Street, Wilbarston,
Market Harborough
LE16 8QG
☎ Rockingham (0536)
771270
*An old ironstone village inn
offering home-cooked food,
real ales and traditional pub
games. Near Rockingham
Forest and castle.*
Bedrooms: 2 twin, 1 triple
Bathrooms: 3 private

Bed & breakfast

per night:	£min	£max
Single	20.00	25.00
Double	30.00	40.00

Half board

per person:	£min	£max
Daily	26.00	39.00

Lunch available
Evening meal 1900 (last
orders 2200)
Parking for 10
Cards accepted: Access, Visa

🕭♿🖩🛌⬛🅜S🖩,❄
✗🍴

Three Swans Hotel &
Restaurant

High Street, Market
Harborough LE16 7NJ
☎ (0858) 466644
Fax (0858) 433101
*15th C coaching inn in the
centre of this historic market
town with quaint shops, tea
rooms and weekly indoor
market. Borders on the
counties of Northamptonshire
and Leicestershire.*
Bedrooms: 3 single,
19 double, 11 twin, 3 triple
Bathrooms: 36 private

Bed & breakfast

per night:	£min	£max
Single	40.00	69.00
Double	55.00	79.00

Lunch available
Evening meal 1800 (last
orders 2200)
Parking for 60

Cards accepted: Access, Visa,
C.Bl, Diners, Amex

🕭♿🖩♿⬛🖩🛌🛏⬛S✂
🅜🕐,🚗🍴4-75🅞🅐🅟❄🆂🅿
🅵🅣

Market town on the edge
of the Lincolnshire Wolds.
The race course and the
picnic site and forest
walks at Willingham
Woods are to the east of
the town.

Bleasby House Farm
♨♨ HIGHLY COMMENDED

Bleasby House, Legsby,
Market Rasen LN8 3QN
☎ (0673) 842383
*1200-acre mixed farm. In
pleasant surroundings only 3
miles from Market Rasen.
Evening meals are available
by prior arrangement. All
rooms have colour TV, tea
and coffee facilities. Single
room has shower.*
Bedrooms: 1 single, 2 twin
Bathrooms: 2 private,
1 public, 1 private shower

Bed & breakfast

per night:	£min	£max
Single	17.00	20.00
Double	30.00	34.00

Half board

per person:	£min	£max
Daily	27.00	29.00

Evening meal 1800 (last
orders 2030)
Parking for 20

🕭🛌⬛🛏🅜S✂🅜📺🖩,
🚗⚲◷↑🍴✗❄

East Farm House
♨♨ HIGHLY COMMENDED

Buslingthorpe, Market Rasen
LN3 5AQ
☎ (0673) 842283
*410-acre arable farm. In a
pretty, rural location, 4 miles
south-west of Market Rasen
on the Middle Rasen to
Lissington road.*
Bedrooms: 1 double, 1 twin
Bathrooms: 1 private,
1 public, 1 private shower

Bed & breakfast

per night:	£min	£max
Single	16.00	17.00
Double	32.00	34.00

Half board

per person:	£min	£max
Daily	26.00	27.00

Evening meal from 1800
Parking for 6

🕭♿🖩🛌⬛🅜🛏S✂🅜📺
🖩,🚗↑🍴❄✗🆂🅵🅣

Waveney
Guesthouse ᴹ
♨♨ APPROVED

Willingham Road, Market
Rasen LN8 3DN
☎ (0673) 843236
*Small, family-sized guesthouse
conveniently situated for
shops, restaurants,
racecourse, golf, woodland
walks and fishing. Non-
smokers only please. Pets and
children welcome.*
Bedrooms: 2 twin, 1 multiple
Bathrooms: 1 private,
1 public

Bed & breakfast

per night:	£min	£max
Single		17.00
Double		30.00

Half board

per person:	£min	£max
Daily		22.00
Weekly		145.00

Lunch available
Evening meal 1800 (last
orders 2000)
Parking for 4

🕭🛏⬛🛌🅜S✂🅜📺
🖩,🚗❄✗🅞🅐🅟🆂🅿

The town lies beside the
narrow valley of the River
Derwent surrounded by
steep wooded hills. Good
centre for exploring
Derbyshire's best scenery.

Farley Farm

Farley, Matlock DE4 5LR
☎ (0629) 582533
*250-acre mixed farm. Built in
1610 of natural stone, set in
open countryside close to
Peak District and many
places of interest.*
Bedrooms: 1 double, 1 twin,
1 triple
Bathrooms: 2 public

Bed & breakfast

per night:	£min	£max
Single	15.00	16.00
Double	28.00	28.00

Half board

per person:	£min	£max
Daily	19.00	19.00
Weekly	133.00	133.00

Evening meal 1700 (last
orders 1900)
Parking for 10

🕭♿🖩⬛S🅜📺🖩,🚗◷✓
❄✗🅞🅐🅟🆂🅿🅵

MATLOCK

Continued

Thornleigh ▲

11 Lime Grove Walk,
Matlock DE4 3FD
☎ (0629) 57626
*Large Edwardian house with
private parking, convenient
for bus/rail stations and
shops. Non-smokers only
please.*
Bedrooms: 1 single,
1 double, 1 triple
Bathrooms: 1 public

Bed & breakfast

per night:	£min	£max
Single	14.00	14.00
Double	28.00	28.00

Half board

per person:	£min	£max
Daily	21.00	21.00

Parking for 3
Open March-October

MATLOCK BATH

Derbyshire
Map ref 4B2

19th C spa town with
many attractions including
several caverns to visit, a
lead mining museum and
a family fun park. There
are marvellous views over
the surrounding
countryside from the
Heights of Abraham, to
which a cable car gives
easy access.
*Tourist Information Centre
☎ (0629) 55082*

Beech Hurst

228 Dale Road, Matlock
Bath, Matlock DE4 3RT
☎ (0629) 56013
*Comfortable Victorian house
overlooking River Derwent.
Friendly family business with
home cooking and log fires.
Ideal for touring Peak
District.*
Bedrooms: 1 double, 1 twin,
1 triple
Bathrooms: 2 public

Bed & breakfast

per night:	£min	£max
Single	14.00	18.00
Double	22.00	28.00

Half board

per person:	£min	£max
Daily	19.00	22.00
Weekly	126.00	150.00

Evening meal 1800 (last
orders 2000)
Parking for 1

The Firs

180 Dale Road, Matlock
Bath, Matlock DE4 3PS
☎ (0629) 582426
*A 250-year-old, comfortable,
elegant house close to all
amenities, Chatsworth, Crich
Tramway Museum and Alton
Towers. Good facilities.*
Bedrooms: 2 double, 1 twin
Bathrooms: 2 public

Bed & breakfast

per night:	£min	£max
Single	20.00	25.00
Double	30.00	34.00

Parking for 4

Temple Hotel ▲

COMMENDED

Temple Walk, Matlock Bath,
Matlock DE4 3PG
☎ (0629) 583911
Fax (0629) 580851
*The hotel nestles comfortably
amid "Little Switzerland"
scenery of picturesque
Matlock Bath, overlooking the
Vale of the River Derwent
from a steep, wooded hillside.
All bedrooms en-suite with
colour TV.*
Bedrooms: 1 single,
7 double, 3 twin, 3 triple
Bathrooms: 14 private

Bed & breakfast

per night:	£min	£max
Single	33.00	39.00
Double	53.00	59.00

Half board

per person:	£min	£max
Daily	44.00	50.00

Lunch available
Evening meal 1830 (last
orders 2200)
Parking for 32
Cards accepted: Access, Visa,
Diners, Amex

MEDBOURNE

Leicestershire
Map ref 4C3

Picturesque village with
medieval bridge.

Homestead House

COMMENDED

5 Ashley Road, Medbourne,
Market Harborough
LE16 8DL
☎ (085 883) 724

*In an elevated position
overlooking the Welland
Valley on the outskirts of
Medbourne, a picturesque
village dating back to Roman
times.*
Bedrooms: 3 twin
Bathrooms: 1 public

Bed & breakfast

per night:	£min	£max
Single	16.00	18.00
Double	28.00	30.00

Half board

per person:	£min	£max
Daily	21.00	26.00

Evening meal 1800 (last
orders 2000)
Parking for 6
Cards accepted: Access, Visa

The Old Rectory

Medbourne, Market
Harborough LE16 8DZ
☎ (085 883) 330
Fax (085 883) 330
*Attractive Georgian listed
house standing in own
grounds in middle of small
conservation village, in
open country between M1 and
A1. Large rooms with open
views.*
Bedrooms: 1 single, 2 twin
Bathrooms: 1 private,
1 public

Bed & breakfast

per night:	£min	£max
Single	18.00	25.00
Double	35.00	40.00

Parking for 2

MELTON MOWBRAY

Leicestershire
Map ref 4C3

Close to the attractive
Vale of Belvoir and
famous for its pork pies
and Stilton cheese which
are the subjects of
special displays in the
museum. It has a
beautiful church with a
tower 100 ft high.
*Tourist Information Centre
☎ (0664) 69946*

Church Cottage

The Green, 14 Main Street,
Holwell, Melton Mowbray
LE14 4SZ
☎ Scalford (066 476) 255
*Charming 18th C listed
cottage with landscaped
gardens on 3 sides. Next to
Holwell Church. En-suite
facilities.*
Bedrooms: 1 double, 1 twin
Bathrooms: 1 private,
1 public

Bed & breakfast

per night:	£min	£max
Single	16.00	16.00
Double	30.00	30.00

Parking for 2

Home Farm

Asfordby Hill, Melton
Mowbray LE14 3QX
☎ (0664) 812634
*200-acre arable & dairy farm.
On the edge of village 1.5
miles from Melton Mowbray.
Traditional farmhouse
hospitality, comfortable
rooms, secluded garden.*
Bedrooms: 1 twin, 1 triple
Bathrooms: 1 public

Bed & breakfast

per night:	£min	£max
Single	13.00	15.00
Double	26.00	30.00

Parking for 2

Manor House ▲

COMMENDED

Church Lane, Saxelbye,
Melton Mowbray LE14 3PA
☎ (0664) 812269
*125-acre dairy farm. Home
cooking and a warm welcome
in this oak-beamed
farmhouse. Parts date back
several hundred years
including a unique 400-year-
old staircase.*
Bedrooms: 1 double, 1 twin,
1 triple
Bathrooms: 1 private,
1 public

Bed & breakfast

per night:	£min	£max
Single	22.00	
Double	30.00	

Half board

per person:	£min	£max
Daily	24.00	
Weekly	158.00	

Evening meal 1900 (last
orders 1200)
Parking for 6
Open April-October

METHERINGHAM

Lincolnshire
Map ref 4C2

Lincolnshire Poacher

High Street, Metheringham,
Lincoln LN4 3DZ
☎ (0526) 20556
*Old and very attractive local
stone-built family-run pub
with open fires in both bars.
15 minutes from Lincoln city
centre.*

Bedrooms: 1 single, 2 double
Bathrooms: 1 public

Bed & breakfast

per night:	£min	£max
Single	14.50	
Double	25.00	

Lunch available
Evening meal 1900 (last orders 2230)
Parking for 30

ॐ 3 ☒ ⏹ ⌨ ▥ ☏ ✗ 🐎

MIDDLETON

Northamptonshire
Map ref 4C3

Valley View
3 Camsdale Walk, Middleton, Market Harborough, Leicestershire LE16 8YR
☎ Rockingham (0536) 770874
An elevated, stone-built house with panoramic views of the Welland Valley. Within easy distance of Market Harborough and Corby.
Bedrooms: 1 double, 1 twin
Bathrooms: 1 public

Bed & breakfast

per night:	£min	£max
Single	15.00	15.00
Double	28.00	28.00

Parking for 2

ॐ ९ ▥ ⑤ ✗ ☏ ▥ 🚗 ✿ 🐎

MINTING

Lincolnshire
Map ref 4D2

Greenfield Farm
Minting, Horncastle
LN9 5RX
☎ Baumber (0507) 578457
335-acre arable farm. Comfortable farmhouse in quiet location but centrally placed for Lincoln, the Wolds, etc. Pretty en-suite shower rooms.
Bedrooms: 1 double, 2 twin
Bathrooms: 2 private, 1 public

Bed & breakfast

per night:	£min	£max
Single	16.00	17.00
Double	32.00	34.00

Parking for 12

ॐ ➤ ◫▥ ⑤ ✗ ☏ ▥ 🚗 ▸ ✓ ✿ 🐎

The town index towards the back of this guide gives page numbers of all places with accommodation.

MORETON PINKNEY

Northamptonshire
Map ref 2C1

Barewell Fields
Listed `HIGHLY COMMENDED`
Moreton Pinkney, Daventry NN11 6NJ
☎ Sulgrave (0295) 760754
200-acre mixed farm. In a peaceful corner of the conservation village of Moreton Pinkney, convenient for many National Trust properties, Stratford and Silverstone, M1 and M40. Evening meals by arrangement only.
Bedrooms: 1 single, 1 double, 1 twin
Bathrooms: 2 public

Bed & breakfast

per night:	£min	£max
Single	15.00	17.00
Double	30.00	34.00

Half board

per person:	£min	£max
Daily	25.00	30.00
Weekly	170.00	200.00

Evening meal 1800 (last orders 1900)
Parking for 4
Open January-November

ॐ 10 ☒ ⌨ ▥ 🅿 ⑤ ☏ ☏ ▥
🚗 ✿ ✗ 🐎

NEWARK

Nottinghamshire
Map ref 4C2

The town has many fine old houses and ancient inns near the large, cobbled market-place. Substantial ruins of the 12th C castle, where King John died, dominate the riverside walk and there are several interesting museums. Sherwood Forest is nearby.
Tourist Information Centre
☎ *(0636) 78962*

Church Farm Guesthouse
Church Lane, South Muskham, Newark NG23 6EQ
☎ (0636) 76997
16th C farmhouse on the edge of a quiet village. Off the B6325 between Newark and the A1. German is spoken.
Bedrooms: 1 double, 2 twin
Bathrooms: 2 public

Bed & breakfast

per night:	£min	£max
Single	15.00	20.00
Double	30.00	35.00

Half board

per person:	£min	£max
Daily	23.00	28.00
Weekly	138.00	168.00

Evening meal 1900 (last orders 1700)
Parking for 5
Cards accepted: Access, Visa

ॐ 10 ⏹ ▥ 🅿 ⑤ ✗ ☏ ▥
🚗 ✿ 🐎

Willow Tree Inn **⋀**
Listed
Front Street, Barnby-in-the-Willows, Newark NG24 2SA
☎ Fenton Claypole (0636) 626613
Heavily beamed inn in a conservation village surrounded by historic places. Close to the Trent and Witham Fisheries, and Newark, off the A17 and A1.
Bedrooms: 1 single, 2 double, 2 triple
Bathrooms: 2 private, 1 public

Bed & breakfast

per night:	£min	£max
Single	18.00	26.00
Double	30.00	40.00

Lunch available
Evening meal 1900 (last orders 2230)
Parking for 50
Cards accepted: Access, Visa

ॐ ♿ ◫ ⏹ ⌨ ⑤ ▥ 🚗 ▸ 🅿 ☏
◐ ✗ 🐎 `DAP` 🌢 `SP` 🏮

NORTHAMPTON

Northamptonshire
Map ref 2C1

A bustling town and a shoe manufacturing centre, with excellent shopping facilities, several museums and parks, a theatre and a concert hall. Several old churches include 1 of only 4 round churches in Britain.
Tourist Information Centre
☎ *(0604) 22677*

10 Church View
Wootton, Northampton NN4 0LJ
☎ (0604) 761626 & 767040
Quiet, friendly, family-run guesthouse, near the M1, Castle Ashby, Billing Aquadrome, Silverstone and County Records Office. Ideal for Collingtree Golf Course and Turners Musical Merry-go-round.
Bedrooms: 1 single, 1 double, 1 twin
Bathrooms: 2 public

Bed & breakfast

per night:	£min	£max
Single	17.00	19.00
Double	34.00	36.00

Parking for 6

ॐ 12 ⏹ ♦ ▥ ⓘ 🅿 ☏ ▥ 🚗
✗ 🐎

Blisworth Hotel & Restaurant **⋀**
Station Road, Blisworth, Northampton NN7 3DS
☎ (0604) 859551
Fax (0604) 859320
Carefully restored 16th C hunting lodge, situated 3 miles from junction 15 on the Northamptonshire M1.
Bedrooms: 3 single, 7 double, 4 twin
Bathrooms: 14 private

Bed & breakfast

per night:	£min	£max
Single	30.00	40.00
Double	47.00	60.00

Half board

per person:	£min	£max
Daily	38.00	48.00
Weekly	250.00	330.00

Lunch available
Evening meal 1900 (last orders 2130)
Parking for 40
Cards accepted: Access, Visa, Diners, Amex

ॐ ♿ ◖ ◫ ⏹ ♦ ⑤ ☏ ▥
🚗 ‡10-120 ◐ ✗ `DAP` 🌢 `SP`
🏮 Ⓣ

The Coach House **⋀**
⇔⇔⇔
8-10 East Park Parade, Northampton NN1 4LA
☎ (0604) 250981
Friendly hotel 1 mile north of the town centre, overlooking a park. Convenient for shops and industrial areas.
Bedrooms: 9 single, 13 double, 5 twin, 3 triple
Bathrooms: 21 private, 2 public, 7 private showers

Bed & breakfast

per night:	£min	£max
Single	20.00	45.00
Double	35.00	60.00

Half board

per person:	£min	£max
Daily	29.00	54.00

Lunch available
Evening meal 1900 (last orders 2130)
Parking for 14
Cards accepted: Access, Visa, Diners, Amex

ॐ ♿ ◖ ◫ ⏹ ♦ ⑤ ✗ ☏
◐ ▥ 🚗 🐎 `DAP` `SP`

NORTHAMPTON

Continued

Hollington Guesthouse ♠
Listed

22 Abington Grove,
Northampton NN1 4QW
☎ (0604) 32584
Comfortable guesthouse, close to town centre and with easy access to M1. TV and tea-making facilities in all rooms.
Bedrooms: 2 single,
2 double, 1 twin, 2 triple
Bathrooms: 2 public
Bed & breakfast

per night:	£min	£max
Single	16.00	
Double	25.00	

Parking for 2

Quinton Green Farm ♠
COMMENDED

Quinton, Northampton
NN7 2EG
☎ (0604) 862484
1200-acre arable & dairy farm. Rambling 17th C farmhouse with lovely views over own farmland. Convenient for Northampton, M1 (junction 15) and Milton Keynes.
Bedrooms: 1 single,
1 double, 1 twin
Bathrooms: 1 public
Bed & breakfast

per night:	£min	£max
Single	15.00	18.00
Double	30.00	36.00

Parking for 8

NORTON

Nottinghamshire
Map ref 4C2

Norton Grange Farm

Norton Cuckney, Norton,
Mansfield NG20 9LP
☎ Mansfield (0623) 842666
172-acre mixed farm. Georgian stone farmhouse in the heart of the Welbeck Estate, a part of the world-famous Sherwood Forest.
Bedrooms: 1 double, 1 twin
Bathrooms: 1 public
Bed & breakfast

per night:	£min	£max
Single	15.00	16.00
Double	30.00	32.00

Parking for 5

NOTTINGHAM

Nottinghamshire
Map ref 4C2

Attractive modern city with a rich history. Outside its castle, now a museum, is Robin Hood's statue. Attractions include 'The Tales of Robin Hood'; the Lace Hall; Wollaton Hall; museums and excellent facilities for shopping, sports and entertainment.
Tourist Information Centre ☎ (0602) 470661 or 773558

Grantham Hotel
👑👑

24-26 Radcliffe Road, West Bridgford, Nottingham
NG2 5FW
☎ (0602) 811373
Family-run hotel offering modern accommodation in a comfortable atmosphere. Convenient for the centre of Nottingham, Trent Bridge and the National Water Sports Centre.
Bedrooms: 13 single,
2 double, 5 twin, 2 triple
Bathrooms: 13 private,
3 public
Bed & breakfast

per night:	£min	£max
Single	20.00	27.00
Double	32.00	38.00

Parking for 20
Cards accepted: Access, Visa

The Milford Hotel ♠
👑👑 **APPROVED**

Pavilion Road, West Bridgford, Nottingham
NG2 5FG
☎ (0602) 811464
Fax (0602) 822204
Family-run hotel. Close to the River Trent, county cricket ground, National Water Sports Centre and the city centre.
Bedrooms: 6 single,
2 double, 5 twin, 1 triple
Bathrooms: 4 public
Bed & breakfast

per night:	£min	£max
Single	19.00	22.00
Double	34.00	38.00

Half board

per person:	£min	£max
Daily	24.00	28.00
Weekly	145.00	177.00

Evening meal 1800 (last orders 1900)
Parking for 14

Cards accepted: Access, Visa, Diners, Amex

OAKHAM

Leicestershire
Map ref 4C3

Pleasant former county town of Rutland has a fine 12th C Great Hall, part of its castle, with a historic collection of horseshoes. An octagonal Butter Cross stands in the market-place and Rutland County Museum, Rutland Farm Park & Rutland Water are other attractions.
Tourist Information Centre ☎ (0572) 724329 & (078 086) 321

Nelson House

11 Market Place, Oakham
LE15 6DT
☎ (0572) 723199
Deceptively large private house, circa 1750 with additions. In the centre of town with views of the castle and Buttercross Market. Secure parking at rear. Non-smokers only please.
Bedrooms: 2 single,
1 double, 1 twin, 1 triple
Bathrooms: 1 public
Bed & breakfast

per night:	£min	£max
Single	15.50	16.00
Double	25.00	30.00

Parking for 2
Open March-November

OUNDLE

Northamptonshire
Map ref 3A1

Historic town situated on the River Nene with narrow alleys and courtyards and many stone buildings, including a fine church and historic inns.
Tourist Information Centre ☎ (0832) 274333

Castle Farm Guesthouse ♠
👑👑

Castle Farm, Fotheringhay,
Peterborough PE8 5HZ
☎ Cotterstock (083 26) 200
850-acre mixed farm. An early 19th C stone farmhouse in beautiful surroundings, with lawns running down to the River Nene and adjoining the Fotheringhay Castle site. 2

rooms can be adapted to family rooms. Packed lunches by arrangement.
Bedrooms: 1 single,
1 double, 4 twin
Bathrooms: 5 private,
1 public
Bed & breakfast

per night:	£min	£max
Single	25.00	30.00
Double	35.00	48.00

Half board

per person:	£min	£max
Daily	26.00	38.50

Evening meal from 1915
Parking for 12

Stable, Grooms and Courtyard Cottages ♠
Listed

30 Market Place, Oundle,
Peterborough PE8 4BE
☎ (0832) 273531
In a garden "oasis" in the centre of historic market town. Regret, no dogs or smokers.
Bedrooms: 2 double, 3 twin
Bathrooms: 5 private
Bed & breakfast

per night:	£min	£max
Single	22.50	27.50
Double	39.00	55.00

Parking for 3
Cards accepted: Access, Visa

PEAK DISTRICT

See under Ashbourne, Ashford in the Water, Bakewell, Bamford, Baslow, Buxton, Castleton, Chinley, Dovedale, Earl Sterndale, Edale, Hartington, Hathersage, Hayfield, Hope, Tideswell, Winster

REDMILE

Leicestershire
Map ref 4C2

Vale of Belvoir village, overlooked by the hilltop castle.

Peacock Farm Guesthouse and Country Restaurant
👑👑

Redmile, Nottingham
NG13 0GQ
☎ Bottesford (0949) 42475
Peter and Marjorie Need welcome you to their old farmhouse in the delightful Vale of Belvoir, close to the

castle. A small licensed restaurant is attached, and there is a sunbed, exercise room and small covered pool.
Bedrooms: 1 single, 2 double, 2 twin, 5 triple
Bathrooms: 6 private, 2 public

Bed & breakfast

per night:	£min	£max
Single		17.50
Double		32.00

Half board

per person:	£min	£max
Daily	29.00	38.50
Weekly	161.00	245.00

Lunch available
Evening meal 1915 (last orders 2030)
Parking for 40
Cards accepted: Access
🐾🛇🏃🛆⒮♥⒯⒯⒯⒥⊟⌽🅿️▲↗
🖾🌸🐎🐈🅰️

ROWLAND

Derbyshire
Map ref 4B2

Rowland Cottage

Rowland, Bakewell DE4 1NR
☎ Great Longstone (0629) 60365
17th C detached stone cottage in private garden, about 1 mile from Great Longstone village. Home cooking and a welcoming atmosphere. Ideal base for walking and touring. Non-smokers preferred.
Bedrooms: 1 double, 1 twin
Bathrooms: 2 private, 1 public

Bed & breakfast

per night:	£min	£max
Single	15.00	20.00
Double	25.00	35.00

Half board

per person:	£min	£max
Daily	20.00	27.50
Weekly	140.00	192.50

Evening meal 1900 (last orders 2100)
Parking for 3
🐾🛆🖾🖵♥⒲🛇⒮⊁⒨
⒯⒯⊟⌽🅿️🌸🐎🎿🐈🐎⒯

SHEARSBY

Leicestershire
Map ref 4C3

Knaptoft House Farm

☷ **HIGHLY COMMENDED**

Bruntingthorpe Road, Shearsby, Lutterworth LE17 6PR
☎ Leicester (0533) 478388
Fax (0533) 478388
145-acre mixed farm. Beautifully-appointed accommodation set in

peaceful rolling countryside close to junction 1 of M6, junction 20 of M1. Excellent pubs and restaurants nearby.
Bedrooms: 1 double, 2 twin
Bathrooms: 1 public, 3 private showers

Bed & breakfast

per night:	£min	£max
Single		17.00
Double		32.00

Parking for 5
🐾3♥⒲🛆⒮🅜⒯⒯⊟▲↗
✓🌸🗙🐎

SHERWOOD FOREST

See under Edwinstowe, Gonalston, Gunthorpe, Laneham, Mansfield, Newark, Southwell, Upton, Wellow

SILVERSTONE

Northamptonshire
Map ref 2C1

Silverthorpe

Abthorpe Road, Silverstone, Towcester NN12 8TW
☎ Towcester (0327) 858020
A large, spacious, modern bungalow with a warm and friendly atmosphere, standing in its own quiet, rural surroundings. 1.5 miles north of Silverstone.
Bedrooms: 3 twin
Bathrooms: 2 private, 2 public

Bed & breakfast

per night:	£min	£max
Single	15.00	20.00
Double	32.00	37.00

Parking for 4
🐾🛆🖾🖵♥⒲⊟🅿️🌸🐎

SKEGNESS

Lincolnshire
Map ref 4D2

Famous seaside resort with 6 miles of sandy beaches and bracing air. Attractions include swimming pools, bowling greens, gardens, Natureland Marine Zoo, golf-courses and a wide range of entertainment at the Embassy Centre. Nearby is Gibraltar Point Nature Reserve.
Tourist Information Centre
☎ *(0754) 764821*

Victoria Inn ⋀

☷☷

Wainfleet Road, Skegness PE25 3RG
☎ (0754) 767333

Friendly, traditional inn with hotel annexe providing home-cooked food. Central for town and beach facilities.
Bedrooms: 1 single, 3 double, 1 twin, 2 triple
Bathrooms: 4 private, 1 public

Bed & breakfast

per night:	£min	£max
Single	13.00	15.00
Double	25.00	29.00

Half board

per person:	£min	£max
Daily	16.00	18.00
Weekly	102.00	108.00

Lunch available
Evening meal 1800 (last orders 2200)
Parking for 20
🐾🖾🖵♥🛆⒮⊁⒯⒯⊟▲
🔍🐎⒮

SLEAFORD

Lincolnshire
Map ref 3A1

Market town whose parish church has one of the oldest stone spires in England and particularly fine tracery round the windows.
Tourist Information Centre
☎ *(0529) 414294*

The Tally Ho Country House Inn

☷ **COMMENDED**

Aswarby, Sleaford NG34 8SA
☎ Culverthorpe (052 95) 205
200-year-old inn carefully converted from stables, offering en-suite bedrooms, real ale, an a la carte restaurant and log fires in winter.
Bedrooms: 2 double, 4 twin
Bathrooms: 6 private

Bed & breakfast

per night:	£min	£max
Single	28.00	30.00
Double	42.00	45.00

Lunch available
Evening meal 1900 (last orders 2100)
Parking for 50
Cards accepted: Access, Visa, Switch
🐾🖵♥🛆⒮🅜⊟▲🌸
🐎🐈⒮

The national Crown scheme is explained in full in the information pages towards the back of this guide.

SNARESTONE

Leicestershire
Map ref 4B3

Snarestone Lodge

Measham Road, Snarestone, Swadlincote, Derbyshire DE12 7DA
☎ Measham (0530) 270535
Fax (0530) 273801
Georgian country house of character, in 4 acres of beautiful grounds through which the Ashby Canal runs. In Ivanhoe country, close to Twycross Zoo, the Battlefield of Bosworth, Calke Abbey and 2 miles from the M42/A42.
Bedrooms: 3 single, 2 twin
Bathrooms: 4 public

Bed & breakfast

per night:	£min	£max
Single	15.00	17.00
Double	35.00	37.50

Evening meal 1900 (last orders 2100)
Parking for 7
🐾🖵♥⒲🛆⒮⊁⒨⒯⒯①⊟
▲🔍🕛↗🌸🗙🐎🐈

SOUTHWELL

Nottinghamshire
Map ref 4C2

Town dominated by the Norman minster which has some beautiful 13th C stone carvings in the Chapter House. Charles I spent his last night of freedom in one of the inns. The original Bramley apple tree can still be seen.

Barn Lodge

Listed **COMMENDED**

Duckers Cottage, Brinkley, Southwell NG25 0TP
☎ (0636) 813435
Smallholding with panoramic views, 1 mile from the centre of Southwell and close to the racecourse, railway station and River Trent.
Bedrooms: 1 double, 1 twin, 1 triple
Bathrooms: 3 private

Bed & breakfast

per night:	£min	£max
Single	20.00	20.00
Double	40.00	40.00

Parking for 3
🐾🛆🖾🖵♥⒲⒮⊟🌸🐎
🅞🅐🅟⒮🐈

Brinkley Hall Farm

Fiskerton Road, Southwell NG25 0TP
☎ (0636) 812268
Continued ▶

SOUTHWELL

Continued

18th C farmhouse in idyllic rural setting with lovely views across the Trent Valley. Within walking distance of charming minster town of Southwell.
Bedrooms: 1 double, 2 twin
Bathrooms: 2 private,
1 public

Bed & breakfast

per night:	£min	£max
Single	15.00	19.00
Double	17.00	32.00

Parking for 10

Crown Hotel
Listed COMMENDED
11 Market Place, Southwell
NG25 0HE
☎ (0636) 812120 & 815572
Town centre listed Georgian building just 50 yards from Southwell Minster, with a carvery and a wide selection of inexpensive food. 11 miles from Nottingham with easy access to Nottinghamshire's tourist attractions.
Bedrooms: 5 double, 2 triple
Bathrooms: 1 private,
1 public, 5 private showers

Bed & breakfast

per night:	£min	£max
Single	27.50	
Double	33.00	

Lunch available
Evening meal 1700 (last orders 2100)
Parking for 7
Cards accepted: Access, Visa

SPALDING

Lincolnshire
Map ref 3A1

Fenland town famous for its bulbfields. A spectacular Flower Parade takes place at the beginning of May each year and the tulips at Springfields show gardens are followed by displays of roses and bedding plants in summer. Interesting local museum.
Tourist Information Centre
☎ (0775) 725468

Stables Motel ⋀

Cowbit Road, Spalding
PE11 2RJ
☎ (0775) 767290
Fax (0775) 767716

Converted from farm buildings, the motel complements the 17th C farmhouse. Three quarters of a mile from the centre of Spalding on the A1073 Peterborough road. Most units are on the ground floor with their own porches and all are equipped with refrigerators and colour TV.
Bedrooms: 3 single,
4 double, 2 twin
Bathrooms: 9 private,
2 public

Bed & breakfast

per night:	£min	£max
Single	17.50	42.00
Double	35.00	70.00

Parking for 40
Cards accepted: Access, Visa, Diners, Amex

STAMFORD

Lincolnshire
Map ref 3A1

Exceptionally beautiful and historic town with many houses of architectural interest, several notable churches and other public buildings all in the local stone. Burghley House, built by William Cecil, is a magnificent Tudor mansion on the edge of the town.
Tourist Information Centre
☎ (0780) 55611

Birch House
Listed
4 Lonsdale Road, Stamford
PE9 2RW
☎ (0780) 54876
Comfortable, family-run detached house on the outskirts of Stamford. All rooms have TV and tea/coffee making facilities. Non-smokers only, please.
Bedrooms: 2 single,
1 double, 1 twin
Bathrooms: 1 public

Bed & breakfast

per night:	£min	£max
Single	14.00	
Double	28.00	

Parking for 4

Bull & Swan
High Street, St Martins,
Stamford PE9 2JL
☎ (0780) 63558
An old coaching house on the old A1 in Stamford offering homely, warm

accommodation with beams and open fires.
Bedrooms: 3 double, 1 twin,
3 triple
Bathrooms: 4 private,
1 public

Bed & breakfast

per night:	£min	£max
Single	30.00	35.00
Double	40.00	45.00

Lunch available
Evening meal 1615 (last orders 2215)
Parking for 16
Cards accepted: Access, Visa

The Lord Burghley Welland House
17-19 Broad Street,
Stamford PE9 1PG
☎ (0780) 63426 & 57028
Town centre, medieval-style free-house with adjoining Georgian restaurant and guesthouse. Close to shopping precinct and within easy reach of all local historic buildings and churches.
Bedrooms: 1 double, 4 twin
Bathrooms: 1 private,
1 public

Bed & breakfast

per night:	£min	£max
Single	18.00	25.00
Double	36.00	40.00

Half board

per person:	£min	£max
Daily	24.00	43.00

Lunch available
Evening meal 1900 (last orders 2200)
Parking for 1
Cards accepted: Access, Visa

The Manor Cottage
Main Road, Collyweston,
Stamford PE9 3PN
☎ (0780) 83209 & 55882
Fine neo-Georgian house with panoramic views, on the main road between Collyweston and Duddington, just 5 miles from Stamford.
Bedrooms: 2 single, 2 twin
Bathrooms: 1 private,
1 public

Bed & breakfast

per night:	£min	£max
Single	15.00	20.00
Double	30.00	40.00

Parking for 10

The Priory ⋀
HIGHLY COMMENDED
Church Road, Ketton,
Stamford PE9 3RD
☎ (0780) 720215

Large, recently restored, 16th C house with delightful gardens and a large conservatory. En-suite rooms with TV, separate residents' lounge and dining room.
Bedrooms: 2 double, 1 twin
Bathrooms: 2 private,
1 public

Bed & breakfast

per night:	£min	£max
Single	20.00	30.00
Double	30.00	50.00

Half board

per person:	£min	£max
Daily	27.50	37.50

Lunch available
Evening meal 1900 (last orders 2100)
Parking for 10
Cards accepted: Access, Visa

STANTON LEES

Derbyshire
Map ref 4B2

Woodside
Stanton Lees, Matlock
DE4 2LQ
☎ Matlock (0629) 734320
Semi-detached house with landscaped garden and spectacular views overlooking the Derwent Valley. In an isolated, picturesque village on the southern plateau of the Peak District, near Bakewell and Matlock.
Bedrooms: 2 double, 2 twin
Bathrooms: 2 private,
4 public

Bed & breakfast

per night:	£min	£max
Double	30.00	

Half board

per person:	£min	£max
Daily	21.00	

Evening meal from 1930
Open April-October

STOKE DOYLE

Northamptonshire
Map ref 3A2

Village whose church has a fine monument by an eminent 18th C sculptor.

Shuckburgh Arms ⋀
COMMENDED
Stoke Doyle, Peterborough
PE8 5TG
☎ Oundle (0832) 272339
Fax (0832) 272339
Fully licensed country inn, offering bed and breakfast,

meals, real ales and a beer garden.
Bedrooms: 2 single,
1 double, 2 twin
Bathrooms: 5 private
Bed & breakfast

per night:	£min	£max
Single	25.00	30.00
Double	40.00	45.00

Half board

per person:	£min	£max
Daily	37.00	42.00

Lunch available
Evening meal 1930 (last orders 2200)
Parking for 40
Cards accepted: Access, Visa

🛇⌨️♿🖪🛏️📺🎬🔳💺💿♨️✕🚲🅿️🏠🍴

STRETTON

Derbyshire
Map ref 4B2

Ivy Beech
Listed

Highstairs Lane, Stretton, Derby DE5 6FD
☎ Chesterfield (0246) 863397
Private house in its own grounds, down a country lane but close to the main trunk road. An ideal centre for touring.
Bedrooms: 1 single, 2 twin
Bathrooms: 2 public
Bed & breakfast

per night:	£min	£max
Single	14.00	14.00
Double	28.00	28.00

Half board

per person:	£min	£max
Daily	21.50	21.50
Weekly	130.00	130.00

Evening meal 1900 (last orders 2000)
Parking for 5
Open March-November

🛇⌨️♿🖪🛏️🆂✕🎬📺🔳💿♨️🚲

TIDESWELL

Derbyshire
Map ref 4B2

Small town with a large 14th C church known as the 'Cathedral of the Peak'. There is a well-dressing ceremony each June with Morris dancing.

Laurel House
The Green, Litton, Buxton SK17 8QP
☎ (0298) 871971
Elegant Victorian house in the heart of the White Peak. Overlooking the green in the village of Litton.

Bedrooms: 1 double, 1 twin
Bathrooms: 1 private,
1 public
Bed & breakfast

per night:	£min	£max
Double	28.00	

Parking for 2

🛇2♿🖪🆂🛏️📺🔳🎬
🆂🅿️🅃

Poppies
Listed

Bank Square, Tideswell, Buxton SK17 8LA
☎ (0298) 871083
Poppies offers a warm welcome, comfortable accommodation and good vegetarian and traditional home cooking in a small restaurant, at the centre of this picturesque mid Peak District village.
Bedrooms: 1 double, 1 twin,
1 triple
Bathrooms: 1 private,
1 public
Bed & breakfast

per night:	£min	£max
Single	12.75	17.00
Double	25.50	34.00

Half board

per person:	£min	£max
Daily	20.75	32.00

Lunch available
Evening meal 1900 (last orders 2130)
Open February-December
Cards accepted: Access, Visa

🛇⌨️♿🆂🔳💿🚲

TOWCESTER

Northamptonshire
Map ref 2C1

Town built on the site of a Roman settlement. It has some interesting old buildings, including an inn featured in one of Dickens' novels. The racecourse lies alongside the A5 Watling Street.

Laurence House
49a High Street, Whittlebury, Towcester NN12 8XH
☎ (0327) 857245
Small guesthouse in a village 3 miles south of Towcester on the A413, convenient for Silverstone and Towcester races. Non-smokers only, please.
Bedrooms: 2 double, 1 twin
Bathrooms: 1 public

| Please mention |
| this guide when |
| making a booking. |

Bed & breakfast

per night:	£min	£max
Single	20.00	20.00
Double	35.00	50.00

Parking for 6

🛇⌨️✕🖪📺🔳💿♨️✕🚲

The Old Vicarage
👑👑 COMMENDED

Church Street, Blakesley, Towcester NN12 8RA
☎ Blakesby (0327) 860200
55-acre mixed farm. Old Victorian vicarage of mellow sandstone, in its own spacious grounds and with private lake. Outdoor pool and hard tennis court.
Bedrooms: 1 twin
Bathrooms: 1 private
Bed & breakfast

per night:	£min	£max
Single	25.00	25.00
Double	30.00	40.00

Parking for 3

🛇⌨️📾♿🖪✕🛏️📺🔳💿🔍♨️⚲♪🅿️♨️✕🚲🏠

UPPER BROUGHTON

Nottinghamshire
Map ref 4C3

Sulney Fields ⋔
Colonel's Lane, Upper Broughton, Melton Mowbray, Leicestershire LE14 3BD
☎ Melton Mowbray (0664) 822204
Large country house with spacious accommodation and fine views of the Vale of Belvoir. Evening meals available by prior arrangement. Discounts for stays of more than 1 night.
Bedrooms: 2 single,
1 double, 2 twin
Bathrooms: 2 public
Bed & breakfast

per night:	£min	£max
Single	18.00	20.00
Double	30.00	35.00

Half board

per person:	£min	£max
Daily	21.00	25.00

Evening meal from 1830
Parking for 2

🛇♿🖪📺🔳💿♨️⚲♨️🚲

| National Crown |
| ratings were correct |
| at the time of going |
| to press but are |
| subject to change. |
| Please check at the |
| time of booking. |

UPPINGHAM

Leicestershire
Map ref 4C3

Quiet market town dominated by its famous public school which was founded in 1584. It has many stone houses and is surrounded by attractive countryside.

Old Rectory ⋔
Belton in Rutland, Oakham LE15 9LE
☎ Belton (057 286) 279
Fax (057 286) 343
A Victorian country house on the edge of charming village. Quiet, friendly atmosphere. 3 miles from Uppingham and 10 minutes from Rutland Water. Accessible from the A47, following signs.
Bedrooms: 1 single,
2 double, 1 twin, 3 triple
Bathrooms: 7 private,
1 public
Bed & breakfast

per night:	£min	£max
Single	19.00	30.00
Double	39.00	55.00

Half board

per person:	£min	£max
Daily	29.00	35.00
Weekly	200.00	240.00

Evening meal 1800 (last orders 1900)
Parking for 6
Cards accepted: Access, Visa

🛇📾♿🖪♿🆂✕🌑🔳💿♨️✕🚲🏠

The Vaults
Market Place, Uppingham, Oakham LE15 9QA
☎ Oakham (0572) 823259
In the market place of this delightful Rutland town in the heart of the East Midlands. Convenient for Leicester, Corby, Peterborough, Melton Mowbray and Rutland Water.
Bedrooms: 3 twin, 1 triple
Bathrooms: 4 private
Bed & breakfast

per night:	£min	£max
Single	30.00	
Double	40.00	

Lunch available
Evening meal 1900 (last orders 2130)
Cards accepted: Access, Visa, Amex

🛇📾♿🖪♿🆂🔳🌑🏠

| We advise you to |
| confirm your |
| booking in writing. |

UPTON

Nottinghamshire
Map ref 4C2

High Barn
Main Street, Upton, Newark
NG23 5TE
☎ Southwell (0636) 813444
A converted barn in a conservation village. Friendly atmosphere in family home of watercolourist Jennie Searle. Studio open to view.
Bedrooms: 1 single, 1 double
Bathrooms: 1 public

Bed & breakfast

per night:	£min	£max
Single	12.50	
Double	25.00	

Parking for 3
🐕 🐎 🖳 🖴 S ⅄ 🅿 🎔 🍴 💰 ✿
✕ 🐾 🏠

Honey Cottage
😊😊 HIGHLY COMMENDED
The Green, Upton, Newark
NG23 5SU
☎ Southwell (0636) 813318
Attractive cottage in the heart of a conservation village, ideal for touring Robin Hood country. Bar and restaurant meals are available in the village pubs. Within easy reach of the A1.
Bedrooms: 2 twin
Bathrooms: 2 private

Bed & breakfast

per night:	£min	£max
Single		24.00
Double		36.00

Parking for 4
🐕 🍴 🖵 💰 🖳 ⅄ 🎔 📺
🍴 💰 ✿ ✕ 🐾

WALTHAM-ON-THE-WOLDS

Leicestershire
Map ref 4C3

Royal Horseshoes
Melton Road, Waltham-on-the-Wolds, Melton Mowbray
LE14 4AJ
☎ (066 478) 289
A listed thatched country inn, approximately 400 years old. The accommodation is separate from the main building.
Bedrooms: 4 twin
Bathrooms: 4 private

Bed & breakfast

per night:	£min	£max
Single	25.00	27.00
Double	40.00	45.00

Half board

per person:	£min	£max
Daily	35.00	35.00

Lunch available
Evening meal 1830 (last orders 2100)
Parking for 50
🐕 🖵 💰 🍴 S 🖳 🎔 🐾 🅿 🏠

WEEDON

Northamptonshire
Map ref 2C1

Globe Hotel 🏛
😊😊😊😊 COMMENDED
High Street, Weedon, Northampton NN7 4QD
☎ (0327) 40336
Fax (0327) 349058
18th C countryside inn with a Royal Charter. Old world atmosphere and freehouse hospitality with good English cooking, available all day. Meeting rooms.
Bedrooms: 4 single, 6 double, 5 twin, 3 triple
Bathrooms: 18 private

Bed & breakfast

per night:	£min	£max
Single	29.50	42.00
Double	40.00	50.00

Half board

per person:	£min	£max
Daily		30.00

Lunch available
Evening meal (last orders 2200)
Parking for 40
Cards accepted: Access, Visa, Diners, Amex
🐕 🖵 ℄ 🍴 🖵 💰 🖳 S 🖳 🎔
🖳 🍴 10-30 ☎ ⌦ 🅿 🏠 T

WELLINGORE

Lincolnshire
Map ref 4C2

Marquis of Granby
High Street, Wellingore,
Lincoln LN5 0HW
☎ Lincoln (0522) 810442
Stone-built public house, approximately 250 years old, just off the A607 Lincoln to Grantham road.
Bedrooms: 1 double, 2 twin
Bathrooms: 3 private

Bed & breakfast

per night:	£min	£max
Single	18.50	20.00
Double	35.00	40.00

Lunch available
Evening meal 1900 (last orders 2200)
Parking for 3
Cards accepted: Access, Visa
🐕 🖵 💰 🖳 🍴 ☎ 🐾

Please check prices
and other details at
the time of booking.

WELLOW

Nottinghamshire
Map ref 4C2

Krefeld
Listed
Eakring Road, Wellow,
Newark NG22 0ED
☎ Mansfield (0623) 861112
With unrestricted views from the front and rear over the surrounding countryside, the house is in the maypole village of Wellow, on the road to Eakring. Close to Sherwood Forest. German spoken.
Bedrooms: 1 double, 1 twin
Bathrooms: 1 public

Bed & breakfast

per night:	£min	£max
Single		13.00
Double		21.00

Parking for 2
🐕 💰 🍴 🖳 💰 🖳 🐾

WESSINGTON

Derbyshire
Map ref 4B2

Crich Lane Farm
Moorwood Moor Lane, Wessington, Derby DE5 6DU
☎ Alfreton (0773) 835186
44-acre dairy farm. 17th C farmhouse just off the A615 Alfreton to Matlock road. Pets for children and a friendly welcome.
Bedrooms: 2 single, 1 double, 1 twin
Bathrooms: 2 public

Bed & breakfast

per night:	£min	£max
Single	14.00	16.00
Double	27.00	30.00

Parking for 10
🐕 🖳 S 🖳 📺 🖳 💰 🐾 🏠

WESTON UNDERWOOD

Derbyshire
Map ref 4B2

Parkview Farm
😊😊 COMMENDED
Weston Underwood,
Ashbourne DE6 4PE
☎ Ashbourne (0335) 60352
370-acre arable & dairy farm. Victorian farmhouse with country house atmosphere. Elegant four-poster bedrooms overlooking the garden and Kedleston Hall and Park.
Bedrooms: 2 double, 1 twin
Bathrooms: 2 public

WINSTER

Derbyshire
Map ref 4B2

Village with some interesting old gritstone houses and cottages, including the 17th C stone market hall, now owned by the National Trust. It is a former lead mining centre.

Brae Cottage
East Bank, Winster, Matlock
DE4 2DT
☎ (0629) 650375
Large self-contained bed and breakfast with bathroom and own garage, in an historic picturesque village. Suitable for 2-4 people.
Bedrooms: 1 double, 1 multiple
Bathrooms: 2 private

Bed & breakfast

per night:	£min	£max
Double	25.00	30.00

Parking for 2
🐕 ℄ 🍴 🖵 🖳 💰 🖳 🎔 ✿ ✕
🐾 🏠

The Dower House
😊😊 HIGHLY COMMENDED
Main Street, Winster,
Matlock DE4 2DH
☎ (0629) 650213
Fax (0629) 650894
An Elizabethan country house with a walled garden, log fires and beams, offering peace and relaxation. Close to Chatsworth and Haddon Hall.
Bedrooms: 1 double, 2 twin
Bathrooms: 3 private, 2 public

Bed & breakfast

per night:	£min	£max
Single	30.00	35.00
Double	45.00	55.00

Parking for 6
Open March-October
🐕 10 🖵 💰 🖳 💰 S ⅄ 🖳 🖳,
🖳 💰 🐾 🏠

Bed & breakfast section (top right):

Bed & breakfast

per night:	£min	£max
Single	18.00	20.00
Double	32.00	36.00

Parking for 10
🐕 🖳 💰 🖵 ⅄ 🖳 📺 🖳, 💰 ✿
✕ 🐾

Half board prices
shown are per
person but in some
cases may be
based on double/
twin occupancy.

WOODHALL SPA

Lincolnshire
Map ref 4D2

Attractive town which was formerly a spa. It has excellent sporting facilities with a championship golf-course and is surrounded by pine woods.

Claremont Guesthouse
☺☺
9-11 Witham Road,
Woodhall Spa LN10 6RW
☎ (0526) 52000
Family-run guesthouse within easy reach of the town's sporting and leisure facilities. We offer personal service and a friendly atmosphere. Evening meal by prior request only.
Bedrooms: 2 single,
2 double, 3 twin, 1 triple
Bathrooms: 1 private,
2 public

Bed & breakfast per night:

	£min	£max
Single	17.50	17.50
Double	30.00	35.00

Lunch available
Parking for 5

🐕☕🖺♨ⓊⓁⓘⓈ🆃📻🍴▶
❄ ᴼᴬᴾ SP

YARDLEY GOBION

Northamptonshire
Map ref 2C1

Old Wharf Farm
Listed
Yardley Gobion, Towcester
NN12 7UE
☎ Milton Keynes (0908)
542454
9-acre smallholding. This unique complex of old farm buildings, with its own working wharf and dry dock on to the Grand Union Canal, is now a family home, smallholding and canal boat maintenance base.
Bedrooms: 1 single,
1 double, 1 triple

Bathrooms: 2 public
Bed & breakfast per night:

	£min	£max
Single	18.00	20.00
Double	34.00	40.00

Parking for 5

🐕☕ⓊⓁⓘⓈ✂♨🍴⛁ 📻♫
🚲 SP 🅿

YOULGREAVE

Derbyshire
Map ref 4B2

Small town in the Peak District with an impressive church, much of which dates from Norman times. There are some interesting monuments in the church and stained glass by William Morris. The stone circle of Arbor Low is nearby.

The Old Bakery
Church Street, Youlgreave,
Bakewell DE45 1UR
☎ (0629) 636887

Separate guest lounge, bathroom and entrance. Information to help you make the best of your stay in this popular village.
Bedrooms: 2 twin
Bathrooms: 1 public
Bed & breakfast per night:

	£min	£max
Single	16.00	17.00
Double	28.00	30.00

Parking for 1

🐕ⓊⓁⓘⓈ✂♨🍴⛁ 📻💈🚲 SP

There are separate sections in this guide listing groups specialising in farm holidays and accommodation which is especially suitable for young people and organised groups.

Thames & Chilterns

You're spoilt for choice in this region of woodlands, downs and waterways, with its abundance of attractions, historic houses and towns and cities rich in heritage. Ramble through the beechwoods of the Chiltern Hills, explore the prehistoric sites of the Berkshire Downs and the charming, sleepy villages of the Oxfordshire Cotswolds, take a trip on the Kennet and

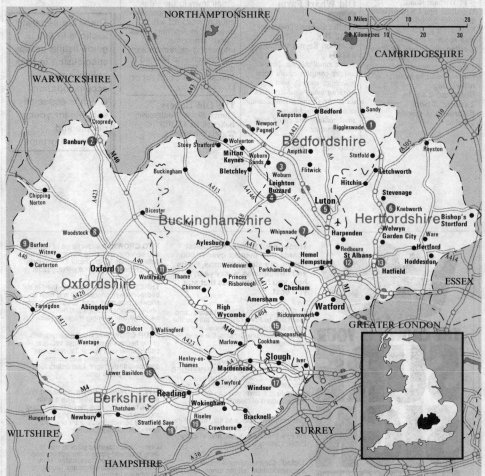

Use the above map to locate places in the "Where to Go, What to See" section opposite.

Use the colour maps at the back of this guide to find places with accommodation.

Avon Canal, or while away a morning watching the boats on the historic waterway of the Thames. Visit the ancient cathedral city of St Albans (Roman Verulamium), Victorian Windsor, admire the architectural splendours of Oxford (the city of dreaming spires) and the glories of Blenheim Palace. You'll find much to delight and memories to treasure.

WHERE TO GO, WHAT TO SEE

George Bernard Shaw chose to live in the village of Ayot St Lawrence on the basis of a graveyard inscription suggesting that a life of 70 years was a short one – he subsequently lived to the age of 94!

The number against each name will help you locate it on the map opposite.

❶ Shuttleworth Collection
Old Warden Aerodrome,
Biggleswade, Bedfordshire
SG18 9ER
Tel: Northill (076 727) 288
Unique historic collection of genuine veteran aircraft from 1909 Bleriot to 1942 Spitfire, all in flying condition. Cars dating from 1898 Panhard.

❶ The Swiss Garden
Biggleswade Road, Old Warden,
Biggleswade, Bedfordshire
Tel: Biggleswade (076 727) 666
Attractive garden dating from the 19th C and taking its name from the tiny Swiss thatched cottage in the centre.

❷ Broughton Castle
Banbury, Oxfordshire OX15 5EB
Tel: Banbury (0295) 262624
Medieval moated house built in 1300 and enlarged between 1550–1600. Home of Lord and Lady Saye and Sele and family home for 600 years. Civil War connections.

❸ Woburn Abbey
Woburn, Bedfordshire MK43 0TP
Tel: Woburn (0525) 290666
18th C Palladian mansion. Contains a collection of English silver, French and English furniture and an important art collection.

❹ Leighton Buzzard Railway
Page's Park Station, Billington
Road, Leighton Buzzard,
Bedfordshire LU7 8TN
Tel: Leighton Buzzard (0525) 373888
Preserved industrial railway, with steam locomotives from India and French Cameroons, diesel collection. This 2ft gauge railway, built in 1919, covers a distance of 5½ miles.

**5 Luton Hoo –
The Wernher Collection**
Luton, Bedfordshire LU1 3TQ
Tel: Luton (0582) 22955
Historic house built in 1767, with paintings, tapestries and porcelain. Jewellery by Carl Faberge, mementoes of the Russian Imperial family.

6 Knebworth House, Gardens and Park
Knebworth, Hertfordshire
SG3 6PY
Tel: Stevenage (0438) 812661
Tudor manor house, refashioned in 19th C by Bulwer-Lytton. Fine collection of manuscripts, portraits. Jacobean banqueting hall, adventure playground, gift shop.

7 Whipsnade Wild Animal Park
Whipsnade, Dunstable, Bedfordshire LU6 2LF
Tel: Whipsnade (0582) 872171
Over 2,000 animals (200 species) in 600-acre setting of parkland. Featuring a chilren's playground, animal centre, steam railway, Tiger Falls, sealions and birds of prey.

8 Blenheim Palace
Woodstock, Oxfordshire OX7 1PS
Tel: Woodstock (0993) 811091
Birthplace of Sir Winston Churchill. Architecture by Vanbrugh, park by Capability Brown. Bronzes, tapestries, furniture, paintings, adventure playground, butterfly house, plant centre, maze.

9 Cotswold Wildlife Park
Bradwell Grove, Burford, Oxfordshire OX8 4JW
Tel: Burford (0993) 823006
Tropical house, aquarium, reptile house, butterfly and insect house, 200 acres of garden and woodland, many wild animals, brass rubbing centre, railway, shop.

10 The Oxford Story
6 Broad Street, Oxford, Oxfordshire OX1 3AJ
Tel: Oxford (0865) 728822
Heritage centre depicting centuries of university history in sights, sounds, personalities and smells. Visitors are transported on moving desks with commentary.

10 Sheldonian Theatre
Broad Street, Oxford, Oxfordshire OX1 3AZ
Tel: Oxford (0865) 277299
Built in 1663, one of Sir Christopher Wren's earliest works. Principal assembly hall for the university and venue for important ceremonies.

11 Waterperry Gardens
Waterperry, Wheatley, Oxfordshire OX9 1JZ
Tel: Kingston Blount (0844) 339254
Ornamental gardens covering 6 acres of the 38-acre 18th C Waterperry House estate. Saxon village church, garden shop and tea shop.

12 Museum of St Albans
St Albans, Hertfordshire AL1 3RR
Tel: St Albans (0727) 56679
Purpose-built as a museum in 1898. Displays include craft tools and local and natural history telling the St Albans story from Roman times to the present day.

A 17th C windmill dominates the skyline near the village of Brill, overlooking the flat countryside of Buckinghamshire and Oxfordshire beyond

13 Hatfield House
Hatfield, Hertfordshire AL9 5NQ
Tel: Hatfield (0707) 262823
Jacobean house built in 1611 and old palace built in 1497. Famous paintings, fine furniture and possessions of Queen Elizabeth I. Extensive park and gardens.

14 Didcot Railway Centre
Didcot, Oxfordshire OX11 7NJ
Tel: Didcot (0235) 817200
Living museum re-creating the golden age of the Great Western Railway. Steam locomotives and trains, engine shed, small relics museum. Steam days and gala events.

15 Bekonscot Model Village
Warwick Road, Beaconsfield, Buckinghamshire HP9 2PZ
Tel: Beaconsfield (0494) 672919
A complete 1930s model village, with zoo, cinema, minster, cricket match, 1,200 inhabitants, model railway.

16 Beale Bird Park
Lower Basildon, Reading, Berkshire RG8 9NH
Tel: Upper Basildon (0491) 671325

Established 35 years ago as the Child-Beale Wildlife Trust, the park features wildfowl, pheasants, highland cattle, rare sheep, llamas, pets' corner, narrow-gauge railway.

⑰ Royalty and Empire Exhibition
Windsor, Berkshire SL4 1PJ
Tel: Windsor (0753) 857837
Adjacent to Windsor Castle, the exhibition celebrates 60 years of Queen Victoria and 40 years of Queen Elizabeth II. Waxworks and special effects are used to depict Royalty.

⑰ Windsor Castle
Windsor, Berkshire
SL4 1NT
Tel: Windsor (0753) 868286
Official residence of HM the Queen and royal residence for 9 centuries. State apartments, Queen Mary's dolls' house, exhibition of the Queen's presents, carriages.

⑰ Windsor Safari Park
Winkfield Road, Windsor, Berkshire SL4 4AY
Tel: Windsor (0753) 830886
African theme park with drive-through game reserves and "African Adventure". Safari road trains and funicular railway pass the elephant gardens, seaworld and bird display.

The Radcliffe Camera in Oxford, built as a library by James Gibbs in 1737 and now part of the Bodleian Library

⑱ Stratfield Saye House
Stratfield Saye, Berkshire
RG7 2BT
Tel: Basingstoke (0256) 882882
House built in 1630. Displays many personal possessions of the Iron Duke, including funeral hearse. Gardens and pleasure grounds.

⑲ Wellington Country Park
Riseley, Reading, Berkshire
RG7 1SP
Tel: Heckfield (0734) 326444
500-acre country park with National Dairy Museum. Miniature steam railway, crazy golf, children's farm and playground, windsurfing, boating, nature trails, deer park, fishing.

FIND OUT MORE

Further information about holidays and attractions in the Thames & Chilterns region is available from Tourist Information Centres in the region, and from the all-England information service on 071-824 8000 (tourist information) and 071-824 8844 (accommodation reservations).

Places to stay

Accommodation entries in this regional section are listed in alphabetical order of place name, and then in alphabetical order of establishment.

The map references refer to the colour maps at the back of the guide. The first figure is the map number; the letter and figure which follow indicate the grid reference on the map.

The symbols at the end of each accommodation entry give information about services and facilities. A 'key' to these symbols is inside the back cover flap, which can be kept open for easy reference.

ABINGDON

Oxfordshire
Map ref 2C1

Attractive former county town on River Thames with many interesting buildings, including 17th C County Hall, now a museum, in the market-place and the remains of an abbey.
Tourist Information Centre
☎ *(0235) 522711*

1 Long Barn
Sutton Courtenay, Abingdon OX14 4BQ
☎ (0235) 848251
17th C village house 8 miles from Oxford, 2 miles from Abingdon. Easy access to Henley and the Cotswolds.
Bedrooms: 1 twin
Bathrooms: 1 private
Bed & breakfast

per night:	£min	£max
Single	12.50	12.50
Double	25.00	25.00

Parking for 3
❄ 8 Ⓤ 📺 ▥ , ☎ ❋ 🐾 🛏

Crooked Chimney Cottage
Little Wittenham, Abingdon OX14 4QX
☎ Clifton Hampden (086 730) 7477
18th C cottage in Thameside hamlet of Little Wittenham at foot of Wittenham Clumps.

Close to Oxford, Abingdon, Wallingford and Didcot.
Bedrooms: 1 double
Bathrooms: 1 private
Bed & breakfast

per night:	£min	£max
Single	20.00	24.00
Double	33.00	36.00

❄ 🍴 🖥 ❖ ➤ Ⓤ 🅰 Ⓢ ✂ ▥,
☎ ✕ 🐾 OAP SP 🛏

AMERSHAM

Buckinghamshire
Map ref 2D1

Old town with many fine buildings, particularly in the High Street. There are several interesting old inns.

The Barn
Listed HIGHLY COMMENDED
Rectory Hill, Old Amersham, Amersham HP7 0BT
☎ (0494) 722701
17th C tithe barn with a wealth of beams. 6 minutes' walk from Amersham station. Easy access to M25 and M40.
Bedrooms: 1 single, 1 twin
Bathrooms: 1 public
Bed & breakfast

per night:	£min	£max
Single	24.00	27.00
Double	45.00	49.50

Parking for 5
❄ 5 🍴 🖥 Ⓤ 📺 ▥ , ☎ ❖
✕ 🐾 🛏

Glory Farm Cottage
Listed
Fagnall Lane, Winchmore Hill, Amersham HP7 0PQ
☎ (0494) 727598
Beamed cottage with homely atmosphere in picturesque Chiltern countryside and close to pubs. 3 miles from Amersham and Beaconsfield.
Bedrooms: 1 double, 1 twin
Bathrooms: 1 public
Bed & breakfast

per night:	£min	£max
Single	20.00	
Double	35.00	

Parking for 3
❄ 🍴 🖥 ❖ Ⓤ ✂ 🅼 📺 ▥ , ☎
❖ ✕ 🐾 🛏

AMPTHILL

Bedfordshire
Map ref 2D1

Busy market town with houses of distinctive Georgian character. Market established in 13thC, where traders sell their wares around the town pump, a Portland-stone obelisk presented to the town in 1785 by Lord Ossory.
Tourist Information Centre
☎ *(0525) 402051*

Pond Farm
Listed
7 High Street, Pulloxhill, Bedford MK45 5HA
☎ Flitwick (0525) 712316

70-acre arable & horses farm. Listed building, an ideal base for touring. Close to Woburn Abbey, Whipsnade Zoo, the Shuttleworth Collection of old aircraft and Luton Airport. Resident Great Dane.
Bedrooms: 1 double, 1 twin, 1 triple
Bathrooms: 1 public
Bed & breakfast

per night:	£min	£max
Single	16.00	22.00
Double	27.00	28.00

Parking for 6
❄ 🖥 Ⓤ 🅰 Ⓢ 📺 ▥ , ☎ ❖ ✕
🐾 🛏 🅣

ASCOT

Berkshire
Map ref 2C2

Small country town famous for its racecourse which was founded by Queen Anne. The race meeting each June is attended by the Royal Family.

54 King Edwards Road
Listed
North Ascot, Ascot SL5 8NY
☎ (0344) 882313 &
Maidenhead (0628) 661380
Detached house close to Ascot racecourse. 5 miles to Windsor, 3 miles to Bracknell and 20 minutes to Heathrow.
Bedrooms: 1 single, 1 double, 1 twin

Bathrooms: 1 public
Bed & breakfast

per night:	£min	£max
Single	15.00	15.00
Double	30.00	30.00

Parking for 5
🛇🌜🍴♨🖵🞘, 🚗 🖬

56 King Edwards Road
Listed

North Ascot, Ascot SL5 8NY
☎ Winkfield Row (0344) 883229
Chalet bungalow in very quiet area. Convenient for Heathrow Airport, trains to London, Windsor, Ascot races, Wentworth, Sunningdale and Berkshire golf-courses.
Bedrooms: 3 single, 1 twin
Bathrooms: 1 private, 2 public
Bed & breakfast

per night:	£min	£max
Single	16.00	18.00
Double	28.00	32.00

Parking for 6
🛇🌜♨🌜🖵 S ⌇ M TV
🞘, 🚗❀🖬

Birchcroft House M
COMMENDED

Birchcroft, Brockenhurst Road, South Ascot, Ascot SL5 9HA
☎ (0344) 20574
Edwardian country house. Superior en-suite accommodation for business and leisure. 15 minutes Bracknell and Windsor, 25 minutes Heathrow. Convenient for Ascot races, golf at Wentworth, Sunningdale or Berkshire.
Bedrooms: 1 double, 2 twin
Bathrooms: 3 private
Bed & breakfast

per night:	£min	£max
Single	28.00	33.00
Double	38.00	44.00

Parking for 6
🛇7🏳🖵♨🖵 S M TV 🞘,
🚗❀🖴🖬

Deepfold House

London Road, Bracknell RG12 6QR
☎ Bracknell (0344) 428367
Early 19th C coach house/ farmhouse in 5 acres of grounds on the A329. A few minutes from Ascot, Bracknell and Windsor. Close to M3, M4, M25 and 20 minutes from Heathrow Airport.
Bedrooms: 2 twin, 1 triple
Bathrooms: 1 private, 1 public

Bed & breakfast

per night:	£min	£max
Single	20.00	30.00
Double	33.00	45.00

Parking for 10
🛇I🌜🖵♨🖵♨🞘,🚗❀🖴
🖬 T

ASTHALL LEIGH

Oxfordshire
Map ref 2C1

Warwick House
Listed

Asthall Leigh, Witney OX8 5PX
☎ (099 387) 336
5-acre mixed farm. Charming country home in quiet village, overlooking open farmland on edge of Windrush Valley in the Cotswolds, between Witney and Burford. All rooms en-suite.
Bedrooms: 2 double, 1 twin
Bathrooms: 3 private
Bed & breakfast

per night:	£min	£max
Single	20.00	25.00
Double	30.00	35.00

Parking for 4
Open April-September
🛇🏇🏳🖵♨🖵♨🖵 🞘, 🚗⌀
🗸❀🖬

ASTON CLINTON

Buckinghamshire
Map ref 2C1

Village far-spread on the escarpment of the Downs, with many Jacobean thatched cottages and an inn which has been receiving travellers since John Hampden's days. 14th C church with its original chancel and fine arch still stands today.

Baywood Guest House

98 Weston Road, Aston Clinton, Aylesbury HP22 5EJ
☎ Aylesbury (0296) 630612
Victorian house with large garden, ducks, geese. Friendly welcome, home-cooked food, open fire. On B4544, off A41.
Bedrooms: 2 single, 2 double, 3 twin
Bathrooms: 3 private, 1 public, 2 private showers
Bed & breakfast

per night:	£min	£max
Single	15.00	20.00
Double	25.00	30.00

Evening meal 1800 (last orders 1830)
Parking for 9
🛇🌜♨🖵 S M TV 🞘, 🚗❀🖬

AYLESBURY

Buckinghamshire
Map ref 2C1

Historic county town in the Vale of Aylesbury. The cobbled market square has a Victorian clock tower and the 15th C King's Head Inn (National Trust). Interesting county museum and 13th C parish church. Twice-weekly livestock market.
Tourist Information Centre
☎ *(0296) 382308*

Apsley Manor Farm
HIGHLY COMMENDED

North Lee Lane, Marsh, Aylesbury HP22 5YA
☎ (0296) 613209
300-acre arable & dairy farm. 15th C Grade II listed manor farmhouse with oak beams, inglenook fireplaces. Lovely views of the Chiltern Hills. 3 miles from Stoke Mandeville.
Bedrooms: 1 double, 1 twin
Bathrooms: 2 private
Bed & breakfast

per night:	£min	£max
Single	25.00	
Double	40.00	

Parking for 12
🛇♨🖵 M TV 🞘, 🚗❀
🗸🖬

The Old Wheatsheaf Inn M

Weedon, Aylesbury HP22 4NS
☎ (0296) 641581
Old Elizabethan coaching inn, furnished with antiques. Courtyard surrounded by cottage and stable-cots. Home-from- home treatment and atmosphere.
Bedrooms: 3 single, 3 double, 2 twin
Bathrooms: 2 private, 3 public
Bed & breakfast

per night:	£min	£max
Single	30.00	35.00
Double	60.00	70.00

Lunch available
Evening meal 1830 (last orders 2200)
Parking for 14
🛇🏇🖵🎜 S ⌇ M TV 🞘, 🚗U
❀🖬 SP 🖬

Wallace Farm M
🍳🍳

Dinton, Aylesbury HP17 8UF
☎ (0296) 748 660
Fax (0296) 748851
150-acre mixed farm. 16th C farmhouse offers comfortable

accommodation in a quiet rural setting. Unspoilt extensive views across the Vale of Aylesbury to the Chiltern Hills. 3 miles from the centre of Aylesbury.
Bedrooms: 1 double, 1 twin, 1 triple
Bathrooms: 3 private
Bed & breakfast

per night:	£min	£max
Single	28.00	
Double	36.00	38.00

Parking for 6
Cards accepted: Access, Visa
🛇🏳🎜♨🖵 M TV 🞘, 🚗
🗸❀🖬🖬

BAMPTON

Oxfordshire
Map ref 2C1

Small market town, well known for its Spring Bank Holiday Monday Fete with Morris Dance Festival.

The Elephant and Castle M

Bridge Street, Bampton, Oxford OX18 2HA
☎ (0993) 850316
Grade II listed country pub with chalet-style rooms.
Bedrooms: 1 double, 2 twin
Bathrooms: 3 private
Bed & breakfast

per night:	£min	£max
Double	34.00	38.00

Parking for 10
🛇10🏇🖵♨🖵🞘,❀🗸🖬🖬

Romany Inn M
Listed

Bridge Street, Bampton, Oxford OX18 2HA
☎ (0993) 850237
Family-run 17th C listed inn, with friendly local clientele. Lounge bar, separate restaurant, log fires.
Bedrooms: 2 double, 4 twin
Bathrooms: 3 private, 1 public
Bed & breakfast

per night:	£min	£max
Single	17.50	25.00
Double	25.00	36.00

Lunch available
Evening meal 1830 (last orders 2200)
Parking for 3
🛇🏇🖵♨ M TV 🞘, 🚗
🖬🖬

The symbols are explained on the flap inside the back cover.

225

BANBURY

Oxfordshire
Map ref 2C1

Famous for its cattle market, cakes and nursery rhyme Cross. Founded in Saxon times, it has some fine houses and interesting old inns. A good centre for touring Warwickshire and the Cotswolds.
Tourist Information Centre
☎ *(0295) 259855*

Belmont Guest House
≋≋
34 Crouch Street, Banbury
OX16 9PR
☎ (0295) 262308
Family-run guesthouse approximately 200 yards from Banbury Cross. Away from the main road.
Bedrooms: 1 single,
3 double, 3 twin, 1 triple
Bathrooms: 5 private,
1 public, 1 private shower

Bed & breakfast per night:	£min	£max
Single	20.00	35.00
Double	30.00	40.00

Parking for 6
Cards accepted: Access, Visa
☒ 7 ♨ ⬚ ♦ ⑤ � ⅷ, ⬚ ⋨ ⚑

College Farmhouse
≋≋
King's Sutton, Banbury
OX17 3PS
☎ (0295) 811473
Period farmhouse set in its own secluded grounds which include a lake and a prolific organic vegetable garden.
Bedrooms: 2 twin
Bathrooms: 2 private,
1 public

Bed & breakfast per night:	£min	£max
Single	24.00	24.00
Double	48.00	48.00

Half board per person:	£min	£max
Daily	34.00	39.00

Lunch available
Evening meal 1930 (last orders 2100)
Parking for 12
☒ ⬚ ♦ ⬚ ⑤ ⬚ ⅷ ⓉⅤ ⅷ. ⬚ ⚘ ⚑

The Lodge
≋≋ COMMENDED
Main Road, Middleton
Cheney, Banbury OX17 2PP
☎ (0295) 710355
200-year-old lodge in lovely countryside, on outskirts of

---

historic village, 3 miles east of Banbury on A422.
Bedrooms: 1 double, 1 twin
Bathrooms: 2 private

Bed & breakfast per night:	£min	£max
Double	40.00	42.00

Parking for 5
☒ 3 ♨ ⅷ ⓉⅤ ● ⅷ. ⬚ ⚘ ⚑

Lowfields
Upper Astrop, King's Sutton,
Banbury OX17 3QN
☎ (0295) 812308
Large Cotswold-stone house in open countryside. Spacious bedrooms, tastefully furnished with antiques. 5 minutes from M40.
Bedrooms: 1 double, 1 twin
Bathrooms: 1 public

Bed & breakfast per night:	£min	£max
Single	15.00	30.00
Double	30.00	60.00

Half board per person:	£min	£max
Daily	25.00	45.00

Evening meal 1930 (last orders 2100)
Parking for 21
☒ ⬚ ⅼ ⬚ ⅷ ⬚ ⑤ ⓉⅤ ⅷ. ⬚ ⮞ ⚘ ⚑ SP ⚑

The Mill Barn
Lower Tadmarton, Banbury
OX15 5SU
☎ Swalcliffe (029 578) 349
Family home offering en-suite ground floor accommodation in a beautifully converted stone barn, set in an acre of grounds. Convenient for Oxford, Stratford-upon-Avon and the Cotswolds.
Bedrooms: 1 double, 1 triple
Bathrooms: 2 private

Bed & breakfast per night:	£min	£max
Single		25.00
Double	35.00	40.00

Parking for 4
☒ ♨ ⬚ ⅷ ♦ ⅷ ⑤ ⅷ ⅷ ⓉⅤ ⅷ. ⬚ ⮞ ⚘ ⚑

The Old Manor
Listed HIGHLY COMMENDED
Cropredy, Banbury
OX17 1PS
☎ (0295) 750235
Fax (0295) 758479
Partially moated manor house alongside Oxford Canal and in centre of village. Rare breed farm animals and private motor museum.
Bedrooms: 1 double, 1 twin
Bathrooms: 2 private

Bed & breakfast per night:	£min	£max
Single	22.50	25.00
Double	40.00	44.00

Parking for 16
Cards accepted: Access, Visa
☒ ⬚ ⬚ ⅷ ⑤ ⅷ ⅷ. ⬚ ⅉ ⚘ ⅷ ⚑ ⚑

Prospect House Guest House ⋔
≋≋≋ COMMENDED
70 Oxford Road, Banbury
OX16 9AN
☎ (0295) 268749
Detached house with lovely grounds, in the most convenient area of town.
Bedrooms: 1 single,
6 double, 2 twin
Bathrooms: 9 private,
1 public

Bed & breakfast per night:	£min	£max
Single	30.00	40.00
Double	40.00	50.00

Half board per person:	£min	£max
Daily	39.50	49.50
Weekly	200.00	

Evening meal 1900 (last orders 2030)
Parking for 10
Cards accepted: Access, Visa
☒ ♨ ⅷ ⬚ ⅷ ♦ ⅷ ⑤ ⅷ ⅷ ⓉⅤ ⅷ. ⬚ ⚘ ⅷ ⚑ ⮝ SP

"Roxtones"
Listed
Malthouse Lane, Shutford,
Banbury OX15 6PB
☎ (0295) 788240
Stone-fronted semi-bungalow with garden surrounds, orchard and lawns. 6 miles from Banbury, 16 miles from Stratford-upon-Avon and 2 miles from Broughton Castle.
Bedrooms: 2 single, 1 double
Bathrooms: 1 public

Bed & breakfast per night:	£min	£max
Single		15.00
Double		25.00

Half board per person:	£min	£max
Daily		21.50
Weekly		150.00

Evening meal 1900 (last orders 2100)
Parking for 3
Open April-September
☒ 7 ⅷ ⅷ ⓉⅤ ⅷ. ⅷ ⚑

Studleigh Farm
Wales Street, King's Sutton,
Banbury OX17 3RR
☎ (0295) 811979
Renovated and modernised farmhouse built circa 1700, on 8 acres of pastureland in

---

a picturesque village. On direct Oxford-London railway lines. Non-smokers only please.
Bedrooms: 1 double, 1 twin
Bathrooms: 2 private

Bed & breakfast per night:	£min	£max
Single	29.00	30.00
Double	38.00	40.00

Parking for 3
⬚ ⅷ ⑤ ⅷ ⓉⅤ ⅷ. ⅉ ⚘ ⅷ ⚑

BEDFORD

Bedfordshire
Map ref 2D1

Busy county town with interesting buildings and churches near the River Ouse which has pleasant riverside walks. Many associations with John Bunyan including Bunyan Meeting House, museum and statue. The Bedford Museum and Cecil Higgins Art Gallery are of interest.
Tourist Information Centre
☎ *(0234) 215226*

No 1 The Grange
≋≋≋ COMMENDED
Sunderland Hill, Ravensden,
Bedford MK44 2SH
☎ (0234) 771771
Elegant, spacious, family-run accommodation in rural surroundings. Two riding schools and Mosbray golf course nearby. Non-smokers please.
Bedrooms: 1 single,
1 double, 1 twin
Bathrooms: 1 private,
2 public

Bed & breakfast per night:	£min	£max
Single		20.00
Double		34.00

Half board per person:	£min	£max
Daily	29.50	32.50

Lunch available
Evening meal 1830 (last orders 1200)
Parking for 10
☒ 3 ⬚ ⅷ ⅷ ⅷ ♦ ⑤ ⅷ ⅷ ⓉⅤ ⅷ. ⬚ ⮞ ⚘ ⅷ ⚑ ⅷ Ⓣ

BERRICK SALOME

Oxfordshire
Map ref 2C2

Lower Farm
≋≋≋ APPROVED
Berrick Salome, Wallingford
OX10 6JL
☎ Stadhampton (0865)
891073

Family home with comfortable rooms, on 24-acre farm with horses. An old house with architecturally interesting connections with the Civil War.
Bedrooms: 2 triple
Bathrooms: 1 private, 1 public
Bed & breakfast

per night:	£min	£max
Single	25.00	30.00
Double	40.00	50.00

Half board

per person:	£min	£max
Daily	30.00	35.00
Weekly	160.00	200.00

Evening meal 1900 (last orders 2100)
Parking for 4

BICESTER

Oxfordshire
Map ref 2C1

Market town with large army depot and well-known hunting centre with hunt established in the late 18th C. The ancient parish church displays work of many periods. Nearby is the Jacobean mansion of Rousham House with gardens landscaped by William Kent.

Manor Farm
Listed

Poundon, Bicester OX6 0BB
☎ (0869) 277212
300-acre arable and mixed farm. 300-year-old farmhouse, tranquil, spacious and comfortable. Take A421 Bicester to Buckingham road. Poundon turn is 3 miles along on right.
Bedrooms: 1 single, 2 triple
Bathrooms: 1 private, 2 public
Bed & breakfast

per night:	£min	£max
Single	15.00	17.00
Double	25.00	30.00

Parking for 12

The town index towards the back of this guide gives page numbers of all places with accommodation.

BIGGLESWADE

Bedfordshire
Map ref 2D1

Busy centre for market gardening set on the River Ivel spanned by a 14th C bridge. Some interesting old buildings in the market-place. Nearby are the Shuttleworth collection of historic aeroplanes and Jordan's Mill.

The New Inn
16A Market Square, Biggleswade SG18 8AS
☎ (0767) 313198
A large public inn dating back to 17th C with big fireplace in lounge bar. All low-beamed ceilings.
Bedrooms: 1 single, 3 twin
Bathrooms: 1 public
Bed & breakfast

per night:	£min	£max
Single	18.00	20.00
Double	36.00	40.00

Half board

per person:	£min	£max
Daily	22.00	24.00

Lunch available
Evening meal 1730 (last orders 1930)
Parking for 1

Old Warden Guest House
Listed

Shop and Post Office, Old Warden, Biggleswade SG18 9HQ
☎ Northill (0767) 627201
Listed, 19th C building, adjacent to shop and post office. Between Biggleswade and Bedford.
Bedrooms: 1 double, 2 twin
Bathrooms: 1 public
Bed & breakfast

per night:	£min	£max
Single	20.00	24.00
Double	34.00	34.00

Parking for 5

National Crown ratings were correct at the time of going to press but are subject to change. Please check at the time of booking.

BISHOP'S STORTFORD

Hertfordshire
Map ref 2D1

Fine old town on the River Stort with many interesting buildings, particularly Victorian, and an imposing parish church. The vicarage where Cecil Rhodes was born is now a museum.
Tourist Information Centre
☎ *(0279) 655261*

46 South Road
Listed

Bishop's Stortford CM23 3JJ
☎ (0279) 503660 & 814316
Private chalet bungalow close to town centre and British Rail station. Convenient for M11/M25, and 15 minutes' drive to Stansted Airport.
Bedrooms: 2 twin
Bathrooms: 1 public
Bed & breakfast

per night:	£min	£max
Single	14.00	17.00
Double	28.00	30.00

Parking for 3

Millers Cottage

Pig Lane, Bishop's Stortford CM22 7PA
☎ (0279) 503487
Thatched cottage over 400 years old set in secluded garden bounded by stream, with ducks, geese and chickens.
Bedrooms: 1 single, 1 double, 1 twin
Bathrooms: 1 public
Bed & breakfast

per night:	£min	£max
Single	15.50	16.50
Double	31.00	33.00

Open March-November

Individual proprietors have supplied all details of accommodation. Although we do check for accuracy, we advise you to confirm the information at the time of booking.

BLETCHINGDON

Oxfordshire
Map ref 2C1

Thatched and stone-roofed cottages surround the village green with magnificent views of Otmoor and the hills beyond.

Stonehouse Farm
Listed

Weston Road, Bletchingdon, Oxford OX5 3EA
☎ Bletchington (0869) 50585
560-acre arable farm. 17th C Cotswold farmhouse. Ideal touring centre. 15 minutes north of Oxford, 20 minutes south of Banbury and 10 minutes from Blenheim Palace. Between the A4260 and A34, junction 9 of M40. 1 hour from Heathrow.
Bedrooms: 1 single, 1 double, 1 twin, 1 triple
Bathrooms: 2 public
Bed & breakfast

per night:	£min	£max
Single	15.00	18.00
Double	28.00	32.00

Parking for 11

BRACKNELL

Berkshire
Map ref 2C2

Designated a New Town in 1949, the town has ancient origins. Set in heathlands, it is an excellent centre for golf and walking. South Hill Park, an 18th C mansion, houses an art centre.
Tourist Information Centre
☎ *(0344) 868196*

Bear Farm

Binfield, Bracknell RG12 5QE
☎ Twyford (0734) 343286
65-acre mixed farm. 17th C oak-beamed farmhouse surrounded by 2 acres of well kept gardens, with en-suite guest bedrooms in an adjoining converted farm building.
Bedrooms: 1 double, 1 twin
Bathrooms: 2 private
Continued ▶

BRACKNELL

Continued

Bed & breakfast

per night:	£min	£max
Single	22.50	25.00
Double	38.50	40.00

Parking for 6
Cards accepted: Access, Visa

BRIMPTON

Berkshire
Map ref 2C2

Manor Farm ⚔

Listed

Brimpton, Reading RG7 4SQ
☎ Woolhampton (0734)
713166
600-acre mixed farm. Working family farm in Brimpton village. Interesting house and chapel, once of the Knights Hospitallers. Close to A4, M4 and M3.
Bedrooms: 1 double, 1 twin
Bathrooms: 1 public
Bed & breakfast

per night:	£min	£max
Single	16.50	20.00
Double	32.00	38.00

Parking for 4

BUCKINGHAM

Buckinghamshire
Map ref 2C1

Interesting old market town surrounded by rich farmland. It has many Georgian buildings, including the Town Hall and Old Jail and many old almshouses and inns. Stowe School nearby has magnificent 18th C landscaped gardens.

Folly Farm

Padbury, Buckingham
MK18 2HS
☎ Winslow (029 671) 2413
500-acre arable farm. On A413 between Winslow and Padbury, 4 miles south of Buckingham. Substantial farmhouse opposite Folly Inn. Convenient for Stowe Landscape Gardens and Silverstone circuit.
Bedrooms: 1 double, 1 twin, 1 multiple
Bathrooms: 1 public

Bed & breakfast

per night:	£min	£max
Single	15.00	16.00
Double	30.00	30.00

Parking for 10

Lockmeadow Farm

COMMENDED

Stratford Road, Buckingham
MK18 7AS
☎ (0280) 812220
30-acre arable farm. 1 mile east of Buckingham on A422, with views over fields and Great Ouse river.
Bedrooms: 1 single, 2 double, 2 twin, 1 triple
Bathrooms: 2 public
Bed & breakfast

per night:	£min	£max
Single	25.00	25.00
Double	36.00	38.00

Parking for 6

BURFORD

Oxfordshire
Map ref 2B1

One of the most beautiful Cotswold wool towns with Georgian and Tudor houses, many antique shops and a picturesque High Street sloping to the River Windrush.
Tourist Information Centre
☎ *(099 382) 3558*

The Dower House

Westhall Hill, Fulbrook,
Oxford OX18 4BJ
☎ (099 382) 2596
Elegant, newly-restored period accommodation in an imposing Cotswold dower house. Superb and tranquil setting, with commanding views over Burford and beautiful surrounding countryside. South-facing bedrooms and picturesque gardens.
Bedrooms: 2 double
Bathrooms: 1 private, 1 public
Bed & breakfast

per night:	£min	£max
Single	15.00	30.00
Double	30.00	34.00

Parking for 3

Please mention this guide when making a booking.

The Highway Hotel ⚔

COMMENDED

High Street, Burford, Oxford
OX8 4RG
☎ (099 382) 2136
Telex Hussey 838736
Family-run, beamed medieval Cotswold hotel offering comfortable modern amenities. Needlecraft centre.
Bedrooms: 7 double, 2 twin, 2 triple
Bathrooms: 9 private, 1 public
Bed & breakfast

per night:	£min	£max
Single	25.00	30.00
Double	35.00	50.00

Cards accepted: Access, Visa, Diners, Amex

Hillborough Hotel ⚔

The Green, Milton-under-Wychwood, Oxford OX7 6JH
☎ Shipton-u-Wychwood
(0993) 830501
Victorian country house facing village green. Open fires. Friendly bar. Restaurant open to non-residents. Leafy conservatory coffee lounge. Pretty gardens.
Bedrooms: 4 double, 3 twin, 3 triple
Bathrooms: 10 private
Bed & breakfast

per night:	£min	£max
Single	39.00	
Double	54.00	

Half board

per person:	£min	£max
Daily	47.00	51.00

Lunch available
Evening meal 1900 (last orders 2130)
Parking for 15
Open February-December
Cards accepted: Access, Visa

Rookery Farm ⚔

Listed COMMENDED

Burford Road, Brize Norton,
Oxford OX18 3NL
☎ Carterton (0993) 842957
2-acre smallholding. 18th C Cotswold farmhouse, pleasantly situated in small Oxfordshire village with lovely views of surrounding countryside. Generous farmhouse breakfast.
Bedrooms: 2 double, 1 twin
Bathrooms: 1 public

Bed & breakfast

per night:	£min	£max
Single	17.00	17.00
Double	34.00	34.00

Parking for 4

The Royal Oak

COMMENDED

26 Witney Street, Burford,
Oxford OX18 4SN
☎ (0993) 823278
17th C inn situated in a quiet position, approximately 100 yards from High Street. Off-street parking available.
Bedrooms: 1 double, 1 twin
Bathrooms: 2 private
Bed & breakfast

per night:	£min	£max
Single	20.00	35.00
Double	40.00	60.00

Lunch available
Evening meal 1900 (last orders 2130)
Parking for 6
Cards accepted: Access, Visa

St. Andrews Bed and Breakfast

Oxford Rd. (A40), Burford,
Oxford OX8 4TU
☎ (099 382) 3281
Cotswold stone house on outskirts of Burford. Panoramic views overlooking Windrush River. Lounge/TV. Ideal base for touring, golfing, riding, walking, cycling.
Bedrooms: 1 double, 1 twin, 1 triple
Bathrooms: 2 public, 1 private shower
Bed & breakfast

per night:	£min	£max
Single	17.50	20.00
Double	30.00	35.00

Parking for 10

Stonefield Barn

Signet Farm, Swindon Road,
Burford, Oxford OX18 4JE
☎ (099 382) 3447
200-year-old converted Cotswold-stone barn and stable block in own grounds. Countryside situation, 1 mile from Burford. Non-smokers only please.
Bedrooms: 2 double, 2 twin
Bathrooms: 2 private, 1 public

We advise you to confirm your booking in writing.

Bed & breakfast

per night:	£min	£max
Single	15.00	20.00
Double	30.00	30.00

Parking for 6

🛏️🚗♿️🎱🍴🔌⚙️🕹️🏦🐾🎠🚲

Warwick House

Listed COMMENDED

25 Lower High Street,
Burford, Oxford OX8 4RN
☎ (099 382) 3438
*Grade II listed building with a
Georgian facade, dating from
1590.*
Bedrooms: 1 double, 2 twin
Bathrooms: 3 private

Bed & breakfast

per night:	£min	£max
Single	15.00	22.50
Double	25.00	35.00

🛏️🖥️🔌⚙️🅿️⚙️🍴🕹️🚲📟🏦

CHALFONT ST GILES

Buckinghamshire
Map ref 2D2

Pretty old village in
wooded Chiltern Hills only
20 miles from London.
Good touring and walking
centre.

Gorelands Corner

Gorelands Lane, Chalfont St
Giles HP8 4HQ
☎ (024 07) 2689
*Family home set in large
garden. Non-smokers only
please.*
Bedrooms: 1 twin
Bathrooms: 1 private

Bed & breakfast

per night:	£min	£max
Single	15.00	
Double	30.00	

Parking for 1

🛏️📟🕹️🔌🅿️🍴🏦🚲

CHEARSLEY

Buckinghamshire
Map ref 2C1

Manor Farm Bed and Breakfast

Listed

Manor Farm, Chearsley,
Aylesbury HP18 0DH
☎ Long Crendon (0844)
208303
*233-acre mixed farm.
Accommodation in old
farmhouse in peaceful setting.
Situated on the right when
entering the village from
Long Crendon direction.*
Bedrooms: 2 single, 1 double

Bathrooms: 2 private,
1 public

Bed & breakfast

per night:	£min	£max
Single		24.00
Double		32.00

Parking for 4

🛏️🔌🅿️📟⚙️🍴🏦⚙️🔌🎠

CHESTERTON

Oxfordshire
Map ref 2C1

Bignell Park Hotel ⚜

🛏️🛏️🛏️ HIGHLY COMMENDED

Chesterton, Bicester
OX6 8UE
☎ Bicester (0869) 241444 &
241192
Fax (0869) 241444
*Cotswold period house circa
1740, set in 2.5 acres with
mature gardens, in rural
Oxfordshire.*
Bedrooms: 1 single,
2 double, 2 twin
Bathrooms: 5 private,
1 public

Bed & breakfast

per night:	£min	£max
Single	45.00	55.00
Double	50.00	90.00

Lunch available
Evening meal 1900 (last
orders 2130)
Parking for 18
Cards accepted: Access, Visa,
Diners, Amex

🛏️🖥️6♿️🍴📟🕹️🔌🅿️📟⚙️🍴
🏦☀️🍴🎱4-30🅿️⚙️📟🏦🚲

CHIEVELEY

Berkshire
Map ref 2C2

The Old Farmhouse

Downend Lane, Chieveley,
Newbury RG16 8TN
☎ (0635) 248361
*Small country farmhouse on
edge of village. Within 1 mile
of M4/A34 junction 13 and
close to Newbury.
Accommodation in self-
contained annexe.*
Bedrooms: 1 double, 1 twin,
1 triple
Bathrooms: 1 private,
1 public

Bed & breakfast

per night:	£min	£max
Single	16.00	20.00
Double	32.00	35.00

Parking for 5

🛏️🔌📟🕹️🔌⚙️🍴🅿️📟⚙️
🏦🍴☀️🚲

CHIPPING NORTON

Oxfordshire
Map ref 2C1

Old market town set high
in the Cotswolds and an
ideal touring centre. The
wide market-place
contains many 16th C and
17th C stone houses and
the Town Hall and Tudor
Guildhall.

The Crown & Cushion Hotel ⚜

🛏️🛏️🛏️🛏️ APPROVED

23 High Street, Chipping
Norton OX7 5AD
☎ (0608) 642533
Fax (0608) 642926
*15th C coaching inn with
indoor pool and leisure
complex. Convenient for M40
motorway, Warwick,
Blenheim, Stratford-upon-
Avon, Cheltenham, Oxford
and the Cotswolds.*
Bedrooms: 29 double,
11 twin
Bathrooms: 40 private

Bed & breakfast

per night:	£min	£max
Single	39.00	55.00
Double	39.00	95.00

Half board

per person:	£min	£max
Daily	35.00	60.00
Weekly	234.00	295.00

Lunch available
Evening meal 1900 (last
orders 2100)
Parking for 23
Cards accepted: Access, Visa,
Diners, Amex

🛏️♿️🔌🍴📟🕹️🔌🅿️⚙️🍴🏦
🅿️🎱3-200☀️🍴🎱🅿️📟⚙️🔌
🏦📺

CRANFIELD

Bedfordshire
Map ref 2D1

Apart from a very few
small cottages and some
Victorian almshouses,
there is little evidence of
Cranfield's past. This is
now one of the most
quickly growing and
heavily populated towns
in Bedfordshire.

The Swan

2 Court Road, Cranfield,
Bedford MK43 0DR
☎ (0234) 750332 & 750772
*Village green pub between
Milton Keynes and Bedford
and only 4 miles from
junctions 13/14 of M1. Pub
games, cosy open fires in
lounge/dining room. Water*

*skiing and parachute club
nearby.*
Bedrooms: 3 double, 3 twin
Bathrooms: 3 private,
1 public

Bed & breakfast

per night:	£min	£max
Single	25.00	35.00
Double	35.00	45.00

Lunch available
Evening meal 1800 (last
orders 2200)
Parking for 30
Cards accepted: Access, Visa

🛏️🔌📟⚙️♿️🍴🔌🅿️🍴🔌🏦⚙️
☀️🍴🎱🅿️⚙️🍴

DEDDINGTON

Oxfordshire
Map ref 2C1

Attractive former market
town with a large market
square and many fine old
buildings.

Earls Farm

Deddington, Banbury
OX5 4TH
☎ (0869) 38243
*230-acre mixed farm. Listed
farmhouse on edge of village.*
Bedrooms: 1 single, 1 twin,
1 triple
Bathrooms: 2 public

Bed & breakfast

per night:	£min	£max
Single	15.00	17.00
Double	30.00	35.00

Parking for 4

🛏️♿️🔌📟🍴📺🕹️🔌🍴⚙️
☀️🚲

Hill Barn

Listed

Milton Gated Road,
Deddington, Banbury
OX5 4TS
☎ (0869) 38631
*Converted barn set in open
countryside with views
overlooking valley and hills.
Banbury - Oxford road, half a
mile before Deddington, turn
right to Milton Gated Road.
Hill Barn is 100 yards on the
right.*
Bedrooms: 1 double, 2 twin
Bathrooms: 1 public

Bed & breakfast

per night:	£min	£max
Single	15.00	15.00
Double	30.00	30.00

Parking for 6

🛏️♿️🔌🍴🅿️☀️🍴🏦

> Map references
> apply to the colour
> maps at the back
> of this guide.

DEDDINGTON

Continued

Unicorn Hotel ⚔

⬙⬙⬙ APPROVED

Market Place, Deddington,
Banbury OX15 0SE
☎ (0869) 38838
Fax (0869) 38036
*17th C Cotswold border
coaching inn, 10 minutes
from M40 junctions 10 and
11, on A4260 Banbury to
Oxford road.*
Bedrooms: 4 single,
3 double, 1 twin, 1 multiple
Bathrooms: 9 private
Bed & breakfast

per night:	£min	£max
Single	30.00	30.00
Double	45.00	45.00

Half board

per person:	£min	£max
Daily	36.00	36.00
Weekly	300.00	300.00

Lunch available
Evening meal 1900 (last
orders 2130)
Parking for 33
Cards accepted: Access, Visa,
Diners, Amex
⬙⬙⬙⬙⬙⬙⬙⬙⬙⬙
⬙⬙£20-60⬙⬙⬙⬙⬙⬙
⬙⬙

DIDCOT

Oxfordshire
Map ref 2C2

Important railway junction
where steam engines can
still be seen at the Didcot
Railway Centre, together
with a recreated station
and a small relics
museum.

Hacca's Cottage

Fieldside, East Hagbourne,
Didcot OX11 9LQ
☎ Abingdon (0235) 814324
*Two cottages combined and
modernised for maximum
comfort. Rural setting in a
delightful village, with views
over fields and downs.*
Bedrooms: 2 single, 1 double
Bathrooms: 3 private,
3 public
Bed & breakfast

per night:	£min	£max
Single	18.00	
Double	36.00	

Evening meal 1800 (last
orders 2000)
Parking for 2
⬙⬙⬙⬙⬙⬙⬙⬙⬙

North Croft Cottage

North Croft, East
Hagbourne, Didcot
OX11 9LT
☎ (0235) 813326
*17th C low white cottage with
oak beams inside and out,
inglenook fireplace and
leaded windows.*
Bedrooms: 3 single, 1 double
Bathrooms: 2 private,
2 public
Bed & breakfast

per night:	£min	£max
Single	25.00	
Double	38.00	

Parking for 4
Open April-October
⬙⬙5⬙⬙⬙⬙⬙⬙⬙⬙⬙
⬙⬙⬙⬙⬙

DUCKLINGTON

Oxfordshire
Map ref 2C1

Walnut Tree Cottage

Back Lane, Ducklington,
Witney OX8 7UE
☎ Witney (0993) 774430
*Large, Cotswold-stone family
home, behind the church.
River Windrush frontage.*
Bedrooms: 2 double
Bathrooms: 1 public
Bed & breakfast

per night:	£min	£max
Double	25.00	30.00

Parking for 2
⬙⬙⬙⬙⬙⬙⬙⬙

DUNSTABLE

Bedfordshire
Map ref 2D1

Modern town with remains
of a 12th C Augustinian
priory in the parish
church. The Dunstable
Downs are famous for
gliding and in the
parkland of Whipsnade
Zoo on the edge of the
Downs many animals
roam freely.
*Tourist Information Centre
☎ (0582) 471012*

Bellows Mill

⬙⬙⬙⬙ COMMENDED

Bellows Mill, Eaton Bray,
Dunstable LU6 1QZ
☎ Eaton Bray (0525)
220548 & 220205
*Delightful old water mill with
converted stables. Tennis
court, fly fishing, games
room. All rooms en-suite with
TV and telephone.*
Bedrooms: 3 double, 2 twin
Bathrooms: 5 private

Bed & breakfast

per night:	£min	£max
Single	30.00	43.48
Double	43.48	45.00

Half board

per person:	£min	£max
Daily	36.44	58.18

Lunch available
Evening meal 1900 (last
orders 2200)
Parking for 12
Cards accepted: Access, Visa
⬙⬙⬙⬙⬙⬙⬙⬙⬙⬙
⬙⬙⬙⬙⬙⬙⬙

ELSTREE

Hertfordshire
Map ref 2D1

North Medburn Farm

Watling Street, Elstree,
Borehamwood WD6 3AA
☎ 081-953 1522
*100-acre arable farm. 150-
year-old farmhouse on A5
between Elstree and Radlett. 5
minutes from nearest station,
12 miles from centre of
London.*
Bedrooms: 1 single,
1 double, 3 twin
Bathrooms: 1 private,
1 public
Bed & breakfast

per night:	£min	£max
Single	15.00	15.00
Double	30.00	30.00

Parking for 4
⬙⬙⬙⬙⬙⬙⬙⬙⬙⬙

FARINGDON

Oxfordshire
Map ref 2B2

Ancient stone-built market
town in the Vale of the
White Horse. The 17th C
market hall stands on
pillars and the 13th C
church has some fine
monuments. A great
monastic tithe barn is
nearby at Great Coxwell.

Barcote Manor

⬙⬙ HIGHLY COMMENDED

Buckland, Faringdon
SN7 8PP
☎ Buckland (036 787) 260
& 330
*Listed manor, set in lovely
gardens, large attractive,
comfortable rooms, views of
surrounding countryside.
Direct access from A420, 1.5
miles from Faringdon towards
Oxford.*
Bedrooms: 1 double, 1 twin
Bathrooms: 2 public

Bed & breakfast

per night:	£min	£max
Single	30.00	35.00
Double	40.00	50.00

Parking for 10
Open April-October
Cards accepted: Visa
⬙⬙⬙⬙⬙⬙⬙⬙⬙⬙
⬙⬙

GOFF'S OAK

Hertfordshire
Map ref 2D1

329 Goffs Lane

Goff's Oak EN7 5QH
☎ (0992) 28524
*Large detached house, close
to countryside yet easy
travelling to London.*
Bedrooms: 1 single,
2 double, 3 twin
Bathrooms: 1 public,
6 private showers
Bed & breakfast

per night:	£min	£max
Single	20.00	25.00
Double	45.00	50.00

Half board

per person:	£min	£max
Daily	25.00	30.00
Weekly	200.00	250.00

Lunch available
Evening meal 1800 (last
orders 2100)
Parking for 6
⬙⬙⬙⬙⬙⬙⬙⬙⬙⬙
⬙⬙⬙⬙⬙⬙⬙⬙⬙⬙

GORING

Oxfordshire
Map ref 2C2

Riverside town on the
Oxfordshire/Berkshire
border, linked by an
attractive bridge to
Streatley with views to the
Goring Gap.

The John Barleycorn

Listed

Manor Road, Goring,
Reading RG8 9DP
☎ (0491) 872509
*16th C inn with exposed
beams. Close to the river,
lovely walks.*
Bedrooms: 1 single,
1 double, 1 triple
Bathrooms: 2 public
Bed & breakfast

per night:	£min	£max
Single	21.00	
Double	35.00	

Lunch available
Evening meal 1900 (last
orders 2200)
Parking for 2
⬙⬙⬙⬙⬙⬙⬙

230

GREAT BRICKHILL

Buckinghamshire
Map ref 2C1

Duncombe Arms
👑👑👑

32 Lower Way, Great
Brickhill, Milton Keynes
MK17 9AG
☎ (052 526) 1226
Fax (052 526) 1350
*Set in 2 acres of gardens in
centre of village. Restaurant
and 2 bars with children's
garden. 18-hole putting green,
16 floodlit petanque pitches,
garden skittles, pitching
American horseshoes, croquet,
garden chess, barbecue,
marquee for 100 people.*
Bedrooms: 3 twin
Bathrooms: 3 private

Bed & breakfast per night:	£min	£max
Single	30.00	32.00
Double	40.00	45.00

Half board per person:	£min	£max
Daily	38.00	40.00

Lunch available
Evening meal 1930 (last
orders 2230)
Parking for 17
Cards accepted: Access, Visa
🕭🖵🛏🛉🕭💷🛁🅿📞🅄🕈❄
📺 SP

GREAT HORWOOD

Buckinghamshire
Map ref 2C1

Mill Farm
Listed

Winslow Road, Great
Horwood, Milton Keynes
MK17 0NY
☎ Winslow (029 671) 2527
*52-acre livestock farm. House
in a quiet location, with views
across the open country. On
B4033 between Winslow and
Great Horwood. Access to
North Bucks Way. Non-
smokers only please.*
Bedrooms: 1 double, 1 triple
Bathrooms: 1 public

Bed & breakfast per night:	£min	£max
Single	15.00	15.00
Double	29.00	29.00

Parking for 25
🕭🖵🛏🛉🛄🛏💷💷❄
🗲 📺

> **Check the
> introduction to this
> region for Where to
> Go, What to See.**

HENLEY-ON-THAMES

Oxfordshire
Map ref 2C2

The famous Thames
Regatta is held in this
prosperous and attractive
town at the beginning of
July each year. The town
has many Georgian
buildings and old
coaching inns and the
parish church has some
fine monuments.

8 Norman Avenue
Listed   COMMENDED

Henley-on-Thames RG9 1SG
☎ (0491) 573099
*Friendly Victorian house in
quiet, private road. Centrally
situated close to station, town
centre and the river. Easy
parking.*
Bedrooms: 1 double, 1 twin,
1 triple
Bathrooms: 1 private,
1 public

Bed & breakfast per night:	£min	£max
Single	18.00	21.00
Double	28.00	36.00

Parking for 2
🕭🛏🖵🛉🛄🛁🗲 📺

Avalon
Listed

36 Queen Street, Henley-on-
Thames RG9 1AP
☎ (0491) 577829
*Spacious Victorian terrace in
a quiet, central location. 2
minutes' walk from river,
station and town centre.*
Bedrooms: 1 twin, 1 triple
Bathrooms: 1 public

Bed & breakfast per night:	£min	£max
Single	20.00	20.00
Double	30.00	30.00

Cards accepted: Access, Visa
🕭 10🖵🛉🛄🛁🗲 📺

Crowsley House

Crowsley Road, Shiplake,
Henley-on-Thames RG9 3JT
☎ Wargrave (0734) 403197
*Attractive house in quiet
riverside village, close to
Henley-on-Thames.
Convenient for Oxford,
London, Windsor and
Heathrow.*
Bedrooms: 1 double, 2 twin
Bathrooms: 1 public

> **Please check prices
> and other details at
> the time of booking.**

Bed & breakfast per night:	£min	£max
Single		16.00
Double		32.00

Parking for 4
🕭 3🛉🖵🛉🛄💷🛁🗲

The Elms

Gallowstree Road,
Rotherfield Peppard, Henley-
on-Thames RG9 5HT
☎ Reading (0734) 723164
*Bed and breakfast near
Henley. Heated swimming
pool. All normal services,
large garden, good parking.
Excellent pub close by.*
Bedrooms: 1 double, 2 twin
Bathrooms: 1 private

Bed & breakfast per night:	£min	£max
Single	14.00	25.00
Double	28.00	50.00

Half board per person:	£min	£max
Daily	21.50	32.50

Evening meal 1930 (last
orders 2000)
Parking for 13
🕭🛉🛄🛁💷🗲 📺💷🛁📞❄
❄ 📺🏠

New Lodge ♨
COMMENDED

Henley Park, Henley-on-
Thames RG9 6HU
☎ (0491) 576340
*Small Victorian lodge in
parkland in area of
outstanding natural beauty.
Lovely walks and views. Only
1 mile from Henley, 45
minutes from Heathrow.*
Bedrooms: 1 double, 1 twin
Bathrooms: 1 private,
1 public

Bed & breakfast per night:	£min	£max
Single	22.00	26.00
Double	29.00	39.00

Parking for 7
🕭🛉🛄💷🛉🛄🛁🗲🗲🆈 📺
💷🛁🅄🕈❄ 📺 OAP SP 🏠

Old Bell House

Northfield End, Henley-on-
Thames RG9 2JG
☎ (0491) 574350
Fax (0491) 571544
*Close to numerous
restaurants, theatre and river.
Public transport (bus and
train) is nearby. Breakfast is
served in the conservatory.*
Bedrooms: 1 triple
Bathrooms: 1 private

Bed & breakfast per night:	£min	£max
Single		20.00
Double		35.00

🕭🛉💷🖵🛉🛄💷🛁🏠

Pennyford House
👑👑

Peppard Common, Henley-
on-Thames RG9 5JE
☎ Rotherfield Greys (0491)
628272 & 628232
*Family home offering evening
meals and packed lunches, by
prior arrangement.*
Bedrooms: 1 single,
3 double, 1 twin
Bathrooms: 3 private,
1 public

Bed & breakfast per night:	£min	£max
Single	15.00	25.00
Double	35.00	50.00

Half board per person:	£min	£max
Daily	22.00	40.00
Weekly	139.00	252.00

Parking for 7
🕭💷🛉🛄🛏🛉🛁🗲 📺💷🛁
❄ ❄🆈 SP

Slaters Farm

Peppard Common, Henley-
on-Thames RG9 5JL
☎ Rotherfield Greys (0491)
628675
*Leave Henley up Gravel Hill
to Peppard. After 3.5 miles,
turn left at T-junction. After a
quarter of a mile The Dog
public house marks the
beginning of Peppard
Common.*
Bedrooms: 1 double, 2 twin
Bathrooms: 2 public

Bed & breakfast per night:	£min	£max
Single	20.00	22.00
Double	35.00	40.00

Evening meal 1900 (last
orders 2030)
Parking for 6
🕭🛉🛄💷 📺🛁📞❄❄🗲🏠

Windy Brow
Listed

204 Victoria Road,
Wargrave, Reading
RG10 8AJ
☎ Reading (0734) 403336
*Friendly accommodation in a
spacious Victorian house with
garden overlooking farmland.
3 miles from Henley-on-
Thames, 12 miles from
Windsor. Heathrow Airport
half an hour away. Colour TV
and tea/coffee facilities in
rooms.*
Bedrooms: 2 double, 2 twin,
1 triple
Bathrooms: 3 private,
2 public

Continued ▶

HENLEY-ON-THAMES

Continued

Bed & breakfast

per night:	£min	£max
Single	17.50	25.00
Double	35.00	40.00

Parking for 7

HIGH WYCOMBE

Buckinghamshire
Map ref 2C2

Famous for furniture-making, historic examples of which feature in the museum. The 18th C Guildhall and the octagonal market house were designed by the Adam brothers. West Wycombe Park and Hughenden Manor (National Trust) are nearby.
Tourist Information Centre
☎ *(0494) 421892*

Clifton Lodge Hotel
COMMENDED

210 West Wycombe Road, High Wycombe HP12 3AR
☎ (0494) 440095 & 29062
Situated on the A40 approximately 1 mile from the M40 Oxford to London motorway. Ideal for touring Thames Valley and Oxford.
Bedrooms: 16 single, 8 double, 5 twin, 2 triple
Bathrooms: 4 public, 2 private showers

Bed & breakfast

per night:	£min	£max
Single	30.00	44.00
Double	52.00	65.00

Half board

per person:	£min	£max
Daily	42.00	64.00

Lunch available
Evening meal 1900 (last orders 2100)
Parking for 20
Cards accepted: Access, Visa, Diners, Amex

National Crown ratings were correct at the time of going to press but are subject to change. Please check at the time of booking.

HITCHIN

Hertfordshire
Map ref 2D1

Once a flourishing wool town. Full of interest, with many fine old buildings centred around the market square. These include the 17th C almshouses, old inns and the Victorian Corn Exchange.
Tourist Information Centre
☎ *(0462) 434738*

Beechlea

Kings Walden Road, Great Offley, Hitchin SG5 3DU
☎ Offley (0462) 768703
Spacious, modern house set in quiet, rural location opposite village church. 10 minutes from Luton Airport, M1 and A1(M).
Bedrooms: 1 single, 1 double, 1 twin
Bathrooms: 1 private, 1 public

Bed & breakfast

per night:	£min	£max
Single	18.00	
Double	32.00	36.00

Parking for 4

HOOK NORTON

Oxfordshire
Map ref 2C1

Quiet town with a history dating back 1000 years when the Normans built and buttressed its chancel walls against attack from the invading Danes.

Pear Tree Inn
COMMENDED

Scotland End, Hook Norton, Banbury OX15 5NU
☎ (0608) 737482
Old beamed pub, near famous Hook Norton brewery. 5 miles from Chipping Norton, close to Banbury and the Cotswolds.
Bedrooms: 1 double
Bathrooms: 1 private

Bed & breakfast

per night:	£min	£max
Single	20.00	25.00
Double	35.00	35.00

Lunch available
Evening meal 1800 (last orders 2000)
Parking for 11

HORTON CUM STUDLEY

Oxfordshire
Map ref 2C1

Village with attractive timbered and thatched cottages, on the edge of Ot Moor. The Oxfordshire Way footpath passes close to the village.

Kings Arms

Horton cum Studley, Oxford OX9 1AY
☎ Stanton-St-John (0867) 35235
18th C inn set on the edge of Ot Moor which surrounds seven villages. Good situation for exploring Oxford and Blenheim.
Bedrooms: 2 single, 5 double, 2 twin
Bathrooms: 9 private

Bed & breakfast

per night:	£min	£max
Single	20.00	20.00
Double	40.00	40.00

Lunch available
Evening meal 1900 (last orders 2200)
Parking for 30
Cards accepted: Access, Visa, Diners, Amex

HUNGERFORD

Berkshire
Map ref 2C2

Attractive town on the Avon Canal and the River Kennet, famous for its fishing. It has a wide High Street and many antique shops. Nearby is the Tudor manor of Littlecote with its large Roman mosaic.

Marshgate Cottage Hotel ♨
COMMENDED

Marsh Lane, Hungerford RG17 0QX
☎ (0488) 682307
Fax (0488) 685475
Family-run canalside hotel ranged around south-facing walled courtyard, linked to 350-year-old thatched cottage. Overlooks marshland and trout streams. Lovely walks, bike hire, bird watching. Important antiques centre. 1 hour from Heathrow. French, German and Scandinavian languages spoken.
Bedrooms: 1 single, 3 double, 3 twin, 1 triple, 1 multiple

Bathrooms: 7 private, 2 public

Bed & breakfast

per night:	£min	£max
Single	25.50	35.50
Double	48.50	

Evening meal 1900 (last orders 2100)
Parking for 9
Cards accepted: Access, Visa, Amex

IBSTONE

Buckinghamshire
Map ref 2C2

The Fox Country Hotel ♨

Ibstone, High Wycombe HP14 3GG
☎ Turville Heath (049 163) 289 & 722
Fax (049 163) 8873
A 300-year-old country inn on the beautiful Chiltern Ridge Way, near the Hambleden/ Thames Valley. Beamed, with open log fires.
Bedrooms: 6 double, 2 twin, 1 triple
Bathrooms: 9 private

Bed & breakfast

per night:	£min	£max
Single	41.00	60.00
Double	58.00	71.00

Lunch available
Evening meal 1900 (last orders 2200)
Parking for 48
Cards accepted: Access, Visa, Amex

IVER

Buckinghamshire
Map ref 2D2

Tower Arms Hotel

2 Thornley Lane South, Richings Park, Iver SL0 9AE
☎ (0753) 652624
Fax (0753) 651112
In country surroundings 10 minutes from Heathrow. Traditional English pub with function room for conferences and weddings.
Bedrooms: 2 single, 2 double, 2 twin
Bathrooms: 3 private, 1 public, 3 private showers

Bed & breakfast

per night:	£min	£max
Single	25.00	37.00
Double	35.00	47.00

Half board per person:	£min	£max
Daily	30.00	50.00
Weekly	200.00	300.00

Lunch available
Evening meal 1830 (last orders 2130)
Parking for 28
Cards accepted: Access, Visa, Diners, Amex
🐴 🖥 ☕ 🔒 [S] 👔 ⊤20-100
✿ 🚌

KINTBURY

Berkshire
Map ref 2C2

Lies between Hungerford and Newbury. A Saxon burial ground has been discovered near the church.

Holt Lodge

Kintbury, Newbury
RG15 0SX
☎ Inkpen (048 84) 244
140-acre livestock farm. A period, family house set in a secluded garden surrounded by wooded farmland. South of the A4, between Kintbury and the Hampshire Downs.
Bedrooms: 1 single, 1 double, 2 twin
Bathrooms: 2 public

Bed & breakfast per night:	£min	£max
Single		18.00
Double		34.00

Half board per person:	£min	£max
Daily		24.00
Weekly		161.00

Evening meal from 2000
Parking for 4
🐴 📰 🖥 ☕ [UL] 🛏 [TV] ▥ 👔 🔍
🎣 🏌 ✿ 🚌 🏠

KNOWL HILL

Berkshire
Map ref 2C2

Laurel Cottage

[Listed]
Bath Road, Knowl Hill, Reading RG10 9UP
☎ Littlewick Green (062 882) 5046
Attractive oak-beamed cottage on the A4. Convenient for Bath, London, Henley, Ascot and Heathrow Airport.
Evening meal by arrangement only.
Bedrooms: 1 single, 2 double, 1 triple
Bathrooms: 1 public

Bed & breakfast per night:	£min	£max
Single	17.50	17.50
Double	30.00	35.00

Half board per person:	£min	£max
Daily	18.00	21.00

Parking for 3
🐴 7 🍽 📰 🖥 [UL] 🔒 ▥ 👔
✈ 🚌

LAMBOURN

Berkshire
Map ref 2C2

Attractive village among the Downs on the River Lambourn. Famous for its racing stables.

Lodge Down 🏠

👑👑
Lambourn, Newbury
RG16 7BJ
☎ Marlborough (0672) 40304
200-acre arable farm. Substantial house in own grounds overlooking the gallops. Off Old Ermin Street road. B4000 from junction 14, M4. Ignore turnings to Lambourn - drive towards Baydon. Lodge Down is situated just before driving over M4.
Bedrooms: 1 single, 1 twin
Bathrooms: 1 private, 1 public

Bed & breakfast per night:	£min	£max
Single	15.00	18.00
Double	30.00	38.00

Half board per person:	£min	£max
Daily	25.00	30.00

Evening meal 1830 (last orders 2030)
Parking for 5
🐴 🍽 📰 ☕ [UL] 🔒 🛏 [TV] ▥ 👔
🏇 🔍 ∪ ⛳ ✿ 🚌 🚌 🚭 [SP]

LEAFIELD

Oxfordshire
Map ref 2C1

The Spindleberry Inn

[Listed] [COMMENDED]
Lower End, Leafield, Oxford
OX8 5QG
☎ Asthall Leigh (099 387) 277
Old Cotswold-stone, family-run inn, within driving distance of Oxford, Stratford, Cheltenham and Blenheim Palace and within easy reach of Witney, Burford and Minster Lovell.
Bedrooms: 1 double, 1 twin
Bathrooms: 1 public

Bed & breakfast per night:	£min	£max
Single	20.00	20.00
Double	29.00	29.00

Half board per person:	£min	£max
Daily	20.45	25.95
Weekly	135.15	173.65

Lunch available
Evening meal 1930 (last orders 2100)
Parking for 30
Cards accepted: Access, Visa
🖥 ☕ 🔒 [S] ▥ 👔 🔍 🏇 🎣 ✈
🚌 🏠

LEIGHTON BUZZARD

Bedfordshire
Map ref 2C1

Large market town with many buildings of interest including a fine 15th C market cross, the 17th C Holly Lodge and a number of old inns. The Grand Union Canal is nearby and in Page's Park is a narrow gauge railway.

The Peacock

1-3 Lake Street, Leighton Buzzard LU7 8RS
☎ (0525) 371174
Oldest building in historic town. Formerly an inn that served ales, from 1441. Oak beams in all rooms.
Bedrooms: 2 double
Bathrooms: 2 private, 2 public

Bed & breakfast per night:	£min	£max
Single	16.00	18.00
Double	32.00	35.00

Half board per person:	£min	£max
Daily	20.00	24.00
Weekly	130.00	150.00

Evening meal 1730 (last orders 2100)
Parking for 6
Open April-September
🐴 🍽 📰 🖥 ☕ [UL] 🔒 🛏 [TV] ▥
👔 🔍 ✿ ✈ 🚌 🚌 [SP] 🏠 [T]

LITTLE WITTENHAM

Oxfordshire
Map ref 2C2

Rooks Orchard

👑👑 [HIGHLY COMMENDED]
Little Wittenham, Abingdon
OX14 4QY
☎ Clifton Hampden (086 730) 7765
Comfortable listed 17th C house surrounded by gardens, in beautiful Thameside village next to Wittenham Clumps and nature reserve. "Superlative breakfasts". 4 miles Wallingford and Didcot, 5 miles Abingdon.
Bedrooms: 1 single, 1 double
Bathrooms: 2 private, 1 public

Bed & breakfast per night:	£min	£max
Single	18.00	22.00
Double	34.00	38.00

Parking for 6
🐴 🖥 ☕ 🔑 [UL] 🔒 [S] 🚭 🛏 [TV] ▥
👔 ✿ 🚌 [OAP] 🚭 [SP] 🏠

LONG HANBOROUGH

Oxfordshire
Map ref 2C1

Old Farmhouse

👑👑 [HIGHLY COMMENDED]
Station Hill, Long Hanborough, Oxford
OX8 8JZ
☎ Freeland (0993) 882097
Vineyard and grazing farm. Period house with inglenook fireplace, beams and flagstones. 3 miles from Woodstock and Blenheim Palace, 15 minutes from Oxford and the Cotswolds.
Bedrooms: 2 double
Bathrooms: 1 private, 1 public

Bed & breakfast per night:	£min	£max
Single	22.00	28.00
Double	33.00	38.00

Parking for 3
🐴 12 ☕ [UL] 🔒 [S] 🚭 🛏 [TV] ▥
👔 ✈ 🚌 🏠

LUTON

Bedfordshire
Map ref 2D1

Bedfordshire's largest town with its own airport, several industries and an excellent shopping centre. The town's history is depicted in the museum and art gallery in Wardown Park. Luton Hoo has a magnificent collection of treasures.
Tourist Information Centre ☎ (0582) 401579
Airport ☎ (0582) 405100

39 Bracklesham Gardens

Stopsley, Luton LU2 4QJ
☎ (0582) 418435

Continued ►

LUTON

Continued

Accommodation in a semi-detached house.
Bedrooms: 1 single, 1 twin
Bathrooms: 2 private
Bed & breakfast

per night:	£min	£max
Single	14.00	14.00
Double	22.00	22.00

Parking for 3

LYFORD

Oxfordshire
Map ref 2C2

Lyford Manor Farm ⋀

HIGHLY COMMENDED

Lyford, Wantage OX12 0EG
☎ Abingdon (0235) 868204
400-acre dairy farm. Comfortable Elizabethan stone farmhouse set in peaceful unspoilt hamlet. Breakfast in conservatory overlooking large garden. Within easy reach of many attractions.
Bedrooms: 1 single, 1 double, 2 twin
Bathrooms: 3 private
Bed & breakfast

per night:	£min	£max
Single	20.00	25.00
Double	36.00	40.00

Parking for 10
Cards accepted: Access, Visa

MAIDENHEAD

Berkshire
Map ref 2C2

Attractive town on the River Thames which is crossed by an elegant 18th C bridge and by Brunel's well-known railway bridge. It is a popular place for boating with delightful riverside walks. The Courage Shire Horse Centre is nearby.
Tourist Information Centre
☎ *(0628) 781110*

Cartlands Cottage

APPROVED

Kings Lane, Cookham Dean, Cookham, Maidenhead SL6 9AY
☎ Marlow (0628) 482196
Delightful timbered character cottage with exposed beams. Traditional cottage garden surrounded by National Trust common land. Very quiet.
Bedrooms: 1 single, 1 triple

Bathrooms: 1 private, 1 public
Bed & breakfast

per night:	£min	£max
Single	16.50	18.50
Double	34.00	36.00

Parking for 4

Moor Farm

COMMENDED

Ascot Road, Holyport, Maidenhead SL6 2HY
☎ (0628) 33761
100-acre mixed farm. 700-year-old medieval manor on working farm in picturesque Holyport village. 4 miles from Windsor, 12 miles from Heathrow.
Bedrooms: 2 twin
Bathrooms: 2 private
Bed & breakfast

per night:	£min	£max
Double	34.00	42.00

Parking for 4

"Sheephouse" ⋀

COMMENDED

Sheephouse Road, Maidenhead SL6 8HJ
☎ (0628) 776902
Fax (0628) 25138
16th C farmhouse in semi-rural area close to the River Thames and with easy access to M4/M40. Sauna, jacuzzi and gym available, country walks nearby. Evening meal by arrangement.
Bedrooms: 2 single, 1 double, 1 twin
Bathrooms: 4 private
Bed & breakfast

per night:	£min	£max
Single	28.50	28.50
Double	42.00	42.00

Half board

per person:	£min	£max
Daily	37.00	37.00

Evening meal 1830 (last orders 1930)
Parking for 12
Cards accepted: Visa

Thamesbrook Guest House

COMMENDED

18 Ray Park Avenue, Maidenhead SL6 8DS
☎ (0628) 783855
In a quiet location near river, Boulters Lock and town centre. Spacious, well-decorated rooms. Pubs and restaurants nearby.

Bedrooms: 1 single, 1 double, 2 twin
Bathrooms: 1 private, 2 public
Bed & breakfast

per night:	£min	£max
Single	18.00	32.00
Double	32.00	38.00

Parking for 6

Tudor House

102 All Saints Avenue, Maidenhead SL6 3LZ
☎ (0628) 35420
Family-run, Tudor-style house in a quiet avenue, close to town centre, station and M4, and 20 minutes from Heathrow Airport.
Bedrooms: 2 twin, 1 triple
Bathrooms: 1 public
Bed & breakfast

per night:	£min	£max
Single	18.00	25.00
Double	30.00	32.00

Parking for 2

MARLOW

Buckinghamshire
Map ref 2C2

Attractive Georgian town on the River Thames, famous for its 19th C suspension bridge. The High Street contains many old houses and there are connections with writers including Shelley and the poet T S Eliot.

2 Hyde Green

Listed

Marlow SL7 1QL
☎ (0628) 483526
Comfortable family home a few minutes' level walk from town centre and River Thames.
Bedrooms: 1 double, 2 twin
Bathrooms: 2 private, 1 public
Bed & breakfast

per night:	£min	£max
Single	20.00	25.00
Double	30.00	35.00

Parking for 2

5 Pound Lane

Listed

Marlow SL7 2AE
☎ (0628) 482649
Older style house, just off town centre, 2 minutes from River Thames. Double room

has own balcony with delightful view.
Bedrooms: 1 double, 1 twin
Bathrooms: 1 public
Bed & breakfast

per night:	£min	£max
Single	18.00	25.00
Double	32.00	38.00

Parking for 2

Acha Pani ⋀

Listed **COMMENDED**

Bovingdon Green, Marlow SL7 2JL
☎ (0628) 483435
Modern house with large garden, in quiet location 1 mile north of Marlow. No children or dogs please.
Bedrooms: 1 single, 1 double, 1 twin
Bathrooms: 1 private, 1 public
Bed & breakfast

per night:	£min	£max
Single	15.00	
Double	25.00	30.00

Parking for 3

Holly Tree House ⋀

HIGHLY COMMENDED

Burford Close, Marlow Bottom, Marlow SL7 3NF
☎ (0628) 891110
Fax (0628) 481278
Detached house set in large gardens with fine views over the valley. Quiet yet convenient location. Large car park. All rooms fully en-suite. Outdoor heated swimming pool.
Bedrooms: 1 single, 4 double
Bathrooms: 5 private
Bed & breakfast

per night:	£min	£max
Single	49.50	57.50
Double	62.50	67.50

Parking for 10
Cards accepted: Access, Visa, Amex

Little Parmoor ⋀

Listed

Frieth, Henley-on-Thames, Oxfordshire RG9 6NL
☎ High Wycombe (0494) 881447
Fax (0494) 883012
Period country house in area of outstanding natural beauty in the Chiltern Hills. Close to Marlow and Henley.
Bedrooms: 1 single, 1 twin
Bathrooms: 1 public

Bed & breakfast

per night:	£min	£max
Single	17.00	20.00
Double	34.00	40.00

Evening meal 1930 (last orders 2100)
Parking for 5

Monkton Farmhouse ₳

Listed COMMENDED

Monkton Farm, Little Marlow, Marlow SL7 3RF
☎ High Wycombe (0494) 521082
Fax (0494) 443905
150-acre dairy farm. 14th C cruckhouse set in beautiful countryside, easily reached by motorway, and close to shopping and sporting facilities.
Bedrooms: 1 single, 1 twin, 1 triple
Bathrooms: 1 public
Bed & breakfast

per night:	£min	£max
Single	18.00	20.00
Double	36.00	40.00

Parking for 6

Sunnyside

Munday Dean, Marlow SL7 3BU
☎ (0628) 485701
Friendly family home in quiet surroundings in an area of outstanding natural beauty. Convenient for Henley, Windsor, M4 or M40.
Bedrooms: 1 single, 1 double, 1 twin
Bathrooms: 1 public
Bed & breakfast

per night:	£min	£max
Single	15.00	17.00
Double	25.00	28.00

Parking for 6

MIDDLE CLAYDON

Buckinghamshire
Map ref 2C1

The Old Rectory

Middle Claydon, Buckingham MK18 2EU
☎ Aylesbury (0296) 730557
Late-Georgian rectory overlooking lakes and parkland. 4 miles from Winslow, next door to Claydon House and convenient for Silverstone, Stowe and Waddesdon.
Bedrooms: 1 double, 1 twin

Bathrooms: 2 private
Bed & breakfast

per night:	£min	£max
Single	27.50	30.00
Double	55.00	55.00

Half board

per person:	£min	£max
Daily	40.00	46.00

Evening meal 1900 (last orders 2100)
Parking for 4

MILTON KEYNES

Buckinghamshire
Map ref 2C1

Designated a New Town in 1967, Milton Keynes offers a wide range of housing and is abundantly planted with trees. It has excellent shopping facilities and 3 centres for leisure and sporting activities. The Open University is based here.
Tourist Information Centre ☎ (0908) 232525

B Line Guest House

72 Watling Street, Fenny Stratford, Milton Keynes MK2 2BY
☎ (0908) 378283
200-year-old house by Watling Street in the old town of Fenny Stratford. Close to shops, pubs, golf, fishing, sports and leisure centres and buses/trains.
Bedrooms: 2 single, 2 twin, 1 triple
Bathrooms: 1 public
Bed & breakfast

per night:	£min	£max
Single	16.00	18.00
Double	32.00	34.00

Half board

per person:	£min	£max
Daily	20.00	22.00

Parking for 6

Chantry Farm

COMMENDED

Pindon End, Hanslope, Milton Keynes MK19 7HL
☎ (0908) 510269
600-acre mixed farm. Stone farmhouse built in 1650 with inglenook fireplaces, surrounded by open countryside. 15 minutes to city centre. Swimming pool, trout lake, table tennis, clay pigeon shooting and coarse fishing on River Tove.
Bedrooms: 1 double, 2 twin
Bathrooms: 2 public, 1 private shower

Bed & breakfast

per night:	£min	£max
Single	15.00	20.00
Double	30.00	40.00

Parking for 7

Cuckoo Hill Farm

Hanslope, Milton Keynes MK19 7HQ
☎ (0908) 510748
50-acre mixed farm. Recently modernised farmhouse on edge of Hanslope village, adjacent to the Milton Keynes Eventing Centre.
Bedrooms: 1 single, 1 double, 2 twin
Bathrooms: 1 public
Bed & breakfast

per night:	£min	£max
Single	15.00	17.00
Double	30.00	34.00

Half board

per person:	£min	£max
Daily	20.00	20.00
Weekly	80.00	100.00

Evening meal from 1930
Parking for 9

Grange Barn

Haversham Village, Milton Keynes MK19 7DX
☎ (0908) 313613
Attractively converted period barn with modern facilities. Comfortable accommodation in a rural setting, 10 minutes from city centre. Non-smokers only please.
Bedrooms: 1 single, 1 double, 1 twin
Bathrooms: 1 public
Bed & breakfast

per night:	£min	£max
Single	17.00	20.00
Double	28.00	32.00

Parking for 6

The Grange Stables

Winslow Road, Great Horwood, Milton Keynes MK17 0QN
☎ Winslow (029 671) 2051
Fax (029 671) 4991
A recently converted stable block offering comfortable and spacious accommodation. Conveniently situated opposite the Swan pub.
Bedrooms: 3 twin
Bathrooms: 1 public, 1 private shower

Bed & breakfast

per night:	£min	£max
Single	24.00	28.20
Double	35.00	41.12

Parking for 5
Cards accepted: Access, Visa

Haversham Grange ₳

Listed APPROVED

Haversham, Milton Keynes MK19 7DX
☎ (0908) 312389
Large 14th C stone house with many interesting features. Set in own gardens backing on to lakes.
Bedrooms: 3 twin
Bathrooms: 3 private, 1 public
Bed & breakfast

per night:	£min	£max
Single	20.00	23.00
Double	40.00	40.00

Parking for 6

Michelville House

Newton Road, Bletchley, Milton Keynes MK3 5BN
☎ (0908) 371578
Clean compact establishment within easy reach of railway station, M1, shopping and sporting facilities. 10 minutes from Milton Keynes shopping centre.
Bedrooms: 10 single, 6 twin
Bathrooms: 4 public
Bed & breakfast

per night:	£min	£max
Single	21.00	25.00
Double	39.00	43.00

Parking for 16

Milford Leys Farm ₳

Castlethorpe, Milton Keynes MK19 7HH
☎ (0908) 510153
120-acre mixed farm. Pleasant farmhouse in own grounds, surrounded by fields. Castlethorpe village is just north of Milton Keynes.
Bedrooms: 2 twin, 1 triple
Bathrooms: 2 public
Bed & breakfast

per night:	£min	£max
Single	15.00	15.00
Double	30.00	30.00

Parking for 5

Mill Farm

COMMENDED

Gayhurst, Newport Pagnell MK16 8LT
☎ Newport Pagnell (0908) 611489

Continued ▶

235

MILTON KEYNES

Continued

505-acre mixed farm. 17th C farmhouse. Tennis, riding and fishing available on the farm. Good touring centre.
Bedrooms: 1 single, 1 twin, 1 triple
Bathrooms: 1 private, 2 public

Bed & breakfast

per night:	£min	£max
Single	15.00	20.00
Double	25.00	35.00

Half board

per person:	£min	£max
Daily	25.00	30.00

Evening meal 1900 (last orders 1600)
Parking for 12

Oldhams Field House

Listed **HIGHLY COMMENDED**

Nash Road, Beachampton, Milton Keynes MK19 6EA
☎ (0908) 568094
235-acre arable farm. Views over open countryside, yet 10 minutes' drive from Milton Keynes centre on the B4033, Stony Stratford to Winslow road. Guests welcome to walk on the farm.
Bedrooms: 1 single, 2 twin
Bathrooms: 2 public

Bed & breakfast

per night:	£min	£max
Single	20.00	
Double	35.00	

Evening meal (last orders 1930)
Parking for 6

Spinney Lodge Farm

Forest Road, Hanslope, Milton Keynes MK19 7DE
☎ (0908) 510267
350-acre arable and mixed farm. Victorian farmhouse in secluded situation. Superb walking facilities in Salcey Forest. 15 minutes Milton Keynes, 8 minutes M1 junction 15.
Bedrooms: 1 double, 1 twin
Bathrooms: 2 private

Bed & breakfast

per night:	£min	£max
Single	17.00	20.00
Double	32.00	40.00

Evening meal 1830 (last orders 1930)
Parking for 4

Swan Revived Hotel M

HIGHLY COMMENDED

High Street, Newport Pagnell MK16 8AR
☎ Newport Pagnell (0908) 610565
Fax (0908) 210995
Telex 826801
Independently owned and family-run, town house hotel, renowned former coaching inn, where guests can enjoy every modern comfort. Convenient for thriving new city of Milton Keynes.
Bedrooms: 20 single, 16 double, 3 twin, 2 triple
Bathrooms: 41 private

Bed & breakfast

per night:	£min	£max
Single	30.00	60.00
Double	55.00	70.00

Half board

per person:	£min	£max
Daily	40.00	70.00

Lunch available
Evening meal 1915 (last orders 2200)
Parking for 18
Cards accepted: Access, Visa, Diners, Amex

Vignoble M

Listed **COMMENDED**

2 Medland, Woughton Park, Milton Keynes MK6 3BH
☎ (0908) 666804
Fax (0908) 666626
In a quiet cul-de-sac within walking distance of the Open University and 2.5 miles from the city centre. A warm welcome in three languages.
Bedrooms: 1 single, 1 double, 1 twin
Bathrooms: 1 private, 2 public

Bed & breakfast

per night:	£min	£max
Single	18.00	20.00
Double	35.00	45.00

Parking for 2

There are separate sections in this guide listing groups specialising in farm holidays and accommodation which is especially suitable for young people and organised groups.

MINSTER LOVELL

Oxfordshire
Map ref 2C1

Picturesque village on the River Windrush with thatched cottages and 19th C houses. Minster Lovell Hall, built in the 15th C by the Lovell family, is the subject of several legends and now stands in ruins in a beautiful riverside setting.

Hill Grove Farm

HIGHLY COMMENDED

Crawley Road, Minster Lovell, Oxford OX8 5NA
☎ Witney (0993) 703120
300-acre mixed farm. Cotswold farmhouse run on a family basis, in an attractive setting overlooking the Windrush Valley. Pleasant rural walks.
Bedrooms: 1 double, 1 twin
Bathrooms: 1 private, 1 private shower

Bed & breakfast

per night:	£min	£max
Double	32.00	38.00

Parking for 4

MOULSFORD ON THAMES

Oxfordshire
Map ref 2C2

White House

Listed

Reading Road, Moulsford, Wallingford OX10 9JD
☎ Cholsey (0491) 651397
Fax (0491) 651751
Homely accommodation in private location with picturesque surroundings. Close to the river, attractive 18-hole golf-course and the Ridgeway path.
Bedrooms: 1 double, 1 twin
Bathrooms: 2 public

Bed & breakfast

per night:	£min	£max
Single	18.00	24.00
Double	36.00	48.00

Parking for 4

The colour maps at the back of this guide pinpoint all places with accommodation.

NEWBURY

Berkshire
Map ref 2C2

Ancient town surrounded by the Downs and on the Kennet and Avon Canal. It has many buildings of interest, including the 17th C Cloth Hall, which is now a museum. The famous racecourse is nearby.
Tourist Information Centre
☎ *(0635) 30267*

Adbury Holt House

Burghclere, Newbury RG15 9BW
☎ (0635) 46061
Fax (0635) 552999
Secluded Victorian mansion set in landscaped grounds. Evening meal available by arrangement.
Bedrooms: 1 single, 2 double, 1 twin, 1 triple
Bathrooms: 2 private, 2 public

Bed & breakfast

per night:	£min	£max
Single	17.50	20.00
Double	35.00	40.00

Half board

per person:	£min	£max
Daily	24.00	

Evening meal 1930 (last orders 2100)
Parking for 20

Cleremede

Fox's Lane, Kingsclere, Newbury RG15 8SL
☎ Kingsclere (0635) 297298
Comfortable house with large attractive garden. Breakfast in conservatory in summer. Near Watership Down and convenient stop on Wayfarers Walk.
Bedrooms: 2 single, 1 twin
Bathrooms: 2 public

Bed & breakfast

per night:	£min	£max
Single	17.00	18.50
Double	32.00	34.00

Parking for 6

Little Paddocks

Listed

Woolhampton Hill, Woolhampton, Reading RG7 5SY
☎ Woolhampton (0734) 713451
Warm welcome to family home with superb views. Good food available in village.

Easy access M4, Oxford, Bath, Heathrow. Excellent walks. Situated 6 miles east of Newbury.
Bedrooms: 1 twin
Bathrooms: 1 private
Bed & breakfast

per night:	£min	£max
Single	15.00	15.00
Double	30.00	30.00

Parking for 10
🛏🍴🗂♿🖥♿📶▥🚗🅿
❀🚲

Mousefield Farm
Listed
Long Lane, Shaw, Newbury
RG16 9LG
☎ (0635) 40333 & 524331
500-acre arable and mixed farm. Farmhouse overlooking our own farmland, set in an area of outstanding natural beauty. Well-kept gardens and plenty of nature trails.
Bedrooms: 1 single,
1 double, 2 twin, 1 triple
Bathrooms: 3 public
Bed & breakfast

per night:	£min	£max
Single	15.00	18.00
Double	30.00	36.00

Half board

per person:	£min	£max
Daily	21.00	24.00
Weekly	130.00	150.00

Lunch available
Evening meal 1800 (last orders 2100)
Parking for 7
🛏🗂♿▥🖥🍴💺📶▥🚗
🚶✓❀🚲🏠

Mrs. R. Shipside
51 Valley Road, Newbury
RG14 6HN
☎ (0635) 45284
On town bus route, 1 mile from town centre, railway station and bus station. Within easy reach of historic and picturesque countryside.
Bedrooms: 2 double
Bathrooms: 1 public
Bed & breakfast

per night:	£min	£max
Single	14.00	14.00
Double	26.00	26.00

Evening meal 1800 (last orders 2000)
Parking for 2
Open April-October
▥🖥📺🖥🚗✓🚲

White Hart Cottage
Westbrook, Newbury
RG16 8DJ
☎ Boxford (048 838) 410
An attractive period cottage in the exceptionally pretty village of Boxford. Ideal for country lovers.

Bedrooms: 1 single,
1 double, 1 twin
Bathrooms: 1 public
Bed & breakfast

per night:	£min	£max
Single	18.00	
Double	36.00	

Half board

per person:	£min	£max
Daily	25.50	

Evening meal 1800 (last orders 2000)
Parking for 3
🛏🗂▥🖥📶▥🚗🚶❀🚲

The White Hart Inn
Hamstead Marshall, Newbury
RG15 0HW
☎ Kintbury (0488) 58201
Traditional rural inn with oak beams and log fire. Comfortable accommodation in barn conversion.
Bedrooms: 2 single, 2 twin, 2 triple
Bathrooms: 6 private
Bed & breakfast

per night:	£min	£max
Single	35.00	40.00
Double	50.00	55.00

Lunch available
Evening meal 1900 (last orders 2200)
Parking for 35
Cards accepted: Access, Visa, Amex
🛏🗂🍴🖥♿🔓📶▥🚗❀
✗🚲

Woodlands Park Farm ⋔
COMMENDED
Ashford Hill, Newbury
RG15 8AY
☎ Headley (0635) 268258 &
Tadley (0734) 814821
240-acre beef farm. Pretty, wooded working farm with Georgian house. Golf, riding, eating and tourist attractions nearby. Close to M4 and M3.
Bedrooms: 1 single,
1 double, 1 twin, 1 triple
Bathrooms: 1 public
Bed & breakfast

per night:	£min	£max
Single	18.00	18.00
Double	36.00	36.00

Evening meal from 1800
Parking for 10
🛏🗂🍴🖥♿🔓🛢✓📶▥
❀🚲

The national Crown scheme is explained in full in the information pages towards the back of this guide.

OXFORD
Oxfordshire
Map ref 2C1

Beautiful university town with many ancient colleges, some dating from the 13th C, and numerous buildings of historic and architectural interest. The Ashmolean Museum has outstanding collections. Lovely gardens and meadows with punting on the Cherwell.
Tourist Information Centre
☎ *(0865) 726871*

21 Lincoln Road
♨
Oxford OX1 4TB
☎ (0865) 246944
Semi-detached home offering ground floor room with separate access to street. Convenient for north and south ring roads, within walking distance of city centre.
Bedrooms: 1 single
Bathrooms: 1 private
Bed & breakfast

per night:	£min	£max
Single	20.00	20.00

Parking for 2
Cards accepted:
♿🗂♿🔓▥🖥✓▥🚗✗🚲

7 Princes Street
Listed
Oxford OX4 1DD
☎ (0865) 726755
Restored Victorian artisan's cottage, furnished with many antiques. Short walk from Magdalen Bridge and central Oxford.
Bedrooms: 1 single, 1 double
Bathrooms: 1 public
Bed & breakfast

per night:	£min	£max
Single	18.00	20.00
Double	28.00	32.00

Parking for 2
🛏🖥♿✓📺▥🚗❀✗🚲

Acorn Guest House
Listed
260 Iffley Road, Oxford
OX4 1SE
☎ (0865) 247998
Situated midway between the centre of town and the ring-road and so convenient for local amenities and more distant attractions.
Bedrooms: 2 single, 1 twin, 3 triple
Bathrooms: 2 public

Bed & breakfast

per night:	£min	£max
Single	18.00	24.00
Double	36.00	42.00

Parking for 5
Cards accepted: Access, Visa, C.Bl
🛏🗂♿▥🖥📶▥🚗🚗✗

All Views
♨♨ COMMENDED
67 Old Witney Road, On main A40, Eynsham, Oxford
OX8 1PU
☎ (0865) 880891
7-acre livestock farm. 1991-built Cotswold stone chalet bungalow, adjacent A40 between Oxford and Witney. Designed with guests' comfort in mind. All rooms have full facilities.
Bedrooms: 1 single,
2 double, 1 twin
Bathrooms: 4 private
Bed & breakfast

per night:	£min	£max
Single	30.00	30.00
Double	40.00	40.00

Parking for 30
🛏8♿📞🍴🗂♿▥🖥♿📺
▥🚗❀✗🚲🈯

Arden Lodge
Listed
34 Sunderland Avenue, Oxford OX2 8DX
☎ (0865) 52076
Modern detached house in select part of Oxford. Within easy reach of country inns, river meadows. Excellent position for Blenheim, Stratford-upon-Avon, Cotswolds, London.
Bedrooms: 1 single,
1 double, 1 twin
Bathrooms: 2 private
Bed & breakfast

per night:	£min	£max
Single	19.00	21.00
Double	32.00	40.00

Parking for 3
🛏🗂♿▥🖥📶▥🚗🚲🈯🅳🈁
🈯🏠

The Bungalow
Listed
Cherwell Farm, Mill Lane, Oxford OX3 0QF
☎ (0865) 57171
Off northern bypass (A40), from Banbury Road roundabout heading towards Marston flyover. Before the flyover there is a turning left onto single road, The Bungalow is a quarter-of-a-mile down the road.
Bedrooms: 2 double, 1 twin
Bathrooms: 1 private,
1 public

Continued ▶

OXFORD

Continued

Bed & breakfast

per night:	£min	£max
Single	18.00	25.00
Double	33.00	45.00

Parking for 4
Open April-October

Hill Farm
Cuddesdon Road, Horspath, Oxford OX9 1JA
☎ Wheatley (0865) 873944 & Mobile phone (0831) 442581
240-acre mixed farm. Stone-built Victorian farmhouse with pretty gardens and lovely views over farmland. Easily found, 5 miles from Oxford city centre.
Bedrooms: 1 triple
Bathrooms: 1 public

Bed & breakfast

per night:	£min	£max
Single	15.00	15.00
Double	30.00	30.00

Parking for 4

Isis Guest House ⋀
COMMENDED
45-53 Iffley Road, Oxford OX4 1ED
☎ (0865) 248894 & 242446
Modernised, Victorian, city centre guesthouse within walking distance of colleges and shops. Easy access to ring road.
Bedrooms: 11 single, 6 double, 18 twin, 2 triple
Bathrooms: 14 private, 10 public

Bed & breakfast

per night:	£min	£max
Single	19.50	25.00
Double	38.00	42.00

Parking for 18
Open June-September
Cards accepted: Access, Visa

Newton House
82-84 Abingdon Road, Oxford OX1 4PL
☎ (0865) 240561
Victorian house within walking distance of city centre.
Bedrooms: 6 double, 4 twin, 1 triple, 1 multiple
Bathrooms: 4 private, 3 public

Bed & breakfast

per night:	£min	£max
Single	17.00	40.00
Double	30.00	42.00

Parking for 8
Cards accepted: Access, Visa

Old Mitre Rooms
Lincoln College, Turl Street, Oxford OX1 3DR
☎ (0865) 279821
The accommodation forms part of the Old Mitre Hotel which is now student accommodation.
Bedrooms: 32 single, 15 twin, 3 triple
Bathrooms: 3 private, 11 public

Bed & breakfast

per night:	£min	£max
Single	17.35	18.50
Double	33.50	36.00

Open July-September

The Ridings
COMMENDED
280 Abingdon Road, Oxford OX1 4TA
☎ (0865) 248364
A warm and friendly welcome awaits you. Cosy, comfortable rooms. Walking distance city centre, close to rail and coach stations.
Bedrooms: 1 single, 2 double
Bathrooms: 2 private, 2 public

Bed & breakfast

per night:	£min	£max
Single	16.00	18.00
Double	32.00	40.00

Parking for 3

Willow Reaches Private Hotel ⋀
COMMENDED
1 Wytham Street, Oxford OX1 4SU
☎ (0865) 721545
Fax (0865) 251139
Comfortable, small hotel in a quiet location, 20 minutes' walk from the city centre. Bridal suite.
Bedrooms: 4 single, 2 double, 2 twin, 1 triple
Bathrooms: 9 private, 1 public

Bed & breakfast

per night:	£min	£max
Single	36.00	41.00
Double	48.00	52.00

Half board

per person:	£min	£max
Daily	51.00	66.00
Weekly	78.00	82.00

Evening meal 1900 (last orders 2100)
Parking for 9
Cards accepted: Access, Visa, Diners, Amex

PANGBOURNE

Berkshire
Map ref 2C2

A pretty stretch of river where the Pang joins the Thames with views of the lock, weir and toll bridge. Once the home of Kenneth Grahame, author of 'Wind in the Willows'.

Weir View Guest House
9 Shooters Hill, Pangbourne, Reading RG8 7DZ
☎ (0734) 842120
House with superb views overlooking falling waters of weir and river. Adjacent to excellent village shops, restaurants and rail-link.
Bedrooms: 1 double, 2 twin
Bathrooms: 1 private, 1 public

Bed & breakfast

per night:	£min	£max
Single	22.00	30.00
Double	38.00	48.00

Parking for 4
Cards accepted: Access, Visa

POTTERS BAR

Hertfordshire
Map ref 2D1

Wilding Guest House
58 Cranborne Crescent, Potters Bar EN6 3AG
☎ (0707) 50533 changing to 650533
Situated 5 minutes' drive from M25 and A1 motorway. 15 minutes from the M1 and A5 and about 30 or 40 minutes from central London. Close to swimming pool, squash courts, children's playground.
Bedrooms: 1 single, 1 double, 1 triple
Bathrooms: 1 public

Bed & breakfast

per night:	£min	£max
Single		14.50
Double		29.00

Half board

per person:	£min	£max
Daily		20.00

Evening meal 1730 (last orders 1930)
Parking for 4

POTTON

Bedfordshire
Map ref 2D1

Westbury Bed and Breakfast
HIGHLY COMMENDED
Deepdale, Potton, Sandy SG19 2NH
☎ (0767) 260770
Country house set in garden and situated in the hamlet of Deepdale, 2 miles east of Sandy on B1042 Bedford-Cambridge road.
Bedrooms: 1 double, 2 twin
Bathrooms: 1 private, 1 public

Bed & breakfast

per night:	£min	£max
Single	16.00	21.00
Double	26.00	31.00

Parking for 3

PUCKERIDGE

Hertfordshire
Map ref 2D1

Little Gosfield Guest House
Cambridge Road, Puckeridge, Ware SG11 1SA
☎ Ware (0920) 821941
Spacious bungalow in 1 acre of grounds. Set in rural village, midway between Cambridge and London, at junction of A10 and A120 roads. Convenient for Stansted Airport and M11 (10 minutes).
Bedrooms: 3 twin, 1 triple
Bathrooms: 2 private, 1 public, 2 private showers

Bed & breakfast

per night:	£min	£max
Single	25.00	35.00
Double	45.00	50.00

Parking for 10
Cards accepted: Access, Visa

> The symbols are explained on the flap inside the back cover.

READING

Berkshire
Map ref 2C2

Busy, modern county town with large shopping centre and many leisure and recreation facilities. There are several interesting museums and the Duke of Wellington's Stratfield Saye is nearby.
Tourist Information Centre
☎ *(0734) 566226*

10 Greystoke Road
Listed COMMENDED
Caversham, Reading
RG4 0EL
☎ (0734) 475784
Private home in quiet, residential area. TV lounge, tea and coffee-making facilities.
Bedrooms: 1 single, 1 double
Bathrooms: 2 public

Bed & breakfast

per night:	£min	£max
Single	16.00	19.00
Double	26.00	30.00

Parking for 2

囲 ⅛ ♙ 📺 🞓. ♙ ✕ 🚗

Belstone
Listed HIGHLY COMMENDED
36 Upper Warren Avenue,
Caversham, Reading
RG4 7EB
☎ (0734) 477435
Large Victorian house in quiet tree-lined avenue, close to river and farmland. Convenient for town centre by car. Non-smokers only please.
Bedrooms: 1 double, 1 twin
Bathrooms: 1 public

Bed & breakfast

per night:	£min	£max
Single	25.00	27.00
Double	35.00	40.00

Parking for 2

♙ 🞓 ⅛ ♙ 📺 🞓. ♙ ✿ ✕ 🚗

The Six Bells
☺☺☺ COMMENDED
Beenham Village, Reading
RG7 5NX
☎ Woolhampton (0734) 713368
Village pub, overlooking farmland. Four miles from Theale M4 junction 12, 1 mile off A4. Newly-built bedrooms. Home cooking always available.
Bedrooms: 1 single, 2 double, 1 twin
Bathrooms: 4 private

Bed & breakfast

per night:	£min	£max
Single		36.00
Double		49.00

Lunch available
Evening meal 1830 (last orders 2130)
Parking for 35
Cards accepted: Access, Visa

🞓☐ ♙ 🞓. ♙ �◗ ♟ ✕ 🚗

Ye Olde Coach House
Listed HIGHLY COMMENDED
127 South View Avenue,
Caversham, Reading
RG4 0BB
☎ (0734) 476627
Old coach house, 5 minutes from river and 15 minutes' walk from Reading town centre. Lovely garden.
Bedrooms: 4 single, 1 double, 1 twin
Bathrooms: 2 public, 6 private showers

Bed & breakfast

per night:	£min	£max
Single	20.00	25.00
Double	35.00	40.00

Parking for 6

🞓 🞓 ☐ ♙ 📺 S ♙ 🞓. ♙ ✿ 🚗 SP

RICKMANSWORTH

Hertfordshire
Map ref 2D2

Old town, where 3 rivers meet, now mainly residential. The High Street is full of interesting buildings, including the home of William Penn. Moor Park Mansion, a fine 18th C house, is now a golf clubhouse.
Tourist Information Centre
☎ *(0923) 776611*

6 Swallow Close
Nightingale Road,
Rickmansworth WD3 2DZ
☎ (0923) 720069
In quiet cul-de-sac, 5 minutes' walk from underground station, 30 minutes to London. Convenient for M25 and Watford. All food home-made. Non-smokers only please.
Bedrooms: 1 single, 1 double, 1 triple
Bathrooms: 1 private, 1 public

Bed & breakfast

per night:	£min	£max
Single	18.00	
Double	36.00	

Parking for 3

🞓 5 🞓 ☐ ♙ 📺 S ♙ 🞓. ♙ ✿ ✕ 🚗

ROTHERFIELD GREYS

Oxfordshire
Map ref 2C2

Shepherds
Shepherds Green,
Rotherfield Greys, Henley-on-Thames RG9 4QL
☎ (0491) 628413
Private, period house with pretty garden set on secluded village green. Warm welcome to guests. Lovely walks nearby. Easy reach of Heathrow Airport, London, Windsor, Oxford, Thames Valley and Chilterns.
Bedrooms: 1 single, 2 double, 1 twin
Bathrooms: 4 private

Bed & breakfast

per night:	£min	£max
Single	21.00	32.00
Double	38.00	48.00

Half board

per person:	£min	£max
Daily	31.00	42.00

Parking for 6

🞓 12 🞓 ☐ ♙ ♙ ⓘ S ✂ ♙
📺 🞓. ♙ ✿ ✕ 🚗

SANDY

Bedfordshire
Map ref 2D1

Small town on the River Ivel on the site of a Roman settlement. Sandy is mentioned in Domesday.

Highfield Farm
☰☰☰ HIGHLY COMMENDED
Great North Road, Sandy
SG19 2AQ
☎ (0767) 682332
300-acre arable farm. Attractive period farmhouse set back in its own grounds. 1 mile north of Sandy roundabout on A1 (southbound).
Bedrooms: 3 double, 2 twin, 1 triple
Bathrooms: 6 private

Bed & breakfast

per night:	£min	£max
Single	18.00	25.00
Double	28.00	35.00

Parking for 8

🞓 🞓 ♙ 📺 ⓘ S ✂ ♙ 📺 🞓. ♙
✿ 🚗

Map references apply to the colour maps at the back of this guide.

SAUNDERTON

Buckinghamshire
Map ref 2C1

Hunter's Gate
Deanfield, Saunderton, High Wycombe HP14 4JR
☎ Bledlow Ridge (024 027) 446
4-bedroomed house with a 1 bedroom flat above garage, in a valley overlooked by Bledlow Ridge, half-a-mile from Wycombe/Princes Risborough road. Set in 5 acres in a quiet area but only half-a-mile to BR station for London.
Bedrooms: 1 single, 3 double
Bathrooms: 1 private

Bed & breakfast

per night:	£min	£max
Double	15.00	15.00

Parking for 4

🞓 🞓 ☐ ♙ 📺 ⓘ S 📺 🞓. ♙
✿ 🚗

SHABBINGTON

Buckinghamshire
Map ref 2C1

Hill House
Mill Lane, Shabbington,
Aylesbury HP18 9HQ
☎ Long Crendon (0844) 208783
Old stone vicarage situated next to the church. Furnished mainly with antiques. Non-smokers only please.
Bedrooms: 1 single, 1 double, 1 twin
Bathrooms: 1 private, 1 public

Bed & breakfast

per night:	£min	£max
Single	17.50	20.00
Double	35.00	40.00

Parking for 8

🞓 12 🞓 ☐ ♙ 📺 ⓘ S ✂ 📺
♙ ✿ ✕ 🚗 🞓

SOUTH MIMMS

Hertfordshire
Map ref 2D1

Best known today for its location at the junction of the M25 and the A1M.
Tourist Information Centre
☎ *(0707) 43233*

The Black Swan
62-64 Blanche Lane, South Mimms, Potters Bar
EN6 3PD
☎ Potters Bar (0707) 44180
Comfortable accommodation in oak-beamed bedrooms or self-contained flats in quietly

Continued ▶

SOUTH MIMMS

Continued

located listed building.
Breakfast provided.
Bedrooms: 2 single,
3 double, 1 twin
Bathrooms: 2 private,
2 public

Bed & breakfast

per night:	£min	£max
Single	20.00	25.00
Double	30.00	35.00

Parking for 7

🛇🎿🏊♿♨ ⛰ ⓈⓉⓋ🏠,📠✿
🚳🐾Ⓣ

ST ALBANS

Hertfordshire
Map ref 2D1

As Verulamium this was
one of the largest towns
in Roman Britain and its
remains can be seen in
the museum. The Norman
cathedral was built from
Roman materials to
commemorate Alban, the
first British Christian
martyr.

25 Ridgmont Road

St Albans AL1 3AG
☎ (0727) 862755
Friendly, informal family
home close to city centre.
Convenient for M1 and M25.
Central London 20 minutes
by train. Non-smokers only
please.
Bedrooms: 2 twin
Bathrooms: 1 public

Bed & breakfast

per night:	£min	£max
Single	14.00	18.00
Double	28.00	30.00

Parking for 1

🛇🖥♿♨ ⛰ ♿Ⓢ✂🏠,📠✿
✕🚳

Care Inns

👑👑👑
29 Alma Road, St Albans
AL1 3AT
☎ (0727) 867310
Comfortable family
atmosphere. Ideally located
close to station, town and
cathedral. All rooms have en-
suite bath/shower and toilet.
Bedrooms: 1 single,
1 double, 1 twin
Bathrooms: 3 private

Bed & breakfast

per night:	£min	£max
Single	20.00	25.00
Double	35.00	

Parking for 5

🛇♿🖥⛰♨ ⓊⓁ🏠,📠
🚳 SP

Newpark House Hotel ᴍ

👑👑
North Orbital Road (A414),
St Albans AL1 1EG
☎ Bowmansgreen (0727)
824839
Fax (0727) 826700
On A414 trunk road
eastbound to A1(M). Pebble-
dash, 3-storey house, small
landscaped garden with patio
and fish pond.
Bedrooms: 9 single, 5 twin
Bathrooms: 5 public

Bed & breakfast

per night:	£min	£max
Single	23.00	26.00
Double	40.00	46.00

Half board

per person:	£min	£max
Daily	30.50	33.50

Evening meal 1800 (last
orders 2030)
Parking for 30
Cards accepted: Access, Visa
🛇🖥♿♨ ⓊⓁ♿Ⓢ🅿ⓉⓋ🏠,📠
✿🚳Ⓣ

The Squirrels

Listed APPROVED
74 Sandridge Road, St
Albans AL1 4AR
☎ (0727) 40497
Edwardian terraced house, 10
minutes' walk from town
centre.
Bedrooms: 1 twin
Bathrooms: 1 private

Bed & breakfast

per night:	£min	£max
Single		15.00
Double		30.00

🛇7🖥♿🔍Ⓢ✂🏠,📠
🚳Ⓣ

STANDLAKE

Oxfordshire
Map ref 2C1

13th C church with an
octagonal tower and spire
standing beside the
Windrush. The interior of
the church is rich in
woodwork.

Blenheim Cottage

Listed
47 Abingdon Road,
Standlake, Witney OX8 7QH
☎ Oxford (0865) 300718
Recently extended and
modernised cottage in a rural
setting on the A415. Situated
at the Witney end of
Standlake.
Bedrooms: 1 twin
Bathrooms: 1 private

Bed & breakfast

per night:	£min	£max
Single		18.00
Double		28.00

Parking for 1
Open May-September
🛇12🎿🖥♿ⓊⓁⓈ🏠,✕
🚳🐾

Hawthorn Cottage

The Downs, Standlake,
Witney OX8 7SH
☎ Oxford (0865) 300588
Charming house overlooking
large, private garden on edge
of village. 1 mile off A415,
Witney/Abingdon road.
Bedrooms: 1 double, 1 twin
Bathrooms: 2 private

Bed & breakfast

per night:	£min	£max
Single	25.00	30.00
Double	35.00	40.00

Parking for 2
🛇2🍴🖥♿ⓊⓁ🏠,✿✕🚳

STANFORD IN THE VALE

Oxfordshire
Map ref 2C2

Cox's Hall

60 High Street, Stanford in
the Vale, Faringdon
SN7 8NQ
☎ (036 77) 10248
Comfortable Georgian house
in a friendly village. Garden
available for guests' use.
Convenient for Oxford and
the Berkshire Downs.
Bedrooms: 1 double, 1 twin
Bathrooms: 2 private

Bed & breakfast

per night:	£min	£max
Single		18.00
Double		30.00

Parking for 6
🍴♿ⓊⓁ✂🏠,✿✕🚳🐾

STOKE ROW

Oxfordshire
Map ref 2C2

Neals Farm

👑
Wyfold, Reading RG4 9JB
☎ Checkendon (0491)
680258
100-acre livestock farm. Very
secluded south-facing
Georgian farmhouse with
home-grown produce and
extensive views. Non-smokers
preferred.
Bedrooms: 1 single,
1 double, 2 twin
Bathrooms: 1 public

Bed & breakfast

per night:	£min	£max
Single		18.00
Double		28.00

Half board

per person:	£min	£max
Daily		26.00

Evening meal from 1930
Parking for 10
🛇♿ⓊⓁ♿Ⓢ✂ⓉⓋ🏠,📠✕
🕙🎵▶✿🚳🐾Ⓣ

STONY STRATFORD

Buckinghamshire
Map ref 2C1

110 Clarence Road

Stony Stratford, Milton
Keynes MK11 1JG
☎ Milton Keynes (0908)
562381
Home furnished with some
antiques.
Bedrooms: 1 single, 2 twin
Bathrooms: 1 public

Bed & breakfast

per night:	£min	£max
Single	17.00	22.00
Double	34.00	44.00

Parking for 8
🛇ⓊⓁ♿Ⓢ✂🅾ⓉⓋ🏠,📠✿✕
🚳🐾

Fegan's View

Listed
119 High Street, Stony
Stratford, Milton Keynes
MK11 1AT
☎ Milton Keynes (0908)
562128 & 564246
Town-house, near local
amenities and convenient for
central Milton Keynes,
Woburn, Silverstone and
Cranfield.
Bedrooms: 1 single, 3 twin
Bathrooms: 1 private,
2 public

Bed & breakfast

per night:	£min	£max
Single	16.00	25.00
Double	32.00	38.00

🛇♿🔍ⓊⓁ♿Ⓢ🅾ⓉⓋ🏠,📠✕
🚳🐾

STRATTON AUDLEY

Oxfordshire
Map ref 2C1

The Old School

Listed COMMENDED
Stratton Audley, Bicester
OX6 9BJ
☎ Bicester (0869) 277371
400-year-old house in tranquil
corner of village and 7
minutes from Bicester. Tea/
coffee and homemade cakes

on arrival. From Bicester take Buckingham road and turn right at sign to Stratton Audley.
Bedrooms: 1 single, 3 twin
Bathrooms: 2 public
Bed & breakfast

per night:	£min	£max
Single	20.00	24.00
Double	40.00	48.00

Parking for 6

THAME

Oxfordshire
Map ref 2C1

Historic market town on the River Thame. The wide, unspoilt High Street has many styles of architecture with medieval timber-framed cottages, Georgian houses and some famous inns.
Tourist Information Centre
☎ *(084 421) 2834*

Crowell End ♠
Crowell Hill, Chinnor, Oxford OX9 4BT
☎ Kingston Blount (0844) 52726
Family house in beautiful and peaceful surroundings, in an area of outstanding natural beauty. Ideal base for walking, riding and touring. Lovely gardens. Horses, ducks and other pets.
Bedrooms: 1 single, 1 double, 1 twin
Bathrooms: 1 private, 2 public
Bed & breakfast

per night:	£min	£max
Single	17.50	
Double	32.00	35.00

Parking for 6

Manor Farm
Listed
Shabbington, Aylesbury, Buckinghamshire HP18 9HJ
☎ Long Crendon (0844) 201103
188-acre livestock farm. In rural setting, within 20 minutes of historic Oxford, on the fringes of the scenic Thames Valley, Chilterns and Cotswolds.
Bedrooms: 2 single, 2 double
Bathrooms: 1 private, 2 public

Bed & breakfast

per night:	£min	£max
Single	15.00	17.50
Double	35.00	35.00

Parking for 10

Stoke Grange
Stoke Talmage, Oxford OX9 7EZ
☎ Tetsworth (0844) 281303
Farmhouse in a quiet location near M40 junction 6, A40 Tetsworth, 5 miles from Thame. Non-smokers only please.
Bedrooms: 2 double, 1 twin
Bathrooms: 3 private, 1 public
Bed & breakfast

per night:	£min	£max
Single	25.00	27.50
Double	42.00	44.00

Parking for 8

TOTTERNHOE

Bedfordshire
Map ref 2D1

Country Cottage
5 Brightwell Avenue, Totternhoe, Dunstable LU6 1QT
☎ Luton (0582) 601287
Cottage-style house on edge of Dunstable Downs, surrounded by the Chiltern Hills. Situated off B489. Turn into Wellhead Road opposite London Gliding Club, first right is Brightwell Avenue.
Bedrooms: 1 single, 1 double, 1 twin
Bathrooms: 1 public
Bed & breakfast

per night:	£min	£max
Single	16.00	
Double	32.00	

Half board

per person:	£min	£max
Daily	22.00	
Weekly	145.00	

Parking for 4

National Crown ratings were correct at the time of going to press but are subject to change. Please check at the time of booking.

UFFINGTON

Oxfordshire
Map ref 2C2

Village famous for the great White Horse cut in the chalk, possibly dating from the Iron Age. Above it is Uffington Castle, a prehistoric hill fort.

The Craven
Fernham Road, Uffington, Faringdon SN7 7RD
☎ (0367) 820449
1-acre mixed farm. Large 17th C thatched farmhouse, originally an inn. Surrounded by lovely scenery on outskirts of pretty village, near the Ridge Way Path.
Bedrooms: 3 single, 2 double, 1 twin
Bathrooms: 1 private, 1 public
Bed & breakfast

per night:	£min	£max
Single	23.00	28.00
Double	35.00	54.00

Half board

per person:	£min	£max
Daily	31.00	38.00

Lunch available
Evening meal 1800 (last orders 1200)
Parking for 11
Cards accepted: Amex

WALLINGFORD

Oxfordshire
Map ref 2C2

Site of an ancient ford over the River Thames, now crossed by a 900-ft-long bridge. The town has many timber-framed and Georgian buildings, Gainsborough portraits in the 17th C Town Hall and a few remains of a Norman Castle.
Tourist Information Centre
☎ *(0491) 26972*

Candleford
17 St John's Road, Wallingford OX10 9AQ
☎ (0491) 33109
Situated near the centre of Wallingford, which lies on the A423, between Oxford and Reading.
Bedrooms: 2 twin
Bathrooms: 1 private, 1 public
Bed & breakfast

per night:	£min	£max
Single	15.00	20.00
Double	25.00	30.00

Half board

per person:	£min	£max
Daily	20.00	

Evening meal 2000 (last orders 2100)
Parking for 1

North Farm
☜☜ COMMENDED
Shillingford Hill, Wallingford OX10 8NB
☎ Warborough (086 732) 8406
500-acre mixed farm. Comfortable farmhouse close to River Thames, in a quiet position with lovely views and walks. Pygmy goats, chickens and sheep.
Bedrooms: 1 double, 1 twin
Bathrooms: 2 private
Bed & breakfast

per night:	£min	£max
Single	25.00	
Double	35.00	40.00

Parking for 4

WARBOROUGH

Oxfordshire
Map ref 2C2

Blenheim House
☜ COMMENDED
11-13 The Green North, Warborough, Wallingford OX10 7DW
☎ (086 732) 8445
Old village house set in 2.5 acres of garden. Swimming pool.
Bedrooms: 1 double, 1 twin
Bathrooms: 2 private
Bed & breakfast

per night:	£min	£max
Single	20.00	25.00
Double	40.00	50.00

Parking for 4

Individual proprietors have supplied all details of accommodation. Although we do check for accuracy, we advise you to confirm the information at the time of booking.

THAMES & CHILTERNS

WARE

Hertfordshire
Map ref 2D1

Interesting riverside town with picturesque summer-houses lining the tow-path of the River Lea. The town has many timber-framed and Georgian houses and the famous Great Bed of Ware is now in the Victoria and Albert Museum.

Ashridge
COMMENDED

3 Belle Vue Road, Ware
SG12 7BD
☎ (0920) 463895
Comfortable, Edwardian residence in quiet cul-de-sac. 10 minutes' walk from Ware and station. Non-smokers only please.
Bedrooms: 2 single, 1 double, 1 twin
Bathrooms: 2 public
Bed & breakfast

per night:	£min	£max
Single	16.50	18.50
Double	33.00	37.00

Half board

per person:	£min	£max
Daily	22.50	24.50

Evening meal 1830 (last orders 1200)
Parking for 4

Eydon Nook

Cambridge Road, High Cross, Ware SG11 1AP
☎ (0920) 467464
Victorian cottage with leaded light windows. On the A10, opposite garage and 1.5 miles north of Ware.
Bedrooms: 1 single, 2 twin
Bathrooms: 1 public
Bed & breakfast

per night:	£min	£max
Single	18.00	25.00
Double	30.00	40.00

Parking for 4

National Crown ratings were correct at the time of going to press but are subject to change. Please check at the time of booking.

WARGRAVE

Berkshire
Map ref 2C2

Attractive village with timber-framed and Georgian houses. The Thames meets the River Loddon nearby and it is a popular place for boating.

Appletree Cottage

Backsideans, Wargrave, Reading RG10 8JS
☎ Reading (0734) 404306
Beautiful, secluded character cottage, just off Wargrave High Street and only 3 miles from Henley-on-Thames. Landscaped garden.
Bedrooms: 1 single, 2 double
Bathrooms: 1 private, 1 public
Bed & breakfast

per night:	£min	£max
Single	17.50	25.00
Double	35.00	50.00

Parking for 2

Dene Croft

Blakes Lane, Wargrave, Reading RG10 9ST
☎ Reading (0734) 403604
Detached house situated 1.5 miles from the centre of Wargrave. In a quiet country position, just 25 miles from Heathrow.
Bedrooms: 1 single, 1 twin
Bathrooms: 1 public
Bed & breakfast

per night:	£min	£max
Single	16.00	18.00
Double	32.00	36.00

Parking for 4
Open January-June, September-November

WATFORD

Hertfordshire
Map ref 2D1

Large town with many industries but with some old buildings, particularly around St Mary's Church which contains some fine monuments. The grounds of Cassiobury Park, once the home of the Earls of Essex, form a public park and golf-course.

33 Courtlands Drive

Watford WD1 3HU
☎ (0923) 220531
Detached house close to M25 and M1, offering bed and

breakfast. Colour TV and tea/coffee-making facilities.
Bedrooms: 2 twin
Bathrooms: 1 public
Bed & breakfast

per night:	£min	£max
Single	15.00	
Double	30.00	

Parking for 5

The Millwards

30 Hazelwood Road, Croxley Green, Rickmansworth WD3 3EB
☎ (0923) 233751 & 226666
Homely canalside residence, convenient for London (Metropolitan line), Moor Park golf-course, Heathrow Airport, Watford and Croxley Business Parks, Wembley Stadium, M1 and M25.
Bedrooms: 1 single, 3 twin
Bathrooms: 2 private, 2 public
Bed & breakfast

per night:	£min	£max
Single	14.00	18.00
Double	26.00	30.00

Parking for 2

WENDOVER

Buckinghamshire
Map ref 2C1

Historic town on the Icknield Way set amid beautiful scenery and spectacular views of the Chilterns. There are many old timbered cottages and inns, one visited by Oliver Cromwell. The church has some interesting carving.
Tourist Information Centre
☎ (0296) 390653

The Black Horse Restaurant

Dunsmore, Aylesbury HP22 6QJ
☎ Aylesbury (0296) 623113
Small, country restaurant with panoramic views from bedrooms. Set high in Chiltern Hills, 1 mile off A413 between Great Missenden and Wendover.
Bedrooms: 2 single, 1 twin
Bathrooms: 3 private, 1 public
Bed & breakfast

per night:	£min	£max
Single	29.00	
Double	52.50	

Lunch available
Evening meal 1900 (last orders 2100)

WESTBURY

Buckinghamshire
Map ref 2C1

Mill Farm House
Listed

Westbury, Brackley, Northamptonshire NN13 5JS
☎ Brackley (0280) 704843
1000-acre mixed farm. A Grade II listed farmhouse, overlooking a colourful garden including a covered heated swimming pool, and situated in the centre of Westbury village.
Bedrooms: 2 double, 1 triple
Bathrooms: 1 public
Bed & breakfast

per night:	£min	£max
Single	16.00	20.00
Double	32.00	40.00

Half board

per person:	£min	£max
Daily	26.00	40.00
Weekly	150.00	200.00

Evening meal 1930 (last orders 2130)
Parking for 8

WESTON-ON-THE-GREEN

Oxfordshire
Map ref 2C1

Pretty village with stocks on the village green and thatched cottages. The church of St Mary's has an attractive setting and a fine tower dating from the 12th C.

Newby Cottage

Weston-on-the-Green, Bicester OX6 8QL
☎ Bletchington (0869) 50662
18th C brick and stone thatched cottage overlooking farmland. Convenient for Oxford, Woodstock, Oxfordshire Way and junction 9 of M40.
Bedrooms: 1 single, 2 double
Bathrooms: 1 public
Bed & breakfast

per night:	£min	£max
Single	14.00	15.00
Double	28.00	30.00

Parking for 3

WINDSOR

Berkshire
Map ref 2D2

Town dominated by the spectacular castle and home of the Royal Family for over 900 years. Parts are open to the public. There are many attractions including the Great Park, Eton, Windsor Safari Park and trips on the river.
Tourist Information Centre
☎ *(0753) 852010*

77 Whitehorse Road
Windsor SL4 4PG
☎ (0753) 866803
A large, semi-detached house in a quiet position, just outside Windsor.
Bedrooms: 2 double, 1 twin
Bathrooms: 2 public

Bed & breakfast

per night:	£min	£max
Single	16.00	18.00
Double	30.00	36.00

Parking for 3
☎ ⛺ 🖵 ⓦ 📺 🛏, ♨ ✿ 🏕

Mrs. B. Clemens
49 Longmead, Windsor
SL4 5PZ
☎ (0753) 866019
Fax (0753) 830964
A home-from-home with private facilities in quiet residential area. 1.25 miles from town centre and Windsor Castle.
Bedrooms: 1 single,
1 double, 1 twin
Bathrooms: 2 private,
1 public

Bed & breakfast

per night:	£min	£max
Single	18.00	20.00
Double	36.00	40.00

Parking for 2
🖵🖵 🖵 ♨ ⓦ Ⓢ ✂ 📺 🛏, ♨
🏕 🐾

The Beeches
19 The Avenue, Datchet,
Slough SL3 9DQ
☎ Slough (0753) 580722
Charming Victorian house with well-appointed spacious rooms and all facilities. Close to River Thames, Windsor and its Safari Park, Thorpe Park. Convenient for Heathrow and motorway links.
Bedrooms: 3 single,
2 double, 2 twin
Bathrooms: 5 private,
1 private shower

Bed & breakfast

per night:	£min	£max
Single		28.50
Double		45.00

Parking for 7
Cards accepted: Access, Visa
☎ ⛺ 🖵 🖵 ♨ 🔌 ⓦ Ⓢ ✂ 📺
🛏, ♨ ✿ 🏕 🐾

Chasela
30 Convent Road, Windsor
SL4 3RB
☎ (0753) 860410
Warm, comfortable, modern house, 1 mile from castle, easy access to M4, M40, M25 and Heathrow. TV in rooms, welcome tray on arrival.
Bedrooms: 1 single, 1 twin
Bathrooms: 1 public

Bed & breakfast

per night:	£min	£max
Single	15.00	17.00
Double	30.00	34.00

Parking for 5
☎ 3 🖵 ♨ ⓦ Ⓢ 🛏, ♨ ✿
🏕 🐾

Crown and Cushion Hotel
84 High Street, Eton,
Windsor SL4 6AF
☎ (0753) 861531
Family-run establishment.
Bedrooms: 6 single,
1 double, 1 twin
Bathrooms: 1 private,
1 public, 1 private shower

Bed & breakfast

per night:	£min	£max
Single	23.00	26.00
Double	35.00	40.00

Half board

per person:	£min	£max
Daily	28.00	31.00
Weekly	140.00	160.00

Lunch available
Evening meal 1730 (last orders 2030)
Parking for 10
Cards accepted: Access, Visa
☎ 10 ♨ 🛆 Ⓢ 🏂 📺 🛏, ♨ ✿
🏕 🐾 🏨

Halcyon House
Listed
131 Clarence Road, Windsor
SL4 5AR
☎ (0753) 863262
A warm welcome at a family-run guesthouse, 10 minutes' walk from the town centre and river. Ideal base for London. Off-street parking.
Bedrooms: 2 double, 2 twin
Bathrooms: 3 private,
1 public

Bed & breakfast

per night:	£min	£max
Double	33.00	40.00

Parking for 6
🖵🖵 🖵 ♨ ⓦ Ⓢ 🏂 📺 🛏, ♨
🏕 🐾

Royal Adelaide Hotel 🅰
♛♛♛♛
Kings Road, Windsor
SL4 2AG
☎ (0753) 863916
Fax (0753) 830682
Close to town centre, overlooking Long Walk and within walking distance of tourist attractions in Windsor.
Bedrooms: 23 single,
11 double, 5 twin, 1 triple
Bathrooms: 40 private

Bed & breakfast

per night:	£min	£max
Single	47.50	60.00
Double	50.00	90.00

Lunch available
Evening meal 1900 (last orders 2130)
Parking for 20
Cards accepted: Access, Visa, Diners, Amex
☎ 🔥 ⛺ 🖵 🖵 ♨ 🛆 Ⓢ 🏂 🅞 🛏,
♨ 🏃 20-100 ▶ ✿ 🏕 🔤 🐾 🆂🅿
🏨 Ⓣ

Tanglewood
Oakley Green, Windsor
SL4 4PZ
☎ (0753) 860034
Picturesque chalet-style guesthouse with pretty garden, in rural area, overlooking open fields. 10 minutes' drive from Windsor on B3024.
Bedrooms: 2 twin
Bathrooms: 1 public

Bed & breakfast

per night:	£min	£max
Double	34.00	34.00

Parking for 2
Open May-September
☎ 🖵 ♨ ⓦ 🛏, ✿ 🏕 🐾

WINSLOW

Buckinghamshire
Map ref 2C1

Small town with Georgian houses, a little market square and a fine church with 15th C wall-paintings. Winslow Hall, built to the design of Sir Christopher Wren in 1700, is open to the public.

Foxhole Farm
Little Horwood Road,
Winslow, Buckingham
MK18 3JW
☎ (029 671) 4550

70-acre livestock farm. Fine modern farmhouse set in pasture and woodland, close to the small market town of Winslow.
Bedrooms: 1 single,
1 double, 1 twin
Bathrooms: 1 public

Bed & breakfast

per night:	£min	£max
Single	17.00	
Double	32.00	

Parking for 6
🖵 ⓦ 🛏, ✿ 🏕 🐾

Manor Farm Stables 🅰
Manor Farm, High Street,
North Marston, Buckingham
MK18 3PS
☎ North Marston (0296)
67252 & 67708
Comfortable converted stables within easy reach of National Trust properties, Milton Keynes and Aylesbury. Breakfast served in farmhouse.
Bedrooms: 2 double, 2 twin
Bathrooms: 4 private

Bed & breakfast

per night:	£min	£max
Single	28.00	36.00
Double	40.00	48.00

Parking for 8
☎ 🔥 ⛺ 🖵 ♨ ⓦ 🛏 🛏, ♨ ♨ ◡
♪ / ✿ 🏕 🐾 🐑 🏨

WITNEY

Oxfordshire
Map ref 2C1

Town famous for its blanket-making and mentioned in the Domesday Book. The market-place contains the Butter Cross, a medieval meeting place, and there is a green with merchants' houses.
Tourist Information Centre
☎ *(0993) 775802*

3 Chapel Lane
Listed COMMENDED
North Leigh, Witney
OX8 6SD
☎ Freeland (0993) 881429
Small Cotswold stone cottage just off the main road, with garden at rear. Log fires, in season.
Bedrooms: 1 single, 1 twin
Bathrooms: 1 public

Bed & breakfast

per night:	£min	£max
Single		15.50
Double		31.00

Continued ▶

WITNEY

Continued

Evening meal from 1800
Parking for 2
Open April-September
Cards accepted:

Ambury Close Farm 🏨
COMMENDED

Barnard Gate, Witney
OX8 6XE
☎ Oxford (0865) 881356
*75-acre hill farm. Off the A40,
on the edge of the Cotswolds.
Witney 3 miles, Burford 10
miles, Oxford 7 miles,
Blenheim Palace 4 miles.
Public telephone available.*
Bedrooms: 2 double, 1 twin,
3 multiple
Bathrooms: 2 private,
2 public

Bed & breakfast

per night:	£min	£max
Single	20.00	24.00
Double	30.00	38.00

Half board

per person:	£min	£max
Daily	28.00	36.00

Evening meal 1830 (last
orders 2030)
Parking for 10

Field View
COMMENDED

Wood Green, Witney
OX8 6DE
☎ (0993) 705485
*Ideal for Oxford University
and the Cotswolds. Situated in
two acres on edge of bustling
market town of Witney.*
Bedrooms: 1 double, 2 twin
Bathrooms: 2 private,
1 private shower

Bed & breakfast

per night:	£min	£max
Single	18.00	22.00
Double	36.00	44.00

Parking for 10

Greystones Lodge Hotel
HIGHLY COMMENDED

34 Tower Hill, Witney
OX8 5ES
☎ (0993) 771898
*Quiet, comfortable private
hotel set in three-quarters of
an acre of pleasant garden.
Conveniently located for
visiting Oxford and the
Cotswolds.*

Bedrooms: 3 single,
4 double, 2 twin, 1 triple,
1 multiple
Bathrooms: 3 private,
1 public, 8 private showers

Bed & breakfast

per night:	£min	£max
Single	23.50	28.90
Double	36.95	45.00

Half board

per person:	£min	£max
Daily	32.00	35.50

Evening meal 1900 (last
orders 1930)
Parking for 20
Cards accepted: Access, Visa,
Diners, Amex

WOBURN

Bedfordshire
Map ref 2D1

Attractive village with
thatched cottages,
Victorian almshouses and
an impressive inn.
Woburn Abbey, an 18th C
mansion set in 3000
acres of parkland, is a
major tourist attraction
with a splendid art
collection.

Serendib B and B

15 Market Place, Woburn,
Milton Keynes MK17 9PZ
☎ (0525) 290464
*Georgian building in historic
Woburn village, near the
abbey, safari park and golf-
course. Comfortable and
friendly atmosphere. 4 miles
from M1, junctions 12 and
13. Sorry, no pets.*
Bedrooms: 1 double, 2 twin
Bathrooms: 1 public

Bed & breakfast

per night:	£min	£max
Double	30.00	35.00

Parking for 2
Cards accepted: Access, Visa

There are separate
sections in this
guide listing groups
specialising in farm
holidays and
accommodation
which is especially
suitable for young
people and
organised groups.

WOODSTOCK

Oxfordshire
Map ref 2C1

Small country town
clustered around the park
gates of Blenheim Palace,
the superb 18th C home
of the Duke of
Marlborough. The town
has well-known inns and
an interesting museum.
Sir Winston Churchill was
born and buried nearby.

Gorselands Farmhouse Auberge 🏨
APPROVED

Boddington Lane, Long
Hanborough, Witney
OX8 6PU
☎ Freeland (0993) 881895
Fax (0993) 882799
*Stone country farmhouse with
exposed beams, snooker
room, conservatory. Near
delightful hamlet of East End
and Roman villa remains.
Evening meals available.
Licensed for wine and beer.
Grass tennis court.*
Bedrooms: 1 single,
2 double, 1 twin, 1 triple
Bathrooms: 2 private,
1 public

Bed & breakfast

per night:	£min	£max
Single	20.00	25.00
Double	25.00	30.00

Half board

per person:	£min	£max
Daily	21.45	24.65
Weekly	135.00	148.00

Evening meal 1900 (last
orders 2100)
Parking for 8
Cards accepted: Access, Visa,
Amex

The Laurels
HIGHLY COMMENDED

Hensington Road,
Woodstock, Oxford
OX20 1JL
☎ (0993) 812583
*Fine Victorian house, located
in the historic town of
Woodstock. A short walk from
Blenheim Palace.*
Bedrooms: 2 double, 1 twin
Bathrooms: 3 private

Bed & breakfast

per night:	£min	£max
Single	25.00	32.00
Double	33.00	40.00

Half board

per person:	£min	£max
Daily	30.00	40.00

Evening meal from 1900

Parking for 4
Cards accepted: Access, Visa

Punch Bowl Inn 🏨
Listed

12 Oxford Street,
Woodstock, Oxford
OX20 1TR
☎ (0993) 811218
*Family-run pub in the centre
of Woodstock, close to
Blenheim Palace. A good
touring centre for Oxford and
the Cotswolds.*
Bedrooms: 2 single,
4 double, 2 twin, 1 triple,
1 multiple
Bathrooms: 3 private,
2 public

Bed & breakfast

per night:	£min	£max
Single	25.00	30.00
Double	35.00	43.00

Lunch available
Evening meal 1830 (last
orders 2130)
Parking for 20
Cards accepted: Access, Visa

The Ridings
Listed

32 Banbury Road,
Woodstock, Oxford
OX20 1LQ
☎ (0993) 811269
*Detached house in a quiet,
rural setting. 10 minutes'
walk to town centre and
Blenheim Palace. Go past the
Tourist Information Centre
for 300 yards then take left
fork along Banbury Road.*
Bedrooms: 2 twin, 1 triple
Bathrooms: 1 private,
1 public

Bed & breakfast

per night:	£min	£max
Single	15.00	20.00
Double	30.00	40.00

Parking for 4
Cards accepted:

Shepherds Hall Inn

Witney Road, Freeland,
Witney OX8 8HQ
☎ Freeland (0993) 881256
*Well-appointed inn offering
good accommodation. Ideally
situated for Oxford,
Woodstock and the Cotswolds,
on the A4095 Woodstock to
Witney road.*
Bedrooms: 1 single,
2 double, 2 twin
Bathrooms: 5 private

Bed & breakfast per night:

	£min	£max
Single	20.00	30.00
Double	35.00	40.00

Lunch available
Evening meal 1900 (last orders 2200)
Parking for 50
Cards accepted: Access, Visa
🏠 📞 🍴 📺 🛁 🚽 🎑 📶 🔌 🌸 🚐

Wynford House
Listed
79 Main Road, Long Hanborough, Oxford OX8 8JX
☎ Freeland (0993) 881402
Charming guesthouse, close to Bladon and Blenheim Palace on A4095. A warm and friendly welcome, comfortable beds and colour TV and tea/coffee facilities in all rooms.
Bedrooms: 1 double, 1 twin, 1 triple

Bathrooms: 1 private, 1 public

Bed & breakfast per night:

	£min	£max
Single	22.00	26.00
Double	32.00	36.00

Half board per person:

	£min	£max
Daily	30.00	34.00

Evening meal 1800 (last orders 2000)
Parking for 4
🏠 📺 🛁 🚽 🎑 📶 ℹ️ ⓢ 🎑 🖩 🍴 🚐
OAP SP

National Crown ratings were correct at the time of going to press but are subject to change. Please check at the time of booking.

Buckinghamshire
Map ref 2C1

Conifers Bed and Breakfast
Listed
29 William Smith Close, Woolstone, Milton Keynes MK15 0AN
☎ Milton Keynes (0908) 674506
Each bedroom has 2 doors, one leading to guests' secluded garden patio.
Bedrooms: 1 single, 2 double, 1 twin
Bathrooms: 1 private, 1 public

Bed & breakfast per night:

	£min	£max
Single	20.00	20.00
Double	35.00	35.00

🎑 📺 🛁 🚽 🖩 🍴 📺 🖩 🌸 🎑 🚐

Berkshire
Map ref 2D2

Clivesden
37 Gloucester Drive, Wraysbury, Staines, Middlesex TW18 4TY
☎ Staines (0784) 464858
Detached private house, 10 minutes' walk from Staines station and close to Heathrow Airport. Spacious garden with fruit trees and stream.
Bedrooms: 1 single, 1 twin
Bathrooms: 1 public

Bed & breakfast per night:

	£min	£max
Single	16.00	16.00
Double	30.00	30.00

Parking for 4
🎑 📺 🛁 🚽 🖩 🍴 🚐 ↗ ✗ 🚐

Key to symbols

Information about many of the services and facilities at establishments listed in this guide is given in the form of symbols. The key to these symbols is inside the back cover flap. You may find it helpful to keep the flap open when referring to the entry listings.

Check the maps

The place you wish to visit may not have accommodation entirely suited to your needs, but there could be somewhere ideal quite close by. Check the colour maps at the back of this guide to identify nearby towns and villages with accommodation listed in the guide, and then use the town index to find page numbers.

East Anglia

Life moves at an easy pace in this region of farmland and fens, breezy beaches, reed-covered marshes, sandy heaths, rustic villages and market towns. Legacies of the past abound – Roman Colchester, Bury St Edmunds, home of the last king of East Anglia, the beautiful wool town of Lavenham and historic Norwich and Ipswich. Visit Cambridge, one of Britain's

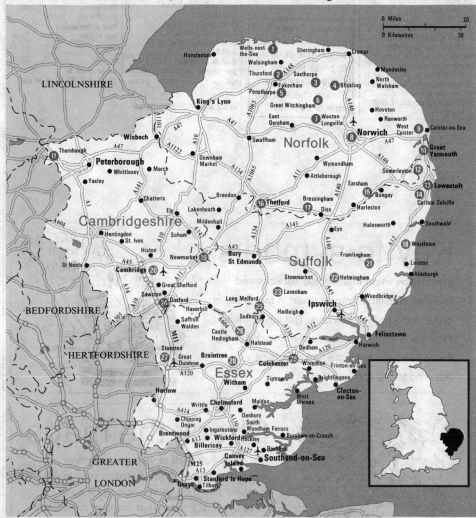

Use the above map to locate places in the "Where to Go, What to See" section opposite.
Use the colour maps at the back of this guide to find places with accommodation.

great university towns, with its romantic cobbled streets, superb old buildings, colleges and museums. There are lively seaside resorts, too – Great Yarmouth has 15 miles of golden beaches and a glittering array of entertainment – while the quieter resorts of the Suffolk coast reflect the charm of this most English of England's regions.

WHERE TO GO, WHAT TO SEE

The number against each name will help you locate it on the map opposite.

1 Holkham Hall
Wells-next-the-Sea, Norfolk
NR23 1AB
Tel: Fakenham (0328) 710227
Classic 18th C Palladian-style mansion, part of a great agricultural estate and a living treasure house of artistic and architectural history.

2 Thursford Collection
Thursford, Norfolk
NR21 OAS
Tel: Thursford (0328) 878477
Musical evenings every Tuesday from end-June to end-September. Mechanical organs and Wurlitzer shows, starring Robert Wolfe.

3 Mannington Gardens and Countryside
Saxthorpe, Norfolk NR11 7BB
Tel: Saxthorpe (026 387) 4175
Gardens with lake, moat and woodland. Outstanding rose collection. Saxon church with Victorian follies. Countryside walks and trails with guide booklets.

4 Blickling Hall
Blickling, Norfolk NR11 6NF
Tel: Aylsham (0263) 733084
Jacobean red brick mansion. Garden, orangery, parkland

Thomas Nashe, who wrote many controversial pamphlets on religious and political matters in the 16th C, was born in Suffolk and educated at Cambridge

and lake. Fine tapestries and furniture.

5 Penshorpe Waterfowl Park
Penshorpe, Fakenham, Norfolk
NR21 0LN
Tel: Fakenham (0328) 851465
Large waterfowl and wildfowl

collection. Information centre, conservation shop, adventure play area, walks and nature trails.

6 Norfolk Wildlife Park
Great Witchingham, Norfolk
NR9 5QS
Tel: Norwich (0603) 872274
Large collection of British and European wildlife in 40 acres of parkland. Pets' corner, steam railway, play areas, model farm and clearwater trout pool.

7 Dinosaur Natural History Park
Weston Longville,
Norfolk NR9 5JW
Tel: Norwich (0603) 870245
Life-size dinosaurs in natural woodland setting. Play area, wooded maze. Bygone museum, information centre, gift shop, picnic area.

8 Sainsbury Centre for Visual Arts
Norwich, Norfolk NR4 7TJ
Tel: Norwich (0603) 56060
Robert and Lisa Sainsbury Collection is wide ranging and of international importance, with the recent addition of new Crescent Wing.

9 Caister Castle and Car Collection
West Caister, Norfolk NR38 5SN
Tel: West Caister (057 284) 251
Important castle with large

private collection of motor vehicles from 1893 to date.

⑩ Pleasure Beach
Great Yarmouth, Norfolk
NR30 3EH
Tel: Great Yarmouth (0493) 844585
Roller coaster, looping star, log flume, magic carpet, monorail, big wheel, galloping horses, rapido express and the condor.

⑪ Sacrewell Farm and Country Centre
Sacrewell, Thornhaugh, Peterborough, Cambridgeshire
PE8 6HJ
Tel: Stamford (0780) 782222
500-acre farm, with working watermill, gardens, shrubberies, nature and general interest trails. 18th C buildings, displays of farm, rural and domestic bygones.

⑫ Somerleyton Hall and Maze
Somerleyton, Suffolk NR32 5QQ
Tel: (0502) 730224
Anglo-Italian style building with state rooms, maze. Garden with azaleas and rhododendrons. Miniature railway, shop and refreshment room.

⑬ Pleasurewood Hills American Theme Park
Lowestoft, Suffolk NR32 5DZ
Tel: Lowestoft (0502) 513626
Tempest chair lift, cine 180, railway pirate ship, fort, Aladdin's cave, parrot shows, rollercoaster, waveswinger, haunted castle, star ride Enterprise.

⑭ East Anglia Transport Museum
Carlton Colville, Suffolk
NR33 8BL
Tel: Lowestoft (0502) 518459
Transport museum with the emphasis on movement.

Working trams, trolley buses, steam roller and 1916 Thornycroft lorry, all in 1930s street scene.

⑮ Otter Trust
Earsham, Suffolk NR35 2AF
Tel: Bungay (0986) 893470
A breeding and conservation headquarters with large collection of otters. Also lakes with collection of waterfowl, deer, etc.

⑯ Charles Burrell Museum
Minstergate, Thetford, Norfolk
Tel: Norfolk (0362) 695333
The Charles Burrell steam museum draws together an impressive collection of exhibits to tell the story of Charles Burrell and Son (1770–1932).

⑰ Bressingham Steam Museum and Gardens
Bressingham, Norfolk IP22 2AB
Tel: Bressingham (037 988) 386
Steam rides through 5 miles of woodland, garden and nursery. Rides on footplate of mainline locomotive. The Victorian Gallopers and over 50 steam engines.

⑱ Minsmere Nature Reserve
Westleton, Saxmundham, Suffolk
IP17 3BY
Tel: Westleton (072 873) 281
Two walks, 2 miles long, with hides on coastal lagoon and reed bed. Birds include avocets, marsh harrier, wildfowl. Shop.

⑲ The National Horseracing Museum
99 High Street, Newmarket, Suffolk CB8 8JL
Tel: Newmarket (0638) 667333
5 permanent galleries telling the story of the development of horseracing. British sporting art.

⑳ Cambridge and County Folk Museum
Cambridge, Cambridgeshire
CB3 0AQ
Tel: Cambridge (0223) 355159
16th C former farmhouse, an inn from 17th C to 1934. Wide variety of objects relating to everyday life of the people of Cambridge.

㉑ Framlingham Castle
Framlingham, Suffolk IP8 9BT
Tel: Suffolk (0728) 723330
12th C curtain walls with 13 towers and Tudor brick chimneys. Built by Bigod family, Earls of Norfolk. Wall walk. 17th C almshouses. Home of Mary Tudor in 1553.

㉒ Helmingham Hall Gardens
Helmingham, Suffolk IP14 6EF
Tel: Helmingham (0473) 890363
Moated and walled garden with many rare roses and possibly the best kitchen garden in Britain. Also Highland cattle and safari rides in park to view red and fallow deer.

㉓ The Priory
Lavenham, Suffolk CO10 9RW
Tel: Lavenham (0787) 247417
Timber-framed house which through the ages has been the home of Benedictine monks, medieval wool merchants and an Elizabethan rector. Herb garden.

㉔ Imperial War Museum
Duxford, Cambridgeshire
CB2 4QR
Tel: Duxford (0223) 835000
Over 120 aircraft plus tanks, vehicles and guns on display. Adventure playground,

Carved in stone in the early 14th C, this old green god can be seen in Norwich Cathedral

The wooden Mathematical Bridge at Queens' College, Cambridge, was originally built without a single nail in 1749 and reconstructed at the beginning of this century

shops, restaurant, narrow gauge railway.

㉕ Kentwell Hall
Long Melford, Suffolk CO10 9BA
Tel: Sudbury (0787) 310207
Mellow red brick Tudor manor surrounded by moat. Family home interestingly restored. Tudor costume display. 15th C moat house, mosaic Tudor Rose maze.

㉖ Colne Valley Railway
Castle Hedingham, Essex
C09 3DZ
Tel: Hedingham (0787) 61174
Complete reconstruction of Victorian/Edwardian rural branch line stations, signal boxes, vintage engines and carriage displays. Museum.

㉗ Mountfitchet Castle
Stansted, Essex CM24 8SP
Tel: Bishops Stortford (0279) 813237
Reconstructed Norman motte and bailey castle and village of Domesday period. Grand hall, church, prison, siege tower, weapons. Domestic animals roam site.

㉘ The Working Silk Museum New Mills
Braintree, Essex CM7 6GB
Tel: Braintree (0376) 553393
Show of textiles and mill shop. Looms and ancient textile machines restored and working. Weaving demonstrations. Evening tours by appointment.

㉙ Colchester Castle
Colchester, Essex
Tel: Colchester (0206) 712931
Norman keep on foundations of Roman temple. Archaeological material includes much on Roman Colchester (Camulodunum).

㉙ Tymperleys Clock Museum
Trinity Street, Colchester, Essex C01 1JN
Tel: Colchester (0206) 712931
Selection of Colchester-made clocks from the Mason Collection, displayed in 15th C house which Bernard Mason restored and presented to the town.

FIND OUT MORE

Further information about holidays and attractions in the East Anglia region is available from:
East Anglia Tourist Board
Toppesfield Hall, Hadleigh, Suffolk IP7 5DN
Tel: (0473) 822922

These publications are available free from the East Anglia Tourist Board:
Bed & Breakfast Touring Map for the East of England
East Anglia, the Real England
Also available are (prices include postage and packing):
East Anglia Guide £3.20
East Anglia Leisure Map £3.20
Gardens to Visit in East Anglia £1

Places to stay

Accommodation entries in this regional section are listed in alphabetical order of place name, and then in alphabetical order of establishment.

The map references refer to the colour maps at the back of the guide. The first figure is the map number; the letter and figure which follow indicate the grid reference on the map.

The symbols at the end of each accommodation entry give information about services and facilities. A 'key' to these symbols is inside the back cover flap, which can be kept open for easy reference.

ALDEBURGH

Suffolk
Map ref 3C2

A prosperous port in the 16th C, now famous for the Aldeburgh Music Festival held annually in June. The 16th C Moot Hall, now a museum, is a timber-framed building once used as an open market.

Brightside

147 Saxmundham Road, Aldeburgh IP15 5PB
☎ (0728) 454058
Pleasantly situated bungalow with large drive, patio and conservatory. On main Saxmundham road.
Bedrooms: 1 double, 1 twin
Bathrooms: 2 private
Bed & breakfast

per night:	£min	£max
Single	17.50	18.00
Double	30.00	35.00

Parking for 18
Open March-October

Tapp Cottage

35 Fawcett Road, Aldeburgh IP15 5HQ
☎ (072 845) 3672
Bed and breakfast in family home. Evening meal by arrangement. Hot drinks available anytime. 4 minutes' walk to town centre and sea.
Bedrooms: 1 double, 1 twin
Bathrooms: 1 public
Bed & breakfast

per night:	£min	£max
Single	14.50	15.00
Double	29.00	30.00

Half board

per person:	£min	£max
Daily	35.00	40.00

Evening meal 1800 (last orders 1800)

ALDHAM

Essex
Map ref 3B2

Old House ⚐
Listed COMMENDED
Ford Street, Aldham, Colchester CO6 3PH
☎ Colchester (0206) 240456
Bed and breakfast in 14th C family home with friendly atmosphere, oak beams, log fires, large garden and ample parking. Between Harwich and Cambridge, Felixstowe and London. On A604, 5 miles west of Colchester.
Bedrooms: 2 single, 2 double, 1 twin, 1 triple
Bathrooms: 1 private, 3 public

Please mention this guide when making a booking.

Bed & breakfast

per night:	£min	£max
Single	20.00	25.00
Double	30.00	45.00

Parking for 8

ARDLEIGH

Essex
Map ref 3B2

2.5 miles north-east of Colchester on the A137. Ardleigh Reservoir has a large bird-watching area.

Bovills Hall ⚐
HIGHLY COMMENDED
Station Road, Ardleigh, Colchester CO7 7RT
☎ (0206) 230217
Comfortable traditionally-furnished manor house with many exposed beams, on edge of Dedham Vale.
Bedrooms: 2 double, 1 twin
Bathrooms: 1 private, 1 public
Bed & breakfast

per night:	£min	£max
Single	23.00	28.00
Double	35.00	40.00

Parking for 6
Open February-November
Cards accepted: Access, Visa

Dundas Place ⚐
COMMENDED
Colchester Road, Ardleigh, Colchester CO7 7NP
☎ (0206) 230625
300-year-old cottage with exposed oak beams throughout, a large open fireplace and a picturesque old world garden. Located in the centre of the village. Four night bed and breakfast package - £110, including use of Ordnance Survey maps and local information.
Bedrooms: 1 double, 2 twin
Bathrooms: 1 public
Bed & breakfast

per night:	£min	£max
Single	17.00	17.00
Double	29.00	29.00

Parking for 2

ATTLEBOROUGH

Norfolk
Map ref 3B1

Market town, mostly destroyed in 1559 by fire, now a cider-making centre. Church with fine Norman tower.

Hill House Farm

Deopham Road, Great Ellingham, Attleborough NR17 1AQ
☎ (0953) 453113
100-acre mixed farm. On the edge of the old Deopham

airbase. Leave the A11 and take the B1077 to Great Ellingham, take turn at bus shelter to Deopham. Farm is half a mile on, second farm on the left.
Bedrooms: 1 single, 2 double, 1 triple
Bathrooms: 1 public

Bed & breakfast

per night:	£min	£max
Single	12.00	
Double	22.00	

Parking for 5

🛇💷🛇⚵ 🅜 ⅏ Ⅲ. 🖃❋✕ 🐾

AYLSHAM

Norfolk
Map ref 3B1

Small town on the River Bure with an attractive market place and interesting church. Nearby is Blickling Hall (National Trust). Also the terminal of the Bure Valley narrow gauge steam railway which runs on 9 miles of the Old Great Eastern trackbed, between Wroxham and Aylsham.

The Beeches
Holman Road, Aylsham, Norwich NR11 6BZ
☎ (0263) 734037
Listed 18th C family house offering elegant accommodation, built around cobbled courtyard in quiet secluded grounds. Close to the town centre.
Bedrooms: 1 double, 1 twin, 1 triple
Bathrooms: 3 private, 1 public

Bed & breakfast

per night:	£min	£max
Single	18.00	20.00
Double	30.00	36.00

Half board

per person:	£min	£max
Daily	46.00	54.00
Weekly	138.00	156.00

Evening meal 1800 (last orders 2000)
Parking for 10

🛇2💷 ⅏ 🅦⚵ 🛇Ⓢ✂🅜 ⅏ Ⅲ. ❋✕ 🐾 SP 🛏

The Old Bank House
3 Norwich Road, Aylsham, Norwich NR11 6BN
☎ (0263) 733843
A warm welcome and elegant accommodation at this listed Georgian house with panelled rooms, Victorian bathrooms, half-tester bed and games room.
Bedrooms: 1 double, 1 twin, 1 triple

Bathrooms: 1 private, 2 public

Bed & breakfast

per night:	£min	£max
Single	15.00	20.00
Double	30.00	30.00

Parking for 3

🛇🛋🖭🅦⚵Ⓢ🅜⅏Ⅲ. 🖃🖾❋✕🐾🖘🛏

The Old Pump House
Holman Road, Aylsham, Norwich NR11 6BY
☎ (0263) 733789
Spacious but homely period house, just off the market place, good centre for touring countryside and coast. Non-smokers only please.
Bedrooms: 3 double, 1 twin, 1 triple
Bathrooms: 3 private, 1 public, 1 private shower

Bed & breakfast

per night:	£min	£max
Single	15.00	20.00
Double	30.00	40.00

Parking for 7

🛇🛋🖵⅏🅦⚵✂🅜⅏Ⅲ. 🖃❋🐾 DAP SP 🛏

BARHAM

Suffolk
Map ref 3B2

Tamarisk House
Sandy Lane, Barham, Ipswich IP6 0PB
☎ (0473) 831825
5 miles from Ipswich and close to Bury St. Edmunds. Village house with beams and ingle nook. Gipping Valley walks and fishing. Local pub and easy car parking.
Bedrooms: 2 double, 1 triple
Bathrooms: 2 public

Bed & breakfast

per night:	£min	£max
Single		20.00
Double		30.00

Parking for 10

🛇💷🖵⅏🆀🅦⚵🅜Ⅲ. 🖃❋ 🐾 DAP

Individual proprietors have supplied all details of accommodation. Although we do check for accuracy, we advise you to confirm the information at the time of booking.

BECCLES

Suffolk
Map ref 3C1

Fire destroyed the town in the 16th C and it was rebuilt in Georgian red brick. The River Waveney, on which the town stands, is popular with boating enthusiasts and has an annual regatta. Home of Beccles and District Museum and the William Clowes Printing Museum.

Rose Cottage
Listed **COMMENDED**
21 Kells Way, Geldeston, Beccles NR34 0LU
☎ Kirby Cane (050 845) 451
Parts of the cottage date back to 1600, with inglenook fireplaces, beams and studwork. Quiet Waveney Valley position in south Norfolk.
Bedrooms: 2 single, 2 double
Bathrooms: 1 public

Bed & breakfast

per night:	£min	£max
Single	14.00	14.00
Double	25.00	25.00

Parking for 3

🛇🖭⚵⅏🅜⅏Ⅲ. 🖃❋✕🐾

Willow Tree Farm (formerly Corner Farmhouse)
Ringsfield Road, Ilketshall St Andrew, Beccles NR34 8NR
☎ (098 681) 380
53-acre dairy farm. Modernised farmhouse in a quiet village, with beams and inglenook fireplace. Small garden, home country cooking.
Bedrooms: 1 single, 1 double, 1 triple
Bathrooms: 2 private, 1 public

Bed & breakfast

per night:	£min	£max
Single	11.50	12.50
Double	23.00	25.00

Parking for 4

🛇🖭🅦⚵✂🅜⅏Ⅲ. 🖃❋🐾

BELAUGH

Norfolk
Map ref 3C1

Barn House
Belaugh, Norwich NR12 8XA
☎ (0603) 782130
In quiet hamlet between Wroxham and Coltishall. 18-hole golf course nearby.
Bedrooms: 2 double, 1 twin
Bathrooms: 2 public

Bed & breakfast

per night:	£min	£max
Single		17.00
Double		26.00

Parking for 3
Cards accepted: Visa

🛇🛋🖭🖵⅏🅦Ⅲ. 🖃Ⓤ⁌ ❋✕🐾

BEYTON

Suffolk
Map ref 3B2

The Grange Farmhouse
🏵🏵
Tostock Road, Beyton, Bury St Edmunds IP30 9AG
☎ (0359) 70184
Traditional 18th C Suffolk farmhouse in an attractive mature garden and meadow setting. 4 miles from Bury St Edmunds.
Bedrooms: 1 double, 2 twin
Bathrooms: 3 private

Bed & breakfast

per night:	£min	£max
Single	18.00	18.00
Double	36.00	36.00

Evening meal from 1830
Parking for 6

🛇🛋🖵⅏🅦⚵Ⓢ🅜⅏Ⅲ. 🖃❋✕🐾🛏

BLAKENEY

Norfolk
Map ref 3B1

Picturesque village on the north coast of Norfolk and a former port and fishing village, 15th C red bricked Guildhall. Marshy creeks extend towards Blakeney Point (National Trust) and are a paradise for naturalists, with trips to the reserve & to see the seals from Blakeney Quay.

Flintstones Guest House ⚿
Listed **COMMENDED**
Wiveton, Holt NR25 7TL
☎ Cley (0263) 740337
Attractive licensed guesthouse in picturesque rural surroundings near village green. 1 mile from Cley and Blakeney with good sailing and bird-watching. All rooms with private facilities. Non-smokers only please.
Bedrooms: 1 double, 1 twin, 3 triple
Bathrooms: 5 private
Continued ▶

BLAKENEY

Continued

Bed & breakfast

per night:	£min	£max
Single	22.50	22.50
Double	34.00	34.00

Half board

per person:	£min	£max
Daily	26.00	26.00
Weekly	168.00	168.00

Evening meal 1900 (last orders 1700)
Parking for 5

🐕🛋️🖵👜🛇Ⓢ⅄🅿📺▥,🅿✦ 🎇🕊️ SP

BLYTHBURGH

Suffolk
Map ref 3C2

Little Thorbyns

Listed COMMENDED

The Street, Blythburgh,
Halesworth IP19 9LS
☎ (050 270) 664
Charming country cottage in village of outstanding natural beauty. Good comfortable accommodation. Close to Minsmere/Southwold and all East Anglia's attractions.
Bedrooms: 1 single,
1 double, 1 twin
Bathrooms: 2 public

Bed & breakfast

per night:	£min	£max
Single	15.00	15.00
Double	30.00	30.00

Half board

per person:	£min	£max
Daily	21.50	21.50
Weekly	145.00	145.00

Parking for 4

🐕👜▥🛇Ⓢ🅿📺▥.🎇🕊️🎇

BRAINTREE

Essex
Map ref 3B2

The Heritage Centre in the Town Hall describes Braintree's former international importance in wool, silk and engineering. St Michael's parish church includes some Roman bricks and Braintree market was first chartered in 1199.
Tourist Information Centre Tel: (0376) 550066.

Spicers Farm

🎇🎇

Rotten End, Wethersfield,
Braintree CM7 4AL
☎ Great Dunmow (0371) 851021

70-acre mixed & arable farm. Farmhouse with large garden in area designated of special landscape value. Lovely views of quiet rural countryside yet convenient for Harwich, Stansted, Cambridge and Constable country. 6 miles north west of Braintree.
Bedrooms: 1 double, 2 twin
Bathrooms: 1 private,
1 public

Bed & breakfast

per night:	£min	£max
Single	15.00	18.00
Double	30.00	36.00

Parking for 10

🐕4🖵👜▥Ⓢ🅿📺▥.🎇 🎇🕊️🎇 SP

BRAMFIELD

Suffolk
Map ref 3C2

Broad Oak Farm

🎇🎇 COMMENDED

Bramfield, Halesworth
IP19 9AB
☎ (098 684) 232
400-acre dairy farm. Farmhouse in rural location, quarter of a mile from road and 1 mile west of A144 which passes through Bramfield. Located 7 miles from Southwold.
Bedrooms: 1 double, 2 twin
Bathrooms: 1 private,
2 public

Bed & breakfast

per night:	£min	£max
Single	13.00	15.00
Double	26.00	30.00

Half board

per person:	£min	£max
Daily	20.00	22.00
Weekly	130.00	136.00

Evening meal 1800 (last orders 2000)
Parking for 6

🐕🖵👜🖢▥👜Ⓢ🅿📺🅿 🔍🎇🕊️🎇

There are separate
sections in this
guide listing groups
specialising in farm
holidays and
accommodation
which is especially
suitable for young
people and
organised groups.

BRENTWOOD

Essex
Map ref 2D2

The town grew up in the late 12th C and then developed as a staging post, being strategically placed close to the London to Chelmsford road. Deer roam by the lakes in the 428 acre park at South Weald, part of Brentwood's attractive Green Belt.
Tourist Information Centre
☎ *(0277) 200300*

Chestnut Tree Cottage 🔺

Great Warley Street, Great Warley Village Green, Brentwood CM13 3JF
☎ (0277) 221727
Attractive country cottage conveniently situated and close to town centre and main line station. London 25 minutes. Leisure facilities and country parks nearby.
Bedrooms: 1 single,
1 double, 1 twin
Bathrooms: 1 private,
1 public

Bed & breakfast

per night:	£min	£max
Single		20.00
Double		35.00

Parking for 3

🐕8🛋️🖵👜🖢🎇▥👜🔒📺▥. 🎇🕊️🎇

BROME

Suffolk
Map ref 3B2

Dawnro Cottage

Eye Road, Brome, Eye
IP23 8AL
☎ Diss (0379) 870727
Pink-washed, timber-framed thatched cottage, Grade II listed, with many exposed beams. Non-smokers only. Pets welcome (free).
Bedrooms: 1 twin
Bathrooms: 1 public

Bed & breakfast

per night:	£min	£max
Single	15.00	15.50
Double	30.00	31.00

Parking for 6

🖵🛢🔧▥Ⓢ⅄🅿📺▥.🅿 🎇🕊️🎇

Check the
introduction to this
region for Where to
Go, What to See.

BRUNDALL

Norfolk
Map ref 3C1

Braydeston House 🔺

🎇🎇 COMMENDED

The Street, Brundall,
Norwich NR13 5JY
☎ Norwich (0603) 713123
A handsome Georgian country residence set in elegant wooded gardens with scenic views down to the River Yare.
Bedrooms: 1 twin
Bathrooms: 1 private

Bed & breakfast

per night:	£min	£max
Double	30.00	35.00

Parking for 1

🐕🖵👜🖢▥Ⓢ▥.🅿🎇 🕊️🎇

BULPHAN

Essex
Map ref 3B3

Bonny Downs Farm

Listed APPROVED

Doesgate Lane, Bulphan,
Upminster RM14 3TB
☎ Basildon (0268) 542129
60-acre mixed farm. Large comfortable farmhouse offering home-cooked food. Conveniently placed for all road links: M25, A13 and A127 to London and south-east England.
Bedrooms: 2 twin, 1 triple
Bathrooms: 1 private,
1 public

Bed & breakfast

per night:	£min	£max
Single	20.00	20.00
Double	30.00	30.00

Evening meal 1800 (last orders 2000)
Parking for 4

🐕🛋️🖵🔧🎇▥👜⅄🅿📺🅿 ▥.🅿🔍🎇🕊️🎇

BUNGAY

Suffolk
Map ref 3C1

Market town and yachting centre on the River Waveney with the remains of a great 12th C castle. In the market-place stands the Butter Cross, rebuilt in 1689 after being largely destroyed by fire. Nearby at Earsham is the Otter Trust.

Abbots Manor

Old Bungay Road, Kirby Cane, Bungay NR35 2HP
☎ (050 845) 703

Thatched Jacobean farmhouse in secluded rural setting, commanding excellent views across the Waveney Valley. Friendly family atmosphere.
Bedrooms: 2 triple
Bathrooms: 1 public
Bed & breakfast

per night:	£min	£max
Single		14.00
Double		28.00

Parking for 4
🐕🖫🕭🛢📶🖺🕾📺🖃❀🍴🏤

Dove Restaurant
♨♨

Wortwell, Harleston, Norfolk IP20 0EN
☎ (098 686) 315
A former railway hotel, now an established restaurant offering accommodation. On the Norfolk/Suffolk border. Good centre for the Waveney Valley.
Bedrooms: 2 double, 1 twin
Bathrooms: 2 private
Bed & breakfast

per night:	£min	£max
Single	15.00	17.50
Double		30.00

Half board

per person:	£min	£max
Daily		22.50
Weekly		135.00

Lunch available
Evening meal 1900 (last orders 2130)
Parking for 16
Cards accepted: Access, Visa
🐕🛢🕭🖫✂🖺📺🖃🛄🏤❀🍴

BURES

Suffolk
Map ref 3B2

Butlers Farm ♠
♨♨ COMMENDED

Colne Road, Bures CO8 5DN
☎ (0787) 227243
100-acre mixed farm. Warm welcome guaranteed at this restored 17th C farmhouse in quiet undulating countryside, 1 mile outside Bures. Adjoins public footpaths.
Bedrooms: 1 double, 2 twin
Bathrooms: 2 private,
1 public
Bed & breakfast

per night:	£min	£max
Single	17.50	25.00
Double	35.00	50.00

Evening meal 1930 (last orders 2100)
Parking for 6
🐕🖫🕭🖫🛢🕭✂🖺📺🖃🛢
🖃✏❀🍴🏤

BURGH ST PETER

Norfolk
Map ref 3C1

Church with unusually narrow thatched nave and 16th C tower overlooking Oulton Broad.

Shrublands Farm
♨♨ COMMENDED

Burgh St Peter, Beccles, Suffolk NR34 0BB
☎ Aldeby (050 277) 241
480-acre mixed farm. Family-run, offering a choice of home-cooked English breakfast. Beccles, Bungay, Lowestoft, Great Yarmouth and Norwich all within easy reach. Indoor pool and food at nearby River Centre.
Bedrooms: 2 double, 1 twin
Bathrooms: 1 private,
2 public
Bed & breakfast

per night:	£min	£max
Single	17.50	18.50
Double	30.00	35.00

Parking for 6
🐕🖫5🖾🕭🖪🛢🕭🖫📺🖢📶
🔍❀🍴🏤

BURNHAM OVERY STAITHE

Norfolk
Map ref 3B1

Domville Guest House

Glebe Lane, Burnham Overy Staithe, King's Lynn PE31 8JQ
☎ Fakenham (0328) 738298
Situated a few hundred yards from Overy Staithe quay, standing in own grounds in a quiet lane, close to the sea. Closed for Christmas.
Bedrooms: 3 single,
1 double, 1 twin
Bathrooms: 2 private,
2 public
Bed & breakfast

per night:	£min	£max
Single	17.00	19.00
Double	34.00	42.00

Half board

per person:	£min	£max
Daily	25.50	27.50
Weekly	160.00	192.00

Evening meal 1900 (last orders 2100)
Parking for 10
🐕🖫6🖾🕭🛢🕭✂🖺❀🍴🏤

We advise you to confirm your booking in writing.

BURY ST EDMUNDS

Suffolk
Map ref 3B2

Ancient market and cathedral town which takes its name from the martyred Saxon King, St Edmund. Bury St Edmunds has many fine buildings including the Athenaeum and Moyses Hall, reputed to be the oldest Norman house in the county.
Tourist Information Centre
☎ *(0284) 764667*

39/40 Well Street
Listed

Bury St Edmunds IP33 1EQ
☎ (0284) 768986
Spacious town centre family house. Car parking available and all amenities within easy walking distance. Warm welcome guaranteed.
Bedrooms: 2 single,
2 double, 1 twin
Bathrooms: 3 public
Bed & breakfast

per night:	£min	£max
Single	16.00	17.50
Double	31.00	33.00

🐕🖾🖫🖫🛢🛢🍴🏤

Elms Farm
♨♨ APPROVED

Depden, Bury St Edmunds IP29 4BS
☎ Chevington (0284) 850289
470-acre mixed farm. 17th C farmhouse in a quiet rural position at the highest point in Suffolk. 7 miles south-west of Bury St Edmunds.
Bedrooms: 1 double, 1 twin
Bathrooms: 1 public
Bed & breakfast

per night:	£min	£max
Single	16.00	18.00
Double	30.00	32.00

Parking for 10
🐕🖫🕭🛢🖺✂🖺🖃❀
🍴🏤SP

Lark House
Listed COMMENDED

22 Mustow Street, Bury St Edmunds IP33 1XL
☎ (0284) 702185
Pretty bedrooms in comfortable, town centre period house adjoining Abbey Gardens and close to cathedral. No smoking please.
Bedrooms: 1 single, 1 twin
Bathrooms: 1 public

Bed & breakfast

per night:	£min	£max
Single	16.00	16.00
Double	32.00	32.00

🍲🖫🕭🖫🖫🛢🖪✂🖺🖃🛢🍴
🏤🏤

The Leys
♨♨

113 Fornham Road, Bury St Edmunds IP32 6AT
☎ (0284) 760225
Lovely, spacious Victorian house in own grounds, close to the A45 and railway station. Pay-phone, home-made bread and preserves.
Bedrooms: 1 double, 1 twin,
1 triple
Bathrooms: 1 private,
1 public
Bed & breakfast

per night:	£min	£max
Single	20.00	25.00
Double	32.00	38.00

Parking for 6
🐕🖫🕭🖫🛢🕭🖫📺🖃🏤

Manorhouse
♨♨ HIGHLY COMMENDED

The Green, Beyton, Bury St Edmunds IP30 9AF
☎ (0359) 70960
Fax (0284) 752561
16th C former farmhouse with 20th C comforts, overlooking delightful village green with its resident geese. 4 miles east of Bury St Edmunds, off A45.
Bedrooms: 1 double, 1 twin
Bathrooms: 2 private
Bed & breakfast

per night:	£min	£max
Double	34.00	36.00

Parking for 5
🐕🖫8🖾🖫🕭🛢🖪🕭✂🖺
🖃🛢❀🍴🏤

South Hill House
Listed

43 Southgate Street, Bury St Edmunds IP33 2AZ
☎ (0284) 755650
Grade II* listed townhouse, reputed to be the school mentioned in Charles Dickens' Pickwick Papers. 10 minutes' walk from town centre, 2 minutes' drive from A45.
Bedrooms: 2 twin, 1 multiple
Bathrooms: 2 private
Bed & breakfast

per night:	£min	£max
Single	20.00	35.00
Double	30.00	45.00

Parking for 3
🐕🖫8🕭🖫🖫⊚❀🍴🏤🏤

BURY ST EDMUNDS

Continued

The Squirrels
9 Garden Close, Great
Barton, Bury St Edmunds
IP31 2SY
☎ (028 487) 684
*Modern 5-bedroom detached
house with large walled
garden. 3 miles from Bury St
Edmunds. Off main A143
Diss/Yarmouth road. Good
rural walks.*
Bedrooms: 2 double, 1 twin
Bathrooms: 1 private,
2 public
Bed & breakfast

per night:	£min	£max
Single	12.00	15.00
Double	24.00	30.00

Parking for 5
🛏🅰️🍳☐♦Ⓤ🅰️§⅄🅰️📺🏧
🚗🐾OAP

CAMBRIDGE

Cambridgeshire
Map ref 2D1

A most important and
beautiful city on the River
Cam with 31 colleges
forming one of the oldest
universities in the world.
Numerous museums,
good shopping centre,
restaurants, theatres,
cinema and fine
bookshops.
*Tourist Information Centre
☎ (0223) 322640*

31 Newton Road
Little Shelford, Cambridge
CB2 5HL
☎ (0223) 842276
*Countryside location 4 miles
south of Cambridge. Spacious,
well-appointed private suite in
owner's house with own
sitting room and kitchen.*
Bedrooms: 1 twin
Bathrooms: 1 private
Bed & breakfast

per night:	£min	£max
Single	28.00	30.00
Double	38.00	40.00

Parking for 2
🛏🅰️10🍳☐♦Ⓤ🅰️📺🏧
🚗🐾✕🚗

33 Westfield Road
Great Shelford, Cambridge
CB2 5JW
☎ (0223) 843583
*Private bungalow, situated on
the outskirts of Cambridge in
village of Great Shelford.
Convenient for M11, A604
and A1.*
Bedrooms: 2 twin
Bathrooms: 1 public
Bed & breakfast

per night:	£min	£max
Single		28.00
Double		35.00

Parking for 3
🛏🅰️🍳☐§🅰️📺🏧
🐾✕🚗

7 Brookfields Mill Road
Cambridge CB1 3NW
☎ (0223) 211259
*A warm and friendly welcome
awaits you. Clean,
comfortable accommodation.
Within walking distance of
city centre and railway
station.*
Bedrooms: 1 double
Bathrooms: 1 private
Bed & breakfast

per night:	£min	£max
Double	35.00	35.00

Parking for 1
🍳☐♦🍳Ⓤ🍳📺🏧🚗✿
✕🚗

Avondale
35 Highfields, Caldecote,
Cambridge CB3 7NX
☎ Madingley (0954) 210746
*Quiet country bungalow, 6
miles from Cambridge off the
A45. Interesting walks. Hire
car facility.*
Bedrooms: 1 twin, 1 triple
Bathrooms: 2 private
Bed & breakfast

per night:	£min	£max
Single	18.00	24.00
Double	28.00	34.00

Parking for 5
🛏🅰️☐♦Ⓤ§🏧🚗✿
🚗SP

Bon Accord House ▲▲
20 St. Margarets Square,
Cambridge CB1 4AP
☎ (0223) 246568 & 411188
*Quietly but conveniently
situated, south of the
fascinating historic centre of
Cambridge. Non-smokers only
please.*
Bedrooms: 5 single,
2 double, 1 twin, 1 triple
Bathrooms: 1 private,
2 public
Bed & breakfast

per night:	£min	£max
Single	19.50	30.00
Double	32.00	46.00

Parking for 13
Cards accepted: Access, Visa
🛏🅰️🍳☐♦Ⓤ🅰️§⅄🅰️🏧
🚗✕

Carlton Lodge
Listed
245 Chesterton Road,
Cambridge CB4 1AS
☎ (0223) 67792
*Small family-run business
within 1 mile of the city
centre.*
Bedrooms: 1 double, 1 twin,
1 triple
Bathrooms: 3 private,
1 public
Bed & breakfast

per night:	£min	£max
Double	34.00	39.00

Parking for 6
🛏🅰️🍳☐♦🍳Ⓤ🍳🅰️§🅰️🏧
🚗✕

Cristinas
👑👑
47 St. Andrews Road,
Cambridge CB4 1DL
☎ (0223) 65855 & 327700
*Small family-run business in
quiet location, a short walk
from city centre and colleges.*
Bedrooms: 3 double, 2 twin,
1 triple
Bathrooms: 5 private,
2 public
Bed & breakfast

per night:	£min	£max
Single	22.00	24.00
Double	34.00	40.00

Parking for 8
🛏🅰️🍳☐♦🍳Ⓤ🅰️🏧🚗✕

Foxhounds
71 Cambridge Road,
Wimpole, Royston,
Hertfordshire SG8 5QD
☎ (0223) 207344
*Formerly a pub, part 17th C.
Comfortable, homely
atmosphere, own bathroom,
sitting room. On main A603,
9 miles from Cambridge.*
Bedrooms: 1 single, 2 twin
Bathrooms: 2 public
Bed & breakfast

per night:	£min	£max
Single	16.00	16.00
Double	30.00	30.00

Parking for 3
🛏🅰️🍳♦Ⓤ§⅄📺🏧🚗✿
✕🚗

Hamden Guest House
Listed
89 High Street, Cherry
Hinton, Cambridge CB1 4LU
☎ (0223) 413263
*Purpose built guesthouse
annexe to a family home with
its own separate entrance
lobby and reception area. All
rooms en-suite with colour TV
and tea and coffee facilities.
On the outskirts of
Cambridge.*
Bedrooms: 4 double
Bathrooms: 4 private

Bed & breakfast

per night:	£min	£max
Single		20.00	25.00
Double		35.00	40.00

Parking for 6
🛏🅰️🍳☐♦Ⓤ§🏧🚗✕
🚗SP

King's Tithe
👑 HIGHLY COMMENDED
13a Comberton Road,
Barton, Cambridge CB3 7BA
☎ (0223) 263610
*Private house, 2 twin
bedrooms with adjacent
bathroom and toilet. Good bar
food available at pubs in local
villages; one pub is
approximately 300 yards from
house.*
Bedrooms: 2 twin
Bathrooms: 1 public
Bed & breakfast

per night:	£min	£max
Single	20.00	22.00
Double	30.00	35.00

Parking for 3
Open February-November
🛏8🍳☐♦Ⓤ🅰️§⅄🏧🚗
✿🚗

Leys Cottage ▲▲
Listed   APPROVED
56 Wimpole Road, Barton,
Cambridge CB3 7AB
☎ (0223) 262482
Fax (0223) 264166
*Part 17th C house with
modern extension in a quiet
and secluded spot but within
easy reach of Cambridge, M11
and A45. On A603
Cambridge-Sandy road.*
Bedrooms: 1 single,
1 double, 1 twin
Bathrooms: 2 private,
1 public
Bed & breakfast

per night:	£min	£max
Single	18.00	20.00
Double		28.00

Evening meal 1900 (last
orders 2030)
Parking for 4
🛏🅰️🍳☐♦Ⓤ🅰️§🅰️📺🏧
🚗✿✕🚗

Manor Farm
👑👑 COMMENDED
Landbeach, Cambridge
CB4 4ED
☎ (0223) 860165
*620-acre mixed farm. Grade II
listed, double-fronted,
Georgian farmhouse,
surrounded by enclosed
garden, in centre of village
next to church.*
Bedrooms: 2 double, 1 twin
Bathrooms: 1 private,
1 public

Bed & breakfast

per night:	£min	£max
Single	20.00	25.00
Double	30.00	35.00

Parking for 4
Open January-November

The Old Rectory

Green End, Landbeach,
Cambridge CB4 4ED
☎ (0223) 861507
Fax (0223) 441276
Spacious, historic former rectory, 4 miles north of Cambridge. Period furnishings throughout. Mural on staircase. Grounds with paddock, rare breed animals. Aga home cooking.
Bedrooms: 1 double, 1 twin, 1 multiple
Bathrooms: 3 private, 1 public

Bed & breakfast

per night:	£min	£max
Single	20.00	20.00
Double	32.00	34.00

Parking for 11

The Old Rectory

Listed COMMENDED

High Street, Swaffham Bulbeck, Cambridge CB5 0LX
☎ (0223) 811986 & 812009
Georgian former vicarage set in own grounds. Located 6 miles from Cambridge and 4 miles from Newmarket.
Bedrooms: 1 double, 1 twin, 1 triple
Bathrooms: 1 private, 1 public

Bed & breakfast

per night:	£min	£max
Single	16.00	26.00
Double	32.00	42.00

Parking for 10

Segovia Lodge

2 Barton Road, Newnham, Cambridge CB3 9JZ
☎ (0223) 354105 & 323011
Within walking distance of the city centre and colleges. Next to cricket and tennis fields. Warm welcome, personal service and both rooms with private facilities. Non-smokers only please.
Bedrooms: 1 double, 1 twin
Bathrooms: 2 private, 1 public

Bed & breakfast

per night:	£min	£max
Double	37.00	40.00

Parking for 4

The Willows

102 High Street, Landbeach, Cambridge CB4 4DT
☎ (0223) 860332
100-acre arable farm. Georgian house with friendly welcome. 2 rooms for up to 6 persons. 3 miles north of Cambridge.
Bedrooms: 1 twin, 1 triple
Bathrooms: 1 public

Bed & breakfast

per night:	£min	£max
Single	15.00	16.00
Double	28.00	30.00

Parking for 4

CARBROOKE
Norfolk
Map ref 3B1

White Hall

HIGHLY COMMENDED

Carbrooke, Thetford IP25 6SG
☎ Watton (0953) 885950
Fax (0953) 885950
Elegant Georgian house in delightful grounds and surrounded by fields. Attractive, spacious accommodation. Good local eating places. Ideal base for touring.
Bedrooms: 2 double, 1 twin
Bathrooms: 1 private, 1 public

Bed & breakfast

per night:	£min	£max
Single	24.00	30.00
Double	32.00	40.00

Parking for 10

CASTLE HEDINGHAM
Essex
Map ref 3B2

Little Chelmshoe House

HIGHLY COMMENDED

Gestingthorpe Road, Great Maplestead CO9 3AB
☎ (0787) 62385 & 60532
Fax (0787) 62312
Secluded 17th C farmhouse, offering quality accommodation surrounded by lovely countryside. Croquet lawn, swimming pool,

whirlpool bath. Free transport to local restaurants.
Bedrooms: 1 double
Bathrooms: 1 private

Bed & breakfast

per night:	£min	£max
Single	35.00	35.00
Double	55.00	55.00

Parking for 9
Cards accepted: Visa, Amex

CAWSTON
Norfolk
Map ref 3B1

Village with one of the finest churches in the country. St Agnes, built in the Perpendicular style, was much patronised by Michael de la Pole, Earl of Suffolk (1414), and has a magnificent hammer-beam roof and numerous carved angels.

Grey Gables Country House Hotel & Restaurant

Norwich Road, Cawston, Norwich NR10 4EY
☎ (0603) 871259
Former rectory in pleasant, rural setting, 10 miles from Norwich, coast and Broads. Wine cellar, emphasis on food. Comfortably furnished with many antiques.
Bedrooms: 2 single, 4 double, 1 twin, 1 triple
Bathrooms: 6 private, 1 public

Bed & breakfast

per night:	£min	£max
Single	18.00	44.00
Double	36.00	56.00

Half board

per person:	£min	£max
Daily	32.00	59.50
Weekly	212.00	224.00

Evening meal 1900 (last orders 2100)
Parking for 15
Cards accepted: Access, Visa

National Crown ratings were correct at the time of going to press but are subject to change. Please check at the time of booking.

CAXTON
Cambridgeshire
Map ref 2D1

The Old Bricklayers Arms

COMMENDED

24 Ermine Street, Caxton, Cambridge CB3 8PQ
☎ (0954) 719228
Listed Grade II village character cottage on A1198, 10 miles west of Cambridge. Traditional and comfortable. Home cooking.
Bedrooms: 2 double
Bathrooms: 1 private, 1 public

Bed & breakfast

per night:	£min	£max
Single	25.00	30.00
Double	35.00	45.00

Half board

per person:	£min	£max
Daily	34.00	39.00
Weekly	190.40	218.40

Evening meal 1930 (last orders 2030)
Parking for 8
Cards accepted: Access, Visa

CHATTERIS
Cambridgeshire
Map ref 3A2

Cross Keys Inn Hotel

APPROVED

16 Market Hill, Chatteris PE16 6BA
☎ (0354) 693036 & 692644
Elizabethan coaching inn built around 1540, Grade II listed. A la carte menu and bar meals available. Friendly atmosphere, oak-beamed lounge with open log fires.
Bedrooms: 1 double, 5 twin, 1 triple
Bathrooms: 5 private, 1 public

Bed & breakfast

per night:	£min	£max
Single	21.00	32.50
Double	32.50	45.00

Lunch available
Evening meal 1900 (last orders 2200)
Parking for 10
Cards accepted: Access, Visa, Diners, Amex

CHEDGRAVE

Norfolk
Map ref 3C1

On the banks of the River
Chet, with its sister village
of Loddon on the
opposite bank. The
church of All Saints has a
richly decorated Norman
doorway.

Hawthorn House
Norwich Road, Chedgrave,
Norwich NR14 6HB
☎ Loddon (0508) 20249
*A large family house, in a
pretty village 150 yards from
the River Chet.*
Bedrooms: 3 double
Bathrooms: 1 public
Bed & breakfast

per night:	£min	£max
Single	18.00	18.00
Double	30.00	30.00

Parking for 3
🛏️🗣️♿️Ⓤ🖾⏣ 🖚

CHEDISTON

Suffolk
Map ref 3C2

Saskiavill 🏠
♨♨♨
Chediston, Halesworth
IP19 OAR
☎ (0986) 873067
*Travelling west from
Halesworth on the B1123,
turn right after 2 miles at the
signpost for Chediston Green.
After crossing the hump-
backed bridge over the
stream, Saskiavill is the
fourth property on the left.*
Bedrooms: 2 double, 2 twin,
1 triple
Bathrooms: 3 private,
2 public
Bed & breakfast

per night:	£min	£max
Single	13.50	15.50
Double	27.00	31.00

Half board

per person:	£min	£max
Daily	16.50	18.50
Weekly	102.00	118.00

Evening meal from 1830
Parking for 8
Open January-October
🛏️3🗣️♿️🖳♿️🖛🕹️Ⓤ🖾📺
🖬 🛢️❋✕🖚 📠 🆂🅿️

> The enquiry
> coupons at the
> back will help you
> when contacting
> proprietors.

CHELMSFORD

Essex
Map ref 3B3

The county town of
Essex, originally a Roman
settlement,
Caesaromagus, thought to
have been destroyed by
Boudicca. Growth of the
town's industry can be
traced in the excellent
museum in Oaklands
Park. 15th C parish
church has been
Chelmsford Cathedral
since 1914.
*Tourist Information Centre
☎ (0245) 283400.*

25 West Avenue
Listed
Maylandsea, Chelmsford
CM3 6AE
☎ Maldon (0621) 740972
Fax (0621) 740945
*Detached four-bedroomed
private residence. From
Maldon on B1018 or from
South Woodham Ferrers on
B1012 to Latchingdon, then
on to Steeple Road to
Maylandsea (about 2 miles).*
Bedrooms: 1 double, 1 twin
Bathrooms: 1 public
Bed & breakfast

per night:	£min	£max
Single	13.00	15.00
Double	26.00	30.00

Parking for 5
🛏️3🗣️♿️🖳♿️✕🖾 🛢️✕🖚

Neptune Cafe Motel
Burnham Road,
Latchingdon, Chelmsford
CM3 6EX
☎ Maldon (0621) 740770
*Transport-type cafe with
single rooms and adjoining
chalet block. 5 miles from
Maldon and Burnham-on-
Crouch.*
Bedrooms: 4 single, 6 double
Bathrooms: 5 private,
1 public
Bed & breakfast

per night:	£min	£max
Single	13.00	13.00
Double	25.00	30.00

Lunch available
Parking for 40
🛏️🗣️🖵🗣️♿️🖳♿️✕🖾✕🖚

Springford
Listed **APPROVED**
8 Well Lane, Galleywood,
Chelmsford CM2 8QY
☎ (0245) 257821
*Family home at Galleywood,
south of Chelmsford. Take
B1007 out of the town or
Galleywood turn-off from A12.*

*Well Lane is near White Boar
pub.*
Bedrooms: 1 single, 2 twin
Bathrooms: 1 public
Bed & breakfast

per night:	£min	£max
Single	13.00	14.00
Double	26.00	30.00

Evening meal 1700 (last
orders 2030)
Parking for 3
🛏️🗣️🖳🛢️Ⓢ✕♿️📺🖾 🛢️Ⓤ
❋🖚

CHOSELEY

Norfolk
Map ref 3B1

Choseley Farmhouse
Choseley, Docking, King's
Lynn PE31 8PQ
☎ Thornham (048 526) 331
*17th C Norfolk farmhouse
with Tudor chimneys.
Foundations are thought to
date back to original abbey of
1250.*
Bedrooms: 1 double, 2 twin
Bathrooms: 1 public
Bed & breakfast

per night:	£min	£max
Double		30.00

Parking for 10
Open July-September
Ⓤ♿️✕🖚🏠

CODDENHAM

Suffolk
Map ref 3B2

Spinney's End
Listed
Spring Lane, Coddenham,
Ipswich IP6 9TW
☎ 0449 (794 51)
*100-acre mixed farm. Large
spacious bungalow set in
attractive landscaped gardens
with farmland views, in a
peaceful location. Full English
breakfast is served and
evening meals are available at
public houses and inns within
1-2 mile radius.*
Bedrooms: 1 double, 1 twin
Bathrooms: 1 public
Bed & breakfast

per night:	£min	£max
Single	15.00	15.00
Double	27.00	27.00

Parking for 12
🖾♿️Ⓤ📺🖾❋✕🖚

> The colour maps
> at the back of this
> guide pinpoint all
> places with
> accommodation.

COLCHESTER

Essex
Map ref 3B2

Britain's oldest recorded
town standing on the
River Colne and famous
for its oysters. Numerous
historic buildings, ancient
remains and museums.
Plenty of parks and
gardens, extensive
shopping centre, theatre
and zoo.
*Tourist Information Centre
☎ (0206) 712920*

2 The Chase
Listed **HIGHLY COMMENDED**
Straight Road, Lexden,
Colchester CO3 5BU
☎ (0206) 540587
*60-year-old house of real
character. Quiet yet
convenient for town and
other facilities. In large
beautiful secluded gardens.*
Bedrooms: 3 twin
Bathrooms: 2 private,
1 public
Bed & breakfast

per night:	£min	£max
Single	20.00	22.00
Double	32.00	35.00

Parking for 6
🛏️5🗣️♿️🖳✕♿️📺🖾 🛢️❋
✕🖚

The Maltings
Listed
Mersea Road, Abberton,
Colchester CO5 7NR
☎ Peldon (0206) 735780
*Attractive period house with a
wealth of beams and an open
log fire, in walled garden with
swimming pool.*
Bedrooms: 1 single, 1 twin,
1 triple
Bathrooms: 1 private,
2 public
Bed & breakfast

per night:	£min	£max
Single	15.00	18.00
Double	30.00	36.00

Parking for 8
🛏️♿️🖳Ⓢ🖾📺🖾 🛢️↘❋
✕🖚🏠

The Old Manse
Listed
15 Roman Road, Colchester
CO1 1UR
☎ (0206) 45154
*Victorian family house in a
quiet square beside the castle
park. 3 minutes' walk from
town centre. Roman wall in
the garden. Non-smokers only
please.*
Bedrooms: 1 double, 2 twin

Bathrooms: 1 private, 3 public

Bed & breakfast

per night:	£min	£max
Single	20.00	25.00
Double	32.00	36.00

Parking for 1

🐎 ♿ 📖 ☐ ☕ [UL] 🍷 [S] 🚭 ♨ 🧺 🚐

Scheregate Hotel 🏅

[Listed] APPROVED

36 Osborne Street, Colchester CO2 7DB

☎ (0206) 573034

Interesting 15th C building, centrally situated, providing accommodation at moderate prices.

Bedrooms: 12 single, 9 twin, 1 triple, 1 multiple

Bathrooms: 1 private, 5 public

Bed & breakfast

per night:	£min	£max
Single	17.50	18.50
Double	34.00	50.00

Parking for 30

🐎 📖 ☕ 🍷 [S] 🍴 [TV] ♨ 🧺 ✈ [OAP] [T]

COLTISHALL

Norfolk
Map ref 3C1

On the River Bure, with an RAF station nearby. The village is attractive with many pleasant 18th C brick houses and a thatched church.

Honeysuckle Cottage

[Listed]

4 Ling Common, Coltishall, Norwich NR12 7AL

☎ (0603) 737075

Semi-detached cottage in a quiet rural setting, overlooking common and backed by farmland.

Bedrooms: 1 single, 1 double, 1 twin

Bathrooms: 1 public

Bed & breakfast

per night:	£min	£max
Single	11.00	12.00
Double	22.00	

Parking for 3

🐎 ☕ [UL] 🍴 [TV] ♨ 🚐

Risings

[Listed]

Church Street, Coltishall, Norwich NR12 7DW

☎ (0603) 737549

Delightful 17th C Dutch gabled country home, 200 yards from Coltishall Staithe, central for all Broadland touring.

Bedrooms: 1 double, 2 twin

Bathrooms: 1 public

Bed & breakfast

per night:	£min	£max
Single	16.00	18.00
Double	30.00	34.00

Parking for 3

Cards accepted: Access, Visa

🐎 ♿ 📖 ☐ ☕ [UL] [S] 🚭 ♨ 🧺 ✿ 🚐 🚫 [SP] 🏛 [T]

COMBERTON

Cambridgeshire
Map ref 2D1

Moat House

👑👑 HIGHLY COMMENDED

65 Green End, Comberton, Cambridge CB3 7DY

☎ (0223) 263978

120-acre arable farm. Attractive farmhouse set in peaceful countryside. Overlooking beautiful rose gardens and moat. Spacious bedrooms. Imperial War Museum, Duxford, and Wimpole Hall close by. No smoking please.

Bedrooms: 1 double, 1 twin

Bathrooms: 1 private, 2 public

Bed & breakfast

per night:	£min	£max
Double	32.00	38.00

Parking for 6

🐎 8 📖 ☐ ☕ [UL] [S] ♨ 🧺 ✿ ✈ 🚐

CROMER

Norfolk
Map ref 3C1

Once a small fishing village and now famous for its fishing boats that still work off the beach and offer freshly caught crabs. A delightful resort with excellent bathing on sandy beaches fringed by cliffs. The town boasts a fine pier, theatre, museum and a lifeboat station.

The Grove Guest House 🏅

👑👑 COMMENDED

95 Overstrand Road, Cromer NR27 0DJ

☎ (0263) 512412

Georgian holiday home in 3 acres, with beautiful walks through fields and woods to the cliffs and beach.

Bedrooms: 2 single, 3 double, 3 twin, 2 multiple

Bathrooms: 6 private, 3 public

Bed & breakfast

per night:	£min	£max
Single	16.50	
Double	33.50	41.00

Half board

per person:	£min	£max
Daily	24.00	27.50
Weekly	149.00	174.00

Evening meal 1830 (last orders 1830)

Parking for 15

Open March-September

🐎 ♿ [UL] 🍷 [S] 🍴 [TV] ♨ 🧺 🔍 ⚑ ✿ ✈ 🚐 [SP] 🏛

DANBURY

Essex
Map ref 3B3

Southways

[Listed]

Copt Hill, Danbury, Chelmsford CM3 4NN

☎ (0245) 223428

Pleasant country house with large garden adjoining an area of National Trust common land.

Bedrooms: 2 twin

Bathrooms: 1 public

Bed & breakfast

per night:	£min	£max
Single	14.00	16.00
Double	26.00	28.00

Parking for 2

🐎 ☕ [UL] ♨ ✿ 🚐

DARSHAM

Suffolk
Map ref 3C2

Priory Farm 🏅

[Listed]

Darsham, Saxmundham IP17 3QD

☎ Yoxford (072 877) 459

135-acre mixed farm. Comfortable 17th C farmhouse, ideally situated for exploring Suffolk and heritage coast. Cycle hire available from own hire fleet.

Bedrooms: 1 single, 1 double, 1 twin

Bathrooms: 1 public

Bed & breakfast

per night:	£min	£max
Single	15.00	20.00
Double	28.00	38.00

Parking for 10

Open March-October

🐎 ☕ [UL] 🚭 [TV] ♨ 🧺 ⛳ ✿ ✈ 🚐

Please check prices and other details at the time of booking.

DEDHAM

Essex
Map ref 3B2

A former wool town. Dedham Vale is an area of outstanding natural beauty and there is a countryside centre in the village. This is John Constable country and Sir Alfred Munnings lived at Castle House which is open to the public.

Little House

[Listed]

High Street, Dedham, Colchester CO7 6HJ

☎ Colchester (0206) 322865

Elegant Grade II listed house situated at quiet west end of high street. Walled garden. Local restaurants. In Constable Country.

Bedrooms: 1 double, 2 twin

Bathrooms: 1 public

Bed & breakfast

per night:	£min	£max
Single	16.00	20.00
Double	32.00	36.00

🐎 ♿ 📖 ☐ ☕ [UL] 🍷 [S] 🚭 🍴 [TV] 🧺 ✿ ✈ 🚐 [OAP] 🚫 [SP] 🏛

May's Barn Farm 🏅

👑👑 HIGHLY COMMENDED

May's Lane, Off Long Rd. West, Dedham, Colchester CO7 6EW

☎ (0206) 323191

300-acre arable farm. Tranquil old farmhouse with outstanding views over the Dedham Vale in Constable country. Quarter mile down unmade lane off Long Road West from B1029 between Dedham and Ardleigh.

Bedrooms: 1 double, 1 twin

Bathrooms: 2 private

Bed & breakfast

per night:	£min	£max
Single		20.00
Double	32.00	35.00

Parking for 6

🐎 ☐ ☕ 🔧 [UL] [S] 🚭 🍴 [TV] ♨ 🧺 ✿ ✈ 🚐

National Crown ratings were correct at the time of going to press but are subject to change. Please check at the time of booking.

DEREHAM

Norfolk
Map ref 3B1

East Dereham is famous for its associations with the poet William Cowper and also Bishop Bonner, chaplain to Cardinal Wolsey. His home is now a museum. Around the charming market-place are many notable buildings.

Chapel Farm
Dereham Road, Whinburgh, Dereham NR19 1AA
☎ (0362) 698433
Farmhouse with heated swimming pool, full-sized snooker table. Dinner can be taken at pub next door. Norwich and coast 30 minutes.
Bedrooms: 4 double, 1 twin
Bathrooms: 2 private,
1 public, 1 private shower

Bed & breakfast

per night:	£min	£max
Single	15.00	15.00
Double	30.00	30.00

Half board

per person:	£min	£max
Daily	15.00	

Parking for 10

Clinton House
Well Hill, Clint Green, Yaxham, Dereham NR19 1RX
☎ (0362) 692079
Attractive 18th C country house in a peaceful setting. Full of character with modern comforts. Breakfast served in beautiful conservatory.
Bedrooms: 2 double, 1 twin
Bathrooms: 2 public

Bed & breakfast

per night:	£min	£max
Single	17.00	19.00
Double	27.00	30.00

Parking for 8

Peacock House
Listed
Peacock Lane, Old Bettley, Dereham NR20 4DG
☎ (0362) 860371
Beautiful period farmhouse in tranquil, rural setting, 3.5 miles north of Dereham on B1110. Traditionally furnished and decorated. Exposed beams and open fires. Non-smoking establishment.

Bedrooms: 1 single, 2 double
Bathrooms: 1 public

Bed & breakfast

per night:	£min	£max
Single	15.00	
Double	30.00	

Parking for 4

DISS

Norfolk
Map ref 3B2

An old market town built around 3 sides of the Mere, a placid water of 6 acres and beside the village green. Although modernised, some interesting Tudor, Georgian and Victorian buildings around the market-place remain. St Mary's Church has a fine knapped flint chancel.

Abbey Farm
Great Green, Thrandeston, Diss IP21 4BN
☎ Mellis (037 973) 422
Restored Elizabethan farmhouse set in 3 acres of peaceful wooded grounds where Shetland ponies roam. Open all year.
Bedrooms: 1 single, 1 double
Bathrooms: 1 private,
1 public

Bed & breakfast

per night:	£min	£max
Single	18.00	20.00
Double	35.00	40.00

Parking for 6

DOWNHAM MARKET

Norfolk
Map ref 3B1

Market town above the surrounding Fens on the River Ouse. Oxburgh Hall (National Trust) is 8 miles east, a magnificent 15th C moated dwelling owned by one family, the Bedingfields, for almost 500 years.

The Dial House
APPROVED
Railway Road, Downham Market PE38 9EB
☎ (0366) 388358
Fax (0366) 382198
Family-run, comfortable Georgian house. Good home cooking. Ideal centre for touring quiet East Anglian countryside, historic houses, bird and wildlife sanctuaries.
Bedrooms: 1 double, 2 twin
Bathrooms: 2 private,
1 public

Bed & breakfast

per night:	£min	£max
Single	17.00	21.00
Double	27.50	32.50

Half board

per person:	£min	£max
Daily	25.50	29.50
Weekly	166.50	191.50

Evening meal 1800 (last orders 2130)
Parking for 5

DULLINGHAM

Cambridgeshire
Map ref 3B2

Coachman's Cottage
Station Road, Dullingham, Newmarket, Suffolk CB8 9UP
☎ Newmarket (0638) 508125
18th C property standing in 103 acres, now being used for stud purposes. 3 miles south of Newmarket, just off B1061.
Bedrooms: 1 single, 2 twin
Bathrooms: 1 private,
1 public

Bed & breakfast

per night:	£min	£max
Single	21.00	
Double	42.00	

Parking for 6

EARLS COLNE

Essex
Map ref 3B2

Riverside Inn Motel
42 Lower Holt Street, Earls Colne, Colchester CO6 2PH
☎ (0787) 223487 & 222281
Fax (0787) 222034
Converted farm buildings in village on the banks of the River Colne. On A604 at Earls Colne by the bridge. All en-suite.
Bedrooms: 2 double, 7 twin, 2 multiple
Bathrooms: 11 private

Bed & breakfast

per night:	£min	£max
Single	24.00	26.00
Double	39.00	43.00

Half board

per person:	£min	£max
Daily	29.00	

Lunch available
Evening meal 1930 (last orders 2200)
Parking for 40
Cards accepted: Access, Visa

EAST BERGHOLT

Suffolk
Map ref 3B2

John Constable, the famous East Anglian artist, was born here in 1776 and at the church of St Mary are reminders of his family's associations with the area. 1 mile south of the village are Flatford Mill and Willy Lott's cottage, both made famous by Constable in his paintings.

Wren Cottage
The Street, East Bergholt, Colchester CO7 6SE
☎ Colchester (0206) 298327
Beamed character cottage in the heart of Constable country. In the middle of the village, an easy walk from Flatford. 30 minutes' drive from Harwich. Off-street parking.
Bedrooms: 1 double,
1 multiple
Bathrooms: 2 private

Bed & breakfast

per night:	£min	£max
Double	34.00	40.00

Parking for 2
Open April-September

EAST HARLING

Norfolk
Map ref 3B2

Roudham House
COMMENDED
Roudham, East Harling, Norwich NR16 2RJ
☎ (0953) 718135
Fax (0953) 717949
From Thetford follow signs to Kilverstone, to Bridgham, left to Roudham. Before church ruins, straight over on to private road. Signposted Roudham House. From Norwich turn off A11 on to B1111 to East Harling, right to Roudham, turn right past church ruins at Roudham. House surrounded by fields and woods.
Bedrooms: 2 double, 1 twin
Bathrooms: 2 private,
1 public

Bed & breakfast

per night:	£min	£max
Single	30.00	
Double	48.00	

Parking for 4

⌨🖵♨🖊🆄🆂🗲🕭📺💻
🎣🔾♨⛵♨⚙✳✕🐾

EAST MERSEA

Essex
Map ref 3B3

Bromans Farm

Listed   HIGHLY COMMENDED

Mersea Island, East Mersea,
Colchester CO5 8UE
☎ West Mersea (0206)
383235
*Arable & horse farm. 14th C
carefully restored farmhouse.
Peaceful atmosphere with oak
beams, log fires, secluded
gardens. Adjacent country
park, nature reserve and
beach. Evening meal by
arrangement.*
Bedrooms: 3 twin
Bathrooms: 2 public

Bed & breakfast

per night:	£min	£max
Single	17.00	19.00
Double	28.00	34.00

🎣♨🆄🖊🆂🕭📺💻🖫🗪
✳♨🐾🏢

ELMSWELL

Suffolk
Map ref 3B2

Kiln Farm Guest House

🖳🖳   COMMENDED

Kiln Lane, Elmswell, Bury St
Edmunds IP30 9QR
☎ (0359) 40442
*Victorian farmhouse and
converted barns set in 3
acres. In quiet lane half a
mile from A1088 roundabout
off A45. Self-catering
accommodation available.*
Bedrooms: 1 single,
1 double, 1 twin, 1 multiple
Bathrooms: 4 private

Bed & breakfast

per night:	£min	£max
Single	16.00	20.00

Half board

per person:	£min	£max
Daily	20.00	25.00

Evening meal 1830 (last
orders 1900)
Parking for 7
Cards accepted:
🎣♨🖵♨🆄🖊🆂🗲🕭💻
🖳🔾🖫✳♨🖫

ELTISLEY

Cambridgeshire
Map ref 2D1

Small village with an
exceptionally large village
green.

The Leeds Arms

🖳🖳🖳   COMMENDED

The Green, Eltisley, St Neots,
Huntingdon PE19 4TG
☎ Croxton (048 087) 283
Fax (048 087) 379
*17th C inn in small country
village dominated by village
green. Pleasant walks and
cricket in summer.*
Bedrooms: 6 single, 3 twin
Bathrooms: 9 private

Bed & breakfast

per night:	£min	£max
Single	27.50	35.00
Double	35.00	42.50

Lunch available
Evening meal 1900 (last
orders 2145)
Parking for 28
Cards accepted: Access, Visa,
Amex
🖧📞⌨🖵♨🛋💻🖫✳✕
🖫 SP

ELY

Cambridgeshire
Map ref 3A2

Until the 17th C when the
Fens were drained, Ely
was an island. The
cathedral, completed in
1189, dominates the
surrounding area. One
particular feature is the
central octagonal tower
with a fan-vaulted timber
roof and wooden lantern.
*Tourist Information Centre
☎ (0353) 662062*

The Black Hostelry

Listed   COMMENDED

The Cathedral Close, The
College, Firmary Lane, Ely
CB7 4DL
☎ (0353) 662612
*One of the finest collections
of medieval domestic
buildings still in use in
England. Situated on the
south side of Ely Cathedral.*
Bedrooms: 1 single,
1 double, 1 twin, 1 triple
Bathrooms: 2 private,
2 public

Bed & breakfast

per night:	£min	£max
Double	45.00	45.00

Parking for 6
🎣⌨🖵♨🆄🆂🗲🕭📺💻
🖫🖫🏢

Forge Cottage

🖳🖳   HIGHLY COMMENDED

Lower Road, Stuntney, Ely
CB7 5TN
☎ (0353) 663275 & (Mobile)
(0831) 833932
*Listed farmhouse with beams
and open fires on a shire
horse farm. Located in centre
of quiet village, 1 mile south
of Ely, in an elevated position
overlooking the Fens to Ely
Cathedral.*
Bedrooms: 1 double, 1 twin
Bathrooms: 2 private

Bed & breakfast

per night:	£min	£max
Single	22.50	30.00
Double	45.00	45.00

Parking for 4
🎣🖵♨🆄🗲🕭💻🖫🛋🗪
✳🖫 T

Highway Chalets

Listed   APPROVED

Tower Road, Ely CB7 4HR
☎ (0353) 663609
*Comfortable warm rooms,
well-equipped and clean. Full
breakfast.*
Bedrooms: 3 single,
2 double, 1 twin
Bathrooms: 3 private,
1 public

Bed & breakfast

per night:	£min	£max
Single	18.00	
Double	31.00	

Parking for 10
🎣🖧🖵♨🆄🆂🕭🖫✳✕🖫

Hill House Farm

🖳🖳🖳

9 Main Street, Coveney, Ely
CB6 2DJ
☎ (0353) 778369
*230-acre arable farm. High
quality en-suite
accommodation and food, in
fine Victorian farmhouse
situated in unspoilt Fenland
village 3 miles west of Ely,
with open views of the
surrounding countryside, and
easy access to Cambridge. No
smoking and no pets, please.*
Bedrooms: 1 double, 1 twin,
1 triple
Bathrooms: 2 private

Bed & breakfast

per night:	£min	£max
Double	32.00	38.00

Half board

per person:	£min	£max
Daily	29.50	32.50

Evening meal 1830 (last
orders 1300)
Parking for 4
🎣⌨🖵♨🆄🗲💻🛋✳
✕🖫

Spinney Abbey

🖳

Stretham Road, Wicken, Ely
CB7 5XQ
☎ (0353) 720971
*200-acre mixed farm.
Spacious Georgian farmhouse
set in 1 acre of garden
adjoining Wicken Fen Nature
Reserve.*
Bedrooms: 1 double, 1 twin,
1 triple
Bathrooms: 1 private,
1 public

Bed & breakfast

per night:	£min	£max
Double	32.00	34.00

Parking for 4
🖫2🖵♨🆄📺💻🛋✳✕
🖫🏢

Springfields

Listed   HIGHLY COMMENDED

Ely Road, Little Thetford,
Ely CB6 3HJ
☎ (0353) 663637
Fax (0353) 663130
*Lovely home, set in 1 acre of
beautiful, tranquil gardens.
Quiet area, yet only 2 miles
from cathedral and city
centre. Non-smokers only
please.*
Bedrooms: 1 double, 2 twin
Bathrooms: 1 private,
1 public

Bed & breakfast

per night:	£min	£max
Single	25.00	30.00
Double	40.00	45.00

Parking for 10
Cards accepted:
🖧⌨🖵♨🆄🆂🛋💻🖫✳
✕🖫

EPPING

Essex
Map ref 2D1

Epping retains its identity
as a small market town
despite its nearness to
London. Epping Forest
covers 2000 acres and at
Chingford Queen
Elizabeth I's Hunting
Lodge houses a display
on the forest's history and
wildlife.

The Conifers

🖳

Theydon Hall Cottages,
Abridge Road, Theydon Bois,
Epping CM16 7NP
☎ Theydon Bois (0992)
813716
*Georgian-style house 7
minutes from the M25. In
beautiful, rural countryside,
only 30 minutes away from
the City. Tea/coffee facilities*

EPPING

Continued

in rooms, with TV and en-suite facilities.
Bedrooms: 2 single,
1 double, 1 twin
Bathrooms: 2 private,
1 public
Bed & breakfast

per night:	£min	£max
Single	18.00	20.00
Double	35.00	40.00

Parking for 6
Open May-October

Parsonage Guest House

Abridge Road, Theydon Bois,
Epping CM16 7NN
☎ (0992) 814242
15th C farmhouse with old English gardens and livery yard. Exit 26 of M25 about 2 miles. 30 minutes from London by underground.
Bedrooms: 1 single,
1 double, 3 twin, 1 triple
Bathrooms: 2 private,
2 public
Bed & breakfast

per night:	£min	£max
Single	30.00	35.00
Double	40.00	45.00

Parking for 10

Uplands ♠

Listed   APPROVED

181a Lindsey Street, Epping
CM16 6RF
☎ (0992) 573733
Private house with rural views. Close to M25, M11 for Stansted Airport and Central Line underground for London. Pay phone available.
Bedrooms: 2 single, 2 triple
Bathrooms: 2 public
Bed & breakfast

per night:	£min	£max
Single	16.00	
Double	32.00	

Parking for 6

ERPINGHAM

Norfolk
Map ref 3B1

Saracens Head Inn ♠♠

Wolterton, Erpingham,
Norwich NR11 7LX
☎ Cromer (0263) 768909
Tuscan coaching inn, built in 1806 by Horace Walpole. Courtyard and walled garden.

At Wolterton off Norwich/ Cromer road.
Bedrooms: 1 double, 1 twin
Bathrooms: 2 private
Bed & breakfast

per night:	£min	£max
Single	25.00	
Double	45.00	

Lunch available
Evening meal 1830 (last orders 2200)
Parking for 30
Cards accepted: Access, Visa, Amex

EYKE

Suffolk
Map ref 3C2

The Old House ♠♠

Eyke, Woodbridge
IP12 2QW
☎ (0394) 460213
Lovely Grade II listed house, 1620. Comfortable and friendly, with beams, open fires, large, interesting garden and views over Deben Valley. Centre of village and edge of heritage coast. Good choice of food.
Bedrooms: 1 single,
2 double, 2 twin, 2 triple
Bathrooms: 6 private,
2 public
Bed & breakfast

per night:	£min	£max
Single	15.00	20.00
Double	26.00	34.00

Half board

per person:	£min	£max
Daily	23.00	28.00

Evening meal 1800 (last orders 1000)
Parking for 9

Please mention this guide when making a booking.

Individual proprietors have supplied all details of accommodation. Although we do check for accuracy, we advise you to confirm the information at the time of booking.

FAKENHAM

Norfolk
Map ref 3B1

Attractive, small market town dates from Saxon times and was a Royal Manor until the 17th C. Its market place has 2 old coaching inns, both showing traces of earlier work behind Georgian facades and the parish church has a commanding 15th C tower.

Old Mill Hotel & Restaurant

Bridge Street, Fakenham
NR21 9AY
☎ (0328) 862100
An old mill recently converted. All rooms en-suite.
Bedrooms: 2 single,
3 double, 5 twin
Bathrooms: 10 private
Bed & breakfast

per night:	£min	£max
Single	35.00	35.00
Double	48.00	48.00

Lunch available
Evening meal 1800 (last orders 2115)
Parking for 3
Cards accepted: Access, Visa, Diners, Amex

FELIXSTOWE

Suffolk
Map ref 3C2

Seaside resort that developed at the end of the 19th C. Lying in a gently curving bay with a 2-mile-long beach and backed by a wide promenade of lawns and floral gardens. Ferry links to the continent.
Tourist Information Centre
☎ *(0394) 276770*

Fludyer Arms Hotel ♠♠

Listed   APPROVED

Undercliff Rd. East,
Felixstowe IP11 7LU
☎ (0394) 283279
Fax (0394) 670754
Closest hotel to the sea in Felixstowe. Two fully licensed bars and family room overlooking the sea. All rooms have superb sea views. Colour TV. Specialises in home-cooked food, with children's and vegetarian menus available.
Bedrooms: 3 single,
4 double, 1 twin, 1 multiple

Bathrooms: 4 private,
2 public
Bed & breakfast

per night:	£min	£max
Single	18.00	26.00
Double	26.00	40.00

Lunch available
Evening meal 1900 (last orders 2100)
Parking for 14
Cards accepted: Access, Visa, Amex

FINCHINGFIELD

Essex
Map ref 3B2

School Green Farm

Listed

Blackmore End, Braintree
CM7 4DS
☎ Great Dunmow (0371) 850679
Lovely 17th C farmhouse. Beautifully furnished large bedrooms. North of Braintree at Blackmore End, Essex/ Suffolk border, close to the famous village of Finchingfield.
Bedrooms: 2 double
Bathrooms: 1 public
Bed & breakfast

per night:	£min	£max
Single	15.00	15.00
Double	30.00	30.00

Parking for 10

FRAMLINGHAM

Suffolk
Map ref 3C2

Pleasant old market town with an interesting church, impressive castle and some attractive houses round Market Hill. The town's history can be traced at the Lanman Museum.

Boundary Farm

Listed   COMMENDED

Saxmundham Road,
Framlingham, Woodbridge
IP13 9NU
☎ (0728) 723401
17th C listed farmhouse in 1.5 acres of garden amidst open countryside. Log fires, warm, friendly atmosphere. Pleasant stay is assured. 1.5 miles out of Framlingham on B1119 road. Ideal location for touring.
Bedrooms: 2 double, 1 twin
Bathrooms: 1 public

Bed & breakfast per night:	£min	£max
Single	20.00	
Double	32.00	

Parking for 6
♘☕[UL][S]🚭🛏[TV]▥🔒∪
🎣✽🚐[SP]🏠

Church Farm

Kettleburgh, Woodbridge IP13 7LF
☎ (0728) 723532
70-acre mixed farm. 350-year-old farmhouse overlooking Deben Valley. On Kettleburgh to Brandeston road. Good home cooking.
Bedrooms: 1 double, 2 twin
Bathrooms: 1 public, 1 private shower

Bed & breakfast per night:	£min	£max
Double	32.00	34.00

Half board per person:	£min	£max
Daily	24.00	25.00

Evening meal 1830 (last orders 2000)
Parking for 6
♘🛏☕[UL]🔒[S]🛏[TV]🎣⛳✓
✽✈🚐

The Falcon Inn

[Listed]
Earl Soham, Framlingham, Woodbridge IP13 7SA
☎ (0728) 685263
15th C inn with exposed beams opposite bowls green and overlooking open fields. 3 miles from Framlingham. Ideal for touring East Anglia.
Bedrooms: 1 double, 1 twin, 1 triple
Bathrooms: 1 public

Bed & breakfast per night:	£min	£max
Single	18.00	18.00
Double	36.00	36.00

Lunch available
Evening meal 1800 (last orders 2130)
Parking for 24
♘☕🔒[S][TV]🍸🔍⛳✽🚐[DAP]
🚭[SP]🏠

The Limes Farmhouse

[Listed] [HIGHLY COMMENDED]
Saxtead Green, Framlingham, Woodbridge IP13 9QH
☎ Earl Soham (0728) 685303
Situated opposite Saxtead Mill, 1.5 miles from Framlingham. Close to the coast, Aldeburgh, Snape and Minsmere. Ideal centre for touring Suffolk.
Bedrooms: 2 double, 2 twin
Bathrooms: 2 private, 1 public

Bed & breakfast per night:	£min	£max
Single	20.00	25.00
Double	36.00	40.00

Half board per person:	£min	£max
Daily	27.00	35.00

Evening meal 1800 (last orders 2030)
Parking for 8
♘12🖥▭☕[UL][S]🛏[TV]▥
🔒✽🚐🏠

Shimmens Pightle 🏆

[COMMENDED]
Dennington Road, Framlingham, Woodbridge IP13 9JT
☎ (0728) 724036
Brian and Phyllis Collett's home is in an acre of landscaped garden overlooking fields, on the outskirts of Framlingham. Locally-cured bacon and home-made marmalade.
Bedrooms: 1 double, 1 twin
Bathrooms: 1 public

Bed & breakfast per night:	£min	£max
Single	18.00	
Double	32.00	

Parking for 4
♘8🛏☕🔍[UL][S]🚭[TV]▥
🔒∪✽✈🚐

FRESSINGFIELD

Suffolk
Map ref 3B2

Chippenhall Hall

[HIGHLY COMMENDED]
Chippenhall Hall, Fressingfield, Eye IP21 5TD
☎ (037 986) 8180 & 733
Fax (037 986) 272
Listed Tudor manor house, heavily beamed and with inglenook fireplaces, in 7 acres, one mile outside Fressingfield on B1116 to Framlingham.
Bedrooms: 3 double
Bathrooms: 3 private

Bed & breakfast per night:	£min	£max
Single	36.00	42.00
Double	46.00	52.00

Half board per person:	£min	£max
Daily	42.00	45.00
Weekly	278.00	297.00

Lunch available
Evening meal 1930 (last orders 1930)
Parking for 12
Cards accepted: Access, Visa
♘12🖥▭☕🔍🔒[S]🚭🛏
[TV]▥🔒🏊∪⛳✽✈🚐🐎🚭
[SP]🏠

Priory House

[Listed]
Priory Road, Fressingfield, Eye IP21 5PH
☎ (037 986) 254
Furnished with antiques, a restored 16th C beamed farmhouse set in quiet, secluded gardens. Telephone for colour brochure. Excellent village pubs/restaurant 7 minutes' walk.
Bedrooms: 1 double, 2 twin
Bathrooms: 1 public

Bed & breakfast per night:	£min	£max
Single	19.00	
Double	34.00	

Parking for 6
♘10☕[UL][S]🛏[TV]▥🔒✽
✈🚐🏠

FRINTON-ON-SEA

Essex
Map ref 3C2

Sedate town that developed as a resort at the end of the 19th C and still retains an air of Victorian gentility. Fine sandy beaches, good fishing and golf.

Hodgenolls Farmhouse

[COMMENDED]
Pork Lane, Great Holland, Frinton-on-Sea CO13 0ES
☎ Clacton (0255) 672054
Early 17th C timber framed farmhouse in rural setting close to sandy beaches, Constable country, historic Colchester and Harwich. Non-smoking establishment.
Bedrooms: 2 double, 1 twin
Bathrooms: 1 public

Bed & breakfast per night:	£min	£max
Double	34.00	34.00

Parking for 5
Open April-October
♘▭☕[UL][S]🚭🛏[TV]▥🔒
✽✈🚐

GARBOLDISHAM

Norfolk
Map ref 3B2

Ingleneuk Lodge 🏆

[COMMENDED]
Hopton Road, Garboldisham, Diss IP22 2RQ
☎ (095 381) 541
Modern single-level home in 10 acres of wooded countryside. South-facing patio, riverside walk. Very friendly atmosphere. On B1111, 1 mile south of village.
Bedrooms: 3 single, 4 double, 2 twin, 2 triple
Bathrooms: 10 private, 1 public

Bed & breakfast per night:	£min	£max
Single	21.00	30.50
Double	34.00	47.00

Half board per person:	£min	£max
Daily	30.50	44.00
Weekly	203.00	273.50

Evening meal 1830 (last orders 1300)
Parking for 20
Cards accepted: Access, Visa, Amex
♘🛏☎▭☕[S]🚭🛏▥🔒🍸
∪✽🚐[SP][T]

Swan House

[Listed] [APPROVED]
Hopton Road, Garboldisham, Diss IP22 2RQ
☎ Diss (095 381) 8221
17th C coaching inn full of character, offering a warm and friendly welcome from Tracy and Michael. Home baking and much more. No smoking throughout.
Bedrooms: 3 double
Bathrooms: 1 public

Bed & breakfast per night:	£min	£max
Single	20.00	20.00
Double	30.00	36.00

Parking for 8
Open March-December
♘▭[UL]🔒[S]🚭▥✽✈🚐🏠

GISSING

Norfolk
Map ref 3B2

The Old Rectory 🏆

[HIGHLY COMMENDED]
Gissing, Diss IP22 3XB
☎ Tivetshall (037 977) 575
Fax (037 977) 4427
Elegant Victorian house in 3 acres. Peaceful, comfortable, tastefully decorated and furnished. Four-course, candlelit dinner available, except Monday and Thursday. Tea/coffee making facilities, colour TV, and an extensive range of toiletries available in all rooms. Indoor pool.
Bedrooms: 1 double, 2 twin
Bathrooms: 3 private

Bed & breakfast per night:	£min	£max
Single	33.00	42.00
Double	46.00	56.00

Continued ►

GISSING

Continued

Half board

per person:	£min	£max
Daily	41.00	46.00
Weekly	247.00	282.00

Evening meal 1945 (last orders 1945)
Parking for 6
Cards accepted: Access, Visa

🐾 ⌂ 🖵 🌙 🕸 🖤 📶 📠 🅂 ⅙ 🅜 📺 🍴, 🍽 ❄ ☕ 🐾 🚲 SP 🎠

GLATTON

Cambridgeshire
Map ref 3A2

Mychelles Mede

40/42 High Haden Road, Glatton, Huntingdon PE17 5RU
☎ Ramsey (0487) 832500
Fax (0487) 832244
Grade II listed thatched period cottage offering bed and breakfast, in quiet village convenient for A1.
Bedrooms: 1 double, 1 multiple
Bathrooms: 1 private, 1 public

Bed & breakfast

per night:	£min	£max
Single	12.50	15.00
Double	27.50	30.00

Parking for 2
🐾 7 🖵 🖤 📶 ⅙ 📺 ❄ ✖ 🎠 🎠

GRAYS

Essex
Map ref 3B3

Stifford Clays Farmhouse

Stifford Clays Road, North Stifford, Grays RM16 3NL
☎ (0375) 375918
Fax (0375) 891135
200-year-old farmhouse with spacious rooms, in two-and-a-half acres of lawns. Easy access to main line railway station to London.
Bedrooms: 4 single, 2 double, 9 twin, 2 multiple
Bathrooms: 11 private, 2 public

Bed & breakfast

per night:	£min	£max
Single	17.00	22.00
Double	27.00	30.00

Parking for 17
Cards accepted: Access, Visa
🐾 🖵 🖵 🖤 📶 ⅙ 🅜 📺 🍴, 🍽 ❄ SP

GREAT BIRCHAM

Norfolk
Map ref 3B1

King's Head Hotel ⋀

Great Bircham, King's Lynn PE31 6RJ
☎ Syderstone (048 523) 265
Family-run country hotel with 3 bars, restaurant and beer garden. Near Sandringham, King's Lynn and the coast.
Bedrooms: 2 double, 3 twin
Bathrooms: 5 private

Bed & breakfast

per night:	£min	£max
Single	35.00	38.00
Double	50.00	58.00

Lunch available
Evening meal 1900 (last orders 2200)
Parking for 80
Cards accepted: Access, Visa
🐾 🖵 🖤 🅜 📺 🍴, 🍽 ❄ ☕ OAP SP 🎠

GREAT DUNMOW

Essex
Map ref 3B2

On the main Roman road from Bishop's Stortford to Braintree. Doctor's Pond near the square, was where the first lifeboat was tested in 1785. Home of the Dunmow Flitch trials held every 4 years on Whit Monday.

Yarrow

🎖 COMMENDED

27 Station Road, Felsted, Great Dunmow CM6 3HD
☎ (0371) 820878
Edwardian house with private garden overlooking open fields and Chelmer Valley. South-facing bedrooms with garden and countryside views.
Bedrooms: 2 double, 1 twin
Bathrooms: 2 public

Bed & breakfast

per night:	£min	£max
Single	11.00	15.00
Double	22.00	30.00

Parking for 8
🐾 🖵 🖵 🖤 📶 ⅙ 📺 🍴, 🍽 ❄ ✖ 🎠

National Crown ratings were correct at the time of going to press but are subject to change. Please check at the time of booking.

GREAT YARMOUTH

Norfolk
Map ref 3C1

One of Britain's major seaside resorts with 5 miles of seafront and every possible amenity including an award winning leisure complex offering a huge variety of all-weather facilities. Busy harbour and fishing centre.
Tourist Information Centre ☎ (0493) 846345 or (accommodation) 846344

Spindrift Private Hotel ⋀

🎖 APPROVED

36 Wellesley Road, Great Yarmouth NR30 1EU
☎ (0493) 858674
Attractively situated small private hotel, close to all amenities and with Beach Coach Station and car park at rear. Front bedrooms have sea views.
Bedrooms: 2 single, 2 double, 1 twin, 2 triple
Bathrooms: 4 private, 1 public

Bed & breakfast

per night:	£min	£max
Single	16.00	25.00
Double	28.00	38.00

Evening meal 1715 (last orders 1300)
Cards accepted: Access, Visa
🐾 3 🖵 🖤 📶 🅜 🍴, 🍽 ✖ 🎠 OAP SP

HADLEIGH

Suffolk
Map ref 3B2

Former wool town, lying on a tributary of the River Stour. The church of St Mary stands among a remarkable cluster of medieval buildings.
Tourist Information Centre ☎ (0473) 822922

Ash Street Farm

🎖 COMMENDED

Ash Street, Semer, Ipswich IP7 6QZ
☎ Bildeston (0449) 741493
Approached down a single track country lane, this fine 15th C farmhouse has lovely views and comfortable, spacious accommodation. Children and dogs welcome; most eccentricities catered for.
Bedrooms: 1 double, 1 triple
Bathrooms: 2 private

Bed & breakfast

per night:	£min	£max
Single	15.00	15.00
Double	26.00	30.00

Half board

per person:	£min	£max
Daily	23.50	23.50

Evening meal 1830 (last orders 2030)
Parking for 8
🐾 🖵 🖤 📶 📠 🅂 ⅙ 🅜 📺 🍴, 🍽 ❄ 🎠 🎠

Gables Hotel ⋀

🎖 COMMENDED

Angel Street, Hadleigh, Ipswich IP7 5EY
☎ (0473) 827169
15th C timbered hall residence in historic market town, recently converted to private hotel offering all modern amenities.
Bedrooms: 1 single, 2 double, 1 twin
Bathrooms: 2 private, 2 public

Bed & breakfast

per night:	£min	£max
Single	22.00	42.00
Double	42.00	62.00

Half board

per person:	£min	£max
Daily	40.00	60.00
Weekly	258.00	378.00

Evening meal 1900 (last orders 2100)
Parking for 6
🐾 🖵 🖤 🅜 📺 🍴, 🍽 ❄ ☕ SP 🎠

Howells

Listed COMMENDED

93 Angel Street, Hadleigh IP7 5EY
☎ Ipswich (0473) 828117
Retired hoteliers offering guests every comfort. Secluded location, near town centre. Large en-suite bedroom, own sitting room with TV.
Bedrooms: 1 double
Bathrooms: 1 private

Bed & breakfast

per night:	£min	£max
Single	18.00	18.00
Double	30.00	30.00

Parking for 1
🖵 📶 🅜 📺 🍴, 🍽 ✖ 🎠

Mount Pleasant Farm ⋀

🎖 APPROVED

Offton, Ipswich IP8 4RP
☎ (0473) 658896
Fax (0473) 658896
8-acre mixed farm. Genuinely secluded, typical Suffolk farmhouse. 30 minutes from the sea and 5 minutes from

water park. Many local beauty spots. Evening meals a speciality.
Bedrooms: 2 double, 1 twin
Bathrooms: 2 private, 1 public

Bed & breakfast per night:	£min	£max
Single	15.00	15.00
Double	25.00	25.00

Half board per person:	£min	£max
Daily	20.50	23.00
Weekly	143.50	161.00

Lunch available
Evening meal 1900 (last orders 1000)
Parking for 10

Town House Fruit Farm
Hook Lane, Hadleigh, Ipswich IP7 5PH
☎ (0473) 823260
85-acre fruit farm. Converted barn close to Constable country and East Anglian wool villages. Near Harwich and Felixstowe.
Bedrooms: 2 double, 1 twin
Bathrooms: 2 public

Bed & breakfast per night:	£min	£max
Single	13.00	
Double	25.00	

Parking for 20

Suffolk
Map ref 3C2

Small market town which grew firstly with navigation on the Blyth in the 18th C and then with the coming of the railways in the 19th C. Opposite the church in a beautiful 14th C building is the Halesworth Gallery.

Fen Way
School Lane, Halesworth
IP19 8BW
☎ (0986) 873574
Bungalow in 7 acres of peaceful meadowland, where the family pets include sheep and lambs.
Bedrooms: 2 double, 1 twin
Bathrooms: 1 public

Bed & breakfast per night:	£min	£max
Single	13.00	14.00
Double	24.00	26.00

Half board per person:	£min	£max
Daily	17.00	19.00
Weekly	115.00	119.00

Evening meal 1800 (last orders 1600)
Parking for 3

Mynholme
☀☀ COMMENDED
40 Holton Road, Halesworth
IP19 8HG
☎ (0986) 875422
Bungalow with character, homely and comfortable, with a peaceful atmosphere and a warm welcome. Attractive garden.
Bedrooms: 2 double
Bathrooms: 1 public

Bed & breakfast per night:	£min	£max
Double	28.00	

Parking for 2

Norfolk
Map ref 3C2

Attractive small town on the River Waveney with 2 market-places and a museum. Candler's House is an outstanding example of an early Georgian town house. At Starston, 1 mile away, is a restored wind-pump.

Weston House Farm
Mendham, Harleston
IP20 0PB
☎ St. Cross (098 682) 206
300-acre mixed farm. 17th C Grade II listed farmhouse set in an acre of garden, overlooking pastureland.
Bedrooms: 2 twin, 1 triple
Bathrooms: 1 private, 1 public

Bed & breakfast per night:	£min	£max
Single	16.50	
Double	29.00	34.00

Half board per person:	£min	£max
Daily	23.00	25.50
Weekly	147.00	161.00

Evening meal 1900 (last orders 2000)
Parking for 6
Open March-November
Cards accepted: Amex

We advise you to confirm your booking in writing.

Suffolk
Map ref 3B2

Giffords Hall
☀☀ COMMENDED
Hartest, Bury St Edmunds
IP29 4EX
☎ (0284) 830464
Georgian farmhouse just outside Hartest village, operating a vineyard and small country living.
Bedrooms: 1 double, 2 twin
Bathrooms: 2 private, 1 public

Bed & breakfast per night:	£min	£max
Double	32.00	36.00

Parking for 20
Cards accepted: Visa

Cambridgeshire
Map ref 3A2

38 High Street
☀ APPROVED
Hemingford Grey, Huntingdon PE18 9BJ
☎ St Ives (0480) 301203
Private detached house in centre of village, with large garden and quiet surroundings. All home cooking. 1 mile from the A604. No smoking.
Bedrooms: 2 single, 2 double
Bathrooms: 1 public

Bed & breakfast per night:	£min	£max
Single	16.00	16.00
Double	32.00	32.00

Half board per person:	£min	£max
Daily	26.00	26.00
Weekly	182.00	182.00

Evening meal 1930 (last orders 1600)
Parking for 4
Open January-November

Norfolk
Map ref 3C1

Mill House
Listed
Field Lane, Hempnall, Norwich NR15 2PB
☎ (0508) 499552
Family accommodation in comfortable Victorian house. Large garden, chickens,

---

donkey. Within easy reach of seaside, Broads, Norwich. Quiet village.
Bedrooms: 2 twin
Bathrooms: 1 public

Bed & breakfast per night:	£min	£max
Single	18.00	20.00
Double	32.00	36.00

Parking for 2

Norfolk
Map ref 3B1

Magnolia House
Cromwell Close, Hethersett
NR9 3HD
☎ (0603) 810749
Norwich 4.5 miles. Large, comfortable house, all rooms with TV, hot and cold water, tea facilities. Residents have own key. Private car park.
Bedrooms: 2 single, 1 double, 1 twin
Bathrooms: 3 public

Bed & breakfast per night:	£min	£max
Single	16.00	20.00
Double	30.00	35.00

Parking for 7

Norfolk
Map ref 3B1

Marsham Arms Inn Ⓜ
☀☀ COMMENDED
Holt Road, Hevingham, Norwich NR10 5NP
☎ (060 548) 268
Old established freehouse and restaurant with 8 self-contained study bedrooms. 5 miles from Norwich airport on the B1149.
Bedrooms: 2 double, 6 twin
Bathrooms: 8 private

Bed & breakfast per night:	£min	£max
Single	35.00	42.00
Double	45.00	52.00

Lunch available
Evening meal 1800 (last orders 2200)
Parking for 100
Cards accepted: Access, Visa, Amex

The symbols are explained on the flap inside the back cover.

EAST ANGLIA

HINGHAM

Norfolk
Map ref 3B1

The Smithy
Low Street, Hardingham,
Norwich NR9 4EL
☎ Attleborough (0953)
851065
*In a peaceful hamlet
surrounded by countryside
between Wymondham and
Dereham. Easy access to
Norwich. Also self-contained
annexe.*
Bedrooms: 1 double, 2 twin
Bathrooms: 2 public
Bed & breakfast

per night:	£min	£max
Single	13.00	15.00
Double	26.00	30.00

Half board

per person:	£min	£max
Daily	18.00	20.00
Weekly	90.00	100.00

Evening meal 1800 (last
orders 2100)
Parking for 7
🛇 ᵁᴸ 🗕 S 🅿 📺 🖃 🌣 🕳
🛵 SP

HINTLESHAM

Suffolk
Map ref 3B2

College Farm
Listed HIGHLY COMMENDED
Hintlesham, Ipswich IP8 3NT
☎ (047 387) 253
*600-acre arable & livestock
farm. Beamed 15th C
farmhouse in quiet position 1
mile west of Hintlesham on
A1071. Comfortable
accommodation with large
garden. Close to Constable
country, Harwich and
Felixstowe.*
Bedrooms: 1 single,
1 double, 1 triple
Bathrooms: 1 private,
1 public
Bed & breakfast

per night:	£min	£max
Single	15.00	19.00
Double	30.00	34.00

Parking for 10
🛇 5 🖃 ᵁᴸ 🖕 S 🗕 🅿 📺 🖃 🖃
☍ ᑌ 🌣 🕳 🛵 ᴼᴬᴾ 🎢

The Old Barn
Listed COMMENDED
Chattisham Lane,
Hintlesham, Ipswich IP8 3PU
☎ (0473) 87498 & 87731
*17th C Suffolk barn with
wealth of exposed timbers,
grounds of 3.5 acres.
Comfortable family
atmosphere. Idyllic country*

setting. Self-contained holiday
cottage also available.
Bedrooms: 1 double
Bathrooms: 1 private
Bed & breakfast

per night:	£min	£max
Single		18.00
Double		30.00

Parking for 3
🛇 🖃 🗕 ᵁᴸ 🖃 🖃 🖃 ☍ ᑌ 🥄 🕳
🌣 🛵 ᴼᴬᴾ SP 🎢

HINXTON

Cambridgeshire
Map ref 2D1

The Old Parsonage
👑👑
Hinxton, Saffron Walden,
Essex CB10 1RS
☎ Saffron Walden (0799)
30630
Fax (0799) 31187
*Georgian house, set in
secluded grounds next to
church. 5 minutes from M11.
Convenient for Duxford Air
Museum, Cambridge and
Saffron Walden.*
Bedrooms: 1 double
Bathrooms: 1 private
Bed & breakfast

per night:	£min	£max
Single		18.00
Double		30.00

Parking for 2
🛇 🖕 ᵁᴸ 🖃 S 🗡 🅿 📺 🖃 🗕 🌣
🕳 🛵 🎢

HITCHAM

Suffolk
Map ref 3B2

Little Causeway
Farmhouse
Hitcham, Ipswich IP7 7NE
☎ Bildeston (0449) 740521
*Tudor farmhouse set in
unspoilt countryside. Close to
Lavenham, Constable
Country, National Trust
properties and within walking
distance of a good village
pub.*
Bedrooms: 2 double
Bathrooms: 1 public
Bed & breakfast

per night:	£min	£max
Double		30.00

Parking for 5
🖕 ᵁᴸ 🅿 📺 🖃 🗕 🕳 🛵 🎢

Mill House
Water Run, Hitcham,
Ipswich IP7 7LN
☎ Bildeston (0449) 740315
& (0860) 886638
*On B1115 Stowmarket to
Sudbury road. Late Regency
house, in 4 acres of grounds,
with garden and tennis court.*

Lavenham, Kersey, Long
Melford and Hadleigh within
10 mile radius. Convenient
for Constable Country.
Bedrooms: 2 double, 1 twin
Bathrooms: 1 private,
1 public
Bed & breakfast

per night:	£min	£max
Single	12.00	12.50
Double	24.00	25.00

Evening meal 1800 (last
orders 2000)
Parking for 10
🛇 🖃 🗕 ᵁᴸ 🖃 🖃 🗕 🍳 🌣 🛵

Wetherden Hall
Listed APPROVED
Hitcham, Ipswich IP7 7PZ
☎ Bildeston (0449) 740412
*270-acre arable and mixed
farm. A warm welcome awaits
you at this attractive
farmhouse on the edge of a
very pretty village. Private
fishing. Good centre for
visiting medieval Lavenham,
Bury St Edmunds, Ipswich,
Cambridge and Constable
country.*
Bedrooms: 1 double, 1 triple
Bathrooms: 1 public
Bed & breakfast

per night:	£min	£max
Single	14.50	15.00
Double	27.00	29.00

Parking for 6
Open April-September
ᵁᴸ 🅿 📺 🖃 🥄 🕳 🛵 🎢

HORSFORD

Norfolk
Map ref 3B1

Church Farm Guest
House
👑👑 COMMENDED
Church Street, Horsford,
Norwich NR10 3DB
☎ Norwich (0603) 898020 &
898582
*Quiet, modernised 17th C
farmhouse. Separate entrance,
lounge and dining room for
guests. Close to city centre,
Broads and coast.*
Bedrooms: 1 double, 2 twin,
2 triple
Bathrooms: 5 private
Bed & breakfast

per night:	£min	£max
Single	17.00	20.00
Double	32.00	38.00

Parking for 20
🛇 🖃 🗕 ᵁᴸ 🖃 🖩 📺 🖃 🗕
🌣 🕳

HUNSTANTON

Norfolk
Map ref 3B1

Seaside resort which
faces the Wash. The
shingle and sand beach is
backed by striped cliffs
and many unusual fossils
can be found here. The
town is predominantly
Victorian. The Oasis
family leisure centre has
indoor and outdoor pools.
Tourist Information Centre
☎ (0485) 532610

Fieldsend House
👑👑 COMMENDED
Homefields Road,
Hunstanton PE36 5HL
☎ (0485) 532593
*Country house style bed and
breakfast. Tastefully furnished
rooms with sea views, ample
parking in grounds.*
Bedrooms: 1 double, 1 twin,
1 multiple
Bathrooms: 1 private,
1 public
Bed & breakfast

per night:	£min	£max
Single	20.00	25.00
Double	34.00	40.00

Parking for 6
🛇 🖃 🗕 ᵁᴸ 🖕 🖤 ᵁᴸ S 🅿 📺
🖃 🗕 🕳 🛵 🎢

INGATESTONE

Essex
Map ref 3B3

Eibiswald
Listed HIGHLY COMMENDED
85 Mill Road, Stock,
Ingatestone CM4 9LR
☎ Stock (0277) 840631
*Anglo-Austrian hospitality.
Comfortable, modern house in
quiet, pleasant rural
surroundings. Railway 4
miles. Convenient for
Chelmsford, Brentwood and
Basildon. 5 minutes from the
A12 on the B1007, signposted
Billericay.*
Bedrooms: 3 double
Bathrooms: 1 private,
1 public
Bed & breakfast

per night:	£min	£max
Single	22.00	26.00
Double	32.00	38.00

Parking for 5
🛇 12 🖃 🗕 ᵁᴸ S 🗡 📺 🖃
🗕 🌣 🕳 🛵 ᵀ

IPSWICH

Suffolk
Map ref 3B2

Interesting county town
and major port on the
River Orwell. Birthplace of
Cardinal Wolsey.
Christchurch Mansion, set
in a fine park, contains a
good collection of
furniture and pictures, with
works by Gainsborough,
Constable and Munnings.
Tourist Information Centre
☎ *(0473) 258070*

Burlington Lodge

Listed

30 Burlington Road, Ipswich
IP1 2HS
☎ (0473) 251868
Victorian town house, close to
town centre yet in a quiet
residential area.
Bedrooms: 2 single, 2 twin
Bathrooms: 4 private
showers

Bed & breakfast

per night:	£min	£max
Single	18.00	20.00
Double	30.00	32.00

Parking for 5
🛇 🕹 ☐ 📺 🔟 ⑤ 🏃 🖿 🗕 🐾

Mount Pleasant

🍴 🍴 COMMENDED

103 Anglesea Road, Ipswich
IP1 3PJ
☎ (0473) 251601
Fax (0473) 252198
Elegant Victorian house in
residential road, just 10
minutes' walk from town
centre. Spacious, attractive
bedrooms, all with
comfortable private
bathrooms.
Bedrooms: 1 single,
2 double, 1 twin
Bathrooms: 4 private

Bed & breakfast

per night:	£min	£max
Single	23.00	25.00
Double	38.00	40.00

Parking for 4
Cards accepted:
🛇 8 🔟 ☐ 🕹 🔟 🖢 🗕 🔟 📺 🔟.
🗕 ✿ 🗙 🐾

Mulberry Hall

Burstall, Ipswich IP8 3DP
☎ Hintlesham (047 387) 348
Attractively furnished 16th C
beamed old farmhouse once
owned by Cardinal Wolsey
(1523). In a small village 5
miles west of Ipswich. Log
fires and home cooking.
Bedrooms: 1 single,
1 double, 1 twin
Bathrooms: 2 public

Bed & breakfast

per night:	£min	£max
Single	16.00	
Double	32.00	36.00

Half board

per person:	£min	£max
Daily	28.00	

Parking for 6
🛇 🕹 🔟 🖆 ⑤ 🏃 📺 🗕 🔍 ✿ 🗙
🐾 🏠

KERSEY

Suffolk
Map ref 3B2

A most picturesque
village, which was famous
for cloth-making, set in a
valley with a water-splash.
The church of St Mary is
an impressive building at
the top of the hill.

Red House Farm

🛇

Kersey, Ipswich IP7 6EY
☎ Boxford (0787) 210245
Listed farmhouse between
Kersey and Boxford, central
for Constable country. Rooms
with wash basins, TV and tea-
making facilities. Twin
bedroom is en-suite.
Bedrooms: 1 double, 1 twin
Bathrooms: 1 private,
1 public

Bed & breakfast

per night:	£min	£max
Single	16.00	18.00
Double	30.00	32.00

Half board

per person:	£min	£max
Daily	22.50	23.50

Evening meal 1900 (last
orders 1000)
Parking for 5
☐ 🖢 🕹 🔟 🖆 ⑤ 📺 🔟. 🗕 🔍 ✿
🐾 🏠

KESSINGLAND

Suffolk
Map ref 3C1

Seaside village whose
church tower has served
as a landmark to sailors
for generations. Nearby is
the Suffolk Wildlife and
Country Park.

The Old Rectory

🍴 🍴 HIGHLY COMMENDED

157 Church Road,
Kessingland, Lowestoft
NR33 7SQ
☎ Lowestoft (0502) 740020
Beautiful late Georgian house
in 2 acres of garden, well
back from road ensuring
peace and quiet. A warm

welcome awaits. Spacious,
comfortable, delightfully
furnished rooms, most with
antiques.
Bedrooms: 2 double, 1 twin,
1 multiple
Bathrooms: 3 private,
2 public

Bed & breakfast

per night:	£min	£max
Single	20.00	22.00
Double	36.00	40.00

Parking for 6
Open May-September
🛇 6 🖢 ☐ 🖢 🕹 🔟 ⑤ 🏃 🔟 📺
🔟. 🗕 ✿ 🔟 🐾 🏠

KING'S LYNN

Norfolk
Map ref 3B1

Combines the attractions
of a busy town, port and
agricultural centre. Many
outstanding buildings. The
Guildhall and Town Hall
are both built of flint in a
striking chequer design.
The Customs House was
built in 1683.
Tourist Information Centre
☎ *(0553) 763044*

25 Friars Street

Listed

King's Lynn PE40 5AW
☎ (0553) 763926
Small town house on ancient
London road into King's
Lynn. About 10 minutes' walk
into historic centre, 3
minutes' walk from riverside.
Very quiet. Non-smokers only
please.
Bedrooms: 1 single, 1 twin
Bathrooms: 1 public

Bed & breakfast

per night:	£min	£max
Single	15.00	15.00
Double	30.00	30.00

☐ 🖢 🔟 ⑤ 🏃 🔟. 🗕 🗙 🐾

Gatton Waters

Hillington, King's Lynn
☎ (0485) 600643
1740 converted Norfolk barn
overlooking private lake. Set
in 20 acres, 2.5 miles from
Sandringham House.
Bedrooms: 1 double, 1 twin
Bathrooms: 1 public

Bed & breakfast

per night:	£min	£max
Single	15.00	15.00
Double	25.00	25.00

Half board

per person:	£min	£max
Daily	20.00	30.00

Parking for 6
Open April-October
📧 🖢 ⑤ 🔟 📺 🔟. 🗕 🔍 ✿
🗙 🐾

Maranatha Guest House 🅰

🛇🛇

115 Gaywood Road,
Gaywood, King's Lynn
PE30 2PU
☎ (0553) 774596
Large carrstone and brick
residence with gardens front
and rear. 10 minutes' walk
from the town centre. Direct
road to Sandringham and the
coast.
Bedrooms: 2 single,
2 double, 2 twin
Bathrooms: 1 private,
2 public

Bed & breakfast

per night:	£min	£max
Single	12.00	15.00
Double	20.00	24.00

Half board

per person:	£min	£max
Daily	14.00	16.00

Lunch available
Evening meal 1800 (last
orders 1800)
Parking for 9
🛇 ☐ 🖢 🖆 ⑤ 🔟 📺 🔟. 🗕

Sixty-One

61 King George V Avenue,
King's Lynn PE30 2QE
☎ (0553) 774485
Quiet locality near college
and sports centre, easy
walking access to town centre.
Considerate attention from
resident owner.
Bedrooms: 1 single, 2 twin
Bathrooms: 1 public

Bed & breakfast

per night:	£min	£max
Single	12.00	15.00
Double	24.00	28.00

Parking for 3
🛇 ☐ 🖢 🔟 🖆 ⑤ 🔟. 🗙

KNEESWORTH

Cambridgeshire
Map ref 2D1

The Grange 🅰

Old North Road, Kneesworth
SG8 5DS
☎ (0763) 248674
18th C farmhouse set in
pretty well-stocked gardens
overlooking farmland.
Breakfast served in Victorian
conservatory. Large en-suite
bedrooms. 20 minutes
Cambridge, M11 and A1(M).
Bedrooms: 2 double, 1 twin
Bathrooms: 3 private

Bed & breakfast

per night:	£min	£max
Single	20.00	35.00
Double	36.00	50.00

Continued ►

265

KNEESWORTH

Continued

Half board

per person:	£min	£max
Daily	30.00	55.00

Evening meal 1900 (last orders 2000)
Parking for 12

🛇🖧🏠♿🛆§💈📺🏧.🛥❀
🍴🏰

LAVENHAM

Suffolk
Map ref 3B2

A former prosperous wool town of timber-framed buildings with the cathedral-like church and its tall tower. The market-place is 13th C and the Guildhall now houses a museum.

Angel Corner 🏍

COMMENDED

17 Market Place, Lavenham, Sudbury CO10 9QZ
☎ (0787) 247168
Fax (0787) 247905
15th C wool merchant's residence with wealth of original timbers. Overlooking Lavenham's historic market place. Attractively restored to family home.
Bedrooms: 1 double, 2 twin
Bathrooms: 1 public

Bed & breakfast

per night:	£min	£max
Single		21.50
Double		35.00

Half board

per person:	£min	£max
Daily	28.50	34.00

Evening meal 1830 (last orders 2100)
Parking for 2
Open February-November

🛇🛆♿🍷§🛏📺🏧.🛥
🍴🏰

Meathe House

HIGHLY COMMENDED

Hill Green, Lavenham, Sudbury CO10 9LS
☎ (0787) 247809
Interesting, spacious, modern house beautifully situated in quiet countryside 1 mile north of Lavenham. Ideal touring base. Non-smokers only please.
Bedrooms: 1 single, 1 double, 1 twin
Bathrooms: 1 public

Bed & breakfast

per night:	£min	£max
Single	18.00	19.00
Double	32.00	34.00

Parking for 5
Open April-October

📺♿🛆🍷🛏📺🏧.❀🍴🏰

LAWSHALL

Suffolk
Map ref 3B2

Brighthouse Farm

COMMENDED

Melford Road, Lawshall, Bury St Edmunds IP29 4PX
☎ Bury St Edmunds (0284) 830385
300-acre arable & livestock farm. A warm welcome awaits at this 200-year-old farmhouse set in 3 acres of gardens. Close to many places of historic interest. Good pubs and restaurants nearby.
Bedrooms: 2 double, 1 twin
Bathrooms: 3 private, 1 public

Bed & breakfast

per night:	£min	£max
Single	14.00	20.00
Double	30.00	40.00

Parking for 10
Open April-October

🛇🛏🛆§🛏📺🏧.🛥🔍❀
🍴🏰

Elmwood House

Listed

Melford Road, Lawshall, Bury St Edmunds IP29 4PX
☎ Bury St Edmunds (0284) 830514 & 830385
Modern country house set in large garden on farm. Situated away from village centre with views of countryside.
Bedrooms: 1 double, 2 twin
Bathrooms: 1 public

Bed & breakfast

per night:	£min	£max
Double	28.00	34.00

Parking for 6
Open January-November

🛇🎿🛆§🛏📺🏧.🛥🔍
❀🍴

LEVINGTON

Suffolk
Map ref 3C2

Attractive farming village with views of the River Orwell.

Redhouse

Listed

Bridge Road, Levington, Ipswich IP10 0LZ
☎ Nacton (0473) 659670

Large Victorian house in 3 acres in tiny village between Ipswich and Felixstowe. Beautiful views over Orwell Estuary. Free-range eggs. Evening meals by arrangement.
Bedrooms: 2 double, 1 triple
Bathrooms: 1 public

Bed & breakfast

per night:	£min	£max
Single	16.00	20.00
Double	30.00	34.00

Half board

per person:	£min	£max
Daily	26.00	30.00

Evening meal from 1830
Parking for 6
Open March-November

🛇🛏♿§🛏📺🏧.∪❀🍴🏰

LINDSELL

Essex
Map ref 3B2

Cowels Cottage

Listed

Cowels Farm Lane, Lindsell, Dunmow CM6 3QG
☎ (0371) 870454
Pink cottage, overlooking farmland in tranquil, secluded garden. Centrally heated, private sitting room and bathrooms, TV.
Bedrooms: 1 single, 1 double, 1 twin
Bathrooms: 3 private, 1 public

Bed & breakfast

per night:	£min	£max
Single		20.00
Double		40.00

Parking for 4

🛇🖧♿🛆§🛏📺🏧.🛥
❀🍴🏰

LINTON

Cambridgeshire
Map ref 2D1

Springfield House

🏠🏠

16 Horn Lane, Linton, Cambridge CB1 6HT
☎ Cambridge (0223) 891383
Period family home close to Church. Spacious rooms with lovely views of garden, river and countryside. Cambridge 10 miles, Saffron Walden and Haverhill 6 miles, Newmarket 12 miles. No-smoking permitted.
Bedrooms: 2 double
Bathrooms: 1 private, 1 public

Bed & breakfast

per night:	£min	£max
Single	17.50	20.00
Double	30.00	35.00

Parking for 4

🛇🖧♿🖥§🛏📺🏧.🛥
❀🍴🏰

LITTLE BARNEY

Norfolk
Map ref 3B1

The Old Brick Kilns 🏍

HIGHLY COMMENDED

Little Barney, Fakenham NR21 ONL
☎ Thursford (0328) 878305
Converted cottages in rural setting. Turn right off A148 Fakenham/Holt road. 200 yards on right to Barney, left into Little Barney, house at end of lane.
Bedrooms: 1 single, 1 double, 1 twin
Bathrooms: 3 private

Bed & breakfast

per night:	£min	£max
Single	21.00	21.00
Double	42.00	42.00

Half board

per person:	£min	£max
Daily	34.00	34.00
Weekly	216.00	216.00

Evening meal 1800 (last orders 1000)
Parking for 8

🛇🖧♿🖥🍷§🛏📺🏧.
🛥❀🍴🏰

LITTLE BENTLEY

Essex
Map ref 3B2

Bentley Manor

Listed

Little Bentley, Colchester CO7 8SE
☎ (0206) 250622 & 261790
Fax (0206) 251820
Telex 988827 Dyson G.
Charming 16th C manor house set in 10 acres of grounds. A family home with ponies and sheep.
Bedrooms: 1 twin, 1 triple
Bathrooms: 2 public

Bed & breakfast

per night:	£min	£max
Single	20.00	25.00
Double	28.00	35.00

Parking for 4

🛇♿🍷§🛏📺🕐
🏧.🛥∪❀🍴🏰🅣

> **Please check prices and other details at the time of booking.**

LITTLE SHELFORD

Cambridgeshire
Map ref 2D1

Little Shelford was developed by academics from nearby Cambridge during Victorian times and there are several old timber-framed buildings.

Long House
11 Church Street, Little Shelford, Cambridge CB2 5HG
☎ (0223) 843055
Small, homely bed and breakfast in the old part of this extended 250-year-old cottage, situated in the centre of the village.
Bedrooms: 2 single, 1 twin
Bathrooms: 1 public
Bed & breakfast

per night:	£min	£max
Single	15.00	17.00
Double	30.00	35.00

Half board

per person:	£min	£max
Daily	22.00	25.00

Parking for 3

LITTLE TEY

Essex
Map ref 3B2

Knaves Farm House
Listed
Great Tey Road, Little Tey, Colchester CO6 1JA
☎ (0206) 211039
Charming early Victorian farmhouse in 1 acre of well-kept garden with traditional Essex barns. 400 yards from A120 towards Great Tey.
Bedrooms: 1 double
Bathrooms: 1 private
Bed & breakfast

per night:	£min	£max
Single	18.00	24.00
Double	29.00	34.00

Evening meal 1800 (last orders 2000)
Parking for 1
Open February-November

National Crown ratings were correct at the time of going to press but are subject to change. Please check at the time of booking.

LITTLE WALSINGHAM

Norfolk
Map ref 3B1

Little Walsingham is larger than its neighbour Great Walsingham and more important because of its long history as a religious shrine to which many pilgrimages were made. The village has many picturesque buildings of the 16th C and later.

Old Rectory
Waterden, Walsingham NR22 6AT
☎ South Creake (0328) 823298
Off the B1355 road, 2 miles from the centre of South Creake village, in peaceful rural surroundings. Large garden, on the Holkham Estate.
Bedrooms: 1 double, 2 twin
Bathrooms: 3 private
Bed & breakfast

per night:	£min	£max
Double	37.00	37.00

Parking for 4

LODDON

Norfolk
Map ref 3C1

Small town on the River Chet. Round the square are some good buildings and the large church of Holy Trinity has many interesting contents. Close by is the 18th C Loddon House.

Stubbs House
Stubbs Green, Loddon, Norwich NR14 6EA
☎ (0508) 20231
200-acre arable farm. Georgian farmhouse now a quiet pleasantly run hotel with personal service and within easy reach of East Anglia's major tourist attractions.
Bedrooms: 3 double, 5 twin, 1 triple
Bathrooms: 3 private, 3 public
Bed & breakfast

per night:	£min	£max
Single	18.00	23.00
Double	32.00	38.00

Half board

per person:	£min	£max
Daily	27.50	33.00
Weekly	157.50	177.50

Evening meal 1830 (last orders 2200)
Parking for 20
Open March-November

LOWESTOFT

Suffolk
Map ref 3C1

Seaside town with wide sandy beaches. Important fishing port with picturesque fishing quarter and also the site of the first recorded lighthouse in England. Home of the famous Lowestoft porcelain and birthplace of Benjamin Britten. Several museums with a maritime flavour.

Church Farm
Listed   HIGHLY COMMENDED
Corton, Lowestoft NR32 5HX
☎ (0502) 730359
220-acre arable farm. Victorian farmhouse with a warm, welcoming atmosphere. Quietly situated on the Suffolk coast between Lowestoft and Great Yarmouth. Clean, comfortable rooms, generous English breakfast.
Bedrooms: 2 double
Bathrooms: 2 private
Bed & breakfast

per night:	£min	£max
Double		32.00

Open March-October

Hall Farm
Listed
Jay Lane, Church Lane, Lound, Lowestoft NR32 5LJ
☎ (0502) 730415
Traditional 16th C Suffolk farmhouse within 2 miles of the sea. Take A12 north from Lowestoft. After 4 miles turn left into Jay Lane. Down private lane on the left, farm is on the right.
Bedrooms: 1 single, 1 double, 1 twin, 1 triple
Bathrooms: 1 private, 1 public
Bed & breakfast

per night:	£min	£max
Single	12.00	14.00
Double	28.00	32.00

Parking for 6
Open March-October

MARGARET RODING

Essex
Map ref 2D1

Greys
Listed
Ongar Road, Margaret Roding, Dunmow CM6 1QR
☎ Good Easter (024 531) 509
Formerly 2 cottages pleasantly situated just off A1060 at telephone kiosk. Beamed throughout, large garden. Tea/coffee available. Children over 10 years welcome. Singles by arrangement. Non-smokers only please.
Bedrooms: 2 double, 1 twin
Bathrooms: 1 public
Bed & breakfast

per night:	£min	£max
Double		32.00

Parking for 6

MATTISHALL

Norfolk
Map ref 3B1

Matsall House
Church Lane, Mattishall, Burgh, Norwich NR20 3QZ
☎ (0362) 858112
New 5-bedroomed house in quiet setting on edge of village. From Mattishall, north down Burgh Lane, turn right after 'phone box, shingle drive on right hand side.
Bedrooms: 2 single, 1 double, 1 twin
Bathrooms: 1 private, 2 public
Bed & breakfast

per night:	£min	£max
Single	15.00	18.00
Double	30.00	35.00

Parking for 4

MAXEY

Cambridgeshire
Map ref 3A1

Abbey House 🅜
APPROVED
West End Road, Maxey, Peterborough PE6 9EJ
☎ Market Deeping (0778) 344642
Listed former rectory, close to historic Stamford. Ideal for touring the eastern shires with their abundance of abbeys, cathedrals, stately
Continued ▶

MAXEY

Continued

homes and attractive stone villages.
Bedrooms: 1 single, 3 double, 3 twin, 1 triple
Bathrooms: 5 private, 1 public

Bed & breakfast per night:	£min	£max
Single	16.00	27.00
Double	28.00	42.00

Parking for 12
🐴 6 ♿ 📺 ☕ [UL] 🍾 [S] 🚭 🛏 [TV] ♨ 🧺 ☎ ❀ ✈ 🚐 🏛

MELTON CONSTABLE

Norfolk
Map ref 3B1

Burgh Parva Hall

Melton Constable NR24 2PU
☎ (0263) 860797
16th C farmhouse with large bedrooms, in rural position on edge of Melton Constable, ideally situated for coast and whole of Norfolk.
Bedrooms: 1 double, 1 twin
Bathrooms: 1 public

Bed & breakfast per night:	£min	£max
Single	15.00	
Double	30.00	

Parking for 3
🐴 ✂ ☕ [UL] [S] 🛏 ♨ 🧺 ❀ 🚐 [SP] 🏛

MUNDESLEY

Norfolk
Map ref 3C1

Small seaside resort with a superb sandy beach and excellent bathing. Nearby is a smock-mill still with cap and sails.

The Grange

High Street, Mundesley-on-Sea, Norwich NR11 8JL
☎ (0263) 721556
Beautiful, well-furnished house with friendly atmosphere, in attractive garden. Ideal for the Broads and Norwich, bird-watching, fishing and the beach.
Bedrooms: 2 double, 1 twin, 1 triple
Bathrooms: 2 public

Bed & breakfast per night:	£min	£max
Single	14.00	16.00
Double	28.00	32.00

Parking for 10
🐴 2 ☕ [UL] 🚭 🛏 [TV] ♨ 🧺 ❀ ✈ 🚐 [SP]

NAYLAND

Suffolk
Map ref 3B2

Charmingly located village on the River Stour owing its former prosperity to the cloth trade. The hub of the village is the 15th C Alston Court. The altar-piece of St James Church was painted by John Constable.

Gladwins Farm M

♛♛

Harpers Hill, Nayland, Colchester CO6 4NU
☎ (0206) 262261
Fax (0206) 263238
22-acre smallholding. Timbered farmhouse in peaceful wooded surroundings in Constable country. Entrance on A134. Trout fishing, tennis. Golf 2 miles. Home and local produce. Brochure.
Bedrooms: 2 single, 1 double, 1 twin, 1 multiple
Bathrooms: 2 private, 1 public

Bed & breakfast per night:	£min	£max
Single	17.50	21.00
Double	35.00	50.00

Parking for 5
Cards accepted: Access, Visa, Amex
🐴 📺 ☕ [UL] [S] 🛏 [TV] ♨ 🧺 🔍 🎣 ⛳ 🎾 ❀ 🚐 [OAP] [SP]

NEATISHEAD

Norfolk
Map ref 3C1

Regency Guest House

♛♛

The Street, Neatishead, Norwich NR12 8AD
☎ Horning (0692) 630233
Ideal location for Broads boating/fishing activities. Accent on personal service. 10 miles from Norwich off A1151. 6 miles from coast. Tea-making facilities/TV in all rooms. Renowned for generous English breakfasts.
Bedrooms: 2 double, 1 twin
Bathrooms: 3 private, 2 public

Bed & breakfast per night:	£min	£max
Single	18.00	
Double	34.00	

Parking for 8
🐴 🗔 📺 ☕ [UL] 🍾 [S] 🚭 🛏 🧺 🎣 ❀ 🚐 [OAP] ✎ [SP] 🏛 [T]

NORFOLK BROADS

See under Aylsham, Beccles, Belaugh, Brundall, Bungay, Burgh St Peter, Cawston, Coltishall, Great Yarmouth, Hevingham, Horsford, Loddon, Lowestoft, Neatishead, North Walsham, Norwich, Oulton Broad, Rollesby, Salhouse, Wroxham

NORTH ELMHAM

Norfolk
Map ref 3B1

Millers Old Cottage M

Listed [COMMENDED]

High Street, North Elmham, Dereham NR20 5JX
☎ (0362) 668813
Large 17th C beamed cottage in historic Saxon village, close to cathedral ruins. Centrally situated, ideal base for touring Norfolk.
Bedrooms: 2 double
Bathrooms: 1 private, 1 public

Bed & breakfast per night:	£min	£max
Single	13.00	17.00
Double	26.00	30.00

Parking for 2
🐴 10 📺 ☕ [UL] [S] 🚭 ♨ 🧺 ❀ ✈ 🚐 [OAP] [SP] 🏛

NORTH WALSHAM

Norfolk
Map ref 3C1

Weekly market has been held here for 700 years. 1 mile south of town is a cross commemorating the Peasants' Revolt of 1381. Nelson attended the local Paston Grammar School, founded in 1606 and still flourishing.

Beechwood Hotel M

♛♛♛ [COMMENDED]

20 Cromer Road, North Walsham NR28 0HD
☎ (0692) 403231
In its own gardens with many roses, shrubs, large trees, extensive lawns and numerous rhododendrons.
Bedrooms: 1 single, 2 double, 3 twin, 5 triple
Bathrooms: 7 private, 2 public

Bed & breakfast per night:	£min	£max
Single	22.00	25.00
Double	44.00	50.00

Half board per person:	£min	£max
Daily	33.00	36.00
Weekly	148.00	209.00

Evening meal 1900 (last orders 1930)
Parking for 11
🐴 5 ♿ ☕ 🛏 [TV] ♨ 🧺 ● ❀ 🚐 [SP] [T]

Geoffrey the Dyer House

♛♛

Church Plain, Worstead, North Walsham NR28 9AL
☎ Smallburgh (0692) 536562
Carefully restored 17th C weaver's residence, full of character and comfort, close to beach, Broads and Norwich. In centre of conservation village.
Bedrooms: 2 double, 1 twin
Bathrooms: 3 private

Bed & breakfast per night:	£min	£max
Single	20.00	23.00
Double	32.00	36.00

Half board per person:	£min	£max
Daily	26.00	29.00

Lunch available
Evening meal 1830 (last orders 2200)
Parking for 4
🐴 🗔 📺 ☕ [UL] 🍾 [S] 🚭 🛏 [TV] ♨ 🚐 🏛

NORWICH

Norfolk
Map ref 3C1

Beautiful cathedral city and county town on the River Wensum with many fine museums and medieval churches. Norman castle, Guildhall and interesting medieval streets. Good shopping centre and market.
Tourist Information Centre ☎ (0603) 666071 or (accommodation) 761082

99 Desmond Drive

Listed [APPROVED]

Old Catton, Norwich NR6 7JR
☎ (0603) 427705
Homely, clean and friendly accommodation in private house situated approximately 4 miles north of Norwich, 2 miles from Airport and 6 miles from Wroxham.
Bedrooms: 1 single, 1 double
Bathrooms: 1 public

Bed & breakfast

per night:	£min	£max
Single	12.00	13.00
Double	22.00	26.00

Parking for 2

♨ 3 ⚒ ♿ ▣ ☎ ♦ ⛔ ⛨ 📺 ▥. 🛏 ☆ ✗ 🚲

Androse House

272 Unthank Road, Norwich
NR2 2AJ
☎ (0603) 54276
Attractive Edwardian family house and garden in fine area near city, university and bus routes. Pleasant bedrooms and a warm welcome.
Bedrooms: 1 double, 1 twin
Bathrooms: 1 public
Bed & breakfast

per night:	£min	£max
Single	16.00	17.00
Double	29.00	32.00

Parking for 3

♨ ♦ ▣ ⛔ ⓢ ⛨ 📺 ▥. 🛏 🚲

Arodet House
⚏

132 Earlham Road, Norwich
NR2 3HF
☎ (0603) 503522
Modernised Victorian guesthouse offering personal attention. Convenient for city centre and university.
Bedrooms: 2 single, 2 double
Bathrooms: 1 private,
1 public
Bed & breakfast

per night:	£min	£max
Single	15.00	16.00
Double	30.00	37.00

♨ ♦ ▣ ⓘ ⓢ ⛨ 📺 ▥. 🛏 🚲

Cumberland Hotel ⚏
⚏⚏⚏ APPROVED

212-216 Thorpe Road,
Norwich NR1 1TJ
☎ (0603) 34550 & 34560
Fax (0603) 33355
*Close to city centre in elevated position with ample private parking.
Independently-run hotel offering personal and friendly service.*
Bedrooms: 9 single,
9 double, 3 twin, 5 triple,
1 multiple
Bathrooms: 27 private,
3 public
Bed & breakfast

per night:	£min	£max
Single	36.50	59.50
Double	44.90	70.00

Half board

per person:	£min	£max
Daily	32.00	44.00
Weekly	199.00	305.00

Lunch available
Evening meal 1830 (last orders 2130)
Parking for 63
Cards accepted: Access, Visa, Diners, Amex, Switch

♨ ⚒ ♿ ▣ ♦ ⛔ ⓢ ⛨ 📺 ▥. 📺 ⓞ ▥. 🛏 ⛽ ⇕ 8-30 🍴 ⓞ̲ᴀ̲ᴘ̲ ⓢ̲ᴘ̲ ⓣ

Gables Farm ⚏
⚏⚏⚏ HIGHLY COMMENDED

Hemblington Hall Road,
Hemblington, Norwich
NR13 4PT
☎ South Walsham (060 549) 548
Fax (060 549) 548
Delightful listed 17th C thatched farmhouse in a large garden surrounded by farmland. Within easy reach of Broads, coast and nature reserves. Non-smokers only please.
Bedrooms: 1 twin, 1 triple,
1 multiple
Bathrooms: 2 private
Bed & breakfast

per night:	£min	£max
Single		21.00
Double		35.00

Parking for 6

♨ 8 ▣ ♦ ⛔ ⓡ ⛨ 📺 ▥. ☆ ✗ 🚲 🏠

Grange Hotel ⚏
⚏⚏⚏ APPROVED

230 Thorpe Road, Norwich
NR1 1TJ
☎ (0603) 34734
Friendly family-run hotel convenient for city, Broadland and coast. Popular a la carte restaurant using fresh local produce. Ample car parking.
Bedrooms: 17 single,
12 double, 4 twin, 2 triple
Bathrooms: 30 private,
2 public
Bed & breakfast

per night:	£min	£max
Single	25.00	35.00
Double	35.00	50.00

Half board

per person:	£min	£max
Daily	37.50	47.50

Lunch available
Evening meal 1830 (last orders 2100)
Parking for 48
Cards accepted: Access, Visa, Diners, Amex

♨ ⚒ ♿ ▣ ♦ ▣ ⛨ ✗ 🚲 ▥. 🛏 ⛽ ⇕ 12-80 🍴 ⚒ ✗ ⓞ̲ᴀ̲ᴘ̲ ⓢ̲ᴘ̲ ⓣ

Kingsley Lodge ⚏
⚏⚏ COMMENDED

3 Kingsley Road, Norwich
NR1 3RB
☎ (0603) 615819
Quiet house in the city centre close to bus station, offering spacious rooms, each with en-
suite bathroom and WC. Non-smokers only please.
Bedrooms: 1 single,
2 double, 1 twin
Bathrooms: 4 private
Bed & breakfast

per night:	£min	£max
Single	23.00	25.00
Double	36.00	36.00

Open February-December

❑ ♦ ▣ ⓢ ⛨ ⛔ ▥. 🛏 ✗ 🚲

The Limes
Listed

188 Unthank Road, Norwich
NR2 2AH
☎ (0603) 54282
Large, comfortable rooms, close to the city centre and university. Run by a young, friendly family. Full fire certificate.
Bedrooms: 2 single,
1 double, 1 twin, 1 triple
Bathrooms: 2 public
Bed & breakfast

per night:	£min	£max
Single	16.00	17.00
Double	30.00	32.00

♨ ❑ ♦ ▣ ⓘ ⓢ 📺 ▥. 🛏 🚲 ⓞ̲ᴀ̲ᴘ̲ ⓢ̲ᴘ̲

Oakfield
⚏⚏⚏ HIGHLY COMMENDED

Yelverton Road, Framingham
Earl, Norwich NR14 7SD
☎ Framingham Earl (050 86) 2605
Bungalow in beautiful, quiet setting next to Framingham Earl church, 4 miles from Norwich. Children over 12 welcome. No smoking allowed. Double room has en-suite facilities.
Bedrooms: 1 single,
1 double, 1 twin
Bathrooms: 1 private,
1 public
Bed & breakfast

per night:	£min	£max
Single	15.00	17.00
Double	28.00	32.00

Parking for 6

♨ 12 ⚒ ♦ ▣ ⛔ ⛨ 📺 ▥. 🛏 ☆ ✗ 🚲 ⓞ̲ᴀ̲ᴘ̲

The Old Rectory ⚏

Watton Road, Little Melton, Norwich NR9 3PB
☎ (0603) 812121 & 810279
Fax (0603) 812121
Beautiful Victorian country house in 3.5 acres. Croquet lawn, pitch and putt. Log fires. 10 minutes from city centre, convenient for Broads and coast.
Bedrooms: 1 single, 2 double
Bathrooms: 1 private,
1 public

Bed & breakfast

per night:	£min	£max
Single	25.00	35.00
Double	40.00	45.00

Parking for 10

♨ 10 ▣ ❑ ♦ ⛔ ⛨ ⛨ 📺 ▥. ∪ ▶ ☆ ⓢ̲ᴘ̲ ⓣ

Shambles Guest House

55 Caernarvon Road,
Norwich NR2 3HZ
☎ (0603) 610704
Large 19th C house. Use of garden. 5 minutes from city centre, just off Earlham road. Evening meal available on request.
Bedrooms: 4 single, 3 twin,
1 triple, 1 multiple
Bathrooms: 1 private,
3 public, 1 private shower
Bed & breakfast

per night:	£min	£max
Single	12.00	18.00
Double	24.00	34.00

Half board

per person:	£min	£max
Daily	18.00	26.00
Weekly	120.00	140.00

Evening meal 1700 (last orders 1900)
Parking for 2

♨ ⚒ ❑ ♦ ▣ ⓘ ⛨ 📺 ▥. 🛏 ☆ ⓞ̲ᴀ̲ᴘ̲ ⓢ̲ᴘ̲

Witton Hall
Listed

Norwich NR13 5DN
☎ (0603) 714580
Elegant Georgian farmhouse in the heart of Norfolk. Peaceful, mature grounds. Swimming pool in walled garden.
Bedrooms: 1 double, 1 twin,
1 triple
Bathrooms: 3 private
Bed & breakfast

per night:	£min	£max
Single	15.00	16.50
Double	30.00	33.00

Parking for 4
Open April-October

♨ ❑ ♦ ▣ ⛔ ⛨ 📺 ▥. 🛏 ⇘ ☆ 🚲

There are separate sections in this guide listing groups specialising in farm holidays and accommodation which is especially suitable for young people and organised groups.

ORFORD

Suffolk
Map ref 3C2

Once a thriving port, now a quiet village of brick and timber buildings, famous for its castle. Orford comes to life during the summer when boats tie up at the quay.

King's Head Inn ⚐

Front Street, Orford, Woodbridge IP12 2LW
☎ (0394) 450271
Tiny inn with open fires, friendly atmosphere and personal service. Proprietor's own cooking with seafood specialities.
Bedrooms: 4 double, 1 twin, 1 triple
Bathrooms: 2 public

Bed & breakfast

per night:	£min	£max
Single	23.00	24.00
Double	38.00	40.00

Lunch available
Evening meal 1900 (last orders 2100)
Parking for 52
Cards accepted: Diners
🛇🖵♿🛏♨ⓈⅢ.🛋🕙🚲
SP 🏰

OULTON BROAD

Suffolk
Map ref 3C1

Oulton Broad is the most southerly of the Broads and is the centre of a very busy boating industry.

Ivy House Farm ⚐

😑😑 HIGHLY COMMENDED

Beccles Road, Oulton Broad, Lowestoft NR33 8HY
☎ Lowestoft (0502) 501353
Farmhouse adjacent to Oulton Broad and nature reserve. Offers log fires and well-appointed en-suite rooms with views.
Bedrooms: 1 double, 2 twin
Bathrooms: 3 private

Bed & breakfast

per night:	£min	£max
Single	30.00	32.00
Double	43.00	45.00

Parking for 8
Cards accepted: Access, Visa
🛇🖵♿🖵🛏♨ⓌⅢ.
🛋🕙🚲

> Please mention this guide when making a booking.

QUIDENHAM

Norfolk
Map ref 3C1

Manor Farm
Listed

Quidenham, Norwich NR16 2NY
☎ (0953) 87540
950-acre arable farm. Large secluded farmhouse set in beautiful surroundings. Home cooking, fresh vegetables, own eggs.
Bedrooms: 2 single, 1 double, 1 twin
Bathrooms: 1 public

Bed & breakfast

per night:	£min	£max
Single	15.00	
Double	30.00	

Half board

per person:	£min	£max
Daily	25.00	

Evening meal 1900 (last orders 2000)
Parking for 10
🛇🖵6♿ⓌⓈ✠🕙Ⅲ.🛋🔍
✿✕

RADWINTER

Essex
Map ref 3B2

The Plough Inn
😑

Sampford Road, Radwinter, Saffron Walden CB10 2TL
☎ (0799) 599222
16th C inn with lovely garden views of countryside. Self-contained accommodation in garden. Lunch and evening meal available in the pub. 5 miles from Saffron Walden and 6 miles from Finchingfield.
Bedrooms: 1 double, 1 twin
Bathrooms: 2 private

Bed & breakfast

per night:	£min	£max
Single	22.00	22.00
Double	36.00	36.00

Lunch available
Evening meal 1900 (last orders 2200)
Parking for 20
♿🖵🖵♨Ⓢ Ⅲ.✿✕🚲🏰

RAMSEY

Cambridgeshire
Map ref 3A2

The Leys

25 Bury Road, Ramsey, Huntingdon PE17 1NE
☎ (0487) 813221 & 710053
Large family house with a friendly atmosphere. On B1040 on the southern

outskirts of Ramsey, between Huntingdon and Peterborough.
Bedrooms: 1 single, 1 twin, 2 triple
Bathrooms: 2 public

Bed & breakfast

per night:	£min	£max
Single	10.00	12.00
Double	20.00	30.00

Parking for 10
🛇🗙♿🖵♨Ⓦ Ⓢ ✠🕙Ⅲ.
🛋✕✿🚲

ROLLESBY

Norfolk
Map ref 3C1

Rollesby Broad forms part of the Ormesby Broad complex and fine views can be seen from the road which runs through the middle.

The Old Court House ⚐

😑😑 COMMENDED

Court Road, Rollesby, Great Yarmouth NR29 5HG
☎ Fleggburgh (0493) 369665
Small family-run hotel set in a peaceful rural location near the Broads. Private bar and swimming pool, games area. Bicycles for hire. Tennis, fishing and riding nearby. Home cooking.
Bedrooms: 2 double, 1 twin, 1 triple, 3 multiple
Bathrooms: 5 private, 2 public

Bed & breakfast

per night:	£min	£max
Double	36.00	43.00

Half board

per person:	£min	£max
Daily	26.00	29.50
Weekly	164.00	185.00

Evening meal 1830 (last orders 2100)
Parking for 20
Open February-November
🛇♿🖵♨Ⓢ✠🕙Ⅲ.🛋
✠🔍🔍♉Ⓤ⬆✿🚲🏰

> Individual proprietors have supplied all details of accommodation. Although we do check for accuracy, we advise you to confirm the information at the time of booking.

SAFFRON WALDEN

Essex
Map ref 2D1

Takes its name from the saffron crocus once grown around the town. The church of St Mary has superb carvings, magnificent roofs and brasses. A town maze can be seen on the common. 2 miles southwest is Audley End, a magnificent Jacobean mansion owned by English Heritage.
Tourist Information Centre
☎ *(0799) 524282*

1 Gunters Cottages
😑😑

Thaxted Road, Saffron Walden CB10 2UT
☎ (0799) 522091
Rebuilt 19th C cottages with views over open farmland. On Thaxted/Saffron Walden road, 2 miles from Saffron Walden.
Bedrooms: 1 single, 2 double
Bathrooms: 1 private, 1 public

Bed & breakfast

per night:	£min	£max
Single		12.00
Double	26.00	30.00

Parking for 6
🛇♿🖵♨ⓌⅢ.✠🕙Ⅲ.,♞
✕🚲

Beam End
😑 COMMENDED

Duck Street, Wendens Ambo, Saffron Walden CB11 4JU
☎ (0799) 41057
Thatched cottage in a quiet lane with lovely peaceful gardens, overlooking open fields. Local pub provides good choice of food.
Bedrooms: 1 double, 1 twin
Bathrooms: 1 public

Bed & breakfast

per night:	£min	£max
Single		18.00
Double		32.00

Parking for 4
🛇12♿🖵♨ⓌⅢ✠🕙Ⅲ.,♞
✿✕🚲🏰

The Delles
Listed HIGHLY COMMENDED

Carmen Street, Great Chesterford, Saffron Walden CB10 1NR
☎ (0799) 30256
Tudor/Georgian house with beautiful gardens in centre of village. Close to Saffron Walden and Duxford, convenient for Cambridge. Half-mile from M11.

Bedrooms: 2 double, 1 twin
Bathrooms: 2 public

Bed & breakfast per night:	£min	£max
Single	16.00	22.00
Double		32.00

Parking for 6
🚸 2 ☰ ▭ ☕ [UL] [S] ✈ [TV] ▥ ✿ 🚌 🏠 [T]

Duddenhoe End Farm
[HIGHLY COMMENDED]
Duddenhoe End, Saffron Walden CB11 4UU
☎ Royston (0763) 838258
230-acre mixed farm. 17th C farmhouse with a wealth of beams and inglenook fireplace, situated in a quiet rural area.
Bedrooms: 2 double, 1 twin
Bathrooms: 3 private

Bed & breakfast per night:	£min	£max
Single	20.00	22.00
Double	35.00	38.00

Parking for 3
🚸 12 ☰ ☕ [UL] ✈ [TV] ▥ ✿ 🚌

Pond Mead
[Listed]
Widdington, Saffron Walden CB11 3SB
☎ (0799) 40201
Large rambling old house with 1.5 acres of garden on the edge of the village of Widdington (population of 650), about 4 miles south of Saffron Walden.
Bedrooms: 1 single, 1 double, 1 triple
Bathrooms: 1 private, 1 public

Bed & breakfast per night:	£min	£max
Single	12.00	17.00

Parking for 5
🚸 ☰ ▭ ☕ [UL] ▥ ✿ 🚌

Rockells Farm
[Crown rating]
Duddenhoe End, Saffron Walden CB11 4UY
☎ Royston (0763) 838053
420-acre arable farm. Georgian house in rolling countryside with plenty of opportunities for walking and sightseeing. The 3-acre lake provides excellent fishing. Stansted Airport 20 minutes by car, Cambridge 30 minutes.
Bedrooms: 1 single, 1 twin, 1 triple
Bathrooms: 3 private, 1 public

Bed & breakfast per night:	£min	£max
Single	16.00	18.00
Double	32.00	36.00

Half board per person:	£min	£max
Daily	23.00	25.00
Weekly	145.00	165.00

Evening meal from 1800
Parking for 4
🚸 [G] ☰ ☕ [UL] 🔒 ✈ [TV] ▥ ✿ 🚌

Rowley Hill Lodge
[Listed]
Little Walden, Saffron Walden CB10 1UZ
☎ (0799) 525975
Secluded and amidst open countryside, this pre-Victorian farm lodge lies only 1 mile from the historic town of Saffron Walden.
Bedrooms: 1 single, 1 twin
Bathrooms: 1 private, 1 public

Bed & breakfast per night:	£min	£max
Single	15.00	15.00
Double	30.00	30.00

Parking for 4
🚸 ▭ ☕ [UL] [S] ▥ ✿ 🚌

Saffron Hotel
[COMMENDED]
10-18 High Street, Saffron Walden CB10 1AY
☎ (0799) 22676
Fax (0799) 513979
Telex 81653
16th C hotel in market town. South of Cambridge, close to Duxford Air Museum and Stansted Airport.
Bedrooms: 5 single, 9 double, 8 twin, 1 triple
Bathrooms: 18 private, 1 public, 2 private showers

Bed & breakfast per night:	£min	£max
Single	30.00	45.00
Double	50.00	80.00

Half board per person:	£min	£max
Daily	43.50	60.00

Lunch available
Evening meal 1830 (last orders 2130)
Parking for 8
Cards accepted: Access, Visa, Diners, Amex
🚸 [G] ☎ ☰ ▭ ☕ 🔒 [S] ✈ ▥ [SP] 🏠 [T]

Map references apply to the colour maps at the back of this guide.

SALHOUSE
Norfolk
Map ref 3C1

Village above the tree-fringed Salhouse Broad. The church of All Saints has a thatched roof and a 14th C arcade.

Brooks Bank
[COMMENDED]
Lower Street, Salhouse, Norwich NR13 6RW
☎ Norwich (0603) 720420
18th C house situated in the centre of Broadland. Guests' own private accommodation. Illustrated brochure. Our pleasure is your comfort.
Bedrooms: 1 double, 1 twin, 1 triple
Bathrooms: 3 private

Bed & breakfast per night:	£min	£max
Single	18.00	22.00
Double	28.00	34.00

Half board per person:	£min	£max
Daily	26.50	30.50

Parking for 4
🚸 3 [G] ☰ ▭ ☕ [UL] 🔒 ✈ [TV] ▥ ✿ 🚌

SHERINGHAM
Norfolk
Map ref 3B1

Holiday resort with Victorian and Edwardian hotels and a sand and shingle beach where the fishing boats are hauled up. The North Norfolk Railway operates from Sheringham Station during the summer. Other attractions include museums, theatre and Splash Fun Pool.

Beeston Hills Lodge
64 Cliff Road, Sheringham NR26 8BJ
☎ (0263) 825936
Family-run Edwardian lodge ideally situated with superb sea views. Next to hills, putting green, cliff walks and near the beach.
Bedrooms: 1 double, 2 twin, 1 triple
Bathrooms: 1 public, 1 private shower

Bed & breakfast per night:	£min	£max
Single	13.50	21.00
Double	27.50	42.00

Parking for 5
Open February-October
🚸 ☰ ▭ ☕ [UL] 🔒 [S] ✈ [TV] ▥ ✿ 🚌 [OAP] [SP] 🏠

Camberley
62 Cliff Road, Sheringham NR26 8BJ
☎ (0263) 823101
In its own grounds, overlooking sea, town and surrounding countryside. Slipway to beach directly opposite. Family-run.
Bedrooms: 3 double
Bathrooms: 3 private, 1 public

Bed & breakfast per night:	£min	£max
Single	16.00	17.00
Double	32.00	34.00

Parking for 3
🚸 ☕ [UL] ✈ [TV] ▥ 🚌 [SP]

The Two Lifeboats Hotel
[APPROVED]
2 The High Street, Sheringham NR26 8JR
☎ (0263) 822401
Fax (0263) 823130
Situated just 30 yards from the beach, with exceptional sea views.
Bedrooms: 3 single, 2 double, 4 twin, 1 triple
Bathrooms: 7 private, 1 public

Bed & breakfast per night:	£min	£max
Single	26.00	
Double	60.00	

Half board per person:	£min	£max
Daily	44.00	
Weekly	278.00	

Lunch available
Evening meal 1830 (last orders 2130)
Cards accepted: Access, Visa
🚸 ▭ ☕ 🔒 [S] ✈ ▥ 🚌 🏠

SHIPDHAM
Norfolk
Map ref 3B1

Massingham Manor
High Street, Shipdham, Thetford IP25 7PA
☎ Dereham (0362) 820228 & 820747
17th C house with beamed ceilings and large inglenook. Traditional farmhouse kitchen, separate dining room and guests' hall/sitting room.
Bedrooms: 1 single, 2 double, 1 twin, 1 triple

Continued ▶

SHIPDHAM

Continued

Bathrooms: 1 private,
2 public
Bed & breakfast

per night:	£min	£max
Single	15.00	18.00
Double	25.00	35.00

Parking for 10
Cards accepted: Access, Visa
🏃 12 🗗 🛏 � 🖐 💷 📺 🛏, 🚗
🌼 ✕ 🛒 SP 🏨

SOUTHEND-ON-SEA

Essex
Map ref 3B3

On the Thames Estuary
and the nearest seaside
resort to London. Famous
for its pier and unique pier
trains. Other attractions
include Peter Pan's
Playground, indoor
swimming pools, indoor
rollerskating and ten pin
bowling.
Tourist Information Centre
☎ *(0702) 355122 or
355120*

Aldridge Guest House

Listed   APPROVED

17 Hartington Road,
Southend-on-Sea SS1 2HR
☎ (0702) 614555
*Friendly accommodation with
comfortable bedrooms, close
to seafront, pier and shops.
Choice of breakfast served in
your room.*
Bedrooms: 1 single,
1 double, 2 twin, 1 triple
Bathrooms: 1 private,
1 public, 1 private shower
Bed & breakfast

per night:	£min	£max
Single	12.00	13.00
Double	22.00	24.00

🏃 🗗 ⓦ 🖐 💷 S 🛏, 🚗 ✕ 🛒
SP T

Roslin Hotel ⋀

⛤⛤⛤   COMMENDED

Thorpe Esplanade, Thorpe
Bay, Southend-on-Sea
SS1 3BG
☎ (0702) 586375
Fax (0702) 586663
*Hotel overlooking the Thames
Estuary in residential Thorpe.
Within easy reach of
Southend and 45 minutes
from London. Live
entertainment Friday and
Saturday.*
Bedrooms: 9 single,
13 double, 14 twin, 4 triple
Bathrooms: 40 private

Bed & breakfast

per night:	£min	£max
Single	38.00	60.00
Double	62.00	70.00

Half board

per person:	£min	£max
Daily	35.00	50.00
Weekly	270.00	310.00

Lunch available
Evening meal 1830 (last
orders 2200)
Parking for 34
Cards accepted: Access, Visa,
Diners, Amex, Switch
🏃 🛁 📞 🖃 🗗 🖐 🔌 🛎 S 📺
◑ 🛏, 🚗 🏊 14-30 DAP 🏊 SP T

SOUTHWOLD

Suffolk
Map ref 3C2

Pleasant and attractive
seaside town with a
triangular market square
and spacious greens
around which stand flint,
brick and colour-washed
cottages. The parish
church of St. Edmund is
one of the greatest
churches in Suffolk.

16 Dunwich Road

Southwold IP18 6LJ
☎ (0502) 722218
*Victorian terrace in
Southwold, 200 yards from
the beach.*
Bedrooms: 2 double, 1 twin
Bathrooms: 1 public
Bed & breakfast

per night:	£min	£max
Single	18.00	25.00
Double	30.00	38.00

🏃 🗗 🖐 💷 🛏, 🏃 🛒

28 Field Stile Road

Southwold IP18 6LD
☎ (0502) 723588
*Tastefully decorated Victorian
house, close to beach and
town centre. Ground floor
bedroom, high standard of
home cooking. Pets welcome.*
Bedrooms: 1 single,
1 double, 1 twin
Bathrooms: 1 public
Bed & breakfast

per night:	£min	£max
Single	24.00	24.00
Double	35.00	35.00

Half board

per person:	£min	£max
Daily	36.00	47.00

Lunch available
Evening meal 1830 (last
orders 2130)
🏃 5 🗗 🔌 🛎 🔌 S 🛏 📺 🛏, 🚗
🛒 🛒

Dunburgh Guest House

28 North Parade, Southwold
IP18 6LT
☎ (0502) 723253
*Elegant, comfortably
furnished Victorian house on
seafront, 5 minutes' walk
from charming town centre.
Friendly atmosphere.*
Bedrooms: 2 double, 1 twin
Bathrooms: 2 private,
2 public
Bed & breakfast

per night:	£min	£max
Single	20.00	22.00
Double	36.00	44.00

Evening meal 1900 (last
orders 1900)
🏃 5 🗗 🔌 🖐 💷 🛎 S 🛏 📺 🛏, 🛒

No 3 Cautley Road

⛤⛤

Southwold IP18 6DD
☎ (0502) 723611
*No 3 is an elegant,
Edwardian family town house.
All en-suite rooms. Evening
meals on request. 5 minutes'
walk to sea and shops.*
Bedrooms: 2 double, 1 twin
Bathrooms: 3 private
Bed & breakfast

per night:	£min	£max
Double	40.00	50.00

Half board

per person:	£min	£max
Daily	30.00	35.00
Weekly	210.00	250.00

Evening meal 1830 (last
orders 2000)
🏃 📞 🖃 🗗 🖐 🔌 💷 S 🛏,
🚗 🛒

STEEPLE BUMPSTEAD

Essex
Map ref 3B2

An interesting building in
the village is the Moot
Hall, which in the 17th C
served as a village school
and was restored as part
of the 1977 Jubilee
celebrations.

Yew Tree House

Listed

15 Chapel Street, Steeple
Bumpstead, Haverhill,
Suffolk CB9 7DQ
☎ (0440) 730364
*Charming Victorian house,
with many period features, in
the centre of Steeple
Bumpstead.*
Bedrooms: 1 double, 1 twin
Bathrooms: 1 public

Bed & breakfast

per night:	£min	£max
Single	17.00	21.00
Double	26.00	35.00

Half board

per person:	£min	£max
Daily	20.50	24.50
Weekly	140.00	168.00

Evening meal 1800 (last
orders 2000)
Parking for 2
🏃 2 🔌 🖐 📺 🛏, ✕ 🛒 🏨

STOKE HOLY CROSS

Norfolk
Map ref 3C1

Salamanca Farm ⋀

⛤⛤

Stoke Holy Cross, Norwich
NR14 8QJ
☎ Framingham Earl (050
86) 2322 changing to (0508)
492322
*175-acre mixed farm.
Victorian house offering full
English breakfast. Set in
beautiful undulating country,
4 miles from Norwich.*
Bedrooms: 3 double, 1 twin
Bathrooms: 1 private,
2 public
Bed & breakfast

per night:	£min	£max
Single	14.00	
Double	28.00	

Parking for 8
🏃 6 🔌 🖐 💷 🖐 🔌 📺 🛏, 🌼 ✕ 🛒

STOWMARKET

Suffolk
Map ref 3B2

Small market town where
routes converge. There is
an open-air museum of
rural life at the Museum
of East Anglian Life.
Tourist Information Centre
☎ *(0449) 676800*

50 Temple Road

Listed

Stowmarket IP14 1AT
☎ (0449) 674673
*Edwardian house with family
atmosphere. Evening meal
available by arrangement.*
Bedrooms: 1 double, 1 twin,
1 triple
Bathrooms: 1 public
Bed & breakfast

per night:	£min	£max
Single	14.00	14.00
Double	28.00	28.00

Half board		
per person:	£min	£max
Daily	19.00	19.00

Evening meal 1830 (last orders 1200)

🛏🚶♿🖥💷🛎🅿📺🎰 ▱🎪

STRATFORD ST MARY

Suffolk
Map ref 3B2

Set in countryside known as Constable Country.

Rosebank
Lower Street, Stratford St Mary, Colchester CO7 6JS
☎ (0206) 322259
Part of 600-year-old Tudor manor house in Constable Country. Gardens with river frontage. Weekend breaks with evening meal November to March.
Bedrooms: 1 double, 2 twin, 1 triple
Bathrooms: 1 private, 1 public

Bed & breakfast		
per night:	£min	£max
Single	16.50	22.00
Double	30.00	33.00

Parking for 6

🛏🚶♿🖥💷♿🅿🖥💷 ▱🎪

Teazles
Listed
Stratford St Mary, Colchester CO7 6LU
☎ Colchester (0206) 323148
Attractive 16th C country house in heart of Constable Country. Just off A12 on B1029 to Dedham, leaving church on right. Refurbished in 1971, now our family home to which we welcome guests.
Bedrooms: 1 single, 1 double, 1 twin
Bathrooms: 1 private, 2 public

Bed & breakfast		
per night:	£min	£max
Single	15.00	17.50
Double	30.00	35.00

Parking for 7

🛏4🚶♿🖥🛎💷📺▱🎪

STUTTON

Suffolk
Map ref 3B2

School Barn 🏠
💷💷 COMMENDED
Holbrook Road, Stutton, Ipswich IP9 2RY
☎ Holbrook (0473) 327397

Traditional Suffolk barn in attractive garden. In centre of Stutton village, opposite Post Office. Close to Alton Water on B1080, Shotley Peninsula.
Bedrooms: 2 double, 1 twin
Bathrooms: 1 private, 2 public

Bed & breakfast		
per night:	£min	£max
Single	24.00	
Double	38.00	48.00

Parking for 3

🏠🚶♿🖥💷📺▱🎪🅿🎪 🎪🏢

SUDBOURNE

Suffolk
Map ref 3C2

Long Meadows
Listed
Gorse Lane, Sudbourne, Woodbridge IP12 2BD
☎ Orford (0394) 450269
Attractive cottage-style bungalow with show garden in rural location within the village. Consideration to guests' comfort and needs paramount.
Bedrooms: 1 single, 1 double, 1 twin
Bathrooms: 1 private, 1 public

Bed & breakfast		
per night:	£min	£max
Single	14.00	15.00
Double	28.00	30.00

Parking for 4

🚶♿🖥💷📺▱🅿🎪🎪

SUDBURY

Suffolk
Map ref 3B2

Former important cloth and market town on the River Stour. Birthplace of Thomas Gainsborough whose home is now an art gallery and museum. The Corn Exchange is an excellent example of early Victorian civic building.

Angel Inn
43 Friars Street, Sudbury CO10 6AG
☎ (0787) 79038
Inn with Tudor exterior and a friendly atmosphere.
Bedrooms: 2 single, 4 double, 1 triple
Bathrooms: 2 public

Bed & breakfast		
per night:	£min	£max
Single	20.00	20.00
Double	30.00	30.00

Half board		
per person:	£min	£max
Daily	20.00	25.00

Lunch available
Evening meal 1800 (last orders 2200)
Cards accepted: Access, Visa

🛏🚶♿🖥💷🛎▱🅿🔑🎰🎪🏢

St. Mary Hall
COMMENDED
Belchamp Walter, Sudbury CO10 7BB
☎ Great Yeldham (0787) 237202
Lovely medieval manor house, with beautiful garden, surrounded by quiet countryside. Tennis court, croquet lawn, swimming pool. From A604 at Great Yeldham on A131 at Sudbury take connecting road. Take turning signed Belchamp Walter 1 mile west of Gestingthorpe.
Bedrooms: 2 single, 1 double, 1 twin
Bathrooms: 2 public

Bed & breakfast		
per night:	£min	£max
Single	22.00	25.00
Double	40.00	50.00

Parking for 4

🛏♿🖥📺▱🅿🔑🎰🎪 🎪🏢

THAXTED

Essex
Map ref 3B2

Small town rich in outstanding buildings and dominated by its hilltop medieval church. The magnificent Guildhall was built by the Cutlers' Guild in the late 14th C. A windmill built in 1804 has been restored and houses a rural museum.

Folly House
💷💷
Watling Lane, Thaxted, Dunmow CM6 2QY
☎ (0371) 830618
Sunny, light, spacious house, with sweeping views over hills, in the historic and picturesque village of Thaxted. Attentive friendly service. Sky TV. Transport to Stansted Airport.
Bedrooms: 1 double, 2 twin
Bathrooms: 1 private, 1 public

Bed & breakfast		
per night:	£min	£max
Single	17.50	20.00
Double	40.00	45.00

Half board		
per person:	£min	£max
Daily	25.00	28.00
Weekly	120.00	150.00

Evening meal 1800 (last orders 2030)
Parking for 4

📺▱🅿🔑🎰🎪

Piggots Mill
💷💷 HIGHLY COMMENDED
Watling Lane, Thaxted, Dunmow CM6 2QY
☎ (0371) 830379
850-acre arable farm. Traditional Essex barn, now a secluded farmhouse in the centre of Thaxted. Garden leads into meadow giving access to attractive walks. Children over 12 welcome.
Bedrooms: 1 double, 1 twin
Bathrooms: 2 private

Bed & breakfast		
per night:	£min	£max
Single	27.00	29.00
Double	39.00	42.00

Parking for 10

🛏12🚶♿🖥♿🖥💷🔑🎰 ▱🅿🔑🎰🎪🎪🎰🏢📺

THETFORD

Norfolk
Map ref 3B2

Small, medieval market town with numerous reminders of its long history: the ruins of the 12th C priory, Iron Age earthworks at Castle Hill and a Norman castle mound. Timber-framed Ancient House is now a museum.

Church Cottage
💷💷 COMMENDED
Breckles, Attleborough NR17 1EW
☎ Great Hockham (0953) 498286
Charming 18th C home in beautiful Breckland. Ideal for touring East Anglia. Own coarse fishing. Heated outdoor swimming pool. Home-made bread. Village 8 miles north-west of Thetford.
Bedrooms: 2 double, 1 twin
Bathrooms: 2 public

Bed & breakfast		
per night:	£min	£max
Single	15.00	15.00
Double	30.00	30.00

Parking for 10

🛏10🎰♿🖥🛎📺▱🅿🔑 🎪🎰🎪🏢

THETFORD

Continued

East Farm

Barnham, Thetford
IP24 2PB
☎ Elveden (084 289) 0231
Friendly, comfortable farmhouse on working farm with large rooms and country views. On outskirts of village. No smoking in bedrooms. En-suite and tea/coffee-making facilities.
Bedrooms: 1 double, 1 twin
Bathrooms: 2 private

Bed & breakfast

per night:	£min	£max
Single	22.00	22.00
Double	38.00	38.00

Parking for 4

Old Bottle House

Cranwich, Mundford,
Thetford IP26 5JL
☎ (0842) 878012
275-year-old former coaching inn, on edge of Thetford Forest. Delicious home cooking, warm welcome.
Bedrooms: 1 single,
1 double, 1 twin, 1 triple
Bathrooms: 1 private,
1 public

Bed & breakfast

per night:	£min	£max
Single	16.50	18.00
Double	33.00	36.00

Half board

per person:	£min	£max
Daily	25.00	32.00
Weekly	145.00	224.00

Evening meal 1800 (last orders 1400)
Parking for 10

THOMPSON

Norfolk
Map ref 3B1

College Farm ⚮

Listed

Thompson, Thetford
IP24 1QG
☎ Caston (095 383) 318
14th C farmhouse, formerly a college of priests. In quiet village away from main road. Meals provided at nearby inns.
Bedrooms: 1 single,
1 double, 2 twin
Bathrooms: 2 public

Bed & breakfast

per night:	£min	£max
Single	16.00	17.00
Double	32.00	34.00

Parking for 10

THORNHAM

Norfolk
Map ref 3B1

The Lifeboat Inn

COMMENDED

Ship Lane, Thornham,
Hunstanton PE36 6LT
☎ (048 526) 236 & 297
Fax (048 526) 323
16th C smugglers' inn just off the main A149, looking across the salt marshes to the sea.
Bedrooms: 3 double, 7 twin,
3 triple
Bathrooms: 13 private

Bed & breakfast

per night:	£min	£max
Single	30.00	35.00
Double	50.00	60.00

Half board

per person:	£min	£max
Daily	40.00	45.00

Lunch available
Evening meal 1900 (last orders 2200)
Parking for 80
Cards accepted: Access, Visa,
Diners

UGLEY

Essex
Map ref 2D1

The Thatch

Listed

Cambridge Road, Ugley,
Bishop's Stortford,
Hertfordshire CM22 6HZ
☎ Rickling (079 988) 440
Partly thatched cottage in half an acre of garden backing on to farmland. Between Stansted and Newport, close to the airport and M11.
Bedrooms: 2 double, 1 twin
Bathrooms: 1 public

Bed & breakfast

per night:	£min	£max
Single	15.00	18.00
Double	30.00	

Parking for 7

WANSFORD

Cambridgeshire
Map ref 3A1

A terminus of the Nene Valley Railway with British and continental steam locomotives and rolling-stock.

Stoneacre

Elton Road, Wansford,
Peterborough PE8 6JT
☎ Stamford (0780) 783283
Rural and secluded with delightful views across the River Nene Valley. Half a mile from Peterborough and Stamford. Large grounds with mini golf-course.
Bedrooms: 3 double, 1 twin,
1 triple
Bathrooms: 3 private,
2 public

Bed & breakfast

per night:	£min	£max
Single	21.00	34.00
Double	27.00	40.00

Parking for 24

WATERBEACH

Cambridgeshire
Map ref 3A2

Denny Abbey has 12th C remains of a church of the Knights Templar.

Goose Hall Farm

Ely Road, Waterbeach,
Cambridge CB5 9PG
☎ (0223) 860235
13-acre market garden. Modern farmhouse in rural setting. 6 miles north of Cambridge on main A10 and close to M11.
Bedrooms: 2 double, 1 twin
Bathrooms: 2 public

Bed & breakfast

per night:	£min	£max
Single	20.00	
Double	30.00	

Parking for 6

WATTON

Norfolk
Map ref 3B1

Moat Farm

Listed

Ashill, Thetford IP25 7BX
☎ Holme Hale (0760)
440357
600-acre mixed farm. Old farmhouse on edge of
Breckland, close to Peddars Way between Watton and Swaffham.
Bedrooms: 1 double, 2 twin
Bathrooms: 2 public

Bed & breakfast

per night:	£min	£max
Single		15.00
Double		30.00

Evening meal 1900 (last orders 2000)
Parking for 10

WELLS-NEXT-THE-SEA

Norfolk
Map ref 3B1

Seaside resort and small port on the north coast. The Buttlands is a large tree-lined green surrounded by Georgian houses and from here narrow streets lead to the quay.

Bay House Bed & Breakfast

Bases Lane, Wells-next-the-Sea NR23 1BT
☎ Fakenham (0328) 711374
Large modern family house in quiet location, a few minutes' walk from town centre and harbour. En-suite/private bathrooms.
Bedrooms: 2 double, 1 twin
Bathrooms: 3 private

Bed & breakfast

per night:	£min	£max
Single	17.50	19.50
Double	35.00	39.00

Evening meal from 1900
Parking for 3
Open March-November

Scarborough House ⚮

COMMENDED

Clubbs Lane, Wells-next-the-Sea NR23 1DP
☎ Fakenham (0328) 710309
& 711661
Spacious licensed Victorian manse with private parking, central for town and quay. Bar, restaurant, four-posters, log fires. Dogs welcome.
Bedrooms: 7 double, 3 triple
Bathrooms: 10 private

Bed & breakfast

per night:	£min	£max
Single	29.00	29.00
Double	48.00	50.00

Half board

per person:	£min	£max
Daily	35.00	40.00
Weekly	241.00	276.00

Evening meal 1930 (last orders 2100)
Parking for 10
Cards accepted: Access, Visa, Amex

WELNEY

Norfolk
Map ref 3A1

Lamb and Flag Inn
Main Street, Welney, Wisbech, Cambridgeshire
PE14 9RB
☎ (035 471) 242
Off A10 at Littleport roundabout on to A1101 Wisbech road. Approximately 3 miles to Welney, pub on this road. Near the river bridge.
Bedrooms: 3 double, 1 twin, 1 triple
Bathrooms: 3 public
Bed & breakfast

per night:	£min	£max
Single	19.00	
Double	35.00	

Lunch available
Evening meal 1900 (last orders 2130)
Parking for 100

WEST BERGHOLT

Essex
Map ref 3B2

The Old Post House
10 Colchester Road, West Bergholt, Colchester
CO6 3JG
☎ (0206) 240379
Formerly the old village post office, within easy reach of historic Colchester and Constable country. Situated on Essex Way.
Bedrooms: 1 double, 1 twin, 1 triple
Bathrooms: 1 private, 1 public
Bed & breakfast

per night:	£min	£max
Single	16.00	18.00
Double	25.00	38.00

Half board

per person:	£min	£max
Daily	22.50	24.50

Parking for 3

WEYBREAD

Suffolk
Map ref 3C2

Pear Tree Farm
Listed
The Street, Weybread, Diss, Norfolk IP21 5TH
☎ Fressingfield (037 986) 753
15th C farmhouse with most beams exposed. Surrounded by fields. Large garden and lawns. Good parking space.
Bedrooms: 1 single, 1 twin, 1 triple
Bathrooms: 1 public
Bed & breakfast

per night:	£min	£max
Single	11.00	12.00
Double	22.00	44.00

Half board

per person:	£min	£max
Daily	17.00	18.00
Weekly	119.00	126.00

Evening meal 1800 (last orders 2000)
Parking for 5
Open January-October

WILLINGHAM

Cambridgeshire
Map ref 3A2

Belsar Lodge
155 Rampton Road, Willingham, Cambridge
CB4 5JF
☎ (0954) 60359
Detached, on outskirts of the village. Equidistant from Ely, Cambridge and Huntingdon. Approach from Cambridge B1049 to Cottenham, Rampton, Willingham or A604 then B1050 to Long Stanton, Willingham.
Bedrooms: 1 double, 2 twin, 1 triple
Bathrooms: 2 public
Bed & breakfast

per night:	£min	£max
Single	14.00	16.00
Double	28.00	32.00

Half board

per person:	£min	£max
Daily	21.50	23.50
Weekly	130.00	150.00

Evening meal 1800 (last orders 2000)
Parking for 6

WISBECH

Cambridgeshire
Map ref 3A1

The town is the centre of the agricultural and flower-growing industries of Fenland. Peckover House (National Trust) is an important example of domestic architecture.
Tourist Information Centre ☎ (0945) 583263

Stratton Farm
COMMENDED
West Drove North, Walton Highway, Wisbech
PE14 7DP
☎ (0945) 880162
22-acre dairy & livestock farm. All ground floor en-suite accommodation in peaceful setting, with heated swimming pool and private fishing. Wheelchair facilities. Non-smokers only please.
Bedrooms: 2 double, 1 twin
Bathrooms: 3 private
Bed & breakfast

per night:	£min	£max
Single	20.00	22.00
Double	40.00	44.00

Parking for 10

WIX

Essex
Map ref 3B2

New Farm House
COMMENDED
Spinnell's Lane, Wix, Manningtree CO11 2UJ
☎ Clacton (0255) 870365
50-acre arable farm. Modern comfortable farmhouse in large garden, 10 minutes' drive to Harwich and convenient for Constable country. From Wix village crossroads, take Bradfield Road, turn right at top of hill; first house on left.
Bedrooms: 3 single, 1 double, 3 twin, 5 multiple
Bathrooms: 7 private, 2 public
Bed & breakfast

per night:	£min	£max
Single	18.50	21.00
Double	35.00	40.00

Half board

per person:	£min	£max
Daily	27.50	30.00
Weekly	192.50	210.00

Evening meal 1830 (last orders 1730)

Parking for 18
Cards accepted: Access, Visa

WOODBRIDGE

Suffolk
Map ref 3C2

Once a busy seaport, the town is now a sailing centre on the River Deben. There are many buildings of architectural merit including the Bell and Angel Inns. The 18th C Tide Mill is now restored and open to the public.

Moat Barn
HIGHLY COMMENDED
Bredfield, Woodbridge
IP13 6BD
☎ Charsfield (047 337) 520
Renovated Suffolk barn with exposed beams and original features, standing in grounds of over 1 acre. In Bredfield village, with pub and church, just 3 miles from the market town of Woodbridge.
Bedrooms: 1 double, 1 twin, 1 multiple
Bathrooms: 1 private, 2 public
Bed & breakfast

per night:	£min	£max
Single	20.00	20.00
Double	30.00	40.00

Parking for 10

WOODHAM FERRERS

Essex
Map ref 3B3

Woolfe's Cottage
The Street, Woodham Ferrers, Chelmsford
CM3 5RG
☎ Chelmsford (0245) 320037
Large converted Victorian cottage in historic village, 12 miles from Chelmsford on the B1418. Many excellent walking trails for ramblers.
Bedrooms: 1 double, 1 twin
Bathrooms: 1 public
Bed & breakfast

per night:	£min	£max
Single	14.00	16.00
Double	25.00	30.00

Continued ▶

We advise you to confirm your booking in writing.

Please check prices and other details at the time of booking.

275

WOODHAM FERRERS

Continued

Half board

per person:	£min	£max
Daily	21.00	23.00

Parking for 2

🐎🌣🐾🎍🚲🐕🛈Ⓢ⇙Ⓜ📺 🏮 ⬛🅿☼✕🐎 ᴅᴀᴘ Ⓢᴘ

WOOLLEY

Cambridgeshire
Map ref 3A2

New Manor Farm
Listed

Woolley, Huntingdon
PE18 0YJ
☎ (0480) 890092
*80-acre livestock farm.
Spacious, comfortable family
farmhouse in quiet pastoral
hamlet only 2 miles from A1.
Large secluded garden.*
Bedrooms: 2 double, 1 twin
Bathrooms: 1 public,
2 private showers
Bed & breakfast

per night:	£min	£max
Double	30.00	30.00

Half board

per person:	£min	£max
Daily	27.50	27.50
Weekly	192.50	192.50

Evening meal 1900 (last
orders 2100)
Parking for 6
Open April-October

🐎🚲🐕☼✕🛈♨Ⓢ⇙Ⓜ📺🏮
⬛☼🐎

WOOLPIT

Suffolk
Map ref 3B2

Village with a number of
attractive timber-framed
Tudor and Georgian
houses. St Mary's Church
is one of the most
beautiful churches in
Suffolk and has a fine
porch. The brass eagle
lectern is said to have
been donated by
Elizabeth I.

The Swan Inn 🏍
Listed COMMENDED

Woolpit, Bury St Edmunds
IP30 9QN
☎ Elmswell (0359) 40482
*16th C inn at centre of
popular village. Well-
appointed ground floor
bedrooms in a quiet annexe,
overlooking a walled garden.*
Bedrooms: 1 single,
1 double, 1 twin, 1 triple

Bathrooms: 1 private,
1 public
Bed & breakfast

per night:	£min	£max
Single	17.50	21.00
Double	32.00	36.00

Parking for 12

🐎🚲🖭🗄🛁🐾⬛✕🐎🏮

WRABNESS

Essex
Map ref 3B2

Wrabness Hall Farm
Listed

Wrabness Hall, Church
Road, Wrabness,
Manningtree CO11 2TQ
☎ Ramsey (0255) 880182
*124-acre arable farm.
Traditional English farmhouse
overlooking River Stour and
Stour Estuary. Many beams
and inglenook fireplaces.
Spacious house, family home
with children, cats, dogs,
horses, ducks, etc. Three-
quarters of a mile off A120.*
Bedrooms: 1 double, 1 twin
Bathrooms: 2 public
Bed & breakfast

per night:	£min	£max
Double	30.00	32.00

🐎🐾🎍🛈Ⓜ📺🏮⬛∪
🖊☼✕🐎🏮

WROXHAM

Norfolk
Map ref 3C1

Yachting centre on the
River Bure which houses
the headquarters of the
Norfolk Broads Yacht
Club. The church of St
Mary has a famous
doorway and the manor
house nearby dates back
to 1623.

Garden Cottage
⬧⬧ HIGHLY COMMENDED

The Limes, 96 Norwich
Road, Wroxham, Norwich
NR12 8RY
☎ (0603) 784376 & 783192
*Converted 18th C barn, 10
minutes' walk from railway
station (North Norfolk/
Norwich). Close to river and
Broads where where day-boat
hire is available.*
Bedrooms: 1 double, 2 twin
Bathrooms: 3 private
Bed & breakfast

per night:	£min	£max
Double	38.00	42.50

Parking for 3
Cards accepted: Access, Visa,
Amex

🛁🖵🐾⬛⇙Ⓜ🏮☼✕🐎 ᴅᴀᴘ

Manor Barn House
⬙⬙ COMMENDED

Back Lane, Rackheath,
Wroxham, Norwich
NR13 6NN
☎ (0603) 783543
*Traditional Norfolk barn
conversion with exposed
beams, in quiet setting with
pleasant gardens. Just off the
A1151, 2 miles from
Wroxham.*
Bedrooms: 3 double, 2 twin
Bathrooms: 4 private,
1 private shower
Bed & breakfast

per night:	£min	£max
Single	16.00	20.00
Double	30.00	35.00

Parking for 8

🐎3🛁🎍🛈⇙Ⓜ📺🏮
⬛∪🖊☼🐎 Ⓢᴘ🏮

Staitheway House
⬙⬙

Staitheway Road, Wroxham,
Norwich NR12 8TH
☎ (0603) 782148
*Fine Victorian house in quiet
location but within easy
walking distance of village
and river.*
Bedrooms: 1 single, 1 twin,
1 triple
Bathrooms: 2 private,
1 public
Bed & breakfast

per night:	£min	£max
Single	16.00	19.50
Double	26.00	30.00

Parking for 3
Open January-November

🐎🖵🐾🛈Ⓜ🛈Ⓢ🏮⬛☼✕
🐎 Ⓣ

WYMONDHAM

Norfolk
Map ref 3B1

Busy market town with a
charming octagonal
market cross. In 1615 a
great fire destroyed most
of its buildings but the
Green Dragon Inn, now
one of the oldest in the
country, survived.

Cobweb Cottage
Listed APPROVED

Queens Street, Spooner Row,
Wymondham NR18 9JU
☎ (0953) 604070
*Delightful old world cottage in
quiet location 2.5 miles from
Wymondham, 15 minutes
from Norwich, central for
touring Norfolk. Homely
accommodation and cooking.
No smoking in
accommodation.*

Bedrooms: 2 single,
2 double, 1 twin
Bathrooms: 3 public
Bed & breakfast

per night:	£min	£max
Single	16.00	18.00
Double	32.00	36.00

Half board

per person:	£min	£max
Daily	26.00	28.00
Weekly	182.00	

Evening meal 1900 (last
orders 2000)
Parking for 6
Cards accepted: Access, Visa

🐎10🛁🎍🛈🐾⇙Ⓜ
📺🏮⬛☼✕🐎 ᴅᴀᴘ 🐾 Ⓢᴘ Ⓣ

Rose Farm
Listed

School Lane, Suton,
Wymondham NR18 9JN
☎ (0953) 603512
*2-acre poultry farm. Homely
farmhouse accommodation
within easy reach of Norwich,
Broads and Breckland. Bus
and train services close by.*
Bedrooms: 2 single,
1 double, 1 triple
Bathrooms: 2 public
Bed & breakfast

per night:	£min	£max
Single	16.00	19.00
Double	32.00	38.00

Half board

per person:	£min	£max
Daily	24.00	27.00
Weekly	160.00	180.00

Parking for 4

🐎🌣🖵🛈Ⓜ🛈Ⓢ⇙Ⓜ📺
🏮⬛🖊🐎

Willow Farm
Listed COMMENDED

Wattlefield, Wymondham
NR18 9PA
☎ (0953) 604679
*Comfortable farmhouse
offering high standard of
hospitality in relaxed
atmosphere. Two miles south
down B1135 from
Wymondham fork right.
Willow Farm three quarters of
a mile on the left.*
Bedrooms: 1 single,
1 double, 1 twin
Bathrooms: 2 public
Bed & breakfast

per night:	£min	£max
Single	15.00	15.00
Double	30.00	30.00

Parking for 3

🐎🌣🖵🐾🛈Ⓜ📺🏮⬛
☼🐎

THE CROWN IS YOUR
SURE SIGN
OF WHERE TO STAY

HOTELS, GUESTHOUSES, INNS, B&Bs & FARMHOUSES

Throughout Britain, the tourist boards now inspect over 17,000 hotels, guesthouses, inns, B&Bs and farmhouses, every year, to help you find the ones that suit you best.

THE CLASSIFICATIONS: **'Listed'**, and then **ONE to FIVE CROWN,** tell you the range of facilities and services you can expect. The more Crowns, the wider the range.

THE GRADES: **APPROVED, COMMENDED, HIGHLY COMMENDED and DE LUXE,** where they appear, indicate the quality standard provided. If no grade is shown, you can still expect a high standard of cleanliness.

Every classified place to stay has a Fire Certificate, where this is required under the Fire Precautions Act, and all carry Public Liability Insurance.

'Listed': Clean and comfortable accommodation, but the range of facilities and services may be limited.

ONE CROWN: Accommodation with additional facilities, including washbasins in all bedrooms, a lounge and use of a phone.

TWO CROWN: A wider range of facilities and services, including morning tea and calls, bedside lights, colour TV in lounge or bedrooms, assistance with luggage.

THREE CROWN: At least one-third of the bedrooms with ensuite WC and bath or shower, plus easy chair, full length mirror. Shoe cleaning facilities and hairdryers available. Hot evening meals available.

FOUR CROWN: At least three-quarters of the bedrooms with ensuite WC and bath/shower plus colour TV, radio and phone, 24-hour access and lounge service until midnight. Last orders for meals 8.30 pm or later.

FIVE CROWN: All bedrooms having WC, bath and shower ensuite, plus a wide range of facilities and services, including room service, all-night lounge service and laundry service. Restaurant open for breakfast, lunch and dinner.

Every Crown classified place to stay is likely to provide some of the facilities and services of a higher classification. More information available from any Tourist Information Centre.

We've checked them out before you check in!

West Country

Land of enchantment, legend and folklore. Land of wild moorland, historic cities, sleepy fishing villages, sophisticated resorts, gardens, gorges, castles and cream teas. From the grandeur of Salisbury, the World Heritage City of Bath and cosmopolitan Bristol, through the resorts of the English Riviera

Use the above map to locate places in the "Where to Go, What to See" section overleaf.

West Country

and brooding Bodmin Moor to the sheltered fishing villages of Cornwall, this is a region of huge charm and eternal fascination. Whether your choice is solitude or stately homes, walking or windsurfing, shopping or sunbathing, the West Country will not disappoint.

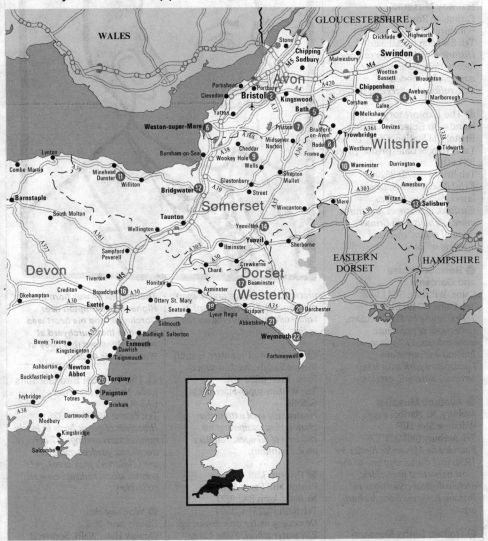

Use the colour maps at the back of this guide to find places with accommodation.

West Country

The number against each name will help you locate it on the map on the previous pages.

1 Great Western Railway Museum
Faringdon Road, Swindon, Wiltshire SN1 5BJ
Tel: Swindon (0793) 526161
Historic Great Western railway locomotives, wide range of nameplates, models, illustrations, posters and tickets.

2 The Exploratory Hands-on Science Centre
Bristol Old Station, Clock Tower Yard, Temple Gate, Bristol, Avon BS1 6QU
Tel: Bristol (0272) 252008
Exhibition of lights, lenses, lasers, bubbles, bridges, illusions, gyroscopes and much more, all housed in Brunel's original engine shed and drawing office.

3 Bowood House and Gardens
Calne, Wiltshire SN11 0LZ
Tel: Calne (0249) 812102
18th C house by Robert Adam. Collections of paintings, watercolours, Victoriana, Indiana and porcelain. Landscaped park with lake, terraces, waterfall, grottos.

4 Avebury Museum
Avebury, Nr Marlborough, Wiltshire SN8 1RF
Tel: Avebury (067 23) 250
Founded by Alexander Keiller in 1930s and containing one of the most important prehistoric archaeological collections in Britain. Remains from Avebury area.

5 Roman Baths Museum
Pump Room, Abbey Church Yard, Bath, Avon BA1 1LZ
Tel: Bath (0225) 461111
Roman baths and temple

precinct, hot springs and Roman monuments. Jewellery, coins, votive offerings from the sacred spring.

6 Tropicana Pleasure Beach
Marine Parade, Weston-super-Mare, Avon BS23 1BE
Tel: Weston-super-Mare (0934) 626581
Heated surf pool with water chutes. Play equipment for children of all ages. Toddlers' pool. Fountains.

7 Priston Mill
Priston Mill Farm, Priston, Nr Bath, Avon BA2 9EQ
Tel: Bath (0225) 423894
Domesday water mill driven by 21ft water wheel. Tithe barn, nature trail, farm animals, cow milking, play areas, trailer rides.

Thomas Hardy was born in Higher Bockhampton near Dorchester and his heart was buried in the churchyard at nearby Stinsford (his body in Westminster Abbey)

8 The Tropical Bird Gardens
Rode, Nr Bath, Somerset BA3 6QW
Tel: Frome (0373) 830326
Hundreds of exotic birds in lovely natural surroundings. 17 acres of woodland, gardens and lakes with children's play areas, pets' corner, steam railway, clematis collection.

9 Wookey Hole Caves and Mill
Wookey Hole, Wells, Somerset BA5 1BB
Tel: Wells (0749) 672243
The most spectacular caves in Britain. Working Victorian paper

mill, "Fairground by Night" exhibition, Edwardian Penny Pier Arcade, archaeological museum, mirror maze.

⑩ Longleat House
Warminster, Wiltshire BA12 7NN
Tel: Warminster (0985) 844551
Great Elizabethan house with lived-in atmosphere. Important libraries and Italian ceilings. Safari park.

⑪ Dunster Castle
Dunster, Nr Minehead, Somerset TA24 6SL
Tel: Dunster (0643) 821314
Fortified home of the Luttrells for 600 years, remodelled 100 years ago. Fine 17th C staircase and plaster ceilings. Terrace garden with rare shrubs.

⑫ Admiral Blake Museum
Blake House, Blake Street, Bridgwater, Somerset TA6 3NB
Tel: Bridgwater (0278) 456127
Battle of Sedgemoor relics, Admiral Blake room, shipping room and John Chubb Picture Gallery. Video films of Battle of Sedgemoor, River Parrot and sailing ship "Irene".

⑬ Salisbury Cathedral
The Close, Salisbury, Wiltshire SP1 2FF
Tel: Salisbury (0722) 328726
Gothic cathedral consecrated in 1258. Famous spire rising to record height of 404 feet was added in 14th C. Ancient clock mechanism dates from 1386. Magna Carta.

⑭ Fleet Air Arm Museum
Royal Naval Air Station, Yeovilton, Somerset BA22 8HT
Tel: Ilchester (0935) 840565
Over 50 historic aircraft, displays and equipment, including Concorde prototype. Falklands campaign, Kamikaze, RNAS 1914–1918, The Wrens and Harrier Jump Jet Story exhibitions.

⑮ Dartington Crystal Ltd
Linden Close, Torrington, Devon EX38 7AN
Tel: Torrington (0805) 23797
Manufacture of hand-made lead crystal glassware by skilled craftsmen, hand-blowing of glassware. Glass centre and glassware exhibition.

⑯ Killerton House
Broadclyst, Nr Exeter, Devon EX5 3LE
Tel: Exeter (0392) 881345
18th C house built for the Acland family, now houses collection of costumes shown in various room settings. 15 acres of hillside garden with rare trees and shrubs.

Most traditions place King Arthur as a West Country man – born at Tintagel, holding court at Camelot (thought to be present-day Cadbury) and taken to die on the Isle of Avalon (Glastonbury Tor)

⑰ Parnham House
Beaminster, Dorset DT8 3NA
Tel: Beaminster (0308) 862204
Tudor manor house with additions and embellishments by John Nash in 1810. Home of John Makepeace and his famous furniture-making workshops. 14 acres of gardens.

⑱ Tintagel Castle
Tintagel, Cornwall PL34 0AA
Tel: Camelford (0840) 770328
Medieval ruined castle on wild, windswept coast. Famous for associations with Arthurian legend. Built largely in 13th C by Richard, Earl of Cornwall, and used as a prison in 14th C.

⑲ Lyme Regis Experience
Marine Parade, Lyme Regis, Dorset DT7 3JH
Tel: Lyme Regis (0297) 443039
Historical tableaux and audio-visual display depicting the history of Lyme from the salt-boiling monks of 774 AD to the present day.

⑳ Dorset County Museum
High West Street, Dorchester, Dorset DT1 1XA
Tel: Dorchester (0305) 262735
Archaeology, natural history and geology of Dorset. Local history and bygones displays. Thomas Hardy material. Gallery for temporary exhibitions.

㉑ Abbotsbury Sub-Tropical Gardens
Abbotsbury, Dorset
Tel: Abbotsbury (0305) 871387
English Heritage Grade I garden, with 20 acres of exotic trees, shrubs and herbaceous plants.

㉒ The Timewalk
Brewers Quay, Hope Square, Weymouth, Dorset DT4 8TR
Tel: Weymouth (0305) 777622

Timewalk through history of Weymouth from the Black Death to World War II.

㉓ Morwellham Quay and Open Air Museum

Morwellham Quay, Nr Tavistock, Devon PL19 8JL
Tel: Tavistock (0822) 863494
Riverside tramway takes visitors underground into a copper mine. Blacksmith's and cooper's workshop, 19th C cottage, water wheels, shire horse carriage rides.

㉔ Dobwalls Family Adventure Park

Dobwalls, Nr Liskeard, Cornwall PL14 6HD
Tel: Liskeard (0579) 20325
Two miles of scenically dramatic miniature railway based on the American railroad scene. Edwardian countryside exhibition. Children's Adventureland.

㉕ Kents Cavern Showcaves

Ilsham Road, Wellswood, Torquay, Devon TQ1 2JF
Tel: Torquay (0803) 294059
Home of earliest people. Story-telling tours are an unforgettable and exciting experience in an extensive and beautiful underground world.

㉖ Plymouth Dome

The Hoe, Plymouth, Devon PL1 2NZ
Tel: Plymouth (0752) 668000
Purpose-built visitor interpretation centre showing the history of Plymouth and its people from Stone Age beginning to satellite technology.

㉗ Trelissick Garden

Feock, Nr Truro, Cornwall TR3 6QL
Tel: Truro (0872) 862090
Large garden, lovely at all seasons. Superb views of estuary and Falmouth harbour. Woodland walks beside the River Fal.

㉘ Land's End

Sennen, Penzance, Cornwall TR19 7AA
Tel: Sennen (0736) 871501
Spectacular cliffs with breathtaking vistas. Superb, multi-sensory Last Labyrinth Show, art gallery, exhibitions and much more.

FIND OUT MORE

Further information about holidays and attractions in the West Country is available from:
West Country Tourist Board 60 St Davids Hill, Exeter EX4 4SY
Tel: (0392) 76351

These publications are available free from the West Country Tourist Board:
England's West Country – Holidays '93
Bed and Breakfast Touring Map for the West Country '93
West Country Inspected Holiday Homes '93
Activity and Leisure Holidays '93
Go West Country 92/93
Places to Visit in Winter 92/93
Also available is:
West Country – Where to Stay 1993 £2.50

According to legend, the White Horse at Westbury was first cut by Alfred the Great

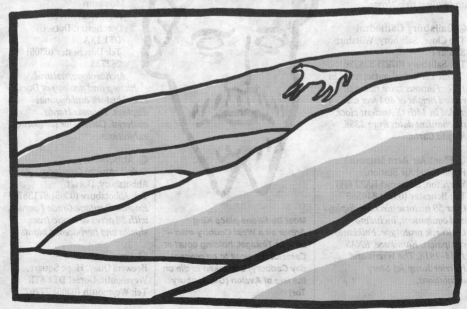

Places to stay

Accommodation entries in this regional section are listed in alphabetical order of place name, and then in alphabetical order of establishment.

The map references refer to the colour maps at the back of the guide. The first figure is the map number; the letter and figure which follow indicate the grid reference on the map.

The symbols at the end of each accommodation entry give information about services and facilities. A 'key' to these symbols is inside the back cover flap, which can be kept open for easy reference.

ABBOTSBURY

Dorset
Map ref 2A3

Beautiful village near Chesil Beach, with a long main street of mellow stone and thatched cottages and the ruins of a Benedictine monastery. High above the village on a hill is a prominent 15th C chapel. Abbotsbury's famous swannery and sub-tropical gardens lie just outside the village.

Swan Lodge

APPROVED

Rodden Row, Abbotsbury, Weymouth DT3 4JL
☎ (0305) 871249

Situated on the B3157 coastal road between Weymouth and Bridport. Swan Inn public house opposite, where food is served all day, is under the same ownership.

Bedrooms: 2 double, 2 twin, 1 triple
Bathrooms: 1 public

Bed & breakfast per night:	£min	£max
Single	27.00	32.00
Double	38.00	46.00

Lunch available
Evening meal 1800 (last orders 2200)
Parking for 10
Cards accepted: Access, Visa
20-80

ALLERFORD

Somerset
Map ref 1D1

Village of picturesque stone and thatch cottages with a packhorse bridge, set in the beautiful Vale of Porlock.

Fern Cottage

COMMENDED

Allerford, Minehead TA24 8HN
☎ Porlock (0643) 862215

Large 16th C traditional Exmoor cottage in National Trust wooded vale. Dramatic scenery and wildlife. Fine classic cooking and comprehensive wine list.

Bedrooms: 3 double, 1 twin, 1 triple
Bathrooms: 1 public

Bed & breakfast per night:	£min	£max
Single	18.25	23.25
Double	36.50	36.50

Half board per person:	£min	£max
Daily	28.00	33.00
Weekly	176.00	176.00

Evening meal 1900 (last orders 1800)
Parking for 7
Cards accepted: Access, Visa, Switch

ALTARNUN

Cornwall
Map ref 1C2

Close to the edge of Bodmin Moor, a hillside village whose fine church is noted for its medieval carved bench-ends and striking Norman font. A packhorse bridge crosses the stream to the church. In the village square is a Georgian Methodist meeting house with a sculpted relief of John Wesley.

Trecollas Farm

Altarnun, Launceston PL15 7SN
☎ Pipers Pool (0566) 86386

90-acre dairy farm. Homely, comfortable, friendly farmhouse near Bodmin Moor, 10 miles from Tintagel. Washbasins, tea/coffee facilities in all bedrooms. Good food served.

Bedrooms: 1 double, 1 twin
Bathrooms: 1 public

Bed & breakfast per night:	£min	£max
Single	11.00	12.00
Double	22.00	24.00

Half board per person:	£min	£max
Daily	17.00	18.00
Weekly	70.00	80.00

Evening meal 1830 (last orders 1900)
Parking for 2
Open April-October

AMESBURY

Wiltshire
Map ref 2B2

Standing on the banks of the River Avon, this is the nearest town to Stonehenge on Salisbury Plain. The area is rich in prehistoric sites.
Tourist Information Centre
☎ (0980) 622833

Mandalay Guest House

15 Stonehenge Road, Amesbury, Salisbury SP4 7BA
☎ Shrewton (0980) 623733

Beautiful bedrooms in house of great character. Fine breakfast served in classical breakfast room overlooking the garden temple. No-smoking policy.

Bedrooms: 1 twin, 1 triple
Bathrooms: 2 private, 1 public

Bed & breakfast per night:	£min	£max
Double	30.00	34.00

Parking for 5

AMESBURY

Continued

Ratfyn Barrow House
Ratfyn Road, Amesbury,
Salisbury SP4 7DZ
☎ Shrewton (0980) 623422
*Comfortable accommodation
in pleasant surroundings off
main road. Site of ancient
barrow, a listed monument.*
Bedrooms: 1 double, 2 twin
Bathrooms: 1 private,
1 public
Bed & breakfast

per night:	£min	£max
Double	25.00	34.00

Parking for 4
Open April-October
☎5🗒♿🆑⚡🛁🌡🅿❄🚭

APPLEDORE

Devon
Map ref 1C1

The first safe haven to be
reached after rounding
Hartland Point, Appledore
stands at the confluence
of the Rivers Torridge and
Taw. Steep, narrow
streets and colour-washed
cottages make this one of
North Devon's prettiest
fishing towns.

Regency House
2 Marine Parade, Appledore,
Bideford EX39 1PJ
☎ Bideford (0237) 473689
*Regency house in one of
north Devon's prettiest fishing
villages. A listed building
overlooking the River
Torridge, within easy reach of
the new Devon link road.*
Bedrooms: 1 single,
4 double, 1 twin
Bathrooms: 2 public,
6 private showers
Bed & breakfast

per night:	£min	£max
Single	13.00	13.00
Double	26.00	26.00

Half board

per person:	£min	£max
Daily	21.00	21.00
Weekly	141.00	141.00

Evening meal 1900 (last
orders 2000)
Cards accepted: Access, Visa
☎🗒♿🆑🅰🛁🌡🅿
🚻❄🚭 OAP SP

Riverside Guest House
4 Marine Parade, Appledore,
Bideford EX39 1PJ
☎ Bideford (0237) 478649
*Home-from-home atmosphere,
overlooking river. Sandy
beach of Westward Ho! only 2*

miles away. Many places to
visit within easy reach.
Bedrooms: 2 double, 1 twin
Bathrooms: 1 private,
1 private shower
Bed & breakfast

per night:	£min	£max
Single	12.00	12.00
Double	24.00	31.00

Half board

per person:	£min	£max
Daily	20.00	23.50
Weekly	120.00	148.00

Evening meal 1830 (last
orders 1000)
☎🗒♿🆑⚡🛁🌡🅿 SP

ASHBRITTLE

Somerset
Map ref 1D1

Higher Westcott Farm
👑👑 APPROVED
Ashbrittle, Wellington
TA21 0HZ
☎ Clayhanger (039 86) 258
*230-acre mixed farm. Family-
run, situated in lovely
countryside on the Devon/
Somerset border. Traditional
farmhouse cooking with
home-produced food. Coarse
and fly fishing nearby. Ideal
for touring Exmoor and
Quantock Hills. Warm
welcome assured.*
Bedrooms: 2 triple
Bathrooms: 1 public
Bed & breakfast

per night:	£min	£max
Single	13.00	14.00
Double	26.00	28.00

Half board

per person:	£min	£max
Daily	17.00	19.00
Weekly	110.00	120.00

Evening meal 1830 (last
orders 1730)
Parking for 4
Open April-October
☎♿⚡🛁🌡🅿🚻❄
🚭

Lower Westcott Farm
👑👑
Ashbrittle, Wellington
TA21 0HZ
☎ Clayhanger (039 86) 296
*220-acre mixed farm. On
Devon/Somerset borders in
peaceful, scenic countryside.
Ideal for touring Exmoor,
Quantocks, coast. Noted for
comfort, homeliness and
farmhouse cooking. All rooms
have spectacular views across
valley.*
Bedrooms: 1 double, 1 twin,
1 triple

Bathrooms: 2 private,
1 public
Bed & breakfast

per night:	£min	£max
Double	26.00	32.00

Half board

per person:	£min	£max
Daily	18.00	22.00
Weekly	135.00	145.00

Evening meal 1800 (last
orders 1700)
Parking for 4
☎♿🆑🅰🛁🌡🅿🚻❄♿
❄🚭🚭

ASHBURTON

Devon
Map ref 1C2

Formerly a thriving wool
centre and important as
one of Dartmoor's 4
stannary towns. Today's
busy market town has
many period buildings.
Ancient tradition is
maintained in the annual
ale-tasting and bread-
weighing ceremony. Good
centre for exploring
Dartmoor or the south
Devon coast.

Wellpritton Farm
👑 HIGHLY COMMENDED
Holne, Newton Abbot
TQ13 7RX
☎ Poundsgate (036 43) 273
*15-acre mixed farm. Plenty of
mouthwatering farm-produced
food in a tastefully
modernised farmhouse on the
edge of Dartmoor. Special
diets catered for by
arrangement. A warm
welcome and caring personal
attention.*
Bedrooms: 2 double, 2 twin
Bathrooms: 3 private,
1 public
Bed & breakfast

per night:	£min	£max
Single	16.00	17.00
Double	32.00	34.00

Half board

per person:	£min	£max
Daily	25.00	25.00
Weekly	140.00	140.00

Evening meal from 1900
Parking for 6
☎🗒♿🆑⚡🛁🌡🅿🚻❄
🍷🏊❄🚭🚭

> The enquiry
> coupons at the
> back will help you
> when contacting
> proprietors.

ASHTON KEYNES

Wiltshire
Map ref 2B2

Village beside the River
Thames, with houses
standing along the edge
of the stream reached by
bridges from the road on
the opposite bank. Nearby
stands the manor, Ashton
House.

Cove House
👑👑
Park Place, Ashton Keynes,
Swindon SN6 6NS
☎ Cirencester (0285)
861226
*Half of 17th C manor house
with southern aspect.
Beautiful walled garden.
Elegant country house
atmosphere. Family service.*
Bedrooms: 1 double, 1 twin
Bathrooms: 2 private
Bed & breakfast

per night:	£min	£max
Single	31.00	32.00
Double	40.00	44.00

Parking for 12
☎🗒♿🆑🆑🛁🌡�tv🅿❄
🚭🏠

AVEBURY

Wiltshire
Map ref 2B2

Set in a landscape of
earthworks and megalithic
standing stones, Avebury
has a fine church and an
Elizabethan manor.
Remains from excavations
may be seen in the
museum. The area
abounds in important
prehistoric sites, among
them Silbury Hill.
Stonehenge stands about
20 miles due south.

New Inn 🏮
Winterbourne Monkton,
Swindon SN4 9NW
☎ (067 23) 240
*Small and friendly country
pub with 1 mile from
Avebury. Packed lunches
prepared if required.*
Bedrooms: 2 double, 3 twin
Bathrooms: 5 private
Bed & breakfast

per night:	£min	£max
Double	33.00	38.00

Half board

per person:	£min	£max
Daily	25.00	32.00

Lunch available
Evening meal 1830 (last orders 2130)
Parking for 20

🛇🕭⌑♨🅿📖 ⏢❀✕🚲

Windmill House

Winterbourne Monkton,
Avebury, Marlborough
SN4 9NN
☎ (067 23) 446
Secluded 18th C former mill house surrounded by open farmland, with magnificent views of Avebury and Marlborough Downs. Home cooking.
Bedrooms: 1 single,
1 double, 1 triple
Bathrooms: 2 public
Bed & breakfast

per night:	£min	£max
Single	14.50	16.50
Double	29.00	33.00

Half board per person:	£min	£max
Daily	23.00	26.00

Evening meal 1800 (last orders 1500)
Parking for 8

🛇🕭 🆄🅻 🅸 🆂 🅼 📺 📖 ⏢ ⏏
✐ ❀ ✕ 🚲 🎣

AVETON GIFFORD

Devon
Map ref 1C3

Marsh Mills

Aveton Gifford, Kingsbridge
TQ7 4JW
☎ Kingsbridge (0548)
550549
5-acre mixed farm. Mill house, now a smallholding, with leat and duck pond, gardens and orchard. Peacefully secluded, just off the A379.
Bedrooms: 2 double, 1 twin
Bathrooms: 1 public
Bed & breakfast

per night:	£min	£max
Single	14.00	15.00
Double	28.00	30.00

Parking for 3

🛇🕭6⏏🆄🅻🅸✕🅼📺⏢❀
✕🚲

There are separate sections in this guide listing groups specialising in farm holidays and accommodation which is especially suitable for young people and organised groups.

AXMINSTER

Devon
Map ref 1D2

This tree-shaded market town on the banks of the River Axe was one of Devon's earliest West Saxon settlements, but is better known for its carpet making. Based on Turkish methods, the industry began in 1755, declined in the 1830s and was revived in 1937.

Fordwater

Axminster EX13 7BB
☎ South Chard (0460)
20257
16th C long thatched, beamed farmhouse with cottage garden close to the peaceful River Kit. Offering a warm and friendly welcome.
Bedrooms: 2 double, 1 twin,
1 triple
Bathrooms: 1 private,
2 public
Bed & breakfast

per night:	£min	£max
Single	17.50	25.00
Double	25.00	35.00

Half board per person:	£min	£max
Daily	22.50	27.50
Weekly	120.00	150.00

Parking for 11

🛇🆄🅻⏏🆄🅻🅸🆂🅼📺📖
🛇❀🚲🅾🅰🅿🅾🆂🅿🏮

BANTHAM

Devon
Map ref 1C3

Village at the mouth of the River Avon, with a fine sandy beach.

Sloop Inn ⋒

🏅🏅 COMMENDED
Bantham, Kingsbridge
TQ7 3AJ
☎ Kingsbridge (0548)
560489 & 5560215
Part 16th C inn in old world fishing village. Some rooms overlook sea and river estuary. Menu majors on local seafood.
Bedrooms: 3 double, 2 triple
Bathrooms: 5 private,
1 public
Bed & breakfast

per night:	£min	£max
Single	25.00	35.00
Double	47.00	52.00

Half board per person:	£min	£max
Daily	36.00	39.00
Weekly	250.00	270.00

Lunch available
Evening meal 1900 (last orders 2200)
Parking for 35

🛇🆄🅻⏏♨🅸📖⏢⏏✐🚲
🅾🅰🅿 🆂🅿

BARNSTAPLE

Devon
Map ref 1C1

At the head of the Taw Estuary, once a shipbuilding and textile town, now an agricultural centre with attractive period buildings, a modern civic centre and leisure centre. Attractions include Queen Anne's Walk, a charming colonnaded arcade and Pannier Market.
Tourist Information Centre
☎ (0271) 47177

The Cedars Lodge Inn

🏅🏅🏅 APPROVED
Bickington Road, Barnstaple
EX31 2HP
☎ (0271) 71784
Fax (0271) 25733
Attractive old house with rooms and lodges set in 3 acres of grounds. Sauna, solarium, squash courts adjoining. Near north Devon link road roundabout.
Bedrooms: 6 double,
14 twin, 4 multiple
Bathrooms: 24 private
Bed & breakfast

per night:	£min	£max
Single	29.50	34.00
Double	39.50	48.00

Lunch available
Evening meal 1830 (last orders 2200)
Parking for 100
Cards accepted: Access, Visa, Amex

🛇🕭⟨♨🆄🅻⏏♨🆂✕🅼
📖⏢⏏🇹12-120 🅱🅰❀🏮🆂🅿

Home Park Farm Accommodation

🏅🏅 COMMENDED
Lower Blakewell, Muddiford,
Barnstaple EX31 4ET
☎ (0271) 42955
70-acre livestock farm. Set in Devonshire countryside, very quiet and peaceful, with outdoor children's play area. Take the A39 Lynton road out of Barnstaple, fork left on to the B3230, turn off main road towards fisheries, continue to end.

Bedrooms: 1 double, 1 triple,
1 multiple
Bathrooms: 3 private
Bed & breakfast

per night:	£min	£max
Single	15.00	18.00
Double	30.00	35.00

Half board per person:	£min	£max
Daily	21.00	25.00
Weekly	135.00	145.00

Lunch available
Evening meal 1800 (last orders 1800)
Parking for 4
Open April, June-October

🛇5⏏♨🆄🅻🅸🆂🅼📺📖⏏
❀🚲🅾🅰🅿🆂🅿

Waytown Farm

🏅🏅 COMMENDED
Shirwell, Barnstaple
EX31 4JN
☎ Newton Tracey (0271)
850396
240-acre mixed farm. Pleasantly situated 17th C farmhouse 3 miles from Barnstaple. Exmoor and beaches within easy reach. Home cooking, relaxed atmosphere. Access at all times.
Bedrooms: 1 double, 1 twin,
1 triple
Bathrooms: 1 public
Bed & breakfast

per night:	£min	£max
Double	36.00	40.00

Half board per person:	£min	£max
Daily	22.00	26.00
Weekly	130.00	145.00

Evening meal 1830 (last orders 1600)
Parking for 6
Open April-November

🛇🆄🅻⏏🆄🅻🅼⏏🅾⏏✐❀✕
🚲🏮

BATCOMBE

Somerset
Map ref 2B2

Village tucked into a fold of the hills, close to the uppermost reaches of the River Alham, giving superb views of the countryside. The church has a splendid 15th C tower.

Batcombe Vale

Batcombe, Shepton Mallet
BA4 6BW
☎ Evercreech (0749) 830246
Peaceful 18th C house in area of outstanding natural beauty, with its own secluded valley of lakes and wild garden.

Continued ▶

BATCOMBE

Continued

Short distance from Glastonbury, Stourhead and Longleat.
Bedrooms: 2 twin, 1 triple
Bathrooms: 1 public
Bed & breakfast per night:

	£min	£max
Single	15.00	17.00
Double	24.00	28.00

Parking for 6
Open March-December

Individual proprietors have supplied all details of accommodation. Although we do check for accuracy, we advise you to confirm the information at the time of booking.

BATH

Avon
Map ref 2B2

Georgian spa city beside the River Avon. Important Roman site with impressive reconstructed baths, uncovered in 19th C. Bath Abbey built on site of monastery where first king of England was crowned (AD 973). Fine architecture in mellow local stone. Pump Room and museums.
Tourist Information Centre
☎ *(0225) 462831*

14 Dunsford Place ⋀

Bathwick Hill, Bath
BA2 6HF
☎ (0225) 464134
Interesting and appealing establishment with a variety of collections from owner's travels. Easy access to the city centre. Non-smokers only please.
Bedrooms: 1 double, 1 twin
Bathrooms: 2 private
Bed & breakfast per night:

	£min	£max
Double	34.00	38.00

Evening meal 1800 (last orders 2000)
Open March-October

Abbey Rise

Listed

97 Wells Road, Bath
BA2 3AN
☎ (0225) 316177
Victorian house with attractively furnished rooms. Full English breakfast. Short walk to city, bus and rail stations.
Bedrooms: 1 double, 1 twin, 1 triple
Bathrooms: 1 private, 1 public
Bed & breakfast per night:

	£min	£max
Double	30.00	42.00

Armstrong House

41 Crescent Gardens, Upper Bristol Road, Bath BA1 2NB
☎ (0225) 442211
Victorian house in central Bath, only a short level walk to all attractions. Enjoy our spacious comfort and caring service.
Bedrooms: 2 double, 1 twin
Bathrooms: 3 private

Bed & breakfast per night: £min £max

	£min	£max
Double	38.00	50.00

Parking for 5
Open March-October

Arosa

124 Lower Oldfield Park, Bath BA2 3HS
☎ (0225) 425778
Friendly, family-owned and run house within easy walking distance of Bath city centre. Tea/coffee facilities and colour TV in all bedrooms.
Bedrooms: 1 triple
Bathrooms: 1 public
Bed & breakfast per night:

	£min	£max
Double	28.00	38.00

Parking for 4

Ashley Villa Hotel ⋀

26 Newbridge Road, Bath
BA1 3JZ
☎ (0225) 421683 & 428887
Comfortably furnished licensed hotel with relaxing informal atmosphere, close to

---

city centre. All rooms en-suite.
Swimming pool.
Bedrooms: 2 single,
7 double, 2 twin, 3 triple
Bathrooms: 14 private

Bed & breakfast

per night:	£min	£max
Single	35.00	39.00
Double	49.00	59.00

Evening meal 1800 (last
orders 2100)
Parking for 10
Cards accepted: Access, Visa

Astor House

14 Oldfield Road, Bath
BA2 3ND
☎ (0225) 429134
*Lovely Victorian house with
comfortable, spacious rooms
and large secluded garden.
Peaceful, elegant atmosphere.*
Bedrooms: 3 double, 4 twin
Bathrooms: 2 public

Bed & breakfast

per night:	£min	£max
Double	30.00	35.00

Parking for 4
Open April-October

Badminton Villa ♠♠

10 Upper Oldfield Road,
Bath BA2 3JZ
☎ (0225) 426347
*Bright and friendly Victorian
family home in quiet location,
with outstanding views of
Bath and just 10 minutes'
walk from city centre. Car
parking.*
Bedrooms: 2 double, 1 twin
Bathrooms: 3 private,
1 public

Bed & breakfast

per night:	£min	£max
Double	48.00	60.00

Parking for 5
Cards accepted: Access, Visa

The Bath Tasburgh ♠♠

HIGHLY COMMENDED

Warminster Road,
Bathampton, Bath BA2 6SH
☎ (0225) 425096 & 463842
Fax (0225) 425096
*Spacious, elegant Victorian
house/hotel with beautiful
views and canal frontage, set
in lovely grounds with easy
access to tourist attractions.
En-suite bathrooms.
Telephones. Private parking.*
Bedrooms: 1 single,
5 double, 3 twin, 3 triple,
2 multiple
Bathrooms: 11 private,
1 public

Bed & breakfast

per night:	£min	£max
Single	32.00	45.00
Double	44.00	65.00

Parking for 15
Cards accepted: Access, Visa,
Diners, Amex

Bloomfield House ♠♠

HIGHLY COMMENDED

146 Bloomfield Road, Bath
BA2 2AS
☎ (0225) 481958
*Fine Regency country house
with superb views over the
city, offering antique
furniture, silk curtains and a
warm welcome.*
Bedrooms: 1 single,
3 double, 1 twin
Bathrooms: 2 private,
1 public

Bed & breakfast

per night:	£min	£max
Single	26.00	40.00
Double	35.00	60.00

Parking for 9
Cards accepted: Access, Visa

Cairngorm Bed and Breakfast

Listed

3 Gloucester Road, Lower
Swainswick, Bath BA1 7BH
☎ (0225) 429004
*Delightful detached bungalow
with superb views, only 2
miles from city. A46 road
from M4. Special off-peak
rates: 3 nights for the price of
2.*
Bedrooms: 1 double, 1 triple
Bathrooms: 2 private

Bed & breakfast

per night:	£min	£max
Double	27.00	32.00

Parking for 3
Open January-November

Carfax Hotel ♠♠

APPROVED

Great Pulteney Street, Bath
BA2 4BS
☎ (0225) 462089
Fax (0225) 443257
*In a famous Georgian street,
surrounded by beautiful Bath
hills. The rear of Carfax
overlooks Henrietta Park. A
well maintained, listed
building.*
Bedrooms: 13 single,
8 double, 15 twin, 3 triple
Bathrooms: 35 private,
3 public

Bed & breakfast

per night:	£min	£max
Single	22.50	47.50
Double	44.50	68.00

Half board

per person:	£min	£max
Daily	30.00	55.00
Weekly	208.25	290.50

Lunch available
Evening meal 1830 (last
orders 2000)
Parking for 17
Cards accepted: Access, Visa,
Amex

Cherry Tree Villa

7 Newbridge Hill, Bath
BA1 3PW
☎ (0225) 331671
*Modernised, tastefully
decorated Victorian house
with friendly atmosphere,
within easy walking distance
of city centre through
pleasant park.*
Bedrooms: 1 single, 1 twin,
1 triple
Bathrooms: 1 public

Bed & breakfast

per night:	£min	£max
Single	15.00	18.00
Double	30.00	34.00

Parking for 4

Church Farm

Monkton Farleigh, Bradford-
on-Avon, Wiltshire BA15 2QJ
☎ (0225) 858583
*52-acre mixed farm. Large
converted barn with en-suite
rooms and guest lounge on
working farm with livery
stables. 10 minutes to Bath.*
Bedrooms: 3 double
Bathrooms: 1 private,
1 public

Bed & breakfast

per night:	£min	£max
Single	18.50	18.50
Double	30.00	35.00

Parking for 5

Devonshire House

143 Wellsway, Bath
BA2 4RZ
☎ (0225) 312495
*Built in 1880, Devonshire
House offers you all the
comforts of home with the
beauty of Bath. No-smoking
house.*
Bedrooms: 1 single,
1 double, 1 triple
Bathrooms: 3 private

Bed & breakfast

per night:	£min	£max
Single	20.00	25.00
Double	38.00	45.00

Parking for 6

Edgar Hotel

APPROVED

64 Great Pulteney Street,
Bath BA2 4DN
☎ (0225) 420619
*Small private hotel,
proprietor-run, in Great
Pulteney Street which leads to
centre of Bath. Roman
remains approximately 600
yards away.*
Bedrooms: 2 single,
9 double, 4 twin, 1 triple
Bathrooms: 16 private

Bed & breakfast

per night:	£min	£max
Single	25.00	30.00
Double	35.00	55.00

Forres Guest House

172 Newbridge Road, Lower
Weston, Bath BA1 3LE
☎ (0225) 427698
*Edwardian family guesthouse
with friendly, informative
hosts, who are ex-teachers
and love Bath. River Avon
and Cotswold Way close by.
Traditional and vegetarian
breakfasts. Colour TV in all
rooms.*
Bedrooms: 2 double, 2 twin,
1 triple
Bathrooms: 1 private,
1 public, 4 private showers

Bed & breakfast

per night:	£min	£max
Single	16.00	20.00
Double	28.00	35.00

Parking for 5
Open April-October

Gainsborough Hotel ♠♠

Weston Lane, Bath BA1 4AB
☎ (0225) 311380
*Spacious and comfortable
country house hotel in own
lovely grounds near the
botanical gardens. High
ground, nice views, close to
the city centre. 5-course
breakfast, friendly staff, warm
welcome.*
Bedrooms: 2 single,
8 double, 4 twin, 2 triple
Bathrooms: 16 private

Continued ▶

BATH

Continued

Bed & breakfast

per night:	£min	£max
Single	30.00	40.00
Double	52.00	62.00

Evening meal 1845 (last orders 1945)
Parking for 18
Cards accepted: Access, Visa, Amex

Green Lane House

1 Green Lane, Hinton Charterhouse, Bath BA3 6BL
☎ (0225) 723631
Fully renovated, attractive stone house built in 1725, and comfortably furnished. Quiet village in beautiful countryside, convenient for Bath, Somerset and Cotswolds.
Bedrooms: 2 double, 2 twin
Bathrooms: 2 private, 1 public
Bed & breakfast

per night:	£min	£max
Single	22.00	35.00
Double	34.00	47.00

Parking for 4
Cards accepted: Access, Visa, Amex

Haute Combe

176 Newbridge Road, Bath BA1 3LE
☎ (0225) 420061
Sunny, south-facing 19th C property, close to park-and-ride scheme for city attractions yet away from the crowds.
Bedrooms: 1 single, 3 double, 1 twin, 2 triple, 1 multiple
Bathrooms: 8 private
Bed & breakfast

per night:	£min	£max
Single	18.00	26.00
Double	30.00	44.00

Evening meal 1900 (last orders 1800)
Parking for 8
Cards accepted: Access, Visa, Amex

> **Please mention this guide when making a booking.**

Haydon House

HIGHLY COMMENDED

9 Bloomfield Park, Bath BA2 2BY
☎ (0225) 444919 & 427351
Edwardian semi-detached house providing tranquillity, elegance and hospitality. Rooms are decorated to a high standard and have colour TV. Ample on-street parking and garages available. Non-smokers only please.
Bedrooms: 1 single, 2 double, 1 twin
Bathrooms: 3 private
Bed & breakfast

per night:	£min	£max
Single	40.00	45.00
Double	55.00	62.00

Parking for 4
Cards accepted: Access, Visa

Kennard Hotel

COMMENDED

11 Henrietta Street, Bath BA2 6LL
☎ (0225) 310472 & 330159
Converted Georgian house in quiet street. A few minutes' level walk to city centre, abbey, Roman Baths, Pump Room and Henrietta Park.
Bedrooms: 2 single, 6 double, 3 twin, 2 triple
Bathrooms: 11 private, 2 public
Bed & breakfast

per night:	£min	£max
Single	25.00	35.00
Double	40.00	55.00

Cards accepted: Access, Visa, Switch

Kinlet Villa Guest House

COMMENDED

99 Wellsway, Bath BA2 4RX
☎ (0225) 420268
Edwardian villa retaining original features and furnishings. Walking distance from city centre, good bus service, unrestricted parking. Non-smokers only, please.
Bedrooms: 1 double, 1 triple
Bathrooms: 1 public
Bed & breakfast

per night:	£min	£max
Double	30.00	32.00

Leighton House

HIGHLY COMMENDED

139 Wells Road, Bath BA2 3AL
☎ (0225) 314769
Elegant and spacious Victorian guesthouse set in gardens with own car park. 10 minutes' walk from city centre. Evening meals available by arrangement Tuesday-Saturday, November-April inclusive.
Bedrooms: 3 double, 3 twin, 2 triple
Bathrooms: 8 private
Bed & breakfast

per night:	£min	£max
Single	40.00	45.00
Double	56.00	64.00

Half board

per person:	£min	£max
Daily	39.00	43.00

Parking for 8
Cards accepted: Access, Visa

The Manor House

COMMENDED

Mill Lane, Monkton Combe, Bath BA2 7HD
☎ (0225) 723128
Restful, rambling 16th C manor beside mill stream in wooded valley designated as an area of outstanding natural beauty, just 2 miles south of city. Inglenook fires, Victorian conservatory, spacious bedrooms. Fine breakfasts served until noon.
Bedrooms: 2 double, 1 twin, 1 triple
Bathrooms: 1 private, 1 public
Bed & breakfast

per night:	£min	£max
Single	20.00	20.00
Double	38.00	45.00

Parking for 6

Marlborough House

1 Marlborough Lane, Bath BA1 2NQ
☎ (0225) 318175 & 466127
Situated within five minutes' level walk of city centre and Royal Crescent. A non-smokers' house. Friendly atmosphere, parking.
Bedrooms: 2 single, 1 double, 1 twin, 1 triple
Bathrooms: 3 private, 1 public, 1 private shower

Bed & breakfast

per night:	£min	£max
Single	18.00	25.00
Double	35.00	50.00

Parking for 3

Meadowland

HIGHLY COMMENDED

36 Bloomfield Park, Bath BA2 2BX
☎ (0225) 311079
Set in its own quiet, secluded grounds only a short drive from the city centre, offering high standards in beautifully appointed accommodation. Non-smokers only please.
Bedrooms: 2 double, 1 twin
Bathrooms: 3 private
Bed & breakfast

per night:	£min	£max
Single	38.00	43.00
Double	48.00	55.00

Parking for 6
Cards accepted: Access, Visa

Membland Guest House

Listed **COMMENDED**

7 Pulteney Terrace, Pulteney Road, Bath BA2 4HJ
☎ (0225) 336712
5 minutes' walk to Roman baths, abbey, train/coach stations, city shops, tranquil canalside. Private parking, comfortable rooms and generous breakfast.
Bedrooms: 1 double, 1 twin
Bathrooms: 1 public, 1 private shower
Bed & breakfast

per night:	£min	£max
Single	20.00	33.00
Double	26.00	36.00

Parking for 2
Open February-December

Newbridge House

HIGHLY COMMENDED

35 Kelston Road, Bath BA1 3QH
☎ (0225) 446676
Fax (0225) 4447541
Palatial country house and restaurant. Set in its own grounds overlooking beautiful valley. Free transport to city centre.
Bedrooms: 2 single, 5 double, 2 twin
Bathrooms: 9 private

Bed & breakfast

per night:	£min	£max
Single	75.00	110.00
Double	95.00	175.00

Lunch available
Evening meal 1900 (last orders 2200)
Parking for 17
Cards accepted: Access, Visa, Diners, Amex

🛇👤☎️🍴🕾🛈Ⓢ🗲♿📺 🏧🚗🛉12✿✗🚬♿

Number Ninety Three

☰☰ COMMENDED

93 Wells Road, Bath
BA2 3AN
☎ (0225) 317977
Pleasant Victorian house, all rooms en-suite. Within very easy walking distance of city centre, British Rail and national coach stations.
Bedrooms: 1 double, 1 twin, 1 triple
Bathrooms: 3 private

Bed & breakfast

per night:	£min	£max
Single	19.00	30.00
Double	38.00	42.50

Half board

per person:	£min	£max
Daily	27.50	38.50
Weekly	192.50	269.50

Cards accepted: Access, Visa, Amex

🛏️🖃👤♿🔌Ⓤ🛈Ⓢ🗲📺🌑 🚬🚗✗🚬ⓄⒶⓅ🏨

Oakleigh House ▲▲

☰☰ COMMENDED

19 Upper Oldfield Park, Bath
BA2 3JX
☎ (0225) 315698
Your comfort is assured at this tastefully modernised Victorian home, quietly situated only 10 minutes from the city centre.
Bedrooms: 3 double, 1 twin
Bathrooms: 4 private

Bed & breakfast

per night:	£min	£max
Single	30.00	45.00
Double	45.00	55.00

Parking for 4
Cards accepted: Access, Visa

🖃🖵♿🔌Ⓤ Ⓢ🗲♿🚬🚗 ✗🚬ⓄⒶⓅⓈⓅ

The Old School House ▲▲

☰☰☰ HIGHLY COMMENDED

Church Street, Bathford, Bath BA1 7RR
☎ (0225) 859593
Pretty Victorian schoolhouse of Bath stone in peaceful conservation area. Views and fine walks overlooking Avon Valley. 3 miles to Bath centre.

All rooms have full private facilities. Dinners, licensed. Non-smoking.
Bedrooms: 3 double, 1 twin
Bathrooms: 4 private, 1 public

Bed & breakfast

per night:	£min	£max
Single	40.00	45.00
Double	60.00	64.00

Half board

per person:	£min	£max
Daily	50.00	65.00
Weekly	330.00	420.00

Evening meal 1900 (last orders 2000)
Parking for 6
Cards accepted: Access, Visa

🛏️👤♿🔌Ⓢ🗲♿🖩🚗✗ 🚬🍴ⓈⓅ🏨

Orchard House ▲▲

☰☰☰ COMMENDED

24 Box Road, Bathford, Bath BA1 7QD
☎ (0225) 859072
Small family-run guesthouse which aims to please, close to city and open countryside. Non-smokers only please.
Bedrooms: 1 double, 2 twin, 1 triple
Bathrooms: 1 private, 1 public

Bed & breakfast

per night:	£min	£max
Double	26.00	36.00

Parking for 4
Cards accepted: Visa

🖵♿🔌Ⓤ🗲♿🖩🚗✿✗ 🚬ⓈⓅ

Poplar Farm ▲▲

Listed COMMENDED

Stanton Prior, Bath BA2 9HX
☎ Mendip (0761) 470382
320-acre mixed farm. In village of Stanton Prior beneath Iron Age fort on Stantonbury Hill. 5 miles west of Bath.
Bedrooms: 3 double
Bathrooms: 1 private, 2 public

Bed & breakfast

per night:	£min	£max
Single	18.00	20.00
Double	30.00	36.00

Parking for 11

🛏️♿Ⓤ🗲📺🖩🚗Ⓤ✿ 🚬🏨

St. Leonards

☰☰

Warminster Road, Bathampton, Bath BA2 6SQ
☎ (0225) 465838
Fax (0272) 865872
Well restored Victorian house overlooking Kennet and Avon canal, in an acre of garden

---

with breathtaking views. 1 mile city centre. King size beds, English breakfast, off-street parking.
Bedrooms: 5 double
Bathrooms: 3 private, 2 public, 2 private showers

Bed & breakfast

per night:	£min	£max
Single	15.00	20.00
Double	30.00	40.00

Parking for 9

🛇🖃🖵♿🔌Ⓤ🛈Ⓢ🗲♿📺 🌑🖩🚗✿🚬ⓈⓅ🏨Ⓣ

Sampford

☰

11 Oldfield Road, Bath BA2 3ND
☎ (0225) 310053
In a quiet residential area half a mile south of city centre off the A367 Exeter road.
Bedrooms: 2 double, 1 twin, 1 triple
Bathrooms: 3 private, 1 public

Bed & breakfast

per night:	£min	£max
Double	28.00	28.00

Parking for 1

🛏️Ⓜ🖵♿🔌Ⓤ🗲♿🖩🚗🚬

Sheridan

☰

95 Wellsway, Bearflat, Bath BA2 4RU
☎ (0225) 429562
Quiet, comfortable family guesthouse. A few minutes' drive from city centre and on main bus route to city and railway station. A non-smoking house.
Bedrooms: 1 single, 1 twin, 1 triple
Bathrooms: 2 public

Bed & breakfast

per night:	£min	£max
Single	15.00	17.00
Double	30.00	34.00

Cards accepted: Visa

🛏️♿Ⓤ Ⓢ🗲♿📺🖩✗ 🚬ⓈⓅ

Wansdyke Cottage

Listed APPROVED

Marksbury Gate, Bath BA2 9HE
☎ Saltford (0225) 873674
Cottage-style accommodation including self-contained suite of bedroom, bathroom, kitchen and lounge. 5 miles west of Bath on A39.
Bedrooms: 1 single, 2 double, 1 twin
Bathrooms: 1 private, 2 public

Bed & breakfast

per night:	£min	£max
Single	15.00	20.00
Double	30.00	35.00

Half board

per person:	£min	£max
Daily	22.00	28.00

Lunch available
Evening meal 1900 (last orders 1700)
Parking for 4

🚬🛏️♿Ⓤ Ⓢ♿📺🖩🚗✿ 🚬🏨Ⓣ

Wellsway Guest House

☰☰

51 Wellsway, Bath BA2 4RS
☎ (0225) 423434
Comfortable, clean, warm, small guesthouse on bus route. Close to local shops, only a few minutes' walk from city centre.
Bedrooms: 1 single, 2 twin, 1 triple
Bathrooms: 1 public

Bed & breakfast

per night:	£min	£max
Single	16.00	18.00
Double	20.00	32.00

Parking for 3

🛏️🖵Ⓤ Ⓢ♿📺🖩🚗▶♿ ⒹⒶⓅⓉ

Wheelwrights Arms ▲▲

Monkton Combe, Bath BA2 7HD
☎ Limpley Stoke (0225) 722287
Ideal centre for sightseeing, a short distance from Bath. Guest rooms are in converted 17th C stables and barn.
Bedrooms: 5 double, 3 twin
Bathrooms: 8 private

Bed & breakfast

per night:	£min	£max
Single	30.00	38.00
Double	46.00	48.00

Half board

per person:	£min	£max
Daily	35.00	37.00

Lunch available
Evening meal 1930 (last orders 2100)
Parking for 31
Cards accepted: Access, Visa

🛏️14🛇👤☎️🖵♿🛈🖩🚗✿ ✗🚬ⓈⓅ🏨

BATHFORD

Avon
Map ref 2B2

Bridge Cottage

Northfield End, Ashley Road, Bathford, Bath BA1 7TT
☎ Bath (0225) 852399
Self-contained ground floor suite including dining room.

Continued ▶

BATHFORD

Continued

Own entrance, all day access. Cottage garden. Convenient for Bath.
Bedrooms: 1 single, 1 triple
Bathrooms: 2 private
Bed & breakfast

per night:	£min	£max
Double	35.00	45.00

Parking for 1
☎🚳🛏🚶♿♨🅿♥🚭🚷🛁
🐾 DAP 🏧

BEAMINSTER

Dorset
Map ref 2A3

Old country town of mellow local stone set amid hills and rural vales. Mainly Georgian buildings; attractive almshouses date from 1603. The 17th C church with its ornate, pinnacled tower was restored inside by the Victorians. Parnham, a Tudor manor house, lies 1 mile south.

Burstock Grange Farm
Broadwindsor, Beaminster
DT8 3LL
☎ Broadwindsor (0308) 68527
300-acre mixed farm. Thatched 13th C farmhouse on family-run farm. Warm and friendly personal attention. Games room and TV lounge. Very quiet.
Bedrooms: 1 single, 1 double, 1 twin
Bathrooms: 1 public
Bed & breakfast

per night:	£min	£max
Single	15.00	15.00
Double	25.00	36.00

Parking for 4
Open April-October
☎ 10 🚶♿🚷🛁📺🛏♦♨
🐾 🏧

The Old Vicarage
Listed

Clay Lane, Beaminster
DT8 3BU
☎ (0308) 863200
Large, spacious mid-Victorian vicarage close to town centre, set in its own grounds of three-quarters of an acre. Hardy's Emminster Vicarage (as in 'Tess of the D'Urbervilles').
Bedrooms: 2 double, 1 twin
Bathrooms: 2 private, 1 public

Bed & breakfast

per night:	£min	£max
Double	27.00	32.00

Parking for 16
Open April-October
☎🚶♿🚷📺🛁🏧 ♨ 🐾🏧

Water Meadow House
🏠🛏

Bridge Farm, Hooke, Beaminster DT8 3PD
☎ (0308) 862619
280-acre dairy & livestock farm. New Georgian-style farmhouse on working dairy farm in quiet village of Hooke, by the river. Good walking country, lovely countryside.
Bedrooms: 1 double, 1 multiple
Bathrooms: 2 private
Bed & breakfast

per night:	£min	£max
Single	18.00	18.00
Double	32.00	36.00

Parking for 4
Open April-September
☎🚳🛏🚶♿🚷♿🅿🚷🛁
🛏♨🗡🐾 DAP SP

BERE FERRERS

Devon
Map ref 1C2

Leeches Farm
Bere Ferrers, Yelverton
PL20 7JF
☎ Tavistock (0822) 840793
Quiet farmhouse with excellent views and swimming pool. Close to River Tamar and River Tavy, Tavistock and Dartmoor 6 miles.
Bedrooms: 1 double, 1 twin
Bathrooms: 2 public
Bed & breakfast

per night:	£min	£max
Double	28.00	32.00

Half board

per person:	£min	£max
Daily	16.00	
Weekly	96.00	

Evening meal 1700 (last orders 2130)
Parking for 6
♿♿♨🚷🛁🗡🐾 🛏🔌♨
🐾 SP

National Crown ratings were correct at the time of going to press but are subject to change. Please check at the time of booking.

BERRYNARBOR

Devon
Map ref 1C1

Small village set in a wooded valley, close to Exmoor and to the wild North Devon coast.

Langleigh House
😊😊 APPROVED

The Village, Berrynarbor, Ilfracombe EX34 9SG
☎ Combe Martin (0271) 883410
Friendly family-run guesthouse providing all home-cooked food, in the beautiful North Devon village of Berrynarbor.
Bedrooms: 1 single, 3 double, 1 twin, 1 triple
Bathrooms: 4 private, 1 public
Bed & breakfast

per night:	£min	£max
Single	14.00	15.50
Double	28.00	31.00

Half board

per person:	£min	£max
Daily	20.00	21.50
Weekly	135.00	144.00

Evening meal 1830 (last orders 1200)
Parking for 6
☎🚳🛏♿♨🅿🛁📺🛁♿♨🐾

BICKINGTON

Devon
Map ref 1D2

Gale Farm
Bickington, Newton Abbot
TQ12 6PG
☎ (0626) 821273
Telex 42585 XONIA
4-acre smallholding. Georgian farmhouse in sheltered valley just off A38. Comfortable sitting room and well-furnished rooms. Traditional cooking with homegrown produce. Tennis court availability can be arranged.
Bedrooms: 2 double, 1 twin
Bathrooms: 2 public
Bed & breakfast

per night:	£min	£max
Single	13.50	15.00
Double	27.00	30.00

Half board

per person:	£min	£max
Daily	23.50	25.00

Evening meal from 1900
Parking for 6
☎🚳🛏♿♨🅿🚷📺🛁♿♨🔌U
♨🐾

Kellinch Farm
😊😊 COMMENDED

Bickington, Newton Abbot
TQ12 6PB
☎ Newton Abbot (0626) 821252
56-acre mixed farm. Attractive 17th C farmhouse. Idyllically set in the heart of the Devonshire countryside.
Bedrooms: 1 double, 1 twin
Bathrooms: 2 private, 1 public
Bed & breakfast

per night:	£min	£max
Double	30.00	30.00

Half board

per person:	£min	£max
Daily	23.50	23.50
Weekly	154.00	154.00

Evening meal from 1900
Parking for 10
☎🚳🔌♨🅿♿🚷🛁📺🔌♨
U♨🗡🐾🅣

BIDEFORD

Devon
Map ref 1C1

The home port of Sir Richard Grenville, the town with its 17th C merchants' houses flourished as a shipbuilding and cloth town. The bridge of 24 arches was built about 1460. Charles Kingsley stayed here while writing Westward Ho!
Tourist Information Centre ☎ (0237) 477676.

Sunset Hotel ♨
😊😊😊 APPROVED

Landcross, Bideford
EX39 5JA
☎ (0237) 472962
Small, elegant country hotel in peaceful, picturesque location 1.5 miles from town, specialising in home cooking. Delightful en-suite bedrooms with beverages and colour TVs. Book with confidence.
Bedrooms: 1 single, 3 double, 2 twin, 2 triple
Bathrooms: 8 private
Bed & breakfast

per night:	£min	£max
Single	25.00	28.00
Double	46.00	53.00

Half board

per person:	£min	£max
Daily	33.00	37.00
Weekly	220.00	245.00

Evening meal 1900 (last orders 1900)
Parking for 10

Open January-November
Cards accepted: Access, Visa
🐾⌨✆🅢🗓⏰📺◐🏠
🅿🖍☀🎣🅳🅰🅿🆂🅃

BISHOP SUTTON

Avon
Map ref 2A2

Village at edge of Chew
Valley Lake.

Centaur
⚜⚜ COMMENDED

Ham Lane, Bishop Sutton,
Bristol BS18 4TZ
☎ Chew Magna (0275)
332321
*Comfortable family house in
the peaceful Chew Valley.
Bishop Sutton is on the A368
between Bath and Weston-
super-Mare.*
Bedrooms: 1 twin, 1 triple
Bathrooms: 1 private,
1 public, 1 private shower
Bed & breakfast

per night:	£min	£max
Single	13.00	16.00
Double	26.00	32.00

Parking for 2
Open January-November
🐾🌢✆🅳📺🏠🎣🎣

Overbrook
⚜⚜ COMMENDED

Stowey Bottom, Bishop
Sutton, Bristol BS18 4TN
☎ (0275) 332648
*Delightful house of character,
in quiet lane by a stream in
Chew Valley. Near Bath,
Bristol, Wells and Cheddar
Gorge.*
Bedrooms: 1 double, 1 twin
Bathrooms: 2 private
Bed & breakfast

per night:	£min	£max
Single	15.00	17.50
Double	30.00	

Half board

per person:	£min	£max
Daily		23.50

Evening meal 1900 (last
orders 2000)
Parking for 8
🐾🅼🌢✆🆄🎣🖉🗓📺🏠
☀🎣🎣

BISHOP'S CAUNDLE

Dorset
Map ref 2B3

Holtwood Farmhouse
⚜⚜ HIGHLY COMMENDED

Bishop's Caundle, Sherborne
DT9 5JY
☎ (0963) 23630

---

*17th C stone farmhouse with
outstanding views over
Blackmore Vale. Home
produce. Exceptional
standards of food and
comfort.*
Bedrooms: 1 double, 1 twin
Bathrooms: 2 private
Bed & breakfast

per night:	£min	£max
Double	45.00	45.00

Half board

per person:	£min	£max
Daily	42.00	42.00

Evening meal 1900 (last
orders 2100)
🐾🌢🎣🆄🅱🅢🖉🗓📺🏠🎣
🍷🎣☀🅱🆂🅿

BISHOP'S LYDEARD

Somerset
Map ref 1D1

Slimbridge Station Farm
⚜⚜ COMMENDED

Bishop's Lydeard, Taunton
TA4 3BX
☎ Bishops Lydeard (0823)
432223
*120-acre dairy farm. Victorian
house next to the privately-
owned West Somerset Steam
Railway which has a limited
number of trains running in
the summer.*
Bedrooms: 1 single,
1 double, 1 twin
Bathrooms: 1 public
Bed & breakfast

per night:	£min	£max
Single	15.00	17.00
Double	30.00	34.00

Parking for 4
🐾🅱🖉⌨🌢🆄🅱🗓📺🏠
☀🎣

BODMIN

Cornwall
Map ref 1B2

County town south-west
of Bodmin Moor with a
ruined priory and church,
containing the casket said
to have held relics of St
Petroc, to whom the
church is dedicated.
Nearby are Lanhydrock
House and Pencarrow
House.
*Tourist Information Centre
Tel (0208) 76616*

Treffry Farm ⚱
⚜⚜ HIGHLY COMMENDED

Lanhydrock, Bodmin
PL30 5AF
☎ (0208) 74405

---

*200-acre dairy farm. Lovely
Georgian farmhouse in
beautiful countryside
adjoining National Trust
Lanhydrock. Central for coast,
moors and towns.*
Bedrooms: 1 double, 2 twin
Bathrooms: 2 private,
1 public, 1 private shower
Bed & breakfast

per night:	£min	£max
Single		18.50
Double		37.00

Half board

per person:	£min	£max
Daily		27.50
Weekly		185.00

Evening meal 1830 (last
orders 1200)
Parking for 3
Open March-September
🐾🅱6🅱⌨🌢🆄🅱🅢🖉
🅱📺🏠◐🅿🎣☀🎣🎣🏵

BOSCASTLE

Cornwall
Map ref 1B2

Small, unspoilt village in
Valency Valley. Active as
a port until onset of
railway era, its natural
harbour affords rare
shelter on this wild coast.
Attractions include
spectacular blow-hole,
Celtic field strips, part-
Norman church. St Juliot
Church nearby, was
restored by Thomas
Hardy.

The Old Coach House ⚱
⚜⚜⚜

Tintagel Road, Boscastle
PL35 0AS
☎ (0840) 250398
*Relax in beautiful 300-year-
old former coach-house. All
en-suite with colour TV.
Licensed. Friendly and
helpful service.*
Bedrooms: 1 single,
3 double, 1 twin, 1 triple
Bathrooms: 6 private
Bed & breakfast

per night:	£min	£max
Single	15.00	22.00
Double	30.00	44.00

Lunch available
Parking for 9
Cards accepted: Access, Visa,
Amex
🐾🅱6🅱⌨⌨🌢🅱🅢🖉🅱
🏠🖉🅾◐☀🎣🎣🆂🏵

We advise you to
confirm your
booking in writing.

BOVEY TRACEY

Devon
Map ref 1D2

Standing by the river just
east of Dartmoor National
Park, this old town has
good moorland views. Its
church, with a 14th C
tower, holds one of
Devon's finest medieval
rood screens.

Corbyns Brimley
⚜⚜ COMMENDED

Higher Brimley, Bovey
Tracey, Newton Abbot
TQ13 9JT
☎ (0626) 833332
*16th C thatched cottage in
foothills of Haytor, within
Dartmoor National Park.
Comfortable and friendly
atmosphere, secluded garden,
panoramic views of
surrounding countryside.
Overseas visitors welcome.
Leave Bovey Tracey on
Haytor road, straight on at
island. Take left at fork,
forward to crossroads. Turn
left, forward to T junction,
turn right. Corbyns is first
thatched cottage two-thirds of
a mile on the right.*
Bedrooms: 2 twin
Bathrooms: 1 private,
1 public
Bed & breakfast

per night:	£min	£max
Single	28.00	30.00
Double	40.00	42.00

Parking for 4
Open February-December
♿🅱⌨🌢🆄🅢🖉📺🅿☀
☀🎣🏵

Lower Elsford Cottage
Listed HIGHLY COMMENDED

Bovey Tracey, Newton Abbot
TQ13 9NY
☎ Lustleigh (064 77) 408
*17th C stone cottage near the
reservoirs at Hennock,
overlooking village of
Lustleigh with outstanding
scenic views. Fishing
available.*
Bedrooms: 1 single, 1 double
Bathrooms: 1 private,
1 public
Bed & breakfast

per night:	£min	£max
Single	15.00	17.00
Double	32.00	36.00

Parking for 4
🐾🅱8🆄🖉🏠🅿☀🎣

BOX

Wiltshire
Map ref 2B2

Lorne House
London Road, Box, Corsham
SN14 9NA
☎ Bath (0225) 742597
Victorian property, recently refurbished, on main A4 road opposite Brunel's famous Box tunnel between Bath and Chippenham. Warm and welcoming.
Bedrooms: 2 double, 1 twin, 1 triple
Bathrooms: 4 private
Bed & breakfast

per night:	£min	£max
Single	20.00	
Double		35.00

Parking for 6
🏃🖵♿🕪Ⅲ🛏🕙S🍴🐾🏧📺Ⅲ🛏🕪

BRADFORD-ON-AVON

Wiltshire
Map ref 2B2

Huddled beside the river, the buildings of this former cloth-weaving town reflect continuing prosperity from the Middle Ages. There is a tiny Anglo-Saxon church, part of a monastery. The part-14th C bridge carries a medieval chapel, later used as a gaol.
Tourist Information Centre
☎ *(022 16) 5797*

Barge Inn
🛏
17 Frome Road, Bradford-on-Avon BA15 2EA
☎ (022 16) 3403
Grade II listed inn on the banks of Kennet and Avon Canal. Canalside gardens. Restaurant open every day.
Bedrooms: 1 double, 2 twin
Bathrooms: 1 private, 1 public
Bed & breakfast

per night:	£min	£max
Single	18.00	20.00
Double	36.00	55.00

Lunch available
Evening meal 1900 (last orders 2200)
Parking for 40
🏃🖵♿Ⅲ🛏🐾❖🍴🏧🛏

Brookfield House
😊😊 HIGHLY COMMENDED
Vaggs Hill, Southwick,
Trowbridge BA14 9NA
☎ Frome (0373) 830615

150-acre dairy farm. Barn converted in 1989, in completely rural location on boundary between Somerset and Wiltshire. South-facing aspects. Farm is 100 yards away.
Bedrooms: 2 double, 1 twin
Bathrooms: 2 private, 2 public
Bed & breakfast

per night:	£min	£max
Single	15.00	26.00
Double	34.00	38.00

Parking for 10
🏃🖵♿Ⅲ🛏🕙S🍴🏧📺🕙Ⅲ🛏❖🏧🛏

Great Ashley House
Ashley Lane, Bradford-on-Avon BA15 2PP
☎ Bath (0225) 868111
Quiet, friendly country house in rural location. Off A363 from Bath. Evening meal by arrangement.
Bedrooms: 2 double, 1 twin
Bathrooms: 2 public
Bed & breakfast

per night:	£min	£max
Single	12.00	12.00
Double	24.00	24.00

Half board

per person:	£min	£max
Daily		18.00

🏃♿Ⅲ🍴🕙📺Ⅲ🛏🐾🍴

Northover House
163 Bath Road, Bradford-on-Avon BA15 1SW
☎ (022 16) 7542
Detached house built in Bath stone, with attractive gardens. Bedrooms with TV, tea and coffee facilities.
Bedrooms: 3 double
Bathrooms: 1 private, 1 public
Bed & breakfast

per night:	£min	£max
Single	20.00	25.00
Double	32.00	38.00

Parking for 6
🏃🖵♿Ⅲ🛏S🍴🕙📺Ⅲ🛏🍴🏧

The Riverside Inn
49 St. Margarets Street,
Bradford-on-Avon BA15 1DE
☎ (022 16) 3526
Fax (0225) 868082
17th C inn on the river in town centre. Pretty restaurant. Good value home cooking. Most rooms overlooking river.
Bedrooms: 1 single, 6 double, 6 twin, 1 triple
Bathrooms: 14 private

Bed & breakfast		
per night:	£min	£max
Single	25.00	28.00
Double	40.00	45.00

Half board		
per person:	£min	£max
Daily	35.00	43.00

Lunch available
Evening meal 1800 (last orders 2200)
Parking for 12
Cards accepted: Access, Visa
🏃🖵♿S Ⅲ🛏◆❖🍴🏧🛏
🛏🏧

BRIDESTOWE

Devon
Map ref 1C2

Small Dartmoor village with a much restored 15th C church, and Great Links Tor rising to the southeast.

White Hart Inn
😊😊
Fore Street, Bridestowe,
Okehampton EX20 4EL
☎ (083 786) 318
17th C inn, family-run for 30 years, primarily noted for good food. En-suite accommodation - a new feature. Close to Dartmoor National Park and Lydford Gorge.
Bedrooms: 2 double
Bathrooms: 2 private
Bed & breakfast

per night:	£min	£max
Single	22.00	
Double	40.00	

Lunch available
Evening meal 1900 (last orders 2130)
Parking for 20
Cards accepted: Access, Visa, Diners, Amex
🍺🖵♿S🍴📺❖🍴🏧

BRIDGERULE

Devon
Map ref 1C2

Lodgeworthy Farm 🏠
😊😊 COMMENDED
Bridgerule, Holsworthy
EX22 7EH
☎ (028 881) 351
180-acre dairy farm. Old Devon longhouse in centre of village, offering a warm welcome and every comfort. Ideal touring centre, good local amenities.
Bedrooms: 1 single, 1 double, 1 multiple
Bathrooms: 2 private, 1 public

Bed & breakfast		
per night:	£min	£max
Single	15.00	17.00
Double	30.00	34.00

Half board		
per person:	£min	£max
Daily	21.00	
Weekly	140.00	

Evening meal 1830 (last orders 1830)
Parking for 5
🏃♿Ⅲ🛏S🍴📺Ⅲ🛏🍴🏧
🍴❖🍴🏧🛏🏧

BRIDGWATER

Somerset
Map ref 1D1

Former medieval port on the River Parrett, now small industrial town with mostly 19th C or modern architecture. Georgian Castle Street leads to West Quay and site of 13th C castle razed to the ground by Cromwell. Birthplace of Cromwellian admiral Robert Blake is now museum. Arts centre.

Chinar
17 Oakfield Road,
Bridgwater TA6 7LX
☎ (0278) 458639
Detached modern house in quiet locality and with attractive small garden. Very comfortable beds and imaginative breakfasts.
Bedrooms: 2 double
Bathrooms: 2 private, 1 public
Bed & breakfast

per night:	£min	£max
Single	14.00	15.00
Double	28.00	30.00

Evening meal 1830 (last orders 1600)
Parking for 2
🏃🍺🖵♿Ⅲ🛏S🍴📺Ⅲ🛏
🍴❖🍴🏧

Waterpitts Farm
Broomfield, Bridgwater
TA5 1AT
☎ Kingston St Mary (0823) 451679
5-acre mixed farm. In quiet secluded part of the Quantock Hills. Convenient for riding, walking, fishing, golf and pub. Midway between Taunton and Bridgwater.
Bedrooms: 1 double, 1 triple
Bathrooms: 1 public

Please check prices and other details at the time of booking.

Bed & breakfast

per night:	£min	£max
Single	14.00	15.00
Double	27.00	29.00

Parking for 20

🐕🐾📺♿🛏📶Ⓢ🍴📺🏠 ⬛
🚭▶✖➕

Dorset
Map ref 2A3

Market town and chief
producer of nets and
ropes just inland of
dramatic Dorset coast.
Old, broad streets built for
drying and twisting, long
gardens for rope-walks.
Grand arcaded Town Hall
and Georgian buildings.
Local history museum has
Roman relics.
Tourist Information Centre
☎ *(0308) 24901.*

Britmead House ⋒

COMMENDED

154 West Bay Road,
Bridport DT6 4EG
☎ (0308) 22941
*Elegant, detached, tastefully
decorated house, renowned
for hospitality, comfort and
meals. 10 minutes' walk to
harbour and beaches.*
Bedrooms: 4 double, 3 twin
Bathrooms: 6 private,
1 private shower

Bed & breakfast

per night:	£min	£max
Single	22.00	32.00
Double	34.00	46.00

Half board

per person:	£min	£max
Daily	28.00	34.50
Weekly	187.25	227.50

Evening meal 1900 (last
orders 1700)
Parking for 8
Cards accepted: Access, Visa,
C.Bl, Diners, Amex

🐕🍴📶📺♿🛏Ⓢ🍴📺🏠
⬛🚭➕📶SP Ⓣ

Lancombes House ⋒

West Milton, Bridport
DT6 3TN
☎ Powerstock (030 885) 375
*35-acre mixed farm.
Converted barn, 8 minutes
from the sea. Panoramic
views. Beautiful walks and
bridleways. Riding facilities.*
Bedrooms: 4 double, 3 twin
Bathrooms: 3 public

Bed & breakfast

per night:	£min	£max
Single	15.00	20.00
Double	20.00	30.00

Half board

per person:	£min	£max
Daily	20.00	25.00

Lunch available
Evening meal 1830 (last
orders 2100)
Parking for 20
Cards accepted: C.Bl, Diners,
Amex

🐕🍴📶🛏📺🏠⬛🚭♿✖
➕📶OAP

The Mill House

Listed

East Road, Bridport
DT6 4AG
☎ (0308) 25147
*Converted Georgian cornmill
with lovely garden, own
stream and meadows. Noted
for our English breakfasts.
Non-smokers only please.*
Bedrooms: 1 single, 2 double
Bathrooms: 1 private,
1 public

Bed & breakfast

per night:	£min	£max
Single	14.00	14.00
Double	27.00	31.00

Half board

per person:	£min	£max
Daily	13.50	15.50
Weekly	85.00	97.00

Parking for 4
Open March-October

🐕🍴10📶🛏Ⓢ🍴✖⬛➕
📶🏠Ⓣ

Avon
Map ref 2A2

A university town and
major port. City grew
around medieval river
docks (Cabot sailed for
Newfoundland in 1497).
Merchant Venturers
founded here 1552. Fine
old churches and
cathedral; wide views of
Avon Gorge from Brunel's
Clifton Bridge.
Tourist Information Centre
☎ *(0272) 260767.*

1 Priory Gardens

High Street, Shirehampton,
Bristol BS11 OBZ
☎ Avonmouth (0272)
825690
*Modern detached house set in
small, attractive, quiet cul-de-
sac off the high street of
Shirehampton. 1 mile from
junction 18 of M5.*
Bedrooms: 1 single, 1 twin
Bathrooms: 1 public

Bed & breakfast

per night:	£min	£max
Single	13.50	13.50
Double	27.00	27.00

Parking for 1

📶🛏Ⓢ🍴📺🏠⬛♿
✖📶

32 Central Avenue

Hanham, Bristol BS15 3PQ
☎ (0272) 676306
*Semi-detached private house
with garden. Approximately 5
miles from centre of Bristol,
east of city, near Bath.*
Bedrooms: 1 single, 1 twin
Bathrooms: 1 public

Bed & breakfast

per night:	£min	£max
Single		12.00
Double		24.00

Parking for 3

🐕3📶🛏🍴📺🏠⬛♿✖📶

Albany Guest House

📶

500 Bath Road, Brislington,
Bristol BS4 3JY
☎ (0272) 778710
*Comfortable, tastefully-
furnished Victorian semi, on
main A4 2 miles from city
centre and 1 mile from
station. Off-road parking.*
Bedrooms: 1 single,
2 double, 1 twin
Bathrooms: 2 private,
1 public

Bed & breakfast

per night:	£min	£max
Single	17.50	20.50
Double	26.50	30.50

Parking for 3

🐕7📶📶🛏Ⓢ🍴📺🏠
⬛✖📶

Cully Hall Farm

Ryedown Lane, Bitton,
Bristol BS15 6JG
☎ (0272) 323177
*105-acre mixed farm. Early
17th C manor house of
historic interest in peaceful
setting, exactly 6 miles from
Bristol and Bath. Elizabeth I
is reputed to have slept here.
Avon Valley Railway within
walking distance.*
Bedrooms: 1 single,
1 double, 1 triple
Bathrooms: 1 public

Bed & breakfast

per night:	£min	£max
Single	16.00	19.00
Double	32.00	35.00

Parking for 12

🐕📶🛏🍴✖🍴📺🏠⬛
🛏▶♿📶🏠

K Linton Homes

Listed

3 Lansdown Road, Clifton
Village, Bristol BS8 3AA
☎ (0272) 737326
*Comfortable, spacious,
Victorian private house in
elegant Clifton village, near
suspension bridge, the downs,
restaurants and shops. 2
miles from city centre.*
Bedrooms: 2 single,
1 double, 1 twin, 1 triple
Bathrooms: 2 public

Bed & breakfast

per night:	£min	£max
Single	17.00	25.00
Double	30.00	40.00

Parking for 2

🐕🍴📶📶📺🛏Ⓢ🏠
⬛📶

Langford Green Farm

Upper Langford, Bristol
BS18 7DG
☎ Churchill (0934) 852368
*120-acre dairy farm. Quiet
picturesque farmhouse with
lovely views, at foot of
Mendip Hills. 15 minutes
from M5 junction 21. Good
local pubs nearby.*
Bedrooms: 1 single,
1 double, 1 triple
Bathrooms: 2 public

Bed & breakfast

per night:	£min	£max
Single	14.00	16.00
Double	28.00	32.00

Parking for 6

🐕📶📺🛏🍴📺🏠⬛♿✖📶

Portbury Priors

Station Road, Portbury,
Bristol BS20 9TN
☎ Pill (0275) 373165
*16th C farmhouse, three
quarters of a mile from
junction 19 of the M5, 8
miles from Bristol centre. Log
fires in winter. Situated close
to the village pub.*
Bedrooms: 1 double, 2 twin
Bathrooms: 2 public

Bed & breakfast

per night:	£min	£max
Single	18.00	20.00
Double	28.00	30.00

Parking for 4

🐕🐾📶Ⓢ🍴📺🏠⬛♿✖
✖📶🏠

Toad Lodge

Listed

12 Cotham Park, Cotham,
Bristol BS6 6BU
☎ (0272) 247080
*Large Georgian residence
within half a mile of city
centre. Offers all amenities,
comfort, attractive decor. Pets
welcome.*

Continued ▶

BRISTOL

Continued

Bedrooms: 1 single, 5 twin,
1 triple
Bathrooms: 2 public
Bed & breakfast

per night:	£min	£max
Single	16.50	16.50
Double	29.00	29.00

Parking for 9

BRIXHAM

Devon
Map ref 1D2

Famous for its trawling
fleet in the 19th C, a
steeply-built fishing port
overlooking the harbour
and fish market. A statue
of William of Orange
recalls his landing here
before deposing James II.
There is an aquarium and
museum. Good cliff views
and walks.
Tourist Information Centre
☎ *(0803) 852861*

Richmond House Hotel

COMMENDED

Higher Manor Road,
Brixham TQ5 8HA
☎ (0803) 882391
*Detached Victorian house
with Laura Ashley interior,
sun trap garden and adjacent
car park. En-suite available.
Convenient for shops and
harbour, yet quiet location.
First left after Golden Lion.*
Bedrooms: 3 single,
1 double, 1 twin, 3 triple,
1 multiple
Bathrooms: 2 private,
2 public
Bed & breakfast

per night:	£min	£max
Single	18.00	
Double	32.00	

Parking for 5
Open February-November
Cards accepted: Access, Visa

National Crown
ratings were correct
at the time of going
to press but are
subject to change.
Please check at the
time of booking.

BUCKFAST

Devon
Map ref 1C2

Situated on the south-
east edge of Dartmoor,
this village is visited for its
handsome 20th C abbey
which occupies the site of
a Cistercian monastery.
The main part was built
from 1906-32 by
untrained Benedictine
monks. The chapel which
was added in the 1960s
has fine stained glass
windows.

Abbey Inn

Buckfast Road, Buckfast,
Buckfastleigh TQ11 0EA
☎ Buckfastleigh (0364)
42343
*Family-run hotel on edge of
the River Dart in Dartmoor
National Park, only 5 minutes
from the A38. High standard
of food, comfort and
hospitality.*
Bedrooms: 2 single,
3 double, 2 twin, 1 triple,
2 multiple
Bathrooms: 2 public,
1 private shower
Bed & breakfast

per night:	£min	£max
Single	20.00	30.00
Double		48.00

Lunch available
Evening meal 1900 (last
orders 2200)
Parking for 26
Cards accepted: Access, Visa

BUDE

Cornwall
Map ref 1C2

Resort on dramatic
Atlantic coast. High cliffs
give spectacular sea and
inland views. Golf course,
cricket pitch, folly, surfing,
coarse-fishing and
boating. Mother-town
Stratton was base of
Royalist Sir Bevil
Grenville.
Tourist Information Centre
☎ *(0288) 354240*

Clovelly House

APPROVED

4 Burn View, Bude
EX23 8BY
☎ (0288) 352761
*In a level location, opposite
golf club and close to all
amenities. All rooms with
tea/coffee facilities, satellite
TV, some en-suite.*

Bedrooms: 2 single,
2 double, 1 twin, 1 triple
Bathrooms: 3 private,
1 public
Bed & breakfast

per night:	£min	£max
Single	14.00	17.00
Double	28.00	35.00

Parking for 2
Open January-October

Lower Northcott Farm

APPROVED

Poughill, Bude EX23 9EL
☎ (0288) 352350
*400-acre mixed farm.
Georgian farmhouse in
secluded grounds with
children's safe play area.
Visitors welcome to wander
around and meet the animals.*
Bedrooms: 1 single, 1 twin,
3 multiple
Bathrooms: 1 private,
2 public
Bed & breakfast

per night:	£min	£max
Single	14.00	
Double	28.00	

Half board

per person:	£min	£max
Daily	20.00	
Weekly	145.00	

Evening meal 1830 (last
orders 1830)
Parking for 4

BUDLEIGH SALTERTON

Devon
Map ref 1D2

Small resort with pebble
beach on coast of red
cliffs, setting for famous
Victorian painting 'The
Boyhood of Raleigh'. Sir
Walter Raleigh was born
at Hayes Barton. A salt-
panning village in
medieval times, today's
resort has some Georgian
houses.
Tourist Information Centre
☎ *(0395) 445275.*

East Cliff

HIGHLY COMMENDED

14 Marine Parade, Budleigh
Salterton EX9 6NS
☎ (0395) 445555
*Large detached Victorian
house on seafront, situated on
the south west coastal path
and offering comfortable
accommodation. Golf-course
and bird watching locally.*
Bedrooms: 2 twin

Bathrooms: 2 private
Bed & breakfast

per night:	£min	£max
Double	40.00	52.00

Parking for 2

Lemprice Farmhouse

Listed

Yettington, Budleigh
Salterton EX9 7BW
☎ Colaton Raleigh (0395)
67037
Fax (0395) 67585
*Georgian farmhouse, with en-
suite facilities, in rural hamlet
between Woodbury and East
Budleigh. Superb walking
country, abundant wildlife.
Three miles beach, 8 miles
M5 junction 30. Home of the
rare barn owl.*
Bedrooms: 1 twin, 1 triple
Bathrooms: 2 private
Bed & breakfast

per night:	£min	£max
Single	18.00	
Double	36.00	

Parking for 10

BURBAGE

Wiltshire
Map ref 2B2

Village close to
Savernake Forest, famous
as a habitat for deer.
Close by are the remains
of Wolf Hall mansion,
where a great banquet in
honour of Jane Seymour
took place in 1536.

The Old Vicarage

HIGHLY COMMENDED

Burbage, Marlborough
SN8 3AG
☎ Marlborough (0672)
810495
Fax (0672) 810663
*Victorian country house in 2-
acre garden, offering peace
and comfort. Within easy
reach of Bath, Salisbury,
Oxford and Windsor.*
Bedrooms: 1 single,
1 double, 1 twin
Bathrooms: 3 private
Bed & breakfast

per night:	£min	£max
Single	35.00	35.00
Double	60.00	60.00

Half board

per person:	£min	£max
Daily	55.00	60.00

Evening meal 2000 (last
orders 1200)
Parking for 10

Cards accepted: Access, Visa, Amex

📞🖨📺↕🎜🛏📶📳♿🅿📺
🍴�↺⛟✗🚲🏤

BURNHAM-ON-SEA

Somerset
Map ref 1D1

Small resort with extensive sands on Bridgwater Bay. Lighthouse is one of the town's attractions, as is the 15th C church whose white marble altar, made by Grinling Gibbons, was salvaged from James II's Whitehall Chapel.
Tourist Information Centre
☎ *(0278) 787852*

Northwick Farm
👑👑 COMMENDED

Mark, Highbridge TA9 4PG
☎ Mark Moor (027 864) 228
50-acre mixed farm. Within 2 miles of the M5 and A38. Picturesque, brick-built Georgian farmhouse with large rooms, quality furnishings, south-facing pleasant gardens. Peacefully situated. Holiday cottage also available.
Bedrooms: 2 double,
1 multiple
Bathrooms: 1 public

Bed & breakfast

per night:	£min	£max
Single	15.00	17.00
Double	30.00	34.00

Half board

per person:	£min	£max
Daily	24.00	27.00
Weekly	150.00	180.00

Evening meal from 1800
Parking for 6
🛇5♿🖴📶🛏S✗🎜📺🖬🚗
�↺⛟✗🚲SP🏤

Prospect Farm
Strowlands, East Brent, Highbridge TA9 4JH
☎ Brent Knoll (0278) 760507
17th C Somerset farmhouse with inglenook fireplaces, bread ovens, beamed ceilings and a colourful history. 3 miles from Burnham-on-Sea. Variety of small farm animals and pets. Children welcome.
Bedrooms: 2 double, 1 twin,
1 triple
Bathrooms: 2 private,
2 public

Please mention this guide when making a booking.

Bed & breakfast

per night:	£min	£max
Single	14.00	16.00
Double	28.00	32.00

Parking for 12
🛇📶🎜📺🖬🚗↺⛟✗🚲🏤

Rookery Farm
👑

Northwick Road, Mark, Highbridge TA9 4PG
☎ Mark Moor (027 864) 235
150-acre dairy farm. Ideal touring area for coast and moors. 5 miles from Burnham-on-Sea, 2 miles from M5 motorway, junction 22. Quiet situation.
Bedrooms: 2 double, 1 triple
Bathrooms: 1 public

Bed & breakfast

per night:	£min	£max
Single	12.00	13.00
Double	23.00	25.00

Parking for 3
🛇♿📶🎜📺🚲

Royal Clarence Hotel ♨
👑👑👑

31 The Esplanade, Burnham-on-Sea TA8 1BQ
☎ (0278) 783138
Fax (0278) 792965
Seafront coaching inn, providing comfortable accommodation and specialising in traditional ales. Good base for touring Somerset.
Bedrooms: 3 single,
8 double, 4 twin, 4 triple
Bathrooms: 17 private,
2 public

Bed & breakfast

per night:	£min	£max
Single	30.00	30.00
Double	45.00	45.00

Half board

per person:	£min	£max
Daily	41.00	41.00
Weekly	203.00	203.00

Lunch available
Evening meal 1900 (last orders 2030)
Parking for 20
Cards accepted: Access, Visa, Diners, Amex
🛇📞🖨📕↕🎜🛏S✗🎜📺
🖬🚗ì20-200🔍📺

CADLEY

Wiltshire
Map ref 2B2

Kingstones Farm
Cadley, Marlborough
SN8 4NE
☎ Marlborough (0672) 512039

700-acre mixed farm. Listed farmhouse in rural setting two miles south of Marlborough, close to Savernake Forest.
Bedrooms: 1 double, 1 twin
Bathrooms: 1 public

Bed & breakfast

per night:	£min	£max
Double	27.50	30.00

Open April-October
🛇📕↕📶🎜🖬🚗✗🚲
SP🏤

CALLINGTON

Cornwall
Map ref 1C2

A quiet market town standing on high ground above the River Lynher. The 15th C church of St Mary's has an alabaster monument to Lord Willoughby de Broke, Henry VII's marshal. A 15th C chapel, 1 mile east, houses Dupath Well, one of the Cornish Holy Wells.

East Cornwall Farmhouse
👑👑 HIGHLY COMMENDED

Fullaford Road, Callington PL17 8AN
☎ Liskeard (0579) 50018
Beautifully situated former count house sympathetically restored in farmhouse style. Close to Cotehele House. Ideal for touring. 1 mile from A390.
Bedrooms: 1 single,
3 double, 1 twin
Bathrooms: 2 private,
1 public

Bed & breakfast

per night:	£min	£max
Single	14.00	16.00
Double	28.00	36.00

Half board

per person:	£min	£max
Daily	21.00	48.00
Weekly	137.20	197.40

Lunch available
Evening meal 1830 (last orders 2030)
Parking for 6
Open February-November
🛇📕↕📶🎜S✗🎜📺
🖬🚗🌸⛟🚲SP🏤

Higher Manaton Farm
Callington PL17 8PX
☎ Stoke Climsland (0579) 370460
90-acre mixed farm. Early 19th C farmhouse in pleasant rural surroundings. Home cooking. Central for touring.

2.5 miles north-west of Callington on the B3257.
Bedrooms: 1 twin, 1 triple
Bathrooms: 1 public

Bed & breakfast

per night:	£min	£max
Single	11.00	14.00
Double	22.00	28.00

Parking for 4
Open March-October
🛇❄📶✗🎜🚗✗🚲

CALNE

Wiltshire
Map ref 2B2

Prosperity from wool in the 15th C endowed this ancient market town with a fine church in the Perpendicular style. To the east are chalk downlands and at Oldbury Castle, an Iron Age fort, a 17th C white horse is carved into the hillside.

Chilvester Hill House
👑👑👑 HIGHLY COMMENDED

Calne SN11 0LP
☎ (0249) 813981 & 815785
Fax (0249) 814217
Professional family accepting guests in their spacious Victorian house. Weekly rates on application.
Bedrooms: 1 double, 2 twin
Bathrooms: 3 private,
1 public

Bed & breakfast

per night:	£min	£max
Single	40.00	50.00
Double	60.00	75.00

Half board

per person:	£min	£max
Daily	48.00	70.00

Evening meal 2000 (last orders 1000)
Parking for 6
Cards accepted: Access, Visa, Diners, Amex
🛇12📕↕🛏S🎜📺🖬
🚗ì↺⛟✗🚲🏤📺

Fenwicks
👑👑 COMMENDED

Buccabank, Lower Goatacre, Lyneham, Calne SN11 9HY
☎ Hilmarton (0249) 76645
Secluded house with charming accommodation and grounds. Close to M4 junctions 16 and 17, Avebury, Marlborough, Castle Combe, Lacock. Within easy reach of Bath and Cotswolds. "Good food" pub 1 mile away.
Bedrooms: 1 double, 1 twin,
1 triple
Bathrooms: 3 private

Continued ▶

295

CALNE

Continued

Bed & breakfast per night:	£min	£max
Single	25.00	28.00
Double	32.00	37.00

Parking for 4
Open February-December
Cards accepted: Amex
9 [UL] [S]

CANNINGTON

Somerset
Map ref 1D1

Quantock Hills village with Brymore House, birthplace of John Pym, a leading statesman in the reign of Charles I, lying to the west. 3 fine old 16th C houses are close by.

Blackmore Farm

COMMENDED
Cannington, Bridgwater TA5 2NE
☎ Combwich (0278) 653442
650-acre mixed farm. Tastefully restored and historic 14th C manor house with four-poster and oak bedsteads. Pleasant rural surroundings. All rooms en-suite.
Bedrooms: 2 double, 1 triple
Bathrooms: 3 private

Bed & breakfast per night:	£min	£max
Single	20.00	40.00
Double	30.00	40.00

Parking for 6
[UL] [S] [TV] [SP]

CASTLE COMBE

Wiltshire
Map ref 2B2

One of England's prettiest villages, in a steep woodland valley by a brook. The Perpendicular church recalls the village's prosperous times as a cloth-weaving centre. No trace remains of the castle, but the 13th C effigy of its founder Walter de Dunstanville lies in the church.

Alicia Cottage

3 School Lane, Castle Combe, Chippenham SN14 7HJ
☎ Chippenham (0249) 782110
300-year-old Cotswold-stone cottage. Comfortable sitting room, log fires. Many fine walks from cottage. Historic city of Bath 12 miles.
Bedrooms: 1 single, 2 double
Bathrooms: 3 private

Bed & breakfast per night:	£min	£max
Single	25.00	30.00
Double	35.00	40.00

Parking for 2
[UL] [TV]

Castle Inn

Castle Combe, Chippenham SN14 7HN
☎ (0249) 782461
Fax (0249) 782461
12th C village inn, providing warmth and hospitality, in a pretty village. Home-cooked food. Ideal for Bath and Stonehenge.
Bedrooms: 1 single, 6 double, 1 twin, 1 triple
Bathrooms: 9 private

Bed & breakfast per night:	£min	£max
Single	35.00	35.00
Double	45.00	55.00

Lunch available
Evening meal 1900 (last orders 2130)
Parking for 6
Cards accepted: Access, Visa, Amex
[S] 12-14 [SP] [T]

CAWSAND

Cornwall
Map ref 1C3

Once a smuggling centre, with old houses sloping down to the quay. Rame Head to the south has panoramic views along the Channel coasts of Devon and Cornwall.

Penmillard Farm

Rame, Cawsand, Torpoint PL10 1LG
☎ (0752) 822215
200-acre dairy farm. Family-run farm set in beautiful Rame Peninsula, close to Mount Edgecumbe Country Park, about 10 miles from Plymouth. Coastal walks, sandy beaches. No smoking home.
Bedrooms: 2 double, 1 twin
Bathrooms: 1 public

Bed & breakfast per night:	£min	£max
Double	26.00	26.00

Parking for 4
Open April-October
[UL] [TV]

CHAGFORD

Devon
Map ref 1C2

Handsome stone houses, some from the Middle Ages, grace this former stannary town on northern Dartmoor. It is a popular centre for walking expeditions and for tours of the antiquities on the rugged moor. There is a splendid 15th C granite church, said to be haunted by the poet Godolphin.

Lawn House

Mill Street, Chagford, Newton Abbot TQ13 8AW
☎ (0647) 433329
Fax (0647) 433124
Small 18th C thatched Georgian house in centre of Chagford, with comfortable rooms and home cooking.
Bedrooms: 4 double, 1 twin
Bathrooms: 2 public

Bed & breakfast per night:	£min	£max
Single	14.00	22.00
Double	26.00	32.00

[UL] [S]

Three Crowns Hotel

APPROVED
High Street, Chagford, Newton Abbot TQ13 8AJ
☎ (0647) 433444
Fax (0647) 433117
13th C hotel of character in picturesque village within Dartmoor National Park. Good cuisine. Function room. 4-poster beds. Log fires.
Bedrooms: 1 single, 8 double, 7 twin, 2 triple
Bathrooms: 15 private, 3 public

Bed & breakfast per night:	£min	£max
Single	22.50	30.00
Double	45.00	60.00

Half board per person:	£min	£max
Daily	35.00	45.00
Weekly	200.00	210.00

Lunch available
Evening meal 1900 (last orders 2130)
Parking for 21
Cards accepted: Access, Visa, Diners, Amex
[S] [TV] [SP]

We advise you to confirm your booking in writing.

CHEDDAR

Somerset
Map ref 1D1

Large village at foot of Mendips just south of the spectacular Cheddar Gorge. Close by are Roman and Saxon sites and famous show caves. Traditional Cheddar cheese is still made here.

Lodgehill Farmhouse

Listed
Rodmead Lane, Westbury-sub-Mendip, Wells BA5 1JQ
☎ Wells (0749) 870207
200-acre mixed farm. Recently built natural stone farmhouse in countryside setting. Uninterrupted views. Large lawns and patio. On A371 between Wells and Cheddar. Closed at Christmas.
Bedrooms: 3 double, 1 twin
Bathrooms: 2 private, 1 public

Bed & breakfast per night:	£min	£max
Single	15.00	18.00
Double	28.00	34.00

Parking for 12
[UL] [SP]

Tor Farm

Listed COMMENDED
Nyland, Cheddar BS27 3UP
☎ (0934) 743710
33-acre mixed farm. On A371 between Cheddar and Draycott (take the road signposted Nyland). Quiet and peaceful on Somerset Levels. Private fishing. Ideally situated for visiting Cheddar, Bath, Wookey Hole, Glastonbury, Wells and coast.
Bedrooms: 1 single, 4 double, 2 twin, 1 triple, 1 multiple
Bathrooms: 5 private, 2 public

Bed & breakfast per night:	£min	£max
Double	30.00	43.00

Evening meal 1900 (last orders 1600)
Parking for 10
[TV] [SP]

CHESELBOURNE

Dorset
Map ref 2B3

Eastfield House

Cheselbourne, Dorchester DT2
☎ Milborne St Andrew (025 887) 251

Beautiful Grade II listed farmhouse in centre of Cheselbourne 9 miles from Dorchester.
Bedrooms: 1 double, 1 twin
Bathrooms: 2 private
Bed & breakfast

per night:	£min	£max
Double	35.00	40.00

Parking for 4
Open March-October
🖵 ♨ ⚘ 🖳 🗲 🅿 📺 🎽 ⟐ 🕯 ✿ 🎭 🏵 🏠

CHEW MAGNA

Avon
Map ref 2A2

Prosperous redstone village in the Mendip Hills with fine houses, cottages and inns of varying periods. High Street rises between railed, raised pavements from a part-Norman church with lofty 15th C tower.

Woodbarn Farm
Listed

Denny Lane, Chew Magna, Bristol BS18 8SZ
☎ (0275) 332599
125-acre mixed farm. Central for touring Bath, Bristol, Wells and Cheddar. 3 minutes from Chew Valley Lake. Friendly, flexible atmosphere. Large farmhouse breakfasts. Warm welcome.
Bedrooms: 1 double, 1 multiple
Bathrooms: 1 private, 1 public
Bed & breakfast

per night:	£min	£max
Single	18.00	20.00
Double	28.00	36.00

Parking for 6
Open March-December
🖵 ♨ ⚘ 🖳 🎽 ♣ 🅿 📺 🎽 🕯 ✿ 🎭

CHICKERELL

Dorset
Map ref 2B3

Stonebank
🏚

14 West Street, Chickerell, Weymouth DT3 4DY
☎ Weymouth (0305) 760120
Charming 17th C former farmhouse, close to coastal path and Chesil Beach. Ideal for exploring the Dorset coast and countryside.
Bedrooms: 2 double
Bathrooms: 2 private
Bed & breakfast

per night:	£min	£max
Double	25.00	30.00

Parking for 2
Open April-September
🖵 ♨ ⚘ 🖳 🗲 🎽 📺 ⟐ ✿ ✂ 🎭 🏵

CHIDEOCK

Dorset
Map ref 1D2

Village of sandstone thatched cottages in a valley near the dramatic Dorset coast. The church holds an interesting processional cross in mother-of-pearl and the manor house close by is associated with the Victorian Roman Catholic church. Seatown has a pebble beach and limestone cliffs.

Mill Cottage
🏚🏚

Mill Lane, Seatown, Chideock, Bridport DT6 6JX
☎ (0297) 89249
Comfortable stone cottage with sea views close to National Trust walks and lovely countryside.
Bedrooms: 1 single, 1 double, 1 twin
Bathrooms: 2 public
Bed & breakfast

per night:	£min	£max
Double	30.00	

Half board

per person:	£min	£max
Daily	27.00	
Weekly	187.00	

Evening meal 1900 (last orders 2000)
Parking for 2
🖵 10 ♨ 🖳 🗲 🎽 📺 ⟐ 🅿 ✿ 🎭 ✂ 🔲 🏵

CHIPPENHAM

Wiltshire
Map ref 2B2

Ancient market town with modern industry. Notable early buildings include the medieval Town Hall and the gabled 15th C Yelde Hall, now a local history museum. On the outskirts Hardenhuish has a charming hilltop church by the Georgian architect John Wood of Bath.
Tourist Information Centre ☎ (0249) 657733.

75 Rowden Hill
🏚

Chippenham SN15 2AL
☎ (0249) 652981
Near National Trust village of Lacock and attractive Castle

Combe. Corsham Court also nearby. Friendly welcome assured.
Bedrooms: 1 single, 1 double, 1 twin
Bathrooms: 1 public
Bed & breakfast

per night:	£min	£max
Single	14.00	
Double	24.00	

Parking for 5
Open April-October
🏠 5 🖵 🖳 📺 ⟐ 🅿 🎭

Oakfield Farm

Easton Piercy Lane, Yatton Keynell, Chippenham SN14 6JU
☎ Castle Combe (0249) 782355
100-acre arable & livestock farm. Friendly welcome on working farm with fine views. Excellent wildlife location. Easy access to Bath, Castle Combe and the Cotswolds.
Bedrooms: 1 single, 1 twin, 1 triple
Bathrooms: 1 private, 1 public
Bed & breakfast

per night:	£min	£max
Single	16.00	16.00
Double	28.00	34.00

Parking for 8
Open March-October
🏠 ⚘ ♨ 🖳 🗲 📺 ⟐ 🅿 ✿ 🎭

CHISELBOROUGH

Somerset
Map ref 2A3

Manor Farm
🏚🏚 COMMENDED

Chiselborough, Stoke sub Hamdon TA14 6TQ
☎ (093 588) 1203
450-acre mixed farm. Mellow hamstone farmhouse offering comfortable facilities, colour TV, tea making in all bedrooms. Ideal for touring or walking in the area.
Bedrooms: 2 double, 1 twin, 1 triple
Bathrooms: 2 public
Bed & breakfast

per night:	£min	£max
Single	17.00	19.00
Double	34.00	38.00

Parking for 4
Open April-October
🏠 🖵🅱 ⚘ 🖳 🎽 📺 ⟐ 🅿 🅿 ⚘
⛳ / ✂ 🎭 🏵 🏠

> **Check the introduction to this region for Where to Go, What to See.**

CHISELDON

Wiltshire
Map ref 2B2

Parsonage Farm

Chiseldon, Swindon SN4 0NJ
☎ Swindon (0793) 740204
400-acre arable farm. 17th C farmhouse, secluded and quiet but close M4 junction 15. Well furnished and comfortable.
Bedrooms: 2 single, 1 double, 1 twin
Bathrooms: 1 public
Bed & breakfast

per night:	£min	£max
Single	22.50	25.00
Double	40.00	40.00

Parking for 10
🏠 ♨ ♣ 🎽 📺 ⟐ 🅿 🅿 ∪ 🎭 🏵

CHITTOE HEATH

Wiltshire
Map ref 2B2

Wayside
🏚🏚🏚 COMMENDED

Chittoe Heath SN15 2EH
☎ Devizes (0380) 850458
Family-run establishment with informal atmosphere, in the heart of Wiltshire, with downs, historic houses and ancient sites. Bath, Salisbury and Marlborough all within 20 mile radius.
Bedrooms: 2 double, 1 triple
Bathrooms: 3 private
Bed & breakfast

per night:	£min	£max
Single	16.00	17.50
Double	32.00	35.00

Half board

per person:	£min	£max
Daily	22.50	25.00

Lunch available
Evening meal 1900 (last orders 2100)
Parking for 14
🏠 🅱 🖵 ♨ ⚘ ♣ 🖳 🅰 🔲 🎽 📺 ⓞ
⟐ 🅿 ✿ 🎭

CHUDLEIGH KNIGHTON

Devon
Map ref 1D2

Tynedale Guest House ⚑
🏚🏚

Chudleigh Knighton TQ13 0ET
☎ (0626) 852317
Former rectory with large garden, in the centre of a quiet village. Good touring
Continued ▶

CHUDLEIGH KNIGHTON

Continued

*centre minutes from A38.
Personal attention assured.*
Bedrooms: 1 single,
2 double, 2 twin, 1 multiple
Bathrooms: 6 private,
3 public

Bed & breakfast

per night:	£min	£max
Single	17.00	19.00
Double	32.00	37.00

Parking for 6

☎ ♿ ♨ ☎ ♦ ⚐ ⓤⓛ Ⓢ ⅄ ⋈
ⓣⓥ ⅲ, ⬛ ✿ 🚲

CHURCHILL

Avon
Map ref 1D1

Village of stone houses,
just off the A38,
dominated by Churchill
Court, seat of some of
the ancestors of the first
Duke of Marlborough and
Sir Winston Churchill.

Lyncombe Lodge & Mendip Riding Centre ♏

Green Hill Road, Churchill,
Bristol BS19 5PQ
☎ (0934) 852335
*160-acre mixed farm. Alpine-
style hunting lodge set in 120
acres of unique woodland in
heart of Mendip Hills.
Farmhouse food, licensed bar,
log fires. Riding school and
180 metre dry ski-slope.
Wonderful walking and riding
countryside.*
Bedrooms: 2 single,
4 double, 5 twin, 4 triple
Bathrooms: 6 private,
5 public

Bed & breakfast

per night:	£min	£max
Single	20.00	25.00
Double	40.00	50.00

Half board

per person:	£min	£max
Daily	28.00	30.00
Weekly	95.00	125.00

Lunch available
Evening meal 1830 (last
orders 1830)
Parking for 40
Cards accepted: Access, Visa

☎ ♿ Ⓢ ⓣⓥ ⅲ, ⬛ ☎ ♦ ⥁ ∪ ✓
✿ ⓄⒶⒻ ⅍ Ⓢⓟ

> **Please check prices
> and other details at
> the time of booking.**

CLEVEDON

Avon
Map ref 1D1

Handsome Victorian
resort on shingly shores
of Severn Estuary. Pier,
golf links with ruined folly,
part-Norman clifftop
church. Tennyson and
Thackeray stayed at
nearby Clevedon Court
just to the east. Medieval
with later additions, the
manor overlooks terraces
with rare plants.

Brighton House

2 Copse Road, Clevedon
BS21 7QL
☎ Bristol (0272) 343566
*Family-run Grade II listed
building just off the seafront.
Comfortable accommodation,
convenient for the M4 and
M5.*
Bedrooms: 2 single,
1 double, 2 twin, 1 multiple
Bathrooms: 2 public

Bed & breakfast

per night:	£min	£max
Single	14.00	

Parking for 3

☎ ♿ ♦ ⚐ ⓤⓛ Ⓢ ⅄ ⋈ ⓣⓥ ⅲ,
⬛ 🚲

Harcot

Listed

18 Leagrove Road, Clevedon
BS21 7QR
☎ Lulsgate (0275) 871509
*Family-run guesthouse, 100
yards from seafront and 5
minutes from M5. Spacious
rooms, sea views.*
Bedrooms: 4 double, 1 twin
Bathrooms: 2 public

Bed & breakfast

per night:	£min	£max
Single	18.00	20.00
Double	25.00	27.00

Parking for 3

☎ ♿ ☎ ♦ ⓤⓛ Ⓢ ⅲ, ⬛ 🚲 Ⓢⓟ

> There are separate
> sections in this
> guide listing groups
> specialising in farm
> holidays and
> accommodation
> which is especially
> suitable for young
> people and
> organised groups.

CLOVELLY

Devon
Map ref 1C1

Clinging to wooded cliffs,
fishing village with steep
cobbled street zigzagging,
or cut in steps, to
harbour. Carrying sleds
stand beside whitewashed
flower-decked cottages.
Charles Kingsley's father
was rector of the church
set high up near the
Hamlyn family's Clovelly
Court.

Fuchsia Cottage

Burscott Lane, Higher
Clovelly, Bideford EX39 5RR
☎ (0237) 431398
*Private house with
comfortable ground floor and
1st floor en-suite
accommodation. Surrounded
by beautiful views of sea and
country. Evening meal by
arrangement.*
Bedrooms: 1 single,
1 double, 1 triple
Bathrooms: 2 private,
1 public

Bed & breakfast

per night:	£min	£max
Single	11.00	
Double	26.00	

Half board

per person:	£min	£max
Daily	17.00	19.00
Weekly	119.00	133.00

Evening meal from 1830
Parking for 3

☎ ♿ ☎ ♦ ⓤⓛ Ⓢ ⅄ ⓣⓥ ⅲ,
⬛ 🚲

COMBE MARTIN

Devon
Map ref 1C1

Seaside village spreading
along its valley to a rocky
beach. Silver was mined
here in the Middle Ages,
market gardening yields
today's produce. An
unusual sight is the Pack
of Cards pub, while the
church with its gargoyles
is noted for panel
paintings on the 15th C
rood screen.

Channel Vista ♏

👑👑👑 COMMENDED

Woodlands, Combe Martin,
Ilfracombe EX34 0AT
☎ (0271) 883514
*Charming, Edwardian period
house, 150 yards from
picturesque cove. All rooms
en-suite, tea/coffee facilities.
Warm welcome, Devon fare.*

Bedrooms: 3 double, 1 twin,
2 triple, 1 multiple
Bathrooms: 7 private

Bed & breakfast

per night:	£min	£max
Single	17.00	19.00
Double	34.00	38.00

Half board

per person:	£min	£max
Daily	24.50	26.50
Weekly	129.50	149.50

Evening meal 1830 (last
orders 1500)
Parking for 9
Open April-October and
Christmas
Cards accepted: Access, Visa,
Amex

☎ ♿ 3 ♦ ⅃ Ⓢ ⋈ ⓣⓥ ⅲ, ⬛ ✿ ✈
ⓄⒶⒻ ⅍ Ⓢⓟ

CONSTANTINE

Cornwall
Map ref 1B3

Hilltop quarrying village
overlooking wooded valley
at the head of a creek on
the Helford River. Shops,
quarrymen's terraces,
handsome church and
chapel are all of granite.
A granite-walled
prehistoric cave, just
north, can be explored.

Trengilly Wartha Inn

👑👑👑 COMMENDED

Nancenoy, Constantine,
Falmouth TR11 5RP
☎ Falmouth (0326) 40332
*Inn with restaurant, serving
real ales and bar meals. From
Falmouth follow signs to
Constantine then signs to
Gweek. Close to the Helford
River and convenient for
beaches. Gweek is also near.*
Bedrooms: 4 double, 2 twin
Bathrooms: 6 private

Bed & breakfast

per night:	£min	£max
Single	32.00	42.00
Double	41.00	55.00

Half board

per person:	£min	£max
Daily	25.00	45.00
Weekly	140.00	250.00

Lunch available
Evening meal 1830 (last
orders 2130)
Parking for 80
Cards accepted: Access, Visa,
Amex

☎ ♿ ☎ ☕ ⚐ ♦ ⓤⓛ Ⓢ ⋈ ⅲ, ⬛ ♦
✿ 🚲 ⓄⒶⒻ ⅍ Ⓢⓟ

COOMBE BISSETT

Wiltshire
Map ref 2B3

Two Bridges
♨♨ COMMENDED

Homington Road, Coombe
Bissett, Salisbury SP5 4LR
☎ (072 277) 531
*Comfortable riverside bed and
breakfast, set in idyllic village
location near Salisbury. TV,
private lounge area and use
of garden. Non-smokers only
please.*
Bedrooms: 1 twin
Bathrooms: 1 private
Bed & breakfast

per night:	£min	£max
Double	32.00	37.00

Parking for 1

CORSHAM

Wiltshire
Map ref 2B2

Growing town with old
centre showing Flemish
influence, legacy of
former prosperity from
weaving. The church,
restored last century,
retains Norman features.
The Elizabethan Corsham
Court, with additions by
Capability Brown, has fine
furniture.

75 High Street
Listed   COMMENDED

Corsham SN13 0HA
☎ (0249) 713366
*Historic 18th C stone house
situated in Corsham High
Street, opposite Flemish
weavers' cottages, and
adjacent to Corsham Court.*
Bedrooms: 1 double, 1 twin,
1 triple
Bathrooms: 1 public
Bed & breakfast

per night:	£min	£max
Single	15.00	16.00
Double	26.00	30.00

Boyds Farm
♨♨ COMMENDED

Gastard, Corsham SN13 9PT
☎ (0249) 713146
*211-acre arable farm.
Attractive 16th C listed
farmhouse in the peaceful
village of Gastard. Bath,
Lacock, Castle Combe and
numerous attractions are
close by.*
Bedrooms: 2 double, 1 triple

Bathrooms: 2 public
Bed & breakfast

per night:	£min	£max
Single	15.00	16.00
Double	28.00	30.00

Parking for 6

Halfway Firs
Listed

5 Halfway Firs, Corsham
SN13 0PJ
☎ Bath (0225) 810552
*Situated 7 miles from Bath on
A4, 5 miles from Chippenham
and 1 mile from Corsham,
overlooking open farmland.*
Bedrooms: 1 single,
1 double, 1 triple
Bathrooms: 1 public
Bed & breakfast

per night:	£min	£max
Single	15.00	16.00
Double	26.00	30.00

Parking for 4

CORTON DENHAM

Somerset
Map ref 2B3

Corton Ash
Listed   APPROVED

Corton Denham, Sherborne,
Dorset DT9 4LS
☎ (0963) 220450
*"In-home" hospitality, modern
house, peaceful hillside
village, ideal for exploring
Dorset/Somerset, local walks.
Near Cadbury, Yeovilton,
Sherborne, between A303 and
A30 routes.*
Bedrooms: 1 double, 1 twin
Bathrooms: 2 private
Bed & breakfast

per night:	£min	£max
Single	13.00	15.00
Double	26.00	30.00

Parking for 8

Individual
proprietors have
supplied all details
of accommodation.
Although we do
check for accuracy,
we advise you to
confirm the
information at the
time of booking.

COVERACK

Cornwall
Map ref 1B3

Fishing village with
thatched cottages on the
Lizard Peninsula. Inland,
Goonhilly Downs is an
area of botanical
importance. 3 miles
offshore are the notorious
Manacles rocks, scene of
numerous shipwrecks.

Bakery Cottage

Coverack, Helston TR12 6TD
☎ St. Keverne (0326)
280474
*Old fisherman's cottage. Home
cooking and friendly service
in quiet fishing village. Safe
bathing beach nearby.*
Bedrooms: 1 double, 1 triple
Bathrooms: 1 public
Bed & breakfast

per night:	£min	£max
Double	25.00	27.00

Half board

per person:	£min	£max
Daily	19.50	20.50

Evening meal 1830 (last
orders 1830)
Parking for 2

CRACKINGTON HAVEN

Cornwall
Map ref 1C2

Tiny village on the North
Cornwall coast, with a
small sandy beach and
surf bathing. The highest
cliffs in Cornwall lie to the
south.

Treworgie Barton ♨
♨♨♨ HIGHLY COMMENDED

Crackington Haven, Bude
EX23 0NL
☎ St Gennys (084 03) 233
*106-acre mixed farm. In
secluded setting 2 miles from
unspoilt cove. Good
farmhouse cooking. Turn
right at Wainhouse corner 10
miles south of Bude on A39,
then follow farm signs.*
Bedrooms: 3 double, 1 twin,
1 multiple
Bathrooms: 5 private
Bed & breakfast

per night:	£min	£max
Double	32.00	44.00

Half board

per person:	£min	£max
Daily	27.00	33.00
Weekly	179.00	221.00

Evening meal from 1830
Parking for 5

Open February-September,
November

CRAFTHOLE

Cornwall
Map ref 1C2

Trewrickle Farm

Crafthole, Torpoint
PL11 3BX
☎ St. Germans (0503) 30333
*375-acre mixed farm. The
farmland, located between
Looe and Plymouth, adjoins
Whitsand Bay and the beach
at Portwrinkle. Children may
join in farm duties. Homely
atmosphere. Home-cooked
food.*
Bedrooms: 2 double, 1 twin,
2 multiple
Bathrooms: 2 public
Bed & breakfast

per night:	£min	£max
Single	13.00	15.00
Double	26.00	30.00

Half board

per person:	£min	£max
Daily	19.00	21.00
Weekly	114.00	120.00

Evening meal from 1800
Parking for 6

CREDITON

Devon
Map ref 1D2

Ancient town in fertile
valley, once prosperous
from wool, now active in
cider-making. Said to be
the birthplace of St
Boniface. The 13th C
Chapter House, the
church governors'
meeting place, holds a
collection of armour from
the Civil War.

Birchmans Farm ♨
♨♨ COMMENDED

Colebrooke, Crediton
EX17 5AD
☎ Bow (0363) 82393
*200-acre mixed farm. In the
centre of Devon within easy
reach of Exeter and
Dartmoor. Home produce. All
rooms en-suite with tea and
coffee-making facilities.*
Bedrooms: 2 double, 1 twin
Bathrooms: 3 private
Bed & breakfast

per night:	£min	£max
Single	12.50	13.50
Double	24.00	26.00

Continued ►

CREDITON

Continued

Half board

per person:	£min	£max
Daily	18.50	18.50
Weekly	125.00	125.00

Evening meal (last orders 1830)
Parking for 6

Hellions Barton

Listed

Upton Hellions, Crediton
EX17 4AE
☎ Morchard Bishop (0363) 776231
Elizabethan barton of interesting character, peaceful, relaxing. 2 miles north of Crediton in the beautiful countryside of the Creedy Valley.
Bedrooms: 1 double, 1 twin, 1 triple
Bathrooms: 1 private, 1 public

Bed & breakfast

per night:	£min	£max
Single	12.00	15.00
Double	24.00	30.00

Parking for 8
Open February-November

CREWKERNE

Somerset
Map ref 1D2

This charming little market town on the Dorset border nestles in undulating farmland and orchards in a conservation area. Built of local sandstone with Roman and Saxon origins. The magnificent St Bartholomew's Church dates from 15th C. St Bartholomew's Fair is held in September.

Broadview ⋒

DE LUXE

43 East Street, Crewkerne
TA18 7AG
☎ (0460) 73424
Secluded colonial-style bungalow, circa 1926, in an acre of feature gardens with many unusual plants. Lovely views. Friendly, relaxing atmosphere and carefully furnished en-suite rooms. Quality, traditional home cooking.
Bedrooms: 1 double, 2 twin
Bathrooms: 3 private

Bed & breakfast

per night:	£min	£max
Single		25.00
Double		37.00

Half board

per person:	£min	£max
Daily		28.00
Weekly		196.00

Evening meal 1830 (last orders 1200)
Parking for 6

Home Farm

Listed

Roundham, Crewkerne
TA18 8RH
☎ (0460) 73447
110-acre livestock farm. Situated on A30, 1 mile west of Crewkerne, 3 miles from Cricket St Thomas. Working farm. TV and tea/coffee-making facilities in all rooms.
Bedrooms: 1 double, 1 twin, 1 triple
Bathrooms: 2 public, 1 private shower

Bed & breakfast

per night:	£min	£max
Single	14.50	18.00
Double	28.00	31.00

Parking for 5

CROYDE

Devon
Map ref 1C1

Pretty village with thatched cottages near Croyde Bay. To the south stretch Saunton Sands and their dunelands Braunton Burrows with interesting flowers and plants, nature reserve and golf-course. Cliff walks and bird-watching at Baggy Point, west of the village.

The Thatched Barn Inn

Croyde, Braunton EX33 1LZ
☎ (0271) 890349
Delightful old inn serving good food in a traditional atmosphere of hospitality.
Bedrooms: 3 double, 5 twin
Bathrooms: 5 private, 1 public

Bed & breakfast

per night:	£min	£max
Single	20.00	30.00
Double	38.00	45.00

Half board

per person:	£min	£max
Daily	40.00	60.00

Lunch available
Evening meal 1800 (last orders 2200)
Parking for 40
Cards accepted: Access, Visa

DARTMOOR

See under Ashburton, Bickington, Bovey Tracey, Bridestowe, Buckfast, Chagford, Holne, Lustleigh, Manaton, Moretonhampstead, North Bovey, Okehampton, Peter Tavy, Postbridge, Tavistock, Throwleigh, Widecombe-in-the-Moor, Yelverton

DARTMOUTH

Devon
Map ref 1D3

Ancient port at mouth of Dart. Has fine period buildings, notably town houses near Quay and Butterwalk of 1635. Harbour castle ruin. In 12th C Crusader fleets assembled here. Royal Naval College dominates from Hill. Carnival, June; Regatta, August.
Tourist Information Centre ☎ *(0803) 834224.*

Boringdon House

COMMENDED

1 Church Road, Dartmouth
TQ6 9HQ
☎ (0803) 832235
Spacious, welcoming Georgian house in large secluded garden overlooking Dartmouth town and harbour. Courtyard parking. Short walk to town centre. Non-smokers only please.
Bedrooms: 1 double, 2 twin
Bathrooms: 3 private

Bed & breakfast

per night:	£min	£max
Single	34.00	40.00
Double	40.00	46.00

Parking for 3
Open March-December

The Captains House

COMMENDED

18 Clarence Street,
Dartmouth TQ6 9NW
☎ Torquay (0803) 832133
18th C listed house. Tasteful decor and personal service. Close to river and shops.
Bedrooms: 1 single, 3 double, 1 twin
Bathrooms: 5 private

Bed & breakfast

per night:	£min	£max
Single	24.00	27.00
Double	34.00	44.00

Cards accepted: Amex

Courtyard House

HIGHLY COMMENDED

10 Clarence Hill, Dartmouth
TQ6 9NX
☎ (0803) 834916
Well-appointed bedrooms for comfortable overnight accommodation with full English breakfast. Located in quaint old street 2 minutes from town centre and river.
Bedrooms: 1 single, 2 double
Bathrooms: 3 private

Bed & breakfast

per night:	£min	£max
Single	20.00	25.00
Double	36.00	44.00

Lunch available
Parking for 2
Cards accepted: Access, Visa

Eastdown House

COMMENDED

Eastdown, Blackawton,
Totnes TQ9 7AP
☎ Blackawton (080 421) 372
Charming early Georgian farmhouse with pretty half-acre garden. Very quiet and peaceful. Only 6 miles from Dartmouth and 2 miles from the coast. Sociable atmosphere. All bedrooms en-suite.
Bedrooms: 2 double, 1 twin
Bathrooms: 3 private

Bed & breakfast

per night:	£min	£max
Double	30.00	34.00

Evening meal 1900 (last orders 2130)
Parking for 4

There are separate sections in this guide listing groups specialising in farm holidays and accommodation which is especially suitable for young people and organised groups.

DEVIZES

Wiltshire
Map ref 2B2

Old market town standing on the Kennet and Avon Canal. Rebuilt Norman castle, good 18th C buildings. St John's church has 12th C work and Norman tower. Museum of Wiltshire's archaeology and natural history reflects wealth of prehistoric sites in the county.
Tourist Information Centre
☎ *(0380) 729408.*

Aspiro
46 The Green, Poulshot, Devizes SN10 1RT
☎ (0380) 828465
On green in exceptionally quiet village. Large secluded garden with much birdlife. Delightful old pub with restaurant nearby. German spoken.
Bedrooms: 1 double, 1 twin, 1 triple
Bathrooms: 1 public

Bed & breakfast per night:	£min	£max
Single	16.00	18.00
Double	28.00	32.00

Half board per person:	£min	£max
Daily	22.00	

Evening meal 1900 (last orders 2000)
Parking for 11

Glenholme Guest House
77 Nursteed Road, Devizes SN10 3AJ
☎ (0380) 723187
Comfortable family home. Both bedrooms with own TV and tea making facilities. Special diets prepared by arrangement.
Bedrooms: 1 twin, 1 triple
Bathrooms: 1 public

Bed & breakfast per night:	£min	£max
Single	16.00	18.00
Double	28.00	30.00

Evening meal 1700 (last orders 1900)
Parking for 2

Pinecroft
Potterne Road, Devizes SN10 5DA
☎ (0380) 721433
Fax (0380) 728368

Comfortable Georgian family house with spacious rooms, exquisite garden and private parking. Only 3 minutes' walk from town centre.
Bedrooms: 2 double, 1 twin, 1 multiple
Bathrooms: 4 private

Bed & breakfast per night:	£min	£max
Single	18.00	20.00
Double	30.00	35.00

Parking for 6
Cards accepted: Access, Visa, Amex

Rathlin Guest House
COMMENDED
Wick Lane, Devizes SN10 5DP
☎ (0380) 721999
Elegant period charm, all rooms en-suite and individually furnished. Quiet location close to town centre. Tranquil gardens. Ample parking.
Bedrooms: 2 double, 1 twin
Bathrooms: 3 private

Bed & breakfast per night:	£min	£max
Single	23.00	23.00
Double	37.00	37.00

Evening meal 1800 (last orders 1930)
Parking for 5

Roundway Hill Farm
Folly Road, Devizes SN10 2HU
☎ (0380) 722928
740-acre arable & livestock farm. Grade II listed farmhouse set in beautiful scenery at the bottom of Roundway Hill, one mile east of Devizes.
Bedrooms: 1 double, 2 twin
Bathrooms: 1 public

Bed & breakfast per night:	£min	£max
Single	14.50	14.50
Double	28.00	28.00

Half board per person:	£min	£max
Daily	21.50	21.50
Weekly	125.00	125.00

Evening meal 1900 (last orders 2115)
Parking for 2

Please mention this guide when making a booking.

DODDISCOMBS-LEIGH

Devon
Map ref 1D2

Riverside village amid hilly countryside just east of Dartmoor. Former manor house stands beside granite church. Spared from the Roundheads by its remoteness, the church's chief interest lies in glowing 15th C windows said to contain Devon's finest collection of medieval glass.

Whitemoor Farm
Doddiscombsleigh, Exeter EX6 7PU
☎ Christow (0647) 52423
284-acre mixed farm. Homely 16th C thatched farmhouse, surrounded by garden and own farmland. Within easy reach of Dartmoor, the coast, Exeter, forest walks, birdwatching and Haldon Racecourse. Evening meal on request with good local inns nearby.
Bedrooms: 2 single, 1 double, 1 twin
Bathrooms: 1 public

Bed & breakfast per night:	£min	£max
Single	14.00	15.00
Double	28.00	30.00

Half board per person:	£min	£max
Daily	20.50	22.50
Weekly	140.00	147.00

Evening meal 1900 (last orders 2000)
Parking for 5

The symbols are explained on the flap inside the back cover.

Individual proprietors have supplied all details of accommodation. Although we do check for accuracy, we advise you to confirm the information at the time of booking.

DORCHESTER

Dorset
Map ref 2B3

Busy medieval county town destroyed by fires in 17th and 18th C. Cromwellian stronghold and scene of Judge Jeffrey's Bloody Assize after Monmouth Rebellion of 1685. Tolpuddle Martyrs were tried in Shire Hall. Museum has Roman and earlier exhibits and Hardy relics.
Tourist Information Centre
☎ *(0305) 267992.*

30 Mountain Ash Road
APPROVED
Dorchester DT1 2PB
☎ (0305) 264811
Comfortable accommodation close to transport, Records Office and museums. Washbasins, TV, beverage facilities in bedrooms. Owner knowledgeable about Dorset.
Bedrooms: 1 single, 1 double, 1 twin
Bathrooms: 1 public

Bed & breakfast per night:	£min	£max
Single	16.50	17.50
Double	33.00	35.00

Parking for 5

Castleview
Listed
8 Edward Road, Dorchester DT1 2HJ
☎ (0305) 263507
Excellent base for touring beautiful Dorset, offering TVs washbasins with softened water and tea/coffee-making facilities in all rooms.
Bedrooms: 2 single, 1 double, 1 twin
Bathrooms: 2 private, 1 public

Bed & breakfast per night:	£min	£max
Single	12.00	13.00
Double ·	24.00	32.00

Parking for 4

Churchview Guest House
Winterbourne Abbas, Dorchester DT2 9LS
☎ Martinstown (0305) 889296

Continued ▶

301

DORCHESTER

Continued

Beautiful 17th C guesthouse set in a small village 5 miles west of Dorchester. Noted for its warm welcome, comfort and delicious home cooking.
Bedrooms: 6 double, 4 twin
Bathrooms: 3 private,
2 public

Bed & breakfast

per night:	£min	£max
Single	15.50	17.50
Double	31.00	35.00

Half board

per person:	£min	£max
Daily	23.50	26.00
Weekly	154.00	170.00

Evening meal 1900 (last orders 1900)
Parking for 10

Five Cross Spinney

Crossways, Dorchester
DT2 8BG
☎ Warmwell (0305) 852171
In quiet rural setting in heart of Thomas Hardy country with many historical attractions. 5 miles from coast and 6 miles east of Dorchester.
Bedrooms: 2 double, 1 twin
Bathrooms: 1 public,
1 private shower

Bed & breakfast

per night:	£min	£max
Single	16.00	
Double	24.00	

Parking for 6

Hyde Farm House

Dorchester Road, Frampton
DT2 9NG
☎ Maiden Newton (0300) 20272
Secluded farmhouse set in 7 acres. Designed for relaxation and comfort. En-suite available. 5 miles north-west of Dorchester.
Bedrooms: 1 double, 2 twin
Bathrooms: 3 private

Bed & breakfast

per night:	£min	£max
Single	25.00	25.00
Double	50.00	50.00

Half board

per person:	£min	£max
Daily	37.50	

Evening meal 1900 (last orders 2100)
Parking for 8

Maumbury Cottage

Listed

9 Maumbury Road,
Dorchester DT1 1QW
☎ (0305) 266726
Homely town centre Victorian house, convenient for all public transport. Dorset owner has intimate local knowledge.
Bedrooms: 1 double, 1 twin
Bathrooms: 1 public

Bed & breakfast

per night:	£min	£max
Double	28.00	30.00

Riverhill House

7 East Hill, Charminster,
Dorchester DT2 9QL
☎ (0305) 265614
Well-appointed accommodation in lovely country house, rural setting 1.5 miles from Dorchester. Full English breakfast and optional home-cooked evening meals. Off-street parking. Every comfort and warm welcome assured. Ideal touring centre.
Bedrooms: 1 double, 2 twin
Bathrooms: 1 private,
2 public

Bed & breakfast

per night:	£min	£max
Single	13.00	13.00
Double	26.00	32.00

Half board

per person:	£min	£max
Daily	20.00	23.00
Weekly	85.00	105.00

Evening meal 1800 (last orders 2030)
Parking for 6

Thornhill House

14 Cornwall Road,
Dorchester DT1 1RT
☎ (0305) 260007
An elegant, spacious Victorian house, in residential area of Dorchester, overlooking the park. Offers good accommodation and service.
Bedrooms: 1 double, 1 twin
Bathrooms: 2 public

Bed & breakfast

per night:	£min	£max
Single	15.00	17.00
Double	30.00	32.00

Vartrees House

Crossways, Moreton,
Dorchester DT2 8BE
☎ Warmwell (0305) 852704
Peaceful, secluded country house set in lovely woodland gardens. Spacious, comfortable accommodation.

On B3390, 5 miles east of Dorchester and near coast. Quarter of a mile Moreton station.
Bedrooms: 1 twin, 1 triple
Bathrooms: 1 public,
2 private showers

Bed & breakfast

per night:	£min	£max
Single	20.00	30.00
Double	32.00	42.00

Evening meal from 1800
Parking for 25

DULVERTON

Somerset
Map ref 1D1

Set among woods and hills of south-west Exmoor, a busy riverside town with a 13th C church. The Rivers Barle and Exe are rich in salmon and trout. The Exmoor National Park Headquarters at Dulverton Information Centre are open throughout the year.

Newhouse Farm

Oakford, Tiverton, Devon
EX16 9JE
☎ Oakford (039 85) 347
42-acre livestock farm. Charming 16th C farmhouse featuring oak beams and inglenook fireplace. Pretty bedrooms with tea trays, en-suite bathrooms available. Many original recipes.
Bedrooms: 2 double, 1 twin
Bathrooms: 2 private,
1 public

Bed & breakfast

per night:	£min	£max
Double	29.00	34.00

Half board

per person:	£min	£max
Daily	24.50	26.00
Weekly	155.00	165.00

Evening meal 1930 (last orders 1700)
Parking for 4

DUNSFORD

Devon
Map ref 1D2

The Royal Oak Inn ₩

Dunsford, Exeter EX6 7DA
☎ Christow (0647) 52256
Victorian country inn, in the heart of a charming thatched village in the Teign Valley.

We specialise in real ales and homemade food.
Bedrooms: 5 double, 2 twin,
1 triple
Bathrooms: 6 private,
1 public

Bed & breakfast

per night:	£min	£max
Single	17.50	25.00
Double	35.00	40.00

Lunch available
Evening meal 1830 (last orders 2100)
Parking for 40
Cards accepted: Access, Visa

DUNSTER

Somerset
Map ref 1D1

Ancient town with views of Exmoor. The hilltop castle has been continuously occupied since 1070. Medieval prosperity from cloth built 16th C octagonal Yarn Market and the church. A riverside mill, packhorse bridge and 18th C hilltop folly occupy other interesting corners in the town.

Burnells Farm

Knowle Lane, Dunster,
Minehead TA24 6UU
☎ (0643) 821841
46-acre mixed farm. Modern, comfortable farmhouse in Exmoor National Park. 1.5 miles from Dunster and 2.5 miles from Minehead.
Bedrooms: 1 double, 1 twin,
1 triple
Bathrooms: 2 public

Bed & breakfast

per night:	£min	£max
Single	15.00	
Double	30.00	

Half board

per person:	£min	£max
Daily	19.50	
Weekly	129.50	

Evening meal from 1900
Parking for 4

Yarn Market Hotel (Exmoor) ₩

25 High Street, Dunster,
Minehead TA24 8SL
☎ (0643) 821425
Fax (0643) 821199
Central and accessible hotel in quaint English village, an ideal location from which to explore the Exmoor National Park.

Bedrooms: 1 double, 1 twin,
1 triple, 1 multiple
Bathrooms: 4 private
Bed & breakfast

per night:	£min	£max
Single	22.50	35.00
Double	45.00	70.00

Half board

per person:	£min	£max
Daily	30.00	38.00
Weekly	215.00	236.00

Lunch available
Evening meal 1800 (last
orders 2000)
Parking for 6
Cards accepted: Access, Visa,
Amex

EAST BRENT
Somerset
Map ref 1D1

Knoll Lodge
Church Road, East Brent,
Highbridge TA9 4HZ
☎ Brent Knoll (0278)
760294
*19th C family home in quiet
lane at foot of Brent Knoll
between Mendip and
Quantock Hills. 2.5 miles to
junction 22 of M5. Non-
smokers only please.*
Bedrooms: 2 double, 1 twin
Bathrooms: 3 private
Bed & breakfast

per night:	£min	£max
Single	18.00	18.00
Double	36.00	36.00

Half board

per person:	£min	£max
Daily	27.50	27.50
Weekly	173.25	173.25

Evening meal 1800 (last
orders 2030)
Parking for 6

EAST KNOYLE
Wiltshire
Map ref 2B3

Sir Christopher Wren, the
famous architect of St
Paul's Cathedral, was
born here in 1632.

The Seymour Arms
East Knoyle, Salisbury
SP3 6AJ
☎ Shaftesbury (0747)
830374
*17th C inn covered with
Virginia creeper, in
conservation area close to*

*places of interest. Extensive
menu and real ales.*
Bedrooms: 2 single,
1 double, 1 twin
Bathrooms: 1 public
Bed & breakfast

per night:	£min	£max
Single	18.00	
Double	36.00	

Lunch available
Evening meal 1900 (last
orders 2200)
Parking for 20
Open February-November
Cards accepted: Access, Visa

EAST TYTHERTON
Wiltshire
Map ref 2B2

Barnbridge
East Tytherton, Chippenham
SN15 4LT
☎ Kellaways (0249) 74280
*Self-contained wing of
country farmhouse enjoying
beautiful views. Tennis court
and private indoor/outdoor
swimming pool.*
Bedrooms: 1 single, 2 twin
Bathrooms: 2 public
Bed & breakfast

per night:	£min	£max
Single	15.00	15.00
Double	28.00	30.00

Half board

per person:	£min	£max
Daily	20.00	20.00

Evening meal 1900 (last
orders 2100)
Parking for 6

EASTERTON
Wiltshire
Map ref 2B2

Eastcott Manor
Easterton, Devizes
SN10 4PL
☎ Lavington (0380) 813313
*In tranquil situation in own
grounds of 20 acres on edge
of Salisbury Plain. Nearest
road B3098.*
Bedrooms: 2 single, 2 double
Bathrooms: 1 public
Bed & breakfast

per night:	£min	£max
Single	20.00	22.00
Double	36.00	40.00

Half board

per person:	£min	£max
Daily	35.00	37.00
Weekly	225.00	235.00

Evening meal 1930 (last
orders 2000)
Parking for 20

ERLESTOKE
Wiltshire
Map ref 2B2

Longwater
COMMENDED
Lower Road, Erlestoke,
Devizes SN10 5UE
☎ Devizes (0380) 830095
*160-acre organic farm.
Overlooking own parkland,
lakes and water bird
conservation area. Coarse
fishing, adjacent to golf-
course. Rare sheep and cattle
on farm. Near National Trust
properties.*
Bedrooms: 2 double, 2 twin,
1 triple
Bathrooms: 5 private
Bed & breakfast

per night:	£min	£max
Single	21.00	21.00
Double	38.00	38.00

Half board

per person:	£min	£max
Daily	29.50	31.50
Weekly	190.00	210.00

Evening meal 1900 (last
orders 1000)
Parking for 8

EXETER
Devon
Map ref 1D2

University city rebuilt after
the 1940s around its
cathedral. Attractions
include 13th C cathedral
with fine west front;
notable waterfront
buildings; Maritime
Museum; Guildhall;
Rougemont House
Museum; Royal Albert
Memorial Museum;
Northcott Theatre.
*Tourist Information Centre
☎ (0392) 265700.*

Clock Tower Hotel
16 New North Road, Exeter
EX4 4HF
☎ (0392) 52493 &
Reservations 424545
Fax (0392) 218445
*Homely accommodation in
the city centre. Coach and
railway stations within 10
minutes' walk. All modern
facilities. En-suite rooms.*
Bedrooms: 3 single,
5 double, 3 twin, 5 triple

Bathrooms: 9 private,
3 public
Bed & breakfast

per night:	£min	£max
Single	15.00	21.50
Double	25.00	45.00

Half board

per person:	£min	£max
Daily	20.00	30.00
Weekly	127.50	187.50

Evening meal 1800 (last
orders 1600)
Cards accepted: Access, Visa

Dolphin Inn
Thorverton, Exeter EX5 5NT
☎ (0392) 860205
*16th C inn, in heart of
beautiful, unspoilt village, one
mile off the old Tiverton road,
six miles north of Exeter.
Originally an important
coaching inn.*
Bedrooms: 3 single,
1 double, 2 twin, 1 triple
Bathrooms: 4 private,
1 public
Bed & breakfast

per night:	£min	£max
Single	18.50	25.50
Double	35.00	47.00

Half board

per person:	£min	£max
Daily	35.00	37.50
Weekly	129.00	185.00

Lunch available
Evening meal 1800 (last
orders 2200)
Parking for 30
Cards accepted: Access, Visa,
Amex

The Grange
Stoke Hill, Exeter EX4 7JH
☎ (0392) 59723
*Country house set in 3 acres
of woodlands, 1.5 miles from
the city centre. Ideal for
holidays and off-season
breaks.*
Bedrooms: 3 double, 3 twin,
1 triple
Bathrooms: 4 private,
2 public
Bed & breakfast

per night:	£min	£max
Single	17.00	19.00
Double	30.00	38.00

Parking for 11

303

EXETER

Continued

Hayne Barton

🛇🛇🛇 COMMENDED

Whitestone, Exeter EX4 2JN
☎ Longdown (039 281) 268
16-acre mixed farm. Listed farmhouse dating from 1086 (Domesday Book) set in gardens, woodland and fields overlooking Alphinbrook Valley. Exeter Cathedral, 4 miles.
Bedrooms: 2 double, 1 twin
Bathrooms: 3 private
Bed & breakfast

per night:	£min	£max
Single	24.00	30.00
Double	42.00	50.00

Half board

per person:	£min	£max
Daily	32.00	38.00
Weekly	210.00	250.00

Evening meal 1930 (last orders 2030)
Parking for 10

🛇🖪🖵♨ 🖵 ⓤⓛ 🛆 🖾 ⚿ ⴄ ⓣⓥ ⬛
🖪 ∪ ↑ ⁄ ✿ 🐾 ⑱ 🔌 ⧖ 🕏 🏠

Meads Guest House

2 St. Davids Hill, Exeter
EX4 3RG
☎ (0392) 74886
Attractive accommodation in interesting Grade II listed building near the Iron Bridge. Convenient for city centre, railway stations and university.
Bedrooms: 1 single,
2 double, 1 twin
Bathrooms: 2 public
Bed & breakfast

per night:	£min	£max
Single	13.00	15.00
Double	26.00	30.00

Half board

per person:	£min	£max
Daily	21.50	23.50

Lunch available
Evening meal 1800 (last orders 0930)

🛇🗝 ⓤⓛ 🛆 🖾 ⓣⓥ ⬛ 🖪 ✿ 🐾 ⑱ 🔌

EXMOOR

See under Allerford, Combe Martin, Dulverton, Dunster, Lynmouth, Lynton, North Molton, Simonsbath, West Anstey, Wheddon Cross, Winsford, Withypool.

We advise you to confirm your booking in writing.

EXMOUTH

Devon
Map ref 1D2

Developed as a seaside resort in George III's reign, set against the woods of the Exe Estuary and red cliffs of Orcombe Point. Extensive sands, small harbour, chapel and almshouses, a miniature railway and A la Ronde, a 16-sided house.
Tourist Information Centre
☎ *(0395) 263744*

The Mews

Knappe Cross, Brixington Lane, Exmouth EX8 5DL
☎ (0395) 272198
Large part of a delightfully secluded mews building in a country setting.
Bedrooms: 1 single, 2 twin
Bathrooms: 1 public
Bed & breakfast

per night:	£min	£max
Single	13.50	15.50
Double	27.00	31.00

Parking for 10

🛇🗝 4 ⬛ 🛆 🖾 ⁄ 🖾 ⬛ ∪ ✿ 🗙 🐾

The Swallows

🛇🛇 COMMENDED

11 Carlton Hill, Exmouth
EX8 2AJ
☎ (0395) 263937
Attractive Georgian house only 300 yards from seafront, pleasantly converted to modern standards and providing comfortable guest accommodation.
Bedrooms: 1 single,
2 double, 2 twin, 1 multiple
Bathrooms: 5 private,
1 public
Bed & breakfast

per night:	£min	£max
Double	32.00	38.00

Evening meal from 1800
Parking for 3

🛇🖵♨ ⓤⓛ 🛆 🖾 ⬛ 🖪 ✿ 🗙 🐾 🖪

FALFIELD

Avon
Map ref 2B2

Whitfield Farm

Falfield, Wotton-under-Edge, Gloucestershire GL12 8DR
☎ (0454) 260334
220-acre arable and mixed farm. Pleasant surroundings but centrally located for easy access to M5 and A38. Pick your own fruit from May to August. Single occupancy available - check for prices.

Bedrooms: 2 double
Bathrooms: 1 public
Bed & breakfast

per night:	£min	£max
Double	30.00	32.00

Parking for 7

🛇 12 ♨ ⓤⓛ ⁄ ⓣⓥ ∪ ✿ 🐾 ⑱
🖪 🏠

FALMOUTH

Cornwall
Map ref 1B3

Busy port and fishing harbour, popular resort on the balmy Cornish Riviera. Henry VIII's Pendennis Castle faces St Mawes Castle across the broad natural harbour and yacht basin Carrick Roads, which receives 7 rivers.
Tourist Information Centre
☎ *(0326) 312300*

Selwood Cottage Guest House

38 Melvill Road, Falmouth
TR11 4DQ
☎ (0326) 314135
Attractive detached house, set off the road in "Britain in Bloom" champion garden. Ideal situation for beaches, town, parks, golf and touring. Friendly atmosphere. Parking in private drive.
Bedrooms: 2 double, 1 twin,
1 triple
Bathrooms: 1 public
Bed & breakfast

per night:	£min	£max
Single	13.00	18.00
Double	24.00	28.00

Parking for 6
Open January-November

🛇🖵♨ ⓤⓛ 🛆 🖾 ⬛ ↑ ✿
🐾 ⑱ 🖪

FIGHELDEAN

Wiltshire
Map ref 2B2

Vale House

Figheldean, Salisbury
SP4 8JJ
☎ Stonehenge (0980) 70713
Secluded house in centre of picturesque village, 4 miles north of Amesbury on A345. Pub food nearby. Stonehenge 2 miles.
Bedrooms: 3 twin
Bathrooms: 2 public
Bed & breakfast

per night:	£min	£max
Single	13.00	13.00
Double	26.00	26.00

Parking for 3
Open May-September

🔔 ♨ ⓤⓛ 🖾 ⓣⓥ ⬛ 🖪 ✿ 🗙 🐾

FLUSHING

Cornwall
Map ref 1B3

Pretty village, popular with holiday yachts, reputedly founded by Dutch construction workers developing Falmouth in Elizabethan times. White and colour-washed cottages stand on the north bank of the Penryn River where it joins the Carrick Roads.

Tregew Farm

Flushing, Falmouth
TR11 5UQ
☎ Falmouth (0326) 374369
350-acre mixed farm. 18th C listed farmhouse set in area of outstanding natural beauty, surrounded by water. Ideally situated for sailing, touring, walking, eating and beaching.
Bedrooms: 1 single,
1 double, 1 twin
Bathrooms: 1 public
Bed & breakfast

per night:	£min	£max
Single	17.50	20.00
Double	25.00	30.00

Parking for 8

🛇 ♨ ⓤⓛ 🛆 🖾 ⓣⓥ ● 🖪 ↑ ✿
🐾 🏠

FONTHILL GIFFORD

Wiltshire
Map ref 2B3

Beckford Arms ⚏

🛇🛇🛇 HIGHLY COMMENDED

Fonthill Gifford, Tisbury,
Salisbury SP3 6PX
☎ Tisbury (0747) 870385
Fax (0747) 51496
Tastefully refurbished, comfortable 18th C inn, between Tisbury and Hindon in area of outstanding beauty. 2 miles A303, convenient for Salisbury.
Bedrooms: 2 single,
4 double, 1 twin
Bathrooms: 5 private,
2 private showers
Bed & breakfast

per night:	£min	£max
Single	29.50	
Double	49.50	

Half board

per person:	£min	£max
Daily	35.00	
Weekly	210.00	

Lunch available
Evening meal 1900 (last orders 2200)

Parking for 42
Cards accepted: Access, Visa
♨♫☎⚑♨⚙ⓘ Ⓢ▥ ⚐
¶☎✿⚘ SP 曲 Ⓣ

FROGMORE

Devon
Map ref 1C3

Globe Inn ⚈
😃 APPROVED

Frogmore, Kingsbridge
TQ7 2NR
☎ (0548) 531351
*Family-run inn on the A379
Kingsbridge to Dartmouth
road, at the head of Frogmore
Creek.*
Bedrooms: 3 double, 2 twin,
1 triple
Bathrooms: 2 private,
2 public
Bed & breakfast

per night:	£min	£max
Single	20.00	25.00
Double	34.00	40.00

Lunch available
Evening meal 1800 (last
orders 2200)
Parking for 20
Cards accepted: Access, Visa,
Switch
♨♫☎♫⚙ⓘ Ⓢ▥ ⟨ TV ⟩▥ ⚐♨
Ʊ✿ ⚘ ☜ SP

FROME

Somerset
Map ref 2B2

Old market town with
modern light industry, its
medieval centre watered
by the River Frome.
Above Cheap Street with
its flagstones and
watercourse is the church
showing work of varying
periods. Interesting
buildings include 18th C
wool merchants' houses.
Local history museum.

Fourwinds Guest
House
😃😃😃 COMMENDED

19 Bath Road, Frome
BA11 2HJ
☎ (0373) 462618
*Chalet bungalow with some
bedrooms on ground floor. TV
and tea-making facilities.
Licensed, good food.*
Bedrooms: 1 single,
2 double, 1 twin, 1 triple,
1 multiple
Bathrooms: 4 private,
2 public
Bed & breakfast

per night:	£min	£max
Single	20.00	25.00
Double	35.00	40.00

Half board

per person:	£min	£max
Daily		30.00

Lunch available
Evening meal 1800 (last
orders 1900)
Parking for 12
♨♫☎♫⚙ⓘ Ⓢ▥ ⚐
✕ ⚘ DAP

Highcroft Farmhouse
West Woodlands, Frome
BA11 5EQ
☎ (0373) 461941
*Comfortable, old, stone
farmhouse with pleasant
gardens in country setting.
Close to Longleat, Stourhead
and Bath.*
Bedrooms: 1 double, 1 twin,
1 multiple
Bathrooms: 1 public,
1 private shower
Bed & breakfast

per night:	£min	£max
Single	11.00	13.00
Double	22.00	26.00

Parking for 12
♨ ▥ ⚑ TV ▥ ✿ ⚘

Ladymead
Berkley Marsh, Frome
BA11 5JE
☎ (0373) 830886
*Peaceful cottage surrounded
by farmland, beautiful views,
4 miles from Longleat, 12
miles from Bath. Ideal
touring base.*
Bedrooms: 2 single,
2 double, 1 twin
Bathrooms: 3 private,
1 public
Bed & breakfast

per night:	£min	£max
Single	13.00	15.00
Double	26.00	30.00

Half board

per person:	£min	£max
Daily	20.00	22.00
Weekly	115.00	130.00

Evening meal 1800 (last
orders 2000)
Parking for 10
♨▥☎♫⚙ⓘ Ⓢ▥ TV
▥⚐✿ ⚘ SP

There are separate
sections in this
guide listing groups
specialising in farm
holidays and
accommodation
which is especially
suitable for young
people and
organised groups.

GLASTONBURY

Somerset
Map ref 2A2

Market town associated
with Joseph of Arimathea
and the birth of English
Christianity. Built around
its 7th C abbey, whose
remains are said to be
the site of King Arthur's
burial. Glastonbury Tor
with its ancient tower
gives panoramic views
over flat country and the
Mendip Hills.

Laverley House ⚈
😃😃

West Pennard, Glastonbury
BA6 8NE
☎ Pilton (0749) 890696
*Grade II listed Georgian
farmhouse in rural position
with views towards Mendips.
On the A361, 4 miles east of
Glastonbury.*
Bedrooms: 1 single,
2 double, 1 triple
Bathrooms: 2 private,
1 public
Bed & breakfast

per night:	£min	£max
Single	18.50	25.00
Double	37.00	37.00

Half board

per person:	£min	£max
Daily	32.50	32.50
Weekly	204.75	246.50

Evening meal 1900 (last
orders 0900)
Parking for 6
Open March-October
♨☎♫⚙ⓘ Ⓢ▥ TV ▥ ⚐
Ʊ¶✿ ⚘ ☜ 曲

Middlewick Farm
Wick, Glastonbury BA6 8JW
☎ (0458) 832351
*Grade II listed 17th C
farmhouse and converted
barns in 20 acres of garden
and paddocks. Take
Glastonbury to Wells road
(A39) for 2 miles, turn right
as you approach Tin Bridge,
then first left. Follow lane for
1 mile, farm is on right.*
Bedrooms: 2 single,
7 double, 2 twin, 1 triple
Bathrooms: 6 private,
3 public
Bed & breakfast

per night:	£min	£max
Single	14.00	16.00
Double	26.00	30.00

Half board

per person:	£min	£max
Daily	21.00	23.00
Weekly	147.00	161.00

Evening meal 1900 (last
orders 2030)
Parking for 20
♨♫☎▥⚙ⓘ Ⓢ✕ ▥ TV ▥ ⚐
✿ ✕ ⚘ DAP SP 曲

Pippin
4 Ridgeway Gardens,
Glastonbury BA6 8ER
☎ (0458) 834262
*Views over Chalice Hill and
Tor. From High Street
continue up Bove Town and
Pippin is third on the right.*
Bedrooms: 1 single,
1 double, 1 twin
Bathrooms: 1 private,
2 public
Bed & breakfast

per night:	£min	£max
Single	12.00	13.00
Double	25.00	26.00

Half board

per person:	£min	£max
Daily	18.00	20.00

Evening meal 1800 (last
orders 1900)
Parking for 2
♨♫☎⚑♫⚙ⓘ Ⓢ✕ ▥ TV ▥
⚐✿ ⚘ DAP SP

Waterfall Cottage
20 Old Wells Road,
Glastonbury BA6 8ED
☎ (0458) 831707
*Old cottage dating from 1695,
with oak beams, inglenook
fireplace and many unusual
features. Panoramic views
from garden. Information and
guidance available on the
mystical/legendary land of
Glastonbury.*
Bedrooms: 1 single, 2 twin
Bathrooms: 1 public
Bed & breakfast

per night:	£min	£max
Single	12.50	15.00
Double	25.00	30.00

Parking for 2
♨♫⚑⚙ⓘ Ⓢ✕ ▥ ▥ ⚐✿✕
⚘ SP 曲

Wick Hollow House
8 Wick Hollow, Glastonbury
BA6 8JJ
☎ (0458) 833595
*Peaceful, self-contained
accommodation with private
sitting room, on ground floor
of lovely house overlooking
Chalice Hill and the Tor.
Special rates for stays of
more than 2 nights.*
Bedrooms: 1 multiple
Bathrooms: 1 private

Continued ▶

Map references
apply to the colour
maps at the back
of this guide.

GLASTONBURY

Continued

Bed & breakfast

per night:	£min	£max
Single	20.00	25.00
Double	30.00	38.00

Parking for 2

🌀🏄⛏️💻☕♨️♿🛡️Ⓢ🅟
📺🛏️🅰️❄️🦽DAP SP

GORRAN HAVEN

Cornwall
Map ref 1B3

Once important in the pilchard fisheries, now a seaside village gathered at the mouth of its valley. A medieval chapel and Methodist church stand among the cottages overlooking the quay and beautiful unspoilt cliffs spread south-west of Dodman Point.

Llawnroc Inn

🌀🏄⛏️

Gorran Haven, St Austell
PL26 6NU
☎ Mevagissey (0726) 843461
Small family-run pub/hotel with a local inn atmosphere and fresh, home-cooked food. All bedrooms face the sea and have magnificent views.
Bedrooms: 3 double, 1 twin, 1 triple, 1 multiple
Bathrooms: 6 private
Bed & breakfast

per night:	£min	£max
Single	20.00	24.00
Double	36.00	44.00

Lunch available
Evening meal 1900 (last orders 2130)
Parking for 36
Cards accepted: Access, Visa, Diners, Amex

🌀🏄⛏️💻☕♨️🅰️Ⓢ🅟📺🛏️
🌀🛡️🔌❄️🦽🅢🅢🆂

GRAMPOUND

Cornwall
Map ref 1B3

Perran House 𝔐

♨️♨️

Fore Street, Grampound,
Truro TR2 4RS
☎ St. Austell (0726) 882066
Delightful listed cottage in the pretty village of Grampound, between St Austell and Truro. Central for touring.
Bedrooms: 1 single,
3 double, 1 twin
Bathrooms: 3 private,
1 public

Bed & breakfast

per night:	£min	£max
Single	13.00	14.50
Double	26.00	33.00

Parking for 6
Cards accepted: Access, Visa

🌀💻☕♨️🅰️🛡️Ⓢ🅟🛏️🌀
🦽🅢📻

GREINTON

Somerset
Map ref 1D1

West Town Farm

♨️♨️ APPROVED

Greinton, Bridgwater
TA7 9BW
☎ Ashcott (0458) 210277
Original part of house is over 200 years old, with large inglenook fire and bread oven, flagstone floors and Georgian front. Listed building. Non-smoking establishment.
Bedrooms: 1 double, 1 twin
Bathrooms: 2 private
Bed & breakfast

per night:	£min	£max
Double	32.00	36.00

Parking for 2
Open March-September

🌀♨️♿Ⓢ❄️🛡️📺🌀❄️
🦽🅢

HARTLAND

Devon
Map ref 1C1

Hamlet on high, wild country near Hartland Point. Just west, the parish church tower makes a magnificent landmark; the light, unrestored interior holds one of Devon's finest rood screens. There are spectacular cliffs around Hartland Point and the lighthouse.

Elmscott Farm

Hartland, Bideford
EX39 6ES
☎ (0237) 441276
650-acre mixed farm. In a coastal setting, quietly situated near the Devon and Cornwall border. Signposted from the main A39, about 4 miles away.
Bedrooms: 2 double, 1 twin, 1 triple, 1 multiple
Bathrooms: 1 public
Bed & breakfast

per night:	£min	£max
Double	25.00	26.00

Half board

per person:	£min	£max
Daily	19.00	20.50

Evening meal 1800 (last orders 2000)
Parking for 8
Open April-October

🌀♨️♿🛡️📺🔌Ⓤ🅟❄️🌀🦽

HAYLE

Cornwall
Map ref 1B3

Former mining town with modern light industry on the Hayle Estuary. Most buildings are Georgian or early Victorian, with some Regency houses along the canal.

Polgrean Farmhouse

Cannonstown, Hayle
TR27 6LY
☎ Penzance (0736) 740219
100-acre arable farm. Grade II listed farmhouse in quiet location between villages of Canons Town and Whitecross, 3 miles from north and south coast beaches.
Bedrooms: 1 single,
2 double, 2 twin
Bathrooms: 1 private,
1 public
Bed & breakfast

per night:	£min	£max
Single	11.00	11.00
Double	22.00	22.00

Parking for 6

🌀♿Ⓢ♨️📺🛏️🌀❄️🦽

Traleste

Angarrack Lane, Connor Downs, Hayle TR27 5JF
☎ (0736) 754928
Detached house in St Ives Bay area. Rural outlook. Full en-suite facilities, remote-control TV, radio, hairdryer, tea/coffee making facilities.
Bedrooms: 1 double, 1 twin
Bathrooms: 2 private
Bed & breakfast

per night:	£min	£max
Single	15.00	15.00
Double	25.00	25.00

Parking for 2
Open April-September

🌀10💻☕♨️🔌Ⓢ🛡️📺
🛏️🌀❄️🦽🅢

National Crown ratings were correct at the time of going to press but are subject to change. Please check at the time of booking.

HELSTON

Cornwall
Map ref 1B3

Handsome town with steep, main street and narrow alleys. In medieval times it was a major port and stannary town. Most buildings date from Regency and Victorian periods. The famous May dance, the Furry, is thought to have pre-Christian origins. A museum occupies the old Butter Market.

Halvanance Farm

Longstone, Sithney, Helston
TR13 0HF
☎ (0326) 572375 & 5563130
62-acre mixed farm. Within 4 miles of Helston and the coast. Hot and cold water in all rooms, shower and tea making facilities. Swimming pool, golf and horse-riding nearby, also Flambards Theme Park and many other attractions.
Bedrooms: 2 double, 1 twin
Bathrooms: 1 public
Bed & breakfast

per night:	£min	£max
Single		13.00
Double		26.00

Half board

per person:	£min	£max
Daily		18.00
Weekly		115.00

Evening meal 1800 (last orders 1600)
Parking for 4
Open April-October

🌀♨️♿Ⓢ📺🌀🦽

Longstone Farm 𝔐

♨️♨️ APPROVED

Trenear, Helston TR13 0HG
☎ (0326) 572483
62-acre dairy farm. In peaceful countryside in west Cornwall. Ideal for touring and beaches. Aero park, horse riding and swimming pool nearby. B3297 to Redruth, left for Coverack Bridges. Right at bottom of the hill, continue left for about 1.5 miles to Longstone Farm.
Bedrooms: 2 double, 1 twin, 2 triple
Bathrooms: 2 public
Bed & breakfast

per night:	£min	£max
Single	13.00	14.00
Double	26.00	28.00

Half board

per person:	£min	£max
Daily	19.50	20.50
Weekly	120.00	130.00

Evening meal 1800 (last orders 0900)
Parking for 6
Open March-October

Riverside

Nantithet, Cury, Helston
TR12 7RB
☎ Mullion (0326) 241027
Small guesthouse, friendly and relaxing, in rural situation midway between Helston and Mullion. Enjoy home-cooking with fresh local produce. Ideal for touring and walking. Within 2 miles of beaches, Mullion Golf Club and Flambards Theme Park.
Bedrooms: 1 single,
1 double, 1 twin, 1 triple,
1 multiple
Bathrooms: 1 private,
1 public

Bed & breakfast

per night:	£min	£max
Single	15.50	15.50
Double	31.00	36.00

Half board

per person:	£min	£max
Daily	24.25	26.75
Weekly	152.25	169.75

Lunch available
Evening meal 1900 (last orders 1600)
Parking for 6

Village with a rebuilt church containing the Tudor Carent tomb.

Fountain Inn Motel ⋀

High Street, Henstridge,
Templecombe BA8 0RA
☎ Stalbridge (0963) 62722
Just off the A30 on the A357 Henstridge to Stalbridge road. Country inn (1700) with modern en-suite motel-type accommodation.
Bedrooms: 6 double
Bathrooms: 6 private

Bed & breakfast

per night:	£min	£max
Single	15.00	25.00
Double	25.00	35.00

Lunch available
Evening meal 1800 (last orders 2230)

Parking for 28
Cards accepted: Access, Visa

Quiet Corner Farm

COMMENDED

Henstridge, Templecombe
BA8 0RA
☎ Stalbridge (0963) 63045
5-acre livestock & fruit farm. Stone farmhouse, part 18th C/Victorian set within a complex of lovely old barns, some converted to holiday cottages. Marvellous views across Blackmoor Vale. In conservation village with post office, pubs, restaurant and shops all within walking distance. Miniature Shetland ponies.
Bedrooms: 2 double,
1 multiple
Bathrooms: 1 private,
1 public, 1 private shower

Bed & breakfast

per night:	£min	£max
Double	32.00	37.00

Parking for 8

Roves Farm

COMMENDED

Sevenhampton, Highworth,
Swindon SN6 7QG
☎ Swindon (0793) 763939
450-acre arable & livestock farm. Spacious, comfortable, quiet accommodation surrounded by beautiful countryside. Panoramic views, farm trail to woods, ponds and river. Signposted in Sevenhampton village.
Bedrooms: 1 twin, 1 triple
Bathrooms: 2 private

Bed & breakfast

per night:	£min	£max
Single	19.50	20.00
Double	32.00	33.00

Parking for 5

Half board prices shown are per person but in some cases may be based on double/ twin occupancy.

Woodland village on south-east edge of Dartmoor. Its 15th C church has a painted medieval screen. Charles Kingsley was born at the vicarage. Holne Woods slope to the River Dart.

Dodbrooke Farm

Listed

Michelcombe, Holne, Newton
Abbot TQ13 7SP
☎ Poundsgate (036 43) 461
Listed 17th C longhouse in idyllic setting at foot of Dartmoor, on farm with animals and large gardens. From Ashburton on A38 take road to Two Bridges, fork left for Holne then follow signs to Michelcombe.
Bedrooms: 2 single, 2 twin
Bathrooms: 1 public

Bed & breakfast

per night:	£min	£max
Single	12.00	13.00
Double	27.00	28.00

Half board

per person:	£min	£max
Daily	19.00	21.00

Evening meal from 1930
Parking for 3
Open January-November

Bookham Stud and Ryewater Farm

Holnest, Sherborne DT9 5PL
☎ (0963) 210248
80-acre horses farm. Old stone farmhouse in peaceful situation, surrounded by beautiful garden. Take A352 from Sherborne, 5 miles on turn left at signpost to Boyshill, half-a-mile on turn left.
Bedrooms: 1 single, 2 twin
Bathrooms: 1 private,
1 public

Bed & breakfast

per night:	£min	£max
Single	14.50	16.00
Double	30.00	50.00

Parking for 22

Busy rural town and centre of a large farming community. Market day attracts many visitors.

The Barton

Pancrasweek, Holsworthy
EX22 7JT
☎ Bridgerule (028 881) 315
200-acre dairy farm. At the Devon/Cornwall border on the A3072, 3.5 miles from Holsworthy and 6 miles from the Cornish coast. Friendly atmosphere and home cooking with home-produced vegetables.
Bedrooms: 2 double, 2 twin,
1 multiple
Bathrooms: 2 public

Bed & breakfast

per night:	£min	£max
Single	12.00	13.00
Double	24.00	26.00

Half board

per person:	£min	£max
Daily	18.50	19.50
Weekly	120.00	130.00

Evening meal 1800 (last orders 1600)
Parking for 5
Open May-September

Leworthy Farm ⋀

Holsworthy EX22 6SJ
☎ (0409) 253488
240-acre mixed farm. Freedom and comfort on a friendly farm. Ideal touring centre, own fishing, shooting, ponies and seasonal entertainment. 10 miles from beach at Bude.
Bedrooms: 2 single,
3 double, 1 twin, 1 triple,
3 multiple
Bathrooms: 3 private,
2 public

Bed & breakfast

per night:	£min	£max
Single	15.00	18.00
Double	30.00	36.00

Half board

per person:	£min	£max
Daily	25.00	30.00
Weekly	160.00	180.00

Evening meal 1800 (last orders 1800)
Parking for 12
Cards accepted: Access

HONITON

Devon
Map ref 1D2

Old coaching town in undulating farmland. Formerly famous for lace-making, it is now an antiques trade centre and market town. Small museum.

Lelamarie M

COMMENDED

Awliscombe, Honiton
EX14 0PP
☎ (0404) 44646
Detached bungalow in third of an acre of patio gardens. On the A373, 2.5 miles from Honiton and 7 miles from Cullompton, M5 junction 28.
Bedrooms: 1 double, 1 twin
Bathrooms: 2 private

Bed & breakfast

per night:	£min	£max
Double	28.00	30.00

Parking for 4

ILFRACOMBE

Devon
Map ref 1C1

Resort of Victorian grandeur set on hillside between cliffs with sandy coves. At the mouth of the harbour stands an 18th C lighthouse, built over a medieval chapel. There are fine formal gardens, museum, Chambercombe Manor, interesting old house, nearby.
Tourist Information Centre
☎ (0271) 863001.

Sunnymeade Country House Hotel M

Dean Cross, West Down, Ilfracombe EX34 8NT
☎ (0271) 863668
Set in over half an acre amid beautiful rolling Devon countryside. Close to beaches and Exmoor. West Down is 4 miles south of Ilfracombe.
Bedrooms: 1 single, 6 double, 1 twin, 1 triple, 1 multiple
Bathrooms: 8 private, 2 public

Bed & breakfast

per night:	£min	£max
Single	15.50	18.50
Double	31.00	37.00

Half board

per person:	£min	£max
Daily	22.50	26.00
Weekly		168.00

Evening meal 1900 (last orders 1830)
Parking for 14
Open April-October
Cards accepted: Access, Visa, Diners, Amex

ILMINSTER

Somerset
Map ref 1D2

Former wool town with modern industry, set in undulating, pastoral country. Fine market square of mellow Ham stone and Elizabethan school house. The 15th C church has a handsome tower and lofty, light interior with notable brass memorials . Nearby is an art centre with theatre and art gallery.

Bay House

Bay Hill, Ilminster TA19 0AT
☎ (0460) 52120
Family-run country guesthouse overlooking rural market town. Large gardens with magnificent views of the Blackdown Hills. Good touring centre.
Bedrooms: 1 single, 2 double, 3 twin, 2 multiple
Bathrooms: 2 public

Bed & breakfast

per night:	£min	£max
Single	20.00	22.00
Double	32.00	35.00

Half board

per person:	£min	£max
Daily	25.00	30.00

Evening meal 1830 (last orders 1000)
Parking for 10

Hermitage

Listed

29 Station Road, Ilminster TA19 9BE
☎ (0460) 53028
Lovely 17th C listed house with beams and inglenooks. Bedrooms (four-poster) overlook 2.5 acres of delightful gardens with hills beyond. Ideal touring centre.
Bedrooms: 1 double, 1 triple
Bathrooms: 1 public

Bed & breakfast

per night:	£min	£max
Single	15.00	17.50
Double	25.00	27.00

Parking for 2

ISLES OF SCILLY

See under St Mary's

KENTISBEARE

Devon
Map ref 1D2

Pretty village at the foot of the Blackdown Hills. The church has a magnificent carved 15th C screen, and nearby is a medieval priest's house with a minstrels' gallery and oak screens.

Knowles House

Broad Road, Kentisbeare, Cullompton EX15 2EU
☎ (088 46) 209
Country house with beautiful gardens and woodland on edge of the Blackdown Hills. 5 minutes M5, junction 28, left on A373, left to Shaldon, 1.5 miles on left.
Bedrooms: 1 double, 1 twin
Bathrooms: 2 private

Bed & breakfast

per night:	£min	£max
Single	15.00	15.00
Double	30.00	30.00

Parking for 4

KING'S NYMPTON

Devon
Map ref 1C1

Great Oakwell Farm

Listed

King's Nympton, Umberleigh EX37 9TE
☎ South Molton (0769) 572810
200-acre dairy farm. Friendly, comfortable, relaxing farmhouse, with glorious views. Ideal for touring Exmoor and the Devon coast from Hartland Point to Minehead.
Bedrooms: 1 single, 2 double
Bathrooms: 2 public

Bed & breakfast

per night:	£min	£max
Single	12.00	13.00
Double	24.00	26.00

Half board

per person:	£min	£max
Daily	19.00	20.00

Evening meal 1900 (last orders 1630)
Parking for 8

KINGSBRIDGE

Devon
Map ref 1C3

Formerly important as a port, now a market town overlooking head of beautiful, wooded estuary winding deep into rural countryside. Summer art exhibitions; Cookworthy Museum.
Tourist Information Centre
☎ (0548) 853195

The Ashburton Arms

Listed COMMENDED

West Charleton, Kingsbridge TQ7 2AH
☎ (0548) 531242
Friendly village freehouse serving real ale and home-cooked food. Comfortable accommodation. Sorry, no pets. No smoking on first floor.
Bedrooms: 2 single, 1 double, 1 twin
Bathrooms: 1 public

Bed & breakfast

per night:	£min	£max
Single	18.00	20.00
Double	33.00	37.00

Lunch available
Evening meal 1900 (last orders 2130)
Parking for 15
Cards accepted: Access, Visa

Burton Farm

COMMENDED

Galmpton, Kingsbridge TQ7 3EY
☎ (0548) 561210
325-acre dairy & livestock farm. In coastal valley, 1 mile from the beach. 16th C farmhouse, tastefully restored. A warm welcome is assured. En-suite rooms.
Bedrooms: 1 single, 3 double, 1 twin, 2 multiple
Bathrooms: 4 private, 2 public

Bed & breakfast

per night:	£min	£max
Single	16.00	19.00
Double	32.00	38.00

Half board

per person:	£min	£max
Daily	24.00	26.00

Evening meal 1830 (last orders 1930)

Parking for 10
Cards accepted: Switch
🐴 ☕ 🔒 [S] 🚭 🛏 [TV] ♨ 👔 🔍 ∪ ✿ 🚐 [SP]

Court Barton Farmhouse

♛♛ COMMENDED

Aveton Gifford, Kingsbridge
TQ7 4LE
☎ (0548) 550312
50-acre mixed farm. Beautiful 16th C manor farmhouse, below the church 100 yards from A379. Splendid hospitality guaranteed.
Bedrooms: 1 single, 3 double, 2 twin, 1 triple
Bathrooms: 6 private, 1 public, 1 private shower

Bed & breakfast per night:	£min	£max
Single	20.00	25.00
Double	32.00	44.00

Parking for 10
🐴 🛋 ☕ [UL] 🔒 [S] 🛏 [TV] ♨ 👔 🍸 🔍 🏃 ⛳ ✿ ✈ 🚐 [SP] 🏛 [T]

South Allington House

♛♛ COMMENDED

Chivelstone, Kingsbridge
TQ7 2NB
☎ Chivelstone (054 851) 272
140-acre mixed farm. Attractive house set in 4 acres of garden with safe play area. Coastal walks leading to safe beaches; sailing, fishing, golf close at hand. Between Start Point and Prawle Point.
Bedrooms: 2 single, 4 double, 3 twin, 2 multiple
Bathrooms: 5 private, 3 public

Bed & breakfast per night:	£min	£max
Single	16.00	17.00
Double	30.00	46.00

Parking for 20
🐴 ☕ [UL] 🔒 🚭 🛏 [TV] ♨ 👔 ⛳ ✓ ✿ ✈ 🚐 🏛

KINGSKERSWELL

Devon
Map ref 1D2

Bickley Mill Inn

Stoneycombe, Kingskerswell, Newton Abbot TQ12 5LN
☎ Torquay (0803) 873201
In the beautiful Stoneycombe Valley, within 3 miles of Torbay. Take the Stoneycombe turning off the A380 main Torquay road and follow signs or, from Newton Abbot, take the A381 road to Totnes at Parkhill Cross.
Bedrooms: 4 double, 1 twin, 2 triple
Bathrooms: 7 private

Bed & breakfast per night:	£min	£max
Single	20.00	25.00
Double	40.00	50.00

Lunch available
Evening meal 1800 (last orders 2145)
Parking for 100
Cards accepted: Access, Visa
🐴 📺 ☕ 🔒 ♨ ✿ 🚐 [OAP] [SP] 🏛

LACOCK

Wiltshire
Map ref 2B2

Village of great charm. Medieval buildings of stone, brick or timber-frame have jutting storeys, gables, oriel windows. Magnificent church, has perpendicular fan-vaulted chapel with grand tomb to benefactor who, after Dissolution, bought Augustinian nunnery Lacock Abbey.

Carpenters Arms

22 Church Street, Lacock, Chippenham SN15 2LB
☎ Chippenham (0249) 730203
Caters for those who enjoy traditional English food and refreshments. Afternoon teas, residents' lounge.
Bedrooms: 2 single, 2 double, 1 twin
Bathrooms: 2 private, 2 public, 1 private shower

Bed & breakfast per night:	£min	£max
Single	30.00	35.00
Double	45.00	65.00

Lunch available
Evening meal 1900 (last orders 2150)
Parking for 5
Cards accepted: Access, Visa, Amex, Switch
🐴 10 🛋 📞 🛋 📺 ☕ 🔒 [S] 🚭 ♨ 👔 🍸 🔍 ✈ 🚐 [SP] 🏛

The Red Lion

High Street, Lacock, Chippenham SN15 2LQ
☎ (024 973) 456
Public house, with bedrooms, specialising in the personal service of home cooked food in traditional bars.
Bedrooms: 2 double, 1 triple
Bathrooms: 2 private, 1 public

Bed & breakfast per night:	£min	£max
Single	32.00	50.00
Double	40.00	50.00

Lunch available
Evening meal 1900 (last orders 2200)
Parking for 3
Cards accepted: Access, Visa
🐴 7 🛋 ☕ 🔒 [TV] ♨ ∪ ⛳ 🚐 🏛

LAMORNA

Cornwall
Map ref 1A3

Popular village by deep, rugged valley winding to rocky cove. Moors just inland have many prehistoric remains, including the 'Merry Maidens' stone circle and 'Pipers' standing stones.

Lamorna Pottery

[Listed]

Lamorna, Penzance
TR19 6NY
☎ St Buryan (0736) 810330
Working pottery since 1947. Lovely walks along the cliff and in the beautiful Lamorna Valley. Gift shop, boutique and restaurant on premises.
Bedrooms: 2 double, 1 twin
Bathrooms: 2 public

Bed & breakfast per night:	£min	£max
Single	11.00	14.00
Double		28.00

Parking for 12
Open March-November
Cards accepted: Access, Visa
🐴 📺 ☕ [UL] 🔒 [S] 🚭 🛏 [TV] ♨ 👔 🚐

LATTON

Wiltshire
Map ref 2B2

Set amid levels of Upper Thames, estate village now owned by co-operative community. Restored Norman church and interesting classic-style wharf-owner's house by disused canal.

Dolls House

[Listed]

The Street, Latton, Swindon
SN6 6DJ
☎ Swindon (0793) 750384
A well maintained 1930s detached family residence showing a splendid collection of dolls. Very close to the Saxon town of Cricklade.
Bedrooms: 1 single, 1 twin, 1 triple
Bathrooms: 2 public

Bed & breakfast per night:	£min	£max
Single	12.00	14.00
Double	23.00	27.00

Evening meal 1800 (last orders 1800)
Parking for 10
Open January-November
🐴 5 🛏 🛋 📺 ☕ 🍷 [UL] 🚭 🛏 [TV] ♨ 👔 ✿ ✈ 🚐

LAUNCESTON

Cornwall
Map ref 1C2

Medieval 'Gateway to Cornwall', county town until 1838, founded by the Normans under their hilltop castle near the original monastic settlement. This market town, overlooked by its castle ruin, has a square with Georgian houses and an elaborately-carved granite church.
Tourist Information Centre
☎ *(0566) 772321*

Middle Tremollett Farm

♛

Coad's Green, Launceston
PL15 7NA
☎ Coad's Green (0566) 82416
118-acre mixed farm. Stone-built house situated at the top of a valley, looking across to Caradon and Sharp Tor on Bodmin Moor.
Bedrooms: 1 double, 1 triple
Bathrooms: 1 public

Bed & breakfast per night:	£min	£max
Single	12.00	16.00
Double	24.00	32.00

Parking for 4
Open March-November
🐴 ☕ [UL] 🔒 🚭 🛏 [TV] ♨ 👔 ∪ ✓ ✿ ✈ 🚐 [OAP] [SP]

Wheatley Farm

♛♛♛ HIGHLY COMMENDED

Maxworthy, Launceston
PL15 8LY
☎ Canworthy Water (056 681) 232
Fax (056 681) 232
232-acre mixed farm. Warmest of welcomes awaits you. Nestling in the quiet heart of Cornwall near coast. Comfort and charm abound. En-suite bedrooms with colour TV. Delicious cooking our speciality.
Bedrooms: 3 double, 1 triple
Bathrooms: 4 private

Bed & breakfast per night:	£min	£max
Double	34.00	40.00

Continued ▶

LAUNCESTON

Continued

Half board

per person:	£min	£max
Daily	26.00	29.00

Evening meal 1830 (last orders 1900)
Parking for 5
Open April-September

🐕🛏♥🆄🆂✂🛗📺🚗♣Ů🌣✗🐾

LEWDOWN

Devon
Map ref 1C2

Small village on the very edge of Dartmoor. Lydford Castle is 4 miles to the east.

Stowford Grange Farm

Listed

Stowford, Lewdown,
Okehampton EX20 4BZ
☎ (056 683) 298
240-acre mixed farm. Listed building, quiet village and inn a quarter of a mile away. Home-cooked food, fresh vegetables and poultry. 10 miles from Okehampton and 7 miles from Launceston.
Bedrooms: 1 single,
2 double, 1 triple
Bathrooms: 2 public
Bed & breakfast

per night:	£min	£max
Single	12.50	14.00
Double	23.00	24.00

Half board

per person:	£min	£max
Daily	16.50	17.00
Weekly	90.00	92.00

Evening meal from 1900
Parking for 5
Open March-October

⛱♥🆄🆂✂🛗📺🛗♪▸✓🌣✗🐾

LISKEARD

Cornwall
Map ref 1C2

Former stannary town with a livestock market and light industry, at the head of a valley running to the coast. Handsome Georgian and Victorian residences and a Victorian Guildhall reflect the prosperity of the mining boom. The large church has an early 20th C tower and a Norman font.

Tregondale Farm

HIGHLY COMMENDED

Menheniot, Liskeard
PL14 3RG
☎ (0579) 342407
180-acre mixed farm. Characteristic farmhouse in beautiful countryside. En-suite facilities. Home-produced food our speciality. Log fires, tennis court. North east of Menheniot, between A38 and A390.
Bedrooms: 1 double, 1 twin,
1 triple
Bathrooms: 1 private,
2 public
Bed & breakfast

per night:	£min	£max
Single	15.00	18.00
Double	30.00	36.00

Half board

per person:	£min	£max
Daily	23.50	26.50
Weekly	150.00	170.00

Evening meal 1900 (last orders 1800)
Parking for 3

🐕♥🆄🆂✂🛗📺🚗Ů🌣✗🐾

Tresulgan Farm

HIGHLY COMMENDED

Menheniot Station, Liskeard
PL14 3PU
☎ Widegates (050 34) 268
145-acre dairy farm. Picturesque farmhouse from modernised 17th C farmhouse which has retained its character. Lots to do in this beautiful area and a warm and friendly welcome awaits you.
Bedrooms: 1 double, 1 triple,
1 multiple
Bathrooms: 1 public
Bed & breakfast

per night:	£min	£max
Single	16.00	17.00
Double	30.00	32.00

Half board

per person:	£min	£max
Daily	22.00	24.00
Weekly	147.00	155.00

Evening meal 1830 (last orders 1930)
Parking for 4

🐕♥🆄🆂🍴📺🛗▪🚗Ů🌣🐾 DAP ◻ SP

Upton Farmhouse

Upton Cross, Liskeard
PL14 5AZ
☎ (0579) 62689
Old Duchy farmhouse with elegant and spacious accommodation. Adjacent to Bodmin Moor and 50 yards from historic Caradon Inn.
Bedrooms: 2 double, 1 twin
Bathrooms: 1 private,
1 public, 1 private shower
Bed & breakfast

per night:	£min	£max
Single	16.00	24.00
Double	32.00	37.00

Parking for 3

🐕♥🆄🆂✂🛗📺🛗🚗Ů
▸🌣🐾 SP

LONG SUTTON

Somerset
Map ref 2A3

The Old Mill

COMMENDED

Knole, Long Sutton,
Langport TA10 9HY
☎ (0458) 241599
Old watermill in idyllic hamlet. Comfortable rooms furnished with antiques. All home comforts. Stream running through spacious garden. Half a mile off A372, between Langport and Podimore.
Bedrooms: 2 double, 1 twin
Bathrooms: 2 private,
1 public
Bed & breakfast

per night:	£min	£max
Single	17.50	22.50
Double	35.00	45.00

Parking for 6

🐕♥10🍴🍲◻♥🆄🆂🐾
📺🚗▸🌣✗🐾 SP 🏵

LOOE

Cornwall
Map ref 1C2

Small resort developed around former fishing and smuggling ports occupying the deep estuary of the East and West Looe Rivers. Narrow winding streets, with old inns; museum and art gallery are housed in interesting old buildings. Shark fishing centre, boat trips; busy harbour.

Bucklawren Farm

COMMENDED

St. Martin-by-Looe, Looe
PL13 1NZ
☎ Widegates (050 34) 738
534-acre arable & dairy farm. Set in glorious countryside with beautiful sea views. Only 1.5 miles from beach. Family and en-suite accommodation with colour TV. Delicious farmhouse cooking.
Bedrooms: 1 double, 1 twin,
3 triple
Bathrooms: 4 private,
1 public
Bed & breakfast

per night:	£min	£max
Single	15.00	20.00
Double	30.00	34.00

Half board

per person:	£min	£max
Daily	23.00	25.00
Weekly	154.00	161.00

Evening meal 1800 (last orders 1800)
Parking for 10
Open March-November

🐕♥🆄🆂✂🛗📺🛗🌢
🛗🚗♪▸🌣🐾 DAP SP 🏵

Coombe Farm ⋒

HIGHLY COMMENDED

Widegates, Looe PL13 1QN
☎ Widegates (050 34) 223
10-acre smallholding. Country house in lovely grounds with superb views to sea. All rooms en-suite. Candlelit dining. Home cooking. Glorious walks and beaches nearby.
Bedrooms: 2 double, 2 twin,
3 triple, 3 multiple
Bathrooms: 10 private
Bed & breakfast

per night:	£min	£max
Double	33.00	45.00

Half board

per person:	£min	£max
Daily	27.00	33.00
Weekly	182.00	224.00

Evening meal 1900 (last orders 1900)
Parking for 12

Individual proprietors have supplied all details of accommodation. Although we do check for accuracy, we advise you to confirm the information at the time of booking.

National Crown ratings were correct at the time of going to press but are subject to change. Please check at the time of booking.

Open March-October

Meneglaze Guest House ⚊
Shutta, Looe PL13 1LU
☎ (0503) 262647
Small guesthouse within easy reach of town, harbour and beach. Friendly atmosphere and personal attention. Ample car parking.
Bedrooms: 1 single,
1 double, 3 triple
Bathrooms: 1 public

Bed & breakfast per night:	£min	£max
Double	30.00	36.00

Parking for 5
Open February-November
Cards accepted: Access, Visa

Pixies Holt ⚊

Shutta, Looe PL13 1JD
☎ (0503) 262726
Built in 1878 for a ship's captain, with views across the two rivers. Only 10 minutes' walk to the fishing port of Looe.
Bedrooms: 1 single,
4 double, 1 twin, 1 triple
Bathrooms: 4 private,
1 public

Bed & breakfast per night:	£min	£max
Single	15.00	18.75
Double	30.00	37.50

Parking for 8
Open March-October
Cards accepted: Access, Visa, Amex

Stonerock Cottage
Listed APPROVED
Portuan Road, Hannafore, Looe PL13 2DN
☎ (0503) 263651
Modernised, old world cottage facing south to the Channel. Ample free parking. 2 minutes from the beach, shops, tennis and other amenities.
Bedrooms: 1 single,
2 double, 1 twin
Bathrooms: 2 public

Bed & breakfast per night:	£min	£max
Single	14.00	16.00
Double	28.00	32.00

Parking for 5
Open March-October

LUSTLEIGH
Devon
Map ref 1D2

Riverside village of pretty thatched cottages gathered around its 15th C church. The traditional Mayday festival has dancing round the maypole. Just west is Lustleigh Cleave, where Dartmoor is breached by the River Bovey which flows through a deep valley of boulders and trees.

Eastwrey Barton Hotel ⚊
HIGHLY COMMENDED
Lustleigh, Newton Abbot TQ13 9SN
☎ (064 77) 338
Well-appointed 17th C country house hotel. Peaceful, relaxing and renowned for good food and personal service.
Bedrooms: 3 double, 3 twin
Bathrooms: 6 private

Bed & breakfast per night:	£min	£max
Single	28.00	28.00
Double	56.00	56.00

Half board per person:	£min	£max
Daily	41.00	41.00
Weekly	264.00	264.00

Evening meal 1930 (last orders 1930)
Parking for 20
Open March-October
Cards accepted: Access, Visa

The Mill ⚊
Lustleigh, Newton Abbot TQ13 9SS
☎ (064 77) 357
12-acre smallholding. Historic riverside millhouse on edge of beautiful Dartmoor village. Exposed beams, antique furniture, home-grown produce.
Bedrooms: 1 single,
2 double, 1 triple
Bathrooms: 2 public

Bed & breakfast per night:	£min	£max
Single		16.50
Double		30.00

Half board per person:	£min	£max
Daily		24.00
Weekly		165.00

Evening meal 1830 (last orders 1600)
Parking for 3

LYME REGIS
Dorset
Map ref 1D2

Pretty, historic fishing town and resort set against the fossil-rich cliffs of Lyme Bay. In medieval times it was an important port and cloth centre. The Cobb, a massive stone breakwater, shelters the ancient harbour which is still lively with boats.
Tourist Information Centre
☎ *(0297) 442138*

Buckland Farm
Raymonds Hill, Axminster, Devon EX13 5SZ
☎ Axminster (0297) 33222
Detached bungalow on A35, set in 5 acres of gardens and paddocks. Comfortable accommodation, friendly atmosphere. Meals available at nearby pub.
Bedrooms: 1 double, 1 twin,
1 triple, 1 multiple
Bathrooms: 1 public

Bed & breakfast per night:	£min	£max
Single	12.00	15.00
Double		25.00

Parking for 6
Open April-October

Haye Farm ⚊
Haye Lane, Lyme Regis DT7 3UD
☎ (0297) 442400
35-acre mixed farm. Comfortable farmhouse accommodation, with spectacular views over glorious hills and valleys, in an area of outstanding natural beauty. Vegetarian and vegan cooking if preferred.
Bedrooms: 2 double, 1 twin
Bathrooms: 1 public

Bed & breakfast per night:	£min	£max
Single	13.50	15.00
Double	24.00	27.00

Parking for 8

Kersbrook Hotel ⚊
HIGHLY COMMENDED
Pound Road, Lyme Regis DT7 3HX
☎ (0297) 442596 & 442576
Thatched, 18th C listed hotel and restaurant in its own picturesque gardens, set high above Lyme Bay. For those who prefer peace and tranquillity.
Bedrooms: 2 single,
7 double, 3 twin
Bathrooms: 12 private

Bed & breakfast per night:	£min	£max
Single	45.00	55.00
Double	60.00	65.00

Half board per person:	£min	£max
Daily	45.50	47.50
Weekly	300.00	325.00

Lunch available
Evening meal 1930 (last orders 2100)
Parking for 16
Open February-November
Cards accepted: Access, Visa, Amex, Switch

Lydwell House
Lyme Road, Uplyme, Lyme Regis DT7 3TJ
☎ (0297) 443522
Pleasant, spacious house in large and lovely gardens. Quiet village location, 10 minutes' walk from the sea.
Bedrooms: 1 single,
2 double, 1 twin, 1 triple
Bathrooms: 1 public,
1 private shower

Bed & breakfast per night:	£min	£max
Single	12.00	12.00
Double	26.00	28.00

Parking for 5
Open February-October

Quambi
HIGHLY COMMENDED
Charmouth Road, Lyme Regis DT7 3DP
☎ (0297) 443117
Detached house in own gardens with pleasant views across Lyme Bay and Lyme Regis, only 5 minutes' walk from seafront.
Bedrooms: 1 single,
3 double, 1 twin, 1 triple
Bathrooms: 5 private,
1 public

Continued ▶

> **Please check prices and other details at the time of booking.**

LYME REGIS

Continued

Bed & breakfast

per night:	£min	£max
Single	20.00	22.00
Double	28.00	38.00

Parking for 7
Open March-October
7 🛴 🔌 UL S 🕽 TV 🛏 🍴 ✹ ✈ 🚗

Southernhaye

😃 COMMENDED

Pound Road, Lyme Regis
DT7 3HX
☎ (0297) 443077
Distinctive Edwardian house in quiet location with panoramic views over Lyme Bay, about ten minutes' walk from town and beach.
Bedrooms: 1 double, 1 twin
Bathrooms: 1 public
Bed & breakfast

per night:	£min	£max
Single	16.00	
Double	28.00	32.00

Parking for 2
🛴 12 🔌 UL S 🕽 TV 🛏 🍴 ✹ ✈ 🚗 T

Springfield

😃 COMMENDED

Woodmead Road, Lyme Regis DT7 3LJ
☎ (029 74) 3409
Elegant Georgian house in walled garden, with well-proportioned, tastefully decorated rooms, enjoying views over sea and countryside.
Bedrooms: 1 single, 1 double, 3 twin, 1 triple, 1 multiple
Bathrooms: 3 private, 2 public
Bed & breakfast

per night:	£min	£max
Single	14.00	18.00
Double	24.00	36.00

Parking for 9
Open February-November
🛴 🔌 UL 🕽 TV 🛏 🍴 ✈ 🚗 ✹ 🚗

White House

😃😃 COMMENDED

47 Silver Street, Lyme Regis DT7 3HR
☎ (0297) 443420
Fine views of Dorset coastline from rear of this 18th C. guesthouse. A short walk from beach, gardens and shops.
Bedrooms: 5 double, 2 twin
Bathrooms: 7 private
Bed & breakfast

per night:	£min	£max
Double	36.00	40.00

Parking for 6
Open April-October
📺🖥🔌🛴 UL 🛏 🕽 🛏 🍴 ✹ 🚗 SP 🏡

LYNMOUTH

Devon
Map ref 1C1

Resort set beneath bracken-covered cliffs and pinewood gorges where 2 rivers meet, and cascade between boulders to the town. Lynton, set on cliffs above, can be reached by water-operated cliff railway from the Victorian esplanade. Valley of the Rocks, to the west, gives dramatic walks.

Coombe Farm ₥

😃😃 COMMENDED

Countisbury, Lynton EX35 6NF
☎ Brendon (059 87) 236
365-acre hill farm. Located half a mile off the A39 and 3 miles from Lynmouth.
Bedrooms: 2 double, 1 twin, 1 triple, 1 multiple
Bathrooms: 2 private, 2 public
Bed & breakfast

per night:	£min	£max
Double	32.00	42.00

Half board

per person:	£min	£max
Daily	27.00	32.00
Weekly	180.00	199.50

Evening meal 1900 (last orders 1700)
Parking for 6
Open March-November
🛴 🔌 🛏 S 🕽 TV 🛏 🍴 ✹ 🚗 SP 🏡

Orchard House Hotel

12 Watersmeet Road, Lynmouth EX35 6EP
☎ Lynton (0598) 53247
In a central location 3 minutes from the harbour, with panoramic views. Large car park opposite.
Bedrooms: 1 single, 5 double, 1 twin, 1 triple
Bathrooms: 1 public, 3 private showers
Bed & breakfast

per night:	£min	£max
Single	15.00	16.50
Double	30.00	36.00

Half board

per person:	£min	£max
Daily	24.00	27.00

Evening meal 1900 (last orders 1900)
Open March-October
🛴 4 🛏 S 🕽 TV 🛏 🍴 ✹ 🚗 OAP SP 🏡

LYNTON

Devon
Map ref 1C1

Hilltop resort on Exmoor coast linked to its seaside twin, Lynmouth, by a water-operated cliff railway which descends from the town hall. Spectacular surroundings of moorland cliffs with steep chasms of conifer and rocks through which rivers cascade.
Tourist Information Centre
☎ (0598) 52225.

Ingleside Hotel ₥

😃😃

Lynton EX35 6HW
☎ (0598) 52223
Family-run hotel with high standards in elevated position overlooking village. Ideal centre for exploring Exmoor.
Bedrooms: 4 double, 1 twin, 2 triple
Bathrooms: 7 private
Bed & breakfast

per night:	£min	£max
Single	25.00	28.00
Double	44.00	50.00

Half board

per person:	£min	£max
Daily	34.00	38.00
Weekly	228.00	256.00

Evening meal 1900 (last orders 1800)
Parking for 10
Open March-October
Cards accepted: Access, Visa
🛴 5 🛏 🖥 🔌 🛏 S 🕽 TV 🛏 🍴 ✹ ✈ 🚗 OAP SP T

Red House Hotel

😃😃😃

Woody Bay, Parracombe, Barnstaple EX31 4QX
☎ Parracombe (059 83) 255
Country house on wooded slope overlooking sea and headland, 3 miles west of Lynton. Beautiful walking and riding country. Home cooking, log fires, sun patio.
Bedrooms: 3 double, 2 twin, 1 triple
Bathrooms: 4 private, 1 public
Bed & breakfast

per night:	£min	£max
Double	41.00	43.00

Evening meal 1930 (last orders 1830)
Parking for 8
Open April-October
🛴 4 🛏 S 🕽 TV 🛏 ✹ 🚗 SP

Sandrock Hotel ₥

😃😃😃 COMMENDED

Longmead, Lynton EX35 6DH
☎ (0598) 53307
Comfortable family-run hotel, quietly situated near local beauty spots, bowls green and tennis courts.
Bedrooms: 2 single, 4 double, 3 twin
Bathrooms: 7 private, 1 public
Bed & breakfast

per night:	£min	£max
Single	18.50	22.50
Double	37.00	45.00

Half board

per person:	£min	£max
Daily	29.00	35.00
Weekly	195.00	225.00

Evening meal 1900 (last orders 2000)
Parking for 9
Open February-November
Cards accepted: Access, Visa, Amex
🛴 🔌 🛏 🖥 🔌 🛴 🛏 S 🕽 🛏 🍴 🚗 🔌 OAP SP T

Victoria Lodge ₥

😃😃😃 COMMENDED

31 Lee Road, Lynton EX35 6BS
☎ (0598) 53203
Elegant Victorian family-run hotel, centrally located, offering a high standard of comfort, hospitality and cuisine. Beautifully decorated en-suite rooms. Four-poster rooms available. Non-smokers only please.
Bedrooms: 8 double, 1 twin, 1 multiple
Bathrooms: 10 private
Bed & breakfast

per night:	£min	£max
Single	23.00	30.00
Double	36.00	60.00

Half board

per person:	£min	£max
Daily	30.50	42.50
Weekly	180.00	245.00

Evening meal 1900 (last orders 2000)
Parking for 8
Cards accepted: Access, Visa
🛴 🖥 🔌 🛴 🔌 🛏 S 🕽 🛏 TV 🛏 🍴 🚗 ✹ ✈ 🚗 🛴 SP

National Crown ratings were correct at the time of going to press but are subject to change. Please check at the time of booking.

MALMESBURY

Wiltshire
Map ref 2B2

Overlooking the River
Avon, an old town
dominated by its great
church, once a
Benedictine abbey. The
surviving Norman nave
and porch are noted for
fine sculptures, 12th C
arches and musicians'
gallery.
Tourist Information Centre
☎ *(0666) 823748*

Bullocks Horn Farm
Listed   COMMENDED
Charlton, Malmesbury
SN16 9OZ
☎ (0666) 577458
*12-acre livestock & horses
farm. Well-appointed
farmhouse in beautiful
peaceful surroundings, with
large well-tended gardens. 2
miles east of Malmesbury,
close to Cotswolds and M4.*
Bedrooms: 2 single,
1 double, 1 twin
Bathrooms: 2 public

Bed & breakfast
per night:	£min	£max
Single	15.00	17.00
Double	30.00	34.00
Parking for 6		

The Chestnuts
Cleverton, Chippenham
SN15 5BT
☎ (0666) 823472
*Well-appointed and charming
country cottage, close to
Cotswolds and M4, 3 miles
east of Malmesbury. Private
and peaceful, offering
comfortable living and home
cooking.*
Bedrooms: 1 single, 1 double
Bathrooms: 1 public

Bed & breakfast
per night:	£min	£max
Single	18.00	20.00
Double	33.00	

Half board
per person:	£min	£max
Daily	27.00	30.00
Weekly	185.00	200.00

Evening meal 1900 (last
orders 2030)
Parking for 8

Flisteridge Cottage
Listed
Flisteridge Road, Upper
Minety, Malmesbury
SN16 9PS
☎ (0666) 860343

*Quiet secluded country
cottage in rural surroundings.
Take A429 Cirencester/
Malmesbury road, turn off at
Crudwell, signpost Oaksey
and Minety, on to C class
road, through Eastcourt and
Flisteridge woods. Cottage is
down gravel drive signposted
on right.*
Bedrooms: 1 single,
1 double, 1 twin
Bathrooms: 1 private,
1 public

Bed & breakfast
per night:	£min	£max
Single	12.50	15.00
Double	25.00	31.00

Parking for 8
Open March-November

Lovett Farm
Little Somerford,
Malmesbury SN15 5BP
☎ (0666) 823268
*65-acre livestock farm.
Modern farmhouse ideally
situated for visiting Bath and
the Cotswolds. Close to M4, 3
miles east of Malmesbury.*
Bedrooms: 1 double, 1 twin
Bathrooms: 1 public

Bed & breakfast
per night:	£min	£max
Single	15.00	
Double	26.00	

Parking for 5

Manor Farm
COMMENDED
Corston, Malmesbury
SN16 0HF
☎ (0666) 822148
*436-acre mixed farm. Guests
enjoy a friendly atmosphere
in a comfortable farmhouse.
Ideally placed for visiting
Bath, Tetbury, Badminton and
the Cotswolds.*
Bedrooms: 2 double, 2 triple,
1 multiple
Bathrooms: 1 private,
1 public, 1 private shower

Bed & breakfast
per night:	£min	£max
Single	14.00	20.00
Double	28.00	40.00

Parking for 12
Cards accepted: Access, Visa,
Diners, Amex

Oakwood Farm
Listed   COMMENDED
Upper Minety, Malmesbury
SN16 9PY
☎ (0666) 860286
*130-acre dairy farm. Quietly
situated family-run farm in
village on edge of Cotswolds.*

*Near St. Leonards Church.
Ideal location for visiting
Bath, Cheltenham, Oxford and
the Cotswolds.*
Bedrooms: 2 double, 1 twin
Bathrooms: 1 public

Bed & breakfast
per night:	£min	£max
Single	13.00	13.00
Double	26.00	26.00

Half board
per person:	£min	£max
Daily	20.00	20.00

Evening meal 1700 (last
orders 2030)
Parking for 5

MANATON

Devon
Map ref 1C2

Scattered village with
whitewashed cottages
and a tree-shaded green,
set in rugged country on
the eastern edge of
Dartmoor. Becka Brook
with its waterfall flows
through the Bovey Valley
nearby and there are
good moorland walks to
Bowerman's Nose, a lofty,
jutting rock stack.

Barracott
COMMENDED
Manaton, Newton Abbot
TQ13 9XA
☎ (0647) 22312
*16th C farmhouse on the edge
of Dartmoor below Easdon
Tor. Sheltered and peaceful
with wide views, ideal for
walking and bird-watching.
Signposted on the B3344.*
Bedrooms: 2 twin
Bathrooms: 1 public

Bed & breakfast
per night:	£min	£max
Double	40.00	45.00

Parking for 4
Open April-October

There are separate
sections in this
guide listing groups
specialising in farm
holidays and
accommodation
which is especially
suitable for young
people and
organised groups.

MARAZION

Cornwall
Map ref 1B3

Old town sloping to
Mount's Bay with views of
St Michael's Mount and a
causeway to the island
revealed at low tide. In
medieval times it catered
for pilgrims. The Mount is
crowned by a 15th C
castle built around the
former Benedictine
monastery of 1044.

Old Eastcliffe
House ▲▲
☺ ☺
Eastcliffe Lane, Marazion
TR17 0AZ
☎ Penzance (0736) 710298
*Attractive Georgian residence,
ideally situated overlooking
own gardens and St Michael's
Mount. Offers a high standard
of accommodation at
affordable prices. Antique
brass beds, full breakfasts.*
Bedrooms: 3 double, 2 twin,
1 triple
Bathrooms: 2 private,
2 public

Bed & breakfast
per night:	£min	£max
Double	34.00	46.00

Parking for 9
Open April-October

MARKET LAVINGTON

Wiltshire
Map ref 2B2

The Old Coach House
☺ ☺
21 Church Street, Market
Lavington, Devizes
SN10 4DU
☎ Lavington (0380) 812879
*Centrally situated in a
Wiltshire village, this 200-
year-old house is within easy
reach of many places of
interest.*
Bedrooms: 1 double, 1 twin
Bathrooms: 2 private

Bed & breakfast
per night:	£min	£max
Single	21.00	23.00
Double	35.00	39.00

Parking for 3

MARLBOROUGH

Wiltshire
Map ref 2B2

Important market town, in a river valley cutting through chalk downlands. The broad main street, with colonnaded shops on one side, shows a medley of building styles, mainly from the Georgian period. Lanes wind away on either side and a church stands at each end.
Tourist Information Centre
☎ *(0672) 513989*

Laurel Cottage Guest House
HIGHLY COMMENDED

Southend, Ogbourne St George, Marlborough
SN8 1SG
☎ Ogbourne St George (067 284) 288
16th C thatched cottage, in a delightful rural setting, a fully modernised family home. Low beamed ceilings and inglenook fireplace. Non-smokers only please.
Bedrooms: 1 single, 2 double, 1 twin
Bathrooms: 2 private, 1 public

Bed & breakfast

per night:	£min	£max
Single	25.00	34.00
Double	32.00	45.00

Half board

per person:	£min	£max
Daily	28.00	34.50

Evening meal from 1900
Parking for 5
Open April-October

The Masons Arms
Lockeridge, Marlborough
SN8 4EQ
☎ Lockerige (067 286) 637
Family-run 18th C former pub in picturesque village, within walking distance of Lockeridge Dene and the Ridge Way Path.
Bedrooms: 1 double, 1 twin
Bathrooms: 1 public

Bed & breakfast

per night:	£min	£max
Single	17.00	20.00
Double	28.00	30.00

Parking for 2

Westerly
Listed COMMENDED

Mildenhall, Marlborough
SN8 2LR
☎ (0672) 514254
Comfortable "en famille" accommodation 1 mile from Marlborough off A345 to Swindon. In village, take first left turn - Westerly is first house on right. Non-smokers only please.
Bedrooms: 2 single, 1 double
Bathrooms: 1 public

Bed & breakfast

per night:	£min	£max
Single	14.00	18.00
Double	28.00	34.00

Half board

per person:	£min	£max
Daily	23.00	

Evening meal from 1800
Parking for 2

MARTINSTOWN

Dorset
Map ref 2B3

Old Post Office
Listed

Martinstown, Dorchester
DT2 9LF
☎ (0305) 889254
Grade II listed Georgian cottage tastefully modernised throughout. Large garden with many small animals. Good rural base, children and pets welcome.
Bedrooms: 1 double, 2 twin
Bathrooms: 2 public

Bed & breakfast

per night:	£min	£max
Single	15.00	17.50
Double	30.00	35.00

Half board

per person:	£min	£max
Daily	30.00	32.50

Evening meal 2000 (last orders 1630)
Parking for 3

Individual proprietors have supplied all details of accommodation. Although we do check for accuracy, we advise you to confirm the information at the time of booking.

MARTOCK

Somerset
Map ref 2A3

Small town with many handsome buildings of Ham stone and a beautiful old church with tie-beam roof. Medieval treasurer's house, Georgian market house, 17th C manor.

Wychwood ⋒
Listed COMMENDED

7 Bearley Road, Martock
TA12 6PG
☎ (0935) 825601
Modern detached property facing south, quiet position, friendly atmosphere, ideal touring location. Just off A303. Close to Montacute House (National Trust) and other historic houses and gardens. Brochure.
Bedrooms: 1 single, 1 double, 1 twin
Bathrooms: 2 private, 1 public

Bed & breakfast

per night:	£min	£max
Single	15.00	17.00
Double	28.00	32.00

Half board

per person:	£min	£max
Daily	21.95	24.95
Weekly	144.00	165.00

Evening meal 1830 (last orders 2000)
Parking for 3

MEETH

Devon
Map ref 1C2

Friars Hele Farm
Listed COMMENDED

Meeth, Okehampton
EX20 3QB
☎ Okehampton (0837) 810282
260-acre mixed farm. A warm welcome awaits you in this spacious farmhouse set in the heart of Devon's beautiful countryside. Facing south, it has breathtaking views of Dartmoor on the horizon with woodland, valleys and private fishing on River Torridge.
Bedrooms: 2 double, 1 twin
Bathrooms: 1 public

Bed & breakfast

per night:	£min	£max
Single	15.00	17.00
Double	32.00	35.00

Half board

per person:	£min	£max
Daily	25.00	30.00
Weekly	170.00	175.00

Lunch available
Evening meal from 1900
Parking for 5

MELKSHAM

Wiltshire
Map ref 2B2

Small industrial town standing on the banks of the River Avon. Old weavers' cottages and Regency houses are grouped around the attractive church which has traces of Norman work. The 18th C Round House, once used for dyeing fleeces, is now a craft centre.
Tourist Information Centre
☎ *(0225) 707424*

Longhope Guest House
9 Beanacre Road, Melksham
SN12 8AG
☎ (0225) 706737
Situated in its own grounds on the A350 Melksham - Chippenham road. Half a mile from Melksham town centre, 10 miles from M4 junction 17.
Bedrooms: 2 single, 1 double, 3 twin, 2 triple
Bathrooms: 8 private

Bed & breakfast

per night:	£min	£max
Single	18.00	20.00
Double	30.00	35.00

Half board

per person:	£min	£max
Daily	26.00	26.00
Weekly	154.00	154.00

Evening meal 1830 (last orders 1900)
Parking for 12

There are separate sections in this guide listing groups specialising in farm holidays and accommodation which is especially suitable for young people and organised groups.

MERE

Wiltshire
Map ref 2B2

Small town with a grand Perpendicular church surrounded by Georgian houses, with old inns and a 15th C chantry house. On the chalk downs overlooking the town is an Iron Age fort.
Tourist Information Centre
☎ *(0747) 861211.*

The Beeches
Chetcombe Road, Mere, Warminster BA12 6AU
☎ (0747) 860687
Comfortable old toll house with interesting carved stairway and gallery. Standing in a beautiful garden at entrance to an early English village.
Bedrooms: 2 double, 1 twin, 1 triple
Bathrooms: 1 public, 1 private shower

Bed & breakfast per night:	£min	£max
Single	18.00	20.00
Double	30.00	37.00

Half board per person:	£min	£max
Daily	27.00	29.00
Weekly	161.00	174.00

Evening meal 1800 (last orders 1900)
Parking for 6
☎ ▥ 📺 🖵 🛏 📺 ▥ U ✓ ❉
🖌 ⚓ SP ▥

Talbot Hotel
▥ APPROVED
The Square, Mere, Warminster BA12 6DR
☎ (0747) 860427
16th C coaching inn with interesting features. Ideal for visits to Stourhead, Longleat, Stonehenge, Salisbury, Bath, Sherborne and Cheddar areas.
Bedrooms: 2 single, 3 double, 1 twin, 1 triple
Bathrooms: 7 private, 1 public

Bed & breakfast per night:	£min	£max
Single	32.50	
Double	53.00	

Lunch available
Evening meal 1900 (last orders 2130)
Parking for 20
Cards accepted: Access, Visa, Amex
☎ 🖳 🖵 🛏 🅂 🖵 ⚓ 🖌
▥ SP ▥

MEVAGISSEY

Cornwall
Map ref 1B3

Small fishing town, a favourite with holidaymakers. Earlier prosperity came from pilchard fisheries, boat-building and smuggling. By the harbour are fish cellars, some converted, and a local history museum is housed in an old boat-building shed. Handsome Methodist chapel; shark fishing, sailing.

Auraville
Trevarth, The Drive, Mevagissey, St Austell PL26 6RX
☎ (0726) 843293
A private residence in quiet and peaceful surroundings, a short walk from the harbour. Central for touring Cornwall.
Bedrooms: 2 double, 2 twin
Bathrooms: 2 public

Bed & breakfast per night:	£min	£max
Single	14.00	
Double	28.00	

Parking for 4
☎ ⚜ 🖳 ▥ 🛏 🅂 🖵 ▥ 📺 🖵 ⚓ ❉
✕ ⚓

Kerry Anna Guest House
▥▥▥ COMMENDED
Treleaven Farm, Mevagissey, St Austell PL26 6RZ
☎ (0726) 843558
200-acre mixed farm. Country house overlooking village, surrounded by rambling farmland, wild flowers and wildlife. Outdoor swimming pool, games barn, putting green. Farm cooking.
Bedrooms: 3 double, 2 twin, 1 multiple
Bathrooms: 6 private, 1 private shower

Bed & breakfast per night:	£min	£max
Double	36.00	46.00

Half board per person:	£min	£max
Daily	28.00	34.00

Evening meal 1830 (last orders 1900)
Parking for 6
Open April-October
☎ 5 ⚜ 🖳 🛏 🅂 🖵 ▥ 🖵 ⚓
⚓ ❉ ✕ ⚓ SP

Rising Sun Inn
⚜
Portmellon Cove, Mevagissey, St Austell PL26 6PL
☎ (0726) 843235
17th C inn right next to the beach at Portmellon Cove, and overlooking Chapel Point and surrounding countryside.
Bedrooms: 3 double, 1 twin, 1 triple
Bathrooms: 5 private

Bed & breakfast per night:	£min	£max
Double	35.00	43.00

Lunch available
Evening meal 1830 (last orders 2130)
Parking for 60
Open March-October
Cards accepted: Access, Visa
☎ ▥ 🖵 🛏 🅂 🖵 ▥ 🖵 ⚓ ⚓ ✕
SP ▥

Steep House ⚜
⚜
Portmellon Cove, Mevagissey, St Austell PL26 2PH
☎ (0726) 843732
Beautifully clean and comfortable house with large garden and covered heated pool. Bedrooms have superb views. Barbecues, Christmas celebrations.
Bedrooms: 6 double, 1 twin
Bathrooms: 7 private

Bed & breakfast per night:	£min	£max
Double	30.00	

Half board per person:	£min	£max
Daily	25.00	
Weekly	165.00	

Lunch available
Evening meal 1900 (last orders 1700)
Parking for 12
Cards accepted: Access, Visa, Amex
☎ 10 🖳 🛏 🅂 🖵 ▥ 📺 ●
🖵 ⚓ ⚓ ❉ ✕ ⚓ OAP ⚓ SP ▥ ⊤

Treleaven Farm Guest House
Mevagissey, St Austell PL26 6RZ
☎ (0726) 842413
200-acre mixed farm. Quiet position overlooking Mevagissey yet only a few minutes walk to the harbour. Closed at Christmas.
Bedrooms: 4 double, 1 twin, 1 multiple
Bathrooms: 6 private, 1 public

Bed & breakfast per night:	£min	£max
Double	32.00	50.00

Half board per person:	£min	£max
Daily	26.00	35.00

Evening meal 1830 (last orders 1800)
Parking for 10
Cards accepted: Access, Visa
☎ 🖳 🛏 🖵 ▥ 🖵 ⚓ ⚓ ❉ ✕
⚓ SP

Tremarne Hotel ⚜
▥▥▥ APPROVED
Polkirt, Mevagissey, St Austell PL26 6UY
☎ (0726) 842213
In a quiet secluded area with views of sea and country. Within easy reach of Mevagissey harbour and Portmellon bathing beach.
Bedrooms: 8 double, 4 twin, 1 triple, 1 multiple
Bathrooms: 14 private, 1 public

Bed & breakfast per night:	£min	£max
Single	23.50	28.00
Double	39.00	48.00

Half board per person:	£min	£max
Daily	27.60	35.00
Weekly	178.00	217.00

Evening meal 1900 (last orders 2000)
Parking for 14
Open February-November
Cards accepted: Access, Visa, Amex
☎ 3 🖳 🖵 🛏 🅂 🖵 ▥ 🖵 ⚓ ⚓
❉ ⚓ SP ▥

MINEHEAD

Somerset
Map ref 1D1

Victorian resort with spreading sands developed around old, steeply-built fishing port on the coast below Exmoor. Former fishermen's cottages stand beside the 17th C harbour; cobbled streets climb the hill in steps to the church. Boat trips, steam railway. Hobby Horse festival 1 May.
Tourist Information Centre
☎*(0643) 702624*

Higher Rodhuish Farm
▥▥ COMMENDED
Rodhuish, Minehead TA24 6QL
☎ Washford (0984) 40253
700-acre mixed farm. Comfortable accommodation with home cooking. Situated in the hamlet of Rodhuish 1.5
Continued ▶

MINEHEAD

Continued

miles off the A39. 6 miles from Minehead.
Bedrooms: 1 double, 1 twin
Bathrooms: 1 private, 2 public

Bed & breakfast

per night:	£min	£max
Single	14.00	16.00
Double	28.00	32.00

Half board

per person:	£min	£max
Daily	20.00	24.50
Weekly	135.00	163.00

Evening meal 1930 (last orders 2030)
Parking for 4
🛇🗝️🖤💷🔌🌡️📺⛅🚗🛄 ✓☼🚲 T

MINETY

Wiltshire
Map ref 2B2

The White Horse

Listed

Minety, Malmesbury
SN16 9QY
☎ Malmesbury (0666) 860284
Recently refurbished country pub with accommodation, restaurant, and function room. Two pleasant beamed bars with open fires. Lakeside setting.
Bedrooms: 2 double
Bathrooms: 2 private showers

Bed & breakfast

per night:	£min	£max
Single		25.00
Double		30.00

Lunch available
Evening meal 1800 (last orders 2200)
Parking for 50
Cards accepted: Access, Visa, Amex
🛇🖤🌡️S🛄,🚗↑20🕯️U✓
🖞☼🚲 SP

MODBURY

Devon
Map ref 1C3

Attractive South Hams town set in rolling countryside, whose Perpendicular church has a rare Devon spire.

Best Park

Mary Cross, Modbury, Ivybridge
☎ (0548) 830776
Secluded, converted farm cottage and barn surrounded

by unspoilt countryside. Own entrance and TV lounge. Ideally situated for Dartmoor, sea and Brittany ferries.
Bedrooms: 1 double, 1 twin, 1 triple
Bathrooms: 1 public

Bed & breakfast

per night:	£min	£max
Single	12.50	13.00
Double	25.00	26.00

Parking for 6
Open April-October
🛇🖏🗝️🖤🔌🛄📺🖳🕯️🚲

MONKTON FARLEIGH

Wiltshire
Map ref 2B2

Fern Cottage

Listed COMMENDED

74 Monkton Farleigh, Bradford-on-Avon BA15 2QJ
☎ (0225) 859412
Delightful stone-built 17th C cottage, set in fine gardens in peaceful conservation village. Well appointed rooms.
Bedrooms: 2 double, 1 twin, 1 triple
Bathrooms: 1 private, 1 public

Bed & breakfast

per night:	£min	£max
Single	20.00	25.00
Double	35.00	45.00

Parking for 5
🛇🗝️🖤🔌UL S🛄🖳,☼🕯️
🚲🏠

MORETON-HAMPSTEAD

Devon
Map ref 1C2

Small market town with a row of 17th C almshouses standing on the Exeter road. Surrounding moorland is scattered with ancient farmhouses, prehistoric sites.

Cookshayes Country Guest House 🅰️

👑👑👑 COMMENDED

33 Court Street, Moretonhampstead, Newton Abbot TQ13 8LG
☎ (0647) 40374
Licensed guesthouse on edge of Dartmoor. Ornamental gardens with ample parking. Traditionally furnished. Accent on food and comfort.
Bedrooms: 1 single, 4 double, 2 twin, 1 triple
Bathrooms: 7 private, 2 public

Bed & breakfast

per night:	£min	£max
Single	15.00	18.00
Double	30.00	36.00

Half board

per person:	£min	£max
Daily	24.00	27.00

Bed & breakfast

per night:	£min	£max
Single	20.00	20.00
Double	32.00	39.00

Half board

per person:	£min	£max
Daily	28.50	32.00
Weekly	192.50	217.00

Evening meal 1900 (last orders 1700)
Parking for 15
Open March-October
Cards accepted: Access, Visa
🛇7🖏🖤🗝️🔌🛇🖤S🖳🛄,
🚗☼🚲 DAP SP T

Great Doccombe Farm

👑👑 COMMENDED

Doccombe, Moretonhampstead, Newton Abbot TQ13 8SS
☎ (0647) 40694
8-acre mixed farm. 300-year-old farmhouse in Dartmoor National Park. Comfortable rooms, farmhouse cooking. Ideal for walking the Teign Valley and Dartmoor.
Bedrooms: 1 double, 1 twin, 1 triple
Bathrooms: 1 private, 2 public

Bed & breakfast

per night:	£min	£max
Single	14.00	17.00
Double	28.00	34.00

Half board

per person:	£min	£max
Daily	22.50	25.50

Evening meal 1800 (last orders 1000)
Parking for 6
Open February-November
🛇🖏🖤🔌UL S🖳🛄,🚗
☼🚲 DAP SP

Great Sloncombe Farm

👑👑 COMMENDED

Moretonhampstead, Newton Abbot TQ13 8QF
☎ Mortenhampstead (0647) 40595
170-acre dairy farm. 13th C Dartmoor farmhouse. Comfortable rooms, central heating, en-suite. Large wholesome farmhouse breakfasts and delicious dinners. Friendly Devonshire welcome.
Bedrooms: 2 double, 1 twin
Bathrooms: 3 private

Bed & breakfast

per night:	£min	£max
Single	15.00	18.00
Double	30.00	36.00

Half board

per person:	£min	£max
Daily	24.00	27.00

Evening meal 1830 (last orders 1000)
Parking for 3
🛇🖏🖤🔌🖤S🖳🛄📺🛄,
🚗☼🚲 SP🏠

Wooston Farm

👑👑 COMMENDED

Moretonhampstead, Newton Abbot TQ13 8QA
☎ (0647) 40367
280-acre mixed farm. Situated within Dartmoor National Park above the Teign Valley, with scenic views and walks. Two rooms en-suite, one with 4-poster bed.
Bedrooms: 2 double, 1 triple
Bathrooms: 2 private, 1 public

Bed & breakfast

per night:	£min	£max
Double	28.00	36.00

Half board

per person:	£min	£max
Daily	22.00	26.00

Evening meal 1800 (last orders 1830)
Parking for 5
🛇3🖏🖤🔌UL🖳✓🖳📺
🚗U☼🚲

MORWENSTOW

Cornwall
Map ref 1C2

Scattered parish on the wild North Cornish coast. The church, beautifully situated in a deep combe by the sea, has a fine Norman doorway and 15th C bench-ends. Its unique vicarage was built by the 19th C poet-priest Robert Hawker. Nearby are Cornwall's highest cliffs.

Cornakey Farm

Morwenstow, Bude EX23 9SS
☎ (028 883) 260
220-acre mixed farm. Convenient coastal walking area with extensive views of sea and cliffs from bedrooms. Home cooking, games room, children welcome. Good touring centre.
Bedrooms: 1 double, 1 triple
Bathrooms: 1 public

Bed & breakfast

per night:	£min	£max
Single	12.00	14.00
Double	24.00	28.00

Half board

per person:	£min	£max
Daily	18.00	20.00
Weekly	112.00	119.00

Evening meal 1830 (last orders 1730)
Parking for 2

🛇 ♨ Ⓤ 🛏 🖩 📺 ⚓ ∪ ✿ ✗ 🚗
🅿 🏛

MULLION

Cornwall
Map ref 1B3

Small holiday village with a golf-course, set back from the coast. The church has a serpentine tower of 1500, carved roof and beautiful medieval bench-ends. Beyond Mullion Cove, with its tiny harbour, wild untouched cliffs stretch south-eastward toward Lizard Point.

Alma House Hotel & Restaurant
Churchtown, Mullion, Helston TR12 7BZ
☎ Helston (0326) 241039
Located in centre of village with sea views across Mount's Bay. Superb candlelit restaurant and bar with a la carte menu.
Bedrooms: 4 double, 1 twin
Bathrooms: 1 private, 1 public

Bed & breakfast per night:	£min	£max
Single	14.50	16.50
Double	29.00	33.00

Half board per person:	£min	£max
Daily	22.25	24.25
Weekly	152.25	166.25

Lunch available
Evening meal 1830 (last orders 2200)
Parking for 18
Open March-October
Cards accepted: Access, Visa, Diners, Amex

🛇 🍽 🖵 ♨ 🛏 Ⓢ ✗ 🕮 🖃
✗ 🚗

MYLOR BRIDGE

Cornwall
Map ref 1B3

Penmere Guest House
😊😊
10 Rosehill, Mylor Bridge, Falmouth TR11 5LZ
☎ Falmouth (0326) 374470
Beautifully restored Victorian property enjoying splendid creek views, close to yachting centres. Lovely garden, perfect for a relaxing stay.
Bedrooms: 2 double, 2 twin, 2 triple
Bathrooms: 4 private, 1 public

Bed & breakfast per night:	£min	£max
Single	19.50	23.00
Double	39.00	46.00

Parking for 6

🛇 🖵 ♨ Ⓤ 🛏 ✗ 🕮 🖩 🖃 ✿
✗ 🚗

NEWQUAY

Cornwall
Map ref 1B2

Popular resort spread over dramatic cliffs around its old fishing port. Many beaches with abundant sands, caves and rock pools; excellent surf. Pilots' gigs are still raced from the harbour and on the headland stands the stone Huer's House from the pilchard-fishing days.
Tourist Information Centre
☎ *(0637) 871345*

Degembris Farmhouse
😊 COMMENDED
St Newlyn East, Newquay TR8 5HY
☎ Mitchell (0872) 510555
165-acre arable farm. 18th C listed Cornish farmhouse overlooking beautiful wooded valley. Our country trail will take you through natural woodland and fields visiting the pond and exploring the valley of the bluebells.
Bedrooms: 1 single, 1 double, 1 twin, 1 triple, 1 multiple
Bathrooms: 2 public

Bed & breakfast per night:	£min	£max
Single	15.00	
Double	30.00	

Half board per person:	£min	£max
Daily	23.00	

Evening meal 1800 (last orders 1000)
Parking for 8
Open April-October

🛇 🖵 ♨ Ⓤ 🛏 📺 🕮 🖃 🖃 ✿
✗ 🚗 🏛

Manuels Farm
😊😊 HIGHLY COMMENDED
Newquay TR8 4NY
☎ (0637) 873577
44-acre mixed farm. In a sheltered valley 2 miles inland from Newquay, offering the peace of the countryside with the charm of a traditional 17th C farmhouse.
Bedrooms: 1 double, 2 triple
Bathrooms: 2 public

Bed & breakfast per night:	£min	£max
Single	14.00	17.00
Double	28.00	34.00

Half board per person:	£min	£max
Daily	22.00	30.00
Weekly	150.00	200.00

Evening meal from 1830
Parking for 6

🛇 ♨ Ⓤ 🛏 Ⓢ ✗ 🕮 📺 🖩 🖃 ✓
✿ 🚗 🏛

NEWTON ABBOT

Devon
Map ref 1D2

Lively market town at the head of the Teign Estuary. A former railway town, well placed for moorland or seaside excursions. Interesting old houses nearby include Bradley Manor dating from the 15th C and Forde House, visited by Charles I and William of Orange.

Bittons
Beech Tree Lane, Ipplepen, Newton Abbot TQ12 5TW
☎ Ipplepen (0803) 812489
Delightfully situated, offering comfort and personal attention. Ideal touring centre within easy reach of the sea and moors.
Bedrooms: 1 single, 2 double, 1 twin, 1 triple
Bathrooms: 2 public

Bed & breakfast per night:	£min	£max
Single	15.00	15.00
Double	30.00	30.00

Parking for 6

🛇 ♨ Ⓤ Ⓢ 🛏 📺 🕮 🖃 ✿
✗ 🚗

NEWTON FERRERS

Devon
Map ref 1C3

Hillside village overlooking wooded estuary of the Yealm, with attractive waterside cottages and yacht anchorage.

Maywood Cottage
Bridgend, Newton Ferrers, Plymouth PL81 ALO
☎ Plymouth (0752) 872372
Cottage on 3 levels, close to River Yealm estuary. Part old, all modernised. Take Bridgend - Noss Mayo road B3186 (leading to Newton Ferrers). Maywood is at bottom of hill on right just before estuary.

Bedrooms: 3 twin
Bathrooms: 2 private, 1 public

Bed & breakfast per night:	£min	£max
Single	17.50	22.50
Double	30.00	40.00

Half board per person:	£min	£max
Daily	24.00	30.00
Weekly	140.00	200.00

Evening meal 1800 (last orders 2030)
Parking for 3

🛇 ♨ Ⓤ 🛏 Ⓢ 🛏 📺 🕮 🖃 ✿
🚗 ⓄⒶⓅ ⤢ 🅿 🏛

NORTH BOVEY

Devon
Map ref 1C2

Picturesque moorland village of thatched cottages gathered around a church and green with shady oak trees, old stone cross and a medieval inn.

Slate Cottage
The Green, North Bovey, Moretonhampstead TQ13 8RB
☎ Moretonhampstead (0647) 40060
18th C cottage in one of the prettiest villages on Dartmoor. Lovely views. 13th C pub within walking distance.
Bedrooms: 2 double
Bathrooms: 2 public

Bed & breakfast per night:	£min	£max
Single	24.50	24.50
Double	39.00	39.00

Parking for 2

🛇 12 🖵 ♨ Ⓤ Ⓢ ✗ 🕮 ✗
🚗 🏛

NORTH MOLTON

Devon
Map ref 1C1

Village on the southern slopes of Exmoor, a centre for local copper mines in the 19th C. A 17th C monument in the church shows the effigies of a mining landlord and his family.

Crangs Heasleigh
Heasley Mill, South Molton EX36 3LE
☎ (059 84) 268
185-acre mixed farm. Devon longhouse on beef and sheep farm within Exmoor National Park. Good centre for touring North Devon and Exmoor.

Continued ▶

NORTH MOLTON

Continued

Bedrooms: 1 single, 1 double, 1 twin, 1 triple
Bathrooms: 1 public

Bed & breakfast per night:	£min	£max
Single	12.00	13.50
Double	24.00	27.00

Parking for 10
🐎 ☕ [UL] 🛋 [TV] ♨ 🧺 ✿ 🐕 🏛

NORTH NEWNTON

Wiltshire
Map ref 2B2

The Woodbridge Inn

North Newnton, Pewsey
SN9 6JZ
☎ Stonehenge (0980) 630266
Fax (0980) 630266
Grade II listed country inn in the beautiful vale of Pewsey on the A345. Two traditional bars, restaurant, trout fishing. Finalist in the Pub Good Food of the Year Award 1992.
Bedrooms: 1 single, 1 double, 1 twin
Bathrooms: 2 public

Bed & breakfast per night:	£min	£max
Single	22.00	22.00
Double	33.00	33.00

Half board per person:	£min	£max
Daily	26.50	32.00
Weekly	169.00	202.00

Lunch available
Evening meal 1800 (last orders 2230)
Parking for 40
Cards accepted: Access, Visa, Amex
🐎 [CH] ▭ ☕ 🔒 [S] 🚭 🛋 [TV] ♨ 🧺 🍷 🔍 ∪ 🎣 ⛳ ✿ ✈ 🐕 [DAP] 🏛 [T]

NORTH TAWTON

Devon
Map ref 1C2

Oaklands Farm

👑

North Tawton EX20 2BQ
☎ Okehampton (0837) 82340
130-acre mixed farm. Centrally situated for north and south Devon coasts and Dartmoor. Very warm welcome. Easy access on level drive. Farmhouse cooking.
Bedrooms: 2 double, 1 triple
Bathrooms: 1 public

Bed & breakfast per night:	£min	£max
Single	13.00	14.00
Double	26.00	28.00

Half board per person:	£min	£max
Daily	20.00	21.00
Weekly	115.00	

Parking for 4
🐎 ☕ [UL] 🔒 [S] 🚭 🛋 [TV] ♨ 🧺 ✿ ✈ 🐕

OKEHAMPTON

Devon
Map ref 1C2

Busy market town near the high tors of northern Dartmoor. The Victorian church, with William Morris windows and a 15th C tower, stands on the site of a Saxon church. A Norman castle ruin overlooks the river to the west of the town. Museum of Dartmoor Life.

Higher Cadham Farm

👑👑 COMMENDED

Jacobstowe, Okehampton
EX20 3RB
☎ Exbourne (083 785) 647
139-acre mixed farm. 16th C farmhouse on a traditional Devon farm, 5 miles from Dartmoor and within easy reach of coast. On the Tarka trail.
Bedrooms: 1 single, 1 double, 1 twin, 1 multiple
Bathrooms: 1 public

Bed & breakfast per night:	£min	£max
Single	12.00	13.00
Double	24.00	26.00

Half board per person:	£min	£max
Daily	19.00	20.00
Weekly	115.00	115.00

Evening meal 1900 (last orders 1700)
Parking for 6
Open March-November
🐎 3 [CH] [CH] ☕ 🔒 [S] 🛋 [TV] ♨ 🧺 🔍 🎾 ✿ ✈ 🐕 [T]

Oxenham Arms 👥

👑👑👑 COMMENDED

South Zeal, Okehampton
EX20 2JT
☎ (0837) 840244
In the centre of Dartmoor village, originally built in the 12th C. Wealth of granite fireplaces, oak beams, mullion windows. Various diets available on request.
Bedrooms: 3 double, 3 twin, 2 triple
Bathrooms: 8 private

Bed & breakfast per night:	£min	£max
Single	40.00	45.00
Double	50.00	60.00

Half board per person:	£min	£max
Daily	40.00	45.00
Weekly	245.00	260.00

Lunch available
Evening meal 1930 (last orders 2100)
Parking for 8
Cards accepted: Access, Visa, Diners, Amex, Switch
🐎 📞 ▭ ☕ 🔒 [S] 🛋 🧺 ⛳ ✿ 🐕 ⊘ [SP] 🏛 [T]

Week Farm

👑👑👑 COMMENDED

Bridestowe, Okehampton
EX20 4HZ
☎ Bridestowe (083 786) 221
180-acre dairy & livestock farm. A warm welcome awaits you at this homely 17th C farmhouse three-quarters of a mile from the A30 and 6 miles from Okehampton. Home cooking and every comfort. Come and spoil yourselves.
Bedrooms: 1 single, 2 double, 1 twin, 2 triple, 1 multiple
Bathrooms: 3 private, 1 public

Bed & breakfast per night:	£min	£max
Single	15.00	19.00
Double	29.00	38.00

Half board per person:	£min	£max
Daily	25.00	29.50
Weekly	170.00	195.00

Evening meal 1900 (last orders 1700)
Parking for 10
Cards accepted: Amex
🐎 [G] ▭ ☕ ☜ [UL] 🔒 [S] 🛋 [TV] ♨ 🧺 ∪ ⛳ ✿ 🐕 [DAP] [SP] 🏛

ORCHESTON

Wiltshire
Map ref 2B2

Cozens House Cottage

Orcheston St. George, Salisbury SP3 4RW
☎ Shrewton (0980) 620257
Beautifully converted 18th C barn, near main house, set in secluded and delightful surroundings, 1 mile from Shrewton off the A360 to Devizes. Also very suitable for self-catering.
Bedrooms: 2 twin
Bathrooms: 1 public

Bed & breakfast per night:	£min	£max
Single	15.00	17.00
Double	30.00	35.00

Parking for 3
Open April-November
🐎 [CH] ☕ [UL] 🛋 [TV] ♨ 🧺 🐕 🏛

OSMINGTON

Dorset
Map ref 2B3

Attractive village near the coast on the road to Weymouth. Close by on a hillside is an equestrian figure of George III, Weymouth's patron, cut into the chalk.

The Beehive

Osmington, Weymouth
DT3 6EL
☎ Preston (0305) 834095
Old stone thatched cottage with modernised interior in picturesque village. Local information readily available. Evening meal with advance notice. Dorset recipes a speciality.
Bedrooms: 2 single, 2 double, 1 twin
Bathrooms: 1 private, 1 public

Bed & breakfast per night:	£min	£max
Single	16.00	18.50
Double	30.00	38.00

Half board per person:	£min	£max
Daily	18.50	28.50

Evening meal 1930 (last orders 0900)
Open February-December
🐎 5 ☕ [UL] 🔒 [S] 🚭 🛋 [TV] ♨ 🧺 ✿ 🐕 [DAP] ⊘ [SP]

OTHERY

Somerset
Map ref 1D1

The Cedars

High Street, Othery, Bridgwater TA7 0QA
☎ Burrowbridge (0823) 698310
Listed Georgian country house set in large garden. Centrally heated, separate lounge. Coffee and tea making facilities in all rooms.
Bedrooms: 2 double, 1 twin
Bathrooms: 2 public

Bed & breakfast per night:	£min	£max
Single		16.00
Double		27.00

Parking for 6
🐎 ☕ [UL] 🚭 🛋 [TV] ♨ 🧺 ✿ 🐕

OTTERTON

Devon
Map ref 1D2

Village on the banks of the River Otter, close to the sea. Beautiful thatched cottages of cob or pinkish stone and a church with a 15th C tower, overlooking the river. A craft centre is housed in an ancient mill nearby. Spectacular red sandstone cliffs rise to 500 ft toward Sidmouth.

Ropers Cottage
♛♛

Ropers Lane, Otterton, Budleigh Salterton EX9 7JF
☎ Colaton Raleigh (0395) 68826
16th C modernised cottage with inglenook fireplace and beams.
Bedrooms: 1 double, 2 twin
Bathrooms: 1 private, 1 public

Bed & breakfast

per night:	£min	£max
Single	15.25	17.25
Double	30.50	34.50

Parking for 4
Open April-October

🛏1🚻🖶📺🖩🚗✖🐾

Spinning Wheel Cottage

Fore Street, Otterton, Budleigh Salterton EX9 7HB
☎ Colaton Raleigh (0395) 68893
Bed and breakfast in pretty, thatched 17th C cottage in beautiful Devon village, within easy distance of tourist areas.
Bedrooms: 1 single, 1 double, 1 twin
Bathrooms: 1 private, 1 public

Bed & breakfast

per night:	£min	£max
Single	18.00	20.00
Double	30.00	34.00

Open April-September

🛏🖶🚻📗🖩🚗🐾

> Individual proprietors have supplied all details of accommodation. Although we do check for accuracy, we advise you to confirm the information at the time of booking.

OTTERY ST MARY

Devon
Map ref 1D2

Former wool town with modern light industry set in countryside on the River Otter. The Cromwellian commander, Fairfax, made his headquarters here briefly during the Civil War. The interesting church, dating from the 14th C, is built to cathedral plan.

Fluxton Farm Hotel ⋈
♛♛♛

Ottery St Mary EX11 1RJ
☎ (0404) 812818
Spacious hotel in former farmhouse with comfortable bedrooms and sitting rooms. Local fresh home-cooked food served in candlelit dining room. Log fires in season. Trout fishing in the River Otter.
Bedrooms: 3 single, 3 double, 4 twin, 2 triple
Bathrooms: 10 private, 1 public

Bed & breakfast

per night:	£min	£max
Single	22.50	25.00
Double	45.00	50.00

Half board

per person:	£min	£max
Daily	28.50	32.00
Weekly	190.00	210.00

Evening meal 1850 (last orders 1800)
Parking for 20

🛏5🖵🚻📗✖🖩📺🖩

Home Farm
♛

Escott, Ottery St Mary EX11 1LU
☎ Honiton (0404) 850241
300-acre mixed farm. Comfortable old farmhouse with oak beams, in parkland setting, off B3176. 1 mile from A30, 6 miles from coast. Optional evening meals.
Bedrooms: 1 double, 1 multiple
Bathrooms: 2 public

Bed & breakfast

per night:	£min	£max
Double	28.00	32.00

Parking for 2
Open April-September

🖶🚻📗📺🚗✖🐾

> Please mention this guide when making a booking.

PADSTOW

Cornwall
Map ref 1B2

Old town encircling its harbour on the Camel Estuary. The 15th C church has notable bench-ends. There are fine houses on North Quay and Raleigh's Court House on South Quay. Tall cliffs and golden sands along the coast and ferry to Rock. Famous 'Obby 'Oss Festival on May Day.

Molesworth Manor

Little Petherick, Wadebridge PL27 7QT
☎ Rumford (0841) 540292
Lovely 17th C manor house near Padstow and the Heritage Coastal Path. Ideally situated for touring, walking, golfing, fishing and relaxing.
Bedrooms: 1 single, 7 double, 1 twin, 1 triple
Bathrooms: 10 private, 1 public

Bed & breakfast

per night:	£min	£max
Single	18.50	18.50
Double	34.00	50.00

Half board

per person:	£min	£max
Daily	28.50	37.50

Lunch available
Evening meal from 1900
Parking for 33

🛏8📗S✖📗🖩🚗U📗 ❋✖🐾

Trevorrick Farm ⋈
Listed **HIGHLY COMMENDED**

St Issey, Wadebridge PL27 7QH
☎ Rumford (0841) 540574
11-acre mixed farm. Delightful, comfortable farmhouse where quality and service come first. Located 1 mile from Padstow, overlooking Little Petherick Creek and the Camel Estuary.
Bedrooms: 2 double, 1 twin
Bathrooms: 2 public

Bed & breakfast

per night:	£min	£max
Single	15.00	17.50
Double	30.00	35.00

Parking for 20

🛏5📗🖶📗S📺🕐🖩 🚗🔍❋✖🐾

> Check the introduction to this region for Where to Go, What to See.

PAIGNTON

Devon
Map ref 1D2

Lively seaside resort with a pretty harbour on Torbay. Bronze Age and Saxon sites are occupied by the 15th C church, which has a Norman door and font. The beautiful Chantry Chapel was built by local landowners, the Kirkhams.
Tourist Information Centre ☎ (0803) 558383.

Bay Cottage Guest House
Listed **COMMENDED**

4 Beach Road, Paignton TQ4 6AY
☎ (0803) 525729
Level position, close to seafront. Delightfully furnished, with pleasing atmosphere. Home cooking. High return trade. Torbay in Bloom award-winners 1986-1992.
Bedrooms: 3 single, 4 double, 1 twin, 1 triple, 1 multiple
Bathrooms: 3 public

Bed & breakfast

per night:	£min	£max
Single	12.50	16.50
Double	25.00	33.00

Half board

per person:	£min	£max
Daily	17.00	21.50
Weekly	105.00	130.00

Evening meal 1800 (last orders 1600)

🛏🖶🚻📗S✖📗📺🖩 🚗❋OAP🖩SP

Sea Spray Hotel

1 Beach Road, Paignton TQ4 6AY
☎ (0803) 553141
Small, clean, comfortable family-run hotel, 50 level yards from the seafront, close town, train and bus stations.
Bedrooms: 1 single, 6 double, 3 twin, 2 triple
Bathrooms: 3 public

Bed & breakfast

per night:	£min	£max
Single	12.00	16.00
Double	24.00	32.00

Half board

per person:	£min	£max
Daily	17.00	22.00
Weekly	107.00	135.00

Continued ▶

PAIGNTON

Continued

Evening meal 1815 (last orders 1815)
Open February-October, December

[symbols]

PELYNT

Cornwall
Map ref 1C2

Trenake Farm

COMMENDED

Pelynt, Looe PL13 2LT
☎ Lanreath (0503) 220216
286-acre mixed farm. 14th C farmhouse, 5 miles from Looe and 3 miles from Talland Bay beach.
Bedrooms: 1 single, 1 double, 1 triple
Bathrooms: 1 public
Bed & breakfast

per night:	£min	£max
Single	12.50	14.50
Double	25.00	29.00

Parking for 6
Open April-October

[symbols]

Trenderway Farm

HIGHLY COMMENDED

Pelynt, Looe PL13 2LY
☎ Polperro (0503) 72214
400-acre mixed farm. 16th C farm with large bedrooms, including four-poster. From Looe take A387 to Polperro. Farm is signposted on main Polperro road.
Bedrooms: 3 double, 1 twin
Bathrooms: 4 private
Bed & breakfast

per night:	£min	£max
Double	23.00	25.00

Parking for 4
Open April-November

[symbols]

There are separate sections in this guide listing groups specialising in farm holidays and accommodation which is especially suitable for young people and organised groups.

PENDEEN

Cornwall
Map ref 1A3

Small village on the beautiful coast road from Land's End to St Ives. A romantic landscape of craggy inland cliffs covered with bracken shelving to a rocky shore. There are numerous prehistoric sites, disused tin mines, a mine museum at Geevor and a lighthouse at Pendeen.

Trewellard Manor Farm

COMMENDED

Pendeen, Penzance
TR19 7SU
☎ Penzance (0736) 788526
300-acre dairy farm. Friendly and comfortable atmosphere, home cooking and seasonal open fires.
Bedrooms: 2 double, 1 twin
Bathrooms: 1 private, 1 public, 1 private shower
Bed & breakfast

per night:	£min	£max
Single	16.50	20.00
Double	28.00	38.00

Parking for 2

[symbols]

PENHALLOW

Cornwall
Map ref 1B3

Lambourne Castle Farm

Penhallow, Truro TR4 9LQ
☎ Truro (0872) 572365
62-acre mixed farm. Stone-built farmhouse, tastefully furnished, with plenty of home-produced farmhouse food cooked by the proprietors.
Bedrooms: 1 double, 1 twin, 2 multiple
Bathrooms: 1 public
Bed & breakfast

per night:	£min	£max
Single	12.00	14.00
Double	24.00	28.00

Half board

per person:	£min	£max
Daily	16.50	19.00
Weekly	110.00	120.00

Evening meal 1830 (last orders 1600)
Parking for 4
Open April-October

[symbols]

PENSFORD

Avon
Map ref 2A2

Green Acres

Stanton Wick, Pensford
BS18 4BX
☎ Mendip (0761) 490397
A friendly welcome awaits you in peaceful setting, off A37/A368. Relax and enjoy panoramic views across Chew Valley to Dundry Hills.
Bedrooms: 1 double, 2 twin
Bathrooms: 3 public
Bed & breakfast

per night:	£min	£max
Single	15.00	17.00
Double	30.00	34.00

Parking for 21

[symbols]

PENZANCE

Cornwall
Map ref 1B3

Resort and fishing port on Mount's Bay with mainly Victorian promenade and some fine Regency terraces. Former prosperity came from tin trade and pilchard fishing. Grand Georgian-style church by harbour. Georgian Egyptian building at head of Chapel Street and Morrab Gardens.
Tourist Information Centre ☎ (0736) 62207

Garswood Guest House

Alexandra Road, Penzance
TR18 4LX
☎ (0736) 62551
Family-run guesthouse close to promenade. All rooms are bright, spacious and have tea and coffee facilities and colour TV.
Bedrooms: 1 single, 2 double, 1 twin, 2 triple
Bathrooms: 2 public
Bed & breakfast

per night:	£min	£max
Single	11.50	12.50
Double	23.00	25.00

Half board

per person:	£min	£max
Daily	17.00	18.50
Weekly	115.00	125.50

Evening meal 1830 (last orders 1900)

[symbols]

Lynwood Guest House

41 Morrab Road, Penzance
TR18 4EX
☎ (0736) 65871
Lynwood offers a warm welcome and is situated between promenade and town centre, close to all amenities.
Bedrooms: 1 single, 1 double, 2 twin, 2 triple
Bathrooms: 3 public
Bed & breakfast

per night:	£min	£max
Single	11.00	13.50
Double	22.00	26.00

Cards accepted: Access, Visa

[symbols]

Menwidden Farm

Listed COMMENDED

Ludgvan, Penzance
TR20 8BN
☎ (0736) 740415
40-acre dairy farm. Centrally situated in west Cornwall. Warm family atmosphere and home cooking. Turn right at Crowlas crossroads on the A30 from Hayle, signpost Vellanoweth on right turn. Last farm on left.
Bedrooms: 4 double, 1 triple, 1 multiple
Bathrooms: 2 public
Bed & breakfast

per night:	£min	£max
Single	12.00	
Double	24.00	

Half board

per person:	£min	£max
Daily	16.00	
Weekly	110.00	

Evening meal 1800 (last orders 1800)
Parking for 8
Open February-November
Cards accepted: Amex

[symbols]

Penalva

APPROVED

Alexandra Road, Penzance
TR18 4LZ
☎ (0736) 69060
Well positioned imposing Victorian hotel, near all amenities, offering full central heating, good food and service. Non-smokers only please.
Bedrooms: 1 single, 3 double, 1 twin
Bathrooms: 5 private
Bed & breakfast

per night:	£min	£max
Double	20.00	32.00

Half board

per person:	£min	£max
Daily	17.00	24.00
Weekly	122.00	164.00

666

Evening meal 1830 (last orders 1900)

Tregoddick House
Listed

Madron, Penzance TR20 8SS
☎ (0736) 62643
Detached period house with walled gardens. Interior has some original fittings, granite fireplaces, etc. Located in attractive village close to West Penwith moors.
Bedrooms: 2 twin
Bathrooms: 2 private

Bed & breakfast

per night:	£min	£max
Double	32.00	35.00

Parking for 2
Open January-November

PERRANPORTH
Cornwall
Map ref 1B2

Small seaside resort developed around a former mining village. Today's attractions include exciting surf, rocks, caves and extensive sand dunes.

Beach Dunes Hotel
COMMENDED

Ramoth Way, Perranporth TR6 0BY
☎ Truro (0872) 572263
Fax (0872) 573824
In the dunes overlooking Perran Beach and adjoining golf-course. Access to beach.
Bedrooms: 5 double, 1 twin, 2 triple
Bathrooms: 8 private

Bed & breakfast

per night:	£min	£max
Single	22.50	25.50
Double	45.00	51.00

Half board

per person:	£min	£max
Daily	27.50	32.50
Weekly	180.00	200.00

Lunch available
Evening meal 1830 (last orders 1930)
Parking for 15
Open March-October
Cards accepted: Access, Visa, Amex, Switch

Mount Pleasant Farm
Carnebo Hill, Goonhavern, Truro TR4 9QH
☎ Truro (0872) 572418

Attractive farmhouse with large gardens and wide views over the village of Goonhavern, on A3075 between Newquay and Perranporth.
Bedrooms: 1 twin, 2 triple
Bathrooms: 2 public

Bed & breakfast

per night:	£min	£max
Single	13.00	16.00
Double	26.00	32.00

Half board

per person:	£min	£max
Daily	20.00	23.00
Weekly	124.00	140.00

Evening meal 1830 (last orders 1500)
Parking for 6

PETER TAVY
Devon
Map ref 1C2

Churchtown
Listed

Peter Tavy, Tavistock PL19 9NN
☎ Mary Tavy (0822) 810477
Large Victorian house in own grounds on edge of village. Secluded and quiet with competition stables attached.
Bedrooms: 1 single, 1 double, 1 triple
Bathrooms: 2 public

Bed & breakfast

per night:	£min	£max
Single	12.00	14.00
Double	24.00	28.00

Parking for 6

PEWSEY
Wiltshire
Map ref 2B2

Totteridge Farmhouse
Milton Lilbourne, Pewsey SN9 5LF
☎ Marlborough (0672) 62402
265-acre mixed farm. 17th C farmhouse set in secluded surroundings . Attractive pond and gardens. Half a mile from Milton Lilbourne.
Bedrooms: 1 single, 1 double, 1 twin
Bathrooms: 2 public

Bed & breakfast

per night:	£min	£max
Single	12.50	15.00
Double	25.00	30.00

Half board

per person:	£min	£max
Daily	17.50	22.50
Weekly	120.00	140.00

Evening meal 1900 (last orders 1600)
Parking for 4

PIDDLETRENTHIDE
Dorset
Map ref 2B3

The Poachers Inn
COMMENDED

Piddletrenthide, Dorchester DT2 7QX
☎ (030 04) 358
Country inn with riverside garden, in beautiful Piddle Valley. Swimming pool. All rooms en-suite, colour TV, tea-making facilities, telephone. Residents' lounge. Brochure available.
Bedrooms: 8 double, 1 twin, 2 multiple
Bathrooms: 11 private

Bed & breakfast

per night:	£min	£max
Single		30.00
Double		46.00

Half board

per person:	£min	£max
Daily		33.00
Weekly		220.00

Lunch available
Evening meal 1700 (last orders 2130)
Parking for 30
Cards accepted: Access, Visa

PLYMOUTH
Devon
Map ref 1C2

Devon's largest city, major port and naval base. Old houses on the Barbican and ambitious architecture in modern centre, with aquarium, museum and art gallery, the Dome - a new heritage centre on the Hoe. Superb coastal views over Plymouth Sound from the Hoe.
Tourist Information Centre
☎ (0752) 264849

Ashleigh House
30 North Road East, Plymouth PL4 6AS
☎ (0752) 664824
Close to city centre attractions, station and ferry terminal.

Bedrooms: 2 twin, 3 triple
Bathrooms: 2 public

Bed & breakfast

per night:	£min	£max
Single		15.00
Double		28.00

Parking for 3

Corner Guest House
98 Devonport Road, Stoke, Plymouth PL3 4DS
☎ (0752) 561908
Centrally situated on the main bus route, close to the Tamar Ferry, Channel ferry and the city centre. Moderately priced accommodation.
Bedrooms: 3 single, 2 double, 2 twin, 2 triple, 1 multiple
Bathrooms: 2 public

Bed & breakfast

per night:	£min	£max
Single	11.50	12.50
Double	23.00	25.00

Parking for 1

Gabber Farm
Listed

Down Thomas, Plymouth PL9 0AW
☎ (0752) 862269
120-acre mixed & dairy farm. On the south Devon coast, near Bovisand and Wembury. Directions are provided. Friendly welcome assured. Special rates for OAPs.
Bedrooms: 1 double, 2 twin, 2 triple
Bathrooms: 1 public

Bed & breakfast

per night:	£min	£max
Single	13.00	13.00
Double	26.00	26.00

Half board

per person:	£min	£max
Daily	19.50	19.50
Weekly	110.00	130.00

Evening meal 1900 (last orders 1800)
Parking for 4
Open March-November

Loma Loma
Listed APPROVED

227 Citadel Road, The Hoe, Plymouth PL
☎ (0752) 661859
Close to historic Barbican, Hoe, bus station and ferry terminal. Only 5 minutes' walk to main shopping centre. Supervised by the proprietors.

Continued ▶

PLYMOUTH

Continued

Bedrooms: 1 single,
2 double, 2 twin, 1 triple
Bathrooms: 1 public,
5 private showers
Bed & breakfast

per night:	£min	£max
Single	15.00	16.00
Double	24.00	28.00

Open March-October
Cards accepted: Access, Visa

Osmond Guest House

42 Pier Street, Plymouth
PL1 3BT
☎ (0752) 229705
*Elegant Edwardian house,
converted to modern
standards, 20 yards from
seafront. Resident proprietors
offer courtesy "pick-up" from
stations.*
Bedrooms: 1 single,
3 double, 1 twin, 2 triple
Bathrooms: 2 private,
2 public, 1 private shower
Bed & breakfast

per night:	£min	£max
Single	14.00	
Double	26.00	34.00

Parking for 4

Phantele Guest House

COMMENDED

176 Devonport Road, Stoke,
Plymouth PL1 5RD
☎ (0752) 561506
*Small family-run guesthouse
about 2 miles from city
centre. Convenient base for
touring. Close to continental
and Torpoint ferries.*
Bedrooms: 2 single,
1 double, 1 twin, 2 triple
Bathrooms: 2 private,
2 public
Bed & breakfast

per night:	£min	£max
Single	13.00	14.00
Double	24.00	31.00

Half board

per person:	£min	£max
Daily	17.50	21.00
Weekly	110.25	126.00

Evening meal 1830 (last
orders 1700)

We advise you to
confirm your
booking in writing.

POLBATHIC

Cornwall
Map ref 1C2

The Copse

Saint Winnolls, Polbathic,
Torpoint PL11 3DX
☎ St. Germans (0503) 30205
*600-acre mixed farm.
Comfortable farmhouse in
peaceful countryside midway
between Plymouth and Looe.
Coast 1 mile, beaches 2 miles.
En-suite rooms. Non-smokers
only, please.*
Bedrooms: 2 double
Bathrooms: 2 private
Bed & breakfast

per night:	£min	£max
Double	30.00	

Parking for 3
Open April-October

POLPERRO

Cornwall
Map ref 1C3

Picturesque fishing village
clinging to steep valley
slopes about its harbour.
A river splashes past
cottages and narrow
lanes twist between. The
harbour mouth, guarded
by jagged rocks, is closed
by heavy timbers during
storms.

Crumplehorn Inn, Mill and Restaurant

Polperro, Looe PL13 2RJ
☎ (0503) 72348
*16th C watermill and
coaching house converted to
comfortable bed and breakfast
and self-catering
accommodation. Local ales.
Fresh fish and seafood
restaurant. Special winter
break tariff.*
Bedrooms: 2 single,
5 double, 3 twin, 4 triple
Bathrooms: 14 private
Bed & breakfast

per night:	£min	£max
Single	23.00	32.00
Double	36.00	54.00

Half board

per person:	£min	£max
Daily	33.00	43.00
Weekly	231.00	301.00

Lunch available
Evening meal 1830 (last
orders 2200)
Parking for 30
Cards accepted: Access, Visa,
Amex

New House

Talland Hill, Polperro, Looe
PL13 2RX
☎ Looe (0503) 72206
*Offering spacious and
comfortable rooms with lovely
garden, harbour and sea
views. Cliff walks and sailing
nearby.*
Bedrooms: 1 single,
1 double, 2 twin
Bathrooms: 2 private,
1 public
Bed & breakfast

per night:	£min	£max
Double	30.00	36.00

Open January-February,
April-December

POLZEATH

Cornwall
Map ref 1B2

Small resort on Padstow
Bay and the widening
Camel Estuary, with
excellent sands and
bathing. Pentire Head
(National Trust), a notable
viewpoint, lies to the
north.

Pheasants Rise

Trebetherick, Polzeath,
Wadebridge PL27 6SA
☎ Trebetherick (0208)
863190
*Bungalow with superb
country views. All rooms TV,
teasmade. 5 minutes from
Polzeath/Daymer Bay
beaches. Excellent walks,
surfing, golf-course.*
Bedrooms: 1 double, 2 twin
Bathrooms: 2 private,
1 public, 1 private shower
Bed & breakfast

per night:	£min	£max
Double	28.00	32.00

Parking for 6
Open March-October

PORT ISAAC

Cornwall
Map ref 1B2

Old fishing port of
whitewashed cottages,
twisting stairways and
narrow alleys. A stream
splashes down through
the centre to the harbour.
Nearby stands a 19th C
folly, Doyden Castle, with
a magnificent view of the
coast.

Trewetha Farm

Port Isaac PL29 3RU
☎ Bodmin (0208) 880256

*20-acre smallholding. 18th C
farmhouse on heritage coast
with sea views and excellent
coastal and countryside
walking. Good area for
birdwatching and
photography. Poultry, sheep
and miniature Shetland
ponies kept on farm.*
Bedrooms: 2 double, 1 triple
Bathrooms: 1 public
Bed & breakfast

per night:	£min	£max
Single	13.50	14.50
Double	25.00	26.00

Parking for 6

PORTREATH

Cornwall
Map ref 1B3

Formerly developed as a
mining port, small resort
with some handsome
19th C buildings. Cliffs,
sands and good surf.

Bensons

1 The Hillside, Portreath,
Redruth TR16 4LL
☎ (0209) 842534
*Situated in a valley
overlooking the sea. Close to
beach and harbour. Ideally
suited for touring Cornwall.
Lovely clifftop walks in
surrounding National Trust
land.*
Bedrooms: 4 double
Bathrooms: 4 private
Bed & breakfast

per night:	£min	£max
Single	25.00	25.00
Double	35.00	35.00

Parking for 5

POSTBRIDGE

Devon
Map ref 1C2

Tiny village in the centre
of Dartmoor National
Park, famous for its stone
clapper bridge, probably
medieval, over the East
Dart River. Broadun Ring
and Broadun Pound are 2
sets of prehistoric
remains nearby.

Penlee Farm

APPROVED

Postbridge, Yelverton
PL20 6TJ
☎ Tavistock (0822) 88207
*Penlee stands above the east
Dart Valley at Postbridge in
the centre of Dartmoor,
offering excellent*

accommodation and livery stabling.
Bedrooms: 1 single, 1 double, 1 twin
Bathrooms: 1 public
Bed & breakfast

per night:	£min	£max
Single	17.00	
Double	34.00	44.00

Open April-September
☷8❒♨◻♥♜📺☎▶ ❀🐾

POWERSTOCK

Dorset
Map ref 2A3

Hilly village of mellow stone houses, overlooked by its church. Partly rebuilt in the 19th C, the church retains a fine Norman chancel arch, gargoyles and 15th C carvings in the south porch.

Powerstock Mill
APPROVED

Powerstock, Bridport
DT6 3SL
☎ (030 885) 213
50-acre dairy farm. Comfortable old farmhouse nestling in a valley, in an area of outstanding natural beauty. Only 4 miles away from beautiful coastline. High tea and babysitting provided on request.
Bedrooms: 2 double, 1 twin
Bathrooms: 1 public
Bed & breakfast

per night:	£min	£max
Single	16.00	18.00
Double	32.00	36.00

Parking for 7
☷♥♞◻♨🔥📺▥⬛
◡♪❀🐾☐SP🏠

REDLYNCH

Wiltshire
Map ref 2B3

Yew Tree Cottage
Listed

Grove Lane, Redlynch, Salisbury SP5 2NR
☎ Downton (0725) 21730
Spacious country cottage and smallholding (sheep and poultry). 1 mile New Forest and near Salisbury. Ideal southern touring centre; walking, riding, fishing (Avon), cycling.
Bedrooms: 1 single, 1 double, 1 twin
Bathrooms: 1 public

Bed & breakfast

per night:	£min	£max
Single	13.00	15.00
Double	26.00	30.00

Parking for 6
☷▥⬛⌖♨🐾📺▥❀🐾🐾

RINGMORE

Devon
Map ref 1C3

Journey's End Inn

Ringmore, Kingsbridge
TQ7 4HL
☎ Bigbury on Sea (0548) 810205
Old inn with a wealth of timbers. Upgraded accommodation and new bathrooms provide modern comfort with old world charm. Short distance south of Ivybridge - off A38 close to Bigbury Bay and National Trust coastline.
Bedrooms: 1 single, 2 double, 1 twin
Bathrooms: 3 private, 1 public
Bed & breakfast

per night:	£min	£max
Single	20.00	20.00
Double	36.00	40.00

Lunch available
Evening meal 1900 (last orders 2200)
Parking for 20
Cards accepted: Access, Visa
☷❒⌖♨◻⬛🔑♨🐾🏠

ROADWATER

Somerset
Map ref 1D1

Glasses Farm

Roadwater, Watchet
TA23 OQH
☎ Washford (0984) 40552
220-acre arable & dairy farm. Thatched 16th C farmhouse near the Brendon Hills. Ideal for walking, riding, quiet holidays looking at local beauty spots. Closed at Christmas.
Bedrooms: 1 double, 2 twin
Bathrooms: 2 public
Bed & breakfast

per night:	£min	£max
Single	16.50	
Double	33.00	

Parking for 6
Open February-November
☷10♨◻♨📺▥⬛
♞◡✓❀🐾🏠

ROWDE

Wiltshire
Map ref 2B2

The Cottage

High Street, Rowde, Devizes
SN10 2PL
☎ Devizes (0380) 721801
Fax (0380) 728002
White thatched 16th C cottage with leaded light windows, beams, inglenook fireplace and outside well.
Bedrooms: 1 single, 1 double, 1 twin, 1 multiple
Bathrooms: 3 public
Bed & breakfast

per night:	£min	£max
Single	15.00	17.00
Double	30.00	34.00

Half board

per person:	£min	£max
Daily	20.00	23.00

Parking for 7
☷♨◻♨◻📺▥⬛❀
☐DAP ☐SP 🏠

Kenavon

Marsh Lane, Rowde, Devizes
SN10 1RF
☎ Devizes (0380) 726892
Double-fronted house situated 300 yards from the famous Cean Hill flight of locks on the Kennet Canal. Indoor heated pool. Evening meal on request.
Bedrooms: 1 single, 2 double
Bathrooms: 1 public
Bed & breakfast

per night:	£min	£max
Single	15.00	18.00
Double	25.00	30.00

Parking for 10
Open April-October
☷◻♨◻♨📺▥⬛🍵❀🐾

RUAN HIGH LANES

Cornwall
Map ref 1B3

Village at the northern end of the Roseland Peninsula.

Penhallow Farmhouse

Ruan High Lanes, Truro
TR2 5LR
☎ Truro (0872) 501245
200-acre mixed farm. Beautiful large farmhouse on traditional farm in Roseland Peninsula. Lovely views. 1 mile from sea. Homemade bread. Honey from own bees.
Bedrooms: 1 single, 3 double, 1 twin
Bathrooms: 1 private, 2 public

Bed & breakfast

per night:	£min	£max
Single	12.00	12.00
Double	24.00	24.00

Parking for 4
Open April-October
☷♥◻♨📺▥⬛🐾✓❀
🐾🏠

SALCOMBE

Devon
Map ref 1C3

Sheltered yachting resort of whitewashed houses and narrow streets in a balmy setting on the Salcombe Estuary. Palm, myrtle and other Mediterranean plants flourish. There are sandy bays and creeks for boating.

Torre View Hotel
COMMENDED

Devon Road, Salcombe
TQ8 8HJ
☎ (0548) 842633
Large detached residence commanding extensive views of the estuary and sea.
Bedrooms: 4 double, 2 twin, 2 triple
Bathrooms: 8 private
Bed & breakfast

per night:	£min	£max
Single	22.00	26.00
Double	42.00	52.00

Half board

per person:	£min	£max
Daily	31.00	36.00
Weekly	216.00	235.00

Evening meal 1900 (last orders 1800)
Parking for 5
Open February-October
Cards accepted: Access, Visa
☷4♨◻✓♨📺▥⬛◡▶
❀🐾🐾☐SP

> Please check prices and other details at the time of booking.

> Individual proprietors have supplied all details of accommodation. Although we do check for accuracy, we advise you to confirm the information at the time of booking.

SALISBURY

Wiltshire
Map ref 2B3

Beautiful city and ancient regional capital set amid water meadows. Buildings of all periods are dominated by the stately cathedral whose spire is the tallest in England. Built between 1220 and 1258, is one of the purest examples of Early English architecture.
Tourist Information Centre
☎ (0722) 334956.

8 Manor Road
Salisbury SP1 1JS
☎ (0722) 334884
Refreshingly quiet Victorian town house, only 5 minutes' walk to the town centre. Friendly, relaxed non-smoking atmosphere.
Bedrooms: 2 single, 1 twin
Bathrooms: 2 public
Bed & breakfast

per night:	£min	£max
Single	12.50	18.00
Double	25.00	30.00

Parking for 1

Avon Lodge Guest House ♠

28 Castle Road, Salisbury SP1 3RJ
☎ (0722) 331359
Victorian house offering a warm welcome and pleasant homely atmosphere. City centre few minutes' walk. Ideal base for touring the South.
Bedrooms: 1 double, 1 twin, 1 triple
Bathrooms: 1 public
Bed & breakfast

per night:	£min	£max
Double	28.00	32.00

Parking for 3

The Bell Inn
Warminster Road, South Newton, Salisbury SP2 0QD
☎ (0722) 743336
300-year-old roadside inn offering full en-suite facilities. Extensive range of bar meals. 6 miles north west of Salisbury.
Bedrooms: 2 double, 1 twin
Bathrooms: 3 private

Bed & breakfast

per night:	£min	£max
Single		18.00
Double	32.00	34.00

Lunch available
Evening meal 1900 (last orders 2100)
Parking for 60

Beulah
Listed
144 Britford Lane, Salisbury SP2 8AL
☎ (0722) 333517
Bungalow in quiet road. 1.25 miles from city centre, overlooking meadows. Evening meal served on request. No-smoking establishment.
Bedrooms: 1 single, 1 triple
Bathrooms: 1 public
Bed & breakfast

per night:	£min	£max
Single	14.50	15.00
Double	29.00	30.00

Half board

per person:	£min	£max
Daily	20.00	21.00
Weekly	130.00	140.00

Evening meal 1800 (last orders 1600)
Parking for 4

Bridge Farm
Bridge Farm, Britford, Salisbury SP5 4DY
☎ (0722) 332376
320-acre arable farm. Attractive 18th C farmhouse in rural setting off the A338, a mile from the edge of the city. Beautiful gardens backing on to river.
Bedrooms: 2 double, 1 twin
Bathrooms: 1 public
Bed & breakfast

per night:	£min	£max
Single	18.00	30.00
Double	32.00	36.00

Parking for 4

Butt of Ale
APPROVED
Sunnyhill Road, Salisbury SP1 3QJ
☎ (0722) 327610
Modern inn with 2 bars and garden. Highest pub in Salisbury giving superb views of the cathedral.
Bedrooms: 1 double, 1 twin
Bathrooms: 1 private, 1 public

Bed & breakfast

per night:	£min	£max
Single	14.50	27.00
Double	46.00	46.00

Half board

per person:	£min	£max
Daily	19.50	37.00
Weekly	140.00	195.00

Lunch available
Evening meal 1830 (last orders 2130)
Parking for 52
Cards accepted: Access, Visa

Byways House ♠

31 Fowlers Road, Salisbury SP1 2QP
☎ (0722) 328364
Fax (0722) 322146
Attractive family-run Victorian house close to cathedral in quiet area of city centre. Car park. Bedrooms en-suite with colour TV. Traditional English and vegetarian breakfasts.
Bedrooms: 4 single, 8 double, 8 twin, 2 triple, 1 multiple
Bathrooms: 19 private, 1 public
Bed & breakfast

per night:	£min	£max
Single	20.00	26.50
Double	35.00	39.00

Half board

per person:	£min	£max
Daily	27.00	33.00
Weekly	189.00	231.00

Evening meal 1800 (last orders 1900)
Parking for 15

Castlewood
♠♠
45 Castle Road, Salisbury SP1 3RH
☎ (0722) 421494 & 324809
Large Edwardian house, tastefully restored throughout. Pleasant 10 minutes' riverside walk to city centre and cathedral.
Bedrooms: 1 single, 1 double, 1 twin, 1 multiple
Bathrooms: 2 private, 1 public
Bed & breakfast

per night:	£min	£max
Single		18.00
Double		28.00

Parking for 4

Cranston Guest House
5 Wain-a-Long Road, Salisbury SP1 1LJ
☎ (0722) 336776
Large detached town house covered in Virginia creeper. 10 minutes' walk from town centre and cathedral.
Bedrooms: 2 single, 2 double, 2 twin, 1 triple
Bathrooms: 5 private, 1 public
Bed & breakfast

per night:	£min	£max
Single	12.00	16.00
Double	30.00	32.00

Evening meal 1800 (last orders 1900)
Parking for 3
Open April-October

Daheim
COMMENDED
3 Willow Close, Laverstock, Salisbury SP1 1QF
☎ (0722) 334536
Delightful spacious modern bungalow in private close beside River Bourne and close to city centre. Breakfast a speciality. German spoken.
Bedrooms: 1 single, 1 twin
Bathrooms: 1 public
Bed & breakfast

per night:	£min	£max
Single	12.50	14.00
Double	25.00	28.00

Parking for 3

Elm Tree Cottage
Stapleford, Salisbury SP3 4LJ
☎ (0722) 790507
Character cottage in a picturesque village with a friendly, warm atmosphere. Home produce, personal service and flower gardens to relax in. Convenient for Salisbury (6 miles), Stonehenge, Avebury, Longleat House and Bath.
Bedrooms: 2 double, 1 triple
Bathrooms: 2 private, 1 public
Bed & breakfast

per night:	£min	£max
Double	32.00	36.00

Parking for 7
Open March-October and Christmas

The Gallery
36 Wyndham Road, Salisbury SP1 3AB
☎ (0722) 324586
A warm welcome awaits you at The Gallery, situated within

easy walking distance of cathedral, museum and shopping centre.
Bedrooms: 1 double, 2 twin
Bathrooms: 3 private

Bed & breakfast

per night:	£min	£max
Double	28.00	34.00

Hayburn Wyke Guest House

72 Castle Road, Salisbury
SP1 3RL
☎ (0722) 412627
Family-run spacious guesthouse adjacent to Victoria Park. Short walk from the cathedral and city centre and Old Sarum. Stonehenge 9 miles.
Bedrooms: 2 double, 2 twin, 2 triple
Bathrooms: 2 private, 1 public

Bed & breakfast

per night:	£min	£max
Single	18.00	25.00
Double	30.00	38.00

Parking for 6

Hillside

Odstock, Salisbury SP5 4JE
☎ (0722) 329746
Bed and breakfast in small country house, in village 3 miles from Salisbury.
Bedrooms: 1 double, 2 twin
Bathrooms: 3 private

Bed & breakfast

per night:	£min	£max
Double	30.00	34.00

Parking for 3

Kelebrae

101 Castle Road, Salisbury
SP1 3RP
☎ (0722) 333628
A family home, opposite Victoria Park within walking distance of city centre. Convenient for Stonehenge. Parking.
Bedrooms: 2 double
Bathrooms: 1 public

Bed & breakfast

per night:	£min	£max
Single	16.00	18.00
Double	30.00	32.00

Parking for 3

Leena's Guest House

50 Castle Road, Salisbury
SP1 3RL
☎ (0722) 335419

Attractive Edwardian house with friendly atmosphere, close to riverside walks and park. Modern facilities include en-suite and ground-floor rooms.
Bedrooms: 1 single, 2 double, 2 twin, 1 multiple
Bathrooms: 4 private, 1 public, 1 private shower

Bed & breakfast

per night:	£min	£max
Single	17.00	
Double	28.00	

Parking for 7

Manor Farm

Great Wishford, Salisbury
SP2 0PG
☎ (0722) 790296
570-acre arable & livestock farm. Country farmhouse, large pleasant room with good views. Just off A36 north of Salisbury and route to West Country. Handy for Stonehenge and Wilton House.
Bedrooms: 1 double
Bathrooms: 1 public

Bed & breakfast

per night:	£min	£max
Double	28.00	32.00

Parking for 1

The Old Bakery

35 Bedwin Street, Salisbury
SP1 3UT
☎ (0722) 320100
16th C house of charm and character, conveniently situated in one of the oldest parts of the city centre.
Bedrooms: 1 single, 1 double, 1 twin
Bathrooms: 2 private, 1 public

Bed & breakfast

per night:	£min	£max
Single	15.00	20.00
Double	30.00	40.00

Pasket House

57 Church Road, Laverstock, Salisbury SP1 1QY
☎ (0722) 327651
Detached spacious residence set in generous garden. Private parking, en-suite facilities, residents' telephone. Reduction for three or more nights.
Bedrooms: 1 double, 1 twin, 1 triple
Bathrooms: 3 private

Bed & breakfast

per night:	£min	£max
Single	18.00	24.00
Double	30.00	35.00

Parking for 4

Richburn Guest House
APPROVED

23 & 25 Estcourt Road, Salisbury SP1 3AP
☎ (0722) 325189
Large, tastefully renovated Victorian house with homely family atmosphere. All modern amenities and large car park. Close to city centre and parks.
Bedrooms: 1 single, 5 double, 2 twin, 1 triple, 1 multiple
Bathrooms: 2 private, 2 public

Bed & breakfast

per night:	£min	£max
Single	16.50	17.50
Double	27.00	36.00

Parking for 12

Swan Inn
APPROVED

Stoford, Salisbury SP2 0PR
☎ (0722) 790236
Fronting the River Wylye, the inn is an excellent centre for visiting Salisbury, Bath, Stonehenge and Longleat. Restaurant with varied menus. Skittles alley, own fishing rights.
Bedrooms: 1 single, 3 double, 2 twin, 2 triple
Bathrooms: 6 private, 1 public, 1 private shower

Bed & breakfast

per night:	£min	£max
Single	18.00	20.00
Double	36.00	40.00

Half board

per person:	£min	£max
Daily	21.75	30.00

Lunch available
Evening meal 1800 (last orders 2130)
Parking for 102

Swaynes Firs Farm
APPROVED

Grimsdyke, Coombe Bissett, Salisbury SP5 5RF
☎ Martin Cross (072 589) 240
15-acre mixed farm. Country farmhouse in pleasant position with good views. Ancient Roman ditch on farm. Peacocks, ducks, chickens and

horses are reared on the farm.
Bedrooms: 2 twin, 1 multiple
Bathrooms: 3 private

Bed & breakfast

per night:	£min	£max
Single	14.00	17.00
Double	30.00	36.00

Parking for 9

SALISBURY PLAIN

See under Amesbury, Figheldean, Market Lavington, Orcheston, Salisbury, Shrewton, South Newton, Warminster, Winterbourne Stoke

SENNEN COVE

Cornwall
Map ref 1A3

The Old Success Inn

Sennen Cove, Lands End
TR19 7DG
☎ (0736) 871232
This 17th C fishermen's inn nestles in one of Cornwall's most beautiful bays, within yards of the superb Whitesands Beach.
Bedrooms: 1 single, 8 double, 2 twin, 1 triple
Bathrooms: 12 private, 1 public

Bed & breakfast

per night:	£min	£max
Single	25.00	35.00
Double	50.00	70.00

Half board

per person:	£min	£max
Daily	35.00	45.00
Weekly	150.00	

Lunch available
Evening meal 1900 (last orders 2130)
Parking for 14
Cards accepted: Access, Visa

SEVERN BEACH

Avon
Map ref 2A2

Rosebush Cottage
COMMENDED

Station Road, Severn Beach, Bristol BS12 3PL
☎ Pilning (0454) 632611
Modern house in garden setting, in village 8 miles from Bristol. All facilities available in rooms.
Bedrooms: 2 single, 2 twin
Continued ▶

SEVERN BEACH

Continued

Bathrooms: 4 private
Bed & breakfast

per night:	£min	£max
Single	18.00	20.00
Double	36.00	40.00

Lunch available
Evening meal 1800 (last
orders 2000)
Parking for 8

🏕️🛁🕳️🖵❄️🎣Ⓢ🅿️TV 📖
Ⓔ🍴☺❄️🚲

SHALDON

Devon
Map ref 1D2

Pretty resort facing
Teignmouth from the
south bank of the Teign
Estuary. Regency houses
harmonise with others of
later periods; there are
old cottages and narrow
lanes. On the Ness, a
sandstone promontory
nearby, a tunnel built in
the 19th C leads to a
beach revealed at low
tide.

Fonthill

🏅 HIGHLY COMMENDED

Torquay Road, Shaldon,
Teignmouth TQ14 0AX
☎ (0626) 872344
*Lovely Georgian family home
in superb grounds
overlooking River Teign.
Comfortable rooms, peaceful.
Restaurants nearby.*
Bedrooms: 3 twin
Bathrooms: 1 private,
1 public
Bed & breakfast

per night:	£min	£max
Single	25.00	28.00
Double	35.00	42.00

Parking for 5
Open February-December

🏕️❄️🖵Ⓢ📖TV 📖🚲🛒🍴
❄️🚲🍴🏠

There are separate
sections in this
guide listing groups
specialising in farm
holidays and
accommodation
which is especially
suitable for young
people and
organised groups.

SHEPTON MALLET

Somerset
Map ref 2A2

Important, stone-built
market town beneath the
south-west slopes of the
Mendips. Thriving rural
industries include glove
and shoe making, dairying
and cider making; the
remains of a medieval
'shambles' in the square
date from the town's
prosperity as a wool
centre.

Hurlingpot Farm

🏅 COMMENDED

Chelynch, Doulting, Shepton
Mallet BA4 4PY
☎ (0749) 880256
*Lovely old farmhouse in an
open country setting, 2 miles
from Shepton Mallet. A361
Chelynch road turn left just
past Poachers Pocket Pub. 16
miles from Bath and Bristol,
8 miles from Wells.*
Bedrooms: 1 double, 1 twin,
1 triple
Bathrooms: 3 private
Bed & breakfast

per night:	£min	£max
Single		25.00
Double		35.00

Parking for 6

🏕️🖵❄️🅿️📖🚲❄️🍴🏠
SP🏠

Kings Arms Inn

🏅 APPROVED

Leg Square, Shepton Mallet
BA4 5LN
☎ (0749) 343781
*17th C inn, affectionately
known as 'The Dusthole',
offering good wholesome
food, traditional en-suite
accommodation and a fine
selection of real ales.*
Bedrooms: 2 double, 1 twin
Bathrooms: 3 private
Bed & breakfast

per night:	£min	£max
Single	25.00	30.00
Double	33.00	40.00

Lunch available
Evening meal 1900 (last
orders 2100)
Parking for 6
Cards accepted: Access, Visa

🏕️🖵❄️🍴Ⓢ📖🖵🛒🍴🔥✓
🚲🏠

The colour maps
at the back of this
guide pinpoint all
places with
accommodation.

SHERBORNE

Dorset
Map ref 2B3

Historic town of
Hamstone, a business
and market centre for a
wide area and a
developing cultural centre
with a range of activities.
The home of Dorset
Opera. In Anglo-Saxon
times it was a cathedral
city and until the
Dissolution there was a
monastery here.
*Tourist Information Centre
☎ (0935) 815341.*

Quinns

🏅 HIGHLY COMMENDED

Marston Road, Sherborne
DT9 4BL
☎ (0935) 815008
*Delightful accommodation in
modern house. All rooms en-
suite, TV, tea/coffee making
facilities. Spacious lounge.
Dinners by arrangement. Car
park.*
Bedrooms: 1 single,
1 double, 1 twin
Bathrooms: 3 private
Bed & breakfast

per night:	£min	£max
Single	20.00	25.00
Double	40.00	50.00

Evening meal from 1900
Parking for 4

🏕️8🖵❄️📖🛒Ⓢ📖📖🚲
🚲SP

SHERSTON

Wiltshire
Map ref 2B2

Widleys Farm

🏅 APPROVED

Sherston, Malmesbury
SN16 0PY
☎ Malmesbury (0666)
840213
*300-acre mixed farm. Close to
100-acre arboretum, easily
reached from M4. Central for
Bath, Bristol and Wales via
the Severn Bridge.*
Bedrooms: 1 double, 1 triple,
1 multiple
Bathrooms: 2 public
Bed & breakfast

per night:	£min	£max
Double	30.00	30.00

Half board

per person:	£min	£max
Daily	23.00	23.00
Weekly	120.00	120.00

Evening meal 1830 (last
orders 1200)

Parking for 6
Open January-November

🏕️🖵❄️🖵📖🛒📖📖🚲🔥Ụ🍴
❄️🍴🚲🏠

SHIPHAM

Somerset
Map ref 1D1

Peaceful village on the
slopes of the Mendip
Hills, once a centre for
calamine mining.

Penscot Farm House Hotel 🅜

Shipham, Winscombe, Avon
BS25 1TW
☎ Winscombe (093 484)
2659
Fax (093 484) 2576
*Cosy old world atmosphere
with log fires in winter, oak
beams and English style food.
Situated in Mendip foothills
with lovely views and walks.*
Bedrooms: 4 single,
7 double, 5 twin, 3 triple
Bathrooms: 13 private,
2 public
Bed & breakfast

per night:	£min	£max
Single		30.00
Double		50.00

Half board

per person:	£min	£max
Daily	34.00	40.00
Weekly	220.00	260.00

Evening meal 1900 (last
orders 2030)
Parking for 40
Open January-November
Cards accepted: Access, Visa,
C.Bl, Diners, Amex

🏕️🛁🕳️🖵🔥🛒📖Ⓢ🍴📖TV
🕐📖🚲♆20-30 Ụ🍴❄️SP
🏠Ⓣ

SHIPTON GORGE

Dorset
Map ref 2A3

Innsacre Country Restaurant

Shipton Gorge, Bridport
DT6 4LJ
☎ Bridport (0308) 56137
*17th C farmhouse hidden in a
sheltered valley. Seriously
good food and informal
atmosphere. Midway
Dorchester and Lyme Regis,
off A35 at Shipton Gorge.*
Bedrooms: 4 double, 1 twin,
1 triple
Bathrooms: 6 private
Bed & breakfast

per night:	£min	£max
Single	40.00	45.00
Double	58.00	66.00

Half board

per person:	£min	£max
Daily	48.00	59.80

Lunch available
Evening meal 1900 (last orders 2200)
Parking for 30
Cards accepted: Access, Visa
🛇📞🖵♿🅟🄿Ⓢ🗡🎇🛆 ⬛🚻☆🎇🐾🆂🄿🏠

SHIRWELL

Devon
Map ref 1C1

The Spinney

♕♕ COMMENDED

Shirwell, Barnstaple
EX31 4JR
☎ Newton Tracey (0271) 850282

Regency former rectory with spacious accommodation, set in over an acre of grounds with views of Exmoor. Meals made from local market-day produce.

Bedrooms: 1 single, 1 double, 1 twin, 2 triple
Bathrooms: 1 private, 2 public

Bed & breakfast

per night:	£min	£max
Single	15.00	20.00
Double	30.00	40.00

Half board

per person:	£min	£max
Daily	21.50	26.50
Weekly	129.00	159.00

Evening meal 1900 (last orders 1730)
Parking for 7
🛇🖵♿🅟Ⓢ🗡🎇📺🄿🛆☆🏠 🆂🄿🏠

SHREWTON

Wiltshire
Map ref 2B2

The Laurels

Salisbury Road, Shrewton,
Salisbury SP3 4EQ
☎ (0980) 620444

A small country living set in attractive village, close to traditional pub, 2 miles from Stonehenge. 18th C house with exposed beams and furnished in character.

Bedrooms: 1 double, 1 twin
Bathrooms: 1 public

Bed & breakfast

per night:	£min	£max
Double	30.00	35.00

Parking for 5
🛇7🖵♿🅟Ⓢ🗡🎇📺🄿☆✕ 🎇🏠

Maddington House

Listed APPROVED

Shrewton, Salisbury SP3 4JD
☎ Amesbury (0980) 620406

Beautiful listed 17th C family home, with attractive period hall and dining room. Stonehenge 2 miles and Salisbury 9 miles.

Bedrooms: 1 double, 1 twin, 1 multiple
Bathrooms: 2 private, 1 public

Bed & breakfast

per night:	£min	£max
Single	17.00	19.50
Double	32.00	34.00

Parking for 6
🛇🖵♿🅄Ⓢ🗡🎇🛆☆ 🎇🏠

SIDMOUTH

Devon
Map ref 1D2

Charming resort set amid lofty red cliffs where the River Sid meets the sea. The wealth of ornate Regency and Victorian villas recalls the time when this was one of the south coast's most exclusive resorts. Museum; August International Festival of Folk Arts.
Tourist Information Centre ☎ (0395) 516441.

Ferndale

♕♕ COMMENDED

92 Winslade Road, Sidmouth
EX10 9EZ
☎ (0395) 515495

Quiet, comfortable, well-modernised Victorian property offering spacious, well-equipped accommodation. Within easy reach of seafront and town centre.

Bedrooms: 1 double, 2 twin
Bathrooms: 2 public

Bed & breakfast

per night:	£min	£max
Single	16.00	19.00
Double	26.00	30.00

Open March-October
🛇9🖵♿🅄🎇📺🄿🛆 ✕🎇

Lower Pinn Farm

♕♕

Pinn, Sidmouth EX10 0NN
☎ (0395) 513733

220-acre mixed farm. In unrivalled east Devon countryside, 2 miles west of Sidmouth. Comfortable, spacious rooms and a relaxed, friendly atmosphere.

Bedrooms: 2 double, 1 twin

Bathrooms: 2 private, 1 public

Bed & breakfast

per night:	£min	£max
Double	32.00	36.00

Parking for 3
Open April-November
🛇🖵🅟♿🄿🎇🛆🚻♿

Pinn Barton Farm

♕♕ COMMENDED

Peak Hill, Pinn Lane,
Sidmouth EX10 0NN
☎ (0395) 514004

330-acre mixed farm. 2 miles from seafront in an area of outstanding natural beauty. A friendly welcome in comfortable surroundings awaits guests. Closed at Christmas.

Bedrooms: 1 double, 1 twin, 1 triple
Bathrooms: 3 private

Bed & breakfast

per night:	£min	£max
Double	34.00	

Parking for 4
🛇📞🖵♿🙏🅄🎇📺🄿🛆 🚻🎵▸☆🎇

Sidling Field

105 Peaslands Road,
Sidmouth EX10 8XE
☎ (0395) 513859

Large bungalow surrounded by garden, backing on to a small paddock. On the outskirts of town, 12 minutes' walk from the seafront.

Bedrooms: 1 double, 1 twin
Bathrooms: 1 public

Bed & breakfast

per night:	£min	£max
Single	15.00	17.00
Double	25.00	27.00

Parking for 4
Open January-November
🛇6🖵♿🅄🎇📺🄿🛆🎇

SIMONSBATH

Somerset
Map ref 1C1

Village beside the beautiful River Barle, deep in Exmoor. From the Middle Ages until the 19th C this was stag-hunting country.

Emmetts Grange Farm Guest House ⚘

♕♕♕ COMMENDED

Simonsbath, Minehead
TA24 7LD
☎ Exford (064 383) 282

1200-acre livestock farm. Attractive country house in a lovely, quiet position 2.5 miles out of Simonsbath on the South Molton road.

Specialises in country cooking.

Bedrooms: 1 single, 1 double, 2 twin
Bathrooms: 2 private, 1 public

Bed & breakfast

per night:	£min	£max
Single	20.00	23.00
Double	40.00	46.00

Half board

per person:	£min	£max
Daily	33.00	36.00
Weekly	200.00	220.00

Evening meal 2000 (last orders 1800)
Parking for 6
Open March-October
🛇🖵♿🙏Ⓢ🎇🄿🛆☆ 🎇🏠

SLAPTON

Devon
Map ref 1D3

Old Walls

Slapton, Kingsbridge
TQ7 2QN
☎ Kingsbridge (0548) 580516

Charming, south-facing 18th C house in elevated position, with beamed bedrooms and sunny conservatory. In centre of village, near sea and Slapton Ley nature reserve.

Bedrooms: 3 twin, 2 triple
Bathrooms: 2 public

Bed & breakfast

per night:	£min	£max
Single	13.50	
Double	27.00	

Half board

per person:	£min	£max
Daily	20.50	

Evening meal from 1850
🛇♿🅄Ⓢ🗡🎇🄿🛆🎇

Start House

♕♕ COMMENDED

Start, Slapton, Kingsbridge
TQ7 2QD
☎ Kingsbridge (0548) 580254

Situated in quiet hamlet, 1 mile from Slapton. Comfortable house overlooking beautiful valley. Large garden. Ideal for wildlife and walking.

Bedrooms: 1 single, 2 double, 1 twin
Bathrooms: 2 private, 1 public

Bed & breakfast

per night:	£min	£max
Single	16.00	
Double	32.00	35.00

Continued ▶

SLAPTON

Continued

Half board

per person:	£min	£max
Daily	26.00	27.50
Weekly	166.00	176.00

Evening meal 1830 (last orders 1000)
Parking for 4
Open January–November

🛇🐕🛏️UL🔒⑤✂️🅿️📺🛏️,🛇✿ 🦽SP🏧

SOMERTON

Somerset
Map ref 2A3

Old market town, important in Saxon times, situated at a gap in the hills south-east of Sedgemoor. Attractive red-roofed stone houses surround the 17th C octagonal market cross and among other handsome buildings are the Town Hall and almshouses of about the same period.

The Lynch Hotel

👑👑 COMMENDED

4 Behind Berry, Somerton
TA11 7PD
☎ (0458) 72316
Comfortable late Georgian house, Grade II listed. Tastefully restored and furnished with antiques. Spacious bedrooms, beautiful grounds, wildlife lake.
Bedrooms: 3 double, 2 twin
Bathrooms: 5 private
Bed & breakfast

per night:	£min	£max
Single	35.00	50.00
Double	45.00	75.00

Parking for 15
Cards accepted: Access, Visa

🛇🏠📞🖂🖵↓🅿🛇🍴,∪ 🦽🏧

The Unicorn at Somerton ♨

West Street, Somerton
TA11 7PR
☎ (0458) 72101
Traditional inn. Home-cooked food and at least 6 real ales, genuine atmosphere, large gardens. Owners' personal attention.
Bedrooms: 1 single, 3 double, 3 twin
Bathrooms: 6 private, 2 public

Bed & breakfast

per night:	£min	£max
Single	25.00	35.00
Double	36.00	45.00

Half board

per person:	£min	£max
Daily	30.00	40.00
Weekly	190.00	250.00

Lunch available
Evening meal 1900 (last orders 2200)
Parking for 45
Cards accepted: Access, Visa, Diners, Amex

🛇🏠📞🖂🖵↓♨⑤🍴,🛇🛇∪ ✿🦽🌳SP🏧

SOUTH MOLTON

Devon
Map ref 1C1

Busy market town at the mouth of the Yeo Valley near southern Exmoor. Wool, mining and coaching brought prosperity between the Middle Ages and the 19th C and the fine square with Georgian buildings, a Guildhall and Assembly Rooms reflects this former affluence.

Kerscott Farm

👑👑

Bishop's Nympton, South Molton EX36 4QG
☎ Bishop's Nympton (0769) 550262
Peaceful old world farmhouse, mentioned in Domesday Book. Beams, inglenook fireplaces, interesting antiques, pretty bedrooms. Country cooking. Wonderful views of Exmoor and surrounding countryside. Non-smokers only please.
Bedrooms: 2 double, 1 twin
Bathrooms: 1 public

Bed & breakfast

per night:	£min	£max
Double	25.00	28.00

Half board

per person:	£min	£max
Daily	18.50	21.50

Evening meal 1830 (last orders 1400)
Parking for 8
Open March–October

🛇8UL⑤✂️📺🍴,🛇✿✕ 🦽🏧

Stowford Cottage

👑👑 HIGHLY COMMENDED

Stowford, Chittlehampton, Umberleigh EX37 9RX
☎ Chittlehampton (0769) 540536
16th C listed thatched Devon longhouse with leaded light

windows, in over an acre of landscaped gardens in rural setting, west of South Molton.
Bedrooms: 1 double, 2 twin
Bathrooms: 2 private, 2 public

Bed & breakfast

per night:	£min	£max
Single	27.00	27.00
Double	44.00	44.00

Half board

per person:	£min	£max
Daily	34.00	34.00

Evening meal from 1900
Parking for 5

🛇10↓UL🔒⑤🅿📺🍴,🛇 🛇∪✿🦽🌳SP🏧

White House

👑👑 APPROVED

Bottreaux Mill, South Molton EX36 3PT
☎ Anstey Mills (039 84) 331
Detached house on B3227, 7 miles east of South Molton, with panoramic views over Exmoor. Warm welcome and personal attention. Comfortable accommodation, log fires, garden produce used.
Bedrooms: 2 double, 1 twin
Bathrooms: 3 private, 1 public

Bed & breakfast

per night:	£min	£max
Single	13.00	16.00
Double	26.00	32.00

Half board

per person:	£min	£max
Daily	18.00	22.00
Weekly	105.00	135.00

Evening meal 1900 (last orders 2000)
Parking for 3
Open April–October

🛇↓UL⑤🅿📺✿🦽OAP SP

SOUTH NEWTON

Wiltshire
Map ref 2B2

Newton Cottage

South Newton, Salisbury
SP2 0QW
☎ Salisbury (0722) 743111
Typically English thatched cottage built in 1679. Offering hospitality, personal attention and a warm comfortable atmosphere. Chalk stream fly fishing tuition by prior arrangement.
Bedrooms: 2 double, 1 twin
Bathrooms: 2 public

Bed & breakfast

per night:	£min	£max
Double	28.00	30.00

Parking for 4

🛇5↓🍴UL⑤📺🍴,🛇 ✿✕🦽🏧

ST AGNES

Cornwall
Map ref 1B3

Small town in a once-rich mining area on the north coast. Terraced cottages and granite houses slope to the church. Some old mine workings remain, but the attraction must be the magnificent coastal scenery and superb walks. St Agnes Beacon offers one of Cornwall's most extensive views.

Penkerris ♨

🛇

Penwinnick Road, St Agnes TR5 0PA
☎ (0872) 552262
Enchanting Edwardian residence in own grounds, just inside St. Agnes on B3277 road. Large lawn for relaxation. Walking distance from magnificent cliffs and beach.
Bedrooms: 1 single, 2 double, 2 twin, 2 triple
Bathrooms: 2 private, 3 public

Bed & breakfast

per night:	£min	£max
Single	12.50	20.00
Double	25.00	30.00

Half board

per person:	£min	£max
Daily	20.00	22.50
Weekly	115.00	140.00

Lunch available
Evening meal 1830 (last orders 1000)
Parking for 8
Cards accepted: Access, Visa

🛇🖂🖵↓🔒⑤📺🛇✿ 🦽SP🏧

ST AUSTELL

Cornwall
Map ref 1B3

Cornwall's china-clay town, on a slope between the clay district's spoil-cones and the clay ports and bathing beaches on St Austell Bay. The traffic-free centre has a fine church of Pentewan stone and an Italianate Town and Market Hall, still a busy market-place.

Poltarrow Farm

👑👑 COMMENDED

St Mewan, St Austell
PL26 7DR
☎ (0726) 67111
45-acre mixed farm. Charming farmhouse set in

peaceful countryside, well placed for discovering all that Cornwall offers. Half-a-mile St Austell - Truro A390, turn right at St Mewan school. Entrance on left.
Bedrooms: 2 double, 1 twin
Bathrooms: 3 private,
1 public
Bed & breakfast

per night:	£min	£max
Single	16.00	

Half board

per person:	£min	£max
Daily	24.00	

Evening meal from 1830
Parking for 5
Cards accepted: Access, Visa

Rescorla Farm

Rescorla, St Austell
PL26 8YT
☎ (0726) 850168
210-acre mixed & dairy farm. Good home cooking. Two guest bathrooms. Panoramic views from the bedrooms. Homely atmosphere is guaranteed.
Bedrooms: 1 double, 2 twin
Bathrooms: 2 public
Bed & breakfast

per night:	£min	£max
Double	25.00	25.00

Half board

per person:	£min	£max
Daily	21.00	21.00

Evening meal 1900 (last orders 2030)
Parking for 4
Open April-October
Cards accepted: Access, Visa

ST DOMINICK

Cornwall
Map ref 1C2

Burcombe Farm

APPROVED

St Dominick, Saltash
PL12 6SH
☎ Liskeard (0579) 50217
Farm dates back to 1722.
Bedrooms: 1 double, 2 twin
Bathrooms: 2 private,
1 public
Bed & breakfast

per night:	£min	£max
Single	17.50	
Double	35.00	

Parking for 5
Open April-October

ST ERME

Cornwall
Map ref 1B3

Pengelly Farm

St Erme, Truro TR4 9BG
☎ Mitchell (0872) 510245
230-acre mixed farm. Well-built farmhouse in quiet surroundings and central for touring. 10 minutes' drive from Truro. Self-catering mobile home also available.
Bedrooms: 1 single,
1 double, 2 triple
Bathrooms: 1 private,
1 public
Bed & breakfast

per night:	£min	£max
Single	11.00	13.00
Double	30.00	32.00

Parking for 6
Open April-October

ST IVES

Cornwall
Map ref 1B3

Old fishing port, artists' colony and holiday town with good surfing beach. Fishermen's cottages, granite fish cellars, a sandy harbour and magnificent headlands typify a charm that has survived since the 19th C pilchard boom.
Tourist Information Centre
☎ *(0736) 796297*

The Grey Mullet

2 Bunkers Hill, Down-a-Long, St Ives TR26 1LJ
☎ Penzance (0736) 796635
18th C listed house in the fishermen's quarter of St Ives. 20 yards from harbour, beaches, shops and car park.
Bedrooms: 1 single,
5 double, 1 twin
Bathrooms: 3 private,
2 public
Bed & breakfast

per night:	£min	£max
Single	15.00	17.00
Double	30.00	38.00

Hobblers Restaurant & Guest House 🏍

Wharf Road, St Ives
TR26 1LG
☎ Penzance (0736) 796439
17th C pilot's house situated directly on harbour front. Three guest bedrooms over licensed old world fresh fish restaurant.

Bedrooms: 1 single,
1 double, 1 twin
Bathrooms: 1 public
Bed & breakfast

per night:	£min	£max
Single	20.00	20.00
Double	30.00	34.00

Evening meal 1800 (last orders 2200)
Open April-October
Cards accepted: Access, Visa, Diners, Amex

Seagulls Guest House

4 Godrevy Terrace, St Ives
TR26 1JA
☎ Penzance (0736) 797273
Panoramic sea views overlooking island and beaches. Superior rooms with private facilities. Reputation for comfort and hospitality. Free private parking.
Bedrooms: 1 single,
3 double, 1 twin, 1 triple,
1 multiple
Bathrooms: 2 private,
1 public, 4 private showers
Bed & breakfast

per night:	£min	£max
Single	12.00	18.00
Double	24.00	36.00

Parking for 10

ST JUST IN ROSELAND

Cornwall
Map ref 1B3

Parish overlooking Carrick Roads on the Roseland Peninsula. The riverside church of St Just has a beautiful setting under a steep slope of tall trees and sub-tropical shrubs.

Commerrans Farm

St Just in Roseland, Truro
TR2 5JJ
☎ Portscatho (0872) 580270
90-acre livestock farm. Close to the River Fal, offering a relaxed atmosphere and home cooking. About 4 miles from beaches. Good area for sailing, bird-watching and walking. Easy reach of tourist attractions.
Bedrooms: 2 double, 1 twin
Bathrooms: 1 public
Bed & breakfast

per night:	£min	£max
Single	12.00	13.50
Double	24.00	27.00

Half board

per person:	£min	£max
Daily	18.00	19.00

Evening meal 1845 (last orders 1500)
Parking for 6
Open April-October

ST KEW

Cornwall
Map ref 1B2

Old village sheltered by trees standing beside a stream. The church is noted for its medieval glass showing the Passion and the remains of a scene of the Tree of Jesse.

Tregellist Farm

COMMENDED

Tregellist, St Kew, Bodmin
PL30 3HG
☎ Bodmin (0208) 880537
125-acre mixed farm. Farmhouse, built in 1989, offering old-fashioned hospitality. Set in tiny hamlet with lovely views and pleasant walks. Central for coast and moors. Children welcome. 1.5 miles from A39.
Bedrooms: 1 double, 1 twin,
1 triple
Bathrooms: 3 private,
1 public
Bed & breakfast

per night:	£min	£max
Single	16.00	20.00
Double	32.00	40.00

Half board

per person:	£min	£max
Daily	24.00	28.00

Evening meal from 1800
Parking for 6
Open February-October

ST MARY'S

Isles of Scilly
Map ref 1A3

Veronica Lodge

COMMENDED

The Garrison, St Mary's, Isles of Scilly TR21 0LS
☎ Scillonia (0720) 22585
Views over town and harbour. Has sheltered gardens and only two minutes' walk from quay. Evening meal available early/late season.
Bedrooms: 2 double, 1 twin
Bathrooms: 1 public

Continued ▶

Please mention this guide when making a booking.

ST MARY'S

Continued

Bed & breakfast

per night:	£min	£max
Double	31.00	35.00

Parking for 1
Open January-November

⚭ 🛏 🎮 🎲 ♨ 🅿 ✕ 🐾

ST MAWGAN

Cornwall
Map ref 1B2

Pretty village on wooded slopes in the Vale of Lanherne. At its centre, an old stone bridge is overlooked by the church with its lofty buttressed tower. Among the ancient stone crosses in the churchyard is a 15th C lantern cross with carved figures.

The Falcon Inn

🏅🏅🏅 COMMENDED

St Mawgan, Newquay
TR8 4EP
☎ Newquay (0637) 860225
16th C wisteria-covered inn with beautiful gardens in the vale of Lanherne. Unspoilt peaceful situation.
Bedrooms: 2 double, 1 twin
Bathrooms: 1 public

Bed & breakfast

per night:	£min	£max
Single	18.00	18.00
Double	36.00	46.00

Lunch available
Evening meal 1830 (last orders 2200)
Parking for 25
Cards accepted: Access, Visa

⛁ ♨ 🅟 🔔 🎮 🎲 ➡ ❄ 🐾

STATHE

Somerset
Map ref 1D1

Black Smock Inn

Langport Road, Stathe,
Bridgwater TA7 0JN
☎ Burrowbridge (0823) 698352
Traditional moorland inn 3 miles west of Langport. High standard accommodation. Panoramic views over Somerset levels. Fishing, hiking, bird watching.
Bedrooms: 4 twin
Bathrooms: 2 private, 1 public

Bed & breakfast

per night:	£min	£max
Double	13.50	15.50

Lunch available
Evening meal 1900 (last orders 2200)
Parking for 40

⚭ 🍴 🖵 🍽 ♨ Ⓢ 🎲 ❄ ✕ 🐾 SP

STOKE ST GREGORY

Somerset
Map ref 1D1

Parsonage Farm

Listed | APPROVED

Stoke St Gregory, Taunton
TA3 6ET
☎ Burrowbridge (0823) 698205
120-acre dairy farm. Large Georgian farmhouse and garden on ridge overlooking the Somerset Levels. Lovely views, good base for touring. Well-stocked coarse fishing half a mile away.
Bedrooms: 2 twin, 1 triple
Bathrooms: 1 public

Bed & breakfast

per night:	£min	£max
Single	15.00	16.00
Double	30.00	32.00

Parking for 8

⚭ 🚲 🖵 ♨ Ⓢ 🎲 🎮 🎲 Ⓤ 🌿 ❄ 🐾

SUTTON MONTIS

Somerset
Map ref 2A3

Parsonage Farm

Listed

Sutton Montis, Yeovil
BA22 7HE
☎ Corton Denham (0963) 220256
120-acre livestock farm. 17th C farmhouse below King Arthur's Cadbury Castle. Unspoilt area and ideal centre for a wide variety of interests. Good local eating places. Babies and toddlers welcome.
Bedrooms: 1 double, 2 twin
Bathrooms: 2 public

Bed & breakfast

per night:	£min	£max
Single	12.00	16.00
Double	24.00	28.00

Parking for 4
Open April-October

♨ 🆄 Ⓢ ✂ 🎲 🎮 ➡ ❄ 🐾 🏫

SUTTON POYNTZ

Dorset
Map ref 2B3

Selwyns

Listed

Puddledock Lane, Sutton Poyntz, Weymouth DT3 6LZ
☎ Preston (0305) 832239
A chalet bungalow in pretty village, 1 mile inland, near Weymouth and White Horse, Osmington. A353 to Preston, turn into Seven Acres road, turn right at top of hill into Puddledock Lane.
Bedrooms: 1 double, 1 twin
Bathrooms: 1 public

Bed & breakfast

per night:	£min	£max
Single	15.00	16.00
Double	25.00	27.00

Evening meal 1800 (last orders 2000)
Parking for 4
Open February-November

⚭ 10 🍳 🖵 ♨ 🆄 Ⓢ 🎲 ➡ Ⓤ ✕ 🐾 OAP SP

Sutton Mill

🏅 COMMENDED

Sutton Poyntz, Preston, Weymouth DT3 6LW
☎ Preston (0305) 835070
Fax (0305) 835062
Sympathetically restored water mill, nestling at the base of south Dorset downs with wonderful views. Water wheel runs as and when water available. Pretty village with mill pond. Special breaks available, please enquire.
Bedrooms: 2 single, 2 double
Bathrooms: 2 public

Bed & breakfast

per night:	£min	£max
Single	18.50	20.00
Double	37.00	40.00

Parking for 3
Cards accepted: Access

⚭ ⛁ ♨ 🆄 Ⓢ ✂ 🎲 🎮 ◐ 🎲 ➡ Ⓤ 🅟 ❄ ✕ 🐾 OAP SP 🏫 Ⓣ

SWINDON

Wiltshire
Map ref 2B2

Swindon's industrial and commercial centre, an important railway town in the 19th C, situated just north of the Marlborough Downs. The railway village created in the mid-19th C has been preserved. Railway museum, art gallery, theatre and leisure centre. *Tourist Information Centre* ☎ *(0793) 530328*

Fairview Guest House

52 Swindon Road, Wootton Bassett, Swindon SN4 8EU
☎ (0793) 852283
Detached guesthouse, west of Swindon, close to the M4 junction 16 (1.25 miles). Ground floor rooms available.
Bedrooms: 3 single, 3 double, 4 twin, 2 triple

Bathrooms: 2 private, 4 public, 3 private showers

Bed & breakfast

per night:	£min	£max
Single	17.00	32.00
Double	33.00	43.00

Half board

per person:	£min	£max
Daily	23.00	38.00

Evening meal 1830 (last orders 1430)
Parking for 17

⚭ 🚲 🚗 🖵 ♨ 🔔 🅟 Ⓢ 🎲 🎮 🎲 ➡ ❄ OAP 🐾 SP

Internos

🏅🏅

3 Turnpike Road, Blunsdon, Swindon SN2 4EA
☎ (0793) 721496
Detached red brick house off A419, 4 miles north of Swindon and 6 miles from M4 junction 15.
Bedrooms: 1 single, 1 twin, 1 triple
Bathrooms: 2 public

Bed & breakfast

per night:	£min	£max
Single	18.00	20.00
Double	30.00	30.00

Parking for 6

⚭ ♨ 🔔 🆁 ♨ Ⓢ 🎲 🎮 🎲 ➡ ✕ 🐾

The Live and Let Live

🏅🏅 COMMENDED

Upper Pavenhill, Purton, Swindon SN5 9DQ
☎ (0793) 770627
Converted stable, 5 miles west of Swindon, north of M4 (junction 16) and Wootton Bassett. At Londis shop turn into Pavenhill. Proceed for half a mile to only right turning - Upper Pavenhill. House is 200 yards on left. Non-smokers preferred.
Bedrooms: 1 twin, 1 triple
Bathrooms: 2 private, 1 public

Bed & breakfast

per night:	£min	£max
Single	18.00	18.00
Double	35.00	35.00

Parking for 3

⚭ 🍳 ♨ 🆄 🔔 Ⓢ ✂ 🎲 🎮 🎲 ➡ ❄ 🐾 SP 🏫

Okus House

105 Bath Road, Swindon
SN1 4AX
☎ (0793) 615086
Fax (0793) 430666
Large Victorian house built in 1878, now restored with all bedrooms en-suite. Situated in Old Town, a few minutes' walk from shops and restaurants.

Bedrooms: 4 single, 1 double, 3 twin, 1 triple
Bathrooms: 9 private

Bed & breakfast per night:	£min	£max
Single		33.00
Double		47.00

Parking for 10
Cards accepted: Access, Visa

Relian Guest House

151-153 County Road, Swindon SN1 2EB
☎ (0793) 521416
Quiet house adjacent to Swindon Town Football Club and near town centre. Close to bus and rail stations. Free car parking.
Bedrooms: 4 single, 2 double, 2 twin
Bathrooms: 2 public

Bed & breakfast per night:	£min	£max
Single	20.00	

Parking for 7

SYDLING ST NICHOLAS

Dorset
Map ref 2B3

Magiston Farm

Sydling St Nicholas
DT2 9NR
☎ Maiden Newton (0300) 20295
400-acre arable farm. 350-year-old farmhouse, set beside the Sydling River in the heart of Dorset's peaceful countryside. 5 miles north of Dorchester.
Bedrooms: 2 single, 1 double, 2 twin
Bathrooms: 1 private, 1 public

Bed & breakfast per night:	£min	£max
Single	15.50	
Double	31.00	

Half board per person:	£min	£max
Daily	25.00	

Evening meal from 1900
Parking for 10

The enquiry coupons at the back will help you when contacting proprietors.

TAUNTON

Somerset
Map ref 1D1

County town, well-known for its public schools, sheltered by gentle hill-ranges on the River Tone. Medieval prosperity from wool has continued in marketing and manufacturing and the town retains many fine period buildings.
Tourist Information Centre ☎ (0823) 274785

Higher Dipford Farm

COMMENDED
Dipford, Trull, Taunton TA3 7NU
☎ (0823) 275770
120-acre dairy farm. Old Somerset longhouse with inglenook fireplaces. Real farmhouse fare using own produce from the dairy. Fresh salmon a speciality. Friendly atmosphere.
Bedrooms: 1 double, 2 twin
Bathrooms: 3 private

Bed & breakfast per night:	£min	£max
Single	27.00	30.00
Double	50.00	54.00

Half board per person:	£min	£max
Daily	42.00	50.00
Weekly	259.00	266.00

Evening meal 1900 (last orders 2130)
Parking for 6
Open April-December
Cards accepted: Amex

North Down Farm

COMMENDED
Wiveliscombe, Taunton TA4 2BL
☎ Wiveliscombe (0984) 23730
102-acre dairy & livestock farm. Family farm on the edge of Exmoor, 10 miles from Taunton, 1.5 miles Wiveliscombe. Magnificent views of Quantocks and Vale of Taunton. Good food, home cooking.
Bedrooms: 1 double, 1 triple
Bathrooms: 1 public

Bed & breakfast per night:	£min	£max
Single	13.50	15.00
Double	27.00	30.00

Half board per person:	£min	£max
Daily	22.00	23.50
Weekly	140.00	150.00

Evening meal 1830 (last orders 1200)
Parking for 6

Prockters Farm

West Monkton, Taunton TA2 8QN
☎ West Monkton (0823) 412269
300-acre mixed farm. 300-year-old farmhouse, with beams, inglenook fireplaces, brass beds, collection of farm antiques. Large garden. Tea and cake on arrival.
Bedrooms: 3 double, 2 twin, 1 triple
Bathrooms: 2 private, 3 public

Bed & breakfast per night:	£min	£max
Single	15.00	19.00
Double	30.00	38.00

Parking for 6
Cards accepted: Amex

Rectory Cottage

Combe Florey, Taunton TA4 3JD
☎ Bishops Lydeard (0823) 432349
Character cottage, 6 miles north west of Taunton, within easy reach of Quantock Hills and Exmoor. Comfortable accommodation and home cooking.
Bedrooms: 1 single, 1 twin, 1 triple
Bathrooms: 1 public

Bed & breakfast per night:	£min	£max
Single	15.00	17.50
Double	30.00	35.00

Half board per person:	£min	£max
Daily	25.00	27.50

Parking for 2

Volis Farm

Hestercombe, Taunton TA2 8HS
☎ Kingston St Mary (0823) 451545
300-acre mixed & dairy farm. Adjacent to Hestercombe Gardens, 400 ft up on the edge of the Quantock Hills. Tranquillity, magnificent views and a warm welcome. 4 miles from the M5.
Bedrooms: 1 double, 2 twin
Bathrooms: 1 public

Bed & breakfast per night:	£min	£max
Single	16.00	20.00
Double	32.00	40.00

Parking for 10
Open March-October

TAVISTOCK

Devon
Map ref 1C2

Old market town beside the River Tavy on the western edge of Dartmoor. Developed around its 10th C abbey, of which some fragments remain, it became a stannary town in 1305 when tin-streaming thrived on the moors. Tavistock Goose Fair, October.

Colcharton

Gulworthy, Tavistock PL19 8HU
☎ (0822) 613047
Charming 16th C farmhouse near moors and within easy reach of many places of interest. Quiet position off main Tavistock/Liskeard road.
Bedrooms: 1 double, 1 twin, 1 triple
Bathrooms: 2 public

Bed & breakfast per night:	£min	£max
Single	18.00	
Double	30.00	

Parking for 6

Mallards Guesthouse

48 Plymouth Road, Tavistock PL19 8BU
☎ (0822) 615171
Tastefully restored Victorian guesthouse. Centre of Tavistock overlooking the park. Quiet, family-run and with home cooking. Close to beautiful Dartmoor.
Bedrooms: 4 double
Bathrooms: 2 private, 2 public

Bed & breakfast per night:	£min	£max
Double	30.00	34.00

Half board per person:	£min	£max
Daily	23.00	25.00
Weekly	147.00	161.00

Evening meal 1830 (last orders 1530)
Parking for 6

TAVISTOCK

Continued

Rubbytown Farm

😊😊 HIGHLY COMMENDED

Gulworthy, Tavistock
PL19 8PA
☎ (0822) 832493
250-acre dairy farm. Well-appointed character farmhouse, overlooking Tamar Valley, with woodland walks and places of interest nearby. Guests assured every comfort. All rooms en-suite with four-poster beds.
Bedrooms: 2 double, 1 twin
Bathrooms: 3 private

Bed & breakfast per night:	£min	£max
Single	17.00	17.00
Double	34.00	34.00

Half board per person:	£min	£max
Daily	27.00	27.00
Weekly	189.00	189.00

Evening meal from 1830
Parking for 6
➰🍴📺♨⬛🛇🔌✗🌙📺🕭🗕🗕
🍴⛲♿Ỻ✗✗🍴🍴 OAP SP 🕮

Wringworthy Farm

Listed

Mary Tavy, Tavistock
PL19 9LT
☎ Mary Tavy (0822) 810434
120-acre livestock farm. Elizabethan farmhouse with modern comforts, in quiet valley near the moors. Within easy reach of sea and well placed for touring.
Bedrooms: 1 double, 1 twin, 1 triple
Bathrooms: 2 public

Bed & breakfast per night:	£min	£max
Single	14.00	16.00
Double	28.00	30.00

Parking for 3
Open April-October
➰🔌♨Ỻ⬛🛇✗🔌📺🕭🗕
🌙🍴🕮

Individual proprietors have supplied all details of accommodation. Although we do check for accuracy, we advise you to confirm the information at the time of booking.

THROWLEIGH

Devon
Map ref 1C2

Charming village below Cawsand Beacon in the Dartmoor National Park, with the Throwleigh stone circle consisting of 6 standing and 36 fallen stones.

Well Farm

😊😊 APPROVED

Throwleigh, Okehampton
EX20 2JQ
☎ Whiddon Down (064 723) 294
260-acre dairy & livestock farm. Guests live as part of the family on this working farm. Walking, riding, fishing and golf in the district.
Bedrooms: 1 double, 1 twin, 2 triple
Bathrooms: 3 private, 1 public

Bed & breakfast per night:	£min	£max
Single	15.00	
Double	30.00	

Half board per person:	£min	£max
Daily	25.00	
Weekly	140.00	

Evening meal 2000 (last orders 1800)
Parking for 6
➰🍴♨Ỻ⬛🛇✗🔌📺🕭🗕
🌙🍴🕮

TINTAGEL

Cornwall
Map ref 1B2

Coastal village near the legendary home of King Arthur. A lofty headland with the ruin of a Norman castle and traces of a Celtic monastery still visible in the turf.

Castle Villa

😊😊 COMMENDED

Molesworth Street, Tintagel
PL34 0BZ
☎ Camelford (0840) 770373 & 770203
Over 150 years old, Castle Villa is within easy walking distance of the 11th C church, post office and King Arthur's castle.
Bedrooms: 1 single, 2 double, 1 twin, 1 multiple
Bathrooms: 1 private, 2 public

Bed & breakfast per night:	£min	£max
Single	12.50	14.50
Double	25.00	34.00

Half board per person:	£min	£max
Daily	22.50	25.50
Weekly	141.75	160.65

Evening meal 1900 (last orders 1000)
Parking for 6
Cards accepted: Access, Visa
➰🔌🍴♨⬛🛇✗🔌📺🕭🗕
🗕🍴 OAP 🛇 SP

St Adwen

St. Nectan's Glen, Trethevy,
Tintagel PL34 0BE
☎ Camelford (0840) 770450
Nestling in 1 acre of gardens at the entrance to glen and waterfall. Between Tintagel and Boscastle on the B3263 at Trethevy.
Bedrooms: 1 single, 1 double, 1 twin, 1 triple
Bathrooms: 1 public

Bed & breakfast per night:	£min	£max
Single	12.50	
Double	25.00	

Parking for 4
Open April-September
➰🍴♨Ỻ⬛🛇✗🔌📺🗕🗕
🌙🍴

Tintagel Arms Hotel & Zorba's Tavern

😊😊 COMMENDED

Fore Street, Tintagel
PL34 0DB
☎ Camelford (0840) 770780
Main street position close to Old Post Office and King Arthur's Castle.
Bedrooms: 7 double, 1 twin
Bathrooms: 8 private

Bed & breakfast per night:	£min	£max
Single	20.00	25.00
Double	35.00	45.00

Lunch available
Evening meal 1800 (last orders 2200)
Parking for 10
Cards accepted: Access, Visa
🔌🍴🔌♨⬛🛇✗🗕🗕
🍴🍴 OAP SP

National Crown ratings were correct at the time of going to press but are subject to change. Please check at the time of booking.

TIVERTON

Devon
Map ref 1D2

Busy market and textile town, settled since the 9th C, at the meeting of 2 rivers. Town houses, Tudor almshouses and parts of the fine church were built by wealthy cloth merchants; a medieval castle is incorporated into a private house; and Blundells School.
Tourist Information Centre
☎ *(0884) 255827*

Great Bradley Farm

😊😊 COMMENDED

Withleigh, Tiverton
EX16 8JL
☎ (0884) 256946
155-acre dairy farm. Enjoy peaceful, beautiful countryside, 20 minutes from M5. Lovely, historic farmhouse offering comfortable, attractive bedrooms. Light suppers available. Non-smokers only please.
Bedrooms: 1 double, 1 twin
Bathrooms: 2 private

Bed & breakfast per night:	£min	£max
Double	33.00	35.00

Parking for 2
Open March-November
➰8♨Ỻ⬛🛇✗🔌📺🕭🗕🌙
🍴🕮

Lower Collipriest Farm

😊😊😊 HIGHLY COMMENDED

Tiverton EX16 4PT
☎ (0884) 252321
221-acre dairy & livestock farm. Lovely thatched farmhouse in beautiful Exe Valley. Of particular interest to naturalists. Traditional and speciality cooking. Coasts and moors within easy reach. Brochure available.
Bedrooms: 2 single, 2 twin
Bathrooms: 4 private

Bed & breakfast per night:	£min	£max
Single	16.50	18.00
Double	36.00	38.00

Half board per person:	£min	£max
Daily	26.00	27.50
Weekly	178.50	182.50

Evening meal 1900 (last orders 1200)
Parking for 4
Open April-October
♨🔌Ỻ⬛🛇✗📺🕭🗕🛇♨
🍴🍴🌙🍴🕮

Prince Regent Hotel

APPROVED

Lowman Green, Tiverton
EX16 4LA
☎ (0884) 252882
Situated in the town close to all amenities and River Lowman. Open all day. Extensive menu. Car park.
Bedrooms: 2 double, 2 twin, 1 triple, 1 multiple
Bathrooms: 2 public

Bed & breakfast

per night:	£min	£max
Single	15.00	18.00
Double	30.00	36.00

Lunch available
Evening meal 1700 (last orders 2100)
Parking for 23
🏧🛏♨🔥📺, 🔌 🚲

Quoit-at-Cross Farm

😊😊😊

Stoodleigh, Tiverton
EX16 9PJ
☎ Oakford (039 85) 280
280-acre mixed farm. 17th C farmhouse, relaxing family home in village. En-suite rooms, colour TV and tea-making. Inglenook dining room, guests' lounge. 10 minutes A361.
Bedrooms: 1 double, 1 multiple
Bathrooms: 2 private

Bed & breakfast

per night:	£min	£max
Double	30.00	

Half board

per person:	£min	£max
Daily	23.00	

Lunch available
Evening meal 1830 (last orders 0900)
Parking for 2
Open April-December
🏧🛏♨🖥📺🍴☕📺🛏, 🔌🔔
🚻✕ 🚲 📶

TORQUAY

Devon
Map ref 1D2

Devon's grandest resort, developed from a fishing village. Smart apartments and terraces rise from the seafront and Marine Drive along the headland gives views of beaches and colourful cliffs.
Tourist Information Centre
☎ (0803) 297428

Aries House

Listed

1 Morgan Avenue, Torquay
TQ2 5RP
☎ (0803) 215655

Family-run guesthouse situated in the town centre, offering easy access to all amenities. Seafront 10 minutes' walk.
Bedrooms: 1 single, 3 double, 1 twin, 4 triple
Bathrooms: 2 public

Bed & breakfast

per night:	£min	£max
Single	11.50	14.50
Double	22.00	28.00

Evening meal 1800 (last orders 1800)
Parking for 2
🏧🛏🖥📺🍴📺🛏, 🔌✕ 📶
🍴 📶📺

The Beehive

Steep Hill, Maidencombe, Torquay TQ1 4TS
☎ (0803) 314647
In a peaceful valley 4 minutes' walk from the beach, close to Torquay harbour and within easy reach of Dartmoor. All rooms have magnificent sea views. Non-smokers only, please.
Bedrooms: 1 single, 1 double, 1 twin
Bathrooms: 1 public

Bed & breakfast

per night:	£min	£max
Single	15.00	16.00
Double	25.00	30.00

Parking for 6
🏧🖥📺♨🖥📺🍴✂📺, ⛵❋✕
📶🍴

Claver Guest House ♨

119 Abbey Road, Torquay
TQ2 5NP
☎ (0803) 297118
A warm welcome awaits you. Close to beach, harbour and all entertainments. Home-cooked food, you'll never leave the table hungry!
Bedrooms: 1 single, 2 double, 1 twin, 2 triple, 2 multiple
Bathrooms: 2 public

Bed & breakfast

per night:	£min	£max
Single	13.00	
Double	26.00	

Half board

per person:	£min	£max
Daily	19.50	
Weekly	110.00	

Evening meal 1800 (last orders 1800)
Parking for 4
Open January-November
🏧🛏🖥📺📺🍴📺🛏, ✕ 📶 📶

Craig Court Hotel

😊😊 **APPROVED**

10 Ash Hill Road, Torquay
TQ1 3HZ
☎ (0803) 294400

Small hotel situated a short distance from the town centre and the harbour. Quiet location with a lovely garden and choice of menus.
Bedrooms: 2 single, 4 double, 2 twin, 2 multiple
Bathrooms: 5 private, 3 public

Bed & breakfast

per night:	£min	£max
Single	16.00	22.00
Double	32.00	44.00

Half board

per person:	£min	£max
Daily	21.50	29.00
Weekly	150.50	189.00

Evening meal 1800 (last orders 0900)
Parking for 10
Open April-October
🏧🛏♨🖥📺📺🛏, 🔌☀🚲
📶🏡📺

Kirkside Guest House

2 Princes Rd East, Torquay
TQ1 1PE
☎ (0803) 293545
Small, friendly, family-run accommodation with colour TV in all bedrooms. Keys to rooms provided - access at all times.
Bedrooms: 3 single, 1 double, 1 twin, 1 triple
Bathrooms: 1 public

Bed & breakfast

per night:	£min	£max
Single	9.50	10.50
Double	18.00	20.00

Half board

per person:	£min	£max
Daily	15.00	16.00
Weekly	105.00	112.00

Evening meal 1830 (last orders 0900)
Parking for 3
🏧2 📺🖥🛏♨📺, 🔌 🚲

Maple Lodge

😊😊 **COMMENDED**

36 Ash Hill Road, Torquay
TQ1 3JD
☎ (0803) 297391
Detached guesthouse with beautiful views. Relaxed atmosphere, home cooking, en-suite and shower rooms. Centrally situated for town and beaches.
Bedrooms: 1 single, 2 double, 1 twin, 2 triple, 1 multiple
Bathrooms: 4 private, 1 public, 2 private showers

Bed & breakfast

per night:	£min	£max
Single	12.00	17.00
Double	25.00	34.00

Half board

per person:	£min	£max
Daily	17.00	22.00
Weekly	125.00	149.00

Evening meal from 1800
Parking for 5
Open March-October
🏧🛏🖥📺🖥📺🛏, 🔌
📶📺📶

TORRINGTON

Devon
Map ref 1C1

Perched high above the River Torridge, with a charming market square, Georgian Town Hall and a museum. The famous Dartington Crystal Factory, Rosemoor Gardens and Plough Arts Centre are all located in the town.

Black Horse

High Street, Torrington
EX38 8HN
☎ (0805) 22121
15th C coaching inn with oak beams, bar and lounge. Separate 36-seat restaurant.
Bedrooms: 2 double, 1 twin
Bathrooms: 3 private

Bed & breakfast

per night:	£min	£max
Single	12.00	16.00
Double	24.00	28.00

Lunch available
Evening meal 1900 (last orders 2100)
🏧📺🛏♨🖥📺🛏, 🔌
📶📺📶📺

Flavills Farm

Kingscott, St Giles in the Wood, Torrington EX38 7JW
☎ (080 52) 3530 & 3250
125-acre mixed farm. 15th C farmhouse in conservation area of picturesque hamlet. Peaceful atmosphere.
Bedrooms: 1 single, 1 double, 1 triple
Bathrooms: 2 public

Bed & breakfast

per night:	£min	£max
Single	12.00	12.00
Double	24.00	24.00

Parking for 6
Open April-September
🏧🐾🖥📺📺🛏☀🚲📶📺

The town index towards the back of this guide gives page numbers of all places with accommodation.

TOTNES

Devon
Map ref 1D2

Old market town steeply built near the head of the Dart Estuary. Remains of medieval gateways, a noble church, 16th C Guildhall and medley of period houses recall former wealth from cloth and shipping, continued in rural and water industries.
Tourist Information Centre
☎ (0803) 863168

2 Antrim Terrace
Totnes TQ9 5QA
☎ (0803) 862638
Comfortable Edwardian Villa overlooking Totnes Castle. Convenient for the town centre and railway station. Non-smokers only please.
Bedrooms: 1 single, 1 double, 1 twin
Bathrooms: 2 public

Bed & breakfast per night:	£min	£max
Single	14.50	15.50
Double	29.00	31.00

Dorsley Park
Higher Plymouth Road, Totnes TQ9 6DN
☎ (0803) 863680
23-acre mixed farm. 160-year-old stone-built cottages offering comfortable accommodation, in a relaxed and friendly atmosphere. Tea and coffee making facilities.
Bedrooms: 1 single, 1 twin, 1 triple
Bathrooms: 2 public

Bed & breakfast per night:	£min	£max
Single	13.00	14.00
Double	26.00	28.00

Parking for 5

The Old Forge at Totnes
HIGHLY COMMENDED
Seymour Place, Totnes TQ9 5AY
☎ (0803) 862174
All modern comforts in a delightful 600-year-old stone building, with beautiful walled garden, cobbled driveway and fully operational smithy workshop. Weekly and off-season discount. Cottage suite suitable for family or disabled guests.
Bedrooms: 1 single, 3 double, 3 twin, 2 multiple
Bathrooms: 8 private, 1 public

Bed & breakfast per night:	£min	£max
Single	30.00	42.00
Double	40.00	60.00

Parking for 10
Cards accepted: Access, Visa

Sea Trout Inn
COMMENDED
Staverton, Totnes TQ9 6PA
☎ (0803) 762274
Delightful beamed country inn, in attractive village by the River Dart, offering food and friendly atmosphere. Good base for walking and touring Dartmoor and south Devon.
Bedrooms: 6 double, 3 twin, 1 triple
Bathrooms: 10 private

Bed & breakfast per night:	£min	£max
Single	37.50	39.50
Double	44.00	50.00

Half board per person:	£min	£max
Daily	33.00	35.00
Weekly	220.00	250.00

Lunch available
Evening meal 1900 (last orders 2145)
Parking for 50
Cards accepted: Access, Visa, Amex

TREBETHERICK

Cornwall
Map ref 1B2

Meadow Garth
Trebetherick, Wadebridge PL27 6SG
☎ (020 886) 2837
Friendly relaxed home with views overlooking Daymer Bay. Peaceful mature gardens surround house. Home-made cream teas in summer. Lovely walks. Wind-surfers' paradise.
Bedrooms: 1 single, 1 double, 1 twin, 1 triple
Bathrooms: 1 public

Bed & breakfast per night:	£min	£max
Single	12.00	14.00
Double	24.00	28.00

Parking for 5

The symbols are explained on the flap inside the back cover.

TROWBRIDGE

Wiltshire
Map ref 2B2

Wiltshire's administrative centre, a handsome market and manufacturing town with a wealth of merchants' houses and other Georgian buildings.
Tourist Information Centre
☎ (0225) 777054

Welam House
COMMENDED
Bratton Road, West Ashton, Trowbridge BA14 6AZ
☎ (0225) 755908
Located in quiet village, garden with trees and lawn with a view of Westbury White Horse. Ideally situated for touring. Bowls and mini-golf for guests.
Bedrooms: 1 double, 1 twin, 1 triple
Bathrooms: 3 private, 1 public

Bed & breakfast per night:	£min	£max
Double	32.00	32.00

Parking for 6
Open March-October

TRURO

Cornwall
Map ref 1B3

Cornwall's administrative centre and cathedral city, set at the head of Truro River on the Fal Estuary. A medieval stannary town, it handled mineral ore from West Cornwall; fine Georgian buildings recall its heyday as a society haunt in the second mining boom.
Tourist Information Centre
☎ (0872) 74555

Lands Vue Country House
APPROVED
Three Burrows, Truro TR4 8JA
☎ (0872) 560242
Offering a warm welcome, relaxed atmosphere, peaceful setting and imaginative home cooking. Panoramic views. In central position, a quarter of a mile off A30.
Bedrooms: 2 single, 1 double, 1 twin
Bathrooms: 1 private, 1 public

Bed & breakfast per night:	£min	£max
Single	14.00	16.00
Double	28.00	36.00

Half board per person:	£min	£max
Daily	22.00	25.00

Evening meal 1900 (last orders 1700)
Parking for 8

Marcorrie Hotel
20 Falmouth Road, Truro TR1 2HX
☎ (0872) 77374
Fax (0872) 41666
Family-run hotel close to the city centre. Ideal for business or holiday, central for touring Cornwall.
Bedrooms: 2 single, 3 double, 5 twin, 2 triple
Bathrooms: 10 private, 1 public, 2 private showers

Bed & breakfast per night:	£min	£max
Single	20.00	30.00
Double	40.00	45.00

Half board per person:	£min	£max
Daily	28.00	38.00
Weekly	200.00	

Evening meal 1900 (last orders 1700)
Parking for 16
Cards accepted: Access, Visa, Amex
10-20

Nanteague Farm Guest House
HIGHLY COMMENDED
Marazanvose, Truro TR4 9DH
☎ Zelah (0872) 540351
Set in 130 acres of farmland and with wonderful views. Ideal base from which to explore Cornwall. En-suite rooms, pool, inland beach and lake, golf-course, floatarium.
Bedrooms: 1 double, 1 triple, 2 multiple
Bathrooms: 4 private, 1 public

Bed & breakfast per night:	£min	£max
Single	14.00	16.50
Double	28.00	33.00

Half board per person:	£min	£max
Daily	21.50	23.50

Evening meal 1900 (last orders 1700)
Parking for 8

Open April-October
Cards accepted: Access, Visa
🏠🍴♿📶🚭🅿️📺🛏️🔥⚞🏧
🔍🚶🅿️✕🚬🏧🎣

Rock Cottage Guest House
COMMENDED
Blackwater, Truro TR4 8EU
☎ (0872) 560252
*18th C beamed cottage with
old world charm. Haven for
non-smokers. Warm, friendly
hospitality, personal service.
Informal atmosphere.
Farmland views.*
Bedrooms: 2 double, 1 twin
Bathrooms: 3 private
Bed & breakfast

per night:	£min	£max
Double	40.00	52.00

Lunch available
Evening meal 1800 (last
orders 1500)
Parking for 4
🍴♿🔍📶🚭🅿️📺🛏️🔥⚞
✕🏧 DAP SP

TRUSHAM
Devon
Map ref 1D2

The Cridford Inn
Trusham, Chudleigh, Newton
Abbot TQ13 ONR
☎ Chudleigh (0626) 853694
*14th C Devon longhouse in
Teign Valley. Specialising in
home-cooked food and real
ale. 1 mile from Dartmoor,
A38 Exeter to Plymouth, turn
off at Teign Valley sign, right
and right again on to B3193
Christow and Trusham, first
right signposted Trusham.*
Bedrooms: 1 double, 2 twin
Bathrooms: 3 private
Bed & breakfast

per night:	£min	£max
Single	25.00	25.00
Double	40.00	40.00

Lunch available
Evening meal 1900 (last
orders 2130)
Parking for 35
Cards accepted: Access, Visa
🏠🍴♿🅿️📶🚭🛏️🔥⚞🏧♿
SP 🔥

UGBOROUGH
Devon
Map ref 1C2

Hillhead Farm
Listed
Ugborough, Ivybridge
PL21 0HQ
☎ Plymouth (0752) 892674
*77-acre mixed farm. Spacious
family farmhouse, surrounded
by fields. All home-cooked
and largely home-grown food.*

---

*From A38 turn off at
Wrangton crossroads, turn
left, take third right over
crossroads, after three-
quarters of a mile turn left,
farm is 75 yards on left.*
Bedrooms: 2 double, 2 twin
Bathrooms: 1 public
Bed & breakfast

per night:	£min	£max
Single		12.00
Double		24.00

Half board

per person:	£min	£max
Daily		18.00
Weekly		112.00

Evening meal 1900 (last
orders 2100)
Parking for 5
🔍🏧♿📶🅿️🚭📺🛏️🔥⚞🏧✓
✿🏧

WADEBRIDGE
Cornwall
Map ref 1B2

Old market town with
Cornwall's finest medieval
bridge, spanning the
Camel at its highest
navigable point. Twice-
widened, the bridge is
said to have been built on
woolpacks sunk in the
unstable sands of the
river bed.

Swan Hotel
COMMENDED
Molesworth Street,
Wadebridge PL27 7DD
☎ (020 881) 2526
*A town hotel with tastefully
decorated public bar and
separate restaurant. Beautiful
function/conference room for
75 people.*
Bedrooms: 1 single,
2 double, 2 twin, 1 triple
Bathrooms: 6 private
Bed & breakfast

per night:	£min	£max
Double		41.00

Lunch available
Evening meal 1800 (last
orders 2130)
Parking for 6
Cards accepted: Access, Visa,
Amex
🏠🍴♿📶🅿️📺🛏️🔥⚞🏧✕
🏧 SP

National Crown
ratings were correct
at the time of going
to press but are
subject to change.
Please check at the
time of booking.

WARMINSTER
Wiltshire
Map ref 2B2

Attractive stone-built town
high up to the west of
Salisbury Plain. A market
town, it originally thrived
on cloth and wheat. Many
prehistoric camps and
barrows nearby, along
with Longleat House and
Safari Park.
*Tourist Information Centre
☎ (0985) 218548*

Otago
♿
3 Portway Lane, Warminster
BA12 8RB
☎ (0985) 212182
*An attractive, quiet house of
unusual design and charm, at
the edge of Salisbury Plain.
Offering home cooking and
comfort.*
Bedrooms: 2 twin
Bathrooms: 2 public
Bed & breakfast

per night:	£min	£max
Single	16.00	18.00
Double	32.00	36.00

Half board

per person:	£min	£max
Daily	24.00	26.00
Weekly	156.00	170.00

Evening meal 1830 (last
orders 2000)
Parking for 3
Open January-November
🏠🍴♿📶🅿️🍴♿📺🛏️🔥
🏧✿🏧

WASHFORD
Somerset
Map ref 1D1

Green Bay
♿
Washford, Watchet
TA23 ONN
☎ (0984) 40303
*Double fronted stone built
cottage approximately 200
years old, situated on main
A39 road at Washford.*
Bedrooms: 2 double, 1 twin
Bathrooms: 1 private,
1 public
Bed & breakfast

per night:	£min	£max
Single	13.50	15.00
Double	27.00	30.00

Half board

per person:	£min	£max
Daily	22.00	
Weekly	145.00	

Evening meal from 1900

Parking for 3
Open March-October
🏠🍴5♿📶🅿️🍴♿📺🛏️🏧✿
✕🏧

WATCHET
Somerset
Map ref 1D1

Small port on Bridgwater
Bay, sheltered by the
Quantocks and the
Brendon Hills. A thriving
paper industry keeps the
harbour busy; in the 19th
C it handled iron from the
Brendon Hills. Cleeve
Abbey, a ruined Cistercian
monastery, is 3 miles to
the south-west.

Wood Advent Farm
COMMENDED
Roadwater, Watchet
TA23 ORR
☎ Washford (0984) 40920
*350-acre mixed farm. Situated
in Exmoor National Park, is
ideal for touring the many
beauty spots. Country
cooking, using mostly home-
produced food.*
Bedrooms: 1 single,
2 double, 1 twin, 2 multiple
Bathrooms: 6 private,
2 public
Bed & breakfast

per night:	£min	£max
Single	16.50	22.50

Half board

per person:	£min	£max
Daily	29.00	35.00
Weekly	145.00	210.00

Lunch available
Evening meal 1900 (last
orders 2100)
Parking for 13
🏠♿📶🍴🅿️🚭📺🛏️🔥⚞🏧♿
🔍🏧🚶🅿️✕✿🏧🔥 T

WATERGATE BAY
Cornwall
Map ref 1B2

Beautiful long board-
riders' beach backed by
tall cliffs, north-west of
Newquay. A small holiday
village nestles in a steep
river valley making a cleft
in the cliffs.

Tregurrian Hotel ⚓
♿♿
Watergate Bay, Newquay
TR8 4AB
☎ St. Mawgan (0637)
860280
*On coast road between
Newquay and Padstow, just
100 yards from golden sandy*
Continued ▶

335

WATERGATE BAY

Continued

beach in an area reputed to have some of the finest beaches and coastline in Europe.
Bedrooms: 4 single, 11 double, 4 twin, 2 triple, 6 multiple
Bathrooms: 22 private, 2 public

Bed & breakfast

per night:	£min	£max
Single	16.00	27.00
Double	32.00	54.00

Half board

per person:	£min	£max
Daily	24.00	35.00
Weekly	120.00	230.00

Lunch available
Evening meal 1845 (last orders 1930)
Parking for 25
Open April-October
Cards accepted: Access, Visa

WELLINGTON

Somerset
Map ref 1D1

Pinksmoor Millhouse

COMMENDED

Pinksmoor Farm, Wellington TA21 0HD
☎ Greenham (0823) 672361
98-acre dairy & livestock farm. Personal service and home cooking. House adjoins old mill and stream with abundant wildlife and scenic walks. Conservation area. En-suite bedrooms with beverage-making facilities and TV.
Bedrooms: 1 double, 1 twin, 1 triple
Bathrooms: 3 private, 1 public

Bed & breakfast

per night:	£min	£max
Single	18.50	19.50
Double	32.00	34.00

Half board

per person:	£min	£max
Daily	26.50	31.00
Weekly	178.50	206.50

Evening meal 1900 (last orders 1600)
Parking for 5

> **Map references apply to the colour maps at the back of this guide.**

WELLS

Somerset
Map ref 2A2

Small city set beneath the southern slopes of the Mendips. Built between 1180 and 1424, the magnificent cathedral is preserved in much of its original glory and with its ancient precincts forms one of our loveliest and most unified groups of medieval buildings.
Tourist Information Centre
☎ (0749) 672552

At the Sign of the Golden Hart

21 St John Street, Wells BA5 1SW
☎ (0749) 674892
Small medieval terraced former ale house of character in city centre. Peaceful and welcoming. Colourful courtyard garden. Open country nearby.
Bedrooms: 2 double, 1 twin
Bathrooms: 2 private, 1 public

Bed & breakfast

per night:	£min	£max
Single	15.00	20.00
Double	30.00	36.00

Half board

per person:	£min	£max
Daily	20.00	25.00
Weekly	120.00	150.00

Evening meal 1900 (last orders 2000)

Beaconsfield Farm 🏍

Easton, Wells BA5 1DU
☎ (0749) 870308
Period character farmhouse on the outskirts of a small village in an area of outstanding beauty. Magnificent views. Pub and restaurant 100 yards.
Bedrooms: 1 double, 2 twin
Bathrooms: 1 public

Bed & breakfast

per night:	£min	£max
Double	28.00	34.00

Parking for 10
Open March-October

Bekynton House

COMMENDED

7 St Thomas Street, Wells BA5 2UU
☎ (0749) 672222
Well-appointed, family-run guesthouse close to cathedral and Bishop's Palace. All

bedrooms with colour TV, most en-suite. Non-smokers only please.
Bedrooms: 1 single, 3 double, 2 twin, 2 triple
Bathrooms: 6 private, 2 public

Bed & breakfast

per night:	£min	£max
Single	21.00	23.00
Double	36.00	45.00

Parking for 7
Cards accepted: Access, Visa

The Coach House

HIGHLY COMMENDED

Stoberry Park, Wells BA5 3AA
☎ Shepton Mallet (0749) 676535
Old coach house in private parkland. Short walk from centre of Wells. Superb views over city and countryside.
Bedrooms: 1 double, 2 twin
Bathrooms: 3 private, 1 public

Bed & breakfast

per night:	£min	£max
Double	36.00	40.00

Parking for 6

Cross Farm

Yarley, Wells BA5 1PA
☎ (0749) 78925
17th C Somerset longhouse, tastefully modernised, offering comfortable facilities. Within easy reach of Wells, Bath, Glastonbury, Cheddar and Wookey Hole. Nearby pubs offer good selection of evening meals.
Bedrooms: 1 double, 1 twin, 1 triple
Bathrooms: 1 public, 1 private shower

Bed & breakfast

per night:	£min	£max
Double	27.00	30.00

Parking for 6

Home Farm

Stoppers Lane, Coxley, Wells BA5 1QS
☎ (0749) 672434
15-acre pig farm. 1.5 miles from Wells, in a quiet spot just off A39. Extensive views of Mendip Hills. Pleasant rooms.
Bedrooms: 1 single, 3 double, 2 twin, 1 triple
Bathrooms: 3 private, 2 public

Bed & breakfast

per night:	£min	£max
Single	15.00	16.50
Double	30.00	37.00

Parking for 12

Littlewell Farm Guest House

HIGHLY COMMENDED

Coxley, Wells BA5 1QP
☎ (0749) 677914
Converted 200-year-old farmhouse with all bedrooms having shower or bathroom en-suite. Located 1 mile south west of Wells.
Bedrooms: 1 single, 2 double, 2 twin
Bathrooms: 3 private, 2 private showers

Bed & breakfast

per night:	£min	£max
Single	19.50	22.00
Double	39.00	41.00

Half board

per person:	£min	£max
Daily	36.00	37.00

Evening meal 1900 (last orders 2000)
Parking for 11

Manor Farm

Old Bristol Road, Upper Milton, Wells BA5 3AH
☎ (0749) 673394
130-acre beef farm. Elizabethan manor house, Grade II* listed, on the slopes of the Mendips, 1 mile north of Wells.
Bedrooms: 2 double, 1 twin
Bathrooms: 1 public

Bed & breakfast

per night:	£min	£max
Single	15.00	18.00
Double	26.00	30.00

Parking for 6

Manor Farm

Dulcote, Wells BA5 3PZ
☎ (0749) 72125
Traditional 17th C farmhouse 1 mile from Wells. Lovely views of cathedral and Mendip Hills. Friendly atmosphere, comfortable accommodation. Garden suite suitable for elderly/disabled. Wholefood breakfast available.
Bedrooms: 1 double, 1 twin
Bathrooms: 2 private

Bed & breakfast

per night:	£min	£max
Single	25.00	33.00
Double	35.00	40.00

Parking for 8

🐾🛁🖳📵♿UL🛗S🎱▥🌙◑❄✕🚲🏧

Stoneleigh House

Roughmoor Lane, Westbury-sub-Mendip, Wells BA5 1HF
☎ (0749) 870668
Superior bed and breakfast in 18th C farmhouse. Lovely views across open countryside. TV, tea/coffee facilities in rooms. Non-smokers only please.
Bedrooms: 1 double, 1 twin
Bathrooms: 2 private

Bed & breakfast

per night:	£min	£max
Double	16.00	17.00

Parking for 3

🐾10📵♿UL S🚳▥🍴.🚲❄✕🚲🏧

Tor Guest House

🏅🏅 APPROVED
20 Tor Street, Wells
BA5 2US
☎ (0749) 672322
Historic, sympathetically restored 17th C building in delightful grounds overlooking the cathedral. Attractive, comfortable, warm bedrooms. 3 minutes' walk to town centre.
Bedrooms: 1 single, 1 double, 6 twin, 1 multiple
Bathrooms: 2 private, 2 public

Bed & breakfast

per night:	£min	£max
Single	20.00	25.00
Double	34.00	44.00

Half board

per person:	£min	£max
Daily	30.00	45.00
Weekly	200.00	300.00

Evening meal 1830 (last orders 1000)
Parking for 11

🐾🛁🖳📵♿UL S🚳▥🌙◑◐.🚲
▸🍴❄✕🚲DAP SP🏧

WEST ANSTEY
Devon
Map ref 1D1

Partridge Arms Farm ⋀

🏅🏅 APPROVED
Yeo Mill, West Anstey, South Molton EX36 3NU
☎ Anstey Mills (039 84) 217
200-acre mixed farm. Old established family farm. Well placed for touring, walking, riding, fishing, Exmoor

---

National Park, north Devon, west Somerset and coastal resorts.
Bedrooms: 3 double, 2 twin, 2 multiple
Bathrooms: 4 private, 1 public

Bed & breakfast

per night:	£min	£max
Single	17.50	20.50
Double	35.00	43.00

Half board

per person:	£min	£max
Daily	25.00	28.00
Weekly	175.00	196.00

Evening meal 1845 (last orders 1800)
Parking for 10

🐾🛁🖳📵♿UL S🚳▥TV▥
🚲◑🌙✕🚲❄🚲🏧

WEST BAGBOROUGH
Somerset
Map ref 1D1

Rising Sun Inn

West Bagborough TA4 3EF
☎ Bishops Lydeard (0823) 432575
16th C thatched inn in beautiful Quantock Hills. Friendly atmosphere with home cooking and attractively furnished rooms. 7 miles from Taunton.
Bedrooms: 3 double, 1 twin
Bathrooms: 4 private

Bed & breakfast

per night:	£min	£max
Single	18.00	18.00
Double	35.00	35.00

Half board

per person:	£min	£max
Daily	40.00	72.00
Weekly	280.00	500.00

Lunch available
Evening meal 1900 (last orders 2130)
Parking for 6

🐾🛁🖳📵♿🏱S🚳▥.
🚲❄✕🚲SP

WEST GRAFTON
Wiltshire
Map ref 2B2

Mayfield

Listed HIGHLY COMMENDED
West Grafton, Marlborough SN8 3BY
☎ Marlborough (0672) 810339
Beautifully decorated 17th C thatched house with happy family atmosphere. Lovely grounds with heated swimming pool and tennis court. Set in peaceful hamlet off A338.

Bedrooms: 1 double, 2 twin
Bathrooms: 2 public

Bed & breakfast

per night:	£min	£max
Single	25.00	30.00
Double	35.00	45.00

Parking for 6

🐾🛁🖳📵♿🌙UL S🚳
TV▥.🚲◑🍴❄✕UL◑❄🚲
🏧T

WEST HUNTSPILL
Somerset
Map ref 1D1

Laburnum House ⋀

Sloway Lane, West Huntspill, Highbridge TA9 3RJ
☎ Burnham-on-Sea (0278) 781830
Fax (0278) 781612
Farmhouse, modernised 5 years ago, 3 letting rooms and 23 holiday lodges. Situated alongside the River Huntspill and nature reserve.
Bedrooms: 5 single, 12 double, 11 twin, 2 triple
Bathrooms: 30 private, 4 public

Bed & breakfast

per night:	£min	£max
Single	28.00	40.00
Double	36.00	40.00

Half board

per person:	£min	£max
Daily	37.00	50.00
Weekly	250.00	340.00

Lunch available
Evening meal 1800 (last orders 2300)
Parking for 150
Cards accepted: Access, Visa, C.Bl, Diners

🐾🛁🖳📵♿🌙🏱S🚳
TV▥.🚲🚲❄✕🚲◑🌙
▸🍴❄DAP🚲SP T

WESTHAY
Somerset
Map ref 1D1

New House Farm

🏅🏅
Burtle Road, Westhay, Glastonbury BA6 9TT
☎ Meare Heath (0458) 860238
Large Victorian farmhouse situated on Somerset Levels near Peat Moors visitor centre. Central for touring this interesting area.
Bedrooms: 3 double
Bathrooms: 1 private, 1 public

Bed & breakfast

per night:	£min	£max
Double	26.00	32.00

Half board

per person:	£min	£max
Daily	22.00	25.00

Evening meal 1830 (last orders 2130)
Parking for 3

🐾🛁♿UL S🚳TV▥.🚲❄
✕🚲🏧

WESTON-SUPER-MARE
Avon
Map ref 1D1

Large, friendly resort developed in the 19th C. Traditional seaside attractions include theatres and a dance hall. The museum shows a Victorian seaside gallery and has Iron Age finds from a hill fort on Worlebury Hill in Weston Woods.
Tourist Information Centre
☎ *(0934) 626838*

Conifers

🏅🏅
63 Milton Road, Weston-super-Mare BS23 2SP
☎ (0934) 624404
Semi-detached corner guesthouse standing back in a large garden. Completely refurbished for bed and breakfast use. 20 years' experience.
Bedrooms: 1 single, 1 double, 1 twin
Bathrooms: 1 private, 1 public

Bed & breakfast

per night:	£min	£max
Single	16.00	19.00
Double	28.00	34.00

Parking for 4
Open January-November

📵♿UL▥.✕🚲

Manacor

🏅 APPROVED
59 Clevedon Road, Weston-super-Mare BS23 1DD
☎ (0934) 629367
Fax (0934) 418403
Homely guesthouse, within easy walking distance of the seafront.
Bedrooms: 1 single, 1 double, 1 twin, 1 triple
Bathrooms: 1 public

Bed & breakfast

per night:	£min	£max
Single	12.00	14.00
Double	24.00	28.00

Open April-October

🐾2UL🚳TV▥.✕🚲

WESTON-SUPER-MARE

Continued

Purn House Farm ₳
APPROVED
Bleadon, Weston-super-Mare
BS24 0QE
☎ Bleadon (0934) 812324
*500-acre mixed farm.
Comfortable 17 C farmhouse
only 3 miles from Weston-
super-Mare. Hot and cold
water, tea-making facilities in
all rooms, en-suite available
with TV. Peaceful yet not
isolated, on bus route to town
centre and station.*
Bedrooms: 1 single,
1 double, 1 twin, 4 multiple
Bathrooms: 4 private,
1 public

Bed & breakfast per night:	£min	£max
Double	30.00	34.00

Half board per person:	£min	£max
Daily	22.00	24.00
Weekly	140.00	146.00

Evening meal 1830 (last
orders 1000)
Parking for 10
Open March-October

Woodspring House
Beach Road, Sand Point,
Weston-super-Mare
BS22 9UD
☎ (0934) 628520
*Attractive country house set
amongst National Trust land,
with outstanding views over
the countryside and sea.*
Bedrooms: 1 single, 2 double
Bathrooms: 2 public

Bed & breakfast per night:	£min	£max
Single	15.00	18.00
Double	30.00	35.00

Parking for 8
Open January-November

There are separate
sections in this
guide listing groups
specialising in farm
holidays and
accommodation
which is especially
suitable for young
people and
organised groups.

WESTWARD HO!

Devon
Map ref 1C1

Small resort, whose name
comes from the title of
Charles Kingsley's famous
novel, on Barnstaple Bay,
close to the Taw and
Torridge Estuary. There
are good sands and a
notable golf-course - one
of the oldest in Britain.

Brockenhurst ₳
COMMENDED
11 Atlantic Way, Westward
Ho!, Bideford EX39 1HX
☎ Bideford (0237) 423346
*Attractive, comfortable,
detached house adjoining the
village centre (shops,
restaurants, pubs). Sea views.
Easy access from North
Devon link road; Bideford 2.5
miles.*
Bedrooms: 2 double, 2 twin
Bathrooms: 4 private

Bed & breakfast per night:	£min	£max
Single	20.00	25.00
Double	35.00	40.00

Parking for 6
Open February-December
Cards accepted: Access, Visa

WEYMOUTH

Dorset
Map ref 2B3

Ancient port and one of
the south's earliest
resorts. Curving beside a
long, sandy beach, the
elegant Georgian
esplanade is graced with
a statue of George III and
a cheerful Victorian
Jubilee clock tower.
*Tourist Information Centre
☎ (0305) 785747.*

Alessandria Hotel
APPROVED
71 Wakeham Easton,
Portland DT5 1HW
☎ Portland (0305) 822270
& 820108
*Well-equipped hotel with
comfortable bedrooms and a
la carte Italian restaurant. All
fresh food cooked to order by
Giovanni himself. Warm,
intimate and friendly
atmosphere.*
Bedrooms: 4 single,
6 double, 4 twin, 2 multiple
Bathrooms: 12 private,
3 public, 4 private showers

Bed & breakfast per night:	£min	£max
Single	20.00	30.00
Double	35.00	50.00

Half board per person:	£min	£max
Daily	25.00	40.00
Weekly	150.00	200.00

Lunch available
Evening meal 1900 (last
orders 2200)
Parking for 15
Cards accepted: Access, Visa,
C.Bl, Amex, Switch

Fairlight
50 Littlemoor Road, Preston,
Weymouth DT3 6AA
☎ (0305) 832293
*Clean comfortable rooms in
detached bungalow, 3 miles
from Weymouth. Good food.
Good area for walking or
water sports. Evening meal by
arrangement.*
Bedrooms: 1 double,
1 multiple
Bathrooms: 1 public

Bed & breakfast per night:	£min	£max
Double	26.00	34.00

Half board per person:	£min	£max
Daily	19.00	23.00
Weekly	114.00	138.00

Evening meal from 1900
Parking for 2

Green Acre
Listed
83 Preston Road, Preston,
Weymouth DT3 6PY
☎ Preston (0305) 832047
*Close to Bowleaze Cove at the
east end of Weymouth.
Detached house with wood-
clad gables.*
Bedrooms: 1 single,
3 double, 1 twin, 2 triple
Bathrooms: 2 public

Bed & breakfast per night:	£min	£max
Single	12.50	15.50
Double	25.00	31.00

Parking for 8

Rosslare
145 Dorchester Road,
Weymouth DT4 7LE
☎ (0305) 785913
*Small, licensed family
guesthouse situated on the
main Dorchester road leading
into Weymouth.*

Bedrooms: 1 single, 2 twin,
4 triple
Bathrooms: 4 private,
1 public

Bed & breakfast per night:	£min	£max
Single	15.00	17.00
Double	28.00	34.00

Half board per person:	£min	£max
Daily	21.00	23.00
Weekly	110.00	125.00

Evening meal 1800 (last
orders 1700)
Parking for 5
Cards accepted: Access, Visa

Tatton House
Buckland Ripers, Weymouth
DT3 4BX
☎ Upwey (030 581) 2840
*440-acre dairy farm. Attractive
Georgian farmhouse, tastefully
modernised, with the
emphasis on friendliness and
comfort. 3 miles north-west of
Weymouth.*
Bedrooms: 1 double, 1 twin,
1 multiple
Bathrooms: 1 public

Bed & breakfast per night:	£min	£max
Double	30.00	35.00

Parking for 6
Open March-October

WHEDDON CROSS

Somerset
Map ref 1D1

Crossroads hamlet in the
heart of Exmoor National
Park.

Little Quarme Farm
Listed
Wheddon Cross, Minehead
TA24 7EA
☎ Timbercombe (0643)
841249
*18-acre livestock & horses
farm. Lovely old secluded
farmhouse with large gardens.
Sun lounge with panoramic
views. Direct access to
footpaths and bridlepaths.
Quarter of a mile from
Wheddon Cross on the B3224
Exford road.*
Bedrooms: 2 double, 1 twin
Bathrooms: 2 public

Bed & breakfast per night:	£min	£max
Double	15.00	16.50

338

Parking for 6
Open May-September
🐎 ☕ [UL] 🚭 ⛽ [TV] [IIII] 🔑 U ✿
✈ 🚌 🏠

WICK ST LAWRENCE

Avon
Map ref 1D1

Icelton Farm

[Listed]
Wick St Lawrence, Weston-super-Mare BS22 OYJ
☎ Weston-super-Mare (0934) 515704
188-acre mixed farm. Situated off junction 21 of M5. Accommodation comprises a double room and family room. Good breakfasts.
Bedrooms: 1 double, 1 triple
Bathrooms: 1 public, 1 private shower

Bed & breakfast per night:	£min	£max
Single	14.00	18.00
Double	28.00	36.00

Parking for 2
Open March-October
Cards accepted: Visa
🐎 ☕ [UL] [S] ⛽ [TV] [IIII] 🔑 U ⛳ ✿
✈ 🚌 🏠

WIDECOMBE-IN-THE-MOOR

Devon
Map ref 1C2

Old village in pastoral country under the high tors of East Dartmoor. The 'Cathedral of the Moor' stands near a tiny square, once used for archery practice, which has a 16th C Church House among other old buildings.

Sheena Tower

👑👑
Widecombe-in-the-Moor, Newton Abbot TQ13 7TE
☎ (036 42) 308
Comfortable moorland guesthouse overlooking Widecombe village, offering a relaxed holiday in picturesque surroundings. Well placed for discovering Dartmoor.
Bedrooms: 1 single, 2 double, 2 triple
Bathrooms: 1 private, 2 public

Bed & breakfast per night:	£min	£max
Single	13.00	15.00
Double	26.00	30.00

Half board per person:	£min	£max
Daily	19.50	21.50
Weekly	133.00	147.00

Evening meal 1900 (last orders 1200)
Parking for 10
Open February-October
🐎 🍽 ☕ 🔒 ⛽ [TV] [IIII] 🔑 ✿ 🚌

WINCANTON

Somerset
Map ref 2B3

Thriving market town, rising from the rich pastures of Blackmoor Vale near the Dorset border, with many attractive 18th C stone buildings. Steeplechase racecourse.

Lower Church Farm

👑👑
Rectory Lane, Charlton Musgrove, Wincanton BA9 8ES
☎ (0963) 32307
60-acre dairy farm. 18th C brick farmhouse with beams and inglenooks, in a quiet area surrounded by lovely countryside. Ideal for touring.
Bedrooms: 2 double, 1 twin
Bathrooms: 2 private, 1 public, 1 private shower

Bed & breakfast	£min	£max
Double	12.00	14.00

Parking for 4
🐎 6 ☕ [UL] 🔒 [S] 🚭 [TV] [IIII] 🔑 ✿
🚌 🏠

WINSFORD

Somerset
Map ref 1D1

Small village on the River Exe in splendid walking country under Winsford Hill. On the other side of the hill is a Celtic standing stone, the Caratacus Stone, and nearby across the River Barle stretches an ancient packhorse bridge, Tarr Steps, built of great stone slabs.

Larcombe Foot

👑👑 COMMENDED
Winsford, Minehead TA24 7HS
☎ (064 385) 306
Comfortable country house in tranquil, beautiful setting, overlooking River Exe. Lovely walks on doorstep. Ideal for touring Exmoor and north Devon coast.
Bedrooms: 1 single, 1 double, 1 twin
Bathrooms: 2 public

Bed & breakfast per night:	£min	£max
Single		16.50
Double		32.00

Parking for 3
Open April-October
🐎 6 ☕ [UL] ⛽ [TV] [IIII] 🔑 U 🎣
✿ 🚌

WINSHAM

Somerset
Map ref 1D2

The Squirrel Inn

Laymore, Winsham, Chard TA20 4NT
☎ (0460) 30298
Modern country pub with good views, on the borders of Dorset, Somerset and Devon.
Bedrooms: 1 double, 2 twin
Bathrooms: 3 private

Bed & breakfast per night:	£min	£max
Single	20.00	22.00
Double	35.00	38.00

Lunch available
Evening meal 1800 (last orders 2130)
Parking for 30
🐎 📺 ☕ 🔒 [S] [IIII] ✿ 🚌

WINTERBOURNE STEEPLETON

Dorset
Map ref 2B3

Sunny Acres

👑👑
Bridport Road, Winterbourne Steepleton, Dorchester DT2 9DX
☎ Martinstown (0305) 889396
Attractive country bungalow set in own 5 acres. Various animals. Ideal for touring. Close to pretty villages and sea. Non-smoking establishment.
Bedrooms: 1 double, 1 twin, 1 triple
Bathrooms: 2 public

Bed & breakfast per night:	£min	£max
Single	13.50	15.50
Double	27.00	31.00

Parking for 4
🐎 12 🍽 ☕ [UL] [S] 🚭 ⛽ [TV] [IIII]
🔑 ✿ ✈ 🚌 [OAP] [SP]

Check the introduction to this region for Where to Go, What to See.

WINTERBOURNE STOKE

Wiltshire
Map ref 2B2

Scotland Lodge

👑👑 APPROVED
Winterbourne Stoke, Salisbury SP3 4TF
☎ Shrewton (0980) 620943 & mobile (0860) 272599
Historic, comfortable country house with private bathrooms. Helpful service. Ideal touring base. French and some German spoken. Self-contained unit also available for self-catering.
Bedrooms: 1 double, 2 twin
Bathrooms: 3 private

Bed & breakfast per night:	£min	£max
Single	20.00	25.00
Double	35.00	45.00

Parking for 5
🐎 📺 ☕ [UL] [S] 🚭 [IIII] 🔑 ✿ ✈
🚌 🏠

WITHYPOOL

Somerset
Map ref 1D1

Pretty village high on Exmoor near the beautiful River Barle. On Winsford Hill (National Trust) are Bronze Age barrows known as the Wambarrows.

Landacre Farm

[Listed]
Withypool, Minehead TA24 7SD
☎ Exford (0643) 83223 & 83487
2000-acre hill farm. Large ground floor en-suite family room. Farm overlooking moor and River Barle. Fantastic views, walking, bird-watching.
Bedrooms: 1 triple
Bathrooms: 1 private

Bed & breakfast per night:	£min	£max
Double	30.00	

Parking for 2
Open April-October
🐎 🍽 📺 ☕ 🔧 [TV] [IIII] 🔑 🎣
✈ 🚌

National Crown ratings were correct at the time of going to press but are subject to change. Please check at the time of booking.

WEST COUNTRY

WOODBURY
Devon
Map ref 1D2

Attractive village, with Woodbury Common to the east, affording a panoramic coastal view from Berry Head to Portland Bill. Woodbury Castle Iron Age fort lies at a height of some 600 ft.

Higher Bagmores Farm
Woodbury, Exeter EX5 1LA
☎ (0395) 32261
200-acre mixed farm. A brick-built farmhouse set in its own garden overlooking the Exe estuary. 2 miles from M5, 5 miles from seaside.
Bedrooms: 1 single, 1 double, 1 triple
Bathrooms: 2 public
Bed & breakfast
per night:	£min	£max
Single	13.00	15.00
Double	26.00	30.00
Parking for 4

WOODFALLS
Wiltshire
Map ref 2B3

Vale View Farm
COMMENDED
Slab Lane, Woodfalls, Salisbury SP5 2NE
☎ Downton (0725) 22116
60-acre livestock farm. Modern, attractive farmhouse in quiet situation close to New Forest. Ideal for walking and touring - many museums and historic places nearby. Non-smokers preferred.
Bedrooms: 1 single, 1 double, 1 twin
Bathrooms: 2 private, 1 public
Bed & breakfast
per night:	£min	£max
Single	14.00	18.00
Double	28.00	36.00
Parking for 3
Open March-November

The national Crown scheme is explained in full in the information pages towards the back of this guide.

WOOKEY
Somerset
Map ref 2A2

Small village below the southern slopes of the Mendips, near the River Axe. 1 mile or so north-east, the river runs through spectacular limestone caverns at Wookey Hole.

Fenny Castle House
COMMENDED
Fenny Castle, Wookey, Wells BA5 1NN
☎ Wells (0749) 672265
Riverside setting overlooking moat and bailey castle. Country house in 60 acres on boundary of levels. Restaurant, lounge bar, delightful accommodation.
Bedrooms: 1 single, 3 double, 2 twin
Bathrooms: 6 private
Bed & breakfast
per night:	£min	£max
Single	28.00	30.00
Double	56.00	60.00
Half board
per person:	£min	£max
Daily	38.00	42.00
Weekly	265.00	
Lunch available
Evening meal 1800 (last orders 2100)
Parking for 60
Cards accepted: Access, Visa, Amex

YELVERTON
Devon
Map ref 1C2

Village on the edge of Dartmoor, where ponies wander over the flat common. Buckland Abbey is 2 miles south-west, while Burrator Reservoir is 2 miles to the east.

Greenwell Farm
Meavy, Yelverton PL20 6PY
☎ (0822) 853563
220-acre hill farm. Fresh country air, breathtaking views and scrumptious farmhouse cuisine. This busy family farm welcomes you to share our countryside and wildlife.
Bedrooms: 1 double, 1 twin, 1 triple
Bathrooms: 2 private

Bed & breakfast
per night:	£min	£max
Double	38.00	44.00
Half board
per person:	£min	£max
Daily	29.00	33.00
Weekly	195.00	225.00
Evening meal 1900 (last orders 1200)
Parking for 8

YEOVIL
Somerset
Map ref 2A3

Lively market town set in dairying country beside the River Yeo, famous for glove making. Interesting parish church. Museum of South Somerset at Hendford Manor.
Tourist Information Centre
☎ (0935) 71279

Southwoods
APPROVED
3 Southwoods, Yeovil BA20 2QQ
☎ (0935) 22178
Charming Edwardian house, close to town centre, ski-slope, wooded beauty spot. Relaxed, friendly atmosphere.
Bedrooms: 1 single, 1 double, 1 twin
Bathrooms: 1 public
Bed & breakfast
per night:	£min	£max
Single	12.50	16.00
Double	25.00	32.00
Parking for 3

Stonecroft Manor Farm
APPROVED
Tintinhull, Yeovil BA22 8PR
☎ Ilchester (0935) 840289
210-acre dairy farm. Large secluded Georgian hamstone farmhouse, in beautiful open country. Private drive off A303 between Tintinhull and Ilchester. Footpath to village, inn and National Trust garden three-quarters of a mile away.
Bedrooms: 1 single, 1 twin, 1 triple
Bathrooms: 1 public
Bed & breakfast
per night:	£min	£max
Single	12.00	14.00
Double	24.00	28.00
Parking for 4

YEOVILTON
Somerset
Map ref 2A3

Cary Fitzpaine
APPROVED
Yeovilton, Yeovil BA22 8JB
☎ Charlton Mackerell (045 822) 3250
600-acre mixed farm. Elegant Georgian manor farmhouse in idyllic setting. 2 acres of gardens. High standard of accommodation.
Bedrooms: 1 single, 1 double, 1 twin, 1 triple
Bathrooms: 1 private, 2 public
Bed & breakfast
per night:	£min	£max
Single	15.00	
Double	28.00	
Parking for 11
Open March-October

Courtry Farm
Bridgehampton, Yeovil BA22 8HF
☎ Ilchester (0935) 840327
590-acre mixed farm. Farmhouse on working farm. Ground floor rooms furnished to high standard. Tennis court. Fleet Air Arm Museum half a mile.
Bedrooms: 1 twin, 1 triple
Bathrooms: 2 private
Bed & breakfast
per night:	£min	£max
Single	18.00	20.00
Double	30.00	30.00

ZEALS
Wiltshire
Map ref 2B2

Pretty village of thatched cottages set high over the Dorset border. Zeals House dates from the medieval period and has some 19th C work. The Palladian Stourhead House (National Trust), in its magnificent gardens, lies further north.

Cornerways Cottage
Longcross, Zeals, Warminster BA12 6LL
☎ Bourton (0747) 840477
18th C cottage with original beams. Ideal position for touring Stourhead, Stonehenge, Shaftesbury and other local attractions. Riding,

340

fishing and walking locally. Close to A303, midway for London or Devon and Cornwall. 2 miles from Stourhead House and Gardens, 4 miles from Longleat.
Bedrooms: 2 double, 1 twin, 1 triple
Bathrooms: 2 private, 4 public

Bed & breakfast

per night:	£min	£max
Single	14.00	18.00
Double	26.00	30.00

Parking for 6

🛏️🚌♿ⓊⓁ🛈§🅟📺〰️🅿️🔌♨️
🚲 OAP

ZENNOR

Cornwall
Map ref 1A3

Boswednack Manor
Zennor, St Ives TR26 3DD
☎ Penzance (0736) 794183

3-acre smallholding. Granite farmhouse with sea and moorland views. Home cooking, peaceful atmosphere. Proprietors are experienced ornithologists and offer various special interest holidays. Non-smoking house.
Bedrooms: 3 double, 1 twin, 1 triple
Bathrooms: 2 private, 2 public

Bed & breakfast

per night:	£min	£max
Single	13.00	17.50
Double	26.00	35.00

Half board

per person:	£min	£max
Daily	19.00	23.50
Weekly	91.00	164.00

Evening meal 1900 (last orders 1200)
Parking for 10

🛏️♿ⓊⓁ🛈§✂️🅟♨️🌸🎿🚲

Country Code

♣ Enjoy the countryside and respect its life and work ♣ Guard against all risk of fire ♣ Fasten all gates ♣ Keep your dogs under close control ♣ Keep to public paths across farmland ♣ Use gates and stiles to cross fences, hedges and walls ♣ Leave livestock, crops and machinery alone ♣ Take your litter home ♣ Help to keep all water clean ♣ Protect wildlife, plants and trees ♣ Take special care on country roads ♣ Make no unnecessary noise

---

Bookings

When enquiring about accommodation you may find it helpful to use the booking enquiry coupons which can be found towards the end of the guide. These should be cut out and mailed direct to the establishments in which you are interested. Do remember to include your name and address.

South of England

Home of Saxon kings, the South of England retains much of its character, and there are abundant reminders of the region's past. Winchester, with its superb cathedral, is the heart of Hampshire, and much of the original architecture survives. Hampshire's rolling chalk downs shelter quaint villages with thatched houses, lovely churches and prehistoric sites. The

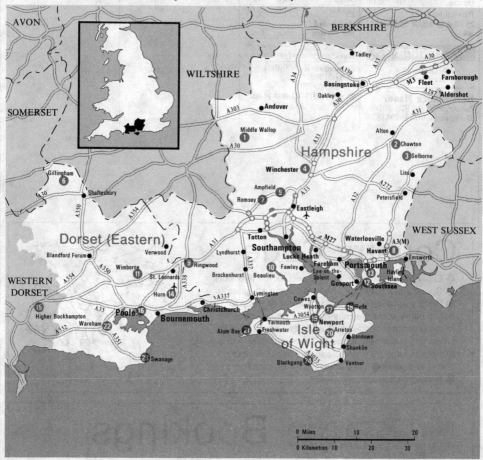

Use the above map to locate places in the "Where to Go, What to See" section opposite.
Use the colour maps at the back of this guide to find places with accommodation.

ancient New Forest was once a royal hunting ground. The coast, too, is rich in interest, from the elegant resorts of Bournemouth and Poole, Dorset's largest harbour town, to the mighty maritime heritage of Portsmouth. And there's the lasting appeal of the Isle of Wight, holiday island of the Victorians and still delighting today's visitors with its unique charms.

WHERE TO GO, WHAT TO SEE

The number against each name will help you locate it on the map opposite.

❶ Museum of Army Flying
Middle Wallop, Hampshire
SO20 8DY
Tel: Andover (0264) 384421
Purpose built museum on the edge of active airfield tells the

story of 100 years of army flying. Exciting and unique collection of aircraft, which fly at weekends.

❷ Jane Austen's House
Chawton, Hampshire GU34 1SD
Tel: Alton (0420) 83262
17th C house where Jane Austen lived from 1809–1817 and wrote or revised her 6 great novels. Letters, pictures, memorabilia, garden with old fashioned flowers.

❸ Romany Folklore Museum and Workshop
Limesend Yard, High Street, Selborne, Hampshire GU34 3JW
Tel: Selborne (042 050) 486
Displays of all aspects of Romany life. Full-size living caravans and tents. Complete wagon builder's workshop (60 years old).

Tennyson lived in Freshwater on the Isle of Wight for 30 years and a monument dedicated to the poet stands atop the chalk downs at the western end of the island

❹ Marwell Zoological Park
Colden Common, Winchester, Hampshire
SO21 1JH
Tel: Owslebury (0962) 777407
Large zoo breeding endangered species. Over 800 animals including big cats, giraffes, deer, zebras, monkeys, hippos and birds.

❺ The Sir Harold Hillier Gardens and Arboretum
Ampfield, Hampshire SO51 0QA
Tel: Braishfield (0794) 68787
Largest collection of trees and shrubs of its kind in the British Isles, planted within an attractive landscape of over 160 acres.

❻ Dorset Rare Breeds Centre
Shaftesbury Road, Gillingham, Dorset SP8 5JG
Tel: Gillingham (0747) 822169
Farm and dairy museums,

lecture hall and tea-rooms. Dorset's largest collection of rare farm animals.

❼ Broadlands
Romsey, Hampshire SO51 9ZD
Tel: Romsey (0794) 516878
Home of the late Lord Mountbatten. Magnificent 18th C house and contents. Superb views across River Test. Mountbatten exhibition and audio-visual presentation.

❼ Paultons Park
Ower, Romsey, Hampshire
SO51 6AL
Tel: Southampton (0703) 814442
A day out for all the family in beautiful surroundings. Lots of fun activities with over 40 different attractions, including bumper boats, kids' kingdom, astroglide.

❽ Sir George Staunton Country Park
Leigh Park, Havant, Hampshire
PO9 5HB
Tel: Havant (0705) 453405
Beautiful Victorian landscape created by Sir George Staunton (Bart), complete with farm animals, buildings, trees and shrubs. All-year interest.

❾ The New Forest Owl Sanctuary
Crow Lane, Crow, Ringwood, Hampshire BH24 3EA
Tel: Ringwood (0425) 476487
Sanctuary for barn owls destined to be released into the wild. Incubation room, hospital unit and 100 aviaries.

⑩ Beaulieu Palace House

Beaulieu, Hampshire SO42 7ZN
Tel: Beaulieu (0590) 612345
The home of Lord and Lady Montagu, the house has been in the family since it was acquired in 1538 following the dissolution of the monasteries by Henry VIII. National Motor Museum, monastic life exhibition, shops.

⑪ Kingston Lacy

Wimborne Minster, Dorset BH21 4EA
Tel: Wimborne (0202) 883402
Historic house recently restored by the National Trust. Fine collection of paintings, garden and park.

⑫ Royal Marines Museum

Southsea, Hampshire PO4 9PX
Tel: Southsea (0705) 819385
History of Royal Marines from 1664 to present day. Dynamic Falklands audio-visual and chilled Arctic display. History gallery featuring a talking head of Hannah Snell.

⑬ Mary Rose Ship Hall and Exhibition

HM Naval Base, Portsmouth, Hampshire PO1 3PZ
Tel: Portsmouth (0705) 812931
Reconstruction and conservation of Henry VIII's warship, and exhibition of the ship's treasures.

⑬ The D Day Museum and Overlord Embroidery

Clarence Esplanade, Portsmouth, Hampshire PO5 3PA
Tel: Portsmouth (0705) 827261
Incorporates Overlord embroidery which depicts Allied invasion of Normandy. Displays of D Day action and some of the vehicles that took part.

⑬ HMS Victory

HM Naval Base, Portsmouth, Hampshire PO1 3PZ
Tel: Portsmouth (0705) 839766
Lord Nelson's flagship at Trafalgar. His cabin, the "cockpit" where he died. Tours of the gun decks.

⑬ HMS Warrior

Victory Gate, HM Naval Base, Portsmouth, Hampshire PO1 3QX
Tel: Portsmouth (0705) 291379
The world's first iron battleship. Four decks completely restored to show life in the Victorian navy of 1860. Cabins, wardroom, engine and cannon.

⑭ Alice in Wonderland Maze

Hurn, Dorset BH23 6BA
Tel: Christchurch (0202) 483004
Hedge maze, Mad Hatter's Tea Garden, Queen of Hearts croquet lawn, Cheshire Cat's adventure playground, Duchess rose and herb garden, rare breeds farmyard.

⑮ Hardy's Cottage and Garden

Higher Bockhampton, Dorset DT2 8QJ
Tel: Dorchester (0305) 262366
Small thatched cottage where the novelist and poet Thomas Hardy was born in 1840, built by his great grandfather and little altered.

The first sight of home for countless seafarers – The Needles lighthouse off the Isle of Wight

16 Brownsea Island
Poole, Dorset BH15 1EE
Tel: Poole (0202) 707744
Island of 500 acres of woodland with beaches, glades and nature reserve. Site of Lord Baden Powell's first scout camp.

16 Compton Acres
Canford Cliffs, Poole, Dorset BH13 7ES
Tel: Canford Cliffs (0202) 700778
Nine separate and distinct gardens of the world. The gardens include Italian, Japanese, sub-tropical, glen, rock, water and heather. Collection of statues.

16 Waterfront Museum
Poole, Dorset BH15 1BW
Tel: Poole (0202) 683138
Displays in the late 15th C town cellars and Oakleys Mill building tell of Poole's maritime history.

17 Butterfly World and Fountain World
Wootton, Ryde, Isle of Wight PO33 4RW
Tel: Isle of Wight (0983) 883430
Tropical indoor garden with butterflies from around the world. Fountain World has many fountains, water features and huge fish. Italian and Japanese garden.

18 Isle of Wight Steam Railway
Railway Station, Havenstreet, Ryde, Isle of Wight PO33 4DS
Tel: Isle of Wight (0983) 882204
Five-mile steam railway using Victorian and Edwardian locomotives and carriages. Souvenir shop, refreshments, children's playground.

19 Newport Roman Villa
Newport, Isle of Wight PO36 1EY
Tel: Isle of Wight (0983) 529720
Underfloor heated bath system, tessellated floors displayed in reconstructed rooms, corn-drying kiln and small site museum of objects recovered.

20 Haseley Manor
Arreton, Isle of Wight PO30 3AN
Tel: Isle of Wight (0983) 865420
Historic manor house dating from medieval times through to the Victorian period. Large working pottery, sweet factory with demonstrations, craft village, garden, pets.

21 The Needles Pleasure Park
Alum Bay, Isle of Wight PO39 OJD
Tel: Isle of Wight (0983) 752401
Chairlift to beach. Famous coloured sand cliffs. View of Needle lighthouse. Glassworks studio, adventure playground. Ride Super X motion simulator and new Carousel.

22 The Tank Museum
Bovington Camp, Wareham, Dorset BH20 6JG
Tel: Bindon Abbey (0929) 463953
Largest and most comprehensive museum collection of armoured fighting vehicles in the world. Over 250 vehicles on show, with supporting displays and video theatres.

23 Swanage Railway
Swanage, Dorset BH19 1HB
Tel: Swanage (0929) 425800

The modern game of cricket originates from Hambledon in Hampshire, where the local team first invented many of its laws in 1774

Enjoy a nostalgic steam train ride on the Purbeck line. Trains run every weekend throughout the year, with daily running at peak times.

24 Blackgang Chine Theme Park
Blackgang Chine, Ventnor, Isle of Wight PO38 2HN
Tel: Isle of Wight (0983) 730330
Theme park with water and clifftop gardens. Dinosaur park, Frontierland, model village, maze, Nurseryland.

FIND OUT MORE

Further information about holidays and attractions in the South of England region is available from:
Southern Tourist Board
40 Chamberlayne Road, Eastleigh, Hampshire SO5 5JH
Tel: (0703) 620006

These publications are available free from the Southern Tourist Board (please telephone [0703] 620555):
Southern England Holidays '93 (a guide to the region and its accommodation)
Take a Break (value for money breaks)
The Isle of Wight Guide
Holiday Parks in the South and South-East (caravan holiday homes, touring parks and camping)
Bed & Breakfast Touring Map

Places to stay

Accommodation entries in this regional section are listed in alphabetical order of place name, and then in alphabetical order of establishment.

The map references refer to the colour maps at the back of the guide. The first figure is the map number; the letter and figure which follow indicate the grid reference on the map.

The symbols at the end of each accommodation entry give information about services and facilities. A 'key' to these symbols is inside the back cover flap, which can be kept open for easy reference.

ABBOTTS ANN

Hampshire
Map ref 2C2

Abbotts Law ♨
HIGHLY COMMENDED

Abbotts Ann, Andover
SP11 7DW
☎ Andover (0264) 710350
Elegant country house on edge of village. Quarter of a mile from junction of A303 and A343 Salisbury road near Andover. Beautiful gardens, Cordon Bleu cuisine, heated pool. B & B price is per room; half board price is per person for 2 sharing room.
Bedrooms: 2 double, 1 twin
Bathrooms: 3 private

Bed & breakfast

per night:	£min	£max
Single	42.00	47.00
Double	42.00	47.00

Half board

per person:	£min	£max
Daily	37.50	40.00

Evening meal 1930 (last orders 1930)
Parking for 10
Open April-October
♨ 2 ⬛ ⬛ □ ♨ ♨ ⬛ ⬛ ⬛ ⬛ ✶
▥ ◪ ✦ ◵ ∪ ↑ ✗ ✗ ⬛ ⬛

Virginia Lodge ♨
Listed COMMENDED

Salisbury Road, Abbotts Ann,
Andover SP11 7NX
☎ Andover (0264) 710713
Spacious comfortable bungalow with large gardens

---

on edge of attractive village. On A343, one mile from A303. Central for Stonehenge, Winchester and Salisbury.
Bedrooms: 1 double, 2 twin
Bathrooms: 1 private,
1 public

Bed & breakfast

per night:	£min	£max
Single	16.00	22.00
Double	30.00	34.00

Parking for 6
♨ 2 ⬛ ♨ ⬛ ⬛ ⬛ ✗ ♨ ⬛ ▥
✶ ⬛

ALRESFORD

Hampshire
Map ref 2C2

Between Old and New Alresford lie the remains of Bishop de Lucy's splendid 12th C reservoir. New Alresford is a pleasant market town and Old Alresford a smaller village with a stream running through the green.

The Milburys

Beauworth, Alresford
SO24 0PA
☎ Bramdean (0962) 771248
Old world inn (1700) with inglenook fireplaces, antiques, minstrels' gallery and a la carte restaurant. No music or pinball, just a proper English pub.
Bedrooms: 1 single,
2 double, 1 twin, 1 triple

Bathrooms: 1 private,
2 public

Bed & breakfast

per night:	£min	£max
Single	28.50	
Double	38.50	

Half board

per person:	£min	£max
Daily	30.00	45.00

Lunch available
Evening meal 1800 (last orders 2200)
Parking for 100
Cards accepted: Access, Visa, Amex
♨ ♨ ⬛ ⬛ ▥ ◪ ↑ ✶ ⬛ ⬛ ✗
⬛ ⬛

The Old Manse

46 East Street, Alresford
SO24 9EQ
☎ (0962) 734396
Grade II listed historic country house, 3 minutes from centre of small country town, surrounding countryside and steam railway. Comfortable and welcoming, own honey and jams.
Bedrooms: 1 single, 1 double
Bathrooms: 2 private,
1 public

Bed & breakfast

per night:	£min	£max
Single	22.00	25.00
Double	37.50	44.00

♨ ♨ ⬛ ⬛ ⬛ ⬛ ✗ ⬛ ▥ ◪ ✶
✗ ⬛ ⬛ ⬛

ALTON

Hampshire
Map ref 2C2

Pleasant old market town standing on the Pilgrim's Way, with some attractive Georgian buildings. The parish church still bears the scars of bullet marks, evidence of a bitter struggle between the Roundheads and the Royalists.
Tourist Information Centre
☎ *(0420) 88448*

Glen Derry

52 Wellhouse Road, Beech,
Alton GU34 4AG
☎ (0420) 83235
Peaceful, secluded family home set in 3.5 acres of garden. Warm welcome assured. Ideal base for Watercress Steam Railway, Winchester and Portsmouth.
Bedrooms: 1 double, 1 triple,
1 multiple
Bathrooms: 1 private,
1 public

Bed & breakfast

per night:	£min	£max
Single	18.00	25.00
Double	28.00	34.00

Parking for 12
♨ ♨ ♨ ⬛ ⬛ ⬛ ✗ ⬛ ⬛ ▥ ◪ ♨
✗ ⬛

AMPORT

Hampshire
Map ref 2C2

Broadwater

Amport, Andover SP11 8AY
☎ Andover (0264) 772240 &
710143
Fax (0264) 710526
*Grade 2 listed thatched
cottage. From A303 (from
Andover) take turn off to
Hawk Conservancy/Amport.
At T junction, turn right, take
first road right (East
Cholderton), Broadwater is
first cottage on the right.*
Bedrooms: 2 twin
Bathrooms: 1 private,
1 public

Bed & breakfast

per night:	£min	£max
Single	17.50	
Double	40.00	

Half board

per person:	£min	£max
Daily	30.00	

Parking for 3
⚭ ⛛ 🚻 🅰 🏮 📺 🛏, 🚗 ✿ 🐾

ANDOVER

Hampshire
Map ref 2C2

Town that achieved
importance from the wool
trade and now has much
modern development. A
good centre for visiting
places of interest.
*Tourist Information Centre
☎ (0264) 324320*

Malt Cottage ⋀

🏅🏅 **HIGHLY COMMENDED**

Upper Clatford, Andover
SP11 7QL
☎ (0264) 323469
*Country house with idyllic 6-
acre garden, lake and stream.
Set in charming Hampshire
village within easy reach of
Salisbury, Romsey,
Stonehenge and London/
Exeter road.*
Bedrooms: 1 double, 1 twin
Bathrooms: 2 private,
2 public

Bed & breakfast

per night:	£min	£max
Double	35.00	42.00

Half board

per person:	£min	£max
Daily	30.00	43.50

Evening meal 1800 (last
orders 2000)
Parking for 5
⚭ 🖥 ⛛ 🚻 📺 🛏, 🚗 ✿ ✗
🐾 🏮

The Old Barn ⋀

Listed **HIGHLY COMMENDED**

Amport, Andover SP11 8AE
☎ (0264) 710410
*Converted old barn, in small
village approximately 3 miles
south west of Andover.
Secluded, but only three-
quarters of a mile from A303.*
Bedrooms: 1 single, 1 double
Bathrooms: 1 public

Bed & breakfast

per night:	£min	£max
Single	15.00	17.00

Half board

per person:	£min	£max
Daily	28.00	30.00

Parking for 4
🖥 ⛛ 🚻 🅰 ✗ 🛏, 🚗 ✿ ✗ 🐾
🏮 🏮

BARTON ON SEA

Hampshire
Map ref 2B3

Seaside village with views
of the Isle of Wight.
Within easy driving
distance of the New
Forest.

Cleeve House ⋀

🏅🏅 **COMMENDED**

58 Barton Court Avenue,
Barton on Sea, New Milton
BH25 7HG
☎ New Milton (0425)
615211
*Large, comfortable, character
family home with beautiful
gardens. Close to sea, within
easy reach of New Forest,
beaches, cliffs, golf and
sailing. No-smoking house.*
Bedrooms: 1 single, 1 twin,
2 triple
Bathrooms: 2 private,
1 public

Bed & breakfast

per night:	£min	£max
Single	15.00	15.00
Double	34.00	37.00

Parking for 8
⚭ ⛛ 🚻 🅰 🏮 ✗ 🚻 📺 🛏, ✿
✗ 🐾

Laurel Lodge

48 Western Avenue, Barton
on Sea, New Milton
BH25 7PZ
☎ New Milton (0425)
618309
*Need pampering? Small,
welcoming establishment with
home cooking. Many local
beaches, cliff top walks. 3
miles from New Forest. Lots
to do - or just relax.*
Bedrooms: 2 double, 1 twin,
1 triple
Bathrooms: 1 private,
2 public

Bed & breakfast

per night:	£min	£max
Double	28.00	33.00

Half board

per person:	£min	£max
Daily	21.50	24.00
Weekly	140.00	158.00

Evening meal from 1830
Parking for 4
⚭ 5 🖥 🚻 ⛛ 🚻 🅰 🏮 📺 🛏,
🐾 🅾 ✗ 🏮

The Ventana Inn

Listed

Marine Drive, Barton on Sea,
New Milton BH25 7DZ
☎ (0425) 610309
*Spectacular sea views from
cliff top hotel. Restaurant,
bars, a la carte menu, bar
meals, children and pets
welcome.*
Bedrooms: 4 double, 1 twin
Bathrooms: 3 private,
2 public

Bed & breakfast

per night:	£min	£max
Double	16.50	19.50

Lunch available
Evening meal 1900 (last
orders 2100)
Parking for 20
Cards accepted: Access, Visa
⚭ 🖥 ⛛ 🏮 🅰 ✗ 🚻 🛏, 🚗 🅰 🕙
🏮 🚭

BASINGSTOKE

Hampshire
Map ref 2C2

Rapidly developing
commercial and industrial
centre. The town is
surrounded by charming
villages and places to
visit.
*Tourist Information Centre
☎ (0256) 817618*

Street Farm House

🏅🏅 **COMMENDED**

The Street, South
Warnborough, Basingstoke
RG25 1RS
☎ (0256) 862225
*Charming Jacobean
farmhouse, offering
comfortable facilities. Well
situated in a pretty, rural
village within easy reach of
London, Guildford and the
south coast.*
Bedrooms: 2 twin, 1 triple
Bathrooms: 1 public,
1 private shower

Bed & breakfast

per night:	£min	£max
Double	30.00	40.00

Half board

per person:	£min	£max
Daily	20.00	25.00

Evening meal from 1930
Parking for 9
Cards accepted: Amex
⚭ 🖥 🚻 ⛛ 🚻 🅰 🏮 ✗ 📺 🛏,
🚗 🕙 ✿ 🐾 🏮

BEAULIEU

Hampshire
Map ref 2C3

Beautifully situated among
woods and hills on the
Beaulieu river, the village
is both charming and
unspoilt. The 13th C
ruined Cistercian abbey
and 14th C Palace House
stand close to the
National Motor Museum.
There is a maritime
museum at Bucklers
Hard.
*Tourist Information Centre
☎ (0590) 612345*

Coollerry Cottage

Masseys Lane, East Boldre,
Beaulieu SO42 7WE
☎ (0590) 612428
*Charming New Forest cottage
in quiet position, close to
motor museum, Bucklers
Hard and Hatchett Pond.
Ideal for forest, coastal and
heathland walks. Sorry no
smokers. Half-price winter
breaks (November-March).*
Bedrooms: 1 double, 1 twin
Bathrooms: 1 public

Bed & breakfast

per night:	£min	£max
Double	28.00	34.00

Parking for 4
⚭ ⛛ 🚻 🏮 ✗ 📺 🛏, 🚗 🐾
🅾 🏮

Harlicks ⋀

Listed

Hatchet Lane, Beaulieu,
Brockenhurst SO42 7WA
☎ (0590) 612375
Fax (0590) 612375
*Delightful house set between
2 farms, with easy access to
Motor Museum, Exbury
Gardens, beaches, riding and
Isle of Wight ferries.*
Bedrooms: 1 single,
1 double, 1 twin, 1 multiple
Bathrooms: 1 public

Bed & breakfast

per night:	£min	£max
Single	15.00	20.00
Double	30.00	50.00

Half board

per person:	£min	£max
Daily	25.00	35.00

Evening meal 1900 (last
orders 2000)
Parking for 6
⚭ 🖥 🖥 ⛛ 🚻 🅰 🏮 ✗ 🚗
🅾 🏮 ✿ 🐾 🅾 🏮

BEAULIEU

Continued

Leygreen Farm House ⚑
Lyndhurst Road, Beaulieu,
Brockenhurst SO42 7YP
☎ (0590) 612355
*Comfortable Victorian
farmhouse with large garden.
Convenient for Beaulieu,
Bucklers Hard museums and
Exbury Gardens.*
Bedrooms: 3 double
Bathrooms: 2 private,
1 public
Bed & breakfast

per night:	£min	£max
Single	16.00	18.00
Double	28.00	34.00

Parking for 6

BLACKFIELD

Hampshire
Map ref 2C3

Village within easy reach
of Beaulieu and the forest
areas.

Scots Pines
West Common, Blackfield,
Southampton SO4 1XJ
☎ Fawley (0703) 897505
*Large house in completely
private grounds 100 yards
from open forest. One and a
half miles from Solent
beaches. Stabling for guests
who would like to bring their
own horse.*
Bedrooms: 1 single,
1 double, 1 twin, 1 triple
Bathrooms: 2 public
Bed & breakfast

per night:	£min	£max
Single	10.00	12.50
Double	20.00	25.00

Parking for 6

Individual
proprietors have
supplied all details
of accommodation.
Although we do
check for accuracy,
we advise you to
confirm the
information at the
time of booking.

BLANDFORD FORUM

Dorset
Map ref 2B3

Almost completely
destroyed by fire in 1731,
the town was rebuilt in a
handsome Georgian style.
The church is large and
grand and the town is the
hub of a rich farming
area.
*Tourist Information Centre
☎ (0258) 454770.*

Fairfield House ⚑
HIGHLY COMMENDED
Church Road, Pimperne,
Blandford Forum DT11 8UB
☎ (0258) 456756
Fax (0258) 480053
*Distinctive, Grade II,
Georgian manor house in 1.5
acres of gardens in peaceful
village. Bedrooms tastefully
furnished, retaining much
antiquity whilst offering
modern facilities. Riding, clay
shooting and golf arranged.
Stables available.*
Bedrooms: 1 single,
1 double, 2 twin, 1 triple
Bathrooms: 4 private,
1 public
Bed & breakfast

per night:	£min	£max
Single	19.50	33.00
Double	39.50	55.00

Lunch available
Evening meal 1900 (last
orders 2100)
Parking for 20
Cards accepted: Access, Visa,
Amex

Farnham Farm House ⚑
Listed APPROVED
Farnham, Blandford Forum
DT11 8DG
☎ Tollard Royal (0725)
516254
*350-acre arable farm. 19th C
farmhouse in the Cranborne
Chase with extensive views to
the south. Within easy reach
of the coast.*
Bedrooms: 1 double, 1 twin,
1 triple
Bathrooms: 1 private,
1 public
Bed & breakfast

per night:	£min	£max
Single	18.00	22.00
Double	35.00	40.00

Parking for 7

Meadow House
Listed
Tarrant Hinton, Blandford
Forum DT11 8JG
☎ Tarrant Hinton (025 889)
498
*Brick and flint farmhouse on
historic Cranborne Chase.
Double glazed, quiet and
comfortable accommodation.
Home-produced English
breakfast.*
Bedrooms: 1 single,
1 double, 1 triple
Bathrooms: 3 public
Bed & breakfast

per night:	£min	£max
Single	14.00	15.00
Double	28.00	30.00

Parking for 6

BOURNEMOUTH

Dorset
Map ref 2B3

Seaside town set among
the pines with a mild
climate, sandy beaches
and fine coastal views.
The town with excellent
shops, a pier, a pavilion,
museums and conference
centre.
*Tourist Information Centre
☎ (0202) 789789*

Belmont Lodge Guest House
21 Grand Avenue,
Southbourne, Bournemouth
BH6 3SY
☎ (0202) 425433
*Delightful family-run hotel
providing good meals. A few
minutes' walk from shops and
sea.*
Bedrooms: 1 single,
2 double, 1 twin, 1 triple,
1 multiple
Bathrooms: 2 public
Bed & breakfast

per night:	£min	£max
Single	12.00	15.00
Double	24.00	30.00

Half board

per person:	£min	£max
Daily	18.50	21.50
Weekly	122.50	143.00

Evening meal from 1800
Parking for 5

We advise you to
confirm your
booking in writing.

The Cottage ⚑
COMMENDED
12 Southern Road,
Southbourne, Bournemouth
BH6 3SR
☎ (0202) 422764
*Charming character family-
run hotel. Restful location.
Noted for home-prepared
fresh cooking, cleanliness and
tastefully furnished
accommodation. Ample
parking. Non-smoking.*
Bedrooms: 1 single,
1 double, 2 twin, 1 triple,
2 multiple
Bathrooms: 4 private,
2 public, 1 private shower
Bed & breakfast

per night:	£min	£max
Single	15.00	19.00
Double	30.00	42.00

Half board

per person:	£min	£max
Daily	21.50	25.50
Weekly	145.00	167.00

Evening meal 1800 (last
orders 1800)
Parking for 8

Egerton House Hotel
Listed
385 Holdenhurst Road,
Queens Park, Bournemouth
BH8 9AN
☎ (0202) 394024
*Tastefully appointed, family-
run hotel, near Bournemouth
and Boscombe town centre
and West Cliff Promenade.
Convenient for public
transport.*
Bedrooms: 2 single,
3 double, 2 twin, 2 triple
Bathrooms: 1 private,
2 public
Bed & breakfast

per night:	£min	£max
Single	14.00	17.00
Double	29.00	31.00

Half board

per person:	£min	£max
Daily	22.00	24.00
Weekly	134.00	150.00

Lunch available
Evening meal 1800 (last
orders 1800)
Parking for 8

The Garthlyn Hotel ⚑
COMMENDED
6 Sandbourne Road, Alum
Chine, Westbourne,
Bournemouth BH4 8JH
☎ (0202) 761016
*Hotel of character with lovely
gardens. Good quality beds,
home cooking and comforts. 4*

minutes' walk to beaches (hut available).
Bedrooms: 6 double, 1 twin, 1 triple, 2 multiple
Bathrooms: 8 private, 1 public

Bed & breakfast

per night:	£min	£max
Single	20.00	26.50
Double	40.00	53.00

Half board

per person:	£min	£max
Daily	27.50	35.00
Weekly	162.00	205.00

Evening meal 1800 (last orders 1900)
Parking for 9
Cards accepted: Access, Visa, Switch

The Golden Sovereigns Hotel

97 Alumhurst Road, Alum Chine, Bournemouth
BH4 8HR
☎ (0202) 762088
Comfortable, interesting small hotel. Beautiful sandy beaches 4 minutes away. Convenient for both Bournemouth and Poole. A warm welcome awaits you.
Bedrooms: 1 single, 3 double, 2 twin, 1 triple, 2 multiple
Bathrooms: 5 private, 2 public

Bed & breakfast

per night:	£min	£max
Single	15.00	26.00
Double	28.00	50.00

Half board

per person:	£min	£max
Daily	21.00	33.00
Weekly	140.00	185.00

Lunch available
Evening meal 1800 (last orders 1630)
Parking for 9
Cards accepted: Access, Visa

Mayfield Private Hotel

46 Frances Road, Bournemouth BH1 3SA
☎ (0202) 551839
Overlooking public gardens with tennis, bowling, putting greens. Central for sea, shops and main rail/coach stations. Some rooms with shower or toilet/shower. Licensed.
Bedrooms: 1 single, 4 double, 2 twin, 1 multiple
Bathrooms: 4 private, 2 public, 1 private shower

Bed & breakfast

per night:	£min	£max
Single	13.00	16.00
Double	26.00	32.00

Half board

per person:	£min	£max
Daily	18.00	21.00
Weekly	104.00	116.00

Evening meal from 1800
Parking for 5
Open January–November

The Osprey

6 Fisherman's Avenue, Southbourne, Bournemouth
BH6 3SQ
☎ (0202) 423673
Family-run establishment in Fisherman's Walk, a leafy glade leading to the sea. Close to town and within easy reach of the New Forest.
Bedrooms: 1 single, 1 double, 2 twin, 2 triple
Bathrooms: 1 private, 1 public

Bed & breakfast

per night:	£min	£max
Single	12.00	16.00
Double	24.00	32.00

Parking for 2

Pinewood Guest House

197 Holdenhurst Road, Bournemouth BH8 8DG
☎ (0202) 292684
Friendly guesthouse, close to rail, coach stations and all amenities. Tea, coffee and satellite TV in all rooms.
Bedrooms: 1 single, 2 double, 1 twin, 4 triple
Bathrooms: 2 public

Bed & breakfast

per night:	£min	£max
Single	14.00	15.00
Double	28.00	30.00

Parking for 8

Rosedene Cottage Hotel
Listed

St Peter's Road, Bournemouth BH1 2LA
☎ (0202) 554102
Old world cottage hotel, quiet, yet in the heart of Bournemouth. A short stroll to pier, shops, gardens, International Centre, theatres and beaches. 20 minutes from Hurn Airport.
Bedrooms: 1 single, 5 double, 1 twin, 1 multiple
Bathrooms: 5 private, 2 public

Bed & breakfast

per night:	£min	£max
Single	16.00	20.00
Double	28.00	36.00

Evening meal 1700 (last orders 2100)
Parking for 8
Cards accepted: Access, Visa, Amex

Seabreeze Hotel

32 St Catherines Road, Southbourne, Bournemouth
BH6 4AB
☎ (0202) 433888
Located opposite beach with glorious sea views and easy access to Bournemouth and Christchurch. Peaceful, small hotel with family atmosphere. Generous home cooking. Children half price. Vegetarians welcome.
Bedrooms: 1 single, 2 double, 2 twin, 1 triple, 2 multiple
Bathrooms: 6 private, 1 public

Bed & breakfast

per night:	£min	£max
Single	14.00	16.00
Double	28.00	32.00

Half board

per person:	£min	£max
Daily	20.00	22.00
Weekly	110.00	140.00

Evening meal 1800 (last orders 1600)
Parking for 8

Sun Haven

39 Southern Road, Southbourne, Bournemouth
BH6 3SS
☎ (0202) 427560
150 yards to sandy beach. Attractive bedrooms, central heating, snacks and tea/coffee facilities. Parking. Ideal for Bournemouth, Christchurch, New Forest and local beauty spots.
Bedrooms: 2 single, 3 double, 1 twin, 2 triple
Bathrooms: 3 public

Bed & breakfast

per night:	£min	£max
Single	14.50	19.50
Double	28.00	38.00

Parking for 6
Open April–September

Tivoli

54 Holloway Avenue, Bear Cross, Bournemouth
BH11 9JS
☎ (0202) 575026

Family-run detached bungalow, conveniently situated for Bournemouth, Poole and surrounding areas. Parking available.
Bedrooms: 1 single, 1 double, 1 triple
Bathrooms: 1 public

Bed & breakfast

per night:	£min	£max
Single	13.00	13.00
Double	26.00	26.00

Parking for 4

Willowdene Hotel
COMMENDED

43 Grand Avenue, Southbourne, Bournemouth
BH6 3SY
☎ (0202) 425370
Detached Georgian house built in 1908 and completely refurbished. Happy atmosphere, no restrictions and access at all times. 200 yards from best beach in England.
Bedrooms: 1 single, 2 double, 1 twin, 2 triple
Bathrooms: 3 private, 2 public

Bed & breakfast

per night:	£min	£max
Single	14.00	15.99
Double	28.00	31.98

Parking for 8
Open April–October

BRAMDEAN

Hampshire
Map ref 2C3

Village astride the A272, 1 mile west of the site of a Roman villa.

Dean Farm
Listed

Kilmeston, Alresford
SO24 0NL
☎ (0962) 771286
200-acre mixed farm. Comfortable, 18th C farmhouse in Kilmeston, a small and peaceful village 1.5 miles off the A272 between Petersfield and Winchester.
Bedrooms: 2 double, 1 triple
Bathrooms: 1 public

Bed & breakfast

per night:	£min	£max
Single	15.00	20.00
Double	30.00	30.00

Parking for 3

BRANSGORE

Hampshire
Map ref 2B3

Situated in extensive woodlands. In the church of St Mary is a lovely Perpendicular font which is said to have come from Christchurch.

Tothill House ⚔

off Forest Road, Bransgore, Christchurch, Dorset BH23 8DZ
☎ (0425) 74414
Edwardian house in secluded woodland garden, offering peace and tranquillity. Wide variety of local activities and places to visit.
Bedrooms: 1 double, 2 twin
Bathrooms: 3 private

Bed & breakfast

per night:	£min	£max
Single	25.00	25.00
Double	50.00	50.00

Parking for 6
Open February-November

BRIGHSTONE

Isle of Wight
Map ref 2C3

Excellent centre for visitors who want somewhere quiet. Calbourne nearby is ideal for picnics and the sea at Chilton Chine has safe bathing at high tide.

Chilton Farm ⚔

Chilton Lane, Brighstone, Newport PO30 4DS
☎ (0983) 740338
600-acre mixed farm. All rooms en-suite in attractive courtyard, converted 18th C stables. Garden and barbecue. Set in beautiful countryside. Close to sea. Colour TV.
Bedrooms: 2 double, 1 twin, 1 triple, 1 multiple
Bathrooms: 5 private

Bed & breakfast

per night:	£min	£max
Single	16.50	17.00
Double	29.00	30.00

Parking for 7
Open March-November

The symbols are explained on the flap inside the back cover.

BROCKENHURST

Hampshire
Map ref 2C3

Attractive village with thatched cottages and a ford in its main street. Well placed for visiting the New Forest.

Moor Cottage

Setley, Brockenhurst SO42 7UG
☎ Lymington (0590) 23630
Lovely country house on forest edge just outside Brockenhurst.
Bedrooms: 2 double, 1 twin
Bathrooms: 1 public

Bed & breakfast

per night:	£min	£max
Single	15.00	
Double	30.00	

Parking for 3

BURLEY

Hampshire
Map ref 2B3

Attractive centre from which to explore the south-west part of the New Forest. There is an ancient earthwork on Castle Hill nearby, which also offers good views.

Bay Tree House

1 Clough Lane, Burley, Ringwood BH24 4AE
☎ (0425) 403215
Friendly country house near centre of village in the heart of the New Forest. Ideal for touring the many places of interest within easy distance.
Bedrooms: 1 single, 1 triple
Bathrooms: 1 public

Bed & breakfast

per night:	£min	£max
Single	15.00	17.00
Double	30.00	37.00

Parking for 4
Open January-November

Rosebay Cottage

Chapel Lane, Burley, Ringwood BH24 4DJ
☎ (042 53) 2471
Delightful, 100-year-old forest cottage. Friendly atmosphere. A few minutes' walk to village centre. Direct access to forest.
Bedrooms: 1 double, 1 twin, 1 triple
Bathrooms: 1 public

Bed & breakfast

per night:	£min	£max
Double	28.00	31.00

Parking for 5

BURSLEDON

Hampshire
Map ref 2C3

Dodwell Cottage ⚔

Dodwell Lane, Bursledon, Southampton SO3 8BD
☎ Southampton (0703) 406074
Friendly bed and breakfast accommodation in 1716 country cottage. Comfortable rooms and sitting room with TV. Home cooking.
Bedrooms: 1 double, 1 twin, 1 triple
Bathrooms: 1 private, 1 public

Bed & breakfast

per night:	£min	£max
Single	16.00	20.00
Double	32.00	40.00

Parking for 6
Cards accepted: Access, Visa, Switch

CADNAM

Hampshire
Map ref 2C3

Village with numerous attractive cottages and an inn close to the entrance of the M27.

Mrs Ann M Dawe

Budd's Farm, Winsor Road, Winsor, Southampton SO4 2HN
☎ Southampton (0703) 812381
200-acre dairy farm. Well-modernised, thatched farmhouse in pretty country garden. Located off A336.
Bedrooms: 1 twin, 1 triple
Bathrooms: 1 public

Bed & breakfast

per night:	£min	£max
Single	15.00	16.00
Double	30.00	32.00

Parking for 3
Open April-October

Le Chanteclerc Restaurant ⚔

Romsey Road, Cadnam, Southampton SO4 2NX
☎ Southampton (0703) 813271 & 812163

Restaurant with rooms, set in attractive grounds on edge of New Forest. Easy access to all main attractions and towns.
Bedrooms: 1 single, 3 double, 2 twin
Bathrooms: 6 private

Bed & breakfast

per night:	£min	£max
Single	28.00	28.00
Double	35.00	35.00

Lunch available
Evening meal 1900 (last orders 2200)
Parking for 20
Cards accepted: Access, Visa, Diners, Amex

CASHMOOR

Dorset
Map ref 2B3

Small village on the A354 Salisbury to Blandford Forum road. To the north-west lies Cranborne Chase.

Cashmoor Guest House

Cashmoor, Blandford Forum DT11 8DN
☎ Handley (0725) 552339
Main part of building is 300 years old, with wealth of exposed beams in dining room, and log fires. Easily located on A354 between Blandford and Salisbury.
Bedrooms: 1 double, 1 twin, 2 triple
Bathrooms: 4 private

Bed & breakfast

per night:	£min	£max
Single	25.00	29.00
Double	35.00	39.00

Half board

per person:	£min	£max
Daily	25.50	27.50
Weekly	148.00	167.00

Lunch available
Evening meal 1900 (last orders 2000)
Parking for 10

CHANDLERS FORD

Hampshire
Map ref 2C3

Mr P Lanham

133 Bournemouth Road, Chandlers Ford, Eastleigh SO5 3HA
☎ (0703) 254801
Three bedroom, detached, family home. Situated in service road, with easy access

to all routes. Pleasant garden with solar heated swimming pool.
Bedrooms: 1 single, 1 double
Bathrooms: 1 public

Bed & breakfast

per night:	£min	£max
Single	14.00	16.00
Double	24.00	28.00

Parking for 2
🐾4🚗♦🅿️🔌♿💷✂️📺🛏️🍽️
🏕️🐕

St Lucia
68 Shaftesbury Avenue,
Chandlers Ford, Eastleigh
SO5 3BP
☎ (0703) 262995
Fax (0703) 262995
Homely accommodation well placed for touring, near Winchester, the south coast and the New Forest. Evening meals, home-grown produce in season. Non-smokers only please.
Bedrooms: 2 single, 2 twin
Bathrooms: 1 public

Bed & breakfast

per night:	£min	£max
Single	14.00	
Double	30.00	

Half board

per person:	£min	£max
Daily	26.00	
Weekly	175.00	

Evening meal 1830 (last orders 1630)
Parking for 5
🐾10🔌🚗♦🔌♿💷✂️🛏️
🅿️🐕✿✂️🏕️📖🐾🆂🅿️

CHRISTCHURCH
Dorset
Map ref 2B3

Tranquil town lying between the Avon and Stour just before they converge and flow into Christchurch Harbour. A fine 11th C church and the remains of a Norman castle and house can be seen.
Tourist Information Centre
☎ *(0202) 471780*

Chalkwood
45 Barrack Road,
Christchurch BH23 1PA
☎ (0202) 474527
Good food and a friendly atmosphere. Children 12 years and under half price sharing parents' room.
Bedrooms: 1 twin, 1 triple
Bathrooms: 1 private,
2 public, 1 private shower

Bed & breakfast

per night:	£min	£max
Single	12.00	13.50
Double	24.00	27.00

Half board

per person:	£min	£max
Daily	17.50	20.00
Weekly	115.00	133.00

Evening meal from 1800
Parking for 2
🐾♦🔌♿📖📺🛏️🅿️✂️
🏕️🆑

COLDEN COMMON
Hampshire
Map ref 2C3

Commons End ⚠
Listed
Main Road, Colden Common,
Winchester SO21 1RR
☎ Twyford (0962) 713477
Modern house with large pleasant garden overlooking fields. Food available at nearby village inn. Winchester, Portsmouth, New Forest within easy reach.
Bedrooms: 1 single, 2 triple
Bathrooms: 1 public

Bed & breakfast

per night:	£min	£max
Single	15.00	15.00
Double	30.00	30.00

Parking for 5
🐾♦🔌♿💷📖📺🛏️🅿️
✿🏕️

COMPTON
Hampshire
Map ref 2C3

Mrs P Neyroud
Listed
Manor House, Place Lane,
Compton, Winchester
SO21 2BA
☎ Twyford (0962) 712162
Comfortable country house, 8 minutes from Shawford railway station and 2 miles from city of Winchester. Non-smokers preferred.
Bedrooms: 1 double
Bathrooms: 1 public

Bed & breakfast

per night:	£min	£max
Single	9.50	9.50
Double	19.00	19.00

Parking for 1
🆑♦🔌✂️🅿️✿✂️🏕️📖

> The colour maps at the back of this guide pinpoint all places with accommodation.

COMPTON ABBAS
Dorset
Map ref 2B3

The Old Forge
Listed
Fanners Yard, Compton
Abbas, Shaftesbury SP7 0NQ
☎ (0747) 811881
Charming bed and breakfast accommodation, 3 miles from Shaftesbury. English country cottage style bedrooms, log fire to relax by. Country house style and atmosphere for the non-smoker.
Bedrooms: 1 single,
2 double, 1 triple
Bathrooms: 2 private,
1 public

Bed & breakfast

per night:	£min	£max
Single	18.00	25.00
Double	36.00	40.00

Parking for 3
🐾♦🔌♿💷✂️📺🛏️🏕️🅿️

COOMBE KEYNES
Dorset
Map ref 2B3

West Coombe Farmhouse
Listed
Coombe Keynes, Wareham
BH20 5PS
☎ Bindon Abbey (0929) 462889
Former farmhouse in quiet hamlet near coast. Turn off B3071 midway between Wool and Lulworth, first house on left in village.
Bedrooms: 1 single,
1 double, 1 twin
Bathrooms: 1 public

Bed & breakfast

per night:	£min	£max
Single	16.00	17.00
Double	30.00	32.00

Evening meal from 1900
Parking for 3
🐾♦🔌💷🅿️📺🛏️✿✂️
🏕️🆂🅿️

> There are separate sections in this guide listing groups specialising in farm holidays and accommodation which is especially suitable for young people and organised groups.

CORFE CASTLE
Dorset
Map ref 2B3

One of the most spectacular ruined castles in Britain. Norman in origin, the castle was a Royalist stronghold during the Civil War and held out until 1645. The village had a considerable marble-carving industry in the Middle Ages.

Bradle Farmhouse
🏅 COMMENDED
Bradle Farm, Church
Knowle, Wareham
BH20 5NU
☎ (0929) 480712
550-acre mixed farm. Built in 1862, set in the heart of Purbeck, 2 miles from the beach and coastal paths. Ideal for families. Evening meals by arrangement with local inn.
Bedrooms: 1 double, 1 twin,
1 triple
Bathrooms: 2 public

Bed & breakfast

per night:	£min	£max
Single	17.00	21.00
Double	30.00	34.00

Evening meal 1830 (last orders 2000)
Parking for 4
🐾♦🔌💷🅿️📺🛏️🅿️✿
✂️🏕️🆂🅿️

Kimmeridge Farmhouse
Kimmeridge, Wareham
BH20 5PE
☎ (0929) 480990
750-acre mixed farm. Farmhouse built in the 16th C, with lovely views of surrounding countryside and sea. Warm family atmosphere and spacious facilities. Evening meals by arrangement with local inn.
Bedrooms: 2 double, 1 twin
Bathrooms: 1 private,
2 public

Bed & breakfast

per night:	£min	£max
Double	30.00	35.00

Parking for 3
🐾🅿️🆑🚗♦🔌🆂🛏️🅿️✿
✂️🏕️🅿️🆂🅿️

> Half board prices shown are per person but in some cases may be based on double/twin occupancy.

CORHAMPTON

Hampshire
Map ref 2C3

Corhampton Lane Farm

Listed

Corhampton, Southampton
SO3 1NB
☎ Droxford (0489) 877506
*600-acre arable farm.
Comfortable 17th C
farmhouse on B3035 Bishops
Waltham to Corhampton road,
in Meon Valley. Historic
Winchester, Portsmouth and
Southampton nearby.*
Bedrooms: 2 twin
Bathrooms: 1 private,
2 public, 1 private shower

Bed & breakfast

per night:	£min	£max
Single	14.00	16.00
Double	28.00	32.00

Parking for 3
Open April-October

♨ ◨ ▯ ▮ ⌁ ⅏ ◪ 📺 ▥ ⚓ ⌖ ✿
✕ ⍝ 🚲

COWES

Isle of Wight
Map ref 2C3

Regular ferry and
hydrofoil services cross
the Solent to Cowes. The
town is the headquarters
of the Royal Yacht
Squadron and Cowes
Week is held every
August.
Tourist Information Centre
☎ *0983 291914.*

Mrs J Gibbons

☺

14 Milton Road, Cowes
PO31 7PX
☎ (0983) 295723
*Close to town centre and
cycle track, on bus route.
Continental or English
breakfast. Quiet river views,
parking.*
Bedrooms: 1 single, 1 twin
Bathrooms: 1 private,
1 public

Bed & breakfast

per night:	£min	£max
Single	12.50	15.00
Double	28.00	30.00

Parking for 2

♨ ⑥ ☎ ◨ ▯ ⅏ ⌁ ▮ ⓢ ✂
▥ ⚓ ∪ ✕ 🚲 🅂🄿 ⊞

Map references
apply to the colour
maps at the back
of this guide.

DAMERHAM

Hampshire
Map ref 2B3

Colt Green ▲▲

♨♨ COMMENDED

North End, Damerham,
Fordingbridge SP6 3HA
☎ (072 53) 240
*Beautiful, tranquil setting. A
genuine welcome, comfort
and good food. Easily
accessible Salisbury/New
Forest. Masses to see and do.
Telephone for directions.*
Bedrooms: 1 double, 2 twin
Bathrooms: 2 private,
1 public

Bed & breakfast

per night:	£min	£max
Single	15.00	25.00
Double	30.00	36.00

Half board

per person:	£min	£max
Daily	27.00	35.00
Weekly	170.00	190.00

Evening meal 1900 (last
orders 2000)
Parking for 3
Open January-November

🐈 ⑥ 🔥 ▯ ⅏ ⓢ ✂ ◪ 📺 ▥,
⚓ ✿ 🚲

DENMEAD

Hampshire
Map ref 2C3

Comparatively modern
town, south-west of the
original settlement.

Forest Gate

♨♨

Hambledon Road, Denmead,
Waterlooville PO7 6EX
☎ Waterlooville (0705)
255901
*Georgian house in 2 acre
garden, on main Hambledon
road B2150, halfway between
Denmead and Hambledon.
Dinner by arrangement.*
Bedrooms: 2 twin
Bathrooms: 2 private

Bed & breakfast

per night:	£min	£max
Single	16.00	18.00
Double	30.00	34.00

Half board

per person:	£min	£max
Daily	25.00	28.50
Weekly	158.00	179.00

Evening meal from 1930
Parking for 4

🐈 ◨ ⅏ ▯ ✂ 📺 ▥ ⚓ ⌖ ✿
✕ 🚲 ⊞

DIBDEN

Hampshire
Map ref 2C3

Small village on the edge
of the New Forest with a
full recreation centre.
Picturesque 13th C
church overlooks
Southampton Water.

Dale Farm Guest House ▲▲

☺

Manor Road, Applemore Hill,
Dibden, Southampton
SO4 5TJ
☎ Southampton (0703)
849632
*Friendly, family-run 18th C
converted farmhouse, in
wooded setting with large
garden. 250 yards from A326,
adjacent to riding stables and
15 minutes from beach.*
Bedrooms: 1 single,
2 double, 2 twin, 1 triple
Bathrooms: 1 public,
1 private shower

Bed & breakfast

per night:	£min	£max
Single	16.50	18.50
Double	29.00	33.00

Half board

per person:	£min	£max
Daily	25.00	27.00
Weekly	145.00	162.00

Evening meal 1800 (last
orders 1100)
Parking for 10

🐈 ⅏ ⚒ ▯ ▮ ⓢ ◪ 📺 ▥ ⚓ ∪
⌖ ✿ ✕ 🅂🄿 ⊞

DROXFORD

Hampshire
Map ref 2C3

Village with numerous
Georgian buildings. Izaak
Walton was a frequent
visitor to the 18th C
rectory now owned by the
National Trust.

The Coach House Motel

Brockbridge, Droxford,
Southampton SO3 1QT
☎ (0489) 877812
*Modern motel accommodation
in area of outstanding beauty,
surrounded by leisure
facilities and adjacent to pub/
restaurant.*
Bedrooms: 2 single, 6 double
Bathrooms: 8 private

Bed & breakfast

per night:	£min	£max
Single	27.50	37.50
Double	37.50	55.00

Parking for 12
Cards accepted: Access, Visa

🐈 ⅏ ▯ ⅏ ▮ ▥, ⚓ ⌖ 🚲
🅂🄿 ⊞

FLEET

Hampshire
Map ref 2C2

The Webbs ▲▲

Listed

12 Warren Close, Fleet,
Aldershot GU13 9LT
☎ (0252) 615063
*Homely, friendly atmosphere.
Families welcome (no age
limit). Close to Fleet station,
A30 and M3.*
Bedrooms: 2 single, 1 twin
Bathrooms: 2 public

Bed & breakfast

per night:	£min	£max
Single		16.00
Double		32.00

Half board

per person:	£min	£max
Daily		24.00

Evening meal 1830 (last
orders 1700)
Parking for 2

🐈 ⅏ ⚒ ◨ ▯ ⅏ ▮ ⓢ ✂ ▥,
⚓ 🚲

FORDINGBRIDGE

Hampshire
Map ref 2B3

On the north-west edge
of the New Forest. A
medieval bridge crosses
the Avon at this point and
gave the town its name. A
good centre for walking,
exploring and fishing.

Cottage Crest

Castle Hill, Woodgreen,
Fordingbridge SP6 2AX
☎ Downton (0725) 22009
*Secluded country cottage
offering quality bed and
breakfast. Set in 4 acres of
picturesque grounds with
glorious views of the River
Avon and surrounding forest.*
Bedrooms: 2 double, 1 twin
Bathrooms: 3 private

Bed & breakfast

per night:	£min	£max
Single	23.00	23.00
Double	36.00	38.00

Parking for 5

🐈 ⑩ ▯ ⅏ ▮ ▥, ✿ ✕ 🚲 ⊞

Hillbury

2 Fir Tree Hill, Camel Green
Road, Alderholt,
Fordingbridge SP6 3AY
☎ (0425) 652582
*Quiet situation with easy
access to M27. Ideal touring*

base for New Forest and south coast. Riding, swimming, golf and fishing nearby. Non-smokers only please.
Bedrooms: 1 single, 1 double, 1 twin, 1 triple
Bathrooms: 1 private, 1 public

Bed & breakfast

per night:	£min	£max
Single	15.00	17.00
Double	30.00	34.00

Parking for 5

Homestead
High Street, Woodgreen, Fordingbridge SP6 2AU
☎ Downton (0725) 22994
Comfortable accommodation in lovely New Forest village setting with views across the Avon Valley to the Dorset hills. Convenient for countryside, coast, walking, fishing, riding, golf, etc. Good food pubs nearby.
Bedrooms: 1 double, 1 twin
Bathrooms: 1 private, 1 public

Bed & breakfast

per night:	£min	£max
Single	15.00	20.00
Double	30.00	40.00

Parking for 4

Partridge Piece
Ogdens, Fordingbridge SP6 2PZ
☎ (0425) 655365
8-acre smallholding. Attractive house in heart of New Forest, 3 miles from Fordingbridge. Superb walking, bird-watching and riding. Catering for horses and riders a speciality.
Bedrooms: 1 single, 1 twin
Bathrooms: 1 private

Bed & breakfast

per night:	£min	£max
Double	25.00	35.00

Parking for 4
Open February-November

The Ship Inn
Market Place, Fordingbridge SP6 1AS
☎ (0425) 652776
Small, family-run inn between Bournemouth and Salisbury. Centrally located for many tourist attractions within the New Forest. Family rooms available.
Bedrooms: 4 twin, 2 triple
Bathrooms: 1 public

Bed & breakfast

per night:	£min	£max
Single	18.00	
Double	35.00	35.00

Lunch available
Evening meal 1800 (last orders 2130)
Parking for 11

FRESHWATER
Isle of Wight
Map ref 2C3

This part of the island is associated with Tennyson, who lived in the village for 30 years. A monument on Tennyson's Down commemorates the poet.

Denehurst
Colwell Road, Freshwater PO40 9SW
☎ (0983) 752571
Small family guesthouse close to beach and downs. Warm welcome, comfortable accommodation and full English breakfast.
Bedrooms: 2 triple, 2 multiple
Bathrooms: 1 public

Bed & breakfast

per night:	£min	£max
Double	30.00	30.00

Parking for 6

FRITHAM
Hampshire
Map ref 2C3

Chapel Lane Cottage
Listed
Fritham, Lyndhurst SO43 7HL
☎ Southampton (0703) 812359
Friendly, comfortable accommodation in small hamlet. Easy access from M27, but very quiet and with direct access to beautiful forest. Non-smokers only please.
Bedrooms: 1 double
Bathrooms: 1 private

Bed & breakfast

per night:	£min	£max
Double	30.00	30.00

Parking for 4

Margarets Mead Farm
Fritham, Lyndhurst SO43 7HJ
☎ Southampton (0703) 813388
20-acre mixed farm. Very quiet, comfortable accommodation in farmhouse

in small hamlet. Ideal for walking in the heart of the New Forest.
Bedrooms: 2 double, 1 twin
Bathrooms: 1 public

Bed & breakfast

per night:	£min	£max
Double	24.00	26.00

Open April-October

HAMBLE
Hampshire
Map ref 2C3

Set almost at the mouth of the River Hamble, this quiet fishing village has become a major yachting centre.

Braymar
Listed
35 Westfield Close, Hamble, Southampton SO3 5LG
☎ Southampton (0703) 453831
Private house, 5 minutes from quiet beach and pretty, sailing village of Hamble, where "Howards Way" was filmed. 15 minutes' drive from Southampton and Portsmouth. Near M27.
Bedrooms: 1 single, 1 double, 2 twin
Bathrooms: 1 public

Bed & breakfast

per night:	£min	£max
Single	12.00	13.00
Double	24.00	26.00

Parking for 3

HAMBLEDON
Hampshire
Map ref 2C3

In a valley, surrounded by wooded downland and marked by an air of Georgian prosperity. It was here that cricket was given its first proper rules. The Bat and Ball Inn at Broadhalfpenny Down is the cradle of cricket.

Cams
Hambledon, Waterlooville PO7 4SP
☎ (0705) 632865
Comfortable, listed family house in beautiful setting with large garden on the edge of Hambledon village. Two pubs within walking distance. Evening meal by arrangement.
Bedrooms: 1 single, 2 twin
Bathrooms: 1 private, 1 public

Bed & breakfast

per night:	£min	£max
Single	15.00	17.00
Double	30.00	34.00

Half board

per person:	£min	£max
Daily	23.00	27.00
Weekly	147.00	165.00

Evening meal from 1900
Parking for 6

Mornington House
Listed
Speltham Hill, Hambledon, Waterlooville PO7 4RU
☎ (0705) 632704
18th C private house with 2 acres of garden and paddock, in the centre of Hambledon behind the George Inn.
Bedrooms: 2 twin
Bathrooms: 1 public

Bed & breakfast

per night:	£min	£max
Single	15.00	15.00
Double	28.00	28.00

Parking for 6

Nightingale Cottage
HIGHLY COMMENDED
Hoegate, Hambledon, Waterlooville PO7 4RD
☎ (0705) 632447
Country house on outskirts of Hambledon, adjacent to Hoegate Common. A quarter of a mile from Rudley Mill and half a mile from B2150.
Bedrooms: 2 double, 1 twin
Bathrooms: 3 private, 1 public

Bed & breakfast

per night:	£min	£max
Single	18.00	22.00
Double	36.00	50.00

Parking for 8
Cards accepted: Access, Visa

Individual proprietors have supplied all details of accommodation. Although we do check for accuracy, we advise you to confirm the information at the time of booking.

353

HAVANT

Hampshire
Map ref 2C3

Once a market town famous for making parchment. Nearby at Leigh Park extensive early 19th C landscape gardens and parklands are open to the public. Right in the centre of the town stands the interesting 13th C church of St Faith.
Tourist Information Centre
☎ *(0705) 480024*

High Towers
14 Portsdown Hill Road, Bedhampton, Havant PO9 3JY
☎ Portsmouth (0705) 471748
Large, detached residence, located on Portsdown Hill with magnificent views overlooking Portsmouth, the sea and surrounding countryside. Near ferries. Non-smokers only, please.
Bedrooms: 1 single, 2 double, 1 triple
Bathrooms: 2 public

Bed & breakfast per night:	£min	£max
Single	20.00	25.00
Double	30.00	40.00

Parking for 6

Holland House Guest House M
33 Bedhampton Hill, Havant PO9 3JN
☎ (0705) 475913
Fax (0705) 470134
Comfortable, friendly guesthouse, ideal for touring, continental ferry port, business and the sea.
Bedrooms: 2 single, 1 double, 1 twin
Bathrooms: 1 private, 1 public

Bed & breakfast per night:	£min	£max
Single	15.00	20.00
Double	17.00	32.00

Evening meal 1700 (last orders 1845)
Parking for 6

The Old Mill Guest House M
Mill Lane, Bedhampton, Havant PO9 3JH
☎ (0705) 454948

Georgian house in large grounds by a lake abundant in wildlife. Modernised, comfortable retreat. John Keats rested here.
Bedrooms: 1 double, 1 twin, 3 triple
Bathrooms: 5 private

Bed & breakfast per night:	£min	£max
Single	25.00	25.00
Double	36.00	36.00

Parking for 10

HAYLING ISLAND

Hampshire
Map ref 2C3

Small, flat island of historic interest, surrounded by natural harbours and with fine sandy beaches, linked to the mainland by a road.

Cockle Warren Cottage Hotel M
36 Seafront, Hayling Island PO11 9HL
☎ (0705) 464961
Lovely farmhouse-style hotel with hens and ducks. French and English country cooking. Home-made bread. Four-poster and Victorian beds. Heated swimming pool. Log fires in winter.
Bedrooms: 5 double
Bathrooms: 5 private

Bed & breakfast per night:	£min	£max
Single	40.00	55.00
Double	56.00	74.00

Evening meal 2000 (last orders 1600)
Parking for 9
Cards accepted: Access, Visa

Newtown House Hotel M
Manor Road, Hayling Island PO11 0QR
☎ (0705) 466131
Fax (0705) 461366
Set in own grounds, a quarter of a mile from seafront. Indoor leisure complex with heated pool, gym, jacuzzi and sauna. Tennis.
Bedrooms: 10 single, 11 double, 4 twin, 3 triple
Bathrooms: 28 private, 2 public

Bed & breakfast per night:	£min	£max
Single	46.50	49.00
Double	55.00	64.00

Half board per person:	£min	£max
Daily	43.00	45.00
Weekly	258.00	

Lunch available
Evening meal 1900 (last orders 2130)
Parking for 45
Cards accepted: Access, Visa, C.Bl, Diners, Amex

HIGHCLERE

Hampshire
Map ref 2C2

Village astride the A343. Highclere Castle was once the principal country residence of the Bishops of Winchester.

The Yew Tree Inn
Hollington Cross, Andover Road, Highclere, Newbury, Berkshire RG15 9SE
☎ (0635) 253360
17th C wayside inn with inglenook fireplaces. Full of character. 60-seater restaurant area.
Bedrooms: 3 double, 1 twin
Bathrooms: 4 private

Bed & breakfast per night:	£min	£max
Single	35.00	
Double	50.00	

Lunch available
Evening meal 1830 (last orders 2200)
Parking for 34
Cards accepted: Access, Visa

HIGHCLIFFE

Dorset
Map ref 2B3

Seaside district of Christchurch some 3 miles to the east. Highcliffe Castle is of interest.

Beverly Glen
1 Stuart Road, Highcliffe, Christchurch BH23 5JS
☎ (0425) 273811
On A337, close to the beach, shops and public transport, with the New Forest a short drive away. Home cooking.
Bedrooms: 1 single, 4 double, 1 twin
Bathrooms: 4 private, 1 public

Bed & breakfast per night:	£min	£max
Single	15.00	17.75
Double	30.00	35.00

Half board per person:	£min	£max
Daily	23.00	26.50
Weekly	150.00	174.00

Evening meal 1800 (last orders 1700)
Parking for 6

Seacroft
45 Wortley Road, Highcliffe, Christchurch BH23 5DR
☎ (0425) 273557
Very stylish, Tudor-beamed throughout, with quality fittings in all rooms. 2 minutes to shops and seafront.
Bedrooms: 3 single, 1 double
Bathrooms: 1 public

Bed & breakfast per night:	£min	£max
Single	14.00	16.00
Double	28.00	30.00

Parking for 3

HYTHE

Hampshire
Map ref 2C3

Changri-La
12 Ashleigh Close, Hythe, Southampton SO4 6QP
☎ (0703) 846664
Spacious comfortable home, in unique position on edge of New Forest, a few minutes' drive from Beaulieu and other places of interest. Golf-course, pony trekking and sports complex nearby.
Bedrooms: 1 single, 1 double, 1 twin
Bathrooms: 2 public

Bed & breakfast per night:	£min	£max
Single	12.00	13.00
Double	24.00	26.00

Parking for 3

IBBERTON

Dorset
Map ref 2B3

Pretty rural village surrounded by open farmland.

Manor House Farm
Ibberton, Blandford Forum DT11 0EN
☎ Hazelbury Bryan (0258) 817339
250-acre dairy & livestock farm. Small 15th C manor house, now a farmhouse with large garden, in a small, quiet

and unspoilt village. 10 miles west of Blandford Forum.
Bedrooms: 2 double, 1 twin
Bathrooms: 1 private,
1 public

Bed & breakfast

per night:	£min	£max
Single	10.00	14.00
Double	20.00	28.00

Parking for 3

ISLE OF WIGHT

See under Brighstone, Cowes, Freshwater, Newtown, Ryde, Ryde-Wootton, Shanklin, Shorwell, Yarmouth

LINWOOD

Hampshire
Map ref 2B3

An area of New Forest farms with camp sites.

High Corner Inn ₩
COMMENDED

Linwood, Ringwood
BH24 3QY
☎ Ringwood (0425) 473973
Fax (0425) 480015
Situated down a drovers' track, in 7 secluded acres in the heart of the New Forest, 4 miles north-east of Ringwood.
Bedrooms: 3 double, 3 twin,
2 triple
Bathrooms: 8 private

Bed & breakfast

per night:	£min	£max
Single	45.50	49.50
Double	69.00	73.00

Half board

per person:	£min	£max
Daily	43.75	47.75
Weekly	271.75	290.00

Lunch available
Evening meal 1900 (last orders 2200)
Parking for 203
Cards accepted: Access, Visa, Diners, Amex

LYMINGTON

Hampshire
Map ref 2C3

Small, pleasant town with bright cottages and attractive Georgian houses, lying on the edge of the New Forest with a ferry service to the Isle of Wight. A sheltered harbour makes it a busy yachting centre.

Admiral House
5 Stanley Road, Lymington
SO41 9SJ
☎ (0590) 674339
House exclusively for guests, with owner next door. 200 yards from countryside conservation area and marinas. Many pubs and restaurants nearby.
Bedrooms: 1 single, 1 twin,
1 triple
Bathrooms: 1 public

Bed & breakfast

per night:	£min	£max
Single	11.00	
Double	22.00	

Altworth ₩
Listed APPROVED

12 North Close, Lymington
SO41 9BT
☎ (0590) 674082
Near centre of town in quiet residential street, 5 minutes from bus and railway stations and close to Isle of Wight ferry. 30 minutes from Southampton and Bournemouth and central to New Forest.
Bedrooms: 1 single,
1 double, 1 triple
Bathrooms: 1 public

Bed & breakfast

per night:	£min	£max
Single	13.00	13.00
Double	23.00	23.00

Open April-October

Cedars ₩
Listed

2 Linden Way, Highfield, Lymington SO41 9JU
☎ (0590) 676468
Bungalow accommodation in quiet, secluded area, ideal for forest and coastal walks. Ground floor annexe rooms, free access and parking. Close to High Street, marinas and ferry.
Bedrooms: 1 double, 2 twin
Bathrooms: 2 private,
1 public

Bed & breakfast

per night:	£min	£max
Single	16.00	18.00
Double	32.00	36.00

Parking for 4

Little Orchard
31 Ramley Road,
Pennington, Lymington
SO41 8HF
☎ (0590) 673430
Lovely family home with private, peaceful garden. Between sea and forest, just off A337. Parking. 1 mile from Lymington town centre. Non-smokers only please.
Bedrooms: 1 single,
1 double, 1 twin
Bathrooms: 2 public

Bed & breakfast

per night:	£min	£max
Single	15.00	15.00
Double	30.00	30.00

Parking for 4

Our Bench ₩
COMMENDED

9 Lodge Road, Pennington, Lymington SO41 8HH
☎ (0590) 673141
Ground floor bedrooms with vanity units and showers. Indoor heated pool, jacuzzi and sauna, large garden. Non-smokers only please. Sorry, no children.
Bedrooms: 1 single, 2 double
Bathrooms: 2 private showers

Bed & breakfast

per night:	£min	£max
Single	14.00	16.00
Double	32.00	36.00

Parking for 5

Wainsford House
Wainsford Road, Everton, Lymington SO41 8LA
☎ (0590) 672654
Principal part of country house, with large rooms. In quiet surroundings, off Wainsford Road between Pennington and Everton. One and a half miles from Lymington.
Bedrooms: 1 single,
1 double, 1 twin
Bathrooms: 1 public

Bed & breakfast

per night:	£min	£max
Single	12.50	13.00
Double	25.00	30.00

Parking for 3
Open April-October

LYNDHURST

Hampshire
Map ref 2C3

The 'capital' of the New Forest, surrounded by attractive woodland scenery and delightful villages. The town is dominated by the Victorian Gothic-style church where the original Alice in Wonderland is buried.
Tourist Information Centre
☎ *(0703) 282269*

Burton House ₩
Romsey Road, Lyndhurst
SO43 7AA
☎ (0703) 282445
Lovely house in half-acre garden, near the village centre. All rooms en-suite shower, WC and washbasin. Parking.
Bedrooms: 1 single,
2 double, 1 twin, 2 triple
Bathrooms: 6 private

Bed & breakfast

per night:	£min	£max
Single	19.00	
Double	30.00	

Parking for 8

Cowpenn Cottage
Fritham, Lyndhurst
SO43 7HH
☎ Southampton (0703) 813119
2-acre smallholding. Situated in the heart of the New Forest. Easy access to coast and neighbouring cities. A warm and cordial welcome assured. Stabling available.
Bedrooms: 2 twin
Bathrooms: 1 private,
1 public

Bed & breakfast

per night:	£min	£max
Single	18.00	18.00
Double	36.00	36.00

Parking for 3
Open March-September

National Crown ratings were correct at the time of going to press but are subject to change. Please check at the time of booking.

Check the introduction to this region for Where to Go, What to See.

Please check prices and other details at the time of booking.

355

LYNDHURST

Continued

Forest Cottage

Listed

High Street, Lyndhurst
SO43 7BH
☎ (0703) 283461
Charming 300-year-old cottage with friendly atmosphere. Natural history library. New Forest maps and reference books. No smoking please.
Bedrooms: 1 single, 1 double, 1 twin
Bathrooms: 2 public

Bed & breakfast

per night:	£min	£max
Single	17.00	
Double	28.00	

Parking for 3

🖙 12 🎛 🛈 🕃 ⅄ ☖ 📺 🛏 🗲 ❄ ✗ 🚲 🆂🅿️

Little Hayes

43 Romsey Road, Lyndhurst
SO43 7AR
☎ (0703) 283000
Lovely Victorian home close to village centre and forest walks. Spacious rooms, sympathetically restored and furnished. Non-smokers only please.
Bedrooms: 2 double, 1 twin
Bathrooms: 1 private, 1 public

Bed & breakfast

per night:	£min	£max
Double	28.00	

Parking for 4

🖙 5 🖵 ❄ ☖ 🛈 🆂 🕃 ⅄ 📺 🛏 🗲 ❄ ✗ 🚲 🅿️ 🆂🅿️

The New Forest Inn

Emery Down, Lyndhurst
SO43 7DY
☎ (0703) 282329
Fax (0425) 472425
New Forest country inn set in woodlands, offering a warm welcome and good food.
Bedrooms: 2 single, 4 double, 2 twin, 3 triple
Bathrooms: 10 private

Bed & breakfast

per night:	£min	£max
Single	25.00	25.00
Double	50.00	50.00

Half board

per person:	£min	£max
Daily	25.00	

Lunch available
Evening meal 1800 (last orders 2130)
Parking for 25
Cards accepted: Access, Visa

🖙 🖵 🌺 ❄ 🍷 🆂 🕃 🛏 🛏 🗲 ❄ 🚲 ╰╯ ♪ ❄ ❄ 🚲 🆂🅿️

MARNHULL

Dorset
Map ref 2B3

Has a fine church and numerous attractive houses.

Moorcourt Farm

Moorside, Marnhull,
Sturminster Newton
DT10 1HH
☎ (0258) 820271
117-acre dairy farm. Friendly, welcoming farmhouse in the Blackmore Vale, 4 miles from Sturminster Newton and 5 miles from Shaftesbury. Central for coast and many places of interest. Children over 10 welcome. Sorry, no pets.
Bedrooms: 2 double, 1 twin
Bathrooms: 2 public

Bed & breakfast

per night:	£min	£max
Single	12.00	13.00
Double	24.00	26.00

Parking for 6
Open April-October

🖙 10 🖵 🖵 ❄ ☖ 🛈 🆂 🕃 📺 🗲 ❄ ✗ 🚲

Old Lamb House

Listed COMMENDED

Walton Elm, Marnhull,
Sturminster Newton
DT10 1QG
☎ (0258) 820491
Large, Georgian house in 4 acre grounds on southern edge of Marnhull village in beautiful Blackmore Vale. Formerly the Lamb Inn, reputedly "Rollivers" in Hardy's "Tess of the D'Urbervilles".
Bedrooms: 2 double
Bathrooms: 1 public

Bed & breakfast

per night:	£min	£max
Double	32.00	32.00

Parking for 4

🖙 🎛 🖵 ❄ ☖ 🛈 🗲 📺 🛏 🗲 ❄ ✗ 🚲

Wisteria House

Listed

New Street, Marnhull,
Sturminster Newton
DT10 1PZ
☎ (0258) 820778
Large Georgian former rectory between Shaftesbury and Sturminster Newton.
Bedrooms: 2 double, 1 twin
Bathrooms: 1 private, 2 public

Bed & breakfast

per night:	£min	£max
Single	15.00	18.00
Double	30.00	34.00

Parking for 6

🖙 🎛 🖵 ❄ 🍷 ☖ 🆂 🛏 📺 🛏 🖵 ❄ 🚲 🅾️🅿️ 🔖 🆂🅿️ 🈁

MILFORD-ON-SEA

Hampshire
Map ref 2C3

Victorian seaside resort with shingle beach and good bathing, set in pleasant countryside and looking out over the Isle of Wight. Nearby is Hurst Castle, built by Henry VIII.

Seawinds

Westminster Road, Milford-on-Sea, Lymington
SO41 0WU
☎ Lymington (0590) 644548
Modern house only steps away from the cliff top and beach. Interesting walks to Milford via cliff top or through woods via river bank.
Bedrooms: 2 double, 1 triple
Bathrooms: 3 private

Bed & breakfast

per night:	£min	£max
Double		36.00

Parking for 3

🖧 🖵 ❄ ☖ 🛈 🗲 📺 🛏 ❄ ✗ 🚲

MILTON ABBAS

Dorset
Map ref 2B3

Sloping village street of thatched houses. A boys' school lies in Capability Brown's landscaped gardens amid hills and woods where the town once stood. The school chapel, former abbey church, can be visited.

Dunbury Heights

Listed COMMENDED

Winterborne Stickland,
Blandford Forum DT11 0DN
☎ (0258) 880445
Always a friendly welcome at this brick and flint cottage. Outstanding views to Poole and Isle of Wight. 6 miles from Blandford Forum and 1 mile from the showpiece village of Milton Abbas.
Bedrooms: 1 double, 1 twin, 1 triple
Bathrooms: 2 public

Bed & breakfast

per night:	£min	£max
Single	15.00	15.00
Double	30.00	30.00

Parking for 10

🖙 ☖ 🆂 🕃 📺 🛏 🖵 ❄ ✗ 🚲

MINSTEAD

Hampshire
Map ref 2C3

Cluster of thatched cottages and detached period houses. The church, listed in the Domesday Book, has private boxes - one with its own fireplace.

Acres Down Farm 🛦

Listed

Minstead, Lyndhurst
SO43 7GE
☎ Southampton (0703) 813693
50-acre mixed farm. Homely New Forest working commoners' farm, in quiet surroundings opening directly on to open forest. Also self-catering cottage.
Bedrooms: 1 double, 1 twin, 1 triple
Bathrooms: 1 public

Bed & breakfast

per night:	£min	£max
Single	13.00	
Double	26.00	

Parking for 6

🖙 ❄ ☖ 🛈 🆂 🗲 ☖ ♪ ❄ ✗ 🚲

Grove House

Newtown, Minstead,
Lyndhurst SO43 7GG
☎ Southampton (0703) 813211
9-acre smallholding. Attractive family home, set in quiet, rural position 3 miles from Lyndhurst, with superb walking, birdwatching and riding (stabling available).
Bedrooms: 1 triple
Bathrooms: 1 public

Bed & breakfast

per night:	£min	£max
Double	28.00	32.00

Parking for 1

🖙 🖵 🖵 ❄ ☖ 🆂 🗲 🛏 ❄ 🚲

National Crown ratings were correct at the time of going to press but are subject to change. Please check at the time of booking.

NEW FOREST

See under Barton on Sea, Beaulieu, Blackfield, Bransgore, Brockenhurst, Burley, Cadnam, Damerham, Dibden, Fordingbridge, Fritham, Hythe, Linwood, Lymington, Lyndhurst, Milford-on-Sea, Minstead, Ringwood, Sway, Tiptoe, Totton

NEWTOWN

Isle of Wight
Map ref 2C3

Clamerkin House ▲▲

Listed | **HIGHLY COMMENDED**

Newtown, Newport
PO30 4PD
☎ Calbourne (0983) 78419
Modernised farmhouse with heated swimming pool, in 12 acres of gardens, woodlands and creekside walks, offering peace and tranquillity. Between Newtown and Porchfield.
Bedrooms: 1 double, 1 twin
Bathrooms: 2 private

Bed & breakfast

per night:	£min	£max
Single	20.00	20.00
Double	34.00	36.00

Parking for 6

OVERTON

Hampshire
Map ref 2C2

Test View

Kingsclere Road, Overton,
Basingstoke RG25 3HA
☎ (0256) 771841
Overton nestles on the edge of the north Hampshire downs 10 miles east of Basingstoke. The guesthouse is in the heart of the conservation area and on the River Test, a trout fisherman's paradise.
Bedrooms: 1 double, 1 twin
Bathrooms: 1 public

Bed & breakfast

per night:	£min	£max
Single	13.50	17.50
Double	27.00	34.00

Parking for 2

The enquiry coupons at the back will help you when contacting proprietors.

OWSLEBURY

Hampshire
Map ref 2C3

Small farming village with Marwell Conservation Zoo close by.

Glasspools Farm House

Longwood Estate,
Owslebury, Winchester
SO21 1JS
☎ (0962) 777218
4000-acre arable farm. Modern farmhouse set in an acre of garden, surrounded by fields and trees.
Bedrooms: 1 double, 1 twin
Bathrooms: 1 public

Bed & breakfast

per night:	£min	£max
Single	14.00	15.00
Double	28.00	30.00

Half board

per person:	£min	£max
Daily	22.00	22.00
Weekly	147.00	147.00

Evening meal 1800 (last orders 2100)
Parking for 2

Miss E A Lightfoot ▲▲

Listed | **HIGHLY COMMENDED**

Tayinloan, Owslebury,
Winchester SO21 1LP
☎ (0962) 777359
Private house with extensive rural views. 4 miles from M3, 11 miles from M27. Easy access to Eastleigh Airport, 9 miles away, and Portsmouth ferries. Non-smokers only please.
Bedrooms: 3 twin
Bathrooms: 3 private, 1 public

Bed & breakfast

per night:	£min	£max
Single	16.50	17.50
Double	30.00	33.00

Parking for 3

Orchard House

Listed

Whaddon Lane, Owslebury,
Winchester SO21 1JL
☎ (0962) 777614
Farmhouse bed and breakfast accommodation in an elegant 19th C barn conversion with excellent views of Hampshire Downs. Evening meal by prior arrangement.
Bedrooms: 1 single, 1 double, 1 twin
Bathrooms: 1 public

Bed & breakfast

per night:	£min	£max
Single	16.00	17.00
Double	32.00	34.00

Half board

per person:	£min	£max
Daily	23.50	24.50
Weekly	140.00	165.00

Evening meal 1900 (last orders 1930)
Parking for 6

PETERSFIELD

Hampshire
Map ref 2C3

Grew prosperous from the wool trade and was famous as a coaching centre. Its attractive market square is dominated by a statue of William III. Close by are Petersfield Heath with numerous ancient barrows and Butser Hill with magnificent views.
Tourist Information Centre
☎ (0730) 268829

Coldhayes ▲▲

Steep Marsh, Petersfield
GU33 6LL
☎ Liss (0730) 892114
200-acre mixed farm. Victorian mansion with beautiful garden and views. Half an hour from Winchester, Chichester and Portsmouth. Adjacent to hamlet of Steep Marsh, 1 mile west of A3 between Petersfield and Liss. Evening meals available on prior request.
Bedrooms: 2 double, 1 twin
Bathrooms: 2 public

Bed & breakfast

per night:	£min	£max
Single	20.00	20.00
Double	40.00	40.00

Half board

per person:	£min	£max
Daily	30.00	30.00

Evening meal from 1930
Parking for 12

Heathlands

64 Heath Road, Petersfield
GU31 4EJ
☎ (0730) 64028
Large, homely Edwardian house, overlooking heath, lake and golf-course. 5 minutes' walk from town centre, 20 minutes from Portsmouth ferries.
Bedrooms: 1 single, 1 double, 1 twin

Bathrooms: 1 private, 1 public

Bed & breakfast

per night:	£min	£max
Single	15.00	15.00
Double	28.00	30.00

Parking for 3

Mrs Mary Bray

Nursted Farm, Buriton,
Petersfield GU31 5RW
☎ (0730) 264278
336-acre arable & livestock farm. Late 17th C farmhouse near Hampshire/West Sussex border, 2 miles south of Petersfield.
Bedrooms: 3 twin
Bathrooms: 1 private, 2 public

Bed & breakfast

per night:	£min	£max
Double	28.00	29.00

Parking for 4

Mrs P A Bushell

Toads Alley, South Lane,
Buriton, Petersfield
GU31 5RU
☎ (0730) 263880
15th C cottage in quiet position overlooking fields. 4 miles from Petersfield village. Shop and 2 village pubs serving food 2 minutes' walk.
Bedrooms: 2 twin
Bathrooms: 1 public

Bed & breakfast

per night:	£min	£max
Single	18.00	19.00
Double	30.00	34.00

Parking for 5

Pillmead House

North Lane, Buriton,
Petersfield GU31 5RS
☎ (0730) 66795
Fax (0730) 64042
Stone-built Victorian house situated in pretty village on edge of downs. Home-cooked meals available. Non-smokers only please.
Bedrooms: 2 twin
Bathrooms: 2 private

Bed & breakfast

per night:	£min	£max
Single	18.50	18.50
Double	35.00	35.00

Half board

per person:	£min	£max
Daily	30.50	30.50

Evening meal 1830 (last orders 2000)
Parking for 2

PETERSFIELD

Continued

Rose Cottage
Listed
1 The Mead, Liss GU33 7DT
☎ (0730) 892378
Semi-detached, 4-bedroom house with lounge and dining area.
Bedrooms: 1 single, 1 double, 1 twin
Bathrooms: 2 public

Bed & breakfast

per night:	£min	£max
Single	16.00	18.00
Double	32.00	36.00

Parking for 1
🛇❑♥ⓤⓛⓈ▥,▄✕🐾

Westmark House
Listed
Sheet, Petersfield GU31 5AT
☎ (0730) 263863
Pleasant Georgian country house, with hard tennis court and heated pool. Turn on to A272 towards Rogate from A3, first house on left.
Bedrooms: 1 single, 1 double
Bathrooms: 1 public

Bed & breakfast

per night:	£min	£max
Single	18.00	18.00
Double	36.00	36.00

Parking for 3
🛇14📺❑♥ⓤⓛ▥,▄🔍
▶❄✕🐾🏕

POOLE

Dorset
Map ref 2B3

Tremendous natural harbour makes Poole a superb boating centre. The harbour area is crowded with historic buildings including the 15th C Town Cellars housing a maritime museum.
Tourist Information Centre
☎ (0202) 673322

The Inn in the Park ⋀⋀
♨♨
26 Pinewood Road, Branksome Park, Poole BH13 6JS
☎ Bournemouth (0202) 761318
Small, friendly, family-owned pub with sun terrace, log fire and easy access to the beach.
Bedrooms: 3 double, 1 twin, 1 triple
Bathrooms: 5 private

Bed & breakfast

per night:	£min	£max
Single	30.00	40.00
Double	40.00	50.00

Lunch available
Evening meal 1900 (last orders 2130)
Parking for 15
Cards accepted: Access, Visa
🛇❑♥▥,▄✕🐾

PORTSMOUTH & SOUTHSEA

Hampshire
Map ref 2C3

There have been connections with the Navy since early times and the first dock was built in 1194. HMS Victory, Nelson's flagship, is here and Charles Dickens' former home is open to the public. Neighbouring Southsea has a promenade with magnificent views of Spithead.
Tourist Information Centre
☎ (0705) 832464

Amberly ⋀⋀
Listed APPROVED
37 Castle Road, Southsea, Hampshire PO5 3DE
☎ (0705) 830563
Centrally situated close to all arrival/departure ferry terminals. Traditionally cooked English evening meals available at reasonable cost.
Bedrooms: 2 twin, 1 triple, 2 multiple
Bathrooms: 2 private, 2 public

Bed & breakfast

per night:	£min	£max
Single	15.00	18.00
Double	36.00	45.00

Half board

per person:	£min	£max
Daily	21.00	24.00
Weekly	147.00	168.00

Evening meal 1800 (last orders 1800)
Cards accepted: Access, Visa, Amex
🛇❑♥ⓤⓛⓈ✕▥,▄🍴
🐾ⓄⒶⓅ

Fortitude Cottage ⋀⋀
Listed HIGHLY COMMENDED
51 Broad Street, Portsmouth, Hampshire PO1 2JD
☎ (0705) 823748
Charming waterside cottage near ancient fortifications, with prettily furnished bedrooms. Good breakfasts, high standard of comfort.

Opposite waterbus for historic ships.
Bedrooms: 1 double, 2 twin
Bathrooms: 1 private, 1 public

Bed & breakfast

per night:	£min	£max
Double	36.00	40.00

🔧❑♥ⓤⓛⓈ✕▥,▄🐾

Hamilton House ⋀⋀
♨♨ COMMENDED
95 Victoria Road North, Southsea, Hampshire PO5 1PS
☎ (0705) 823502
Delightful family-run guesthouse, 5 minutes by car to ferry terminals and tourist attractions. Some en-suite rooms available. Breakfast served from 6am.
Bedrooms: 1 single, 2 double, 2 twin, 1 triple, 2 multiple
Bathrooms: 4 private, 2 public

Bed & breakfast

per night:	£min	£max
Single	14.00	16.00
Double	28.00	32.00

Cards accepted:
🛇📺❑♥ⓤⓛⓈⓐ✕⋈
ⓉⓋ▥,▄❄🐾ⓄⒶⓅ

The Saltings ⋀⋀
♨♨ HIGHLY COMMENDED
19 Bath Square, Portsmouth, Hampshire PO1 2JL
☎ (0705) 821031
Elegant town house on waterfront, overlooking Portsmouth Harbour entrance. Attractively furnished rooms with spectacular views. Within strolling distance of Maritime Heritage and museums.
Bedrooms: 1 double, 1 twin
Bathrooms: 1 public

Bed & breakfast

per night:	£min	£max
Double	36.00	40.00

🛇📺❑♥ⓤⓛⓐⓈ✕▥,
▄✕🐾🏕

Waverley Park Lodge Guest House
⋀⋀
99 Waverley Road, Southsea, Hampshire PO5 2PL
☎ (0705) 730402
Comfortable Victorian guesthouse. Close to maritime Portsmouth. Midweek and reduced weekly bookings. Bookable car space. Chef owner.
Bedrooms: 1 single, 2 double, 1 twin, 2 triple
Bathrooms: 1 public

Bed & breakfast

per night:	£min	£max
Single	14.00	15.00
Double	26.00	28.00

Half board

per person:	£min	£max
Daily	22.00	23.00

Evening meal 1800 (last orders 1800)
Cards accepted: Access, Visa
🛇❑♥🔍ⓤⓛⓐⓈ✕⋈ⓉⓋ▥,
▄ⓄⒶⓅⓈⓅ

RINGWOOD

Hampshire
Map ref 2B3

Market town by the River Avon comprising old cottages, many of them thatched. Although just outside the New Forest, there is heath and woodland nearby and it is a good centre for horse-riding and walking.

Cafe Renoir
12-14 High Street, Ringwood BH24 1AF
☎ (0425) 479700
Central position, warm friendly welcome. Meals available 0815-2100 in licensed restaurant or garden. Biggest breakfast in town!
Bedrooms: 1 twin, 2 triple
Bathrooms: 1 public

Bed & breakfast

per night:	£min	£max
Single	14.50	15.00
Double	30.00	31.00

Half board

per person:	£min	£max
Daily	34.00	35.00

Lunch available
Evening meal 1700 (last orders 2100)
Parking for 2
Cards accepted: Access, Visa
🛇❑♥ⓐⓈ✕✕

Homeacres ⋀⋀
♨♨ COMMENDED
Homelands Farm, Three Legged Cross, Wimborne Minster, Dorset BH21 6QZ
☎ Verwood (0202) 822422
270-acre mixed farm. Large chalet bungalow of traditional design, with inglenook fireplace in drawing room. Extensive garden, with access to large patio from drawing room.
Bedrooms: 1 single, 1 twin, 3 triple
Bathrooms: 4 private, 1 public

Bed & breakfast

per night:	£min	£max
Single	15.00	19.50
Double	28.00	39.00

Parking for 8

⬠♿⬡🅿♿Ⓢ✕🅼📺 🏚🚗☎🕻♪✿🚲

Picket Hill House
Picket Hill, Ringwood
BH24 3HH
☎ (0425) 476173
Large country house, with direct access to New Forest, offering comfortable accommodation and good breakfast. Ideal for walkers/ riders. Overseas guests particularly welcome. Accommodation for 2 horses by prior arrangement.
Bedrooms: 1 double, 1 twin
Bathrooms: 2 private

Bed & breakfast

per night:	£min	£max
Double	30.00	36.00

Parking for 6

⬠10⬡♿🅿Ⓢ✕📺🏚🕻 ✿✕🚲

ROMSEY
Hampshire
Map ref 2C3

Town grew up around the important abbey and lies on the banks of the River Test, famous for trout and salmon. Broadlands House, home of the late Lord Mountbatten, is open to the public.
Tourist Information Centre
☎ *(0794) 512987*

Country Accommodation, The Old Post Office ⚲

COMMENDED

New Road, Michelmersh, Romsey SO51 0NL
☎ (0794) 68739
In pretty village location, interesting conversion from old forge, bakery and post office. All ground floor rooms, some beamed. On-site parking.
Bedrooms: 1 double, 2 twin, 1 triple
Bathrooms: 4 private

Bed & breakfast

per night:	£min	£max
Single	25.00	25.00
Double	35.00	35.00

Parking for 10

⬠♿🖵🅼Ⓢ🅼📺🏚✕ 🚲🏨

Hazeldene
♔♔
Sandy Lane, Belbins, Romsey SO51 0PD
☎ Braishfield (0794) 68388
Secluded quality accommodation set in 3.5 acres. Spacious modern rooms. Large guest lounge, ample parking facilities, only a few minutes' drive to New Forest, Salisbury, Stonehenge, Winchester.
Bedrooms: 1 double, 1 twin
Bathrooms: 1 private, 1 public

Bed & breakfast

per night:	£min	£max
Double	36.00	40.00

Parking for 6

♿⬡🕻🅼🅰🅼📺🏚🚗🕻✿ ✕🚲

Highfield House
♔♔ HIGHLY COMMENDED
Newtown Road, Awbridge, Romsey SO51 0GG
☎ (0794) 40727
Recently-built house, overlooking golf-course, in unspoilt rural village. Delightful setting and charming gardens. Home cooking a speciality.
Bedrooms: 1 double, 2 twin
Bathrooms: 3 private, 1 public

Bed & breakfast

per night:	£min	£max
Single	18.00	18.00
Double	40.00	40.00

Evening meal from 1900
Parking for 10

⬠12🖵♿🅼📺🅰Ⓢ🅼 📺🏚🚗🕻✕🚲

Miss R K Chambers
8 The Meads, Romsey SO51 8HB
☎ (0794) 512049
Small town house in pleasant, quiet location in town centre, with view of the abbey.
Bedrooms: 1 double, 1 twin
Bathrooms: 1 public

Bed & breakfast

per night:	£min	£max
Single	18.00	
Double	28.00	30.00

Parking for 1
Open April-October

⬠5🅼♿🅼Ⓢ🅼🏚✕🚲

Spursholt House
Salisbury Road, Romsey SO51 6DJ
☎ (0794) 512229
Fax (0794) 523142
The house dates from Cromwell's time, with extensive grounds and gardens, a large parterre and

roses, and beautiful views over Romsey.
Bedrooms: 2 double, 1 twin
Bathrooms: 1 private, 3 public

Bed & breakfast

per night:	£min	£max
Single	15.00	20.00
Double	25.00	35.00

Half board

per person:	£min	£max
Daily	25.00	30.00

Evening meal 1900 (last orders 2100)
Parking for 5

⬠♿🕻🅼🅰Ⓢ✕🅼📺🏚🚗 🕻✿🚲🏨

ROPLEY
Hampshire
Map ref 2C2

Village on the Alresford to Alton Mid Hants Railway.

Belmont House
Gilbert Street, Ropley, Alresford SO24 0BY
☎ (0962) 772344
Dating back to the 19th C, the house is set in a beautiful garden in a quiet country lane. 1 hour by car from Heathrow and Gatwick Airport.
Bedrooms: 1 twin
Bathrooms: 1 private

Bed & breakfast

per night:	£min	£max
Single	17.00	19.00
Double	34.00	38.00

Parking for 5

⬠5🕻🖵♿🅼🅰✕🅼🏚🚗 🕻✿✕🚲🏨

RYDE
Isle of Wight
Map ref 2C3

The island's chief entry port, connected to Portsmouth by ferries and hovercraft. 7 miles of sandy beaches with a half-mile pier, esplanade and gardens.
Tourist Information Centre
☎ *(0983) 562905*

Keys Lodge
Church Road, Binstead, Ryde PO33 3SY
☎ (0983) 63640
Listed, 17th C, thatched character cottage, with oak beams and lovely grounds. In quiet village, near church and 10 minutes' walk from main Binstead road and shops.
Bedrooms: 2 double, 1 twin
Bathrooms: 1 public

Bed & breakfast

per night:	£min	£max
Single	13.50	14.00
Double	27.00	28.00

Parking for 3
Open April-October

🖵♿🅼🏚✿✕🚲🏨

Rodborough ⚲
25 Queens Road, Ryde PO33 3BG
☎ (0983) 65370
Close to town centre and ferries. One room has magnificent sea views. All usual facilities and car park. Warm welcome and super breakfast.
Bedrooms: 2 double, 1 twin
Bathrooms: 1 private, 2 private showers

Bed & breakfast

per night:	£min	£max
Single	15.00	18.00
Double	14.00	16.00

Parking for 3
Open April-October

⬠🖵♿🅼Ⓢ✕🅼🏚🚲

RYDE-WOOTTON
Isle of Wight
Map ref 2C3

Village runs uphill from Wootton Creek, popular with yachtsmen for its sailing school and boat yards.

Ashlake Farmhouse
Ashlake Farm Lane, Wootton Bridge, Ryde PO33 4LF
☎ (0983) 882124
Lovely 17th C farmhouse with grounds sloping down to Wootton Creek. Happy, calm atmosphere and friendly service.
Bedrooms: 1 double, 1 twin, 1 triple
Bathrooms: 1 private, 2 public

Bed & breakfast

per night:	£min	£max
Single	15.00	20.00
Double	25.00	32.00

Half board

per person:	£min	£max
Daily	20.00	30.00

Evening meal 1900 (last orders 2100)
Parking for 6

⬠6🖵♿🕻🅼Ⓢ✕🅼📺 🏚🚗♪✿🚲🏨 ⟦OAP⟧⟦SP⟧🏨

The symbols are explained on the flap inside the back cover.

SELBORNE

Hampshire
Map ref 2C2

Village made famous by Gilbert White, who was a curate here and is remembered for his classic book 'The Natural History of Selborne', published in 1788. His house is now a museum.

Mrs A Rouse
Listed

8 Goslings Croft, Selborne, Alton GU34 3HZ
☎ (042 050) 285
Family home, set on edge of historic village, adjacent to National Trust land. Ideal base for walking and touring. Non-smokers only please.
Bedrooms: 1 twin
Bathrooms: 1 private
Bed & breakfast

per night:	£min	£max
Single	19.50	19.50
Double	29.50	29.50

Parking for 1
Cards accepted: Access, Visa

SHAFTESBURY

Dorset
Map ref 2B3

Hilltop town with a long history. The ancient and cobbled Gold Hill is one of the most attractive in Dorset. There is an excellent small museum containing a collection of buttons for which the town is famous.
Tourist Information Centre
☎ *(0747) 53514.*

Brookside
Listed

Dover Street, Stour Row, Shaftesbury SP7 0QH
☎ East Stour (0747) 85491
Stone-built cottage in rural setting, with open landscape views. 4 miles south-west of Shaftesbury in Thomas Hardy country.
Bedrooms: 2 single, 1 double
Bathrooms: 1 private,
1 public
Bed & breakfast

per night:	£min	£max
Single	16.00	17.50
Double	30.00	32.00

Parking for 4

The Mitre Inn
23 High Street, Shaftesbury SP7 8JE
☎ (0747) 52488
An old inn, modernised, with panoramic views of North Dorset and the Blackmoor Vale.
Bedrooms: 3 double, 1 twin, 1 triple, 1 multiple
Bathrooms: 2 public
Bed & breakfast

per night:	£min	£max
Single		30.00
Double		40.00

Lunch available
Evening meal 1830 (last orders 2130)
Cards accepted: Access, Visa, Switch

Paynes Place Barn ⋀
New Road, Shaftesbury SP7 8QL
☎ (0747) 55016
Converted stone barn with beautiful views, en-suite facilities, friendly service and evening meal by prior arrangement. Half a mile from Shaftesbury town centre on B3081.
Bedrooms: 2 double, 2 twin
Bathrooms: 4 private
Bed & breakfast

per night:	£min	£max
Single	18.00	22.00
Double	36.00	40.00

Half board

per person:	£min	£max
Daily	28.00	30.00

Evening meal 1830 (last orders 2030)
Parking for 10

SHANKLIN

Isle of Wight
Map ref 2C3

Set on a cliff with gentle slopes leading down to the beach, esplanade and marine gardens. The picturesque, old thatched village nestles at the end of the wooded chine.
Tourist Information Centre
☎ *(0983) 862942*

Apse Manor Country House ⋀

COMMENDED

Apse Manor Road, Shanklin PO37 7PN
☎ (0983) 866651
Recently restored 16th C manor house in a lovely country setting, 1.5 miles

from Shanklin. Ideal for a relaxing holiday in beautiful surroundings.
Bedrooms: 4 double, 2 twin, 1 triple
Bathrooms: 7 private
Bed & breakfast

per night:	£min	£max
Double	52.00	52.00

Half board

per person:	£min	£max
Daily	36.00	38.00
Weekly	230.00	250.00

Evening meal 1900 (last orders 1915)
Parking for 12
Cards accepted: Access, Visa

Hazelwood Hotel ⋀

14 Clarence Road, Shanklin PO37 7BH
☎ (0983) 862824
Small, friendly comfortable hotel in a quiet tree-lined road, close to all amenities.
Bedrooms: 1 single, 3 double, 2 twin, 1 triple, 3 multiple
Bathrooms: 8 private, 1 public
Bed & breakfast

per night:	£min	£max
Single	15.00	16.00
Double	30.00	32.00

Half board

per person:	£min	£max
Daily	20.00	21.00
Weekly	126.00	135.00

Evening meal 1800 (last orders 1600)
Parking for 5
Open March-October
Cards accepted: Access, Visa, Amex

Loretta House
15 Atherley Road, Shanklin PO37 7AT
☎ (0983) 866733
Small, comfortable guesthouse, 3 minutes from sea. All beds have continental quilts. Open Easter and Bank Holidays.
Bedrooms: 1 single, 1 double, 2 triple
Bathrooms: 1 public
Bed & breakfast

per night:	£min	£max
Single	12.00	14.00
Double	24.00	28.00

Open February-November

Osborne House Hotel ⋀

HIGHLY COMMENDED

Esplanade, Shanklin PO37 6BN
☎ (0983) 862501
Tastefully modernised Victorian residence, 25 yards from the sea, where bookings are accepted on a daily basis. Dining room is non-smoking.
Bedrooms: 1 single, 9 double, 2 twin
Bathrooms: 12 private, 2 public
Bed & breakfast

per night:	£min	£max
Single		30.00
Double		60.00

Half board

per person:	£min	£max
Daily		43.00

Evening meal 1900 (last orders 2000)
Open January-October
Cards accepted: Access, Visa

Summercourt Hotel ⋀

6 Popham Road, Shanklin PO37 6RF
☎ (0983) 863154
Spacious Tudor-style house with large pleasant garden, in a quiet position in Shanklin Old Village. Near sea and shops, adjacent to Rylstone Gardens and Shanklin Chine.
Bedrooms: 1 double, 2 twin, 2 triple, 1 multiple
Bathrooms: 3 private, 1 public
Bed & breakfast

per night:	£min	£max
Single	17.00	20.00
Double	30.00	36.00

Parking for 6

SHILLINGSTONE

Dorset
Map ref 2B3

Village in the River Stour valley.

Church House
Church Road, Shillingstone, Blandford Forum DT11 0SL
☎ Child Okeford (0258) 860646
Charming, 18th C listed thatched country house, near Blandford. Private suite for 2-6 guests. Good food, beautiful gardens, views and countryside.
Bedrooms: 2 double, 1 triple
Bathrooms: 1 public

Bed & breakfast

per night:	£min	£max
Single	18.00	22.00
Double	34.00	40.00

Half board

per person:	£min	£max
Daily	25.00	32.00

Lunch available
Evening meal 1800 (last orders 1930)
Parking for 3

🛇 10 🌡 ♨ ⑭ 🛊 Ⓢ ⅍ 🌊 ⑲ 🏧, 🛆 ∪ ↟ ❋ ✕ 🐾 🆂🅿 🏘

The Willows Tea Rooms

5 Blandford Road,
Shillingstone, Blandford
Forum DT11 0SG
☎ Child Okeford (0258)
861167
Old world cottage of cob and flint. Tea rooms have huge inglenook fireplace and beams. Set in lovely countryside overlooking Hambledon Hill.
Bedrooms: 1 single,
1 double, 1 twin
Bathrooms: 1 private,
1 public

Bed & breakfast

per night:	£min	£max
Single	15.00	18.00
Double	26.00	32.00

Parking for 10
Open February-December

🛇 1 🌡 🛏 ⅍ ⑭ 🛊 ⅍ 🏧, 🛆 ✕ 🐾 🆂🅿

SHORWELL

Isle of Wight
Map ref 2C3

Cheverton Farm

Listed

Shorwell, Newport PO30 3JE
☎ (0983) 741017
560-acre arable & livestock farm. Farmhouse in beautiful downland setting 1 mile from Shorwell. Excellent walking and riding, with good food locally. 10 minutes' car journey to sea. Stabling available. Riding and clay pigeon shooting by arrangement.
Bedrooms: 1 double, 1 twin
Bathrooms: 2 public

Bed & breakfast

per night:	£min	£max
Single	13.50	15.50
Double	27.00	31.00

Parking for 6
Open February-November

🛇 🍴 ♨ ⑭ Ⓢ ⅍ ⑲ 🏧, 🛆 ∪ ╱ ❋ ✕ 🐾 🆂🅿 🏘

SIXPENNY HANDLEY

Dorset
Map ref 2B3

The Barleycorn House

♨ ♨

Deanland, Sixpenny Handley,
Salisbury, Wiltshire SP5 5PD
☎ Handley (0725) 552583
Fax (0725) 552090
Converted 17th C inn retaining original period features, in peaceful surroundings with many nearby walks. Relaxed atmosphere and home cooking.
Bedrooms: 1 single,
1 double, 1 twin
Bathrooms: 2 private,
1 public

Bed & breakfast

per night:	£min	£max
Single	16.00	
Double	32.00	

Half board

per person:	£min	£max
Daily	23.50	
Weekly	153.30	

Evening meal from 1830
Parking for 5

🛇 ⑭ ♨ ⑭ 🛊 🛏 ⑲ 🏧, 🛆 ❋ 🐾

SOUTHAMPTON

Hampshire
Map ref 2C3

One of Britain's leading seaports with a long history, now a major container port. In the 18th C it became a fashionable resort with the assembly rooms and theatre. The old Guildhall and the Wool House are now museums. Sections of the medieval wall can still be seen.
Tourist Information Centre
☎ *(0703) 221106*

Ashelee Lodge ⋀

Listed

36 Atherley Road, Shirley,
Southampton SO1 5DQ
☎ (0703) 222095
Homely guesthouse, garden with pool. Near station, M27 and Sealink ferryport. Good touring base for New Forest, Salisbury, Winchester, etc. Evening meal by arrangement.
Bedrooms: 2 single,
1 double, 1 twin
Bathrooms: 1 public

Bed & breakfast

per night:	£min	£max
Single	12.50	13.50
Double	25.00	27.00

Evening meal from 1800
Parking for 2

🛇 ⑭ 🛊 Ⓢ ⅍ ⑲ 🏧, 🛆 ⅊ ❋ 🐾

Bartley Villa Guest House ⋀

283 Salisbury Road,
Testwood, Totton,
Southampton SO4 3LZ
☎ (0703) 870736
Detached, Victorian house with warm reception assured. Close to M27 and M271. Bus stop to Southampton, Romsey, Salisbury, etc, outside house.
Bedrooms: 1 single,
2 double, 1 triple
Bathrooms: 1 public

Bed & breakfast

per night:	£min	£max
Single	17.50	17.50
Double	35.00	35.00

Half board

per person:	£min	£max
Daily	21.00	21.00
Weekly	147.00	147.00

Lunch available
Evening meal 1700 (last orders 1000)
Parking for 5

🛇 🍴 ⑭ 🛇 ♨ ⑭ 🛊 Ⓢ ⅍ ⑲ 🏧, 🛆 ❋ 🐾 🆗 🅣

Cedar Lodge

Listed **APPROVED**

100 Cedar Road, Portswood,
Southampton SO2 1AH
☎ (0703) 226761
Small guesthouse, with friendly service and easy access to Southampton centre and university.
Bedrooms: 1 double, 2 twin
Bathrooms: 1 public

Bed & breakfast

per night:	£min	£max
Single	14.00	15.00
Double	28.00	30.00

Half board

per person:	£min	£max
Daily	22.00	23.00
Weekly	150.00	160.00

Evening meal from 1900

🛇 ⑭ ♨ ⑭ 🛊 🏧, 🛆 ❋ 🐾

Mayview Guest House

Listed

30 The Polygon,
Southampton SO1 2BN
☎ (0703) 220907
Small, family-run guesthouse in the city centre, providing a comfortable stay in clean and friendly surroundings.
Bedrooms: 1 single,
1 double, 1 twin, 1 triple
Bathrooms: 1 public

Bathrooms: 2 public

Bed & breakfast

per night:	£min	£max
Single	12.00	12.00
Double	24.00	24.00

🛇 ⑭ ♨ ⑭ Ⓢ ⑲ 🏧, 🛆 ❋ 🐾

Verulam House

181 Wilton Road, Shirley,
Southampton SO1 5HY
☎ (0703) 773293
Built in 1905. High ceilings, cornice in downstairs rooms, large hall and circular landing. All rooms are a comfortable size and warm. Car parking space.
Bedrooms: 1 single,
1 double, 1 twin
Bathrooms: 2 public

Bed & breakfast

per night:	£min	£max
Single	14.00	14.00
Double	28.00	28.00

Half board

per person:	£min	£max
Daily	22.00	22.00
Weekly	150.00	150.00

Evening meal 1900 (last orders 1900)
Parking for 3
Cards accepted: Visa

🛇 3 ⑭ 🛇 ♨ ↟ ⑭ 🛊 ⑲ 🏧, 🛆 ❋ 🐾

SOUTHSEA

Hampshire

See under Portsmouth & Southsea

SPARSHOLT

Hampshire
Map ref 2C2

Village in high position on the downs. Nearby is Farley Mount Bronze Age Barrow and Horse Monument.

Sparsholt College ⋀

Listed

Sparsholt, Winchester
SO21 2NF
☎ (096 272) 441
Study and en-suite accommodation with full catering and recreational facilities, set in attractive rural grounds. Free car parking. Ideal base for touring. Special rates for groups. Individuals and families welcome.
Bedrooms: 306 single,
1 double, 4 twin
Bathrooms: 222 private,
20 public

Continued ▶

SPARSHOLT

Continued

Bed & breakfast

per night:	£min	£max
Single	14.60	17.00
Double	21.90	25.50

Half board

per person:	£min	£max
Daily	24.68	27.00
Weekly	99.00	145.00

Lunch available
Evening meal 1700 (last orders 1900)
Parking for 200
Open April-May, July-September
Cards accepted: Access, Visa, C.Bl, Diners, Amex

STOCKBRIDGE

Hampshire
Map ref 2C2

Set in the Test Valley which has some of the best fishing in England. The wide main street has houses of all styles, mainly Tudor and Georgian.

Carbery Guest House ⋀

COMMENDED

Salisbury Hill, Stockbridge
SO20 6EZ
☎ Andover (0264) 810771
Fine old Georgian house in an acre of landscaped gardens and lawns, overlooking the River Test. Games and swimming facilities, riding and fishing can be arranged. Ideal for touring the south coast and the New Forest.
Bedrooms: 4 single, 4 double, 2 twin, 1 triple
Bathrooms: 8 private, 1 public

Bed & breakfast

per night:	£min	£max
Single	20.00	27.50
Double	40.00	45.00

Half board

per person:	£min	£max
Daily	30.00	37.50
Weekly	200.00	250.00

Evening meal 1900 (last orders 1800)
Parking for 12

STOURPAINE

Dorset
Map ref 2B3

Stourpaine Guest House

Stourpaine Stores, Stourpaine, Blandford Forum DT11 8TA
☎ (0258) 453168
Turn-of-the-century village shop and post office.
Bedrooms: 1 double, 1 twin, 1 triple
Bathrooms: 1 public

Bed & breakfast

per night:	£min	£max
Single	15.00	
Double	26.00	28.00

Parking for 4

STUDLAND

Dorset
Map ref 2B3

On a beautiful stretch of coast and good for walking, with a National Nature Reserve to the north. The Norman church is the finest in the country, with superb rounded arches and vaulting. Brownsea Island, where the first scout camp was held, lies in Poole Harbour.

Bankes Arms Hotel

Studland, Swanage
BH19 3AU
☎ (092 944) 225
Old inn in coastal village with sea views and miles of sandy beaches. Morning and evening bar meals, en-suite accommodation.
Bedrooms: 1 single, 3 double, 2 twin, 3 triple
Bathrooms: 5 private, 1 public

Bed & breakfast

per night:	£min	£max
Single	20.00	25.00
Double	39.00	47.00

Lunch available
Evening meal 1900 (last orders 2130)
Parking for 20
Cards accepted: Access, Visa

Purbeck Down

The Glebe, Studland, Swanage BH19 3AS
☎ (092 944) 257
Spacious, Scandinavian-style house, in peaceful, secluded

surroundings, encompassed by National Trust land. Near beaches and cliffs.
Bedrooms: 1 double, 1 twin, 1 triple
Bathrooms: 1 private, 1 public

Bed & breakfast

per night:	£min	£max
Single	15.50	29.00
Double	29.00	38.00

Parking for 3

STURMINSTER NEWTON

Dorset
Map ref 2B3

Every Monday this small town holds a livestock market. One of the bridges over the River Stour is a fine medieval example and bears a plaque declaring that anyone 'injuring' it will be deported.

The Old Bridge Cottage Restaurant

Listed   COMMENDED

The Bridge, Sturminster Newton DT10 2BS
☎ (0258) 72689
Attractive 17th C cottage restaurant in the heart of the Blackmore Vale, overlooking the famous medieval bridge and working mill.
Bedrooms: 1 double, 2 twin
Bathrooms: 1 private, 1 public

Bed & breakfast

per night:	£min	£max
Single	20.00	27.00
Double	36.00	44.00

Half board

per person:	£min	£max
Daily	28.00	37.00

Lunch available
Evening meal 1800 (last orders 2130)
Parking for 8
Cards accepted: Access, Visa

SUTTON SCOTNEY

Hampshire
Map ref 2C2

Dever View

COMMENDED

17 Upper Bullington, Sutton Scotney, Winchester SO21 3RB
☎ Winchester (0962) 760566
Modernised, warm, comfortable cottage with

large, pretty garden, in quiet country lane surrounded by fields, but only half-a-mile from main roads, A34, A303. A real home-from-home.
Bedrooms: 2 twin
Bathrooms: 2 public

Bed & breakfast

per night:	£min	£max
Single	18.00	18.00
Double	30.00	30.00

Half board

per person:	£min	£max
Weekly	95.00	95.00

Parking for 7

Mrs V Keel

HIGHLY COMMENDED

Knoll House, Wonston, Sutton Scotney, Winchester SO21 3LR
☎ Winchester (0962) 760273 & 883550
Take Andover Road from Winchester to Sutton Scotney. Turn right at village hall to Wonston. Situated on right hand side almost opposite Wonston Arms.
Bedrooms: 1 double, 1 twin
Bathrooms: 1 private

Bed & breakfast

per night:	£min	£max
Single	15.00	15.00
Double	30.00	30.00

Half board

per person:	£min	£max
Daily	22.00	22.00
Weekly	148.00	148.00

Evening meal 1830 (last orders 2030)
Parking for 2

SWANAGE

Dorset
Map ref 2B3

Began life as an Anglo-Saxon port, then a quarrying centre of Purbeck marble. Now the safe, sandy beach set in a sweeping bay and flanked by downs is good walking country, making it an ideal resort.
Tourist Information Centre ☎ *(0929) 422885*

Horseshoe House Hotel ⋀

9 Cliff Avenue, Swanage
BH19 1LX
☎ (0929) 422194
Elegant family-run hotel, 4 minutes from beach, offering

cuisine and comfort of a good standard.
Bedrooms: 2 single, 2 double, 1 twin, 3 triple
Bathrooms: 4 private, 1 public, 2 private showers

Bed & breakfast per night:	£min	£max
Single	17.00	21.00
Double	34.00	42.00

Parking for 5
Open April-October

Leyland

APPROVED
Quarr Farm Lane, Valley Road, Swanage BH19 3DY
☎ Corfe Castle (0929) 480573
Modern Purbeck stone house surrounded by open countryside. 2.5 miles from Swanage and the ancient village of Corfe Castle.
Bedrooms: 4 double, 1 twin, 1 triple
Bathrooms: 2 public

Bed & breakfast per night:	£min	£max
Single	12.00	14.50
Double	25.00	29.00

Parking for 8
Open April-September

Maycroft

Old Malthouse Lane, Langton Matravers, Swanage BH19 3HH
☎ (0929) 424305
Comfortable Victorian home in quiet position, with magnificent views of sea and countryside. Close to coastal path and the amenities of the Isle of Purbeck.
Bedrooms: 1 double, 1 twin
Bathrooms: 1 public

Bed & breakfast per night:	£min	£max
Single	17.50	20.00
Double	28.00	32.00

Parking for 4
Open February-November

Sea Glimpse

2 Stafford Road, Swanage BH19 2BQ
☎ (0929) 425035
Situated 100 yards from shops and beach, quiet home with friendly service. Ideal location for Dorset coastline and countryside. Non-smokers only please.
Bedrooms: 2 double, 1 multiple
Bathrooms: 3 private

Bed & breakfast per night:	£min	£max
Single	15.00	20.00
Double	30.00	40.00

SWAY

Hampshire
Map ref 2C3

Small village on the south-western edge of the New Forest. It is noted for its 220-ft tower, Peterson's Folly, built in the 1870s by a retired Indian judge to demonstrate the value of concrete as a building material.

The Nurse's Cottage

Listed
Station Road, Sway, Lymington SO41 6BA
☎ Lymington (0590) 683402
Fax (0590) 683402
Situated in the heart of this thriving New Forest village, the District Nurse's former residence provides an ideal touring centre, with excellent road/rail access to the area's many attractions.
Bedrooms: 1 single, 1 double, 1 twin
Bathrooms: 2 private, 1 public

Bed & breakfast per night:	£min	£max
Single	17.50	18.50
Double	30.00	36.00

Half board per person:	£min	£max
Daily	23.50	27.00
Weekly	166.50	184.00

Evening meal 1900 (last orders 2000)
Parking for 6
Cards accepted: Access, Visa, C.Bl, Switch

Redwing Farm

Pitmore Lane, Sway, Lymington SO41 6BW
☎ Lymington (0590) 683319
24-acre farm. Beamed, cottage rooms with modern facilities and warm hospitality. Ideal sightseeing base in the New Forest.
Bedrooms: 1 single, 2 double
Bathrooms: 2 public

Bed & breakfast per night:	£min	£max
Single	15.00	16.00
Double	30.00	32.00

Parking for 10

Please mention this guide when making a booking.

TIPTOE

Hampshire
Map ref 2C3

Candleford House

Listed
Middle Road, Tiptoe, Lymington SO41 0FX
☎ Lymington (0590) 682069
Modern, Georgian-style house, not overlooked, within walking distance of forest. Central for Lymington, Milford-on-Sea, Bournemouth and Southampton.
Bedrooms: 1 double, 1 twin
Bathrooms: 1 public

Bed & breakfast per night:	£min	£max
Double	29.00	

Parking for 3

TOTTON

Hampshire
Map ref 2C3

Jubilee Cottage

303 Salisbury Road, Totton, Southampton SO4 3LZ
☎ Southampton (0703) 862397
Victorian house convenient for Romsey, M27, New Forest, continental and Isle of Wight ferries. Bed and breakfast accommodation with private facilities.
Bedrooms: 1 twin, 1 triple
Bathrooms: 1 private, 2 public

Bed & breakfast per night:	£min	£max
Single	12.50	15.00
Double	22.00	28.00

Parking for 2

National Crown ratings were correct at the time of going to press but are subject to change. Please check at the time of booking.

WAREHAM

Dorset
Map ref 2B3

This site has been occupied since pre-Roman times and has a turbulent history. In 1762 fire destroyed much of the town, so the buildings now are mostly Georgian.
Tourist Information Centre ☎ (0929) 552740.

Cherry Bank Guest House

32 Furzebrook Road, Stoborough, Wareham BH20 5AX
☎ (0929) 552986
Small country guesthouse at the foot of the Purbeck Hills, with access to RSPB heathland.
Bedrooms: 1 double, 1 twin, 1 triple
Bathrooms: 1 private, 1 public

Bed & breakfast per night:	£min	£max
Single	16.00	18.00
Double	32.00	37.00

Parking for 5
Open April-September

WEST LULWORTH

Dorset
Map ref 2B3

Well-known for Lulworth Cove, the almost landlocked circular bay of chalk and limestone cliffs.

Graybank Guest House

Main Road, West Lulworth, Wareham BH20 5RL
☎ (092 941) 256
Comfortably furnished, Victorian guesthouse 5 minutes' walk from Lulworth Cove. Ideal base for walking and visiting Dorset beauty spots. Car park.
Bedrooms: 1 single, 2 double, 2 twin, 2 multiple
Bathrooms: 3 public

Bed & breakfast per night:	£min	£max
Single	16.00	18.00
Double	30.00	34.00

Parking for 7
Open January-October

WEST LULWORTH

Continued

Newlands Farm

Listed **APPROVED**

West Lulworth, Wareham
BH20 5PU
☎ (092 941) 376
*750-acre arable & livestock
farm. 19th C farmhouse, with
outstanding views to sea and
distant Purbeck Hills. At
Durdle Door, 1 mile west of
Lulworth Cove.*
Bedrooms: 1 double, 1 triple
Bathrooms: 1 public,
2 private showers
Bed & breakfast

per night:	£min	£max
Double	36.00	36.00

Parking for 10

The Old Barn ⚘

Listed

West Lulworth, Wareham
BH20 5RL
☎ (092 941) 305
*Converted old barn in
peaceful, picturesque coastal
village. Choice of rooms with
continental breakfast or
please-yourself-rooms. Well
placed for touring Dorset.*
Bedrooms: 2 single,
2 double, 2 twin, 1 multiple
Bathrooms: 3 public
Bed & breakfast

per night:	£min	£max
Single	15.00	18.00
Double	30.00	40.00

Parking for 9

WEST MEON

Hampshire
Map ref 2C3

The Court House

West Meon, Petersfield
GU32 1JG
☎ (0730) 829336
*Small manor house
(previously Bishop's Court),
parts of which are 400 years
old. Gardens have River Meon
and old village pond.*
Bedrooms: 1 single,
1 double, 3 twin, 1 triple
Bathrooms: 1 private,
4 public
Bed & breakfast

per night:	£min	£max
Single	15.00	
Double	25.00	

Parking for 10

WICKHAM

Hampshire
Map ref 2C3

Lying in the Meon Valley,
this market town is built
around the Square and in
Bridge Street can be seen
some timber-framed
cottages. Still the site of
an annual horse fair.

Montrose ⚘

▲▲▲ HIGHLY COMMENDED

Solomons Lane, Shirrell
Heath, Southampton
SO3 2HU
☎ (0329) 833345
*Attractive, comfortable
accommodation in lovely
Meon Valley, offering comfort
and personal attention.
Equidistant from main towns
and convenient for
continental ferries and
motorway links.*
Bedrooms: 2 double, 1 twin
Bathrooms: 1 private,
1 public
Bed & breakfast

per night:	£min	£max
Single	20.00	23.00
Double	35.00	40.00

Parking for 6

Mount Folly Cottage ⚘

Southwick Road, North
Boarhunt, Fareham
PO17 6JH
☎ (0329) 833582
*Country cottage, set in
delightful surroundings,
offering homely
accommodation. Ideally
situated on B2177 for M27
and ferry port.*
Bedrooms: 1 single,
1 double, 1 triple
Bathrooms: 1 public
Bed & breakfast

per night:	£min	£max
Single	14.00	14.00
Double	28.00	28.00

Parking for 6
Cards accepted: Access, Visa

National Crown
ratings were correct
at the time of going
to press but are
subject to change.
Please check at the
time of booking.

WIMBORNE MINSTER

Dorset
Map ref 2B3

Market town centred on
the twin-towered Minster
Church of St Cuthberga
which gave the town the
second part of its name.
Good touring base for the
surrounding countryside,
depicted in the writings of
Thomas Hardy.
*Tourist Information Centre
☎ (0202) 886116*

Acacia House

2 Oakley Road, Wimborne
Minster BH21 1QJ
☎ (0202) 883958
Fax (0202) 881943
*Beautifully decorated rooms
are what the discerning
traveller expects. What comes
as a surprise is Eveline
Stimpson's tea and cake
welcome.*
Bedrooms: 1 single,
2 double, 1 twin
Bathrooms: 1 private,
2 public
Bed & breakfast

per night:	£min	£max
Single	14.50	17.50
Double	29.00	35.00

Parking for 3

Ashton Lodge

▲▲ COMMENDED

10 Oakley Hill, Wimborne
Minster BH21 1QH
☎ (0202) 883423
*Large, detached, family
house, with attractive gardens
and relaxed, friendly
atmosphere. Off-street parking
available. Pay phone.*
Bedrooms: 1 single,
1 double, 1 twin, 1 triple
Bathrooms: 2 private,
3 public
Bed & breakfast

per night:	£min	£max
Single	16.50	16.50
Double	33.00	33.00

Parking for 4

Granville

54 Wimborne Road West,
Wimborne Minster
BH21 2DP
☎ (0202) 886735 & (0860)
268443
Fax (0202) 695428
*Detached, double-fronted
house in country setting, with
sweeping drive, in three*

*quarters of an acre garden.
Ample parking space.*
Bedrooms: 1 single, 3 twin,
1 triple
Bathrooms: 2 private,
1 public
Bed & breakfast

per night:	£min	£max
Single	16.00	26.00
Double	28.00	38.00

Half board

per person:	£min	£max
Daily	20.00	34.00
Weekly	140.00	258.00

Evening meal 1800 (last
orders 2100)
Parking for 11
Cards accepted: Access, Visa

Northill House ⚘

▲▲▲ COMMENDED

Horton, Wimborne Minster
BH21 7HL
☎ Witchampton (0258)
840407
*Mid-Victorian former
farmhouse, modernised to
provide comfortable
bedrooms. Log fires and
cooking using fresh produce.*
Bedrooms: 5 double, 3 twin,
1 triple
Bathrooms: 9 private
Bed & breakfast

per night:	£min	£max
Single	35.00	35.00
Double	60.00	60.00

Half board

per person:	£min	£max
Daily	42.50	47.50
Weekly	267.75	299.25

Evening meal 1930 (last
orders 1830)
Parking for 12
Open February-December
Cards accepted: Access, Visa,
Amex

Mr & Mrs R Cook

96 West Boro, Wimborne
Minster BH21 1NH
☎ (0202) 884039
*Modern, friendly home, a few
minutes' walk from town
centre.*
Bedrooms: 1 single, 1 double
Bathrooms: 1 public
Bed & breakfast

per night:	£min	£max
Single	12.00	
Double	24.00	

Open April-October

WINCHESTER

Hampshire
Map ref 2C3

King Alfred the Great made Winchester the capital of Saxon England. A magnificent Norman cathedral, with one of the longest naves in Europe, dominates the city. Home of Winchester College founded in 1382.
Tourist Information Centre
☎ (0962) 840500

Mrs C P Tisdall
32 Hyde Street, Winchester
SO23 7DX
☎ (0962) 851621
Attractive 18th C town house close to city centre and recreational amenities.
Bedrooms: 1 double, 1 triple
Bathrooms: 1 public

Bed & breakfast

per night:	£min	£max
Single	15.00	16.00
Double	24.00	26.00

♨ 3 ♦ ⅏ 📺 🛏. ⊁ 🎪

Cathedral View ⋀
🏵🏵🏵 COMMENDED

9A Magdalen Hill,
Winchester SO23 8HJ
☎ (0962) 863802
Edwardian guesthouse with views across historic city and cathedral. 5 minutes' walk from city centre. En-suite facilities, TV, parking.
Bedrooms: 3 double, 2 twin, 1 triple
Bathrooms: 3 private, 1 public

Bed & breakfast

per night:	£min	£max
Single	27.50	33.00
Double	35.00	45.00

Half board

per person:	£min	£max
Daily	37.50	43.00
Weekly	236.25	261.90

Evening meal 1900 (last orders 0900)
Parking for 4
♨ ⅏ 🖵 ♦ ⅏ Ⓢ ⊁ ♨ 📺 🛏. 🖪 ✿ SP

Mrs Christine Leonard ⋀
🏵🏵 COMMENDED

Dellbrook, Hubert Road, St Cross, Winchester SO23 9RG
☎ (0962) 865093
Comfortable, spacious Edwardian house in quiet area of Winchester close to water meadows and 12th C St. Cross Hospital.

Bedrooms: 1 twin, 2 triple, 1 multiple
Bathrooms: 3 private, 1 public

Bed & breakfast

per night:	£min	£max
Double	34.00	38.00

Evening meal 1800 (last orders 1400)
Parking for 4
♨ ⅏ ⅏ 🛊 Ⓢ ♨ 📺 🛏. 🖪 ✿ 🎪 OAP

The Farrells ⋀
🏵

5 Ranelagh Road, St Cross, Winchester SO23 9TA
☎ (0962) 869555
Comfortable Victorian house close to city centre, St. Cross Hospital and water meadows.
Bedrooms: 1 double, 1 twin, 1 triple
Bathrooms: 2 private, 2 public

Bed & breakfast

per night:	£min	£max
Single	14.00	15.50
Double	30.00	39.00

♨ 5 ♦ ⅏ 🛊 ⅏ ⊁ 📺 🛏. ⊁ 🎪

Mrs J Maguire
62 Middlebrook Street, Winchester SO23 8DP
☎ (0962) 862188
Friendly, comfortable Victorian town house in heart of the city, just minutes away from cathedral, recreation centre and river park.
Bedrooms: 2 single, 1 twin, 1 triple
Bathrooms: 1 private, 2 public

Bed & breakfast

per night:	£min	£max
Single	15.00	16.00
Double	30.00	32.00

Open April-October
♨ 🖵 ♦ ⅏ 🛊 Ⓢ ⊁ 🛏. 🖪 ✿ ⊁ 🎪 Ⓣ

Little Hayes
🏵🏵 COMMENDED

School Hill, Itchen Abbas, Winchester SO21 1BE
☎ Itchen Abbas (096 278) 208
Well-appointed country house with beautiful views, set in 3 acres. 3 miles east of Winchester off B3047 going towards Alresford. Maps available.
Bedrooms: 2 single, 1 twin
Bathrooms: 2 private, 2 public

We advise you to confirm your booking in writing.

Bed & breakfast

per night:	£min	£max
Single	18.50	18.50
Double	37.00	37.00

Parking for 12
♨ 8 ⅏ 🖵 ♦ ♨ ⅏ ⊁ ♨ 📺 🛏. 🖪 ⚲ ✿ ⊁ 🎪

Markland House
44 St Cross Road, Winchester SO23 9PS
☎ (0962) 854901
Delightful Victorian house, close to cathedral, college, St Cross Hospital, water meadows and town centre. A warm welcome awaits you.
Bedrooms: 2 double, 1 twin
Bathrooms: 3 private

Bed & breakfast

per night:	£min	£max
Double	42.00	42.00

Parking for 3
Open January-November
Cards accepted: Access, Visa
♨ ⅏ 🖵 ♦ ⅏ 🛏. 🖪 ✿ 🎪

Mrs O M Fetherston-Dilke
🏵🏵

85 Christchurch Road, Winchester SO23 9QY
☎ (0962) 868661
Comfortable, friendly Victorian family house in St. Cross, Winchester. Ideal for exploring city and Hampshire. Off-street parking. Non-smokers preferred.
Bedrooms: 1 single, 1 double, 1 twin
Bathrooms: 2 public

Bed & breakfast

per night:	£min	£max
Single	16.50	18.00
Double	33.00	36.00

Parking for 3

Mrs R M Curtis
10c Edgar Road, Winchester SO23 9SJ
☎ (0962) 854985
Comfortable accommodation only 3 minutes' walk from the city centre.
Bedrooms: 1 single, 1 double, 1 twin
Bathrooms: 1 public

Bed & breakfast

per night:	£min	£max
Single	17.00	18.00
Double	29.00	30.00

Parking for 3
♨ ⅏ 🛏. 🎪

Ridgeway ⋀
🏵🏵 HIGHLY COMMENDED

Lower Baybridge Lane, Owslebury, Winchester SO21 1JN
☎ (0962) 777601

Country house offering delightful self-contained suite of bedroom/sitting room, kitchen and shower room/WC. Comfortably accommodates up to 3 people. Set in 8 acres surrounded by beautiful countryside, yet only 6 miles south of Winchester. Superb walking and riding area. Ideal touring location.
Bedrooms: 1 triple
Bathrooms: 1 private, 1 public

Bed & breakfast

per night:	£min	£max
Single	22.00	26.00
Double	34.00	38.00

Parking for 5
Cards accepted: Access, Visa
♨ 8 ⅏ ♨ ⅏ 🖵 ♦ ♨ ⅏ ⊁ ♨ 📺 🛏. 🖪 ♉ ✿ ⊁ 🎪 OAP SP

Shawlands ⋀
🏵🏵 COMMENDED

46 Kilham Lane, Winchester SO22 5QD
☎ (0962) 861166
Attractive, modern house, situated in a quiet, elevated position overlooking open countryside. Delightful garden. 1.5 miles from city centre.
Bedrooms: 2 double, 1 twin
Bathrooms: 1 private, 2 public

Bed & breakfast

per night:	£min	£max
Single	18.00	20.00
Double	32.00	36.00

Parking for 4
♨ ⅏ 🛊 Ⓢ ♨ 📺 🛏. 🖪 ✿ ⊁ 🎪

Stratton House ⋀
Listed

Stratton Road, St Giles Hill, Winchester SO23 8JQ
☎ (0962) 863919 & 864529
Fax (0962) 842095
A lovely old Victorian house with an acre of grounds, in an elevated position on St Giles Hill.
Bedrooms: 1 single, 2 double, 1 twin, 2 triple
Bathrooms: 1 private, 3 public, 2 private showers

Bed & breakfast

per night:	£min	£max
Single	19.00	22.00
Double	38.00	44.00

Continued ▶

The colour maps at the back of this guide pinpoint all places with accommodation.

WINCHESTER

Continued

**Half board
per person:** £min £max
Daily 25.00 28.00
Weekly 165.00 186.00
Evening meal 1800 (last orders 1600)
Parking for 8
🛇🖵👶🖵🗎Ⓢ⒨📺🖨️🚗
✿🚲 ᴅᴀᴘ ꜱᴘ 🏠 Ⓣ

Mrs V Edwards ⋀

Listed COMMENDED

Sycamores, 4 Bereweeke Close, Winchester SO22 6AR
☎ (0962) 867242
Detached house with open garden, in a quiet area 10 minutes' walk from the railway station. Family home.
Bedrooms: 1 double, 2 twin
Bathrooms: 1 private,
1 public
**Bed & breakfast
per night:** £min £max
Single 16.00 16.00
Double 32.00 32.00
🛇7🍴🖵🖵👶Ⓦ⒮🍽️🖨️
🗎✿🏹🚲

WINTERBORNE STICKLAND

Dorset
Map ref 2B3

Restharrow

🏵️🏵️ HIGHLY COMMENDED

North Street, Winterborne Stickland, Blandford Forum DT11 0NH
☎ Milton Abbas (0258) 880936
Comfortable accommodation in pretty village at head of Winterborne Valley, in the "Heart of Dorset." Friendly base for exploring the county.
Bedrooms: 2 double
Bathrooms: 2 private
**Bed & breakfast
per night:** £min £max
Double 30.00 36.00
Parking for 3
🛇🍴🍴🖵👶🗜️Ⓦ🗎Ⓢ🍴
📺🖨️🗎🏹🚲 ꜱᴘ

The enquiry coupons at the back will help you when contacting proprietors.

YARMOUTH

Isle of Wight
Map ref 2C3

Small, historic port on the Solent in the west of the island. A good, central starting-point for exploring the island.

The George Hotel ⋀

Quay Street, Yarmouth PO41 0PE
☎ (0983) 760331
Hotel open all year round. Specialises in fish dishes. A haven for yachtsmen with garden going down to Solent, private beach and moorings. Bars with bar food and log fires. Full a la carte restaurant.
Bedrooms: 3 single,
5 double, 3 twin, 2 triple
Bathrooms: 10 private,
3 public
**Bed & breakfast
per night:** £min £max
Single 35.00 40.00
Double 70.00 80.00
**Half board
per person:** £min £max
Daily 50.00 55.00

Lunch available
Evening meal 1900 (last orders 2230)
Cards accepted: Access, Visa, Diners, Amex
🛇🍴🗜️🍴🖵🗎Ⓢ🍽️🖨️🗎
✿🏠
[Ad] Display advertisement appears on this page

YATELEY

Hampshire
Map ref 2C2

Beechwood House

Vicarage Road, Yateley Green, Yateley, Camberley, Surrey GU17 7QT
☎ (0252) 872395
Secluded, character house with all comforts, set in a conservation area overlooking farmland. No children under 12 years. No pets. Non-smokers only please.
Bedrooms: 1 double, 1 twin
Bathrooms: 2 public
**Bed & breakfast
per night:** £min £max
Single 21.00 23.00
Double 34.00 36.00
Parking for 3
🛇12🖵👶🏹Ⓦ🗎Ⓢ🍴🖨️🗎
✿🏹🚲

"THE GEORGE"
YARMOUTH I·O·W

A first class hotel in a superb position, originally the home of the Governor of the Isle of Wight, Admiral Sir Robert Holmes, 1640. Little has changed since.
In prime position overlooking Solent with huge gardens and beach beside Yarmouth Castle. Restaurant with Normandy flavour. Own lobsters, crabs, mussels and other shellfish direct by sea from St. Vaast in France. Four bars, original panelling and bedrooms en suite.

Tel: 0988 760331

National Accessible Scheme

◆

If you are a wheelchair user or someone who has difficulty walking, look for the national "Accessible" symbol when choosing where to stay.

All the places that display the symbol have been checked by a Tourist Board inspector against criteria that reflect the practical needs of wheelchair users.

At the moment, the Tourist Boards are concentrating their inspections on hotels, guesthouses, inns, B&Bs, farmhouse acommodation and self-catering holiday homes. There are plans to extend the scheme to holiday caravan parks and visitor attractions in 1994.

◆

There are three categories of accessibility:

Category 1: Accessible to all wheelchair users including those travelling independently

Category 2: Accessible to a wheelchair user with assistance

Category 3: Accessible to a wheelchair user able to walk short distances and up at least three steps

◆

The National Accessible Scheme forms part of the Tourism for All campaign that is being promoted by all three national Tourist Boards.

A leaflet giving more information on the scheme is available free from any Tourist Information Centre, whose staff will also be pleased to help with finding suitable accommodation in the area.

Additional help and guidance can be obtained from the Holiday Care Service, 2 Old Bank Chambers, Station Road, Horley, Surrey RH6 9HW.
Tel: (0293) 774535. Fax: (0293) 784647.
Minicom: (0293) 776943 (24-hour answering).

◆

South East England

The gateway to England, this region has the largest stretch of resorts in Britain along its lovely coastline. From Bognor Regis, with its five miles of sandy beaches, to the yachting centre of Whitstable, there's a vast choice and infinite variety. Inland, there are the tranquil hamlets of the South Downs, the valley woodlands and summits of the North Downs, and the Weald of Kent, home of orchards and oasthouses. Savour the sense of history in the historic towns of Tunbridge Wells, Canterbury and Chichester and visit some of the stately homes and gardens with which the region is so richly endowed. South East England is a different world.

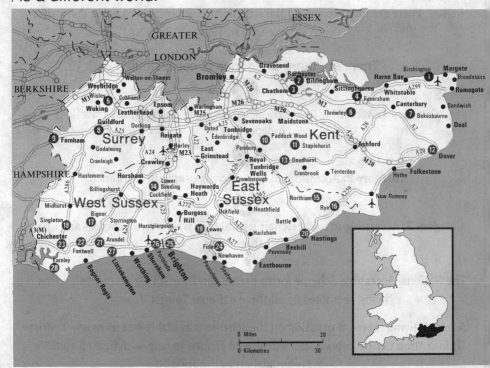

Use the above map to locate places in the "Where to Go, What to See" section opposite.

Use the colour maps at the back of this guide to find places with accommodation.

WHERE TO GO, WHAT TO SEE

The number against each name will help you locate it on the map opposite.

1 Powell Cotton Museum, Quex House and Gardens
Quex Park, Birchington, Kent CT7 0BH
Tel: Thanet (0843) 42168
Regency house with period furniture. Museum with ethnograhic collections, diorama of African and Asian animals, weapons, archaeology, Chinese porcelain.

2 Royal Engineers Museum
Gillingham, Kent
Tel: Medway (0634) 406397
The characters, lives and work of Britain's soldier-engineers, 1066–1945. Medals, uniforms, scientific and technical equipment. Collection of ethnography and decorative arts.

3 The Historic Dockyard
Chatham, Kent ME4 4TE
Tel: Medway (0634) 812551
Historic 18th C 80-acre dockyard, now a living museum. Former HMS Gannet undergoing restoration. Sail and colour loft, ordnance mews, "Wooden Walls" gallery.

4 Brogdale Horticultural Trust
Faversham, Kent ME13 8XZ
Tel: Faversham (0795) 535286
National Fruit Collection with 4,000 varieties of fruit in 30 acres of orchard: apples, pears, cherries, plums, currants, quinces, medlars, etc.

5 The Royal Horticultural Society's Garden
Wisley, Surrey GU23 6QB
Tel: Guildford (0483) 224434
World famous RHS establishment with 250 acres of vegetable, fruit and ornamental gardens. Trial grounds, glasshouses, rock garden, ponds, rose gardens, model and specialist gardens.

6 Belmont
Throwley, Kent ME13 0HH
Tel: Eastling (0795) 890202
Late 18th C country mansion designed by Samuel Wyatt, seat of the Harris family since 1801. Harris clock collection, mementoes of connections with India. Gardens and pinetum.

7 Howletts Zoo Park
Bekesbourne, Canterbury, Kent CT4 5EL
Tel: Canterbury (0227) 721286
55-acre parkland with large gorilla and tiger collection and many other animals.

8 Guildford Cathedral
Guildford, Surrey GU2 5UP
Tel: Guildford (0483) 65287
Anglican cathedral, foundation stone laid in 1936 and consecrated in 1961. Notable glass engravings, embroidered kneelers, modern furnishings. Brass rubbing centre.

9 Birdworld and Underwaterworld
Farnham, Surrey GU10 4LD
Tel: Bentley (0420) 22140
20 acres of garden and parkland with ostriches, flamingoes, hornbills, parrots, emus, pelicans, etc. Penguin island, tropical fish, plant area, seashore walk.

9 Museum of Farnham
Farnham, Surrey GU9 7DX
Tel: Farnham (0252) 715094
Built in 1718, Willmer House has displays on history and archaeology of town. 18th C furniture, paintings and other changing exhibitions. William Cobbett memorabilia.

Charles Dickens – seen here conjuring up a product of his imagination – lived in Broadstairs during the time that he wrote "David Copperfield"

10 Whitbread Hop Farm
Beltring, Paddock Wood, Kent TN12 6PY
Tel: Maidstone (0622) 872068
Large collection of Victorian oasts, rural museums, play area, animal village, birds of prey, pottery workshop, Whitbread shire horses. Hop story exhibition.

11 Iden Croft Herbs
Frittenden Road, Staplehurst, Kent TN12 0DH
Tel: Staplehurst (0580) 891432
Large herb farm with walled garden and variety of aromatic gardens, demonstrating the beauty and use of herbs. Thyme rockery of special interest.

12 Dover Castle and Hellfire Corner
Dover, Kent CT16 1HU
Tel: Dover (0304) 201628
One of most powerful medieval fortresses in Western Europe. St Mary in Castro Saxon church, Roman lighthouse, Hellfire Corner. All the Queen's Men exhibition and Battle of Waterloo model.

The Royal Pavilion at Brighton – described by William Cobbett as "a square box, a large Norfolk turnip and four onions"

⑮ Great Dixter House and Gardens
Northiam, Rye, East Sussex
TN31 6PH
Tel: Northiam (0797) 253160
Fine example of 15th C manor house with antique furniture and needlework. Unique great hall restored by Lutyens, who also designed the garden – topiary, meadow garden, flower beds.

⑯ Rye Town Model Sound and Light Show
Stand Quay, Rye, East Sussex
TN31 7AY
Tel: Rye (0797) 226696
Fascinating combination of detailed town model of the ancient town with dramatic sound and light effects, telling the story of Rye through the ages.

⑰ Bignor Roman Villa
Bignor, West Sussex RH20 1PH
Tel: Sutton (079 87) 259
Remains of large villa containing some of the finest mosaic pavements outside Italy. 80ft long corridor mosaic and Roman artefacts display.

⑱ Weald and Downland Open Air Museum
Singleton, West Sussex PO18 0EU
Tel: Singleton (024 363) 348
Open-air museum of rescued historic buildings from South East England reconstructed on downland country park site. 35 buildings include medieval farmstead and watermill.

⑲ The Old Needlemakers
West Street, Lewes, East Sussex
BN7 2NZ
Tel: Lewes (0273) 471582
Converted 19th C candle factory housing craft workshops. Candle makers, stained glass, leather crafts and other specialist shops.

⑬ Bedgebury National Pinetum
Nr Goudhurst, Kent TN17 2SL
Tel: Goudhurst (0580) 211044
The Forestry Commission's superb collection of specimen conifers, in 150 acres with lake and streams. Rhododendrons and azaleas. Visitor centre.

⑭ Leonardslee Gardens
Lower Beeding, West Sussex
RH13 6PP
Tel: Lower Beeding (0403) 891212
Renowned spring-flowering shrub garden in a valley: rhododendrons, camellias, azaleas, lakes, paths. Good views, autumn tints, rock garden, bonsai exhibition, alpine house.

⑮ Brickwall House and Gardens
Northiam, Rye, East Sussex
TN31 6NL
Tel: Rye (0797) 223329
Formal garden with terracotta entrance gates. 18th C bowling alley, sunken topiary garden, yew hedges, chess garden. Jacobean house with 17th C plaster ceilings.

⑳ A Smuggler's Adventure at St Clement's Caves

Hastings, East Sussex TN34 3HY
Tel: Hastings (0424) 422964
One acre of caves, housing the largest smuggling exhibition in the country. Museum, audio-visual show and 50 life-size figures with dramatic sound and lighting effects.

㉑ The Wildfowl and Wetlands Centre

Mill Road, Arundel, West Sussex BN18 9PB
Tel: Arundel (0903) 883355
Wildfowl and Wetlands Trust's reserve in 60 acres of watermeadows. Tame swans, ducks, geese and many wild birds. Film theatre and visitor centre with gallery.

㉒ Denmans Garden

Fontwell, West Sussex BN18 0SU
Tel: Eastgate (0243) 542808
Walled, gravel and water gardens, natural layout of trees, climbers and wall shrubs for all-year interest. Glass areas. School of Garden Design.

㉓ Pallant House

Chichester, West Sussex PO19 1TJ
Tel: Chichester (0243) 774557
Queen Anne residence containing Bow Porcelain collection, Hussey and Kearley painting collections, Rembrandt to Picasso, sculptures by Moore, temporary exhibitions. Old kitchen.

A folly was built by the London, Brighton and South Coast railway in 1841 as a home for the keeper of the Clayton Tunnel

㉔ Charleston Farmhouse

Firle, Lewes, East Sussex BN8 6LL
Tel: Ripe (0323) 811265
17th–18th C farmhouse, home of Vanessa and Clive Bell and Duncan Grant. House and contents decorated by the artists. Newly restored garden room. Traditional flint-walled garden.

㉕ Brighton Sea Life Centre

Brighton, East Sussex BN2 1TB
Tel: Brighton (0273) 604234
Ocean life on a grand scale featuring over 35 displays of fascinating marine creatures, and a whale and dolphin exhibition. Themed talks.

㉖ Foredown Tower Countryside Centre

Portslade, East Sussex BN41 2EW
Tel: Brighton (0273) 422540
Converted water tower 1909, housing exhibitions on the Downs and water. Camera obscura gives views of South Downs and coast. Touch screen computer. Local history exhibitions.

㉗ Smarts Amusement Park

Littlehampton, West Sussex BN17 5LL
Tel: Littlehampton (0903) 721200
Large indoor and outdoor amusement park for all ages. Many rides including dodgems, Waltzer, Cyclone Roller Coaster, waterslides.

㉘ Earnley Butterflies and Gardens

Earnley, West Sussex PO20 7JR
Tel: Birdham (0243) 512637
Ornamental butterfly house, covered theme gardens, bird garden, children's play area, small animal farm.

FIND OUT MORE

Further information about holidays and attractions in the South East England region is available from:
South East England Tourist Board
The Old Brew House, Warwick Park, Tunbridge Wells, Kent TN2 5TU
Tel: (0892) 540766

These publications are available free from the South East England Tourist Board:
South East England Accommodation Guide
Holiday Selector
Take a Break 1992/93
Diary of Events
Places to Visit Open in Winter
Also available are the following (prices include postage and packing):
Hundreds of Places to Visit in the South East £2.35
Leisure Map for South East England £3.60

Places to stay

Accommodation entries in this regional section are listed in alphabetical order of place name, and then in alphabetical order of establishment.

The map references refer to the colour maps at the back of the guide. The first figure is the map number; the letter and figure which follow indicate the grid reference on the map.

The symbols at the end of each accommodation entry give information about services and facilities. A 'key' to these symbols is inside the back cover flap, which can be kept open for easy reference.

ABINGER HAMMER

Surrey
Map ref 2D2

Lying in some of the most beautiful wooded land in the country, this village is notable for the clock on which the figure of a blacksmith strikes the hours on a bell. The 'Hammer' takes its name from an old forge where cannon balls were made in the 16th C.

Crossways Farm

Raikes Lane, Abinger Hammer, Dorking RH5 6PZ
☎ Dorking (0306) 730173
200-acre arable & livestock farm. 17th C listed farmhouse. Good centre for London, the South East and airports. Large comfortable rooms.
Bedrooms: 1 twin, 1 triple
Bathrooms: 2 private, 1 public

Bed & breakfast

per night:	£min	£max
Double	30.00	36.00

Half board

per person:	£min	£max
Daily	23.00	26.50
Weekly	160.00	172.00

Evening meal 1900 (last orders 1900)
Parking for 3

ALBOURNE

West Sussex
Map ref 2D3

Great Wapses Farm

Wineham, Henfield BN5 9BJ
☎ (0273) 492544
33-acre mixed farm. Attractive Tudor and Georgian farmhouse in rural, peaceful surroundings with horses, calves and other animals. Four poster bed, tennis court.
Bedrooms: 2 double, 1 twin
Bathrooms: 3 private

Bed & breakfast

per night:	£min	£max
Single	22.00	24.00
Double	34.00	36.00

Parking for 7
Cards accepted: Amex

ALBURY

Surrey
Map ref 2D2

High Dudgeon

Heath Lane, Albury Heath, Albury, Guildford GU5 9DB
☎ Shere (048 641) 2223
18th C cottage on heath above Shere, with lovely views. Complete with own staircase and inglenook in separate sitting room. Heated swimming pool. On Albury Heath opposite cricket pitch (right hand track down to cottage).

Bedrooms: 1 double
Bathrooms: 1 private

Bed & breakfast

per night:	£min	£max
Double	50.00	50.00

Parking for 3
Open February-November

ALDINGTON

Kent
Map ref 3B4

Once the home of Elizabeth Barton, the 'Holy Maid' or 'Nun of Kent'.

Hogben Farm

Church Lane, Aldington, Ashford TN25 7EH
☎ (0233) 720219
Small 16th C country house, surrounded by pretty garden and 17 acres of farmland. Convenient for Channel ports, Canterbury, Rye, Tenterden and Romney Marsh.
Bedrooms: 1 double, 2 twin
Bathrooms: 1 private, 1 public

Bed & breakfast

per night:	£min	£max
Single	15.00	17.00
Double	30.00	34.00

Half board

per person:	£min	£max
Daily	23.00	25.00
Weekly	150.00	165.00

Evening meal from 2000
Parking for 4

ARDINGLY

West Sussex
Map ref 2D3

Famous for the South of England Agricultural Showground and public school. Nearby is Wakehurst Place (National Trust), the gardens of which are administered by the Royal Botanic Gardens, Kew.

Jordans

Church Lane, Ardingly, Haywards Heath RH17 6UP
☎ (0444) 892681
Victorian country house set in beautiful gardens opposite medieval village church. Behind South of England Showground, close to many facilities and 20 minutes from Gatwick.
Bedrooms: 1 single, 1 twin
Bathrooms: 2 private, 1 public

Bed & breakfast

per night:	£min	£max
Single	20.00	22.00

Half board

per person:	£min	£max
Daily	38.00	40.00

Parking for 5

Open January-July,
September-December
🖵📶🕯📶📠🛏🖏.�· ⛽ Ⓟ ✵
✕ 🍴 🏠

ARUNDEL

West Sussex
Map ref 2D3

Pleasant town on the
River Arun, dominated by
Arundel Castle, home of
the Dukes of Norfolk.
There are many 18th C
houses and the Toy and
Military Museum, Wildfowl
Trust Reserve and
Heritage Centre.
Tourist Information Centre
☎ *(0903) 882268*

Arundel Vineyards ⚑
Listed COMMENDED
The Vineyard, Church Lane,
Lyminster, Arundel
BN17 7QF
☎ (0903) 883393
*Modern farmhouse in English
vineyard surrounded by open
countryside, 1.5 miles due
south of Arundel. Signposted
A284 Arundel to Lyminster/
Littlehampton road.*
Bedrooms: 2 twin
Bathrooms: 1 private,
1 private shower

Bed & breakfast
per night:	£min	£max
Single		22.00
Double		36.00

Parking for 15
🛏4🖨📶🖵🌀🛆🛈Ⓢ✉📺
◐🛏.�·✵✕🍴🏠

Castle View
Restaurant and Tea
Rooms
63 High Street, Arundel
BN18 9AJ
☎ (0903) 883029
*Rooms opposite castle in 16th
C listed building in
conservation area. Very
central and ideally situated
for visiting many local
attractions. Family-run.*
Bedrooms: 1 twin, 1 triple
Bathrooms: 2 private
showers

Bed & breakfast
per night:	£min	£max
Double	30.00	36.00

Lunch available
Open February-October
🛏6🖨🛈Ⓢ✉🖏🛈🏠

Mill Lane House
Slindon, Arundel BN18 0RP
☎ Slindon (0243) 65440
changing to 814440
*House situated in beautiful
National Trust village.
Magnificent views to coast.*

---

*Pubs within easy walking
distance. One mile from A29/
A27 junction.*
Bedrooms: 1 single,
3 double, 2 twin, 1 triple
Bathrooms: 7 private,
1 public

Bed & breakfast
per night:	£min	£max
Single		22.00
Double		33.00

Half board
per person:	£min	£max
Daily	25.00	30.50
Weekly	164.50	197.50

Evening meal 1900 (last
orders 1000)
Parking for 7
🛏🖨🖵🛈Ⓢ✉🖏🛈🖏.�·
🏠OAPSP🏠

Pindars ⚑
Listed
Lyminster, Arundel
BN17 7QF
☎ (0903) 882628
*Traditional country house
near Arundel. South-facing
bedrooms and dining room.
Beautiful garden.*
Bedrooms: 1 double, 1 twin
Bathrooms: 1 public

Bed & breakfast
per night:	£min	£max
Single	14.00	16.00
Double	30.00	34.00

Parking for 8
Open March-October
🛏10🖭🖵🌀🛈🖏.�·
✕🏠

ASHFORD

Kent
Map ref 3B4

Once a market centre for
the farmers of the Weald
of Kent and Romney
Marsh. The town centre
has a number of Tudor
and Georgian houses.
Tourist Information Centre
☎ *(0233) 629165*

Barnfield
🏠🏠🏠 HIGHLY COMMENDED
Pested Lane, Challock,
Ashford TN25 4BQ
☎ Challock (0233) 74380
*Set in beautiful Kent
countryside close to Leeds
Castle, Chilham and
Canterbury. Easy access to
M25 and M2.*
Bedrooms: 2 double, 1 twin
Bathrooms: 2 private,
1 public

Bed & breakfast
per night:	£min	£max
Single	15.00	15.00
Double	30.00	30.00

Half board
per person:	£min	£max
Daily	22.00	22.00
Weekly	154.00	154.00

Evening meal 1900 (last
orders 2100)
Parking for 10
🛏🖨🖵🌀📶🛈Ⓢ✉🖏📺
🛏.�·Ⓟ✵🏠OAP✵SP

Fishponds Farm
🏠🏠
Pilgrims Way, Brook,
Ashford TN25 5PP
☎ (0233) 812398
*Rural farmhouse with lake in
Wye Downs Nature Reserve, 3
miles south-east of Wye on
lane to Brabourne.*
Bedrooms: 1 double, 1 twin
Bathrooms: 2 private

Bed & breakfast
per night:	£min	£max
Single	15.00	15.00
Double	28.00	28.00

Parking for 10
🛏🖵🌀📶🛈.✵✕🏠

Meadowside
Church Road, Mersham,
Ashford TN25 6NT
☎ (0233) 626458
*1.5 miles from M20,
convenient for channel ports,
Canterbury, Rye and Weald.
Large comfortable rooms en-
suite (shower), tea-making,
colour TV. Non-smokers only
please.*
Bedrooms: 1 double, 1 twin
Bathrooms: 2 private

Bed & breakfast
per night:	£min	£max
Single	20.00	20.00
Double	36.00	40.00

Parking for 2
🛏10🖭🖵🌀📶🛈.
✵✕🏠

One Mile Oast ⚑
Church Hill, Kingsnorth,
Ashford TN23 3EX
☎ (0233) 624576
*In pleasant rural
surroundings 1 mile from
Kingsnorth crossroads and
2.5 miles from Ashford.
Converted Kent oast with
circular bedrooms. Good
centre for exploration. Small
livestock enterprise.*
Bedrooms: 2 double, 1 twin
Bathrooms: 2 public

Bed & breakfast
per night:	£min	£max
Single	15.00	18.00
Double	25.00	28.00

Parking for 5
🛏🖨🖵📶Ⓢ✉📺🛈🏠🏠

Warren Cottage ⚑
🏠🏠🏠 APPROVED
136 The Street,
Willesborough, Ashford
TN25 0NB
☎ (0233) 621905 & 632929
Fax (0233) 623400
*300-year-old guesthouse with
oak beams, open fireplaces
and a cosy atmosphere. On
old coaching route with easy
access to M20 and a short
drive from many places of
interest.*
Bedrooms: 2 single, 2 double
Bathrooms: 4 private,
1 public

Bed & breakfast
per night:	£min	£max
Single	25.00	38.00
Double	45.00	50.00

Half board
per person:	£min	£max
Daily	34.00	39.00
Weekly	238.00	273.00

Lunch available
Evening meal 1830 (last
orders 2130)
Parking for 7
Cards accepted: Access, Visa
🛏🖨🖭🖵🌀🖏📶🛈Ⓢ✉🖏
📺🛈.�·✵🏠🏠

AYLESFORD

Kent
Map ref 3B3

Stone Cottage
77 Mill Hall, Aylesford
ME20 7JN
☎ Maidstone (0622) 719562
*Victorian stone cottage with
beams. Comfortable friendly
accommodation, welcome
drink, very close to Aylesford
station. Close to M2 and M20.*
Bedrooms: 1 double, 1 triple
Bathrooms: 1 public

Bed & breakfast
per night:	£min	£max
Single	12.50	20.00
Double	25.00	40.00

Half board
per person:	£min	£max
Daily	17.50	26.00
Weekly	85.00	180.00

Evening meal 1750 (last
orders 1900)
🛏6🖭🖵🌀🛈Ⓢ✉🖏🛈.🛆
✕🏠

BARCOMBE

East Sussex
Map ref 2D3

Camoys Farmhouse ⚑
🏠🏠
Barcombe, Lewes BN8 5BH
☎ (0273) 400662
Continued ▶

373

BARCOMBE

Continued

850-acre mixed farm. A modern yet comfortable farmhouse in a quiet location with lovely views. Conveniently situated in central Sussex for sea, historic buildings and gardens.
Bedrooms: 1 single, 2 twin, 1 triple
Bathrooms: 1 private, 1 public

Bed & breakfast

per night:	£min	£max
Double	34.00	44.00

Parking for 4

Wootton Cottage
Hamsey Road, Barcombe, Lewes BN8 5TG
☎ Brighton (0273) 400486
Old family home set in heart of the Sussex countryside with extensive orchard and gardens. 3.5 miles from county town of Lewes and 11 miles from Brighton and Haywards Heath.
Bedrooms: 1 single, 1 double, 1 twin
Bathrooms: 1 private, 1 private shower

Bed & breakfast

per night:	£min	£max
Single	13.00	14.00
Double	30.00	32.00

Parking for 12

BATTLE

East Sussex
Map ref 3B4

The Abbey at Battle was built on the site of the Battle of Hastings, when William defeated Harold II and so became the Conqueror in 1066. The museum has a fine collection relating to the Sussex iron industry.
Tourist Information Centre
☎ *(042 46) 3721.*

Abbey Hotel ⋔
APPROVED
84 High Street, Battle
TN33 0AQ
☎ (042 46) 2755
Recently refurbished 17th C inn located on now vanished site of the historic battle of 1066. Friendly informal atmosphere.
Bedrooms: 8 double

Bathrooms: 8 private

Bed & breakfast

per night:	£min	£max
Single	30.00	35.00
Double	40.00	49.50

Evening meal 1900 (last orders 2130)
Cards accepted: Access, Visa

Kitchenham Farm
Ashburnham, Battle
TN33 9NP
☎ Ninfield (0424) 892221
700-acre arable and mixed farm. Friendly family atmosphere in beautiful 18th C farmhouse in superb countryside steeped in history. Large comfortable rooms.
Bedrooms: 1 double, 1 twin, 1 triple
Bathrooms: 2 public

Bed & breakfast

per night:	£min	£max
Single	15.00	20.00
Double	30.00	30.00

Half board

per person:	£min	£max
Daily	23.00	25.00
Weekly	147.00	147.00

Evening meal from 1900
Parking for 5

Lilac Cottage
Whatlington Road, Battle
TN33 0ND
☎ (042 46) 2389
Period cottage set in beautiful lakeside gardens. Pretty bedrooms with en-suite bathrooms, tea/coffee facilities. Private parking. Enjoy breakfast served on our lakeside terrace (weather permitting). Village inn walking distance for evening meals.
Bedrooms: 1 single, 1 double, 1 twin
Bathrooms: 2 private, 1 public

Bed & breakfast

per night:	£min	£max
Single	15.00	17.00
Double	30.00	34.00

Parking for 3

Moonshill Farm ⋔

The Green, Ninfield, Battle
TN33 9JL
☎ (0424) 892645
10-acre mixed farm. Modernised farmhouse in Ninfield village centre, in the heart of "1066" country. A

warm welcome and Sussex home cooking. Pub opposite.
Bedrooms: 2 double, 3 twin
Bathrooms: 3 private, 1 public

Bed & breakfast

per night:	£min	£max
Single	15.00	17.50
Double	30.00	35.00

Parking for 12
Open January-November

Netherfield Hall
Netherfield, Battle
TN33 9PQ
☎ (042 46) 4450
Comfortable, spacious, character building in quiet, rural surroundings in historic area. Take A2100 from Battle to London. First turning on left to Netherfield. After 3 miles there is a church on the right and Netherfield Hall is opposite.
Bedrooms: 2 double, 1 twin, 1 triple
Bathrooms: 2 private, 1 public, 1 private shower

Bed & breakfast

per night:	£min	£max
Single	25.00	30.00
Double	35.00	45.00

Parking for 7

Priory House Hotel ⋔
COMMENDED
17 High Street, Battle
TN33 0EA
☎ (042 46) 3366
Charming Queen Anne family-run hotel offering value for money and clean accommodation. English food.
Bedrooms: 3 double, 3 triple
Bathrooms: 5 private, 1 public

Bed & breakfast

per night:	£min	£max
Single	21.00	24.00
Double	35.00	39.00

Half board

per person:	£min	£max
Daily	23.00	27.00

Lunch available
Evening meal 1900 (last orders 2100)
Cards accepted: Access, Visa

Wakeford House
Potmans Lane, Lunsford Cross, Bexhill-on-Sea
TN39 5JL
☎ Ninfield (0424) 892013
Large detached country house with lovely 1 acre garden. Quiet lane off A269 Ninfield

to Bexhill road. Battle 8 minutes.
Bedrooms: 1 single, 2 double, 1 triple
Bathrooms: 2 public

Bed & breakfast

per night:	£min	£max
Single	16.50	20.00
Double	33.00	37.00

Parking for 7

BEXHILL-ON-SEA

East Sussex
Map ref 3B4

Popular resort with beach of shingle and firm sand at low tide. The De la Warr Pavilion has good entertainment facilities.
Tourist Information Centre
☎ *(0424) 212023*

Buenos Aires
Listed
24 Albany Road, Bexhill-on-Sea TN40 1BZ
☎ (0424) 212269
Well-established guesthouse adjacent to seafront, theatre and town centre, offering comfortable accommodation and a friendly atmosphere.
Bedrooms: 1 double, 1 twin, 1 triple, 1 multiple
Bathrooms: 1 public

Bed & breakfast

per night:	£min	£max
Single	17.00	17.00
Double	28.00	30.00

Half board

per person:	£min	£max
Daily	20.50	23.50
Weekly	138.00	158.00

Evening meal 1800 (last orders 1200)

Tudor Court
Ninfield Road, Ninfield, Battle TN39 5JR
☎ Ninfield (0424) 892231
Rambling Tudor family house with oak panelling, beams and open fires. Small library, tennis court and large garden. Car park.
Bedrooms: 1 double, 2 twin, 1 triple
Bathrooms: 1 private, 2 public

Bed & breakfast

per night:	£min	£max
Single	20.00	25.00
Double	33.00	38.00

Parking for 7

BIDDENDEN

Kent
Map ref 3B4

Perfect village with black and white houses, a tithe barn and a pond. Part of the village is grouped around a green with a village sign depicting the famous Biddenden Maids. It is an important centre of the Flemish weaving industry, hence the beautiful Old Cloth Hall.

Bettmans Oast
HIGHLY COMMENDED

Hareplain Road, Biddenden, Ashford TN27 8LJ
☎ (0580) 291463
Grade II listed oast house and converted barn set in 10 acres near Sissinghurst Castle, quarter mile from Three Chimneys pub. Lovely gardens and log fires in winter.
Bedrooms: 1 twin, 1 multiple
Bathrooms: 1 private, 1 public

Bed & breakfast per night:	£min	£max
Single	20.00	20.00
Double	30.00	35.00

Half board per person:	£min	£max
Daily	25.00	27.50

Evening meal 1830 (last orders 2100)
Parking for 4

Bishopsdale Oast ⋀
Listed

Biddenden, Ashford TN27 8DR
☎ (0580) 291027 & 292065
Fax (0580) 292321
18th C. double kiln oast. Outstanding rooms, business facilities, professional cooks. Tenterden two miles, Cranbrook five miles. Signpost on bend.
Bedrooms: 2 double
Bathrooms: 2 private

Bed & breakfast per night:	£min	£max
Single	30.00	35.00
Double	50.00	60.00

Half board per person:	£min	£max
Daily	37.50	45.00
Weekly	227.50	280.00

Lunch available
Evening meal 1830 (last orders 2000)
Parking for 6

BILLINGSHURST

West Sussex
Map ref 2D3

Small town lying 100 ft above sea level in undulating and unspoilt countryside.

Blue Idol Guest House ⋀
Listed

Coolham, Horsham RH13 8QP
☎ Coolham (0403) 741241
Historic building founded by William Penn, set in lovely grounds up quiet lane off the A272 between Billingshurst and Coolham.
Bedrooms: 2 single, 2 double, 1 triple
Bathrooms: 2 public

Bed & breakfast per night:	£min	£max
Single	16.00	20.00
Double	28.00	30.00

Evening meal 1900 (last orders 1900)
Parking for 20

Wooddale Cottage
Listed

Billingshurst RH14 9DU
☎ (0403) 782996
Delightful old farmhouse set in large water gardens surrounded by over 100 acres of wooded farmland, 1 mile north east of Billingshurst.
Bedrooms: 1 single, 1 double, 1 twin
Bathrooms: 1 public

Bed & breakfast per night:	£min	£max
Single	15.00	18.00
Double	30.00	36.00

Half board per person:	£min	£max
Daily	22.50	28.50

Parking for 3

> The colour maps at the back of this guide pinpoint all places with accommodation.

BIRCHINGTON

Kent
Map ref 3C3

Town on the north coast of Kent with sandy beaches and rock pools. Powell Cotton Museum is in nearby Quex Park.

Woodchurch Farmhouse

Woodchurch, Birchington CT7 0HE
☎ Thanet (0843) 832468
6-acre arable farm. This Elizabethan farmhouse provides a warm welcome and ensures a comfortable stay. An excellent base for exploring south-east Kent.
Bedrooms: 1 single, 2 double, 1 twin
Bathrooms: 1 public

Bed & breakfast per night:	£min	£max
Single		14.50
Double		29.00

Parking for 6

BIRDHAM

West Sussex
Map ref 2C3

An area much favoured by yachtsmen, as Birdham Pool forms part of Chichester Harbour.

Saint Christophers

Main Road, Birdham, Chichester PO20 7HS
☎ Chichester (0243) 512141
Comfortable well appointed large rooms close to Birdham/Chichester marinas and beaches. Friendly welcome, especially for families. On A286 south of Chichester.
Bedrooms: 1 double, 1 triple
Bathrooms: 1 public

Bed & breakfast per night:	£min	£max
Single	14.00	14.00
Double	28.00	30.00

Parking for 6

> National Crown ratings were correct at the time of going to press but are subject to change. Please check at the time of booking.

BOUGHTON MONCHELSEA

Kent
Map ref 3B4

Pleasant village mainly built of ragstone, a material that has been quarried nearby for over 7 centuries and was used in the building of Westminster Abbey.

Iden Farmhouse

Heath Road, Boughton Monchelsea, Maidstone ME17 4JE
☎ (0622) 743714
Grade II, 16th C farmhouse in quiet area surrounded by orchards, about 2 miles from Leeds Castle. 40 minutes to Canterbury and Gatwick, and close to main line station for London.
Bedrooms: 1 single, 1 double, 1 twin
Bathrooms: 3 private

Bed & breakfast per night:	£min	£max
Single	14.00	16.00
Double	26.00	30.00

Parking for 10
Open April-October

BRASTED

Kent
Map ref 2D2

The Mount House ⋀

Brasted, Westerham TN16 1JB
☎ Westerham (0959) 563617
Fax (0959) 563617
Large early Georgian village house in centre of village. Occupied as a family residence. Listed Grade II.
Bedrooms: 1 single, 1 double, 1 twin
Bathrooms: 1 private, 1 public

Bed & breakfast per night:	£min	£max
Single	20.00	20.00
Double	40.00	40.00

Parking for 3

> The town index towards the back of this guide gives page numbers of all places with accommodation.

BRENCHLEY

Kent
Map ref 3B4

In the centre of this village is a small green, around which stand half-timbered, tile-hung and weatherboarded houses.

Bull Inn at Brenchley ▲

♛♛ [COMMENDED]

High Street, Brenchley, Tonbridge TN12 7NQ
☎ (089 272) 2701

Victorian village inn set in the heart of the Weald of Kent. Comfortable accommodation with traditional English ales and home-cooked food. 10 per cent discount for weekly half board.

Bedrooms: 1 single, 2 double, 1 twin, 1 triple
Bathrooms: 4 private, 1 public

Bed & breakfast per night:	£min	£max
Single	24.00	40.00
Double	30.00	45.00

Half board per person:	£min	£max
Daily	24.00	55.00

Lunch available
Evening meal 1830 (last orders 2130)
Parking for 10

🐴 🛏 📖 □ ☕ 💨 🔒 [S] 🚭 🪑 [TV] ◐ ♨ ◣ 🍷 🔍 ∪ ⚑ ⛳ ✽ ✈ 🚐 ↘ [SP] 🏛

BRIGHTLING

East Sussex
Map ref 3B4

The Glebe House

Brightling, Robertsbridge TN32 5HE
☎ (042 482) 295

Old rectory in Brightling, on Robertsbridge road out of village. Accommodation in 17th C wing. Beamed, Gothic lancet windows, antique furniture. Beautiful garden with panoramic views.

Bedrooms: 2 single, 2 double
Bathrooms: 1 public

Bed & breakfast per night:	£min	£max
Single		20.00
Double		40.00

Parking for 2
Open April-October

🐴 🛏 💨 [UL] [S] 🪑 ♨ ◣ ✽ 🚐 🏛

BRIGHTON & HOVE

East Sussex
Map ref 2D3

First and largest seaside resort in the south east. Attractions include the Dome, Royal Pavilion, Theatre Royal, Volks Railway, Sea Life Centre, Palace Pier, Stanmer Park, Marina, Conference and Exhibition Centre and 'The Lanes'. Neighbouring Hove is a resort in its own right with interesting Museum of Art and King Alfred's Leisure Centre.
Tourist Information Centre ☎ (0273) 23755; for Hove (0273) 746100 or 778087

Aannabelles Olde English Lodging House ▲

9 Charles Street, Brighton BN2 1TG
☎ (0273) 605845 & 677419
Fax (0273) 621703

Established in 1790 in the heart of Brighton. Still retaining the charm of yesteryear but with all modern facilities. Restaurant.

Bedrooms: 2 single, 2 double, 1 twin
Bathrooms: 5 private

Bed & breakfast per night:	£min	£max
Single	29.50	29.50
Double	69.50	69.50

Half board per person:	£min	£max
Daily	39.50	39.50
Weekly	276.50	276.50

Evening meal from 1800
Parking for 6
Cards accepted: Access, Visa, C.Bl, Diners

🐴 🛏 ☎ □ ☕ 💨 🔒 [S] 🪑 ♨ ◣ ✈ 🚐 [SP] 🏛 [T]

Amblecliff Hotel

♛♛♛

35 Upper Rock Gardens, Brighton BN2 1QF
☎ (0273) 681161

Featured on 2 TV programmmes and in the "Sunday Times". Close to seafront, town centre and conference centre.

Bedrooms: 3 single, 8 double, 2 twin
Bathrooms: 10 private, 2 public

Bed & breakfast per night:	£min	£max
Single	16.00	19.00
Double	32.00	52.00

Evening meal 1800 (last orders 1800)
Parking for 3
Cards accepted: Access, Visa, Diners, Amex

🐴 5 🛏 ☎ 📖 □ ☕ 💨 🔒 [S] 🚭 🪑 [TV] ♨ ◣ ✈ [OAP] [SP] [T]

'Brighton' Marina House Hotel ▲

♛♛♛

8 Charlotte Street, Marine Parade, Brighton BN2 1AG
☎ (0273) 605349 & 679484
Fax (0273) 605349

Cosy, well-maintained elegant hotel, offering a warm welcome, cleanliness, comfort and hospitality. English breakfast, licensed restaurant. Central for Palace Pier, conferences and exhibitions, adjacent to the sea and a few minutes from the Marina, Royal Pavilion and all amenities. Flexible breakfast, check-in and check-out times.

Bedrooms: 3 single, 7 double
Bathrooms: 7 private, 1 public

Bed & breakfast per night:	£min	£max
Single	13.50	29.00
Double	29.00	41.00

Half board per person:	£min	£max
Daily	22.50	38.00
Weekly	150.00	259.00

Lunch available
Evening meal 1830 (last orders 1700)
Cards accepted: Access, Visa, Diners, Amex

🐴 🛁 📖 □ ☕ 💨 🔒 [S] 🪑 [TV] ♨ ◣ ✈ [OAP] ↘ [SP] [T]

Cavalaire House ▲

♛♛ [COMMENDED]

34 Upper Rock Gardens, Brighton BN2 1QF
☎ (0273) 696899
Fax (0273) 600504

Close to all amenities, offering rooms with or without private facilities. Book 7 nights and get 1 night free.

Bedrooms: 1 single, 3 double, 3 twin, 2 triple
Bathrooms: 3 private, 1 public, 4 private showers

Bed & breakfast per night:	£min	£max
Single	17.00	19.00
Double	28.00	42.00

Cards accepted: Access, Visa, Diners, Amex

🐴 📖 □ ☕ 💨 [UL] [S] 🚭 🪑 ♨ ◣ 🚐 ↘

Granada House Hotel

35 Walsingham Road, Hove, Brighton BN3 4FE
☎ (0273) 723855

Small, comfortable, modernised hotel situated 250 yards from Hove seafront. Easy parking.

Bedrooms: 3 twin
Bathrooms: 1 public

Bed & breakfast per night:	£min	£max
Double	32.00	34.00

Open January-November

□ [UL] 🔒 ♨ ◣ ✈ 🚐

Griffon Guest House

59 Montefiore Road, Hove, Brighton BN3 6EP
☎ (0273) 732760

Small, friendly guesthouse with showers in all rooms, tea- making facilities, colour TV and central heating. Unrestricted street parking and full English breakfast. Three bedrooms offering flexible accommodation.

Bedrooms: 1 single, 2 twin
Bathrooms: 3 private showers

Bed & breakfast per night:	£min	£max
Single	14.00	14.50
Double	27.00	28.00

🐴 □ ☕ [UL] [S] ♨ ◣ ✈ 🚐 [T]

Melford Hall Hotel ▲

♛♛

41 Marine Parade, Brighton BN2 1PE
☎ (0273) 681435

Listed building well positioned on seafront and within easy walking distance of all the entertainment that Brighton has to offer. Many rooms with sea views.

Bedrooms: 4 single, 14 double, 7 twin
Bathrooms: 23 private, 2 public, 2 private showers

Bed & breakfast per night:	£min	£max
Single	25.00	32.00
Double	44.00	.54.00

Parking for 12
Cards accepted: Access, Visa, Diners, Amex

🐴 🛁 🛏 📖 □ ☕ 💨 [UL] [S] 🪑 [TV] ♨ ◣ ✈ [OAP] [SP] 🏛 [T]

Queensbury Hotel ▲

♛♛ [APPROVED]

58 Regency Square, Brighton BN1 2GB
☎ (0273) 25558 changing to 325558
Fax (0273) 24800 changing to 324800

Family-run bed and breakfast, close to the beach, shopping, entertainment and exhibition/conference centres, but just far enough away to avoid the traffic noise.

Bedrooms: 1 single,
7 double, 4 twin, 4 triple
Bathrooms: 10 private,
3 public, 5 private showers
Bed & breakfast

per night:	£min	£max
Single	20.00	45.00
Double	30.00	58.00

Cards accepted: Access, Visa

The Regency Hotel **
28 Regency Square,
Brighton BN1 2FH
☎ (0273) 202690
Fax (0273) 220438
*Small, smart, family-managed
hotel with licensed bar and
sea views. Children welcome.
Arrangements made for
theatre, excursions, car and
boat hire, dining out.
Christmas packages.*
Bedrooms: 4 single,
7 double, 2 twin, 1 multiple
Bathrooms: 10 private,
1 public
Bed & breakfast

per night:	£min	£max
Single	32.00	37.00
Double	50.00	60.00

Half board

per person:	£min	£max
Daily	30.00	45.00
Weekly	180.00	230.00

Evening meal 1900 (last
orders 2100)
Cards accepted: Access, Visa,
Diners, Amex

Royal Promenade Hotel
3-5 Percival Terrace, Marine
Parade, Brighton BN2 1FA
☎ (0273) 675516
Fax (0273) 670181
*Overlooking marina.
Conferences and secretarial
service. Speciality holidays
include Art and Colour,
Writing Skills, Self-
development, Houses and
Gardens, Cookery, Alternative
Cures for Stress.*
Bedrooms: 9 single,
10 double, 16 twin, 5 triple
Bathrooms: 40 private
Bed & breakfast

per night:	£min	£max
Single	25.00	40.00
Double	40.00	60.00

Half board

per person:	£min	£max
Daily	35.00	45.00
Weekly	230.00	300.00

Lunch available
Evening meal 1830 (last
orders 2115)
Parking for 6

Cards accepted: Access, Visa,
Diners, Amex

St. James's Guest House
39 St. James's Avenue,
Brighton BN2 1QD
☎ (0273) 690111
*Comfortable, quiet, friendly
family-run accommodation.
Centrally located close to
seafront, shopping,
entertainment and the Royal
Pavilion.*
Bedrooms: 1 twin, 1 triple
Bathrooms: 1 public
Bed & breakfast

per night:	£min	£max
Single	16.00	20.00
Double	26.00	30.00

Open January-November

Whitehaven Hotel **
34 Wilbury Road, Hove,
Brighton BN3 3JP
☎ (0273) 778355
Fax (0273) 731177
*Elegant family-managed hotel
with garden and easy
parking, on quiet wide road
near sea and shops. All
bedrooms extensively
equipped and with en-suite
facilities.*
Bedrooms: 6 single,
5 double, 4 twin, 2 triple
Bathrooms: 17 private
Bed & breakfast

per night:	£min	£max
Single	40.00	55.00
Double	60.00	75.00

Half board

per person:	£min	£max
Daily	41.00	45.00

Lunch available
Evening meal 1900 (last
orders 2130)
Cards accepted: Access, Visa,
C.Bl, Diners, Amex

There are separate
sections in this
guide listing groups
specialising in farm
holidays and
accommodation
which is especially
suitable for young
people and
organised groups.

BURWASH
East Sussex
Map ref 3B4

Village of old houses,
many from the Tudor and
Stuart periods. One of the
old ironmasters' houses is
Bateman's (National
Trust) which was the
home of Rudyard Kipling.

Woodlands Farm
Listed
Heathfield Road, Burwash,
Etchingham TN19 7LA
☎ (0435) 882794
*55-acre mixed farm.
Modernised 16th C farmhouse
set away from road, amidst
fields and woods. Friendly
welcome and fresh food. Near
Batemans.*
Bedrooms: 2 double, 2 twin
Bathrooms: 1 private,
2 public
Bed & breakfast

per night:	£min	£max
Single	16.50	
Double	28.00	36.00

Parking for 4
Open April-December

BUXTED
East Sussex
Map ref 2D3

Small Wealden village
near the towns of
Crowborough and
Uckfield, within easy
reach of the Ashdown
Forest.

Buxted Inn
High Street, Buxted, Uckfield
TN22 4LA
☎ (082 573) 3510
*Family-run Victorian inn in
the High Weald of East
Sussex, within easy reach of
Eastbourne and Brighton.
Close to Tunbridge Wells and
Ashdown Forest. Chef/
proprietor.*
Bedrooms: 1 single,
1 double, 1 twin, 1 triple
Bathrooms: 2 public
Bed & breakfast

per night:	£min	£max
Single	17.50	18.50
Double	35.00	37.00

Half board

per person:	£min	£max
Daily	25.00	

Lunch available
Evening meal 1800 (last
orders 2200)

Parking for 40
Cards accepted: Visa, Diners,
Amex

CANTERBURY
Kent
Map ref 3B3

Place of pilgrimage since
the martyrdom of Becket
in 1170 and the site of
Canterbury Cathedral.
Visit St Augustine's
Abbey, St Martin's (the
oldest church in England),
Royal Museum and the
Canterbury Tales. Nearby
is Howletts Zoo Park.
Tourist Information Centre
☎ (0277) 766567

Abberley House
Listed
115 Whitstable Road,
Canterbury CT2 8EF
☎ (0227) 450265
*Family-run guesthouse within
walking distance of the city
and university. Non-smokers
only please.*
Bedrooms: 1 single,
1 double, 1 twin
Bathrooms: 1 public
Bed & breakfast

per night:	£min	£max
Single	16.00	19.00
Double	30.00	34.00

Parking for 2

Anchor Guest House **
25 North Lane, Canterbury
CT2 7EE
☎ (0227) 768105
*Charming 15th C hall-house
with crown post roof,
formerly the Blue Anchor
coaching inn. Medieval beams
and floors.*
Bedrooms: 1 double, 1 twin,
2 triple
Bathrooms: 2 private,
2 public
Bed & breakfast

per night:	£min	£max
Double	34.00	46.00

Open April-October
Cards accepted: Access, Visa,
Amex

Bower Farm House
Stelling Minnis, Canterbury
CT4 6BB
☎ Stelling Minnis (022 787)
430
*Delightful heavily beamed
17th C farmhouse between the*
Continued ►

CANTERBURY

Continued

villages of Stelling Minnis and Bossingham. Canterbury and Hythe are approximately 7 miles away.
Bedrooms: 2 double, 1 twin
Bathrooms: 1 public,
1 private shower
Bed & breakfast

per night:	£min	£max
Single	16.00	16.00
Double	32.00	32.00

Parking for 8

Cathedral Gate Hotel ⚅

APPROVED

36 Burgate, Canterbury
CT1 2HA
☎ (0227) 464381
Fax (0227) 462800
Central position at main entrance to the cathedral. Car parking nearby. Baby listening service. Old world charm at reasonable prices. English breakfast extra.
Bedrooms: 5 single,
7 double, 8 twin, 4 triple,
2 multiple
Bathrooms: 13 private,
3 public, 3 private showers
Bed & breakfast

per night:	£min	£max
Single	20.00	44.00
Double	40.00	66.00

Evening meal 1900 (last orders 2100)
Parking for 12
Cards accepted: Access, Visa, Diners, Amex

Clare-Ellen Guest House ⚅

HIGHLY COMMENDED

9 Victoria Road, Wincheap,
Canterbury CT1 3SG
☎ (0227) 760205
Victorian house with large, elegant en-suite rooms, 8 minutes' walk from city centre. 5 minutes to BR Canterbury East station. Car park and garage available.
Bedrooms: 1 single,
2 double, 1 twin, 1 triple
Bathrooms: 4 private,
2 public
Bed & breakfast

per night:	£min	£max
Single	18.00	22.00
Double	38.00	44.00

Parking for 9

The Corner House ⚅

Listed

113 Whitstable Road,
Canterbury CT2 8EF
☎ (0227) 761352
Just a few minutes' walking distance from city, university, shops and restaurants. Spacious family house and friendly hospitality.
Bedrooms: 1 double, 2 twin
Bathrooms: 2 public
Bed & breakfast

per night:	£min	£max
Single	18.00	25.00
Double	28.00	34.00

Parking for 4

Courtney Guest House ⚅

Listed COMMENDED

4 London Road, Canterbury
CT2 8LR
☎ (0227) 769668
Excellently situated opposite St Dunstans Church. Rooms not overlooked. Clear views to University at rear, cathedral and city at front.
Bedrooms: 1 double, 1 twin,
1 triple, 1 multiple
Bathrooms: 1 private,
1 public, 2 private showers
Bed & breakfast

per night:	£min	£max
Single	20.00	30.00
Double	26.00	36.00

Parking for 3
Cards accepted: Access, Visa

Crockshard Farmhouse

Crockshard Lane, Wingham,
Canterbury CT3 1NY
☎ (0227) 720464
Large Regency farmhouse and family home in pleasant countryside with beautiful gardens and farmyard animals. 7 miles Canterbury, 13 miles Dover.
Bedrooms: 3 multiple
Bathrooms: 1 private,
3 public
Bed & breakfast

per night:	£min	£max
Single	20.00	25.00
Double	30.00	35.00

Half board

per person:	£min	£max
Daily	25.00	27.50
Weekly	150.00	165.00

Evening meal 1800 (last orders 2000)
Parking for 12
Cards accepted: Amex

Ersham Lodge Hotel ⚅

12 New Dover Road,
Canterbury CT1 3AP
☎ (0227) 463174
Fax (0227) 455482
Delightfully appointed rooms furnished with exquisite taste and elegance. Colour TV, telephone, radio, hairdryer. Well-stocked bar, bright breakfast room, pleasant patio. Close to amenities.
Bedrooms: 1 single,
3 double, 8 twin, 2 triple
Bathrooms: 12 private,
1 public, 2 private showers
Bed & breakfast

per night:	£min	£max
Single	43.00	52.00
Double	54.00	61.00

Parking for 12
Cards accepted: Access, Visa, Amex

The Farmhouse, Upper Mystole Park Farm

HIGHLY COMMENDED

Pennypot Lane, Mystole,
Canterbury CT4 7BT
☎ (0227) 730589
75-acre fruit farm. Modern farmhouse in the heart of Kent and with magnificent views. Set between historic Canterbury and beautiful Chilham (A28). Dover 25 minutes.
Bedrooms: 1 double, 1 twin,
1 triple
Bathrooms: 1 private,
1 public
Bed & breakfast

per night:	£min	£max
Single	16.00	18.00
Double	30.00	32.00

Half board

per person:	£min	£max
Daily	22.00	23.00
Weekly	132.00	138.00

Evening meal 1830 (last orders 2000)
Parking for 6

Kenfield House ⚅

Listed

Kenfield, Petham,
Canterbury CT4 5RN
☎ Petham (0227) 700721
Large Georgian former farmhouse with Tudor origins set in own grounds of 6 acres in valley, 4.5 miles from Canterbury.
Bedrooms: 1 double, 1 twin,
1 triple
Bathrooms: 1 public

Bed & breakfast

per night:	£min	£max
Single	15.00	18.00
Double	30.00	36.00

Half board

per person:	£min	£max
Daily	21.00	24.00
Weekly		160.00

Evening meal from 1900
Parking for 6

Lyon House ⚅

Petham, Canterbury
CT4 5QY
☎ (0227) 700326
18th C villa in centre of village.
Bedrooms: 1 double, 1 twin,
1 triple
Bathrooms: 3 private
Bed & breakfast

per night:	£min	£max
Single	18.00	18.00
Double	36.00	36.00

Half board

per person:	£min	£max
Daily	23.00	23.00
Weekly	138.00	138.00

Evening meal from 1930
Parking for 4

Magnolia House ⚅

HIGHLY COMMENDED

36 St. Dunstans Terrace,
Canterbury CT2 8AX
☎ (0227) 765121
Georgian house in attractive city street. Close to university, gardens, river and city centre. Very quiet house within a walled garden, ideal for guests to relax in.
Bedrooms: 1 single,
4 double, 1 twin
Bathrooms: 6 private
Bed & breakfast

per night:	£min	£max
Single	28.00	35.00
Double	45.00	50.00

Half board

per person:	£min	£max
Daily	32.50	45.00

Parking for 4
Cards accepted: Access, Visa, Amex, Switch

Millers Quern ⚅

Listed HIGHLY COMMENDED

40a Ivy Lane, Canterbury
CT1 1TU
☎ (0227) 769222
Listed 14th C cottage for discerning visitors. Elegantly furnished, patio garden. Near

*city wall. Self-catering also
available.*
Bedrooms: 1 single, 1 double
Bathrooms: 1 private,
1 public
Bed & breakfast

per night:	£min	£max
Single	15.00	80.00
Double	45.00	83.00

Parking for 1

🛇⛔♿🏧👃⛺📺🛏🌀🚲
⛔♿📶♿📞

The Old Coach House ⋀

⚜⚜⚜ COMMENDED

Dover Road, (A2), Barham,
Canterbury CT4 6SA
☎ (0227) 831218
Fax (0227) 831932
*On A2, midway between
Canterbury and Dover.
Convenient for ferries.
Maison Francaise.*
Bedrooms: 2 double, 2 twin,
1 triple
Bathrooms: 5 private
Bed & breakfast

per night:	£min	£max
Single	37.50	42.00
Double	44.00	52.00

Half board

per person:	£min	£max
Daily	48.00	56.50

Lunch available
Evening meal 1900 (last
orders 2100)
Parking for 80
Cards accepted: Access, Visa,
Diners, Amex

🛇🖂⛔👃🏧♿🔆♿📺🛏🌀
🛝🅿✔♿🌸🚲⛔♿📞

Pilgrims Hotel ⋀

⚜⚜⚜⚜ COMMENDED

18 The Friars, Canterbury
CT1 2AS
☎ (0227) 464531
Fax (0227) 762514
*Comfortable and friendly city
centre hotel. All rooms en-
suite. Bar, restaurant. 2
minutes from cathedral,
opposite Marlowe.*
Bedrooms: 5 single,
7 double, 2 twin, 1 multiple
Bathrooms: 15 private
Bed & breakfast

per night:	£min	£max
Single	35.00	45.00
Double	45.00	55.00

Lunch available
Evening meal 1800 (last
orders 2200)
Parking for 10
Cards accepted: Access, Visa

🛇🏧⛔🖂⛔👃🏧♿🛏🌀
🛝🅿⛔♿📞

Pointers Hotel ⋀

⚜⚜⚜ COMMENDED

1 London Road, Canterbury
CT2 8LR
☎ (0227) 456846
*Family-run Georgian hotel
close to city centre, cathedral
and university.*
Bedrooms: 2 single,
8 double, 2 twin, 2 triple
Bathrooms: 8 private,
2 public, 2 private showers
Bed & breakfast

per night:	£min	£max
Single	30.00	38.00
Double	42.00	58.00

Half board

per person:	£min	£max
Daily	34.00	51.00

Evening meal 1930 (last
orders 2030)
Parking for 10
Cards accepted: Access, Visa,
Diners, Amex

🛇🖂⛔👃🏧♿🌀⛔♿
♿🛝

St Stephens Guest House ⋀

Listed COMMENDED

100 St. Stephens Road,
Canterbury CT2 7JL
☎ (0227) 767644
*Mock-Tudor house set in
attractive garden within easy
walking distance of the city
centre and cathedral. Colour
TV in rooms. Car park.*
Bedrooms: 2 single,
6 double, 2 twin, 1 triple
Bathrooms: 8 private,
1 public
Bed & breakfast

per night:	£min	£max
Single	17.50	
Double	35.00	42.00

Parking for 8
Cards accepted: Access, Visa

🛇🏧⛔👃🏧♿🔆♿🌀🛝
🌸✖♿📞

The Tanner Of Wingham ⋀

Listed APPROVED

44 High Street, Wingham,
Canterbury CT3 1AB
☎ (0227) 720532
*Old English licensed
restaurant and tearooms, built
in 1620. Oak-beamed but with
all modern facilities, in a
small village between
Canterbury and Sandwich.*
Bedrooms: 1 single,
1 double, 1 twin, 2 multiple
Bathrooms: 1 public
Bed & breakfast

per night:	£min	£max
Single	20.00	20.00
Double	39.00	39.00

Half board

per person:	£min	£max
Daily	23.25	31.50

Evening meal 1900 (last
orders 2100)
Cards accepted: Access, Visa

🛇🖂👃♿🛏🌀🛝🅿⛔♿
🛝♿📞

Thanington Hotel ⋀

⚜⚜⚜ HIGHLY COMMENDED

140 Wincheap, Canterbury
CT1 3RY
☎ (0227) 453227
*Up-market bed and breakfast,
5 minutes' walk from city
centre and 30 minutes from
Dover. En-suite bedrooms,
indoor swimming pool,
snooker room. Colour
brochure available.*
Bedrooms: 5 double, 3 twin,
2 multiple
Bathrooms: 10 private
Bed & breakfast

per night:	£min	£max
Single	38.00	45.00
Double	55.00	62.00

Parking for 12
Cards accepted: Access, Visa,
Amex

🛇♿🖂⛔👃🏧♿🔆♿📺
🌀🛝🌸♿🌸🚲⛔♿📞

Well House

⚜⚜

The Green, Chartham,
Canterbury CT4 7JW
☎ (0227) 738762
*In a very quiet position, on
village green next to 15th C
church. Just off A28, 2 miles
from Canterbury.*
Bedrooms: 1 double, 1 twin
Bathrooms: 2 private
Bed & breakfast

per night:	£min	£max
Single		16.00
Double		28.00

Parking for 2

🛇⛔👃♿🅿♿🌀🛝🌸🚲

The Willows ⋀

⚜ COMMENDED

Howfield Lane, Chartham
Hatch, Canterbury CT4 7HG
☎ (0227) 738442
*A friendly welcome awaits
you. Situated 2 miles from
city centre. Breakfast is taken
in the conservatory
overlooking attractive garden.*
Bedrooms: 1 double, 1 twin
Bathrooms: 1 public
Bed & breakfast

per night:	£min	£max
Single	15.00	
Double	36.00	

Parking for 6

🛇🏧⛔👃♿🏧♿🔆♿🌀🛝
🌸✖♿🛝

Yorke Lodge ⋀

⚜⚜⚜ COMMENDED

50 London Road, Canterbury
CT2 8LF
☎ (0227) 451243
Fax (0227) 451243
*Spacious, elegant Victorian
town house close to city
centre. Relax and enjoy a
special bed and breakfast.*
Bedrooms: 1 single, 4 double
Bathrooms: 5 private
Bed & breakfast

per night:	£min	£max
Double	18.00	23.00

Half board

per person:	£min	£max
Daily	34.00	40.00

Parking for 4
Cards accepted: Access, Visa,
Amex

🛇🖂⛔👃♿🏧♿📞♿🔆♿
📺🌀🛝🌸🚲⛔♿🛝♿📞

CHARING

Kent
Map ref 3B4

Delightful village with
many 15th C houses. The
parish church has a fine
timbered roof with painted
beams and a medieval
pulpit.

Barnfield ⋀

Listed COMMENDED

Charing, Ashford TN27 0BN
☎ (023 371) 2421
*500-acre arable farm. Kent
hall farmhouse built 1420
with wealth of character. On
A20, leave Charing
roundabout by London exit.
After 400 yards take first left
signed Hook Lane, continue
for 2.5 miles to house on left
with white mail rail fence.*
Bedrooms: 2 single,
1 double, 1 twin
Bathrooms: 1 public
Bed & breakfast

per night:	£min	£max
Single	18.00	20.00
Double	36.00	40.00

Half board

per person:	£min	£max
Daily	29.50	31.50
Weekly	177.00	189.00

Evening meal 1900 (last
orders 1900)
Parking for 21

🛇⛔👃♿🔆♿🛏🌀🛝🌸🚲
🌸🅿♿✖🌸🚲♿📞

> **Map references
> apply to the colour
> maps at the back
> of this guide.**

CHARTHAM

Kent
Map ref 3B3

The first separate village beyond the outskirts of Canterbury, with a combination of medieval and modern architecture and two greens.

Bridge House
Listed
The Green, Chartham, Canterbury CT4 7JW
☎ (0227) 738354
Delightful 5-year-old well-equipped house on banks of River Stour. Tea/coffee upon request. Colour TV. Canterbury 3 miles on A28.
Bedrooms: 2 twin
Bathrooms: 2 public
Bed & breakfast

per night:	£min	£max
Single	15.99	15.99
Double	26.00	26.00

Parking for 5
ⓈⓍ▯▯▮▯▥▮▯◪▯

CHICHESTER

West Sussex
Map ref 2C3

The county town of West Sussex with a beautiful Norman cathedral. Noted for its Georgian architecture but also has modern buildings like the Festival Theatre. Surrounded by places of interest, including Fishbourne Roman Palace and Weald and Downland Open-Air Museum.
Tourist Information Centre
☎ (0243) 775888

5 Willowbed Avenue
Chichester PO19 2JD
☎ (0243) 786366
Select quiet area 12 minutes' walk from town and within easy reach of public transport. Friendly large house off A27, junction B2145. No smoking please.
Bedrooms: 2 single, 1 twin
Bathrooms: 1 public,
1 private shower
Bed & breakfast

per night:	£min	£max
Single	13.00	15.00
Double	28.00	30.00

Parking for 3
Ⓢ8▯▯▥▯▥▮▯◪▯
▥◪

Barford
Bosham Lane, Bosham,
Chichester PO18 8HL
☎ (0243) 573393
Comfortable cottage-style bungalow in the centre of a picturesque village and within a few minutes' walk of the harbour. Cycle hire available.
Bedrooms: 2 double, 1 twin
Bathrooms: 1 public
Bed & breakfast

per night:	£min	£max
Single	17.00	20.00
Double	32.00	36.00

Half board

per person:	£min	£max
Daily	23.50	25.50
Weekly	164.50	178.50

Evening meal 1800 (last orders 2100)
Parking for 1
Ⓢ▯▥▯▯▥Ⓢ▮▯▥▥
▯◇▯▥▯▯◪Ⓢ▯Ⓣ

Hedgehogs
45 Whyke Lane, Chichester PO19 2JT
☎ (0243) 780022
About half mile from city centre, bus/railway stations and theatre. Secluded garden. Guests' own bathroom, TV lounge. Weekly terms available. Cyclists and hikers welcome.
Bedrooms: 1 double, 1 twin
Bathrooms: 2 public
Bed & breakfast

per night:	£min	£max
Single	13.00	17.00
Double	26.00	34.00

Parking for 4
Ⓢ▯▥Ⓢ▥Ⓢ▥▥▯
▥◇▯

Stanes Farm
Funtington, Chichester PO18 9DW
☎ Bosham (0243) 575558
Quiet, comfortable converted Sussex barn at foot of South Downs. Set in farmland, three-quarters of a mile north of Funtington.
Bedrooms: 1 double, 1 twin
Bathrooms: 1 public
Bed & breakfast

per night:	£min	£max
Single	17.50	25.00
Double	35.00	35.00

Parking for 6
Open March-October
Ⓢ▯▥▯▥▥▥▯◇▥

White Lodge
Lavant Road, Chichester PO19 4QY
☎ (0243) 527495
Beautifully appointed private house where guests are welcomed as friends. A knowledge of local history a

speciality and guided tours of the area are available on request. Non-smokers only please.
Bedrooms: 1 single, 2 twin
Bathrooms: 2 public,
1 private shower
Bed & breakfast

per night:	£min	£max
Single	16.00	22.00
Double	32.00	40.00

Parking for 6
Ⓢ▯▥▯▥▯▥▮▯◇▥◪

Woodpeckers
56 The Avenue, Hambrook,
Chichester PO18 8TY
☎ Bosham (0243) 573856
Quiet cosy bungalow in rural setting between South Downs and Chichester Harbour. Hospitality is our speciality. Good meals at village inn.
Bedrooms: 2 twin
Bathrooms: 1 public
Bed & breakfast

per night:	£min	£max
Double	31.00	31.00

Parking for 2
Ⓢ12▯▥▯▯▥▥▯
▥◇▥

CHIDDINGFOLD

Surrey
Map ref 2D2

Old village grouped round a green, with a 13th C inn. The church preserves some of the medieval glass for which the village was once famous.

Greenaway
Pickhurst Road,
Chiddingfold, Godalming GU8 4TS
☎ Wormley (0428) 682920
Fax (0428) 685078
Situated in picturesque village, 1 hour from Gatwick and Heathrow, 40 minutes to coast. 16th C listed building, peaceful garden, friendly household. Inglenook fireplaces and a wealth of beams.
Bedrooms: 1 single,
1 double, 1 twin
Bathrooms: 1 private,
1 public
Bed & breakfast

per night:	£min	£max
Single	25.00	35.00
Double	50.00	60.00

Parking for 3
Ⓢ▯▥▯▥▥▯◇▥◪▥

Please check prices and other details at the time of booking.

CHIDDINGSTONE

Kent
Map ref 2D2

Pleasant village of 16th and 17th C, preserved by the National Trust, with an 18th C "castle" and attractive Tudor inn.

Hoath Holidays ♠
Listed APPROVED
Hoath House, Chiddingstone Hoath, Edenbridge TN8 7DB
☎ Cowden (0342) 850362
Tudor family house with beamed and panelled rooms and extensive gardens.
Bedrooms: 2 twin
Bathrooms: 1 public
Bed & breakfast

per night:	£min	£max
Single	15.00	20.00
Double	25.00	39.00

Parking for 8
Ⓢ▯▥Ⓢ▥▥▯Q▯◇▥
▥▥

CHILHAM

Kent
Map ref 3B3

Extremely pretty village of mostly Tudor and Jacobean houses. The village rises to the spacious square with the castle and the 15th C church. The grounds of the Jacobean House, laid out by Capability Brown, are open to the public.

Jullieberrie House ♠
🛏🛏
Canterbury Road, Chilham, Canterbury CT4 8DX
☎ Canterbury (0227) 730488
Modern house with lovely views over lake and woodland. On the A28 Ashford to Canterbury road, close to Chilham village.
Bedrooms: 1 double, 2 twin
Bathrooms: 1 private,
1 public
Bed & breakfast

per night:	£min	£max
Single	20.00	25.00
Double	27.00	33.00

Half board

per person:	£min	£max
Daily	30.00	42.00

Evening meal from 1900
Parking for 5
Ⓢ▯▥▯▯▥▥▯◇▥

380

The Woolpack Inn 🏛

APPROVED

High Street, Chilham,
Canterbury CT4 8DL
☎ Canterbury (0227)
730208
Fax (0227) 751090
*A fine bed and victuals have
been offered here for 200
years. Dine on Kentish fare
and enjoy the friendly bar.*
Bedrooms: 1 single,
7 double, 6 twin, 1 triple
Bathrooms: 13 private

Bed & breakfast

per night:	£min	£max
Single	35.00	40.00
Double	45.00	56.00

Lunch available
Evening meal 1900 (last
orders 2130)
Parking for 40
Cards accepted: Access, Visa,
Diners, Amex, Switch
🛇🖧🖳📞🖃🖂♦🔥🚿
📺🛏🍴🗼🐾

CLIFTONVILLE

Kent

See under Margate

COBHAM

Kent
Map ref 3B3

73 Sallows Shaw

Sole Street, Cobham,
Gravesend DA13 9BP
☎ Meopham (0474) 814546
*Attractive bungalow in quiet
Dickens village. 7 miles from
historic Rochester and easy
access to M25/M20/M2,
London and tourist
attractions. One hour Channel
ports. Good food and warm
welcome.*
Bedrooms: 1 double
Bathrooms: 1 private

Bed & breakfast

per night:	£min	£max
Single	15.50	15.50
Double	29.00	30.00

Parking for 2
🖧🖃♦🔥💷🔆📺🛏🍴🚶
🍴🚐

National Crown
ratings were correct
at the time of going
to press but are
subject to change.
Please check at the
time of booking.

COPTHORNE

Surrey
Map ref 2D2

Residential village on the
Surrey/West Sussex
border, near Crawley and
within easy reach of
Gatwick Airport.

Broad Oak

Listed

West Park Road, Copthorne,
Crawley, West Sussex
RH10 3EX
☎ (0342) 714882
*Modernised country house
built in early 1920s, set in
beautiful secluded garden.
Courtesy transport provided
for Gatwick travellers. Dining-
out facilities nearby. Non-
smokers only please.*
Bedrooms: 1 single, 1 twin,
1 triple
Bathrooms: 1 public

Bed & breakfast

per night:	£min	£max
Single	23.00	24.00
Double	38.00	39.00

Parking for 6
🛇♦💷🔆🗝🔆🖂📺🛏🍴🖂🔍
🚶🍴🚐🗼

CRANBROOK

Kent
Map ref 3B4

Old town, a centre for the
weaving industry in the
15th C. The 72-ft-high
Union Mill is a 3-storeyed
windmill, still in working
order.

Hancocks Farmhouse

Tilsden Lane, Cranbrook
TN17 3PH
☎ (0580) 714645
*Lovely old timber-framed
house quietly situated on the
edge of Cranbrook. Furnished
with antiques. Inglenook with
log fires. Beautiful garden.*
Bedrooms: 1 double, 2 twin
Bathrooms: 1 private,
1 public

Bed & breakfast

per night:	£min	£max
Single	20.00	25.00
Double	34.00	40.00

Half board

per person:	£min	£max
Daily	30.00	34.00

Evening meal 1900 (last
orders 2030)
Parking for 3
🛇🖧🖂♦🔥💷🔆🔆🛏🍴📺
🛏🍴🚐🗼🚐🔆🐾

Tolehurst Barn 🏛

Cranbrook Road, Frittenden,
Cranbrook TN17 2BP
☎ (0580) 714385
*Converted 17th C barn in
farmland - quiet and rural, all
modern conveniences, beams.
On A229, convenient for the
heart of Kent and places of
historic interest. Only 5
minutes from Sissinghurst.*
Bedrooms: 2 double, 1 twin
Bathrooms: 3 private

Bed & breakfast

per night:	£min	£max
Single	17.00	17.00
Double	34.00	34.00

Half board

per person:	£min	£max
Daily	25.00	25.00

Evening meal 1900 (last
orders 2100)
Parking for 6
🛇♦🖃🔥💷🔆🛏🍴📺🛏🍴
🍴🔆🚐🗼🗼

The White Horse Inn

High Street, Cranbrook
TN17 3EX
☎ (0580) 712615
*Victorian public house and
restaurant in the centre of the
smallest town in Kent, once
the capital of the Weald.*
Bedrooms: 1 double, 1 twin,
1 triple
Bathrooms: 1 public

Bed & breakfast

per night:	£min	£max
Single	20.00	
Double	30.00	

Half board

per person:	£min	£max
Daily	25.00	

Lunch available
Evening meal 1830 (last
orders 2130)
Parking for 12
Cards accepted: Access, Visa
🛇🖃♦🛏🍴🗼🍴🔆🔆
🐾🗼

CRAWLEY

West Sussex
Map ref 2D2

One of the first New
Towns built after World
War II, but it also has
some old buildings. Set in
magnificent wooded
countryside.

Caprice Guest House 🏛

Listed **APPROVED**

Bonnetts Lane, Ifield,
Crawley RH11 0NY
☎ (0293) 528620

*Small, friendly, family-run
guesthouse surrounded by
farmland and close to all
amenities. 10 minutes south
of Gatwick Airport.*
Bedrooms: 1 double, 2 twin
Bathrooms: 1 private,
1 public

Bed & breakfast

per night:	£min	£max
Single	25.00	30.00
Double	35.00	45.00

Parking for 6
🛇🖧🖃♦💷🔆🛏🍴📺🛏🍴🖂
🗼🚐

Europa Gatwick 🏛

COMMENDED

Balcombe Road,
Maidenbower, Crawley
RH10 4SR
☎ (0293) 886666
Fax (0293) 886680
*Mediterranean-style courtyard
property 6 miles from
Gatwick Airport. First class
conference facilities and
health club.*
Bedrooms: 158 double,
20 twin
Bathrooms: 178 private,
1 public

Bed & breakfast

per night:	£min	£max
Single	45.00	
Double	55.00	

Half board

per person:	£min	£max
Daily	65.00	

Lunch available
Evening meal 1830 (last
orders 2230)
Parking for 250
Cards accepted: Access, Visa,
C.Bl, Diners, Amex
🛇🖧🖳📞🖃🖂♦🔥🚩🛏🔆
🛏🔆🖂🛏🖂♦🔆⏰7-150🔆🗼
🔆🚶🔆🗼🐾🗼

School Cottages Guest House

Listed **APPROVED**

2 School Cottages, Rusper
Road, Ifield Green, Crawley
RH11 0HL
☎ (0293) 518813
*Near Crawley, in village
dating back to the 11th C,
with 13th C church. The
cottages date from 1850s.
Close to Gatwick Airport.
Courtesy transport from
airport and return.*
Bedrooms: 2 single,
1 double, 1 twin
Bathrooms: 1 public

Continued ▶

Please mention
this guide when
making a booking.

CRAWLEY

Continued

Bed & breakfast

per night:	£min	£max
Single	30.00	35.00
Double	40.00	45.00

Evening meal 1800 (last orders 2100)
Cards accepted: Access, Visa

🛏🖰🗓❖🖵🖽🅰🅸🗓↙🛏⌗.🖎✗
🚗🖳 OAP SP 🏠 🅣

White Lodge

10 Langley Lane, Ifield,
Crawley RH11 0NA
☎ (0293) 546222
Family-run 200-year-old lodge in quiet private lane. Good home cooking, vegetarians welcome. Non-smokers only. 10 minutes from Gatwick.
Bedrooms: 1 single,
1 double, 1 twin, 1 triple
Bathrooms: 2 public

Bed & breakfast

per night:	£min	£max
Single	25.00	35.00
Double	35.00	45.00

Parking for 6
Cards accepted: Access, Visa

🛏6🖵❖🖍🅰🖽🗓⌗.🖎❖
✗🚗

CRAWLEY DOWN

West Sussex
Map ref 2D2

Oak Tree Cottage

Sandhill Lane, Crawley
Down, Crawley RH10 4LB
☎ Copthorne (0342) 714750
Modernised cottage with large garden in quiet country lane, 4 miles north-east of Crawley off B2028 and 15 minutes from Gatwick.
Bedrooms: 2 twin
Bathrooms: 1 public

Bed & breakfast

per night:	£min	£max
Single	22.00	24.00
Double	34.00	36.00

Parking for 5

🛏🖰🗓🖵❖🖍🅰🖽🛏⌗.🖎❖
✗🚗

CROCKENHILL

Kent
Map Ref 2D2

The "Dees"

56 Old Chapel Road,
Crockenhill, Swanley
BR8 8LJ
☎ Swanley (0322) 667645
Crockenhill is adjacent to M25, M20. Easy access to Brands Hatch, London, Kent and Sussex coast and country.

Nice double room with full private facilities.
Bedrooms: 1 single, 1 double
Bathrooms: 1 private,
1 public

Bed & breakfast

per night:	£min	£max
Double	25.00	35.00

Parking for 2

🛏🖰🖵❖🖍🅰🖽🅂↙🗓⌗.
🖎❖✗🚗 OAP SP

CUCKFIELD

West Sussex
Map ref 2D3

The High Street is lined with Elizabethan and Georgian shops, inns and houses and was once part of the London to Brighton coach road. Nearby Nymans (National Trust) is a 30-acre garden with fine topiary work.

Ousedale

Listed

Brook Street, Cuckfield,
Haywards Heath RH17 5JJ
☎ Haywards Heath (0444)
450548
Comfortable quiet family chalet bungalow home with lovely gardens and views, one mile north of Cuckfield on B2036. Easy parking.
Bedrooms: 1 single,
1 double, 1 twin
Bathrooms: 2 public

Bed & breakfast

per night:	£min	£max
Single	17.50	20.00
Double	30.00	33.00

Parking for 6

🖰🖵🗓❖🖍🅰🖽🗓⌗.🖎❖
✗🚗

Stonecroft

Broad Street, Cuckfield,
Haywards Heath RH17 5DY
☎ Haywards Heath (0444)
455275
Victorian property with large garden, on A272. Within easy reach of Gatwick Airport.
Bedrooms: 1 single,
1 double, 1 twin
Bathrooms: 1 public

Bed & breakfast

per night:	£min	£max
Single	17.50	17.50
Double	30.00	30.00

Parking for 5

🛏🗓❖🖍🅰🖽🗓⌗.🖎❖
✗🚗

> We advise you to confirm your booking in writing.

DARTFORD

Kent
Map ref 2D2

Industrial town probably most famous for the Dartford Tunnel and now the new Queen Elizabeth II bridge across the Thames. Large Orchard Theatre has a fine variety of entertainment.
Tourist Information Centre
☎ (0322) 343243

Rosedene Guest House

284 & 286 Lowfield Street,
Dartford DA1 1LH
☎ (0322) 277042
Small, homely bed and breakfast guesthouse near Dartford town and countryside. Close to Dartford Tunnel, M25, A20/M20, A2/M2, on A225. Hot and cold water and colour TV in all rooms. Off-road parking.
Bedrooms: 2 single, 3 twin,
1 triple, 1 multiple
Bathrooms: 3 public

Bed & breakfast

per night:	£min	£max
Single	22.00	25.00
Double	34.00	36.00

Parking for 6
Cards accepted: Visa

🛏🖵❖🖽🅰🅸↙🖍🗓⌗.
🖎❖✗🚗

DEAL

Kent
Map ref 3C4

Coastal town and popular holiday resort. Deal Castle was built by Henry VIII as a fort and the museum is devoted to finds excavated in the area. Also the Time-Ball Tower Museum. Angling available from both beach and pier.
Tourist Information Centre
☎ (0304) 369576

Finglesham Grange

♛♛ HIGHLY COMMENDED

Finglesham, Deal CT14 0NQ
☎ Sandwich (0304) 611314
Georgian country house in 4.5 acres of secluded grounds situated outside Finglesham village, just 4 miles from Deal and Sandwich.
Bedrooms: 1 double, 2 twin
Bathrooms: 3 private

Bed & breakfast

per night:	£min	£max
Single		25.00
Double	45.00	45.00

Half board

per person:	£min	£max
Daily	32.50	35.00

Evening meal 1900 (last orders 1700)
Parking for 5

🖽🅰🖍🗓⌗.🖎❖🚗🏠🅣

DIAL POST

West Sussex
Map ref 2D3

Small village on the main road from Horsham to the coast at Worthing.

Swallows Farm

♛♛

Swallows Lane, Dial Post,
Horsham RH13 8NN
☎ Partridge Green (0403)
710385
210-acre mixed farm. Georgian farmhouse in the quiet Sussex countryside half a mile off A24, within easy reach of coast, downs and many places of historic interest. Gatwick Airport 35 minutes' drive.
Bedrooms: 1 double, 2 twin
Bathrooms: 2 public

Bed & breakfast

per night:	£min	£max
Single	18.00	20.00
Double	30.00	35.00

Half board

per person:	£min	£max
Daily	25.00	27.00

Evening meal from 1830
Parking for 4
Open March-October

🛏10🖵❖🖑🖽🗓⌗.🖎🚗🔌
❖✗🚗🏠

DORKING

Surrey
Map ref 2D2

Ancient market town and a good centre for walking, delightfully set between Box Hill and the Downs.

Bulmer Farm

♛♛

Holmbury St Mary, Dorking
RH5 6LG
☎ (0306) 730210
30-acre beef farm. 17th C character farmhouse with beams and inglenook fireplace, in the Surrey hills. Choice of twin rooms in the house or double/twin en-suite rooms in tastefully converted barn adjoining the house. Village is 5 miles from Dorking.
Bedrooms: 3 double, 5 twin

Bathrooms: 5 private,
2 public

Bed & breakfast

per night:	£min	£max
Double	30.00	36.00

Parking for 10

The Dene

Hole Hill, Westcott, Dorking
RH4 3LS
☎ (0306) 885595
*Large country house in seven
acres of park-like gardens on
slopes of Ranmore. Beautiful
views towards Leith Hill.*
Bedrooms: 1 double, 1 twin
Bathrooms: 1 public

Bed & breakfast

per night:	£min	£max
Single	20.00	
Double	28.00	34.00

Half board

per person:	£min	£max
Daily	21.00	27.00

Evening meal 1800 (last
orders 2100)
Parking for 10

Mark Ash

Abinger Common, Dorking
RH5 6JA
☎ (0306) 731326
*Victorian house in lovely
garden opposite village green.
Area of outstanding natural
beauty. 1 mile off A25.
Dorking 4 miles, Guildford 8
miles. Convenient for Gatwick
Airport.*
Bedrooms: 1 double, 1 twin
Bathrooms: 1 private,
2 public, 1 private shower

Bed & breakfast

per night:	£min	£max
Single		25.00
Double		40.00

Parking for 4

Steyning Cottage

Horsham Road, South
Holmwood, Dorking
RH5 4NE
☎ (0306) 888481
*Detached tile-hung house
adjacent to A24, opposite
Holmwood Common and
within walking distance of
Leith Hill. Gatwick Airport
approximately 20 minutes
away. French spoken.*
Bedrooms: 1 single, 2 twin
Bathrooms: 1 public

Bed & breakfast

per night:	£min	£max
Single	13.00	18.00
Double	24.00	30.00

Half board

per person:	£min	£max
Daily	19.00	25.00
Weekly	77.00	154.00

Evening meal 1900 (last
orders 2000)
Parking for 4

Tanhouse Farm

Rusper Road, Newdigate,
Dorking RH5 5BX
☎ Newdigate (0306) 631334
*16th C listed farmhouse in
lovely countryside, half a mile
south of Newdigate village.
Large garden with ponds and
wildlife. New golf course
being constructed within half
a mile.*
Bedrooms: 2 twin
Bathrooms: 2 public

Bed & breakfast

per night:	£min	£max
Double	26.00	31.00

The Waltons

5 Rose Hill, Dorking
RH14 2EG
☎ (0306) 883127
*House retains all its period
features. Central location with
beautiful views. Surrounded
by National Trust land.
Friendly atmosphere.*
Bedrooms: 1 double, 1 twin
Bathrooms: 2 public

Bed & breakfast

per night:	£min	£max
Single	15.00	20.00
Double	30.00	35.00

Half board

per person:	£min	£max
Daily	23.50	28.50
Weekly	164.50	199.50

Evening meal 1800 (last
orders 2100)
Parking for 3

Individual
proprietors have
supplied all details
of accommodation.
Although we do
check for accuracy,
we advise you to
confirm the
information at the
time of booking.

DOVER

Kent
Map ref 3C4

A Cinque Port and busiest
passenger port in the
world. Still a historic town
and seaside resort beside
the famous White Cliffs.
The White Cliffs
Experience attraction
traces the town's history
through the Roman,
Saxon, Norman and
Victorian periods.
Tourist Information Centre
☎ *(0304) 205108.*

Castle House

10 Castle Hill Road, Dover
CT16 1QW
☎ (0304) 201656
Fax (0304) 210197
*Listed building, circa 1830, 2
minutes from docks, castle
and town centre. Extra car
parking available locally.*
Bedrooms: 4 double, 1 twin
Bathrooms: 3 private,
2 private showers

Bed & breakfast

per night:	£min	£max
Single	19.00	30.00
Double	28.00	40.00

Evening meal from 1800
Parking for 4
Cards accepted: Access, Visa

Charlton Green Guest House

COMMENDED

12 Frith Road, Dover
CT16 2PY
☎ (0304) 210647
*Victorian townhouse built in
1886 - recently restored. Close
to docks.*
Bedrooms: 2 double, 1 twin
Bathrooms: 2 private,
1 public

Bed & breakfast

per night:	£min	£max
Single	15.00	20.00
Double	28.00	35.00

Evening meal 1800 (last
orders 1900)
Parking for 3

Coldred Court Farm

HIGHLY COMMENDED

Church Road, Coldred, Dover
CT15 5AQ
☎ (0304) 830816
*7-acre wood farm. 1620
farmhouse full of old world
charm, with modern facilities.*

*Situated 1 mile from the A2,
5 minutes from Dover.*
Bedrooms: 2 double, 1 twin
Bathrooms: 3 private

Bed & breakfast

per night:	£min	£max
Single		18.50

Evening meal 1800 (last
orders 1930)
Parking for 13

Dell Guest House

233 Folkestone Road, Dover
CT17 9SL
☎ (0304) 202422
*Victorian house with modern
facilities. Convenient for
Dover Priory railway station,
docks and hoverport. Ideal
overnight stay for the
continental traveller.*
Bedrooms: 2 single,
1 double, 3 multiple
Bathrooms: 2 public

Bed & breakfast

per night:	£min	£max
Single	16.00	18.00
Double	26.00	32.00

Parking for 6

East Lee Guest House

108 Maison Dieu Road,
Dover CT16 1RT
☎ (0304) 210176
Fax (0304) 210176
*Non-smoking Victorian
residence furnished in
traditional English style.
Convenient for town centre,
buses, trains and ferries.*
Bedrooms: 3 double, 1 twin
Bathrooms: 4 private,
1 public

Bed & breakfast

per night:	£min	£max
Double	26.00	36.00

Parking for 4
Cards accepted: Access, Visa

Esther House

Listed COMMENDED

55 Barton Road, Dover
CT16 2NF
☎ (0304) 241332
*Non-smoking B and B with
warm Christian atmosphere.
Close to ferries and town
centre. Ideal for short breaks
and overnight stops to
Continent. Early breakfasts.*
Bedrooms: 1 single, 1 twin,
1 triple
Bathrooms: 1 public

Continued ▶

383

DOVER
Continued

Bed & breakfast

per night:	£min	£max
Single	12.00	16.00
Double	24.00	32.00

Half board

per person:	£min	£max
Daily	20.00	28.00
Weekly	128.00	178.00

Messines Guest House
Listed

Upper Road, Dover
CT16 1HP
☎ (0304) 209744
Spanish-style bungalow in large garden, situated below Dover Castle between Bleriot Memorial and Langdon Cliffs.
Bedrooms: 2 double, 1 twin
Bathrooms: 2 public

Bed & breakfast

per night:	£min	£max
Double	22.00	24.00

Parking for 6

Number One Guest House

1 Castle Street, Dover
CT16 1QH
☎ (0304) 202007
Georgian town house, in an historic street, ideally situated for the port, Heritage Centre, restaurants, banks. Garage parking available.
Bedrooms: 2 double, 2 twin, 1 triple
Bathrooms: 5 private

Bed & breakfast

per night:	£min	£max
Double	28.00	36.00

Parking for 10

Woodpeckers

Chapel Lane, St-Margarets-at-Cliffe, Dover CT15 6BQ
☎ (0304) 852761
10 minutes from Dover docks, in the quiet village of St. Margarets, behind the village pond. En-suite facilities.
Bedrooms: 1 twin, 1 triple
Bathrooms: 2 private

Bed & breakfast

per night:	£min	£max
Single	17.00	17.00
Double	28.00	28.00

Half board

per person:	£min	£max
Daily	23.00	26.00

Evening meal 1830 (last orders 2000)
Parking for 4

EAST DEAN
East Sussex
Map ref 2D3

Pretty village on a green near Friston Forest and Birling Gap.

Birling Gap Hotel ⋀
APPROVED

East Dean, Eastbourne BN20 0AB
☎ Eastbourne (0323) 423197
Fax (0323) 423030
Magnificent Seven Sisters clifftop position, with views of country, sea, beach. Superb downland walks. Old world "Thatched Bar" and "Oak Room Restaurant". Coffee shop and games room, function and conference suite.
Bedrooms: 1 single, 4 double, 2 twin, 2 triple
Bathrooms: 9 private, 1 public

Bed & breakfast

per night:	£min	£max
Single	30.00	45.00
Double	47.00	55.00

Half board

per person:	£min	£max
Weekly	143.00	288.00

Lunch available
Evening meal 1800 (last orders 2130)
Parking for 100
Cards accepted: Access, Visa, Diners, Amex, Switch
☎20-240

EAST GRINSTEAD
West Sussex
Map ref 2D2

A number of fine old houses stand in the High Street, one of which is Sackville College, founded in 1609.

Cranston House
Cranston Road, East Grinstead RH19 3HW
☎ (0342) 323609
Detached house in quiet location near town centre, 15 minutes' drive from Gatwick. Parking facilities available whilst away.
Bedrooms: 1 double, 1 twin, 1 triple
Bathrooms: 1 public

Bed & breakfast

per night:	£min	£max
Single	22.00	26.00
Double	32.00	36.00

Half board

per person:	£min	£max
Daily		27.00

Evening meal 1900 (last orders 1900)
Parking for 4
Cards accepted: Access

Middle House, Cookhams
Listed

Sharpthorne, East Grinstead RH19 4HU
☎ (0342) 810566
Central portion of large 100-year-old country house, with open southerly aspect. In village south of East Grinstead.
Bedrooms: 1 single, 1 double, 1 twin
Bathrooms: 1 private, 1 public, 1 private shower

Bed & breakfast

per night:	£min	£max
Single	20.00	22.00
Double	44.00	50.00

Parking for 4

EAST SUTTON
Kent
Map ref 3B4

The Shant Hotel & Prince of Wales
Off A274, East Sutton, Maidstone ME17 3DT
☎ Maidstone (0622) 842235 & 8843409
Privately-owned Kentish inn with comfortable old world atmosphere. Signposted off A274 6 miles from Maidstone/Leeds roundabout. Good food.
Bedrooms: 2 single, 13 double, 1 twin
Bathrooms: 16 private

Bed & breakfast

per night:	£min	£max
Single	40.00	
Double	55.00	

Lunch available
Evening meal 1830 (last orders 2200)
Parking for 60
Cards accepted: Access, Visa, Amex

EASTBOURNE
East Sussex
Map ref 3B4

One of the finest, most elegant resorts on the south-east coast situated beside Beachy Head. Long promenade, plenty of gardens, theatres, Towner Art Gallery, 'How We lived Then' Museum and Aquarium.
Tourist Information Centre
☎ (0323) 411400

Bay Lodge Hotel ⋀
COMMENDED

61-62 Royal Parade, Eastbourne BN22 7AQ
☎ (0323) 32515 changing to 732515
Fax (0323) 35009 changing to 735009
Small seafront hotel opposite Redoubt Gardens, close to bowling greens, sailing clubs and entertainments. Large sun-lounge. All double/twin bedrooms are en-suite.
Bedrooms: 3 single, 5 double, 4 twin
Bathrooms: 9 private, 2 public

Bed & breakfast

per night:	£min	£max
Single	16.00	22.00
Double	32.00	45.00

Half board

per person:	£min	£max
Daily	24.00	34.00
Weekly	139.00	189.00

Evening meal 1800 (last orders 1800)
Open March-October and Christmas
Cards accepted: Access, Visa

Edelweiss Private Hotel ⋀

10-12 Elms Avenue, Eastbourne BN21 3DN
☎ (0323) 32071 changing to 732071
Family-run hotel within easy walking distance of the seafront, pier, shops, theatres, coach and railway stations. En-suite double available at extra cost.
Bedrooms: 3 single, 6 double, 5 twin, 1 triple
Bathrooms: 1 private, 4 public

Bed & breakfast

per night:	£min	£max
Single	13.00	15.00
Double	26.00	30.00

Half board per person:	£min	£max
Daily	16.00	18.50
Weekly	92.00	120.00

Evening meal 1800 (last orders 1500)
Cards accepted: Access, Visa
🛇💪🖵🕯📺🖩 Ⓢ🅿TV🖩,
🛏✕🕯SP🏠

EASTLING

Kent
Map ref 3B3

Carpenters Arms

The Street, Eastling,
Faversham ME13 0AZ
☎ (079 589) 0234
*Listed building dating from
around 1380, with inglenooks,
saloon bar. 4 miles from A2/
M2/A20.*
Bedrooms: 3 double
Bathrooms: 3 private

Bed & breakfast

per night:	£min	£max
Single	32.00	32.00
Double	40.00	42.00

Half board per person:	£min	£max
Daily	45.00	55.00

Lunch available
Evening meal 1830 (last
orders 2230)
Parking for 20
Cards accepted: Access, Visa,
Amex
🛇10💪🖵🕯📺📺TV🖩,
🛏∪↑🕯✕🏠🏠

EGHAM

Surrey
Map ref 2D2

In attractive and historic
area beside the Thames,
near Thorpe Park,
Britain's first theme park,
with 400 acres of lakes
and parkland.

Beau Villa

44 Grange Road, Egham
TW20 9QP
☎ (0784) 435115
*Warm family home in a small
town. Convenient for
Heathrow (10 minutes),
Windsor, Ascot, M25, M4 and
BR to London.*
Bedrooms: 1 single,
1 double, 1 twin
Bathrooms: 1 private,
1 public

Bed & breakfast

per night:	£min	£max
Single	16.50	16.50
Double	30.00	35.00

Half board per person:	£min	£max
Daily		22.00

Evening meal from 2000
Parking for 2
🛇10💪🖵🕯📺Ⓢ✕🖩,
🛏🏠

Milton Park Farm

Stroude Road, Egham
TW20 9UW
☎ (0784) 439295
*3-acre mixed farm. Once a
farmhouse, now a private
residence standing in 3 acres
of land with a half-acre pond.
Letting accommodation in a
new ground floor annexe.*
Bedrooms: 1 double, 2 twin
Bathrooms: 3 private

Bed & breakfast

per night:	£min	£max
Single	30.00	35.00
Double	40.00	50.00

Parking for 32
🛇💪📞🕯🖵🕯📺📺Ⓢ◐
🖩.🛏∪♪🕯🏠

ELHAM

Kent
Map ref 3B4

In the Nailbourne Valley
on the chalk downlands,
this large village has an
outstanding collection of
old houses. Abbot's
Fireside, built in 1614, has
a timbered upper storey
resting on brackets
carved into figures.

Tye

Collards Lane, Elham,
Canterbury CT4 6UF
☎ (0303) 840271
*Country house, less than a
mile from the village,
beautifully situated on top of
a hill with lovely views and
walks. Very quiet.*
Bedrooms: 1 single, 1 twin,
1 private
Bathrooms: 1 public

Bed & breakfast

per night:	£min	£max
Single	16.00	16.00
Double	32.00	32.00

Parking for 6
🛇10📺🕯🖵✕📺TV🖩,🕯
✕🏠

ENGLEFIELD GREEN

Surrey
Map ref 2D2

4, Fircroft ⋀

Bagshot Road, Englefield
Green, Egham TW20 0RS
☎ Egham (0784) 432893

*Three bedroomed detached
house.*
Bedrooms: 1 single, 2 double
Bathrooms: 1 public

Bed & breakfast

per night:	£min	£max
Single	16.00	16.00
Double	32.00	32.00

Parking for 3
Cards accepted: Access
🛇🖵🕯📺TV🖩,🏠🖫

EWELL

Surrey
Map ref 2D2

Nonsuch Palace, begun
by Henry VII, has long
since disappeared but the
fine park remains and is
open to the public.

Tuum House

Epsom Road, Ewell, Epsom
KT17 1LJ
☎ 081-393 1682
*Detached house near East
Street and Epsom Road
junction, almost between
Epsom and Ewell on the
same side as Texaco petrol
station.*
Bedrooms: 2 single, 2 double
Bathrooms: 2 public

Bed & breakfast

per night:	£min	£max
Single	15.00	15.00
Double	25.00	25.00

Parking for 5
Cards accepted: Visa
🛇🕯🖵✕TV🖩,🕯🏠

EWHURST

Surrey
Map ref 2D2

Village in the heart of the
Surrey countryside, with
Hurtwood Common,
Winkworth Aboretum and
Leith Hill nearby.

High Edser ⋀
Listed

Shere Road, Ewhurst,
Cranleigh, Surrey GU6 7PQ
☎ Guildford (0483) 278214
*14th-15th C family home set
in area of outstanding natural
beauty. 6 miles from
Guildford and Dorking. Non-
smokers only please.*
Bedrooms: 1 double, 1 twin
Bathrooms: 1 public

Bed & breakfast

per night:	£min	£max
Single	18.00	18.00
Double	35.00	35.00

Parking for 7
🛇🖵🕯📺🖩✕TV🖩,
🛏🕯✕🏠🏠

FARNHAM

Surrey
Map ref 2C2

Town noted for its
Georgian houses. Willmer
House (now a museum)
has a facade of cut and
moulded brick with fine
carving and panelling in
the interior. The 12th C
castle has been occupied
by Bishops of both
Winchester and Guildford.
Tourist Information Centre
☎ (0252) 715109

1 Broomleaf Corner

Farnham GU9 8BG
☎ (0252) 721930
*Quiet secluded position
minutes' walk from town
centre, station, Farnham
Maltings and theatre.
Candlelit dinner by
arrangement.*
Bedrooms: 1 single, 2 twin
Bathrooms: 1 public

Bed & breakfast

per night:	£min	£max
Single	16.00	18.00
Double	30.00	32.00

Parking for 2
🛇🕯🖵🕯📺Ⓢ🖩,🛏🕯
✕🏠

FAVERSHAM

Kent
Map ref 3B3

Historic town, once a port,
dating back to prehistoric
times. Abbey Street has
more than 50 listed
buildings. Roman and
Anglo-Saxon finds can be
seen in a museum in the
Maison Dieu at Ospringe.
Fleur de Lis Heritage
Centre.
Tourist Information Centre
☎ (0795) 534542

Frith Farm House
👑👑👑

Otterden, Faversham
ME13 0DD
☎ Eastling (0795) 890701
*Georgian country house in
area of outstanding natural
beauty. All bedrooms with en-
suite facilities.*
Bedrooms: 2 double, 1 twin
Bathrooms: 3 private

Continued ▶

**Please check prices
and other details at
the time of booking.**

FAVERSHAM

Continued

Bed & breakfast

per night:	£min	£max
Double		40.00

Evening meal from 1800
Parking for 13

🛇 12 🗗 🖾 ▱ 🍴 📶 🛈 Ⓢ
✂ 🗡 ▦ 🛆 T ∪ ✝ ✕ ᾧ
🕭 Ⓣ

Leaveland Court
Leaveland, Faversham
ME13 ONP
☎ Challock (0233) 740596
*300-acre arable farm. Grade
II* listed 15th C timbered
farmhouse in quiet rural
setting adjacent to Leaveland
church. 5 minutes from M2
Faversham, 20 minutes from
Canterbury.*
Bedrooms: 1 double, 2 twin
Bathrooms: 3 private
Bed & breakfast

per night:	£min	£max
Single	17.50	
Double	35.00	

Half board

per person:	£min	£max
Daily	25.50	

Evening meal 1830 (last
orders 2030)
Parking for 6

🛇 🖾 ▱ 🍴 🔌 📶 🛈 Ⓢ ✂ 🎞
🛆 ✿ ᾧ 🕭

The Oaks
Abbotts Hill, Ospringe,
Faversham ME13 0RR
☎ (0795) 532936
*In quiet rural setting with
attractive gardens, 1 mile
south of Ospringe, via Water
Lane. Excellent base for
touring Kent.*
Bedrooms: 1 twin
Bathrooms: 1 private
Bed & breakfast

per night:	£min	£max
Single	15.00	17.00
Double	30.00	30.00

Parking for 3

▱ 🔌 📶 🎞 🛆 ✿ ✕ ᾧ OAP ⌽
SP 🕭

Owens Court Farm
Selling, Faversham
ME13 9QN
☎ CANTERBURY (0227)
752247
*265-acre fruit farm. Georgian
farmhouse. A2 from
Faversham, half a mile
towards Canterbury. Turn
right to Selling, opposite Shell
garage. First public road
right.*
Bedrooms: 1 single, 1 twin,
1 triple
Bathrooms: 1 public

Bed & breakfast

per night:	£min	£max
Single	14.00	15.00
Double	28.00	30.00

Parking for 4

🛇 🖾 🔌 📶 Ⓢ ✂ 🗡 TV 📶 🛆
✿ 🗡 ᾧ 🕭

Queens Head Inn ⚜
Listed APPROVED
111 The Street, Boughton-
under-Blean, Faversham
ME13 9BH
☎ Canterbury (0227) 751369
*16th C village inn with
gardens, 2 miles from
Canterbury and Faversham.
Lunches and evening meals.
Weekly rates available.
Licensed. No music in bar
area/dining room.*
Bedrooms: 2 double, 1 twin,
2 triple
Bathrooms: 2 public
Bed & breakfast

per night:	£min	£max
Single	25.00	30.00
Double	28.00	38.00

Lunch available
Evening meal 1900 (last
orders 2130)
Parking for 25

🛇 🖾 ▱ 🔌 🗑 🛈 Ⓢ 📶 📶 🍴 ⚓
▷ ✕ ᾧ OAP SP 🕭

The Railway Hotel ⚜
Preston Street, Faversham
ME13 8PE
☎ (0795) 533173
*Opposite main railway station
in historic town. Parts of
building are 17th C and
Victorian.*
Bedrooms: 1 single,
2 double, 3 twin, 1 triple
Bathrooms: 7 private
Bed & breakfast

per night:	£min	£max
Single	18.50	22.50
Double	37.00	45.00

Half board

per person:	£min	£max
Daily	27.00	34.50

Lunch available
Evening meal 1800 (last
orders 2130)
Parking for 20
Cards accepted: Access, Visa

🛇 📞 🖾 ▱ 🔌 🛈 Ⓢ TV 📶 🛆
🗡 SP 🕭

White Horse Inn ⚜
♛♛♛ COMMENDED
Boughton, Faversham
ME13 9AX
☎ Canterbury (0227)
751700 & 751343
Fax (0227) 751090
*15th C coaching inn with oak
beams and inglenook
fireplace. In centre of village*

---

*yet only 10 minutes' drive
from Canterbury.*
Bedrooms: 6 double, 5 twin,
2 triple
Bathrooms: 13 private
Bed & breakfast

per night:	£min	£max
Single	35.00	40.00
Double	45.00	56.00

Lunch available
Evening meal 1900 (last
orders 2130)
Parking for 50
Cards accepted: Access, Visa,
Diners, Amex, Switch

🛇 🖾 🔥 📞 🖾 ▱ 🔌 🛈 Ⓢ 📶 🛆 ▷ 🍴
🗡 SP 🕭

Willowmore Guesthouse
2 London Road, Faversham
ME13 8RX
☎ (0795) 538326
*Large comfortable Victorian
house, 7 miles from
Canterbury. Personally
supervised by the proprietor
to ensure your stay is
enjoyable.*
Bedrooms: 1 single,
1 double, 1 triple
Bathrooms: 2 public,
3 private showers
Bed & breakfast

per night:	£min	£max
Single	20.00	22.00
Double	28.00	30.00

🛇 ▱ 🔌 📶 🛈 📶 🛆 ∪ ✝ ✿ ᾧ

FINDON

West Sussex
Map ref 2D3

Downland village well-
known for its annual
sheep fair and its racing
stables. The ancient
landmarks, Cissbury Ring
and Chanctonbury Ring,
and the South Downs
Way, are nearby.

Findon Tower
Cross Lane, Findon,
Worthing BN14 0UG
☎ (0903) 873870
*Elegant Edwardian country
house in large secluded
garden. Spacious
accommodation with en-suite
facilities. Warm welcome,
relaxed and peaceful
atmosphere. Rural views,
snooker room. Good selection
of food in village restaurants
and pubs.*
Bedrooms: 1 single,
1 double, 1 twin, 1 multiple
Bathrooms: 3 private

Bed & breakfast

per night:	£min	£max
Single	20.00	25.00
Double	35.00	40.00

Parking for 10

🛇 🖾 🔌 📶 🛈 Ⓢ 📶 TV 📶 🛆 🔍 ✿
ᾧ 🕭

FOLKESTONE

Kent
Map ref 3C4

Popular resort and
important cross-channel
port. The town has a fine
promenade, the Leas,
from where the orchestral
concerts and other
entertainments are
presented. Horse-racing
at Westenhanger.
Tourist Information Centre
☎ *(0303) 58594*

Abbey House Hotel ⚜
♛♛
5-6 Westbourne Gardens, off
Sandgate Road, Folkestone
CT20 2JA
☎ (0303) 255514
*Friendly well-equipped hotel
close to the promenade and
bandstand. All rooms with TV,
tea and coffee facilities, some
en-suite. Unrestricted street
parking.*
Bedrooms: 3 single,
2 double, 5 twin, 4 triple
Bathrooms: 2 private,
4 public
Bed & breakfast

per night:	£min	£max
Single	17.00	19.00
Double	32.00	36.00

Half board

per person:	£min	£max
Daily	24.00	26.00
Weekly	160.00	175.00

Lunch available
Evening meal 1830 (last
orders 1930)
Cards accepted: Access

🛇 🖾 ▱ 🔌 🛈 Ⓢ ✂ 🗡 TV ◑
🛆 🍴 🔍 🗡 ✿ 🕭 OAP 📶 SP Ⓣ

Pigeonwood House Grove Farm
Arpinge, Folkestone
CT18 8AQ
☎ (0303) 275539
*Traditional farmhouse with
wonderful views in area of
outstanding natural beauty.
Perfect for walks, yet only 20
minutes from ports.*
Bedrooms: 1 double, 1 twin,
2 triple
Bathrooms: 1 public

Bed & breakfast per night:	£min	£max
Single	13.50	15.00
Double	28.00	30.00

Evening meal 1800 (last orders 2000)
Parking for 6
Open March-November
🐴 4 ♿ 🫖 [UL] 🔒 🚭 🛏 [TV] ♨ 🧴 🧲 ✿ 🐕

FONTWELL

West Sussex
Map ref 2D3

Tiny village between Arundel and Chichester, with Fontwell Park Racecourse.
Tourist Information Centre
☎ (0243) 543269

Woodacre

Arundel Road, Fontwell, Arundel BN18 0SD
☎ (024 365) 301
Family-run, non-smoking bed and breakfast established in 1981, with a friendly home atmosphere, offering weekly healthier lifestyle courses.
Bedrooms: 5 double, 2 twin
Bathrooms: 2 private, 2 public

Bed & breakfast per night:	£min	£max
Single	15.00	20.00
Double	35.00	40.00

Half board per person:	£min	£max
Daily	22.50	27.50
Weekly	150.00	175.00

Parking for 20
🐴 ♿ [UL] 🔒 [S] 🚭 ◐ ♨ 🧴 ✿ 🐕

FULKING

West Sussex
Map ref 2D3

Small, pretty village nestling on the north side of the South Downs near the route of the South Downs Way.

Downers Vineyard

Clappers Lane, Fulking, Henfield BN5 9NH
☎ Brighton (0273) 857484
18-acre vineyard & grazing farm. Quiet rural position 1 mile north of the South Downs and Devil's Dyke; 8 miles from Brighton.
Bedrooms: 1 double, 1 triple
Bathrooms: 2 public

Bed & breakfast per night:	£min	£max
Single	17.00	20.00
Double	30.00	35.00

Evening meal 1930 (last orders 1930)
Parking for 6
🐴 ♿ 🫖 [UL] [TV] ♨ 🧴 ✿ 🐕

GATWICK AIRPORT

West Sussex

See under Copthorne, Crawley, Crawley Down, East Grinstead, Horley, Horsham, Leigh, Lingfield, Newdigate, Redhill, Reigate, Smallfield

GILLINGHAM

Kent
Map ref 3B3

The largest Medway Town merging into its neighbour Chatham. The Royal Engineers Museum is an interesting and developing attraction.
Tourist Information Centre
☎ (Farthing Corner Motorway Services) (0634) 360323.

Mrs B L Penn

178 Bredhurst Road, Wigmore, Gillingham ME8 0QX
☎ Medway (0634) 233267
Private house in quiet residential area. En-suite rooms available. Children welcome. Close to M2/M20, castles and countryside.
Bedrooms: 2 twin, 1 triple
Bathrooms: 2 private, 2 public

Bed & breakfast per night:	£min	£max
Single	18.00	20.00
Double	30.00	32.00

Parking for 2
🐴 ♿ 🖥 [UL] 🔒 🛏 [TV] ♨ 🧴 ✿ ✈ 🐕

GODALMING

Surrey
Map ref 2D2

Several old coaching inns are reminders that the town was once a staging point. The old Town Hall is now the local history museum. Charterhouse School moved here in 1872 and is dominated by the 150-ft Founder's Tower.

"Coturnix House"

Rake Lane, Milford, Godalming GU8 5AB
☎ (0483) 416897
Modern house in rural setting, 200 yards from Milford station on village edge. Easy access to motorways, trains and coast.
Bedrooms: 1 single, 2 double, 1 twin
Bathrooms: 1 private, 1 public

Bed & breakfast per night:	£min	£max
Single	17.00	
Double	34.00	

Half board per person:	£min	£max
Daily	25.00	

Evening meal 1900 (last orders 2000)
Parking for 5
🐴 10 ⛳ 📋 🖥 🫖 [UL] 🔒 [S] 🚭 🛏 [TV] ♨ 🧴 ✿ 🐕 [SP] [T]

Fairfields

The Green, Elstead, Godalming GU8 6DF
☎ Farnham (0252) 702345
High quality facilities in quiet modern detached house with 1 acre of grounds in centre of village. Guildford 8 miles, Farnham and Godalming 5 miles. Excellent pub food adjacent. Non-smokers only please.
Bedrooms: 1 double, 2 twin
Bathrooms: 3 private

Bed & breakfast per night:	£min	£max
Single	17.50	20.00
Double	35.00	35.00

Parking for 6
♿ 📋 🖥 🫖 [UL] [S] 🚭 ♨ 🧴 ✿ ✈ 🐕

GOUDHURST

Kent
Map ref 3B4

Village on a hill surmounted by a square-towered church with fine views of orchards and hopfields. Achieved prosperity through weaving in the Middle Ages. Finchcocks houses a museum of historic keyboard instruments.

Green Cross Inn

Station road, Goudhurst, Cranbrook TN17 1HA
☎ (0580) 211200
Family-run inn situated in the heart of the Kent countryside, offering a fine selection of traditional ales and fare.
Bedrooms: 1 single, 2 double, 1 twin
Bathrooms: 1 public

Bed & breakfast per night:	£min	£max
Single	25.00	25.00
Double	36.00	40.00

Lunch available
Evening meal 1900 (last orders 2130)
Parking for 25
Cards accepted: Access, Visa, Diners, Amex
🐴 🖥 🫖 🔒 [S] [TV] ♨ ✿ 🐕 [SP]

Tattlebury House

Cranbrook Road, Goudhurst, Cranbrook TN17 1BS
☎ (0580) 211995
Large Georgian family house with extensive grounds and panoramic views. Spacious rooms, four-poster bed, TV lounge. Free-range hens and peacock.
Bedrooms: 1 double, 1 twin, 1 triple
Bathrooms: 1 private, 1 public

Bed & breakfast per night:	£min	£max
Single	20.00	25.00
Double	30.00	35.00

Parking for 3
🐴 📋 [UL] [S] 🚭 🛏 [TV] ♨ 🧴 ✿ 🐕 🏠

GRAVESEND

Kent
Map ref 3B3

Industrial riverside town where the Thames pilots are based. The statue of the Red Indian princess, Pocahontas, stands by St George's church.
Tourist Information Centre
☎ (0474) 337600

Shamrock Guest House

117/119 Milton Road, Gravesend DA12 2PG
☎ (0474) 365557
Bed and breakfast establishment, one minute from town centre. 50 miles from Dover and 26 miles from London.
Bedrooms: 4 single, 9 double, 6 twin, 2 triple
Bathrooms: 7 public

Bed & breakfast per night:	£min	£max
Single	15.00	
Double	26.00	

Parking for 8
🐴 ♿ 🖥 🫖 [UL] 🚭 🛏 [TV] ◐ ♨ 🧴 ● ✈

GREAT BOOKHAM

Surrey
Map ref 2D2

The Lodge

2 Park Green, Great
Bookham, Leatherhead
KT23 3NL
☎ (0372) 459642
*Quiet location. Easy parking.
Conveniently situated near
junctions 9 and 10 of M25,
midway between Heathrow
and Gatwick.*
Bedrooms: 1 double, 1 twin
Bathrooms: 1 public,
1 private shower
Bed & breakfast

per night:	£min	£max
Single	16.00	18.00
Double	32.00	32.00

🛇🖙♿🔒🆑🗓️📶🐾

GUILDFORD

Surrey
Map ref 2D2

Bustling town with many
historic monuments, one
of which is the Guildhall
clock jutting out over the
old High Street. The
modern cathedral
occupies a commanding
position on Stag Hill.
Tourist Information Centre
☎ *(0483) 444007*

Abeille House

119, Stoke Road, Guildford
GU1 1ET
☎ (0483) 32200
*Owner-run, friendly
guesthouse offering a warm
welcome and hearty breakfast.
Overlooking Stoke Park but 5
minutes from town centre.*
Bedrooms: 2 single, 2 twin
Bathrooms: 1 public
Bed & breakfast

per night:	£min	£max
Single	18.00	20.00
Double	34.00	36.00

Parking for 2

Appletrees 🏠

COMMENDED

Malthouse Lane, Fox Corner,
Worplesdon, Guildford
GU3 3PS
☎ Worplesdon (0483)
232079
*Secluded residence in
woodland area away from
main road. 4 miles from
Guildford and Woking town
centres. Easy commuting to
London.*
Bedrooms: 1 double, 2 twin,
1 triple

Bathrooms: 1 private,
2 private showers
Bed & breakfast

per night:	£min	£max
Single	20.00	22.00
Double	32.00	34.00

Parking for 5

Blanes Court Hotel

Albury Road, Guildford
GU1 2BT
☎ (0483) 573171
Fax (0483) 32780
*Bed and breakfast
accommodation, mostly en-
suite rooms, all with colour
TV, tea/coffee facilities.
Garden lounge, cosy bar
serving snacks. In a quiet
area within easy walking
distance of town and country.*
Bedrooms: 7 single,
3 double, 2 twin, 2 triple
Bathrooms: 10 private,
1 public
Bed & breakfast

per night:	£min	£max
Single	25.00	45.00
Double	45.00	60.00

Half board

per person:	£min	£max
Daily	33.00	38.00

Parking for 20
Cards accepted: Access, Visa,
Amex

Cherry Trees

Gomshall Lane, Shere,
Guildford GU5 9HE
☎ Shere (048 641) 2288
*Quiet, comfortable home in
beautiful garden situated in
lovely village at foot of the
North Downs. Convenient for
local pub, restaurant and
public transport.*
Bedrooms: 1 single, 2 twin
Bathrooms: 1 private,
3 public
Bed & breakfast

per night:	£min	£max
Single	15.50	22.50
Double	30.00	35.00

Parking for 5
Open April-October

Dene Croft 🏠

1 Denmark Road, Guildford
GU1 4DA
☎ (0483) 506938
*Bright, well decorated and
newly furnished with large
bedrooms. Each bedroom
supplied with colour TV, tea/
coffee/chocolate facilities, hot
and cold water. Parking
facilities.*

Bedrooms: 1 single,
4 double, 3 triple
Bathrooms: 1 public
Bed & breakfast

per night:	£min	£max
Single	17.00	20.00
Double	35.00	40.00

Parking for 5

Eastfield

Pyle Hill, Sutton Green,
Woking GU21 0SR
☎ (0483) 730304
*Separate ground floor wing of
attractive family home in
quiet, rural situation. Garden
with pool; good pubs and
walking nearby. Between
Woking and Guildford. Non-
smokers only please.*
Bedrooms: 1 double
Bathrooms: 1 private
Bed & breakfast

per night:	£min	£max
Double	32.00	36.00

Parking for 5

Hillcote

11 Castle Hill, Guildford
GU1 3SX
☎ (0483) 63324
*Peaceful house in quiet part
of Guildford, but close to town
centre, shops, theatre and
river.*
Bedrooms: 1 single, 2 twin
Bathrooms: 2 public
Bed & breakfast

per night:	£min	£max
Single	13.00	13.00
Double	26.00	26.00

Parking for 4

Mr. & Mrs. J.Cook, Beevers Farm

Chinthurst Lane, Bramley,
Guildford GU5 0DR
☎ (0483) 898764
*In peaceful location near
village and restaurants, 2
miles from Guildford. Non-
smokers only please. Take
Station Road turn-off at
Bramley roundabout, then
first left over bridge. Beevers
is third on left.*
Bedrooms: 1 twin, 1 triple,
1 multiple
Bathrooms: 1 private,
2 public
Bed & breakfast

per night:	£min	£max
Double	26.00	42.00

Parking for 10
Open March-November

Mulberry Corner

East Shalford Lane,
Guildford GU4 8AE
☎ (0483) 573885
*One mile south of Guildford
on A281, first left after sign
for Shalford, between church
and Sea Horse pub. Beautiful
country with river walks from
the house. Guildford centre 5
minutes away.*
Bedrooms: 1 double, 1 twin
Bathrooms: 1 public
Bed & breakfast

per night:	£min	£max
Double	28.00	32.00

Parking for 3

The Old Malt House 🏠

Bagshot Road, Worplesdon,
Guildford GU3 3PT
☎ Worplesdon (0483)
232152
*Old country house in
extensive grounds with
swimming pool and ancient
trees. Easy access to
Heathrow, Gatwick and
central London.*
Bedrooms: 1 double, 1 twin,
1 multiple
Bathrooms: 2 public
Bed & breakfast

per night:	£min	£max
Single	18.00	20.00
Double	28.00	30.00

Parking for 4

HADLOW

Kent
Map ref 3B4

Attractive village with a
medieval church and
modern Agricultural
College. Dominated by a
fascinating folly tower.

Goblands Farm

Court Lane, Hadlow,
Tonbridge TN11 0LT
☎ (0732) 850853
Fax (0732) 850974
*Converted barn on working
farm in quiet rural situation.
Off A26 through Hadlow
village, half a mile along
Court Lane, over small
crossroads, next farm on left.*
Bedrooms: 1 single,
1 double, 1 twin
Bathrooms: 1 public

> Check the
> introduction to this
> region for Where to
> Go, What to See.

Bed & breakfast

per night:	£min	£max
Single	16.00	18.00
Double	30.00	32.00

Parking for 11

♿⛽🚗♿⛰Ⓢℹ️🚫♨️📺 ▦ ❏⟁ᛏ♣️✕🚬⛪

Leavers Oast

Stanford Lane, Hadlow,
Tonbridge TN11 0JN
☎ (0732) 850924
*Beautiful twin oast in heart of
Weald. Central for historic
houses and gardens. Close to
very good train service to
London.*
Bedrooms: 1 double, 1 twin
Bathrooms: 2 private

Bed & breakfast

per night:	£min	£max
Single	25.00	27.50
Double	48.00	54.00

Half board

per person:	£min	£max
Daily	40.00	42.50
Weekly	262.00	280.00

Evening meal 1830 (last
orders 2030)
Parking for 3

🚬15⛽❏♿⚐🅿️ ⛰Ⓢ📺 ▦.
❏☀️✕🚬⛪

HAILSHAM

East Sussex
Map ref 2D3

An important market town
since Norman times and
still one of the largest
markets in Sussex. 2
miles west, at Upper
Dicker, is Michelham
Priory, an Augustinian
house founded in 1229.
Tourist Information Centre
☎ *(0323) 840604*

Blackstock Farm ⋔

Listed	COMMENDED

Grove Hill, Hellingly,
Hailsham BN27 4HF
☎ (0323) 844453
*220-acre mixed farm.
Substantial Victorian
farmhouse with commanding
views of surrounding
countryside. Well placed for
access to towns and many
tourist attractions.*
Bedrooms: 1 double, 1 triple
Bathrooms: 1 public

Bed & breakfast

per night:	£min	£max
Double	27.00	30.00

Parking for 8
Open April-September
Cards accepted: Access

🚬7❏♿⚐⛰▦. ❏🚶✎☀️
✕🚬

HALSTEAD

Kent
Map ref 2D2

April Cottage

Otford Lane, Halstead,
Sevenoaks TN14 7EG
☎ Knockholt (0959) 533082
& (0732) 866038
*Late 18th C cottage
overlooking farmland. Within
easy reach of many historic
houses and places of interest.
Twenty miles from London.
Non-smokers requested. Use
of garden room, garden
furniture and equipment.
Riding and swimming by
arrangement.*
Bedrooms: 2 single, 2 double
Bathrooms: 2 private

Bed & breakfast

per night:	£min	£max
Single	15.00	25.00
Double	30.00	40.00

Half board

per person:	£min	£max
Daily	23.00	33.00

Lunch available
Evening meal 1900 (last
orders 2100)
Parking for 5

🚬12❏♿⚐♨️⛰Ⓢℹ️🚫
♨️📺 ❏∪☀️✕🚬⛪🅳🅰🅿️🆂🅿️
⛪🆃

HARRIETSHAM

Kent
Map ref 3B4

Village beneath the North
Downs, close to the North
Downs Way. Of interest
are many old houses and
the church with its fine
Norman font.

Mannamead ⋔
♨️

Pilgrims Way, Harrietsham,
Maidstone ME17 1BT
☎ (0622) 859336
*Quiet, comfortable home with
pretty garden. Situated on
peaceful and historic
Pilgrims' Way, 4 miles from
Leeds Castle. Excellent base
for touring.*
Bedrooms: 1 single,
1 double, 1 twin
Bathrooms: 1 public

Bed & breakfast

per night:	£min	£max
Single	15.00	20.00
Double	28.00	32.00

Parking for 4

🚬♿♨️⛰🚫📺 ▦.☀️✕🚬

HARTFIELD

East Sussex
Map ref 2D2

Pleasant village in
Ashdown Forest, the
setting for A A Milne's
'Winnie the Pooh' stories.

Stairs Farmhouse ⋔

Listed	COMMENDED

High Street, Hartfield
TN7 4AB
☎ (0892) 770793
*17th C modernised farmhouse
with various period features,
in picturesque village. Close
to Pooh Bridge and Hever
Castle. Views over open
countryside. Home produced
additive free breakfast
provided. Tea room and farm
shop.*
Bedrooms: 1 double, 1 twin,
1 triple
Bathrooms: 2 public

Bed & breakfast

per night:	£min	£max
Single	25.00	30.00
Double	34.00	40.00

Lunch available
Parking for 10

🚬♨️❏♿⚐⛰Ⓢ✕▦. ❏
⛲☀️✕🚬🆂🅿️⛪

HASLEMERE

Surrey
Map ref 2C2

Town set in hilly, wooded
countryside, much of it in
the keeping of the
National Trust. Its
attractions include the
educational museum and
the annual music festival.

Blackdown Park Farm

Fernden Lane, Haslemere
GU27 3LA
☎ (0428) 654999
*Converted stone stable block
on single level, with
outstanding views over
parkland and wonderful
walks. One hour from
Gatwick, Heathrow and
London.*
Bedrooms: 2 double, 1 twin,
1 triple
Bathrooms: 3 private,
1 public, 1 private shower

Bed & breakfast

per night:	£min	£max
Single	15.00	18.00
Double	30.00	35.00

Evening meal 1800 (last
orders 1930)
Parking for 6
Open April-December

🚬♨️❏♿⚐♨️⛰📺 ▦. ❏
∪✎☀️🚬

HASTINGS

East Sussex
Map ref 3B4

Ancient town which
became famous as the
base from which William
the Conqueror set out to
fight the Battle of
Hastings. Later became
one of the Cinque Ports,
now a leading resort.
Castle, Hastings
Embroidery inspired by
the Bayeux Tapestry and
Sealife Centre.
Tourist Information Centre
☎ *(0424) 718888*

Argyle Guest House
♨️♨️

32 Cambridge Gardens,
Hastings TN34 1EN
☎ (0424) 421294
*Homely and pleasantly
furnished town centre
guesthouse near seafront and
stations. After 15 years of
hospitality a warm welcome
assured.*
Bedrooms: 2 single,
3 double, 3 twin, 3 triple
Bathrooms: 5 private,
1 public

Bed & breakfast

per night:	£min	£max
Single	15.00	
Double	26.00	

🚬4♨️♿⚐♨️📺 ▦.❏✕
🅳🅰🅿️⛪🆃

Filsham Farm House

111 Harley Shute Road, St.
Leonards-on-Sea, Hastings
TN38 8BY
☎ (0424) 433109
*Historic Sussex farmhouse
with inglenook fireplaces, old
beams and antique
furnishings, providing
comfortable accommodation
in a traditional setting.*
Bedrooms: 2 double, 1 twin
Bathrooms: 1 private,
1 public

Bed & breakfast

per night:	£min	£max
Single	20.00	20.00
Double	30.00	40.00

Evening meal from 1900
Parking for 4

🚬♨️❏❏♿⚐⛰Ⓢ♨️📺 ▦.
❏☀️✕🚬⛪

Norton Villa Guest House

Hill Street, Old Town,
Hastings TN34 3HU
☎ (0424) 428168
*Built in 1850 into the rock
face overlooking the Old
Town, sea and harbour. Lanes*
Continued ▶

HASTINGS

Continued

and steps lead in all directions allowing visitors to explore this interesting area. 4 poster bed. Parking overnight on premises. Also self-catering cottage.
Bedrooms: 2 double, 1 twin, 1 triple
Bathrooms: 4 private, 1 public

Bed & breakfast

per night:	£min	£max
Single	18.00	25.00
Double	32.00	40.00

Parking for 6

Parkside House ⋀
♦♦♦ DE LUXE

59 Lower Park Road, Hastings TN34 2LD
☎ (0424) 433096
2-storey Victorian house opposite Alexandra Park. 10 minutes' walk to town centre and beaches. Quiet location. No parking restrictions. No smoking throughout.
Bedrooms: 1 single, 2 double, 2 twin
Bathrooms: 4 private, 1 public, 1 private shower

Bed & breakfast

per night:	£min	£max
Single	20.00	30.00
Double	38.00	46.00

Half board

per person:	£min	£max
Daily	28.00	32.00
Weekly	175.00	205.00

Evening meal 1800 (last orders 1200)

HAWKHURST

Kent
Map ref 3B4

Village in 3 parts: Gill's Green, Highgate and the Moor. There is a colonnaded shopping centre, large village green, church and inn which is associated with the Hawkhurst smuggling gang.

Conghurst Farm
♦♦ COMMENDED

Conghurst Lane, Hawkhurst, Cranbrook TN18 4RW
☎ (0580) 753331
500-acre arable & livestock farm. Georgian farmhouse on Kent/Sussex border 2 miles

from Hawkhurst, in peaceful countryside.
Bedrooms: 1 double, 2 twin
Bathrooms: 1 private, 2 public

Bed & breakfast

per night:	£min	£max
Single	17.50	20.00
Double	33.00	40.00

Half board

per person:	£min	£max
Daily	27.50	30.00
Weekly	165.00	180.00

Evening meal 1900 (last orders 1100)
Parking for 8
Open February-October

Tudor Court Hotel ⋀
♦♦♦♦

Rye Road, Hawkhurst, Cranbrook TN18 5DA
☎ (0580) 752312
Fax (0580) 753966
Telex 957565
Picturesque country house hotel superbly located in the Weald of Kent, on A268 Rye road. Ideal for Kent and Sussex beauty spots and nearby Camber Sands. Special half board rates for 2 nights or more.
Bedrooms: 5 single, 6 double, 7 twin
Bathrooms: 18 private

Bed & breakfast

per night:	£min	£max
Single	49.00	
Double	78.00	

Half board

per person:	£min	£max
Daily	51.50	61.50
Weekly	257.00	270.00

Lunch available
Evening meal 1930 (last orders 2115)
Parking for 53
Cards accepted: Access, Visa, Diners, Amex

There are separate sections in this guide listing groups specialising in farm holidays and accommodation which is especially suitable for young people and organised groups.

HAYWARDS HEATH

West Sussex
Map ref 2D3

Busy market town and administrative centre of mid-Sussex, with interesting old buildings and a modern shopping centre.

Barbara Pettitt Mattagami

61 Franklynn Road, Haywards Heath RH16 4DS
☎ (0444) 453506
Family home close to shops and restaurants. Gatwick Airport 13 minutes by rail. On the A272 in the centre of Sussex. Non-smokers only please.
Bedrooms: 2 single, 2 twin
Bathrooms: 2 public

Bed & breakfast

per night:	£min	£max
Single	20.00	25.00
Double	30.00	35.00

Parking for 4

HEADCORN

Kent
Map ref 3B4

Small town with timbered houses used in the 17th C as cloth halls by Flemish weavers. Headcorn Vineyards and Flower Nursery are open to visitors.

Vine Farm
♦♦

Waterman Quarter, Headcorn, Ashford TN27 9JJ
☎ (0622) 890203
50-acre livestock farm. Quietly situated 16th C farmhouse in rural location with extensive gardens and ponds. Comfortable accommodation. Close to Sissinghurst and Leeds Castle.
Bedrooms: 1 single, 1 double, 1 twin
Bathrooms: 3 private

Bed & breakfast

per night:	£min	£max
Double	40.00	44.00

Parking for 3
Open February-November

Please mention this guide when making a booking.

HEATHFIELD

East Sussex
Map ref 2D3

Old Heathfield is a pretty village which was one of the major centres of the Sussex iron industry.

Little London End

Little London, Heathfield TN21 0BB
☎ Horam Road (043 53) 2659
Elegant Edwardian country house in fourteen acres of interesting grounds, plus over eight acres of woodland with stream.
Bedrooms: 1 single, 1 twin
Bathrooms: 2 private

Bed & breakfast

per night:	£min	£max
Single	20.00	20.00
Double	40.00	40.00

HERSTMONCEUX

East Sussex
Map ref 3B4

Pleasant village noted for its woodcrafts and with the beautiful 15th C Herstmonceux Castle (not currently open to visitors).

Court Lodge ⋀

Wartling, Hailsham BN27 1RY
☎ (0323) 832150
400-acre mixed farm. 15th C farmhouse 3 miles north of A27. Restaurant and bar meals at nearby inn. Good fishing and birdwatching.
Bedrooms: 1 twin, 1 triple
Bathrooms: 1 public

Bed & breakfast

per night:	£min	£max
Single	17.50	20.00
Double	30.00	35.00

Parking for 6
Open February-December

Hole Farm

Bodle Street, Herstmonceux, Hailsham BN27 4QJ
☎ Hestmonceux (0323) 833254
Traditional Sussex farmhouse with large garden. Turn off A271 at Windmill Hill, signed Bodle Street. Through village, keeping the White Horse pub on your right. Sharp left opposite Ebenezer Strict Baptist Chapel. At bottom of

*hill turn right, across cattle
grid, signed Hole Farm.*
Bedrooms: 1 single,
1 double, 1 twin
Bathrooms: 1 public
Bed & breakfast

per night:	£min	£max
Single	15.00	20.00
Double	30.00	40.00

Parking for 5

🏃♿⚑🖵📺▥🖩➡🛡✓❀✕⚘🐾

The Stud Farm
🏅🏅 **COMMENDED**

Bodle Street Green,
Herstmonceux, Hailsham
BN27 4RJ
☎ (0323) 833201
*70-acre mixed farm. Upstairs,
2 bedrooms and bathroom let
as one unit to party of 2, 3 or
4. Downstairs, twin-bedded
room with shower, WC and
handbasin en-suite, sunroom.*
Bedrooms: 1 double, 2 twin
Bathrooms: 1 private,
1 public
Bed & breakfast

per night:	£min	£max
Single	22.00	25.00
Double	34.00	38.00

Parking for 3

🏃♿♨⚑▥✂📺▥✕⚘

Surrey
Map ref 2D2

Town on the London to
Brighton road, just north
of Gatwick Airport, with
an ancient parish church
and 15th C inn.

Chalet Guest House
🏅🏅 **COMMENDED**

77 Massetts Road, Horley
RH6 7EB
☎ (0293) 821666
Fax (0293) 821619
*Family-run modern
guesthouse. Convenient for
Gatwick Airport, motorways,
railway station, local bus,
shops, pubs and restaurants.*
Bedrooms: 3 single,
1 double, 1 twin, 1 triple
Bathrooms: 5 private,
1 public
Bed & breakfast

per night:	£min	£max
Single	22.00	29.50
Double	40.00	48.00

Parking for 14
Cards accepted: Access, Visa

🏃♿♨⚑🖵S✂📺▥➡❀✕⚘🐾T

The Gables Guest House 🏾
Listed

50 Bonehurst Road, Horley
RH6 8QG
☎ (0293) 774553
*Approximately 2 miles from
Gatwick and the railway
station. Long term parking.
Transport to the airport
available.*
Bedrooms: 3 single,
7 double, 9 twin, 3 triple
Bathrooms: 6 private,
4 public
Bed & breakfast

per night:	£min	£max
Single	25.00	26.00
Double	32.00	39.00

Parking for 25

🏃♿♨⚑🖵▥📺▥➡❀✕T

Gainsborough Lodge 🏾
🏅🏅 **COMMENDED**

39 Massetts Road, Horley
RH6 7DT
☎ (0293) 783982
*Extended Edwardian house
set in attractive garden. Five
minutes' walk from Horley
station and town centre. Five
minutes' drive from Gatwick
Airport.*
Bedrooms: 3 single,
2 double, 5 twin, 2 triple
Bathrooms: 12 private
Bed & breakfast

per night:	£min	£max
Single	27.50	36.50
Double	39.50	46.50

Parking for 16
Cards accepted: Access, Visa

🏃♿🖵♿▥✂📺▥➡❀✕⚘
🏾SP T

Gorse Cottage
66 Balcombe Road, Horley
RH6 9AY
☎ (0293) 784402
Fax (0622) 784402
*Small, friendly, private
accommodation in pleasant
residential area. 5 minutes
from Horley station, 2 miles
from Gatwick, 40 minutes
from London.*
Bedrooms: 2 single, 1 twin,
1 triple
Bathrooms: 1 public
Bed & breakfast

per night:	£min	£max
Single	20.00	22.00
Double	30.00	32.00

Parking for 4

🏃✆♿⚑▥📺▥⚘

The Lawn Guest House 🏾
🏅🏅 **HIGHLY COMMENDED**

30 Massetts Road, Horley
RH6 7DE
☎ (0293) 775751
*Ideal for travellers using
Gatwick. Pleasantly situated.
Few minutes' walk to town
centre, pubs and restaurants.
Good base for London and
the south coast. Non-smokers
only please.*
Bedrooms: 1 double, 4 twin,
1 triple, 1 multiple
Bathrooms: 3 private,
2 public
Bed & breakfast

per night:	£min	£max
Double	35.00	42.00

Parking for 10
Cards accepted: Access, Visa,
Diners, Amex

🏃♿⚑🖵♨▥✂📺▥➡❀
⚘T

Prinsted Guest House
Listed

Oldfield Road, Horley
RH6 7EP
☎ (0293) 785233
*Detached, Edwardian
guesthouse in a quiet position
with spacious accommodation,
including large family rooms.
Close to Gatwick, London 30
minutes by train.*
Bedrooms: 1 double, 2 twin,
3 triple
Bathrooms: 3 public,
1 private shower
Bed & breakfast

per night:	£min	£max
Single	27.00	35.00
Double	35.00	40.00

Parking for 10
Cards accepted: Amex

🏃♿⚑🖵♿▥📺▥➡✕
⚘T

Springwood Guest House
58 Massetts Road, Horley
RH6 7DS
☎ (0293) 775998
*Elegant detached Victorian
house in pleasant residential
road close to Gatwick Airport.
Long-term car parking, with
transport.*
Bedrooms: 1 single,
1 double, 3 twin, 1 triple,
1 multiple
Bathrooms: 2 public
Bed & breakfast

per night:	£min	£max
Single	20.00	20.00
Double		32.00

Parking for 10

🏃♿⚑🖵♿▥▥➡✕⚘

Stone Court
64, Smallfield Road, Horley
RH6 9AT
☎ (0293) 774482
*Gatwick departures: stay in a
warm, comfortable Tudor
house. Spacious rooms, guest
lounge, private parking.
Transport to airport arranged.
30 minutes from London and
coast.*
Bedrooms: 1 single, 2 twin,
1 triple
Bathrooms: 2 public
Bed & breakfast

per night:	£min	£max
Single	20.00	35.00
Double	33.00	35.00

Parking for 9

🏃8♿♨⚑▥✂🅿📺▥➡❀
✕⚘SP🐾T

West Sussex
Map ref 2D2

Busy town with much
modern development but
still retaining its old
character. The museum in
Causeway House is
devoted chiefly to local
history and the
agricultural life of the
county.
*Tourist Information Centre
☎ (0403) 211661*

Brookfield Farm Hotel 🏾
🏅🏅 **APPROVED**

Winterpit Lane, Plummers
Plain, Horsham RH13 6LU
☎ Lower Beeding (0403)
891645 & 891568
Fax (0403) 891499
*In beautiful countryside in a
central position, ideal for
touring. Convenient for
Gatwick Airport. Lift service
and long-term car parking
available. Family-run. A warm
welcome assured.*
Bedrooms: 5 single,
5 double, 5 twin, 2 triple
Bathrooms: 15 private,
1 public
Bed & breakfast

per night:	£min	£max
Single	30.00	35.00
Double	40.00	45.00

Lunch available
Evening meal 1850 (last
orders 2150)
Parking for 100
Cards accepted: Access, Visa,
Diners, Amex, Switch

🏃♿♨🖵✆🗝➡🅿S🏾
📺▥➡🍴46-75🐟🐾🦴∪
♪▸❀⚘SP

HORSHAM

Continued

The Old Post House
Plummers Plain, Horsham
RH13 6NU
☎ (0403) 891776
*Charming 19th C guesthouse,
4 miles south-east of Horsham
on A279, opposite Lower
Beeding church. Close to
Nymans and Leonardslee
Gardens. 12 miles Gatwick.
Reduced rates November-
March.*
Bedrooms: 2 single,
2 double, 1 twin, 1 triple
Bathrooms: 3 private,
1 public

Bed & breakfast

per night:	£min	£max
Single	25.00	34.00
Double	38.00	44.00

Half board

per person:	£min	£max
Daily	25.00	40.00
Weekly	140.00	225.00

Evening meal 1830 (last
orders 2030)
Parking for 8
🛇🌣🖬🗗🚾🛏🛎🛏🖫🗙🛋🚶⊡🕯🐕✖️🕳️⌂

Saxtons Farm
🏅 HIGHLY COMMENDED
Nuthurst, Horsham
RH13 6LG
☎ Lower Beeding (0403)
891231
*100-acre mixed farm. Family-
run farm with home cooking,
close to Gatwick Airport and
within easy reach of south
coast resorts and London.
Non-smokers preferred.*
Bedrooms: 1 single,
1 double, 1 twin
Bathrooms: 2 public

Bed & breakfast

per night:	£min	£max
Single	21.00	21.00
Double	36.00	36.00

Parking for 8
🛇🗗🛏🚾🗙🛏🖫🛋🔥
✦🎿✖️🕳️⌂

Westlands Guest House
🏅 HIGHLY COMMENDED
Brighton Road, Monks Gate,
Horsham RH13 6JD
☎ (0403) 891383
*Elegant large Victorian house,
situated in Sussex countryside
on the A281 Horsham/
Cowfold/Brighton road. Close
to village pubs, Gatwick, coast
and places of interest.*
Bedrooms: 2 double, 1 twin,
1 triple
Bathrooms: 2 private

Bed & breakfast

per night:	£min	£max
Single	27.50	30.00
Double	35.00	40.00

Parking for 8
🛇🗗🔥🖬🗗🚾🛏🖫🛏🖫🌣
✖️🕳️

HOVE
East Sussex

*See under Brighton &
Hove*

HUNTON
Kent
Map ref 3B4

The Woolhouse
Grove Lane, Hunton,
Maidstone ME15 0SE
☎ (0622) 820778
*300-year-old brick Kentish
barn conversion in quiet rural
location. Comfortable, pretty,
beamed, leaded lights and
lovely garden.*
Bedrooms: 2 single,
1 double, 1 twin
Bathrooms: 4 private

Bed & breakfast

per night:	£min	£max
Single	17.50	20.00
Double	35.00	40.00

Parking for 12
🛋🖫🔥🚾🖬🛋🔍🌣🕳️⌂

HYTHE
Kent
Map ref 3B4

Once one of the Cinque
Ports, the town today
stands back from the sea.
The Royal Military Canal
is the scene of a summer
pageant, the Romney,
Hythe and Dymchurch
Railway terminates here
and Port Lympne Zoo
Park, Mansion and
Gardens is nearby.

Holly Tree Cottage
58 Swan Lane, Selllindge,
Ashford TN25 6HB
☎ Sellindge (0303) 813332
*Cottage in village. Close to
main road and shops and 4
miles from coast.*
Bedrooms: 1 double, 1 triple
Bathrooms: 2 public

Bed & breakfast

per night:	£min	£max
Single	16.00	17.50
Double	30.00	33.00

Parking for 3
🛇🖫8🔥🖬🗗🚾🛏🖬🛋
🕳️🕾

Lucys
📟
Lucys Hill, Hythe CT21 5ES
☎ (0303) 262018
*Large ragstone Victorian
house, south facing. Hillside
position above Hythe. All
rooms have sea views.
Delightful old established
terraced garden.*
Bedrooms: 1 single,
1 double, 1 twin
Bathrooms: 2 public

Bed & breakfast

per night:	£min	£max
Single	20.00	22.50
Double	40.00	43.00

Parking for 3
🛇🖫10🖫🔥🗗🚾🖫🗙🖬
🔍🎿✖️🕳️⌂

LAMBERHURST
Kent
Map ref 3B4

Long village street passes
over the River Teise and
has retained much of its
ancient character.
Scotney Castle Gardens
(National Trust) and
Lamberhurst Vineyards
are close by.

Hook Green House
Hook Green, Lamberhurst,
Tunbridge Wells TN3 8LR
☎ (0892) 890504
*Delightful 18th C farmhouse
in large garden overlooking
wooded farmland. Friendly,
family atmosphere and home
cooking. Hand-made ceramics
on sale. Non-smokers
preferred. Discount for 4
nights or more.*
Bedrooms: 1 single, 2 double
Bathrooms: 2 public

Bed & breakfast

per night:	£min	£max
Double	26.00	32.00

Half board

per person:	£min	£max
Daily	20.00	26.00

Evening meal 1900 (last
orders 1200)
Parking for 4
🛇🖫🗗🔥🖬🗗🚾🛏🖬🛋🌣
🕳️⌂

LANCING
West Sussex
Map ref 2D3

The Old Post Office
🏅 COMMENDED
West Street, Sompting,
Lancing BN15 0AP
☎ (0903) 200914
*Original old building c1882,
just off A27 between Worthing*

*and Lancing. Formerly used
as the village Post Office and
store.*
Bedrooms: 1 single,
2 double, 2 twin
Bathrooms: 2 public

Bed & breakfast

per night:	£min	£max
Single	15.00	18.00
Double	30.00	36.00

Half board

per person:	£min	£max
Daily	22.00	25.00
Weekly	130.00	145.00

Evening meal 1830 (last
orders 1930)
Open June-September
🗗🔥🖫🚾🖬🌣✖️🕳️⌂

LAUGHTON
East Sussex
Map ref 2D3

Once the home of the
Sussex Pelham family, the
village has views towards
Firle Beacon.

Spences Farm
Laughton, Lewes BN8 6BX
☎ Halland (0825) 840489
*200-acre mixed farm. A
delightful farmhouse ideal for
walking or quiet holidays.
Basins in bedrooms.*
Bedrooms: 1 twin, 1 triple
Bathrooms: 1 public

Bed & breakfast

per night:	£min	£max
Single	17.50	
Double	32.00	

Parking for 6
🛇🖫🔥🖫🚾🛏🖬🛋⌣🎵
🖋️🌣🕳️

LEATHERHEAD
Surrey
Map ref 2D2

Old county town in the
Green Belt, with the
modern Thorndike
Theatre.

Bronwen
Crabtree Drive, Givons
Grove, Leatherhead
KT22 8LJ
☎ (0372) 372515
*Large family house in the
Green Belt at Leatherhead.
Adjoins open farmland and is
close to National Trust areas
of Headley Heath and Box
Hill. 20 minutes from
Gatwick, 30 minutes from
Heathrow, 40 minutes from
central London.*
Bedrooms: 2 single,
2 double, 1 twin, 1 triple
Bathrooms: 1 private,
1 public

Bed & breakfast

per night:	£min	£max
Single	19.00	22.00
Double	38.00	44.00

Half board

per person:	£min	£max
Daily	30.00	32.00

Lunch available
Evening meal 1900 (last orders 2100)
Parking for 4

ㅎ🏃🏠🔌👜🛇🛏🖃 📺🏧 🚗🌸🗙🥾

Clifton

3 Spring Grove, Fetcham, Leatherhead KT22 9NN
☎ Bookham (0372) 450329
Modern bungalow. Quiet residence. Special diets if required, by prior arrangement. Off-street parking.
Bedrooms: 1 double
Bathrooms: 1 private shower

Bed & breakfast

per night:	£min	£max
Single	25.00	
Double	30.00	

Evening meal 1700 (last orders 2300)
Parking for 1

🏃🖂🏠🔌👜🛇🛏🖃 🚗🌸

Surrey
Map ref 2D2

Barn Cottage

Church Road, Leigh, Reigate RH2 8RF
☎ Dawes Green (030 678) 347
Lovely cottage, picturesque gardens 100 yards from "The Plough" (listed pub). Opposite church rebuilt in 15th C. Gatwick 15 minutes (transport arranged).
Bedrooms: 1 double, 1 twin
Bathrooms: 1 private, 1 public

Bed & breakfast

per night:	£min	£max
Single	20.00	25.00
Double	40.00	45.00

Half board

per person:	£min	£max
Daily	32.00	40.00

Evening meal 1930 (last orders 2100)
Parking for 4

🏃🖂🔌👜🛇👜🛏🖃📺🏧 🚗🌸🔍🗙🥾

> The symbols are explained on the flap inside the back cover.

Kent
Map ref 3B4

Shops, inns and houses, many displaying timber-work of the late Middle Ages, surround a square which is the centre of the village. The 14th C parish church has one of the best examples of a Kentish tower.

Dog and Bear Hotel ⚠

🏆 🏆 COMMENDED

The Square, Lenham, Maidstone ME17 2PG
☎ Maidstone (0622) 858219
Fax (0622) 859415
15th C coaching inn retaining its old world character and serving good Kent ale, lagers and fine wines with home cooking. En-suite rooms. Large car park and function room.
Bedrooms: 5 single, 12 double, 5 twin, 3 triple
Bathrooms: 25 private

Bed & breakfast

per night:	£min	£max
Single	35.00	40.00
Double	45.00	56.00

Lunch available
Evening meal 1900 (last orders 2130)
Parking for 26
Cards accepted: Access, Visa, Diners, Amex

🏃🖂🔌🍷🖂🏠🔌👜🛇🛏🖃 🚗🏧🌸🏰

East Sussex
Map ref 2D3

Historic county town with Norman castle. The steep High Street has mainly Georgian buildings. There is a folk museum at Anne of Cleves House and the archaeological museum is in Barbican House.
Tourist Information Centre
☎ *(0273) 483448*

Barn House ⚠

Rodmell, Lewes BN7 3HF
☎ (0273) 477865
Attractive converted barn near Glyndebourne, Newhaven ferry, Brighton, Sussex University and 'Virginia Woolf' village. All rooms en-suite. Golf and walking.
Bedrooms: 1 single, 6 double
Bathrooms: 7 private

Bed & breakfast

per night:	£min	£max
Single	20.00	25.00
Double	45.00	50.00

Parking for 12
Cards accepted: Access, Visa

ㅎ 12 🏃🏠🔌👜🛇🛏🖃 📺🏧 🚗🖂🕐👤🌸🗙🥾 🅿

The Black Horse Inn

Western Road, Lewes BN7 1RS
☎ (0273) 473653
Public house selling locally brewed real ale and guest beers. 8 miles from Brighton, 3 miles from Glyndebourne.
Bedrooms: 3 double, 1 twin
Bathrooms: 1 public

Bed & breakfast

per night:	£min	£max
Single	23.75	24.50
Double	40.00	41.00

Lunch available
Open February-November
Cards accepted: Access, Visa

🖂👜🛇🛏🖃 🚗🌸🥾

European

7 Dorset Road, Lewes BN7 1TH
☎ 476703
3-storey Victorian terraced house, in quiet road 1 minute from station and Lewes High Street. Parking nearby.
Bedrooms: 2 single, 1 twin
Bathrooms: 1 public

Bed & breakfast

per night:	£min	£max
Single	15.00	15.00
Double	30.00	30.00

🔌👜🛏📺🖃 🚗🗙🥾

Felix Gallery

Listed

2 Sun Street, (Corner Lancaster Street), Lewes BN7 2QB
☎ (0273) 472668
Fully-modernised period house in quiet location 3 minutes' walk from town centre, Records Office and castle. Colour TV.
Bedrooms: 1 single, 1 twin
Bathrooms: 1 public

Bed & breakfast

per night:	£min	£max
Single	21.00	23.00
Double	34.00	36.00

Cards accepted: Access, Visa

ㅎ 4 🔌👜🛇🛏🖃 🚗🗙🥾

Glyndebourne Farm

Glynde, Lewes BN8 6SH
☎ Ringmer (0273) 812391
400-acre mixed farm. Comfortable old farmhouse in peaceful location. Close to Glyndebourne Opera House. Newhaven ferry 5 miles.

Beautiful downland views and walks. 1 mile off A27.
Bedrooms: 1 double, 2 twin
Bathrooms: 1 private, 1 public

Bed & breakfast

per night:	£min	£max
Single	18.50	18.50
Double	37.00	37.00

Parking for 6

🔌👜🛇🛏📺🚗🌸🗙🥾🏰

The Ram Inn

Firle, Lewes BN8 6NS
☎ Glynde (0273) 858222
17th C coaching inn in quiet unspoilt village of Firle, close to South Downs Way, Charleston Farmhouse and Glyndebourne.
Bedrooms: 1 single, 2 double, 2 twin
Bathrooms: 1 public

Bed & breakfast

per night:	£min	£max
Single	25.00	27.50
Double	50.00	65.00

Lunch available
Evening meal 1900 (last orders 2100)
Parking for 20
Cards accepted: Access, Visa

🔌👜🛇🗙🖃 🚗🌸🥾 🅿🏰

Kent
Map ref 3B3

Woodgate ⚠

🏆 COMMENDED

Birling Road, Leybourne, West Malling ME19 5HT
☎ West Malling (0732) 843201
Family home with antiques, lovely gardens and tropical bird aviaries. Four attractive guest rooms, two overlooking garden. Good food.
Bedrooms: 2 single, 2 double
Bathrooms: 1 private, 1 public

Bed & breakfast

per night:	£min	£max
Single	16.00	18.00
Double	32.00	40.00

Half board

per person:	£min	£max
Daily	28.50	32.00

Parking for 6

🏃🖂🔌🍷🔳👜🛇🛏🗙📺🖃 🚗🌸🏰

> The enquiry coupons at the back will help you when contacting proprietors.

LINDFIELD

West Sussex
Map ref 2D3

Reputed to be the finest village street in Sussex. Georgian and Tudor buildings lie behind grass verges and lime trees. The 13th C church is at one end and a large village green with a pond at the other.

Little Lywood
Ardingly Road, Lindfield, Haywards Heath RH16 2QX
☎ (0444) 892571
Charming 16th C cottage in extensive grounds. Accommodation in modern wing. Beautiful rural setting between Gatwick and Brighton.
Bedrooms: 1 double
Bathrooms: 1 private
Bed & breakfast

per night:	£min	£max
Single		21.00
Double		36.00

Parking for 2

LINGFIELD

Surrey
Map ref 2D2

Wealden village with many buildings dating back to the 15th C. Nearby there is horse racing at Lingfield Park.

Oaklands
Felcourt, Lingfield RH7 6NF
☎ (0342) 834705
Spacious country house dating from the 16th C, set in its own grounds close to Lingfield. Transport and term parking for Gatwick Airport by arrangement.
Bedrooms: 1 single, 1 twin, 1 triple
Bathrooms: 1 private, 2 public
Bed & breakfast

per night:	£min	£max
Single	16.00	19.00
Double	32.00	38.00

Half board per person:	£min	£max
Daily	22.00	25.00
Weekly	98.00	

Lunch available
Evening meal 1900 (last orders 2100)
Parking for 10

Stantons Hall Farm
Eastbourne Road, Blindley Heath, Lingfield RH7 6LG
☎ (0342) 832401
18-acre mixed farm. 18th C family-run farmhouse. Close to M25 London Orbital, Lingfield Racecourse and Gatwick Airport.
Bedrooms: 1 single, 1 double, 1 twin, 1 triple
Bathrooms: 1 private, 1 public, 2 private showers
Bed & breakfast

per night:	£min	£max
Single	14.00	20.00
Double	28.00	32.00

Parking for 6

LYMINSTER

West Sussex
Map ref 2D3

Sandfield House ♠
APPROVED
Lyminster, Littlehampton BN17 7PG
☎ Littlehampton (0903) 724129
Spacious country-style family house in 2 acres. Between Arundel and sea, in area of great natural beauty.
Bedrooms: 1 double, 1 twin
Bathrooms: 1 public
Bed & breakfast

per night:	£min	£max
Double	34.00	38.00

Parking for 4

LYNSTED

Kent
Map ref 3B3

Village noted for its charming half-timbered houses and cottages, many of which date from the Tudor period.

Forge Cottage
Lynsted, Sittingbourne ME9 0RH
☎ Teynham (0795) 521273
Historic half-timbered cottage with oak beams and inglenook, in a picturesque village. Walled garden with terraced lawns. Good touring centre.
Bedrooms: 1 double, 1 twin, 1 triple
Bathrooms: 2 public

We advise you to confirm your booking in writing.

Bed & breakfast

per night:	£min	£max
Single		20.00
Double	26.00	30.00

MAIDSTONE

Kent
Map ref 3B3

Busy county town of Kent on the River Medway has many interesting features and is an excellent centre for excursions. Museum of Carriages, Museum and Art Gallery, Archbishop's Palace, Allington Castle, Mote Park.
Tourist Information Centre
☎ (0622) 673581

Grangemoor Hotel ♠
♛♛♛ COMMENDED
St. Michael's Road, Maidstone ME16 8BS
☎ (0622) 677623
Fax (0622) 678246
One hour from London and the Kent coast, in a quiet position on the edge of town. The hotel has rear gardens, restaurant and bar.
Bedrooms: 10 single, 15 double, 15 twin, 7 triple
Bathrooms: 47 private, 3 public
Bed & breakfast

per night:	£min	£max
Single	33.00	48.00
Double	46.00	56.00

Lunch available
Evening meal 1830 (last orders 2200)
Parking for 79
Cards accepted: Access, Visa

The Hazels
13 Yeoman Way, Bearsted, Maidstone ME15 8PQ
☎ (0622) 37943
Detached family home with guest bathroom and lounge. Quiet location with easy access to M20. Views across Len Valley.
Bedrooms: 2 twin
Bathrooms: 1 public
Bed & breakfast

per night:	£min	£max
Single	15.00	17.00
Double	30.00	34.00

Parking for 2

Homestead ♠
Greenhill, Otham, Maidstone ME15 8RR
☎ (0622) 862234

Part 16th C farmhouse in peaceful village setting, near Maidstone and Leeds Castle. From M20 take exit 8 then A20 towards Bearsted/ Maidstone. After Tudor Park Hotel, turn left into Otham Lane. After 1 mile, at top of hill, turn sharp left down unmade drive.
Bedrooms: 2 double, 1 twin
Bathrooms: 2 private, 1 public
Bed & breakfast

per night:	£min	£max
Single	16.00	18.00
Double	30.00	36.00

Parking for 3

Raigersfeld House
Mote Park
Ashford Road, Maidstone ME14 4AE
☎ (0622) 687377 & 685211
Fax (0622) 691013
Three/four hundred-year-old farmhouse, inside Mote Park (400 acres) plus lake. Near leisure centre, town centre. Leeds Castle 4 miles.
Bedrooms: 1 single, 2 double, 1 twin, 1 triple
Bathrooms: 1 private, 2 public
Bed & breakfast

per night:	£min	£max
Single	15.00	18.00
Double	25.00	28.00

Parking for 10
Open January-October

Wealden Hall House
♛♛
East Street, Hunton, Maidstone ME15 0RA
☎ (0622) 820246
16th C Grade II Wealden hall house offering comfortable accommodation. Four-poster bed. Set in 1 acre of gardens, 8 miles from Leeds Castle.
Bedrooms: 1 single, 3 double
Bathrooms: 1 private, 1 public
Bed & breakfast

per night:	£min	£max
Single		16.00
Double		32.00

Parking for 6

West Belringham ♠
♛♛
Chart Road, Sutton Valence, Maidstone ME17 3AW
☎ (0622) 843995
Modern bungalow with panoramic views in quaint

historic village. Home-made cakes with tea/coffee on arrival. Easy access to London and coast, 10 minutes from Leeds Castle and motorway (M20). Evening meals available at local pubs.
Bedrooms: 1 twin, 1 triple
Bathrooms: 1 public
Bed & breakfast

per night:	£min	£max
Double	30.00	34.00

Parking for 5
Open March-October

The White Lodge
Loddington Lane, Linton, Maidstone ME17 4AG
☎ (0622) 743129
South-facing Regency house overlooking the Weald of Kent. Charming garden of 2.5 acres with 2 ponds stocked with carp. Tranquil setting. Friendly atmosphere. Good local pubs for evening meals. 15 minutes from Leeds Castle.
Bedrooms: 2 single, 1 double, 3 twin
Bathrooms: 1 private, 2 public
Bed & breakfast

per night:	£min	£max
Single	16.00	17.00
Double	32.00	34.00

Parking for 10

Willington Court ∧∧
COMMENDED
Willington Street, Maidstone ME15 8JW
☎ (0622) 38885
17th C Tudor-style house, traditionally furnished. Antiques, four-poster bed. Adjacent to Mote Park and near Leeds Castle.
Bedrooms: 1 single, 2 double, 1 twin
Bathrooms: 2 private, 1 public
Bed & breakfast

per night:	£min	£max
Single	17.00	17.00
Double	32.00	40.00

Parking for 6
Cards accepted: Access, Visa, Diners, Amex

The national Crown scheme is explained in full in the information pages towards the back of this guide.

MARDEN
Kent
Map ref 3B4

The village is believed to date back to Saxon times, though today more modern homes surround the 13th C church.

Tanner House ∧∧
Tanner Farm, Goudhurst Road, Marden, Tonbridge TN12 9ND
☎ Maidstone (0622) 831214
Fax (0622) 832472
105-acre mixed farm. Tudor farmhouse in centre of attractive family farm. Inglenook dining room. Off B2079. Car essential. Shire horses bred on farm.
Bedrooms: 1 double, 2 twin
Bathrooms: 3 private
Bed & breakfast

per night:	£min	£max
Double	33.00	40.00

Half board

per person:	£min	£max
Daily	28.50	32.00
Weekly	180.00	202.00

Evening meal 1900 (last orders 1800)
Parking for 3
Cards accepted: Access, Visa, Amex

MARGATE
Kent
Map ref 3C3

Oldest and most famous resort in Kent. Many Regency and Victorian buildings survive from the town's early days. There are 9 miles of sandy beach. 'Dreamland' is a 20-acre amusement park and the Winter Gardens offers concert hall entertainment.
Tourist Information Centre
☎ (0843) 220241

The Malvern Hotel ∧∧
29 Eastern Espl, Cliftonville, Margate CT9 2HL
☎ Thanet (0843) 290192
Overlooking sea, promenade and lawns. Close to all amenities, shopping, indoor/outdoor bowling greens, entertainments and Channel ports. Parking outside and opposite hotel. TV and tea making facilities. En-suite

shower and toilet most rooms (no baths).
Bedrooms: 1 single, 5 double, 3 twin, 1 multiple
Bathrooms: 8 private, 1 public
Bed & breakfast

per night:	£min	£max
Double	35.00	40.00

Evening meal 1800 (last orders 1200)
Cards accepted: Access, Visa, Diners, Amex

MATFIELD
Kent
Map ref 3B4

Village with Georgian houses, green and pond.

Hodges Farmhouse
Dundle Lane, Kippings Cross, Matfield, Tonbridge TN12 7HD
☎ Pembury (089 282) 3704
250-year-old former farmhouse with wealth of old beams and inglenook fireplace. At intersection of A21 and B2160 south of Pembury.
Bedrooms: 1 single, 1 double
Bathrooms: 1 public
Bed & breakfast

per night:	£min	£max
Single	15.00	20.00
Double	30.00	35.00

Parking for 3

MAYFIELD
East Sussex
Map ref 2D3

On a ridge offering wide views of the Sussex Weald. Fire swept through the village in 1389, thus the oldest houses in the main street date from the 15th C.

Brook Farm
Argos Hill, Salters Green, Mayfield TN20 6NP
☎ (0435) 873269
65-acre beef farm. 15th C yeoman's cottage with a wealth of oak beams on a family-run farm, deep in the Sussex countryside.
Bedrooms: 1 single, 2 triple
Bathrooms: 2 public
Bed & breakfast

per night:	£min	£max
Single	13.00	13.00
Double	26.00	26.00

Half board

per person:	£min	£max
Daily	18.00	18.00

Evening meal 1900 (last orders 1200)
Parking for 5

MEREWORTH
Kent
Map ref 3B3

The Octagon
Mereworth Road, Mereworth, Maidstone ME18 5JQ
☎ Maidstone (0622) 812472
Octagonal toll house surrounded by Kent countryside. Easy access to London and Kent coast. Just off A26 between Tonbridge and Maidstone.
Bedrooms: 1 twin
Bathrooms: 1 private
Bed & breakfast

per night:	£min	£max
Single	25.00	25.00
Double	35.00	35.00

Half board

per person:	£min	£max
Daily	38.00	38.00
Weekly	228.00	228.00

Evening meal 1900 (last orders 2100)
Parking for 6

MINSTER
Kent
Map ref 3B3

Cherry Tree Lodge
451 Minster Road, Minster, Sheerness ME12 3NS
☎ (0795) 874958
Large family home with secluded garden in the historic village of Minster. Easy access to main island towns and Olau ferry terminal.
Bedrooms: 1 single, 2 twin
Bathrooms: 1 private, 1 public
Bed & breakfast

per night:	£min	£max
Single	15.00	
Double	30.00	

Parking for 6

Map references apply to the colour maps at the back of this guide.

395

MINSTER-IN-THANET

Kent
Map ref 3C3

Small town in rural setting has a noteworthy parish church with 15th C choir stalls.

Durlock Lodge

Durlock, Minster-in-Thanet, Ramsgate CT12 4HD
☎ Thanet (0843) 821219
Listed country house near ancient abbey in quiet village overlooking countryside. Plenty of character, beams, four poster bed. Self-catering cottage also available.
Bedrooms: 2 double, 1 triple
Bathrooms: 3 private
Bed & breakfast

per night:	£min	£max
Single	25.00	35.00
Double	35.00	45.00

Parking for 6

NEW ROMNEY

Kent
Map ref 3B4

Capital of Romney Marsh. Now 1 mile from the sea, it was one of the original Cinque Ports. Romney, Hythe and Dymchurch Railway's main station is here.

The White House

Madeira Road, Littlestone, New Romney TN28 8QP
☎ (0679) 62253
Large detached residence in corner position close to seafront and golf-course. Approximately 1 mile from New Romney town.
Bedrooms: 1 double, 3 twin, 1 triple
Bathrooms: 1 public
Bed & breakfast

per night:	£min	£max
Single	13.50	15.00
Double	27.00	30.00

Half board

per person:	£min	£max
Daily	19.50	21.50
Weekly	129.50	143.50

Evening meal from 1830
Parking for 5
Cards accepted: C.Bl

NEWDIGATE

Surrey
Map ref 2D2

Village concerned with the Weald iron industry. The attractive 13th C church was once called 'Hunter's Church' because of its connections with deer hunting.

Sturtwood Farm ᴍ

Partridge Lane, Newdigate, Dorking RH5 5EE
☎ (030 677) 308
200-acre mixed farm. Attractive 18th C working farmhouse, 12 minutes from Gatwick. Courtesy parking available.
Bedrooms: 1 single, 1 twin
Bathrooms: 1 private, 1 public
Bed & breakfast

per night:	£min	£max
Single	17.00	20.00
Double	34.00	40.00

Half board

per person:	£min	£max
Daily		25.00

Evening meal 1900 (last orders 1600)
Parking for 8

NINFIELD

East Sussex
Map ref 3B4

Village with fine country views, standing on high ground to the north of Bexhill.

Fir Tree House

The Green, Ninfield, Battle TN33 9JQ
☎ (0424) 892792
Oak-beamed family house, 250 years old, in village 4 miles from Battle. Good evening meals at village pub within walking distance.
Bedrooms: 2 twin
Bathrooms: 1 public
Bed & breakfast

per night:	£min	£max
Double		26.00

Parking for 2
Open April-October

United Friends Public House

The Green, Ninfield, Battle TN33 93L
☎ (0424) 892462

On A271 Bexhill-Hailsham road 200 yards from Standard Hill (Battle of Hastings). Attached is 150-year-old cottage (original village pub).
Bedrooms: 1 single, 1 double, 2 twin, 1 triple
Bathrooms: 5 private
Bed & breakfast

per night:	£min	£max
Single		16.50
Double		33.00

Evening meal 1900 (last orders 2130)
Parking for 30
Cards accepted: Access, Visa

OXSHOTT

Surrey
Map ref 2D2

Apple Tree Cottage

3 Oakshade Road, Oxshott, Leatherhead KT22 0LF
☎ (0372) 842087
Attractive cottage accommodation in a quiet location, convenient for London (30 minutes), Wisley RHS Gardens and many National Trust properties. Non-smokers only please.
Bedrooms: 1 double, 1 twin
Bathrooms: 1 public
Bed & breakfast

per night:	£min	£max
Single	30.00	35.00
Double	47.00	51.00

Parking for 2

OXTED

Surrey
Map ref 2D2

Pleasant town on the edge of National Trust woodland and at the foot of the North Downs. Chartwell, the former home of Sir Winston Churchill, is close by.

The New Bungalow Old Hall Farm ᴍ

Listed
Tandridge Lane, Oxted RH8 9NS
☎ South Godstone (0342) 892508
44-acre mixed farm. Spacious, modern bungalow set in the centre of a small farm and reached by a private drive.
Bedrooms: 2 double, 1 twin
Bathrooms: 1 public

Bed & breakfast per night:	£min	£max
Single	22.00	25.00
Double	32.00	35.00

Parking for 5
Open January-November

PARTRIDGE GREEN

West Sussex
Map ref 2D3

Small village between Henfield and Billingshurst.

The Bushes ᴍ

Littleworth Lane, Littleworth, Partridge Green, Horsham RH13 8JF
☎ (0403) 710495
Detached small country house in the hamlet of Littleworth, near Partridge Green. Landscaped garden. Gatwick Airport 20 minutes by car. Near Horsham.
Bedrooms: 1 single, 2 double, 1 twin
Bathrooms: 1 private, 2 public
Bed & breakfast

per night:	£min	£max
Single	16.00	21.00
Double	30.00	36.00

Parking for 7

Pound Cottage Bed and Breakfast ᴍ

Mill Lane, Littleworth, Partridge Green, Horsham RH13 8JU
☎ (0403) 710218 & 711285
Pleasant country house in quiet surroundings. 8 miles from Horsham, 20 minutes from Gatwick. Just off the West Grinstead to Steyning road.
Bedrooms: 1 single, 1 double, 1 twin
Bathrooms: 1 public
Bed & breakfast

per night:	£min	£max
Single	15.00	15.00
Double	30.00	30.00

Half board

per person:	£min	£max
Daily	20.00	20.00
Weekly	140.00	140.00

Evening meal from 1830
Parking for 8

PENSHURST

Kent
Map ref 2D2

Village in a hilly wooded setting with Penshurst Place, the ancestral home of the Sidney family since 1552, standing in delightful grounds with a formal Tudor garden.

Swale Cottage
Listed HIGHLY COMMENDED
Old Swaylands Lane, Off Poundsbridge Lane, Penshurst, Tonbridge TN11 8AH
☎ (0892) 870738
Charmingly converted Grade II* listed barn in idyllically tranquil wooded valley. Three attractively furnished en-suite rooms. Close to Penshurst Place, Hever and Chartwell. Gatwick is 30 minutes' drive. Near A26, off the B2176.
Bedrooms: 2 double, 1 twin
Bathrooms: 3 private

Bed & breakfast per night:	£min	£max
Single	28.00	32.00
Double	40.00	48.00

Parking for 7

PETWORTH

West Sussex
Map ref 2D3

Town dominated by Petworth House, the great 17th C mansion, set in 2000 acres of parkland laid out by Capability Brown. The house contains wood-carvings by Grinling Gibbons.

Calebs Brook ⋒
Kirdford, Petworth RH14 0JY
☎ (040 377) 224
17th C farmhouse in lovely gardens. Period furniture.
Bedrooms: 2 single, 1 twin
Bathrooms: 1 public

Bed & breakfast per night:	£min	£max
Single	20.00	25.00
Double	40.00	50.00

Parking for 6

Drifters
Dunctun, Petworth GU28 0JZ
☎ (0798) 42706
Quiet, country village house overlooking meadowland.

English breakfast. Pleasant country walks. Pub, restaurants short distance away.
Bedrooms: 1 double, 2 twin
Bathrooms: 1 private, 1 public

Bed & breakfast per night:	£min	£max
Single	20.00	
Double	28.00	36.00

Evening meal from 1700
Parking for 3

Eastwood Farm
Graffham, Petworth GU28 0QF
☎ Graffham (079 86) 317
Fax (0798) 6317
Country house in 15 acres of lovely grounds with swimming pool, tennis court and lakes. Wonderful walking, riding, wildlife and sightseeing area.
Bedrooms: 1 single, 1 double, 1 twin
Bathrooms: 1 public, 1 private shower

Bed & breakfast per night:	£min	£max
Single	15.00	17.00
Double	30.00	34.00

Parking for 4

Northhurst Farm
Lurgashall, Petworth GU28 9HA
☎ North Chapel (0428) 707227
Listed 16th C farmhouse between Petworth and Midhurst, on outskirts of typical English village. Spectacular views of local hills.
Bedrooms: 1 single, 2 twin
Bathrooms: 2 private

Bed & breakfast per night:	£min	£max
Single	12.00	14.00
Double	35.00	37.00

Parking for 3
Open February-November

Upfolds
Balls Cross, Petworth GU28 9JP
☎ Kirdford (040 377) 284
Family home, comfortably furnished with antiques. Modernised cottage, about 170 years old, located 3 miles from Petworth on Kirdford road in rural situation adjacent to nature conservancy area.
Bedrooms: 1 single, 1 double, 1 twin
Bathrooms: 1 public

Bed & breakfast per night:	£min	£max
Single	15.00	17.00
Double	30.00	34.00

Parking for 4

White Horse Inn ⋒
HIGHLY COMMENDED
The Street, Sutton, Pulborough RH20 1PS
☎ Sutton (079 87) 221
Fax (079 87) 291
Pretty Georgian village inn close to South Downs Way. Roman villa 1 mile. Garden, log fires. 4 miles Petworth, 2 miles Pulborough.
Bedrooms: 3 double, 2 twin
Bathrooms: 5 private

Bed & breakfast per night:	£min	£max
Single	38.00	44.00
Double	48.00	54.00

Half board per person:	£min	£max
Daily	36.00	39.00
Weekly	176.00	199.00

Lunch available
Evening meal 1900 (last orders 2145)
Parking for 12
Cards accepted: Access, Visa, C.Bl

PEVENSEY BAY

East Sussex
Map ref 3B4

Small but popular resort, with spacious beach, near the village of Pevensey.

Driftwood
36, Eastbourne Road, Pevensey Bay, Pevensey BN24 6HJ
☎ Eastbourne (0323) 768530
A warm welcome and hearty breakfast await in our comfortable family home. Village centre, beach and good pub grub 2 minutes' walk. Beautiful countryside. Non-smokers please.
Bedrooms: 1 double, 1 triple, 1 multiple
Bathrooms: 1 public

Bed & breakfast per night:	£min	£max
Single	15.00	18.00
Double	25.00	28.00

Parking for 2

Montana
The Promenade, Pevensey Bay, Pevensey BN24 6HD
☎ Eastbourne (0323) 764651
Quiet seafront position with own beach. Close to amenities. Private parking for cars and small boats. Non-smokers only please.
Bedrooms: 1 single, 2 twin
Bathrooms: 1 public

Bed & breakfast per night:	£min	£max
Single	13.00	15.00
Double	23.00	27.50

Parking for 4

RAMSGATE

Kent
Map ref 3C3

Popular holiday resort with good sandy beaches. At Pegwell Bay is the replica of a Viking longship. Terminal for car-ferry service to Dunkirk.
Tourist Information Centre
☎ (0843) 591086

Belvidere Guest House
26 Augusta Road, Ramsgate CT11 8JS
☎ Thanet (0843) 588809
Friendly family-run guesthouse on East Cliff, minutes from beach, ferry terminal and shops.
Bedrooms: 2 double, 1 twin, 2 triple, 1 multiple
Bathrooms: 2 public

Bed & breakfast per night:	£min	£max
Single	12.00	15.00
Double	24.00	28.00

Half board per person:	£min	£max
Daily	18.00	21.00
Weekly	115.00	126.00

Lunch available
Evening meal 1930 (last orders 2000)
Parking for 12

National Crown ratings were correct at the time of going to press but are subject to change. Please check at the time of booking.

397

REDHILL

Surrey
Map ref 2D2

Part of the borough of Reigate and now the commercial centre with good shopping facilities. Gatwick Airport is 3 miles to the south.

Lynwood Guest House
50 London Road, Redhill RH1 1LN
☎ (0737) 766894
Conveniently situated close to Redhill town centre and railway station. Under 15 minutes by train or car from Gatwick Airport.
Bedrooms: 3 single, 1 double, 1 twin, 3 triple
Bathrooms: 2 private, 1 public, 7 private showers

Bed & breakfast

per night:	£min	£max
Single	25.00	28.00
Double	38.00	40.00

Parking for 8
Cards accepted: Access, Visa

🛇🖄🖳🖀🗠📺🕙🛏🖁 🗙 ᴼᴬᴾ ⬚ SP

REIGATE

Surrey
Map ref 2D2

Old town on the edge of the North Downs with modern developments. Just outside the town on Reigate Heath stands an old windmill, which has been converted into a church.

Beechwood House
♨♨
39 Hatchlands Road, Redhill RH1 6AP
☎ (0737) 761444 & 764277
Victorian house with easy access to all amenities and

Gatwick Airport. 10 minutes' walk from mainline station (Victoria 30 minutes). Licensed bar.
Bedrooms: 2 double, 4 twin, 1 triple, 2 multiple
Bathrooms: 5 private, 1 public, 2 private showers

Bed & breakfast

per night:	£min	£max
Single	25.00	45.00
Double	50.00	60.00

Half board

per person:	£min	£max
Daily	37.50	57.50

Lunch available
Evening meal 1800 (last orders 2000)
Parking for 9
Cards accepted: Access, Visa, Diners, Amex

🛇🖄🖳🖀🗠🛏🖁📺 🕮🖀🍴🔆🗠 ᴼᴬᴾ ⬚ SP 🎪

RIPE

East Sussex
Map ref 2D3

Lulham Cottage ⋔
Ripe, Lewes BN8 6AY
☎ (0323) 811438
Quietly situated detached country house in unspoilt rural location having lovely views to South Downs. Between A22 and A27 and within 5 miles of Glyndebourne.
Bedrooms: 1 single, 1 double
Bathrooms: 1 private, 1 public

Bed & breakfast

per night:	£min	£max
Single	17.50	17.50
Double	38.50	38.50

Parking for 2

🛇 3 Ⓜ 🖳🖀🗠🛏🖁 🖀 🕙 🎵 🍴 🔆 🎪

ROBERTSBRIDGE

East Sussex
Map ref 3B4

Small town in well-wooded country near the River Rother, with a number of old timber and boarded houses. An important local industry is the making of Gray-Nicolls cricket bats.

Parsonage Farm
Salehurst, Robertsbridge TN32 5PJ
☎ (0580) 880446
300-acre arable & livestock farm. 15th C farmhouse with beams and panelling. Relaxed atmosphere. Within easy reach of south coast resorts and many places of historic interest and natural beauty.
Bedrooms: 1 single, 1 twin, 1 triple
Bathrooms: 1 public

Bed & breakfast

per night:	£min	£max
Single	14.00	14.00
Double	28.00	28.00

Half board

per person:	£min	£max
Daily	21.00	21.00
Weekly	135.00	135.00

Evening meal from 1830
Parking for 20
Open January-August, November-December

🛇🖄🖳🖀📺🛏🖁🎵🔆🗠 🎪 🖁

National Crown ratings were correct at the time of going to press but are subject to change. Please check at the time of booking.

ROCHESTER

Kent
Map ref 3B3

Ancient cathedral city on the River Medway. Has many places of interest connected with Charles Dickens (who lived nearby) including the fascinating Dickens Centre. Also massive castle overlooking the river and Guildhall Museum.
Tourist Information Centre ☎ (0634) 843666

The Old Priory
Mill Road, Frindsbury, Rochester ME2 3BT
☎ (0634) 714053 & 718823
Fax (0634) 717716
Victorian house set in beautiful garden, within easy reach of historic Rochester, A2/M2, railway and buses. Transport available.
Bedrooms: 2 single, 2 twin, 2 triple
Bathrooms: 2 public

Bed & breakfast

per night:	£min	£max
Single		12.00
Double		24.00

Parking for 10

🛇🖄🖳🖀 S 🛏🖁📺🛏🖁 🖀🔆🗙 🎪 🖁

ROGATE

West Sussex
Map ref 2C3

Trotton Farm
♨♨ COMMENDED
Trotton GU31 5EN
☎ Midhurst (0730) 813618
Fax (0730) 816093
Farmhouse just off the A272, access through yard. Accommodation and lounge in a converted cart shed

---

adjoining farmhouse. All
rooms with en-suite shower.
Bedrooms: 2 twin
Bathrooms: 2 private
Bed & breakfast

per night:	£min	£max
Double	35.00	40.00

ROTTINGDEAN

East Sussex
Map ref 2D3

The quiet High Street
contains a number of fine
old buildings and the
village pond and green
are close by.

Braemar Guest House

Steyning Road, Rottingdean,
Brighton BN2 7GA
☎ Brighton (0273) 304263
Family-run guesthouse, proud
of its cheerful atmosphere, in
an old world village where
Rudyard Kipling once lived.
Bedrooms: 5 single,
6 double, 3 twin, 2 triple
Bathrooms: 3 public,
2 private showers
Bed & breakfast

per night:	£min	£max
Single	14.00	15.00
Double	28.00	30.00

RYE

East Sussex
Map ref 3B4

Cobbled, hilly streets and
fine old buildings make
Rye, once a Cinque Port,
a most picturesque town.
Noted for its church with
ancient clock, potteries
and antique shops, and
the Ypres Tower Museum.
Town Model sound and
light show gives a good
introduction to the town.
Tourist Information Centre
☎ *(0797) 226696*

Aviemore Guest House M
APPROVED

28/30 Fishmarket Road, Rye
TN31 7LP
☎ (0797) 223052
Owner-run, friendly
guesthouse offering a warm
welcome and hearty breakfast.
Overlooking "Town Salts" and
the River Rother. 2 minutes
from town centre.
Bedrooms: 1 single,
4 double, 3 twin

Bathrooms: 4 private,
2 public
Bed & breakfast

per night:	£min	£max
Single	15.00	28.00
Double	28.00	38.00

Half board

per person:	£min	£max
Daily	21.00	34.00
Weekly	147.00	175.00

Evening meal 1800 (last
orders 2200)
Cards accepted: Access, Visa,
Amex

Barons Grange
Readers Lane, Iden, Rye
TN31 7UU
☎ Iden (0797) 280478
400-acre mixed farm. Listed
Georgian farmhouse with
attractive gardens, hard
tennis court and swimming
pool. Comfortable bedrooms.
2.5 miles from Rye.
Bedrooms: 1 double, 1 twin,
1 triple
Bathrooms: 3 private
Bed & breakfast

per night:	£min	£max
Single	17.50	20.00
Double	30.00	40.00

Jeake's House M
HIGHLY COMMENDED

Mermaid Street, Rye
TN31 7ET
☎ (0797) 222828
Fax (0797) 225758
Recapture the past in this
historic building, in a
cobblestoned street at the
heart of the old town.
Honeymoon suite available.
Bedrooms: 1 single,
7 double, 1 twin, 2 triple
Bathrooms: 10 private,
2 public
Bed & breakfast

per night:	£min	£max
Single	21.50	21.50
Double	39.00	53.00

Cards accepted: Access, Visa,
Amex

Kimblee M
COMMENDED

Main Street, Peasmarsh, Rye
TN31 6UL
☎ Peasmarsh (0797) 230514
& (0831) 841004
Country house with views
from all aspects, 250 metres
from pub/restaurant and 5
minutes' drive on the A268
from Rye. Warm welcome.

Bedrooms: 3 double
Bathrooms: 2 private
Bed & breakfast

per night:	£min	£max
Single	15.00	18.00
Double	30.00	35.00

Parking for 4
Cards accepted: Access, Visa

The Old Vicarage
Listed COMMENDED
Rye Harbour, Rye TN31 7TT
☎ (0797) 222088
Imposing Victorian former
vicarage, quietly situated close
to sea and nature reserve.
Antique furniture and open
fires. Good English breakfast.
Bedrooms: 1 double, 1 twin
Bathrooms: 1 public
Bed & breakfast

per night:	£min	£max
Single	18.00	20.00
Double	32.00	36.00

Parking for 4

Mrs. Pat Sullivin Cliff Farm
Military Road, Iden Lock,
Rye TN31 7QE
☎ Iden (0797) 280331
180-year-old house in
peaceful, elevated position
with views over Romney
Marsh. Free coarse fishing
nearby. 2 miles east of Rye
on the Military Road towards
Appledore, turn left at the
"hanging milk churn" sign.
Bedrooms: 1 double, 1 twin,
1 triple
Bathrooms: 1 public
Bed & breakfast

per night:	£min	£max
Double	13.50	14.50

Parking for 5
Open March-October

Saint Margarets
Dumbwomans Lane,
Udimore, Rye TN31 6AD
☎ (0797) 222586
Comfortable, friendly chalet
bungalow with sea views. Car
parking. En-suite facilities.
B2089, 2 miles west of Rye.
Bedrooms: 1 double, 1 twin
Bathrooms: 2 private
Bed & breakfast

per night:	£min	£max
Double	25.00	27.00

Parking for 3

Strand House M
COMMENDED

Winchelsea TN36 4JT
☎ (0797) 226276
Fine old 15th C house with
oak beams and inglenook
fireplaces. Located just off
A259. 10% discount for
weekly terms except in high
season.
Bedrooms: 8 double, 1 twin,
1 triple
Bathrooms: 8 private,
1 public
Bed & breakfast

per night:	£min	£max
Single	25.00	30.00
Double	36.00	50.00

Evening meal 1830 (last
orders 1900)
Parking for 15

Top o'The Hill at Rye M
COMMENDED

Rye Hill, Rye TN31 7NH
☎ (0797) 223284
Fax (0797) 227030
Small friendly inn offering
fine traditional food and
accommodation. Central for
touring Kent and Sussex
Channel ports nearby. Large
car park, garden.
Bedrooms: 3 double, 2 twin,
1 triple
Bathrooms: 6 private
Bed & breakfast

per night:	£min	£max
Single	15.00	21.00
Double	30.00	36.00

Lunch available
Evening meal 1900 (last
orders 2100)
Parking for 32
Cards accepted: Access, Visa

SANDWICH

Kent
Map ref 3C3

Delightful old market
town, once a Cinque Port,
now 2 miles from the sea.
Many interesting old
buildings including the
16th C Barbican and the
Guildhall which contains
the town's treasures.
Several excellent golf-
courses.

St. Crispin Inn
The Street, Worth, Deal
CT14 0DF
☎ (0304) 612081
Continued ▶

SANDWICH

Continued

Old country inn, heavily beamed bars, log fires, antique furniture in bedrooms. Good home-cooked food, real ales. Best village pub in Kent (awarded 1988). Large pretty garden. Good location for golf-courses and ferries.
Bedrooms: 4 twin, 3 triple
Bathrooms: 7 private
Bed & breakfast

per night:	£min	£max
Single	33.00	33.00
Double	48.00	48.00

Lunch available
Evening meal 1800 (last orders 2130)
Parking for 30
Cards accepted: Access, Visa, Switch
♿ ♨ 🏠 📞 💷 🖬 ⬛ ✿ ♠

SARRE

Kent
Map ref 3C3

Crown Inn (The Famous Cherry Brandy House) ⋔

😋😋😋 COMMENDED

Ramsgate Road, Sarre, Birchington CT7 0LF
☎ Thanet (0843) 47808
Fax (0843) 47914
An ideal centre for exploring Canterbury, Thanet and east Kent. Our unique liqueur has been available here since 1650.
Bedrooms: 9 double, 2 twin, 1 triple
Bathrooms: 12 private
Bed & breakfast

per night:	£min	£max
Single	35.00	40.00
Double	45.00	56.00

Lunch available
Evening meal 1900 (last orders 2130)
Parking for 27
Cards accepted: Access, Visa, Diners, Amex, Switch
♿ ♨ 🏠 📞 💷 🛏 💷 🐾 📺 🖬 ⬛ ✿ ♠ SP 🏠 T

National Crown ratings were correct at the time of going to press but are subject to change. Please check at the time of booking.

SEAFORD

East Sussex
Map ref 2D3

The town was a bustling port until 1579 when the course of the River Ouse was diverted. The downlands around the town make good walking country, with fine views of the Seven Sisters cliffs.
Tourist Information Centre
☎ (0323) 897426

Fairy Cross

Stonewood Close, Seaford BN25 3UX
☎ (0323) 896784
Tranquil country house atmosphere and personal service. 1 mile from the sea. Bordering Seven Sisters Country Park. Convenient for Alfriston, Eastbourne, Brighton, many National Trust properties and Newhaven ferry.
Bedrooms: 1 single, 3 twin, 1 triple
Bathrooms: 1 private, 2 public
Bed & breakfast

per night:	£min	£max
Single	16.00	
Double	30.00	34.00

Parking for 4
♿ ♨ 🖬 💷 ✕ 🐾 📺 🖬 ✿ ✕ 🐾 OAP SP 🏠

SEDLESCOMBE

East Sussex
Map ref 3B4

Pretty village with a long, wide green on which stands a water pump under a gable-roofed shelter. Nearby is the Pestalozzi Children's Village.

Spilsted Vineyard

Stream Lane, Sedlescombe, Battle TN33 0PB
☎ (042 487) 0036 & 0793
15th C oak-beamed farmhouse. On working vineyard in picturesque Sedlescombe village near historic town of Battle and local country pubs.
Bedrooms: 3 double
Bathrooms: 1 private, 1 public
Bed & breakfast

per night:	£min	£max
Single	25.00	30.00
Double	35.00	38.50

Parking for 30
Cards accepted: Access, Visa
🏠 📞 🖬 📞 ♨ ♠ 💷 🖬 ⬛ ⬛ ✿ ✕ 🐾 🖬 ♠ U ♨ ✿ ✕ 🐾 ♠ 🏠

SEVENOAKS

Kent
Map ref 2D2

Set in pleasant wooded country, with a distinctive character and charm. Nearby is Knole (National Trust), home of the Sackville family and one of the largest houses in England, set in a vast deer park.
Tourist Information Centre
☎ (0732) 450305

Holmesdale House

High Street, Brasted, Westerham TN16 1HS
☎ Westerham (0959) 564834
Large Victorian (and part 17th C) house on the A25 opposite the Bull Inn at Brasted, between Sevenoaks and Westerham.
Bedrooms: 1 single, 1 double, 1 twin, 2 triple
Bathrooms: 3 private, 1 public, 2 private showers
Bed & breakfast

per night:	£min	£max
Single	20.00	26.00
Double	36.00	42.00

Parking for 6
♿ ♨ 🏠 📞 ♨ 🖬 💷 🛏 💷 🖬 ⬛ ⬛ ✿ ✕ 🐾 🏠 T

Moorings Hotel ⋔

😋😋😋

97 Hitchen Hatch Lane, Sevenoaks TN13 3BE
☎ (0732) 452589
Fax (0732) 456462
Friendly family hotel offering high standard accommodation for tourists and business travellers. Near British Rail station for fast trains to London.
Bedrooms: 5 single, 3 double, 12 twin, 2 triple
Bathrooms: 20 private, 2 public, 1 private shower
Bed & breakfast

per night:	£min	£max
Single	30.00	45.00
Double	40.00	60.00

Half board

per person:	£min	£max
Daily	40.00	55.00
Weekly	240.00	330.00

Evening meal 1900 (last orders 2100)

Parking for 22
Cards accepted: Access, Visa
♿ ♨ 🏠 📞 ♨ 💷 📺 ⬛ 🖬 ⬛ 🏠 T

Nearly Corner

Heaverham, Sevenoaks TN15 6NQ
☎ (0732) 62039
A 15th C friendly family house in a small peaceful hamlet, just below the North Downs amid farming country. Non-smokers only please.
Bedrooms: 1 single, 1 double, 1 twin
Bathrooms: 2 public
Bed & breakfast

per night:	£min	£max
Single		15.00
Double		30.00

Parking for 3
♿ ♨ 🖬 ✕ 💷 🖬 ⬛ ✿ ✕ 🐾

Stone Ridge ⋔

😋😋

168 Maidstone Road, Borough Green, Sevenoaks TN15 8JD
☎ Borough Green (0732) 882053
Fax (0732) 885903
Comfortable Edwardian country house with friendly atmosphere in beautiful surroundings. Convenient for famous Kentish attractions, motorways and London. Non-smokers preferred.
Bedrooms: 1 double, 1 multiple
Bathrooms: 2 private
Bed & breakfast

per night:	£min	£max
Single	20.00	25.00
Double	30.00	38.00

Half board

per person:	£min	£max
Daily	20.00	30.00
Weekly	120.00	180.00

Parking for 4
Cards accepted: Access, Visa
♿ ♨ 🖬 💷 ✕ 📺 🖬 ⬛ ✿ ✕ OAP SP 🏠

Individual proprietors have supplied all details of accommodation. Although we do check for accuracy, we advise you to confirm the information at the time of booking.

SHEERNESS

Kent
Map ref 3B3

Commercial port, formerly a naval base and now a holiday resort with a long promenade and a sand and shingle beach. Terminal for car-ferry service to Vlissingen in Holland.
Tourist Information Centre
☎ *(0795) 665324*

Alexandra Guest House ⋈

♛
122 Alexandra Road,
Sheerness ME12 2AU
☎ (0795) 666888
Attractive family house providing accommodation of a high standard. Close to Olau Line ferry.
Bedrooms: 1 single,
1 double, 1 twin, 1 triple
Bathrooms: 1 public

Bed & breakfast

per night:	£min	£max
Single	12.00	14.00
Double	24.00	27.00

Half board

per person:	£min	£max
Daily	16.00	

Evening meal 1800 (last orders 2000)
Parking for 3
⛨🦲🖳🛏♿🛉🍴🕭🛗✕
🚗Ⓣ

SMALLFIELD

Surrey
Map ref 2D2

Small village between Horley and Lingfield, named after local estate.

Chithurst Farm

Chithurst Lane, Horne,
Smallfield, Horley RH6 9JU
☎ (0342) 842487
92-acre dairy farm. Recently renovated 16th C listed farmhouse, with genuine beamed rooms, inglenook fireplaces and attractive garden. Set in a quiet country lane, yet convenient for Gatwick and motorways.
Bedrooms: 1 single,
1 double, 1 triple
Bathrooms: 1 public

Bed & breakfast

per night:	£min	£max
Single	13.50	18.50
Double	27.00	30.00

Parking for 3
Open February-November
⛨🦲🖳🛏♿🖳✕🕭🛏♿✕
🚗🏠

SMARDEN

Kent
Map ref 3B4

Pretty village with a number of old, well-presented buildings. The 14th C St Michael's Church is sometimes known as the 'Barn of Kent' because of its 36-ft roof span.

Chequers Inn ⋈

Smarden, Ashford TN27 8QA
☎ (023 377) 217 & 623
15th C inn with oak beams, centrally situated for visiting many stately homes. 5 golf-courses nearby. Food always available.
Bedrooms: 2 single,
3 double, 2 twin, 1 triple
Bathrooms: 2 public

Bed & breakfast

per night:	£min	£max
Single	19.00	22.00
Double	34.00	38.00

Lunch available
Evening meal 1800 (last orders 2200)
Parking for 18
Cards accepted: Access, Visa, Switch
⛨🖳♿🛏♿S🛏♿🕭✕🚗

ST NICHOLAS AT WADE

Kent
Map ref 3C3

Village in the Isle of Thanet with ancient church built of knapped flint.

Streete Farm House

Court Road, St Nicholas at Wade, Birchington CT7 0NH
☎ Thanet (0843) 47245
90-acre arable and mixed farm. 16th C farmhouse on the outskirts of the village, with original oak-panelled dining room.
Bedrooms: 1 single,
1 double, 1 twin
Bathrooms: 1 public

Bed & breakfast

per night:	£min	£max
Single	13.00	15.00
Double	26.00	30.00

Parking for 4
⛨3🖳🛏♿🖳🕭✕🚗🏠

STAPLE

Kent
Map ref 3C3

The Three Tuns Inn

Listed
Staple, Canterbury CT3 1LN
☎ (0304) 812317
Family-run 17th C country inn, 9 miles south of Canterbury, 5 miles to Sandwich. Double and family rooms, most en-suite. Bar and restaurant meals, tea/coffee facilities. Beer garden.
Bedrooms: 2 double, 2 triple
Bathrooms: 3 private

Bed & breakfast

per night:	£min	£max
Single	20.00	35.00
Double	40.00	50.00

Lunch available
Evening meal 1900 (last orders 2200)
Parking for 60
Cards accepted: Access, Visa
⛨🛏♿🖳🕭✕🚗

STAPLEHURST

Kent
Map ref 3B4

Little Pagehurst Oast

Pagehurst Road, Staplehurst,
Tonbridge TN12 0JD
☎ (0580) 891651
Fax (0580) 891651
Grade II listed converted oast/barn in peaceful countryside. Ideal touring base. Close to Leeds, Sissinghurst, Scotney and Bodiam Castles. Friendly family home.
Bedrooms: 1 single, 1 double
Bathrooms: 1 private,
1 public

Bed & breakfast

per night:	£min	£max
Single	17.50	20.00
Double	35.00	40.00

Parking for 9
⛨🖳🛏♿S✕🕭🖳🛏♿SP🏠

STELLING MINNIS

Kent
Map ref 3B4

Off the Roman Stone Street, this isolated village lies deep in the Lyminge Forest, south of Canterbury.

Great Field Farm

Misling Lane, Stelling Minnis, Canterbury G4 6DE
☎ (022 787) 223
42-acre mixed farm. Modern traditional farmhouse in

lovely countryside. Ideally located for touring, port, beaches, etc. Midway Canterbury and Folkestone just off B2068.
Bedrooms: 1 single,
1 double, 1 twin
Bathrooms: 1 private,
1 public

Bed & breakfast

per night:	£min	£max
Single	14.50	16.00
Double	29.00	32.00

Parking for 6
⛨🦲🖳🛏♿🖳🕭✕Ů❋🚗

STEYNING

West Sussex
Map ref 2D3

This village has an interesting jumble of building styles. Half a mile to the east is Bramber Castle, a ruin now in the care of the National Trust.

Springwells Hotel

High Street, Steyning
BN44 3GG
☎ (0903) 812446
18th C Georgian house in Downland market town. Four-poster beds, walled garden, pool, conservatory. Many special discounts available.
Bedrooms: 2 single,
6 double, 1 twin, 1 multiple
Bathrooms: 8 private,
2 public, 1 private shower

Bed & breakfast

per night:	£min	£max
Single	25.00	40.00
Double	40.00	83.00

Evening meal 1915 (last orders 2130)
Parking for 6
Cards accepted: Access, Visa, Diners, Amex
⛨🦲📞🖳🛏♿S🖳🛏♿🖳
♿🚲❋🚗SP🏠

STORRINGTON

West Sussex
Map ref 2D3

Small town within easy reach of walks over the South Downs and the popular Sussex coast.

Greenacres Farm ⋈

♛♛♛ COMMENDED
Washington Road,
Storrington, Pulborough
RH20 4AF
☎ Worthing (0903) 742538
Family-run bed and breakfast set in 6 acres at the foot of the downs, 20 minutes from Worthing and the sea. Central

Continued ▶

STORRINGTON

Continued

*for touring the south.
Swimming pool.*
Bedrooms: 1 single, 2 twin,
3 triple, 1 multiple
Bathrooms: 6 private,
1 public

Bed & breakfast

per night:	£min	£max
Single	18.00	25.00
Double	36.00	40.00

Half board

per person:	£min	£max
Daily	43.50	48.00

Evening meal 1830 (last
orders 2000)
Parking for 30
Cards accepted: Access, Visa,
Amex

🏃🏡🛏🍴🖊🚪♿📶 ⓊⓁ Ⓢ
🖊🛏🚗↑☊∪✤📶 DAP SP

TENTERDEN

Kent
Map ref 3B4

Most attractive market
town with a broad main
street full of 16th C
houses and shops. The
tower of the 15th C parish
church is the finest in
Kent.

Finchden Manor

HIGHLY COMMENDED

Appledore Road, Tenterden
TN30 7DD
☎ (058 06) 4719
*Early 15th C manor house,
Grade II listed, with
inglenook fireplaces, panelled
rooms and beams. Set in 4
acres of gardens and grounds.*
Bedrooms: 1 single, 2 double
Bathrooms: 2 private,
3 public

Bed & breakfast

per night:	£min	£max
Single	21.00	24.00
Double	42.00	48.00

Parking for 4
🏃10📶♿🛏🖊 ⓊⓁ🛏📺📶✤
🐾📶

West Cross House Hotel

COMMENDED

2 West Cross, Tenterden
TN30 6JL
☎ (058 06) 2224 changing
to (0580) 762224
*Private hotel in fine, spacious
Georgian house on wide tree-
lined main street of attractive
Kent town, convenient for
touring.*
Bedrooms: 1 single,
2 double, 2 twin, 2 triple

Bathrooms: 2 public

Bed & breakfast

per night:	£min	£max
Single	16.00	16.00
Double	32.00	34.00

Parking for 7
Open March-October

🏃♿📶📺📶 ⚲📶

Woolpack Hotel

👑👑

26 High Street, Tenterden
TN30 6AP
☎ (058 06) 2934
*Delightful 15th C coaching
inn with creaking boards,
lovely ship beams and secret
passages. Log fires in the
inglenook fireplaces. Beer
garden.*
Bedrooms: 1 single,
1 double, 2 twin, 1 multiple
Bathrooms: 1 public

Bed & breakfast

per night:	£min	£max
Single	18.00	22.00
Double	36.00	42.00

Half board

per person:	£min	£max
Daily	27.00	31.00
Weekly	150.00	200.00

Lunch available
Evening meal 1800 (last
orders 2100)
Parking for 28
Cards accepted: Access, Visa,
Switch

🏃📶☎📞🛏♿ Ⓢ🖊📶 ⚲📞
✤🐾📶 DAP SP 📶 Ⓣ

TONBRIDGE

Kent
Map ref 2D2

Ancient town, built on the
River Medway, has a long
history of commercial
importance and is still a
thriving town. Attractive
gardens surround the
remains of the Norman
castle.
*Tourist Information Centre
☎ (0732) 770929*

Poplar Farm Oast

Three Elm Lane, Golden
Green, Tonbridge TN11 0LE
☎ (0732) 850723
*Kentish farm in a quiet
position overlooking
surrounding farmland.
Situated off A26 and central
for touring this historic area.*
Bedrooms: 2 double, 1 twin
Bathrooms: 1 public

Bed & breakfast

per night:	£min	£max
Double	16.00	19.00

Parking for 4
Open January-November

🏃♿ ⓊⓁ📞Ⓢ🖊📶📺📶 ⚲∪
✤🐾📶

TUNBRIDGE WELLS

Kent
Map ref 2D2

This 'Royal' town became
famous as a spa in the
17th C and much of its
charm is retained, as in
the Pantiles, a shaded
walk lined with elegant
shops. Also a new
heritage attraction 'A Day
at the Wells'. Rich in
parks and gardens and a
good centre for walks.
*Tourist Information Centre
☎ (0892) 515675.*

17 Claremont Road

Tunbridge Wells TN1 1SY
☎ (0892) 38938
*Comfortably furnished,
centrally situated Victorian
house, 5 minutes' walk from
shops and station. Private
parking.*
Bedrooms: 1 single,
1 double, 1 twin
Bathrooms: 1 public

Bed & breakfast

per night:	£min	£max
Single		15.00
Double		30.00

Parking for 4
🛏♿📶 ⓊⓁ Ⓢ📶 ✖📶

Bankside

6 Scotts Way, Tunbridge
Wells TN2 5RG
☎ (0892) 531776
*Family house in quiet cul-de-
sac within walking distance of
Pantiles and town centre.
English breakfast, off-street
parking.*
Bedrooms: 1 single,
1 double, 1 twin
Bathrooms: 1 public

Bed & breakfast

per night:	£min	£max
Single	13.50	15.00
Double	27.00	30.00

Parking for 4
🏃📶12♿📶 Ⓢ🖊📺📶
✖📶

Blurtings

149, Forest Road, Tunbridge
Wells TN2 5EX
☎ (0892) 530615
*Friendly, informal atmosphere
in very pleasant home with
beautiful garden.*
Bedrooms: 2 single, 2 twin
Bathrooms: 2 public

Bed & breakfast

per night:	£min	£max
Single	16.00	18.00
Double	32.00	36.00

Parking for 2
🏃♿📶 ⓊⓁ Ⓢ📶📺📶 ⚲↑
✤📶

Chequers

Camden Park, Tunbridge
Wells TN2 5AD
☎ (0892) 532299
*Friendly family house, origins
1840. Part-walled garden.
Unique private location, 10
minutes from Pantiles, high
street, railway station.
Peaceful, comfortable, central
base. Non-smokers only
please.*
Bedrooms: 1 single, 1 twin
Bathrooms: 1 private,
1 public

Bed & breakfast

per night:	£min	£max
Single	18.00	20.00
Double	28.00	33.00

Parking for 5
🏃📞♿📶 ⓊⓁ Ⓢ🖊📶📶 ⚲
✤📶

Hamsell Wood Farm

Eridge, Tunbridge Wells
TN3 9JY
☎ Langton (0892) 864326
*Old farmhouse on a hill with
excellent views of woodlands
and farmland. Five minutes
from the village store, church
and public house. A26
between Tunbridge Wells and
Crowborough.*
Bedrooms: 1 double, 1 twin
Bathrooms: 1 public

Bed & breakfast

per night:	£min	£max
Single	17.00	20.00
Double	28.00	32.00

Parking for 6
🏃📞♿ ⓊⓁ📶 DAP SP

Jordan House

68 London Road, Tunbridge
Wells TN1 1DT
☎ (0892) 523983
*17th C town house with old
world ambience, overlooking
Tunbridge Wells Common and
near town centre and station.
Non-smokers preferred.*
Bedrooms: 1 double, 1 twin
Bathrooms: 2 private

Bed & breakfast

per night:	£min	£max
Single	18.00	25.00
Double	36.00	40.00

Half board

per person:	£min	£max
Daily	30.00	35.00
Weekly	100.00	120.00

Evening meal 1830 (last orders 2030)

🛏 10 🕙 🖳 🅜 🅢 🖳 🖳 📺 🏛, 🍽 🚭 🆂🅿 🏧

Manor Court Farm 🏔
🍴🍴

Ashurst, Tunbridge Wells
TN3 9TB
☎ Fordcombe (0892) 740 279
350-acre mixed farm. Georgian farmhouse. Guests welcome to explore the farm. Many footpaths and lovely views. Tennis and fishing by arrangement with owner. On the A264, half a mile east of Ashurst village (Tunbridge Wells to East Grinstead road).
Bedrooms: 1 single, 1 twin, 1 triple
Bathrooms: 3 public

Bed & breakfast

per night:	£min	£max
Single	16.00	18.00
Double	32.00	36.00

Parking for 12

🛏 🕙 🖳 🅐 🅢 ⁄ 🖳 📺 🕐 🖳, 🍽 🍵 🔍 🍴 🚭 🆗 🆂🅿 🏧

Number Ten 🏔
Listed

Modest Corner,
Southborough, Tunbridge
Wells TN4 0LS
☎ (0892) 522450
Attractively located at the back of Southborough Common. All guest facilities on ground floor. No passing traffic. Good public transport to Tunbridge Wells and London. Homely atmosphere.
Bedrooms: 2 twin
Bathrooms: 1 public

Bed & breakfast

per night:	£min	£max
Single	18.50	20.00
Double	35.00	38.00

Parking for 2

🛏 🍳 🖳 🖳 🕙 🖳 🅐 🅢 🖳, 🍽 🚭

The Old Parsonage 🍴🍴 HIGHLY COMMENDED

Church Lane, Frant,
Tunbridge Wells TN3 9DX
☎ Frant (0892) 750773
Former Georgian rectory, built by the Marquess of Abergavenny for his son. Elegant reception rooms and conservatory. En-suite bedrooms, including four-posters.
Bedrooms: 2 double, 1 twin
Bathrooms: 3 private

Bed & breakfast

per night:	£min	£max
Single	25.00	35.00
Double	45.00	52.00

Parking for 12

🛏 🖳 🖳 🖳 🅢 ⁄ 🖳 📺 🖳, 🍽 🍵 🚭

UCKFIELD

East Sussex
Map ref 2D3

Once a medieval market town and centre of the iron industry, Uckfield is now a busy country town on the edge of the Ashdown Forest.

Dale Hamme
Piltdown, Uckfield TN22 3XY
☎ Nutley (082 571) 2422
15th C hall house with oak beams and inglenook fireplaces in idyllic rural location. On A272 going east, take second left after Piltdown Man pub (Down Street, signposted Nutley), after 1 mile turn left, house on left hand side.
Bedrooms: 2 single, 2 twin
Bathrooms: 2 private, 1 public

Bed & breakfast

per night:	£min	£max
Single	16.00	16.00
Double	36.00	36.00

Parking for 14

🛏 🕙 🖳 🅢 🖳, 🕐 🌣 🚭 🏛

Hooke Hall 🏔
🍴🍴 HIGHLY COMMENDED

250 High Street, Uckfield
TN22 1EN
☎ (0825) 761578
Fax (0825) 768025
Elegant Queen Anne town house, recently completely refurbished, with individual comfortably designed rooms equipped to a high standard. Friendly and informal atmosphere.
Bedrooms: 3 double, 3 twin
Bathrooms: 6 private

Bed & breakfast

per night:	£min	£max
Single	35.00	60.00
Double	55.00	100.00

Half board

per person:	£min	£max
Daily	50.00	80.00

Evening meal 1930 (last orders 2100)
Parking for 7
Cards accepted: Access, Visa
🛏 12 🅜 🖳 🖳 🕙 🍵 🅢 🖳 🖳, 🍽 🍵 🕇20 🕐 🍴 🚭 🆂🅿 🏛

Old Mill Farm
High Hurstwood, Uckfield
TN22 4AD
☎ Buxted (0825) 732279
50-acre beef farm. Situated in picturesque valley, off A26. Gatwick, Crowborough, Uckfield and Ashdown Forest nearby.
Bedrooms: 3 twin
Bathrooms: 1 private, 2 public, 3 private showers

Bed & breakfast

per night:	£min	£max
Single	17.00	17.00
Double	34.00	34.00

Half board

per person:	£min	£max
Daily	22.00	25.00
Weekly	154.00	175.00

Evening meal 1800 (last orders 2030)
Parking for 6
🛏 🕙 🖳 🖳 🖳 🅐 🅢 📺 🖳, 🍽 🌣 🍴 🚭 🏛

South Paddock 🏔
🍴🍴 COMMENDED

Maresfield Park, Uckfield
TN22 2HA
☎ (0825) 762335
Comfortable quiet country house accommodation set in 3.5 acres of landscaped gardens. Home-made preserves and log fires. Within easy reach of Gatwick, Brighton, Glyndebourne, Ashdown Forest.
Bedrooms: 2 twin
Bathrooms: 1 public

Bed & breakfast

per night:	£min	£max
Single	27.00	34.00
Double	42.00	50.00

Parking for 6
🛏 5 🖳 🖳 🕙 🍵 🅐 🅐 📺 🖳, 🍽 🔍 🕐 🌣 🍴 🚭 🆗 🆂🅿

WADHURST

East Sussex
Map ref 3B4

Village in the Sussex Weald. The village sign depicts an anvil, recalling the iron industry, and also an oasthouse, showing that this is hop country.

Best Beech Hotel
Mayfield Lane, Best Beech,
Wadhurst TN5 6JH
☎ (089 288) 2046
Quiet, rural public house set in pretty Sussex countryside and surrounded by beech trees.
Bedrooms: 2 double, 3 twin
Bathrooms: 2 private, 1 public, 1 private shower

Bed & breakfast

per night:	£min	£max
Single	18.00	25.00
Double	30.00	40.00

Half board

per person:	£min	£max
Daily	25.00	45.00

Lunch available
Evening meal 1900 (last orders 2130)
Parking for 30
Cards accepted: Access, Visa
🛏 🖳 🕙 🍵 🍵 ⁄ 🖳, 🍽 🚭

Cheviots 🏔
🍴🍴 COMMENDED

Cousley Wood, Wadhurst
TN5 6HD
☎ (0892) 782952
On B2100 between Lamberhurst and Wadhurst. Comfortable bed and breakfast in modern country house with extensive garden. Home cooking. Convenient base for walking and motoring. Close to Bewl Water.
Bedrooms: 2 single, 2 twin
Bathrooms: 2 private, 1 public

Bed & breakfast

per night:	£min	£max
Single	17.00	22.00
Double	34.00	44.00

Half board

per person:	£min	£max
Daily	30.00	35.00
Weekly	210.00	245.00

Evening meal from 1800
Parking for 4
Open March-November
🛏 🖳 🖳 🖳 🕙 🅐 🅢 ⁄ 🖳 🖳, 🍽 🌣 🍴 🚭 🆂🅿

Kirkstone
🍴🍴

Mayfield Lane, Wadhurst
TN5 6HX
☎ (089 278) 3204
Large Victorian house in countryside near Tunbridge Wells. Large garden, fine views.
Bedrooms: 1 twin, 1 triple
Bathrooms: 2 public

Bed & breakfast

per night:	£min	£max
Single	16.00	18.00
Double	32.00	32.00

Parking for 4
🛏 🖳 🅐 🅐 📺 🖳, 🍽 🌣 🚭

Half board prices shown are per person but in some cases may be based on double/ twin occupancy.

WEST CHILTINGTON

West Sussex
Map ref 2D3

Well-kept village caught in the maze of lanes leading to and from the South Downs.

New House Farm ⚑
COMMENDED
Broadford Bridge Road, West Chiltington, Pulborough RH20 2LA
☎ (0798) 812215
50-acre mixed farm. 15th C farmhouse with oak beams and inglenook for log fires. 40 minutes' drive from Gatwick. Within easy reach of local inns and golf-course.
Bedrooms: 1 double, 2 twin
Bathrooms: 3 private

Bed & breakfast per night:	£min	£max
Single	18.00	22.00
Double	36.00	44.00

Parking for 6
Open January-November

WEST CLANDON

Surrey
Map ref 2D2

Ways Cottage
Lime Grove, West Clandon, Guildford GU4 7UT
☎ Guildford (0483) 222454
Rural detached house in quiet location, five miles from Guildford. Easy reach of A3 and M25. Close to station on Waterloo/Guildford line.
Bedrooms: 1 single, 1 twin
Bathrooms: 1 private, 1 public

Bed & breakfast per night:	£min	£max
Single	15.00	18.50
Double	30.00	30.00

Half board per person:	£min	£max
Daily	22.50	26.50

Evening meal 1800 (last orders 2100)
Parking for 2

The town index towards the back of this guide gives page numbers of all places with accommodation.

WEST MALLING

Kent
Map ref 3B3

Became prominent in Norman times when an abbey was established here.

Westfields Farm
Listed
St. Vincents Lane, Addington, West Malling ME19 5BW
☎ (0732) 843209
A farmhouse of character, approximately 500 years old, in rural setting. Within easy reach of London, Canterbury, Tunbridge Wells and the coast. Reductions for children. Golf nearby.
Bedrooms: 1 single, 1 double, 2 twin
Bathrooms: 2 public

Bed & breakfast per night:	£min	£max
Single	16.00	16.00
Double	32.00	32.00

WESTERHAM

Kent
Map ref 2D2

This small country town near the Kent/Surrey border sits in the wooded slopes of the glorious North Downs. Made famous as the birthplace of General Wolfe and close to Churchill's house at Chartwell.

Oak Mount
18 Aperfield Road, Biggin Hill, Westerham TN16 3LU
☎ (0959) 75443
On North Downs, 3 miles north of Westerham on A233. Ideal for touring London and South East. Special diets catered for.
Bedrooms: 1 triple, 1 multiple
Bathrooms: 2 private, 1 public

Bed & breakfast per night:	£min	£max
Single	15.00	25.00
Double	26.00	38.00

Parking for 3

Please check prices and other details at the time of booking.

WHITSTABLE

Kent
Map ref 3B3

Seaside resort and yachting centre on Kent's north shore. The beach is shingle and there are the usual seaside amenities and entertainments and a museum.
Tourist Information Centre
☎ *(0227) 275482.*

The Nestings
3 Pier Avenue, Whitstable CT5 2HH
☎ (0227) 261600
Pleasant house 200 yards from safe, clean beaches and within easy walking distance of Whitstable and Herne Bay. Shops nearby.
Bedrooms: 1 single, 1 double, 1 twin
Bathrooms: 1 public

Bed & breakfast per night:	£min	£max
Single	12.00	14.00
Double	24.00	28.00

Parking for 2

WILMINGTON

East Sussex
Map ref 2D3

The Long Man of Wilmington, a great figure cut out of the turf of Windover Hill, overlooks the village. Its origin is a mystery. Wilmington Priory houses an interesting agricultural museum.

Crossways Restaurant & Hotel
Wilmington, Polegate BN26 5SG
☎ Polegate (0323) 482455
Fax (0323) 487811
Georgian-style hotel and restaurant, run by chef/proprietor, in 2 acres of grounds. Directly opposite the Long Man of Wilmington and Wilmington Priory.
Bedrooms: 2 single, 3 double, 2 twin
Bathrooms: 6 private, 1 public

Bed & breakfast per night:	£min	£max
Single	32.00	36.00
Double	52.00	62.00

Half board per person:	£min	£max
Daily	48.00	

Evening meal 1930 (last orders 2100)
Parking for 25
Open February-December
Cards accepted: Access, Visa

WINCHELSEA

East Sussex
Map ref 3B4

Edward I laid out the present town on its hilltop site in the 13th C to replace the ancient Cinque Port which was eventually engulfed by the sea.

The New Inn ⚑
APPROVED
German Street, Winchelsea TN36 4EN
☎ Rye (0797) 226252
Traditional country inn, central in Winchelsea, providing accommodation and a selection of meals and snacks served in comfortable bars.
Bedrooms: 2 double, 1 twin, 1 triple, 2 multiple
Bathrooms: 1 public, 2 private showers

Bed & breakfast per night:	£min	£max
Double	29.00	36.00

Lunch available
Evening meal 1830 (last orders 2130)
Parking for 16
Cards accepted: Access, Visa, Diners, Amex

WITTERSHAM

Kent
Map ref 3B4

Village in the Isle of Oxney with a well-preserved 18th C post mill, Stocks Mill, open to the public.

Knoll House
Wittersham, Tenterden TN30 7HN
☎ (0797) 270258
In peaceful rural surroundings, set well back off the road. Only 500 yards from main Rye to Tenterden road. Ideal touring centre.
Bedrooms: 1 single, 1 double, 1 twin
Bathrooms: 2 public

404

Bed & breakfast

per night:	£min	£max
Single	13.00	14.00
Double	27.00	28.00

Parking for 4
Open March-November

WOKING

Surrey
Map ref 2D2

One of the largest towns in Surrey, which developed with the coming of the railway in the 1830s. Old Woking was a market town in the 17th C and still retains several interesting buildings.

Elm Lodge

Elm Road, Horsell, Woking
GU21 4DY
☎ (0483) 763323
Fax (0344) 845656
Comfortable Victorian home in a quiet location overlooking woodland, yet five minutes from town centre and main line station.
Bedrooms: 3 double
Bathrooms: 1 public

Bed & breakfast

per night:	£min	£max
Single	28.00	28.00
Double	40.00	40.00

Half board

per person:	£min	£max
Daily	40.00	40.00

Evening meal 1800 (last orders 2000)
Parking for 6
Cards accepted:

Mayford House
The Mayford Centre

Smarts Heath Road, Woking
GU22 0PP
☎ (0483) 730554
Non-smokers only please. Rooms all have colour TV, tea and coffee-making facilities. Extra bed/put-ups available. Payphone, fax and secretarial services available. Post Office, newsagent and restaurant nearby.
Bedrooms: 2 single, 1 double, 1 twin
Bathrooms: 1 public

Bed & breakfast

per night:	£min	£max
Single	17.00	20.00
Double	34.00	40.00

Parking for 4

WORTHING

West Sussex
Map ref 2D3

Largest town in West Sussex, a popular seaside resort with extensive sand and shingle beaches. Seafishing is excellent here. The museum contains finds from Cissbury Ring.
Tourist Information Centre
☎ *(0903) 210022*

Aspen House
COMMENDED

13 Winchester Road, Worthing BN11 4DJ
☎ (0903) 230584
Edwardian house in quiet location near town, sea and station. All bedrooms beautifully modernised and furnished. Breakfast served in elegant period dining room.
Bedrooms: 1 single, 2 double, 1 twin
Bathrooms: 3 private, 1 private shower

Bed & breakfast

per night:	£min	£max
Single	19.00	22.00
Double	38.00	44.00

Parking for 2

Cherry Tree House

30 Madeira Avenue, Worthing BN11 2BA
☎ (0903) 236128
Double-fronted Victorian house with friendly atmosphere, close to sea, shops and bowling green.
Bedrooms: 2 double, 1 twin
Bathrooms: 1 private, 1 public

Bed & breakfast

per night:	£min	£max
Single	13.00	15.00
Double	26.00	30.00

Parking for 2

Marimac

9 Ash Grove, Worthing BN11 1PD
☎ (0903) 200715
Small friendly bed and breakfast establishment very near shops, parks and seafront.
Bedrooms: 1 double, 2 twin
Bathrooms: 1 public, 2 private showers

Please mention this guide when making a booking.

Bed & breakfast

per night:	£min	£max
Double	29.00	32.00

Open April-October

Moorings Hotel
COMMENDED

4 Selden Road, Worthing BN11 2LL
☎ (0903) 208882
Fax (0903) 823872
Victorian house, tastefully renovated and retaining many original features. Close to the beach, Beach House Park, Aquarena, children's playground and town centre.
Bedrooms: 2 single, 2 double, 2 twin, 2 triple
Bathrooms: 8 private

Bed & breakfast

per night:	£min	£max
Single	24.00	
Double	40.00	44.00

Half board

per person:	£min	£max
Daily	28.00	32.00
Weekly	176.00	200.00

Evening meal 1900 (last orders 1930)
Parking for 5
Cards accepted: Access, Visa, Switch

Seaspray

12 Alexandra Road, Worthing BN11 2DX
☎ (0903) 230352
Family-run Victorian guesthouse, walking distance to seafront, championship bowling greens, main shops, children's playground, municipal swimming pool. Unrestricted parking.
Bedrooms: 1 single, 2 twin, 1 triple
Bathrooms: 1 public

Bed & breakfast

per night:	£min	£max
Single	14.00	15.00
Double	28.00	30.00

Half board

per person:	£min	£max
Daily	19.00	20.00

Open May-September

Tudor Guest House

5 Windsor Road, Worthing BN11 2LU
☎ (0903) 210265
Comfortable bedrooms, satellite TV, English or continental breakfast. 1 minute from seafront, restaurants. Close to town

---

centre, entertainment, bowling greens, Beach House Park. Parking on premises.
Bedrooms: 4 single, 2 double, 2 twin, 1 triple
Bathrooms: 1 public, 1 private shower

Bed & breakfast

per night:	£min	£max
Single	11.00	14.50
Double	22.00	29.00

Parking for 5

WROTHAM

Kent
Map ref 3B3

Below Wrotham Hill close to the North Downs Way, the village has an impressive 14th C church and several interesting old buildings, some dating from Elizabethan times.

The Bull Hotel

Bull Lane, Wrotham, Sevenoaks TN15 7RF
☎ Borough Green (0732) 885522
Privately-run 14th C coaching inn, in secluded historic village close to M20 and M25. Half an hour from Gatwick and London.
Bedrooms: 1 single, 3 double, 5 twin, 1 triple
Bathrooms: 6 private, 1 public

Bed & breakfast

per night:	£min	£max
Single	35.00	40.00
Double	45.00	50.00

Lunch available
Evening meal 1900 (last orders 2200)
Parking for 50
Cards accepted: Access, Visa, C.Bl, Diners, Amex

There are separate sections in this guide listing groups specialising in farm holidays and accommodation which is especially suitable for young people and organised groups.

WYE

Kent
Map ref 3B4

Well known for its agricultural and horticultural college. The Olantigh Tower, with its imposing front portico, is used as a setting for part of the Stour Music Festival held annually in June.

New Flying Horse Inn ⚔
Upper Bridge Street, Wye, Ashford TN25 5AN
☎ (0233) 812297
17th C former coaching inn with oak beams and gleaming brasses. Ideal for touring and walking in Kent countryside and coast.
Bedrooms: 4 double, 3 twin, 1 triple
Bathrooms: 4 private, 2 public

Bed & breakfast per night:	£min	£max
Single	25.00	35.00
Double	35.00	50.00

Lunch available
Evening meal 1830 (last orders 2130)
Parking for 50
Cards accepted: Access, Visa, Amex

🛏 🍴 🛎 📞 🖨 🚶 🛗 S 🅿 ⅲ 🚐 ✿ SP 🛏 T

Use your *i*'s

🛈 Tourist information ➤

There are more than 600 Tourist Information Centres throughout England offering friendly help with accommodation and holiday ideas as well as suggestions of places to visit and things to do.

In your home town there may be a centre which can help you before you set out. You'll find the address of your nearest Tourist Information Centre in your local Phone Book.

FAMILY LEISURE GUIDES

Golf ◆ Birdwatching ◆ Horse Riding ◆ Horse Racing

A series of colourful guides to sporting and leisure pursuits together with all the nearby major attractions you and the family can visit.

- ◆ **GOLF** features over 140 golf-courses that welcome visiting players
- ◆ **BIRDWATCHING** features over 120 RSPB and Wildlife Trust reserves
- ◆ **HORSE RIDING** gives details of over 100 riding schools, all approved by BHS
- ◆ **HORSE RACING** has comprehensive details of all 61 professional racecourses

Each guide has over 200 pages full of practical information, including how to get there, facilities available, catering, etc.

Published in association with the National Tourist Boards for England, Scotland, Wales and Northern Ireland by Charles Letts.
Available in large-format paperback from bookshops, price £9.95.

UK ACTIVITY HOLIDAYS

UK Activity Holidays gives hundreds of ideas for holidays and activity breaks throughout England, Scotland, Wales and Northern Ireland and is ideal for all who are seeking something to do with their holiday time.

There are holidays for adults and children, beginners and experts.

Holiday suggestions include learning to sail, surf, canoe or ski and multi-activity holidays which involve tackling five or six sports in a week. If you're not quite so energetic, take life easy exploring our heritage or the countryside or learn a new skill such as picture framing or glass blowing. For something completely different, there are "Whodunnit" murder parties or learn-to-drive weekends.

Available in paperback from bookshops, price £4.50.

Farm Holiday Groups

This section of the guide lists groups specialising in farm and country based holidays. Most offer bed and breakfast accommodation (some with evening meal) and self-catering accommodation.

To obtain further details of individual properties please contact the group(s) direct, indicating the time of the year when the accommodation is required and the number of people to be accommodated. You may find the booking enquiry coupons (pages 441–450) helpful when making contact.

The cost of sending out brochures is high, and the groups would appreciate written enquiries being accompanied by a stamped and addressed envelope (at least 9" x 4½").

The "b&b" prices shown are per person per night; the self-catering prices are weekly terms per unit.

The symbol 🐄 before the name of a group indicates that it is a member of the Farm Holiday Bureau, set up by the Royal Agricultural Society of England in conjunction with the English Tourist Board.

Bed & Breakfast (GB)
Mr J. Ette, Bed & Breakfast (GB),
PO Box 66, Henley-on-Thames,
Oxfordshire RG9 1XS
Tel: (0491) 578803
Fax: (0491) 410806
Over 500 carefully selected bed and breakfast hosts in London, England, Scotland, Wales and Ireland, all bookable through one central reservations office.
500 properties offering bed and breakfast: £13.50–£42 b&b.
Short stays also available.

🐄 **Bedfordshire Farm and Country Holiday Group**
Mrs S. Mousley, Lea Cottage, Old Harrowden Road, Bedford,
Bedfordshire MK42 0TB
Tel: (0234) 740182

*Good selection of bed and breakfast and self-catering properties in rural areas.
Whether your visit is for business or pleasure, we look foward to welcoming you to our homes in the country.*
11 properties offering bed and breakfast: £13–£20 b&b.
12 self-catering units: from £100.

🐄 **Derbyshire Dales and Dovedale Farm and Country Holiday Group**
Mrs A. Whitfield, Waldley Manor, Marston Montgomery, Nr Doveridge, Derbyshire DE6 5LR
Tel: (0889) 590287
Friendly and welcoming farm and country based quality bed and breakfast and self-catering

accommodation within 10 miles of Ashbourne, the gateway to Dovedale.
22 properties offering bed and breakfast: £12–£29.50 b&b.
20 self-catering units: low season (October–April) £75–£110; high season (late July–September) £150–£350.
Self-catering short breaks available out of season.
Caravan pitches available.

🐄 **Exmoor Holiday Group**
Mrs T. Cody-Boutcher, Little Quarme Farm, Wheddon Cross, Nr Minehead, Somerset TA24 7EA
Tel: (0643) 841249
Cosy self-catering cottages, old-world farmhouses with superb

AYE, IT'S BEEN A GOOD YEAR— I'VE HAD A BUMPER CROP OF HOLIDAY MAKERS!

VALE FARM

KenPyne

food, offering excellent value for money and a warm welcome. All situated in the glorious surroundings of the Exmoor National Park.
20 properties offering bed and breakfast: £14–£24 b&b.
32 self-catering units: £80–£400.
Short breaks also available.
Tent pitches available.

Heart of Devon Farm Holiday Group
Mrs H. Hann, Great Bradley Farm, Withleigh Cross, Tiverton, Devon EX16 8JL
Tel: (0884) 256946
Variety of working farms in and around the lovely Exe Valley, offering self-catering accommodation or bed and breakfast with optional evening meal. Friendly, welcoming atmosphere assured.
11 properties offering bed and breakfast: £10–£18 b&b.
9 self-catering units: low season (November–May) £100–£275; high season (mid-July–September) £275–£450.
Short breaks also available.

Kent Farm Holidays
Mrs D. Day, Great Cheveney Farm, Goudhurst Road, Marden, Tonbridge, Kent TN12 9LX
Tel: (0622) 831207
Fax: (0622) 831786
Mrs R. Bannock, Court Lodge Farm, Teston, Maidstone, Kent ME18 5AQ
Tel: (0622) 812570
Fax: (0622) 814200
Wide selection, from traditional farm cottages to modern farm-building conversions. Many with interesting architectural features and leisure facilities, many welcome non-smokers. Peaceful touring caravan and camping park.
19 properties offering bed and breakfast: £16–£30 b&b.
38 self-catering units: low season (October–April) from £90; high season (May–September) £120–£664.
Discounted short breaks available in low season.

South Pennine Farm Accommodation
Jane Neave, Leaches Farm, Ashworth, Rochdale, Lancashire OL11 5UN
Tel: (0706) 41116/7 or 228520

Pennine hill farms, 200 to 300-year-old houses but with all mod cons. Remote moorland and dramatic scenery, yet only 20 minutes' drive to the heart of Manchester and the airport.
7 properties offering bed and breakfast: £15–£20 b&b.
7 self-catering units: low season £90–£150; high season £100–£300.
Short breaks also available.
Tent pitches available.

Thames Valley Farm & Country House Accommodation
Mrs M. Palmer, Monkton Farm, Little Marlow, Buckinghamshire SL7 3RF
Tel: (0494) 521082
Fax: (0494) 443905
Excellent accommodation on working farms and in country houses in the Thames Valley area.
29 properties offering bed and breakfast: £15–£35 b&b.
3 self-catering units: low season £138–£175; high season £168–£230.
Caravan pitches available.

Warwickshire Farm Holidays
Miss D. Lea, Crandon House, Avon Dassett, Leamington Spa, Warwickshire CV33 0AA
Tel: (0295) 770652
A warm welcome at farmhouses offering serviced and self-catering accommodation in comfortable and homely surroundings, situated in historic and picturesque "Shakespeare Country".
27 properties offering bed and breakfast: £12–£27 b&b.
25 self-catering units: low season (October–April) £70–£350; high season (May–September) £80–£450.
Caravan and tent pitches available.

Group & Youth Section

Most of the accommodation establishments listed in this guide are particularly suitable for people looking for relatively low-cost places to stay in England.

Many of them make a special point of providing safe, budget-priced accommodation for young people, for families or for large groups. These establishments, ranging from Youth Hostels, YMCAs and YWCAs through budget and student hotels to the seasonally available campuses of universities and colleges, are listed individually in the pages which follow.

Information on organisations which specialise in this type of accommodation is given below – please contact the organisations direct for further details.

YOUTH HOSTELS

The Youth Hostels Association (England and Wales) provides basic accommodation, usually in single-sex bunk-bedded rooms or dormitories, with self-catering facilities. Most hostels also provide low-cost meals or snacks. At the time of going to press, a night's stay at a Youth Hostel will cost between £3.40 and £19.50.

In spite of the word "youth" in the name, there is in fact no upper age limit. Indeed, many Youth Hostels also offer family accommodation, either in self-contained annexes (with kitchen, living room and bathroom) or by letting the smaller, four-to-six bed dormitories as private units.

Groups are very welcome at Youth Hostels, whether for educational or leisure pursuits: some hostels offer field study facilities and many more have classrooms. The YHA also offers a wide range of adventure holidays and special interest breaks.

Youth Hostels – from medieval castles to shepherds' huts – can be found all over the country, both in countryside and coastal locations and in towns and cities.

You need to be a member of the YHA in order to take advantage of the facilities. Membership entitles you to use not only the 250 hostels in England and Wales but also the thousands of Youth Hostels in other parts of the British Isles and around the world. Membership costs £3 (under 18) or £9 (over 18). Family membership is available at £9 (single-parent family) or £18 (two-parent family).

Further information from:
Youth Hostels Association
National Office, Trevelyan House, 8 St Stephen's Hill, St Albans, Hertfordshire AL1 2DY
Tel: (0727) 55215
Fax: (0727) 44126

YWCA & YMCA

The Young Women's Christian Association, founded in 1855, has grown into the world's largest women's organisation. Among its many activities is the running of over 60 hostels in Britain (known as YWCAs) which offer safe, reasonably priced self-catering accommodation, mostly in single rooms, either on a permanent or temporary basis.

Most YWCAs take short-stay visitors only during the summer months when their permanent residents – in many cases, students – are on holiday. However, some of the hostels do accept short-stay visitors all the year round. And although the word "women" appears in the name of the organisation, many of the residences now take men and boys as well as women and girls.

The Young Men's Christian Association (YMCA), founded in 1844, operates on much the same basis as the YWCA, taking people of both sexes at its 50-plus residences around the country either on a permanent or short-stay basis.

Special budget accommodation is also available in July and August at some YMCAs as part of the Inter-Point Programme, set up to provide accommodation and advice for Inter-Railers.

Further information from:
YWCA HQ
Clarendon House, 52 Cornmarket Street, Oxford OX1 3EJ
Tel: (0865) 726110
YMCA
National Council, 640 Forest Road, Walthamstow, London E17 3DZ
Tel: 081-520 5599
For details of the Inter-Point Programme, contact:
Y Training Services, Manchester
Tel: 061-881 5321

UNIVERSITIES & COLLEGES

Accommodation in universities and colleges offers excellent value for money at dozens of city centre, seaside and countryside campus locations around England.

This type of accommodation is particularly suitable for groups, whether on a leisure trip or participating in a conference or seminar. Beds available on campus vary from 30 to 3,000. There is a wide selection of meeting room facilities to choose from, with a maximum capacity of 2,000 people, and banqueting facilities for up to 1,500.

Most accommodation is in single "study bedrooms", with a limited number of twin and family rooms.

Availability is mainly during the academic vacation periods (usually July to September and for four-week periods at Christmas and Easter), with some venues offering short-stay accommodation throughout the year.

For relaxation, there is a wide choice of recreational facilities, with most venues providing TV rooms, bars and restaurants and a variety of sporting activities, ranging from tennis, squash and swimming to team sports.

Activity and special interest holidays are also on offer as are many self-catering flats and houses.

Further information from:
British Universities Accommodation Consortium (BUAC)
Box No 860, University Park, Nottingham NG7 2RD
Tel: (0602) 504571
Fax: (0602) 422505

Higher Education Accommodation Consortium (HEAC)
36 Collegiate Crescent, Sheffield S10 2BP
Tel: (0742) 683759
Fax: (0742) 661203

OTHER ACCOMMODATION

In addition to the above main providers on a countrywide basis of budget accommodation for young people and groups, there are, of course, the many individual student and budget hotels around England and also such places as outdoor and field study centres.

Some of these feature in the following pages but for more information on what is available in a particular area, please contact a local Tourist Information Centre.

Places to stay

Accommodation entries in this section are listed in alphabetical order of place name, and then in alphabetical order of establishment.

The map references refer to the colour maps at the back of the guide. The first figure is the map number; the letter and figure which follow indicate the grid reference on the map.

The symbols at the end of each accommodation entry give information about services and facilities. A 'key' to these symbols is inside the back cover flap, which can be kept open for easy reference.

AMBLESIDE

Cumbria
Map ref 5A3

Market town situated at the head of Lake Windermere and surrounded by fells. The historic town centre is now a conservation area and the country around Ambleside is rich in historical and literary association. Good centre for touring, walking and climbing.
Tourist Information Centre ☎ *(05394) 32582.*

Iveing Cottage Holiday Centre ♠
YWCA, Old Lake Road, Ambleside LA22 0DJ
☎ (053 94) 32340
Contact: The Director
Centrally located on old coaching road between Ambleside and lake. Ideal for fell-walking, rambling or climbing. Parties or individuals.
Bedrooms: 1 single, 3 double/twin, 6 dormitories. Total number of beds: 50
Bathrooms: 7 public
Bed & breakfast

per person:	£min	£max
Daily	11.75	12.50

Lunch available
Evening meal 1800 (last orders 1800)

Parking for 9
Open February-November
🛏 🖳 🛉 Ⓢ ✂ 🛋 📺 🅿 ♨ 🍴
SP 📷

ASKRIGG

North Yorkshire
Map ref 5B3

The name of this Dales village means 'ash tree ridge'. It is centred on a steep main street of high, narrow 3-storey houses and thrived on cotton and later wool in 18th C. Once famous for its clock making.

Low Mill Residential Youth Centre
Askrigg, Leyburn DL8 3HZ
☎ Wensleydale (0969) 50432
Contact: The Warden
A residential youth centre offering outdoor education courses for able-bodied and disabled young people. In the Yorkshire Dales National Park.
For groups only
Total number of beds: 40
Bed & breakfast

per person:	£min	£max
Daily	20.00	

🖳 Ⓢ 🛋 📺 🅿 🔍 ✗ 🚲 📷

> We advise you to confirm your booking in writing.

BATH

Avon
Map ref 2B2

Georgian spa city beside the River Avon. Important Roman site with impressive reconstructed baths, uncovered in 19th C. Bath Abbey built on site of monastery where first king of England was crowned (AD 973). Fine architecture in mellow local stone. Pump Room and museums.
Tourist Information Centre ☎ *(0225) 462831*

The City of Bath YMCA ♠
International House, Broad Street Place, Bath BA1 5LN
☎ (0225) 460471
Contact: Mr M Goff
Open to those of both sexes and all ages. Centrally located and only minutes away from Bath's major attractions. A convenient base for city and west country tours.
Minimum age 17
Bedrooms: 69 single, 13 double/twin, 4 triple, 2 dormitories. Total number of beds: 135
Bathrooms: 26 public
Bed & breakfast

per person:	£min	£max
Daily	9.20	11.75

Lunch available
Evening meal 1700 (last orders 1800)
🛏 ♨ 🖳 🛉 Ⓢ ✂ 🛋 📺 🅿 ♨ 🍴
🛇 🔍 ✗ 📷

BELFORD

Northumberland
Map ref 5B1

Small market town on the old coaching road, close to the coast, the Scottish border and the north-east flank of the Cheviots. Built mostly in stone and very peaceful now that the A1 has by-passed the town, Belford makes an ideal centre for excursions to the moors and coast.

Bearsports Outdoor Centres
Windy Gyle, Belford NE70 7QE
☎ (0668) 213289
Fax (0668) 213775
Contact: Mr P Clark
Outdoor activity holidays for individuals, families and groups. Expert instruction, excellent equipment and locations. Quality accommodation and food, catering for up to 130 in 4 centres. Approved by RYA, BCU, BAHA and MLTB.
Minimum age 8
Bedrooms: 6 dormitories. Total number of beds: 45
Bathrooms: 8 public

Bed only

per person:	£min	£max
Daily	5.00	

Bed & breakfast

per person:	£min	£max
Daily	12.00	

Lunch available
Evening meal 1830 (last orders 1930)
Cards accepted: Access, Visa

BIRMINGHAM

West Midlands
Map ref 4B3

Britain's second city, with many attractions including the City Art Gallery, Barber Institute of Fine Arts, 17th C Aston Hall, science museum, railway museum, 2 cathedrals and 10-acre Botanical Gardens. It is well placed for exploring Shakespeare country.
Tourist Information Centre
☎ *021-643 2514.*

James Gracie Conference Centre ᴹ
38 Wake Green Road, Moseley, Birmingham
B13 9PE
☎ 021-449 4137
Fax 021-442 4035
Contact: Mr. D J Morgan
Set in large gardens about 4 miles from New Street station and the city centre, approximately 7 miles from National Exhibition Centre and airport. Convenient for M6.
Minimum age 15
Bedrooms: 114 single, 8 double/twin. Total number of beds: 129
Bathrooms: 56 private, 21 public

Bed & breakfast

per person:	£min	£max
Daily	37.00	41.15

Full board

per person:	£min	£max
Weekly	367.50	367.50

Lunch available
Evening meal 1800 (last orders 2000)
Parking for 83

BISHOP AUCKLAND

Durham
Map ref 5C2

Busy market town on the bank of the Wear. The Palace, a castellated Norman manor house altered in the 18th C, stands in beautiful gardens. Open to the public and entered from the market square by a handsome 18th C gatehouse, the park is a peaceful retreat of trees and streams.

Weardale House ᴹ
Ireshopeburn, Bishop Auckland, County Durham
Contact: Mr Chris Jones, Y.M.C.A. Residential Office, Herrington Burn, Houghton-le-Spring, Tyne and Wear
DH4 4JW
☎ 091-385 2822 & 385 3085
Fax 091-385 2267
Multi-activity outdoor centre.
Minimum age 7
Bedrooms: 3 single, 8 dormitories. Total number of beds: 70
Bathrooms: 8 public
Full board

per person:	£min	£max
Weekly	97.00	105.75

Lunch available
Parking for 10

BLACKFIELD

Hampshire
Map ref 2C3

Village within easy reach of Beaulieu and the forest areas.

Mopley Farm Equestrian Centre & Guest House
Mopley Farm, Mopley Road, Blackfield, Southampton
SO4 1YH
☎ Fawley (0703) 898197
Contact: Mrs. A Rumsam
Countryside activity centre, offering holidays/weekends for DIY horse-owners, trout and coarse fishermen, walking and bird-watching enthusiasts. Dogs welcome.
Bedrooms: 2 single, 2 double/twin, 1 dormitory.
Total number of beds: 7
Bathrooms: 2 public
Bed & breakfast

per person:	£min	£max
Daily	13.00	15.00

Full board

per person:	£min	£max
Weekly	85.00	95.00

> Individual proprietors have supplied all details of accommodation. Although we do check for accuracy, we advise you to confirm the information at the time of booking.

BOURNEMOUTH

Dorset
Map ref 2B3

Seaside town set among the pines with a mild climate, sandy beaches and fine coastal views. The town has wide streets with excellent shops, a pier, a pavilion, museums and conference centre.
Tourist Information Centre
☎ *(0202) 789789*

Bournemouth Central YMCA ᴹ
Westover Road, Bournemouth BH1 2BS
Contact: Mr A Whitmore, Bournemouth Central YMCA, Delta House, 56 Westover Road, Bournemouth, Dorset
BH1 2BS
☎ (0202) 290451 & 551087
In town centre overlooking the sea, 100 yards from beach. Facilities include sports hall, fitness suite, snooker parlour, table tennis rooms, dance studio, sunbed, laundry and restaurant.
Bedrooms: 58 single, 1 double/twin, 2 triple, 1 quadruple, 3 dormitories. Total number of beds: 100
Bathrooms: 18 private, 10 public
Bed only

per person:	£min	£max
Daily	8.25	8.25

Bed & breakfast

per person:	£min	£max
Daily	15.50	16.00

Lunch available
Evening meal 1700 (last orders 1800)

BRASSINGTON

Derbyshire
Map ref 4B2

Hopton Cottage

High Peak Trail,
Brassington, Derby DE4
Contact: Chief Planning and
Highways Officer, County
Offices, Matlock, Derbyshire
DE4 3AG
☎ Matlock (0629) 580000
*Hopton Cottage provides
simple accommodation for
groups willing to cater for
themselves. It is particularly
suited to small groups
undertaking active pursuits or
field studies.*
For groups only
Minimum age 5
Bedrooms: 2 dormitories.
Total number of beds: 12
Bathrooms: 2 public

Bed only

per person:	£min	£max
Daily		3.40

Parking for 5

BROMPTON-BY-SAWDON

North Yorkshire
Map ref 5D3

William Wordsworth, the
renowned Lakeland poet,
was married in the parish
church in 1802 to Mary
Hutchinson of Gallows
Hill.

Wydale Hall

York Diocesan Centre,
Brompton-by-Sawdon,
Scarborough YO13 9DG
☎ Scarborough (0723)
859270
Contact: The Warden
*Beside the North York Moors
and 9 miles from the coast.
This conference/holiday
centre is ideal for any holiday
group.*
Bedrooms: 9 single,
17 double/twin, 2 triple,
2 quadruple. Total number
of beds: 57
Bathrooms: 11 public

Bed & breakfast

per person:	£min	£max
Daily	17.25	25.00

Full board

per person:	£min	£max
Weekly	223.25	250.00

Please check prices
and other details at
the time of booking.

CAMBRIDGE

Cambridgeshire
Map ref 2D1

A most important and
beautiful city on the River
Cam with 31 colleges
forming one of the oldest
universities in the world.
Numerous museums,
good shopping centre,
restaurants, theatres,
cinema and fine
bookshops.
*Tourist Information Centre
☎ (0223) 322640*

Cambridge Y.M.C.A.

Queen Anne House, Gonville
Place, Cambridge CB1 1ND
☎ (0223) 356998
Contact: Mrs. P Bishop
*A young people's residency,
in the centre of Cambridge
overlooking Parkers Piece.
Near railway and bus stations.
Very busy - not suitable for
guests expecting peace and
quiet.*
Minimum age 16
Bedrooms: 95 single,
31 double/twin. Total
number of beds: 157
Bathrooms: 24 public

Bed & breakfast

per person:	£min	£max
Daily	16.00	20.50

Lunch available
Evening meal 1615 (last
orders 1845)

CANTERBURY

Kent
Map ref 3B3

Place of pilgrimage since
the martyrdom of Becket
in 1170 and the site of
Canterbury Cathedral.
Visit St Augustine's
Abbey, St Martin's (the
oldest church in England),
Royal Museum and the
Canterbury Tales. Nearby
is Howletts Zoo Park.
*Tourist Information Centre
☎ (0277) 766567*

University of Kent at Canterbury

Conference Office, The
University, Canterbury
CT2 7NZ
☎ (0227) 769186
Fax (0227) 452196
Telex 965449
Contact: Mr. P Jordan
*The university, with its fine
views of Canterbury, offers
value for money
accommodation and meals.*

*Bedrooms with private
facilities now available.*
Minimum age 16
Bedrooms: 1400 single,
56 double/twin. Total
number of beds: 1512
Bathrooms: 103 private, 160
public

Bed & breakfast

per person:	£min	£max
Daily	17.25	30.80

Lunch available
Evening meal 1800 (last
orders 1900)
Parking for 1997
Open January, March-April,
July-September, December

CARLISLE

Cumbria
Map ref 5A2

Near Scottish border, this
cathedral city suffered
years of strife through the
centuries, often changing
hands between England
and Scotland. The red
sandstone cathedral is
the second smallest in
England. Castle founded
in 1092 now houses a
museum.
*Tourist Information Centre
☎ (0228) 512444*

Carlisle Racecourse

Durdar Road, Carlisle
CA2 4TS
Contact: Mrs Ann Bliss,
Brackenridge,
Brackenthwaite, Wigton,
Cumbria CA7 8AS
☎ (069 73) 42634
Fax (069 73) 42634
*On southern outskirts of
Carlisle, 2 miles from
junction 42 of M6. Several
function rooms. Meals in
licensed "Old Tote Bar" or
racecourse hostel.*
For groups only
Minimum age 4
Bedrooms: 10 quadruple,
1 dormitory. Total number of
beds: 48
Bathrooms: 8 public

Bed only

per person:	£min	£max
Daily	6.50	7.50

Bed & breakfast

per person:	£min	£max
Daily	8.00	10.00

Full board

per person:	£min	£max
Weekly	84.00	108.00

Lunch available
Evening meal 1700 (last
orders 2100)
Parking for 100

COVENTRY

West Midlands
Map ref 4B3

Modern city with a long
history. It has many
places of interest
including the post-war and
ruined medieval
cathedrals, art gallery and
museums, some 16th C
almshouses, St Mary's
Guildhall, Lunt Roman fort
and the Belgrade Theatre.
*Tourist Information Centre
☎ (0203) 832303*

Coventry University

Priory Halls of Residence,
Priory Street, Coventry
CV1 5FB
☎ (0203) 838758
Fax (0203) 838445
Contact: Mrs. H Wheway
*University student halls of
residence, offering out-of-term
accommodation. Situated in
the city centre beside
Coventry Cathedral and sports
centre.*
Bedrooms: 546 single,
2 double/twin. Total number
of beds: 550
Bathrooms: 2 private, 200
public

Bed only

per person:	£min	£max
Daily		12.00

Bed & breakfast

per person:	£min	£max
Daily		16.50

Lunch available
Open January, March-April,
July-September, December
Cards accepted: Access, Visa

Individual
proprietors have
supplied all details
of accommodation.
Although we do
check for accuracy,
we advise you to
confirm the
information at the
time of booking.

DURHAM

Durham
Map ref 5C2

Ancient city with its Norman castle and cathedral set on a bluff high over the Wear. A market and university town and regional centre, spreading beyond the market-place on both banks of the river. July Miners' Gala is a celebrated Durham tradition.

Tourist Information Centre
☎ 091-384 3720

College of St. Hild & St. Bede ⛰
University of Durham,
Leazes Road, Durham
DH1 1SZ
☎ 091-374 3069
Contact: Mr P A Warburton

College set in spacious grounds in the medieval City of Durham, providing a splendid base for exploring Northumbria.

Minimum age 10
Bedrooms: 374 single, 30 double/twin. Total number of beds: 434
Bathrooms: 53 public

Bed & breakfast per person:	£min	£max
Daily	12.30	15.50

Full board per person:	£min	£max
Weekly	167.30	189.70

Parking for 200
Open March-April, July-September
🐴 [S] 🪑 [TV] ▥ ◢ 🏌 🎾 🐕 🚌

Collingwood College ⛰
South Road, Durham,
County Durham DH1 3LT
☎ 091-374 4565
Fax 091-374 4595
Contact: Mrs Sylvia Hall

Durham's newest residential college set in woodland one mile south of the city.

Bedrooms: 295 single, 3 double/twin. Total number of beds: 301
Bathrooms: 56 public

Bed & breakfast per person:	£min	£max
Daily	14.19	

Full board per person:	£min	£max
Weekly	178.57	

Lunch available
Evening meal 1800 (last orders 1900)
Parking for 70
Open March-April, July-September and Christmas
🐴 🛏 ☕ 🔒 [S] 🪑 [TV] ▥ ◢ ⊤10-120 🏓 🎾 ∪ ⚑ 🐕 [SP]

Durham University Business School ⛰
Mill Hill Lane, Durham,
County Durham DH1 3LB
☎ 091-374 2202
Contact: Ms Alison Fairlamb

Modern university complex offering 60 study bedrooms and full conference facilities. Close to the centre of historic Durham with pleasant woodland surroundings.

Minimum age 15
Bedrooms: 60 single. Total number of beds: 60
Bathrooms: 60 private

Bed only per person:	£min	£max
Daily		40.00

Bed & breakfast per person:	£min	£max
Daily		46.00

Lunch available
Parking for 60
📠 🖥 🔒 [S] [TV] ▥ ◢ 🐕 🚌

Saint Chad's College University of Durham ⛰
18 North Bailey, Durham,
County Durham DH1 3RH
☎ 091-374 3370 & 374 3364
Contact: Mr I Blacklock

Traditional college welcomes conferences, groups or individuals at its quiet central location beside the cathedral, overlooking gardens and river.

Bedrooms: 56 single, 66 double/twin, 2 triple. Total number of beds: 150
Bathrooms: 6 private, 32 public

Bed only per person:	£min	£max
Daily	9.00	12.00

Bed & breakfast per person:	£min	£max
Daily	12.00	17.50

Full board per person:	£min	£max
Weekly	125.00	

Lunch available
Evening meal 1800 (last orders 1930)
Parking for 15
Open January, March-April, June-September, December
🐴 🛏 ☕ 🔒 [S] 🚭 🪑 [TV] ▥ ◢ ⊤25-150 [OAP] [SP] 🏠

St. Cuthberts Society
12 South Bailey, Durham,
County Durham DH1 3EE
☎ 091-374 3464
Contact: Mrs H Bowler

3 old stone houses with riverside gardens, 5 minutes' walk from the city centre and close to the cathedral.

Bedrooms: 50 single, 23 double/twin, 3 triple.
Total number of beds: 114
Bathrooms: 21 public

Bed & breakfast per person:	£min	£max
Daily	13.50	

Open July-September
🐴 ☕ [UL] [S] 🚭 🪑 [TV] ▥ ◢ 🐕 🚌

St. John's College ⛰
University of Durham,
3 South Bailey, Durham
DH1 3RJ
☎ 091-374 3566
Contact: Mr Martin Clemmett

College buildings are skilfully adapted 18th C houses adjacent to Durham Cathedral and Castle.

Bedrooms: 96 single, 12 double/twin. Total number of beds: 120
Bathrooms: 25 public

Bed only per person:	£min	£max
Daily	13.75	13.75

Bed & breakfast per person:	£min	£max
Daily	15.50	15.50

Evening meal 1800 (last orders 1930)
Open March-April, July-September, December
🐴 🔒 [S] 🪑 [TV] ▥ ◢ ⊤ 🏓 🐕 [OAP] 🏠

ENGLEFIELD GREEN

Surrey
Map ref 2D2

Anugraha Hotel
Wick Lane, Englefield Green,
Egham, Surrey TW20 0XN
☎ (0784) 34355
Fax (0784) 430596
Telex 928116 ANUGRA G
Contact: Mr Mauro Bernesi

Anugraha is a hotel and conference centre recently created from an English country house and incorporating the most modern architectural and technical features.

Bedrooms: 37 single, 67 double/twin. Total number of beds: 172
Bathrooms: 104 private

Bed & breakfast per person:	£min	£max
Daily	35.00	140.00

Lunch available
Evening meal 1900 (last orders 2200)
Parking for 350
Cards accepted: Access, Visa, C.Bl, Diners, Amex
🐴 🛏 ▣ 📞 📠 🖥 ☕ 💨 🔒 [S] 🚭 ▥ ◢ ⊤2-800 🎾 ⚑ 🍃 [SP] 🏠 [T]

ILKLEY

West Yorkshire
Map ref 4B1

This moorland town is famous for its ballad. The 16th C manor house, now a museum, displays local prehistoric and Roman relics. Popular walk leads up Heber's Ghyll to Ilkley Moor, with the mysterious Swastika Stone and White Wells, 18th C plunge baths.

Tourist Information Centre
☎ (0943) 602319.

Glenmoor Centre ⛰
Wells Road, Ilkley LS29 9JF
☎ (0943) 816359
Fax (0943) 216359
Contact: Mrs M Cairns

Attractive accommodation for residential and day conferences in a beautiful setting, just on the edge of Ilkley Moor. Day delegate rate from £18.50 per person, 24-hour rate £64.00 per person.

For groups only
Bedrooms: 13 single, 9 double/twin. Total number of beds: 31
Bathrooms: 6 private, 6 public
Lunch available
Evening meal 1700 (last orders 1900)
Parking for 15
🚸 🛏 🔒 [S] 🚭 🪑 [TV] ▥ ◢ [SP] 🏠

The enquiry coupons at the back will help you when contacting proprietors.

The colour maps at the back of this guide pinpoint all places with accommodation.

The town index towards the back of this guide gives page numbers of all places with accommodation.

LIVERPOOL

Merseyside
Map ref 4A2

Liverpool became a major port in the 18th C. Landmarks include 2 cathedrals, Town Hall, Walker Art Gallery, Merseyside Maritime Museum, excellent shopping centre, entertainment and sports facilities (Aintree Racecourse). Speke Hall (National Trust).
Tourist Information Centre ☎ *051-709 3631 or 708 8854*

Christian Alliance Housing Association
Mildmay House,
6 Blackburne Place,
Liverpool L8 7PQ
☎ 051-709 1417
Contact: Miss Rosh Cundall
Self-catering hostel based on cluster flatlets, with shared laundry and recreational facilities.
Bedrooms: 51 single,
3 double/twin. Total number of beds: 57
Bathrooms: 6 private, 28 public

Bed only

per person:	£min	£max
Daily		7.00

☎4🛏♿🖵🖫📺🎱🎿♥🐕🏊

LONDON

See colour maps 6 & 7

Astor College
99 Charlotte Street, London
W1P 1LD
☎ 071-580 7262
Contact: Miss M C Hill
Centrally located student accommodation 3 minutes' walk from Goodge Street underground station and close to shops, restaurants and the British Museum.
Minimum age 10
Bedrooms: 210 single,
13 double/twin. Total number of beds: 236
Bathrooms: 1 private, 43 public

Bed only

per person:	£min	£max
Daily	12.50	21.95

Lunch available
Open January, April, July-September, December

☎🖫🖵📺🎱🎿♥🎾⛳🐕🏊

Brunel University Conference Centre
Conference Office, Brunel University, Uxbridge, Middlesex UB8 3PH
☎ Uxbridge (0895) 274 000
Fax (0895) 232 806
Telex 261173 G
Contact: Mr Carl Woodall
En-suite or standard bedrooms, cafeteria or silver service meals, purpose-built theatres and classrooms, audio and visual aids and sports facilities all available.
Minimum age 12
Bedrooms: 790 single. Total number of beds: 790
Bathrooms: 300 private, 85 public

Bed & breakfast

per person:	£min	£max
Daily	13.00	24.00

Full board

per person:	£min	£max
Weekly	169.00	300.00

Lunch available
Evening meal 1800 (last orders 2000)
Parking for 2000
Open April-September

☎12🛏♿♥🖫🖵📺🖫🎱🎿♥🎾⛳🐕🏊 DAP

Campbell House
Taviton Street, London
WC1H 0BX
☎ 071-380 7079
Contact: Mr R L Sparvell
Specially reconstructed Georgian housing providing self-catering accommodation in a peaceful, central London location.
Minimum age 10
Bedrooms: 60 single,
40 double/twin. Total number of beds: 140
Bathrooms: 25 public

Bed only

per person:	£min	£max
Daily	12.15	14.50

Open June-September

☎🎱🖫🛏🎿🖵📺🖫🖫🎾⛳

Central University of Iowa Hostel
7 Bedford Place, London
WC1B 5JA
☎ 071-580 1121
Contact: Ms. W Bristow
Old Georgian house near the British Museum. Closest underground stations are Russell Square and Holborn.
Bedrooms: 1 single,
6 double/twin,
5 dormitories. Total number of beds: 30
Bathrooms: 7 public

Bed & breakfast

per person:	£min	£max
Daily	14.50	15.50

Open May-August

☎🖫♿🖵📺🖫🎱🎾⛳🐕🏊

Curzon House Hotel ♨
58 Courtfield Gardens, London SW5 0NF
☎ 071-581 2116
Contact: Mr. C A Otter
Budget accommodation with free use of kitchen, dining room and TV lounge. Homely and friendly atmosphere guaranteed. Weekly rates are for November to June.
Bedrooms: 2 single,
5 double/twin,
12 dormitories. Total number of beds: 58
Bathrooms: 10 private, 5 public

Bed & breakfast

per person:	£min	£max
Daily	12.00	26.00

Full board

per person:	£min	£max
Weekly	65.00	120.00

Cards accepted: Access, Visa

☎🎱🖫📺🎱🎾⛳ SP T

Driscoll House Hotel
172 New Kent Road, London SE1 4YT
☎ 071-703 4175
Contact: Mr. T Driscoll
Long or short term accommodation offered to teachers, students and tourists. B & B price includes dinner; weekly full-board price excludes weekday lunch.
Minimum age 18
Bedrooms: 200 single. Total number of beds: 200
Bathrooms: 14 public

Bed & breakfast

per person:	£min	£max
Daily	27.00	27.00

Full board

per person:	£min	£max
Weekly	130.00	130.00

Lunch available
Evening meal 1730 (last orders 1900)

🖫🖵 S 🖫📺🖫🎱🎾⛳🐕🏊

Ealing YMCA
25 St Marys Road, Ealing, London W5 5RE
☎ 081-579 6946
Contact: Mrs. S Herring
A new residential centre. Each room with colour TV. Le Jardin restaurant on premises.
Minimum age 16
Bedrooms: 129 single,
14 double/twin. Total number of beds: 157

Bathrooms: 14 private, 28 public

Bed & breakfast

per person:	£min	£max
Daily		22.00

Full board

per person:	£min	£max
Weekly		94.92

🖵 S 📺🖫🎱🎾⛳🐕🏊

Inchmont Hotel
25 Collingham Place, South Kensington, London SW5 0EN
Contact: Mr Louise Zweig,
88 Greencroft Gardens, Swiss Cottage, London NW6
☎ 071-624 7665
Friendly international, student and young traveller style hostel/hotel. Comfortable TV lounge, dining room, laundry room. Few minutes' walk from Gloucester Road underground station, near to South Kensington for museums.
Minimum age 15
Bedrooms: 1 single,
5 double/twin, 2 triple,
3 quadruple, 3 dormitories. Total number of beds: 47
Bathrooms: 8 private, 4 public

Bed only

per person:	£min	£max
Daily		9.00

Bed & breakfast

per person:	£min	£max
Daily	28.00	30.00

Evening meal 1830 (last orders 2230)

🛏🖵♿🖫📺🖫🎱🎾⛳ SP T

Ingram Court ♨
King's College London, Chelsea Campus, 552 Kings Road, London SW10 0AU
Contact: Mrs J M Fennell, King's Campus Vacation Bureau, King's College London, 552 Kings Road, London SW10 0UA
☎ 071-351 6011
Fax 071-352 7376
Telex 8954102 BBS LON G
Student bedrooms in small residences grouped around a quiet courtyard, on a spacious green campus. Other halls of residence available in Westminster, Wandsworth, Champion Hill and the Sloane Square end of the King's Road.
Bedrooms: 107 single,
7 double/twin. Total number of beds: 121
Bathrooms: 30 public

Bed & breakfast

per person:	£min	£max
Daily	15.90	20.00

Parking for 20

Open March-April, July-September, December

🐕🚶♿️🈴🍴📺🛏🍽🅿️🔍🎾🈺

International House Woolwich ⛰

109 Brookhill Road, London
SE18 6RZ
☎ 081-854 1418
Fax 081-855 9257
Contact: Mr B Siderman
*Purpose-built student hostel.
Self-contained flats for
married couples and children.
Full en-suite facilities also
available. Short-term visitor
accommodation available July-
September.*
Bedrooms: 85 single,
21 double/twin. Total
number of beds: 127
Bathrooms: 21 private, 18
public

Bed & breakfast

per person:	£min	£max
Daily	8.29	12.13

Parking for 21
Open April, July-September,
December

🐕🈴🍴📺🛏🍽🛏🎾🈺🍴

International Students Hostel

99 Frognal, London
NW3 6XR
☎ 071-794 6893 & 794
8095
Contact: Sr. P S Taylor
*Only 20 minutes by
underground from central
London. Hampstead Heath
and Hampstead underground
nearby. Budget rates for
students.*
For females only
Minimum age 16
Bedrooms: 17 single,
2 double/twin,
4 dormitories. Total number
of beds: 40
Bathrooms: 14 public

Bed only

per person:	£min	£max
Daily	8.00	14.50

Bed & breakfast

per person:	£min	£max
Daily	8.50	15.00

Evening meal from 1845

🐕🈴🍴📺🛏🍽🍴🎾

John Adams Hall (Institute of Education) ⛰

15-23 Endsleigh Street,
London WC1H 0DH
☎ 071-387 4086
Fax 071-383 0164
Telex 94016519 DICE G
Contact: Ms Sue Waller
*An assembly of Georgian
houses, the hall has retained
its old glory. Close to Euston,*

---

*King's Cross and St. Pancras
stations.*
Bedrooms: 126 single,
21 double/twin, 13 triple.
Total number of beds: 170
Bathrooms: 1 private, 26
public

Bed & breakfast

per person:	£min	£max
Daily	17.00	21.40

Evening meal 1730 (last
orders 1830)
Open January, March-April,
July-September, December
Cards accepted: Access, Visa

🐕🈴🍴📺🛏🍽🛏🍴12-70🎾🈺🍴

Kent House ⛰

325 Green Lanes, London
N4 2ES
☎ 081-802 0800 & 802
9070
Fax 081-802 9070
Contact: The Manager
*Special off-season and weekly
rates for young tourists.
Facilities for self-catering.
Adjacent to Manor House
underground station and 10
minutes from central London.*
Minimum age 16
Bedrooms: 3 single,
13 double/twin,
3 dormitories. Total number
of beds: 34
Bathrooms: 6 public

Bed only

per person:	£min	£max
Daily	10.00	18.00

Bed & breakfast

per person:	£min	£max
Daily	12.50	20.00

Parking for 4

🐕🍴🈴🍴📺🛏🍴🎾🈺

King's Fund College

2 Palace Court, Bayswater,
London W2 4HS
☎ 071-727 0581
Contact: Ms T Thorne
*Management college with
extensive conference and
overnight accommodation
facilities, opposite Kensington
Gardens. Bed only price is
weekend rate and B and B
price is weekday rate, both
based on 2 sharing room.*
Bedrooms: 14 single,
4 double/twin. Total number
of beds: 22
Bathrooms: 18 private

Bed only

per person:	£min	£max
Daily	17.50	

Bed & breakfast

per person:	£min	£max
Daily	30.00	

Lunch available
Evening meal 1900 (last
orders 1945)
Cards accepted: Access, Visa

🐕🍴♿️🍴🈴🍴📺🛏🍴🍴🎾🈺🍴

Lancaster Hall Hotel (Youth Annexe)

35 Craven Terrace,
Lancaster Gate, London
W2 3EL
☎ 071-723 9276
Fax 071-706 2870
Contact: Mr E A Wallis
*Within easy walking distance
of Hyde Park, Kensington
Gardens and Marble Arch.
Close to public transport.*
Bedrooms: 3 single,
7 double/twin, 4 triple,
3 quadruple. Total number
of beds: 41
Bathrooms: 5 public

Bed & breakfast

per person:	£min	£max
Daily	14.00	20.00

Evening meal 1800 (last
orders 2100)
Parking for 13
Cards accepted: Access, Visa,
Switch

🐕🈴🍴📺🛏🍽🛏🍴20-120🎾🍴

Lee Abbey International Students Club

57-67 Lexham Gardens,
London W8 6JJ
☎ 071-373 7242
Fax 071-244 8702
Contact: Miss. J Facey
*A hostel primarily for
international students, run by
a Christian Community. Short
term, non-student visitors
welcome in holiday season.
Lift serving all floors. First
Aid qualified personnel.*
Minimum age 18
Bedrooms: 52 single,
37 double/twin, 8 triple.
Total number of beds: 150
Bathrooms: 19 private, 28
public

Bed & breakfast

per person:	£min	£max
Daily	14.00	21.50

Lunch available
Evening meal 1800 (last
orders 1900)
Parking for 1

🐕🍴♿️🈴🍴📺🛏🍽🛏🍴🎾🍴🈺🍴

London Friendship Centre

Peace Haven, 3 Creswick
Road, London W3 9HE
☎ 081-992 0221
Contact: Mr. P O'Nath
*Comfortable residential hostel
most suitable for groups of*

---

*young people and school
parties, open throughout the
year. Individuals also
welcome.*
Minimum age 12
Bedrooms: 2 single,
6 double/twin, 2 triple,
1 quadruple, 5 dormitories.
Total number of beds: 50
Bathrooms: 5 public

Bed & breakfast

per person:	£min	£max
Daily	9.20	15.00

Lunch available
Evening meal 1700 (last
orders 1900)

🐕🈴🍴📺🛏🍽🛏🍴🎾🈺🍴

Lords Hotel ⛰

20-22 Leinster Square,
London W2 4PR
☎ 071-229 8877
Fax 071-229 8377
Telex 298716 LORDS G
Contact: Mr N G Ladas
*Bed and breakfast
accommodation in central
London. Residents' bar, direct-
dial telephone, radio. Most
rooms with private facilities.*
Bedrooms: 11 single,
28 double/twin,
26 dormitories. Total
number of beds: 145
Bathrooms: 32 private, 17
public

Bed & breakfast

per person:	£min	£max
Daily	14.00	40.00

Cards accepted: Access, Visa,
C.Bl, Diners, Amex, Switch

🐕🍴♿️🈴🍴📺🛏🍴🎾🈺🍴

Newham Youth Trust

Newham Youth Lodge,
315 Roman Rd., East Ham,
London E6 3SQ
Contact: Mr G P Owen, c/-
Ravenhill Centre, Ravenhill
Road, London E13 9BU
☎ Administrative secretary
081-472 4435
Fax 081-470 7302
*Short stay hostel dormitory
accommodation for groups of
12 people or more only (no
individuals please). Bookings
especially welcome from
affiliated members of the
Trust, registered Youth Clubs
and organisations.*
For groups only
Minimum age 10
Bedrooms: 2 double/twin,
4 dormitories. Total number
of beds: 26
Bathrooms: 3 public

Bed only

per person:	£min	£max
Daily		4.50

Parking for 2

🐕11🈴🍴📺🍴🎾

417

LONDON

Continued

O'Callaghan's
205 Earls Court Road,
London SW5 9AN
☎ 071-370 3000 & 081-540 5958
Contact: Mr. B J Browning
Central London low-budget guesthouse for tourists and students. Open all year round.
Minimum age 16
Bedrooms: 4 double/twin, 3 triple, 3 quadruple. Total number of beds: 26
Bathrooms: 3 public
Bed & breakfast

per person:	£min	£max
Daily	10.00	12.00

◨ 📺 🖿 ❧ ✕ 🕪

Passfield Hall ⋀
1 Endsleigh Place, London WC1H 0PW
☎ 071-387 7743 & 387 3584
Contact: Ms. J Martin
University hall of residence with washbasin in all rooms, suitable for families. Central for Oxford Street and the West End.
Bedrooms: 100 single, 34 double/twin, 10 triple.
Total number of beds: 198
Bathrooms: 36 public
Bed & breakfast

per person:	£min	£max
Daily	17.50	21.00

Open March-April, July-September
◔ ◨ ⑤ 🕭 📺 🖿 ❧ ◕

Polytechnic of Central London Halls of Residence ⋀
35 Marylebone Road,
London NW1 5LS
Contact: Ms N Chanson,
309 Regent Street, London W1R 8AL
☎ 071-911 5000
Fax 071-911 5141
Telex 25964
Halls of residence in central London offering well-appointed single and double study bedrooms on self-catering or meals basis. Further 2 residences available in central London near Oxford Circus and Waterloo. For groups only
Minimum age 7
Bedrooms: 220 single. Total number of beds: 220
Bathrooms: 131 public
Bed only

per person:	£min	£max
Daily	13.00	18.00

Bed & breakfast

per person:	£min	£max
Daily	15.00	22.00

Full board

per person:	£min	£max
Weekly	150.00	230.00

Lunch available
Evening meal 1700 (last orders 1900)
Parking for 7
Open April-September
Cards accepted: Access, Visa, Switch
◔ ⑦ 🕭 ⑤ 🕭 📺 🖿, ❧ ⑦ ◕
✕ ◕ 🗶 ◔ ✕ 🕪 SP

Ramsay Hall ⋀
20 Maple Street, London W1P 5GB
☎ 071-387 4537
Contact: Mr Hugh Ewing
Central London location, good value, comfortable accommodation in pleasant surroundings.
Minimum age 14
Bedrooms: 390 single, 10 double/twin. Total number of beds: 416
Bathrooms: 70 public
Bed & breakfast

per person:	£min	£max
Daily	17.50	19.00

Evening meal 1800 (last orders 1900)
Open January, March-April, June-September, December
◔ ◈ 🕭 ⑤ ✕ 🕭 📺 🖿, ❧ ⑦ 15-100 ◕ 🗶

Rywin House
36 Christchurch Avenue,
Brondesbury, London NW6 7BE
☎ 081-459 5434
Contact: Mr. P Horsley
In a quiet residential area with British Rail and London Transport stations nearby. Short walk to local tennis courts.
Bedrooms: 2 single, 1 double/twin, 6 dormitories. Total number of beds: 23
Bathrooms: 3 public
Bed & breakfast

per person:	£min	£max
Daily	14.50	14.50

◨ 🕭 🕭 📺 🖿, ✕ 🕪

Wellington Hall ⋀
King's College London,
71 Vincent Square, London SW1P 2PA
Contact: Mrs. J M Fennell,
King's College London,
552 Kings Road, London SW10 0UA
☎ 071-351 6011
Telex 8954102 BBS LON
Delightfully situated in a quiet, green central London square, combining modern

(continued)
facilities with traditional style. 6 additional campus halls of residence throughout central London.
Bedrooms: 39 single, 43 double/twin. Total number of beds: 125
Bathrooms: 22 public
Bed & breakfast

per person:	£min	£max
Daily	17.50	23.80

Open March-April, July-September, December
⑤ 🕭 📺 🖿, ❧ 🗶 🕪 🕮

MANCHESTER

Greater Manchester
Map ref 4B1

The industrial capital of the North, second only to London as a commercial, financial, banking and newspaper centre. Victorian architecture. 15th C cathedral and the exciting Granada Studios Tour development. Superb shopping centre.
Tourist Information Centre
☎ 061-234 3157/3158 or 061-436 3344.

The Manchester Conference Centre and Hotel
P.O. Box 88, Sackville Street, Manchester M60 1QD
☎ 061-200 4065
Fax 061-200 4090
Contact: Mr A F Yates
Modern year-round conference centre and hotel, in Manchester city centre. Standard and en-suite rooms. Conferences and groups a speciality.
Bedrooms: 1601 single, 182 double/twin. Total number of beds: 1965
Bathrooms: 528 private, 300 public
Bed only

per person:	£min	£max
Daily	12.00	49.50

Bed & breakfast

per person:	£min	£max
Daily	17.00	53.40

Full board

per person:	£min	£max
Weekly	150.00	580.00

Lunch available
Evening meal 1830 (last orders 2100)
Parking for 700
Cards accepted: Access, Visa, Diners, Amex, Switch
◔ 🕭 🕭 ⑤ ✕ 🕭 📺 🖿, ❧ ⑦ 🗶
◕ 🗶 ◕ 🗶 ◕ 🕪 SP

MATFIELD

Kent
Map ref 3B4

Village with Georgian houses, green and pond.

Old Cryals
Cryals Road, Matfield,
Tonbridge TN12 7HN
☎ Brenchley (089 272) 2372
Contact: Mr C Charrington
Hostel-type accommodation for 12, in two rooms for 4 and 8. Comfortable sitting/dining room with microwave oven, TV, freezer, dishwasher. Self-catering only.
Bedrooms: 2 dormitories.
Total number of beds: 12
Bathrooms: 2 public
Bed only

per person:	£min	£max
Daily	5.00	6.00

Parking for 12
Open March-November
◔ ⑤ 🗢 ◔ ◨ 🕭 📺 🖿, ❧ ◕
◔ 🕪 SP

NEWCASTLE UPON TYNE

Tyne and Wear
Map ref 5C2

Commercial and cultural centre of the North East, with a large indoor shopping centre, Quayside market, museums and theatres which offer an annual 6 week season by the Royal Shakespeare Company. Norman castle keep, medieval alleys, old Guildhall.
Tourist Information Centre
☎ 091-261 0691 or 230 0030

Newcastle Polytechnic ⋀
Coach Lane Campus Halls of Residence, Coach Lane,
Newcastle upon Tyne NE7 7XA
Contact: Ms S Cowell,
Newcastle upon Tyne Polytechnic, Elison Building, Ellison Place, Newcastle upon Tyne NE1 8ST
☎ 091-235 8024
Fax 091-235 8017
Accommodation in modern halls of residence, set in pleasant grounds, 3 miles from the city centre. Bed and breakfast with or without evening meal for groups or parties.
Bedrooms: 144 single, 50 double/twin. Total number of beds: 244

Bathrooms: 44 public

Bed only

per person:	£min	£max
Daily	9.10	12.10

Bed & breakfast

per person:	£min	£max
Daily	13.50	17.00

Full board

per person:	£min	£max
Weekly	128.00	232.50

Lunch available
Evening meal 1730 (last orders 1930)
Parking for 200
Open April, July-September

🛏🍴🏧§🖊🏐📺🎞🛥🏹🕯✗

North Eastern YWMCA Hostel

Jesmond House, Clayton Road, Newcastle upon Tyne, Tyne & Wear NE2 1UJ
☎ 091-281 1233
Contact: Mr B Garnon
New, custom-built accommodation in a good residential area with easy access by Metro and bus to the city centre. All bedrooms have wash basins.
Minimum age 18
Bedrooms: 80 single. Total number of beds: 80
Bathrooms: 12 public

Bed & breakfast

per person:	£min	£max
Daily		13.65

Full board

per person:	£min	£max
Weekly		67.65

Parking for 20

§ 🏐📺🎞🛥✗🚲

NEWPORT

Shropshire
Map ref 4A3

Small market town on the Shropshire Union Canal has a wide High Street and a church with some interesting monuments. Newport is close to Aqualate Mere which is the largest lake in Staffordshire.

Edgmond Hall Residential Centre

Edgmond, Newport TF10 8JY
☎ (0952) 810799
Contact: Mr. C B Matthews
Good quality dormitory accommodation suitable for school parties. Available for courses or accommodation only.
For groups only
Minimum age 8

Bedrooms: 3 double/twin, 4 dormitories. Total number of beds: 44
Bathrooms: 9 public

Bed only

per person:	£min	£max
Daily	7.00	8.50

Bed & breakfast

per person:	£min	£max
Daily	12.50	14.00

Full board

per person:	£min	£max
Weekly	95.00	135.00

Lunch available
Parking for 20

🛏8🎿🏐§🖊🏐📺🎞🛥🔍SP🏠

NORWICH

Norfolk
Map ref 3C1

Beautiful cathedral city and county town on the River Wensum with many fine museums and medieval churches. Norman castle, Guildhall and interesting medieval streets. Good shopping centre and market.
Tourist Information Centre
☎ *(0603) 666071 or (accommodation) 761082*

Norwich Y.M.C.A.

48 St. Giles Street, Norwich NR2 1LP
☎ (0603) 620269
Contact: Mr. B Balfour
Comfortable, friendly hostel for long or short stays, in central Norwich and close to shops, theatres and public transport. Snooker, weight-training, gymnasium. Parties welcome.
Minimum age 17
Bedrooms: 75 single, 16 double/twin. Total number of beds: 107
Bathrooms: 17 public

Bed & breakfast

per person:	£min	£max
Daily		12.50

🛏🏐📺🎞🛥🛥✗🚲🏠

Y.W.C.A.

Marjorie Hinde House, 61 Bethel Street, Norwich NR2 1NR
☎ (0603) 625982
Contact: Mrs Sylvia Phillips
Comfortable hostel for long or short stays. Central position near shops, theatres, gardens, library and public transport.
For females only
Bedrooms: 20 single, 7 double/twin. Total number of beds: 34
Bathrooms: 7 public

Bed only

per person:	£min	£max
Daily	7.31	8.77

Full board

per person:	£min	£max
Weekly		34.20	41.00

🛏🍴🏐📺🎞🛥🛥✗🚲

OTTERBURN

Northumberland
Map ref 5B1

Small village set at the meeting of the River Rede with Otter Burn, the site of the Battle of Otterburn in 1388. A peaceful tradition continues in the sale of Otterburn tweeds in this beautiful region, which is ideal for exploring the Border country and the Cheviots.

Otterburn Hall

Otterburn NE19 1HE
☎ (0800) 591527
Fax 091-385 2267
Contact: Mrs K Hutchinson
Family holiday hotel, conference venue and training establishment in 100 acres. Offering special interest holidays. Prices quoted include dinner.
Minimum age 8
Bedrooms: 3 single, 33 double/twin, 16 triple, 7 quadruple, 1 dormitory. Total number of beds: 135
Bathrooms: 27 private, 8 public

Bed & breakfast

per person:	£min	£max
Daily	28.00	33.00

Lunch available
Evening meal 1900 (last orders 1900)
Parking for 40
Cards accepted: Visa

🛏🍴🏧§🖊🏐📺🎞🛥🔍🏹🕯
🏹🔍∪🏐OAP🏐SP🏠

Individual proprietors have supplied all details of accommodation. Although we do check for accuracy, we advise you to confirm the information at the time of booking.

OXFORD

Oxfordshire
Map ref 2C1

Beautiful university town with many ancient colleges, some dating from the 13th C, and numerous buildings of historic and architectural interest. The Ashmolean Museum has outstanding collections. Lovely gardens and meadows with punting on the Cherwell.
Tourist Information Centre
☎ *(0865) 726871*

Hill End Residential and Field Study Centre ⚠

Eynsham Road, Farmoor, Oxford OX2 9NJ
☎ (0865) 863510
Contact: Mrs J Ledger
Residential field study centre on a rural site of special scientific interest within 3 miles of Oxford city centre.
For groups only
Minimum age 3
Bedrooms: 1 double/twin, 2 triple, 1 quadruple, 21 dormitories. Total number of beds: 181
Bathrooms: 8 public

Bed only

per person:	£min	£max
Daily		5.70

Parking for 75

🛏🍴🏐📺🎞🖊🏐🕯🔍∿🔍
✗🏠

St Edmund Hall ⚠

Queens Lane, Oxford OX1 4AR
☎ (0865) 279006 & 279007
Contact: Miss Pauline Linieres
Only surviving medieval hall in Oxford. Oldest Oxford church in grounds, Saxon crypt.
For groups only
Minimum age 18
Bedrooms: 133 single, 40 double/twin, 2 dormitories. Total number of beds: 215
Bathrooms: 2 private, 38 public

Bed & breakfast

per person:	£min	£max
Daily	24.09	29.37

Lunch available
Evening meal 1800 (last orders 1945)
Open January, March-April, June-October, December

🍴🏧§🏐📺🎞🛥🏹12-90
✗🏠

419

PORTSMOUTH & SOUTHSEA

Hampshire
Map ref 2C3

There have been connections with the Navy since early times and the first dock was built in 1194. HMS Victory, Nelson's flagship, is here and Charles Dickens' former home is open to the public. Neighbouring Southsea has a promenade with magnificent views of Spithead.
Tourist Information Centre
☎ *(0705) 832464*

Portsmouth YMCA ⚠

Penny Street, Portsmouth, Hampshire PO1 2NN
☎ (0705) 864341
Contact: Mrs D Wade
Comfortable, reasonably priced accommodation adjacent to beaches and road/rail interchange. Family and youth groups most welcome. Brochure available.
Bedrooms: 80 single, 20 double/twin, 5 dormitories. Total number of beds: 130
Bathrooms: 15 public
Bed & breakfast

per person:	£min	£max
Daily	9.25	10.25

Evening meal 1715 (last orders 1800)
🛏🍴🖥🅂♿🅟📺🖩🗄🏃
🔒✕🐕🆂🅿🎜

PULBOROUGH

West Sussex
Map ref 2D3

Here is Parham, an Elizabethan mansion with unusually tall, mullioned windows and a long gallery measuring 158 ft. The house and the surrounding park and garden can be visited. In the grounds stands the church of St Peter.

Lodge Hill Residential Centre

Watersfield, Pulborough
RH20 1LZ
☎ Bury (West Sussex) (0798) 831411
Contact: The Secretary
Residential centre in South Downs near Pulborough, suitable for courses and conferences. Comfortable accommodation.
For groups only

Minimum age 8
Bedrooms: 2 single, 17 double/twin, 9 triple, 6 dormitories. Total number of beds: 58
Bathrooms: 15 public
Bed & breakfast

per person:	£min	£max
Daily	22.00	28.50

Full board

per person:	£min	£max
Weekly	230.00	280.00

Lunch available
Evening meal 1700 (last orders 2000)
Parking for 40
Open March-May, August-September, December
🛏8🍴🅂♿🅟📺🖩🗄🛡
🔒🔑⛵✕🆂🎜

RAMSGATE

Kent
Map ref 3C3

Popular holiday resort with good sandy beaches. At Pegwell Bay is the replica of a Viking longship. Terminal for car-ferry service to Dunkirk.
Tourist Information Centre
☎ *(0843) 591086*

The Regency Hotel and School of English ⚠

Royal Crescent, Ramsgate
CT11 9PE
☎ Thanet (0843) 591212
Fax (0843) 850035
Telex 96454 REGRAM G
Contact: Miss. J A Beech
Historic building overlooking flowered lawns and sea. Late-night snack bar, bar and discotheque. Indoor pool, sauna, sandy beaches. Very lively young atmosphere.
Minimum age 16
Bedrooms: 29 single, 56 double/twin, 4 dormitories. Total number of beds: 89
Bathrooms: 16 private, 12 public
Bed & breakfast

per person:	£min	£max
Daily	24.00	30.00

Lunch available
🛏🅂♿🅟📺🖩🗄🆂🎜

The colour maps at the back of this guide pinpoint all places with accommodation.

RIPPONDEN

West Yorkshire
Map ref 4B1

Main Calderdale village on the River Ryburn with walks to Ryburn Reservoir and Blackstone Edge Roman Road where part of the Roman pavement is still visible. A pleasant main street of traditional houses leads down to the stocks and there is a spired church and a 16th C packhorse bridge.

Stones Environmental Training Centre

Rochdale Road, Ripponden, Sowerby Bridge HX6 4LA
Contact: Mr. C Haigh, Upper Oakes, Dyson Lane, Ripponden, Sowerby Bridge, West Yorkshire HX6 4JX
☎ Halifax (0422) 824030
Self-catering activity centre for organised groups such as educational, ecclesiastical and uniformed organisations. Based on a former primary school with opportunities for environmental and outdoor pursuits.
For groups only
Bedrooms: 6 dormitories.
Total number of beds: 42
Bathrooms: 4 public
Bed only

per person:	£min	£max
Daily		3.00

Parking for 20
🛏🖥🅂♿🖩🗄🗄🔒✕🎜

RYDAL

Cumbria
Map ref 5A3

Small hamlet next to Rydal Water, a small, beautiful lake sheltered by Rydal Fell. Once the home of William Wordsworth, Rydal Mount is open to the public. It is a good centre for walking and touring.

Rydal Hall ⚠

Rydal, Ambleside LA22 9LX
☎ (053 94) 32050
Contact: Rev. Peter Walker
Groups and individuals are welcome at this central Lakeland mansion run by a small Christian community. Set amidst 30 acres of grounds.
Bedrooms: 10 single, 15 double/twin, 4 triple, 1 quadruple. Total number of beds: 56
Bathrooms: 8 public

Full board

per person:	£min	£max
Weekly	206.50	293.65

🛏♿🅂♿🅟📺🖩🗄🛡🔒⛵✕
✕🎜🐕🎜

SKIPTON

North Yorkshire
Map ref 4B1

Pleasant market town with farming community atmosphere, at gateway to Dales, with a Palladian Town Hall, parish church and fully roofed castle at the top of High Street.
Tourist Information Centre
☎ *(0756) 792809*

Halton Gill Bunk Barn

Halton Gill, Skipton
BD23 5QN
Contact: Mr. & Mrs. J Cowan Manor Farm, Halton Gill, Skipton, North Yorkshire BD23 5QN
☎ Arncliffe (0756) 770241
Accommodation for groups up to 40, particularly walkers. Near the Pennine Way and Dales Way and in the heart of the Yorkshire Dales.
Bedrooms: 2 double/twin, 6 dormitories. Total number of beds: 40
Bathrooms: 4 public
Bed only

per person:	£min	£max
Daily	4.00	6.00

Lunch available
Parking for 15
🛏♿🅂♿🖩🗄🗄✕🎜🐕🎜

SOUTHAMPTON

Hampshire
Map ref 2C3

One of Britain's leading seaports with a long history, now a major container port. In the 18th C it became a fashionable resort with the assembly rooms and theatre. The old Guildhall and the Wool House are now museums. Sections of the medieval wall can still be seen.
Tourist Information Centre
☎ *(0703) 221106*

Southampton YMCA ⚠

George Williams House, Cranbury Place, Southampton SO2 0LG
☎ (0703) 221202
Contact: The Executive Director
Educational groups welcome from home and overseas.

Bookings also welcome from individuals and couples.
Minimum age 10
Bedrooms: 74 single,
4 double/twin. Total number of beds: 82
Bathrooms: 15 public
Bed & breakfast

per person:	£min	£max
Daily	12.00	14.00

🛏🖥Ⅱ🗐📺🎦�e 🛆🎔
📶Ⓣ

SOWERBY BRIDGE

West Yorkshire
Map ref 4B1

Busy little town in the Calder Valley near the Calder Hebble Canal.

Mill Bank Centre ♏

AMIT (Personal and Training Services), Mill Bank, Sowerby Bridge HX6 3DY
☎ Halifax (0422) 824388 & 824472
Contact: Mr J Haymer
Well-equipped residential centre with conference facilities, in a converted chapel overlooking a Pennine conservation village. Centrally heated, with carpets and Continental quilts. Prices vary according to number in group - please ask for details.
For groups only
Minimum age 10
Bedrooms: 1 single,
2 double/twin,
2 dormitories. Total number of beds: 25
Bathrooms: 6 public
Bed & breakfast

per person:	£min	£max
Daily	18.00	

Lunch available
Parking for 10

🛏🛋🖥♿🖥🎦🗐📺Ⅲ🛆
🎔Ⓤ🗙🎦 📶Ⓣ

STOKE ROCHFORD

Lincolnshire
Map ref 3A1

Stoke Rochford Hall ♏

Stoke Rochford, Grantham NG33 5EJ
☎ Great Ponton (047 683) 337
Fax (0476) 83534
Contact: Peter Robinson
Conference centre/hotel based in superb Victorian mansion with excellent communication links. 6 miles south of Grantham within a quarter-of-a-mile of the A1.
Bedrooms: 86 single,
86 double/twin. Total number of beds: 213

Bathrooms: 58 private, 10 public
Bed & breakfast

per person:	£min	£max
Daily	52.85	73.45

Parking for 500
Cards accepted: Access, Visa, Diners, Amex

🛏Ⓐ🖥🎦📺Ⅲ🛆🎦🗙�e
🎦🎦🎔ⓊⒻ🗙🎦🎦📶

STOKE-ON-TRENT

Staffordshire
Map ref 4B2

Famous for its pottery. Factories of several famous makers, including Josiah Wedgwood, can be visited. The City Museum has one of the finest pottery and porcelain collections in the world.
Tourist Information Centre ☎ (0782) 411222 or 284600.

Staffordshire University ♏

College Road, Stoke-on-Trent ST4 2DE
☎ (0782) 744585
Contact: Mr. M J Howells
Student village within 5 minutes' walk of Stoke railway station and with easy access to the Potteries. Good sports facilities. Also a student hall of residence on the outskirts of Stafford.
Minimum age 7
Bedrooms: 713 single,
32 double/twin. Total number of beds: 777
Bathrooms: 176 public
Bed only

per person:	£min	£max
Daily		15.00

Bed & breakfast

per person:	£min	£max
Daily		17.00

Parking for 800
Open July-September

🛏Ⓐ🖥♿🎦🗐🖥Ⅲ🛆
🎦20-350🗙🎦🔌�e🗙🗐Ⓣ

Individual proprietors have supplied all details of accommodation. Although we do check for accuracy, we advise you to confirm the information at the time of booking.

STRATFORD-UPON-AVON

Warwickshire
Map ref 2B1

Famous as Shakespeare's home town, Stratford's many attractions include his birthplace, New Place where he died, the Royal Shakespeare Theatre and Gallery, 'The World of Shakespeare' audio-visual theatre and Hall's Croft (his daughter's house).
Tourist Information Centre ☎ (0789) 293127.

Stratford-upon-Avon Youth Hostel

Hemmingford House, Alveston, Stratford-upon-Avon CV37 7RG
☎ (0789) 297093
Fax (0789) 205513
Contact: The Warden
Large house in attractive grounds, in village 2 miles from Stratford-upon-Avon. Convenient for visits to Shakespeare's birthplace and other famous properties including Royal Shakespeare Theatre and Warwick Castle.
Minimum age 5
Bedrooms: 2 double/twin,
5 quadruple, 17 dormitories.
Total number of beds: 154
Bathrooms: 9 public
Bed only

per person:	£min	£max
Daily	5.50	8.25

Bed & breakfast

per person:	£min	£max
Daily	6.90	10.20

Lunch available
Evening meal 1700 (last orders 2000)
Parking for 20
Cards accepted: Access, Visa

🛏Ⓐ🖥🖊🗐🖥🎦Ⅲ🎔�e
🗙🗐Ⓣ

WICK

Avon
Map ref 2A2

Wick Court Centre

Wick, Bristol BS15 5RB
☎ Bristol (0272) 373562
Contact: Mr N Chiswell Jones
Low cost accommodation especially suitable for young people. Minimum group size 25. Beautiful surroundings. Adventure playground, hard tennis court, river.
For groups only
Bedrooms: 2 double/twin,
13 dormitories. Total number of beds: 58

Bathrooms: 1 private, 3 public
Bed only

per person:	£min	£max
Daily	7.05	7.05

Full board

per person:	£min	£max
Weekly	105.00	113.00

Parking for 15

🛏🖥🗐🖥🎦Ⅲ🛆🎔�e
🔌🎦

WOLVERHAMPTON

West Midlands
Map ref 4B3

Modern industrial town with a long history, a fine parish church and an excellent art gallery. There are several places of interest in the vicinity including Moseley Old Hall and Wightwick Manor with its William Morris influence.
Tourist Information Centre ☎ (0902) 312051

University of Wolverhampton ♏

Molineux Street, Wolverhampton WV1 1SB
Contact: Mr. W Wilson, Residential Services Office, The Bungalow, Deanery Row, Wolverhampton WV1 1SB
☎ (0902) 321274
Fax (0902) 321267
Telex Polwol 336301
The university offers single study bedroom accommodation on four sites, in Wolverhampton for 600, at Compton Park, Wolverhampton for 120, at Dudley for 360 and at Walsall for 350.
Bedrooms: 1418 single,
20 double/twin. Total number of beds: 1458
Bathrooms: 130 public
Bed only

per person:	£min	£max
Daily		12.50

Bed & breakfast

per person:	£min	£max
Daily		16.75

Lunch available
Evening meal 1700 (last orders 2000)
Parking for 1000

🛏🖥🗐🖥🎦Ⅲ🛆🎦🎔10-
375�e🎦🎦�e🗙

The symbols are explained on the flap inside the back cover.

421

YORK

North Yorkshire
Map ref 4C1

Ancient walled city nearly 2000 years old containing many well-preserved medieval buildings. Its Minster has over 100 stained glass windows. Attractions include Castle Museum, National Railway Museum, Jorvik Viking Centre and York Dungeon.
Tourist Information Centre ☎ (0904) 621756 or 643700 or 620557

Fairfax House ⋀

99 Heslington Road, York
YO1 5BJ
☎ (0904) 432095
Contact: Mrs. A E Glover
Student residence in quiet spacious grounds, within walking distance of town centre. Reduced rates for children under twelve and senior citizens.

Bedrooms: 93 single. Total number of beds: 93
Bathrooms: 14 public

Bed & breakfast

per person:	£min	£max
Daily	13.00	17.00

Open March-April, July-September

🐕 🛁 🖊 ⓤⓛ ⋀ ⓉⓋ 🏨 ☕ 🍴 ♿

University College of Ripon and York Saint John ⋀

Lord Mayor's Walk, York
YO3 7EX
☎ (0904) 656771 & 656771
Fax (0904) 612512
Contact: Mrs A Cheetham
Well-appointed college accommodation overlooking the city walls. Emphasis on standards of cuisine; bars, TV, swimming pool, squash and tennis. Full audio-visual service. Suitable for holidays or conferences.

Bedrooms: 281 single, 19 double/twin. Total number of beds: 300
Bathrooms: 52 public

Bed only

per person:	£min	£max
Daily	18.50	18.50

Bed & breakfast

per person:	£min	£max
Daily	21.37	21.37

Full board

per person:	£min	£max
Weekly	271.25	271.25

Lunch available
Evening meal from 1800
Parking for 180
Open January, March-April, June-September, December

🐕 🛁 🖊 🅢 🖍 ⋀ ⓉⓋ 🏨 ☕ 🍴 ♿ ✿ 🔍 🎿 🎣 🏓

York Youth Hotel ⋀

11-13 Bishophill Senior, York YO1 1EF
☎ (0904) 625904 & 630613
Fax (0904) 612494
Contact: Ms Maureen Sellers
Dormitory-style accommodation in the city

centre. Private rooms, TV lounge, snack shop, evening meals, packed lunches, games room, residential licence, disco and 24-hour service.
Minimum age 2
Bedrooms: 7 single, 14 double/twin, 1 triple, 4 quadruple, 5 dormitories.
Total number of beds: 120
Bathrooms: 8 public

Bed only

per person:	£min	£max
Daily	7.00	12.30

Bed & breakfast

per person:	£min	£max
Daily	9.30	14.60

Full board

per person:	£min	£max
Weekly	105.00	148.00

Evening meal 1700 (last orders 1900)
Cards accepted: Access, Visa

🐕 🛁 🖊 🅢 🖍 ⋀ ⓉⓋ 🏨 ☕ 🍴 🎣 🆂🅿 🏠 🆃

Key to symbols

Information about many of the services and facilities at establishments listed in this guide is given in the form of symbols. The key to these symbols is inside the back cover flap. You may find it helpful to keep the flap open when referring to the entry listings.

Advertisers

When requesting further information from advertisers in this guide, you may find it helpful to use the advertisement enquiry coupons which can be found towards the end of the guide. These should be cut out and mailed direct to the companies in which you are interested. Do remember to include your name and address.

Information Pages

General advice and information

MAKING A BOOKING

When enquiring about accommodation, as well as checking prices and other details you will need to state your requirements clearly and precisely – for example:

1. Arrival and departure dates with acceptable alternatives if appropriate.
2. The accommodation you need. For example: double room with twin beds, private bath and WC.
3. The terms you want. For example: room only; bed & breakfast; bed, breakfast and evening meal (half board); bed, breakfast, lunch and evening meal (full board).
4. If you will have children with you give their ages, state whether you would like them to share your room or have an adjacent room and mention any special requirements such as a cot.
5. Tell the management about any particular requirements such as a ground floor room or special diet.

Misunderstandings can occur very easily over the telephone so we recommend that all bookings should be confirmed in writing if time permits.

When first enquiring in writing about a reservation you may find it helpful to use the booking enquiry coupons (pages xxx–xxx) which can be cut out and mailed to the establishment(s) of your choice.

Remember to include your name and address and please enclose a stamped and addressed envelope – or an international reply coupon if writing from outside Britain.

Please note that the English Tourist Board does not make reservations. You should address your enquiry direct to the establishment.

DEPOSITS AND ADVANCE PAYMENTS

For reservations made weeks or months ahead a deposit is usually payable and the amount will vary according to the length of booking, time of year, number in party and so on. The deposit will be deducted from the total bill at the end of your stay.

More and more establishments, particularly larger hotels in big towns, now require payment for the room on arrival if a prior reservation has not been made – especially if you arrive late and/or with little luggage. Regrettably this practice has become necessary because of the number of guests who have left without paying their bills.

If you are asked to pay on arrival it may be advisable to see your room first to ensure that it meets your requirements.

CANCELLATIONS

When you accept offered accommodation, on the telephone or in writing, you are entering into a legally binding contract with the proprietor. This means that if you cancel a reservation, fail to take up the accommodation or leave prematurely the proprietor may be entitled to compensation if the accommodation cannot be re-let for all or a good part of the booked period. If a deposit has been paid it is likely to be forfeited and an additional payment may be demanded.

However, no such claim can be made by the proprietor until after the booked period, during which time every effort should be made to re-let the accommodation. Any circumstances which might lead to repudiation of a contract may also need to be taken into account and, in the case of a dispute, legal advice should be sought by both parties.

It is therefore in your own interests to advise the management immediately if you have to change your travel plans, cancel a booking or leave prematurely.

Travel and holiday insurance protection policies are available quite cheaply and will safeguard you in the event of your having to cancel or curtail your holiday. Your insurance company or travel agent can advise you further on this. Some hotels also offer insurance schemes.

ARRIVING LATE

If you will be arriving late in the evening it is advisable to say so at the time of booking; if you are delayed on your way, a telephone call to inform the management that you will be late might help to avoid problems on arrival.

SERVICE CHARGES AND TIPPING

Many establishments now levy a service charge automatically and if so this fact must be stated clearly in the offer of accommodation at the time of booking. If the offer is then accepted by you the service charge becomes part of the contract.

At establishments where a service charge of this kind is made there is no need for you to give tips to the staff unless some

AH, YES, A TIP – NEVER PLANT YOUR GERANIUMS IN NOVEMBER

particular or exceptional service has been rendered. In the case of meals the usual amount is 10% of the total bill.

TELEPHONE CALL CHARGES

There is no restriction on the charges that can be made by hotels for telephone calls made through their switchboard or via direct-dial telephones in bedrooms. Unit charges are frequently considerably higher than British Telecom's standard charges. Hoteliers claim that they need to charge higher rates to defray the cost of providing the service.

Although it is a condition of a national Crown rating that a hotel's unit charges are displayed alongside telephones, it is not always easy to see how these compare with the standard charges. Before using a hotel telephone for long-distance calls within Britain or overseas, you may wish to ask how the charges compare.

SECURITY OF VALUABLES

Property of value may be deposited for safe-keeping with the proprietor or manager of the establishment who should give you a receipt and will then generally be liable for the value of the property in the case of loss. For your peace of mind we advise you to adopt this procedure. In establishments which do not accept articles for safe custody, you are advised to keep valuables under your personal supervision.

You may find that proprietors of some establishments disclaim, by notice, liability for property brought on to their premises by a guest; however, if a guest engages overnight accommodation in a hotel the proprietor is only permitted to restrict his liability to the minimum imposed upon him under the Hotel Proprietors Act, 1956. Under this Act, a proprietor of a hotel is liable for the value of the loss or damage to any property (other than a motor

car or its contents) of a guest who has engaged overnight accommodation, but if the proprietor has a notice in the form prescribed by that Act, liability is limited to the sum of £50 in respect of one article and a total of £100 in the case of any one guest.

These limits do not apply, however, if you have deposited the property with the proprietor for safe-keeping or if the property is lost through the default, neglect or wilful act of the proprietor or his staff.

To be effective, any notice intended to disclaim or restrict liability must be prominently displayed in the reception area of, or in the main entrance to, the premises.

CODE OF CONDUCT

All establishments appearing in this guide have agreed to observe the following Code of Conduct:
1. To ensure high standards of courtesy and cleanliness; catering and service appropriate to the type of establishment.
2. To describe fairly to all visitors and prospective visitors the amenities, facilities and services provided by the establishment, whether by advertisement, brochure, word of mouth or any other means. To allow visitors to see accommodation, if requested,

before booking.
3. To make clear to visitors exactly what is included in all prices quoted for accommodation, meals and refreshments, including service charges, taxes and other surcharges. Details of charges, if any, for heating or for additional services or facilities available should also be made clear.
4. To adhere to, and not to exceed, prices current at time of occupation for accommodation or other services.
5. To advise visitors at the time of booking, and subsequently of any change, if the accommodation offered is in an unconnected annexe, or similar, or by boarding out, and to indicate the location of such accommodation and any difference in comfort and amenities from accommodation in the main establishment.
6. To give each visitor, on request, details of payments due and a receipt if required.
7. To deal promptly and courteously with all enquiries, requests, reservations, correspondence and complaints from visitors.
8. To allow an English Tourist Board representative reasonable access to the establishment, on request, to confirm that the Code of Conduct is being observed.

COMMENTS AND COMPLAINTS

Accommodation establishments have a number of legal and statutory responsibilities to their customers in areas such as the provision of information on prices, the provision of adequate fire precautions and the safeguarding of valuables. Like other businesses, they must also meet the requirements of the Trade Descriptions Acts 1968 and 1972 when describing and offering accommodation and facilities. All establishments appearing in this guide have declared that they fulfil all applicable statutory obligations.

The establishment descriptions and other details appearing in this guide have been provided by proprietors and they have paid for their entries to appear.

The English Tourist Board cannot guarantee the accuracy of the information in this guide and accepts no responsibility for any error or misrepresentation. All liability for loss, disappointment, negligence or other damage caused by reliance on the information contained in this guide, or in the event of bankruptcy or liquidation or cessation of trade of any company, individual or firm mentioned, is hereby excluded. Prices and other details should always be carefully checked at the time of booking.

We naturally hope that you will not have any cause for complaint but problems do inevitably occur from time to time. If you are dissatisfied, make your complaint to the management at the time of the incident. This gives the management an opportunity to take action at once to investigate and to put things right without delay. The longer a complaint is left the more difficult it is to deal with effectively.

In certain circumstances the English Tourist Board may look into complaints. However, the Board has no statutory control over establishments or their methods of operation and cannot become involved in legal or contractual matters.

We find it very helpful to receive comments about establishments in "Where to Stay" and suggestions on how to improve the guide. We would like to hear from you. Our address is on page 16.

Key to symbols

Information about many of the services and facilities at establishments listed in this guide is given in the form of symbols. The key to these symbols is inside the back cover flap. You may find it helpful to keep the flap open when referring to the entry listings.

About the guide entries

LOCATIONS

LOCATIONS

Establishments are listed in this guide under the name of the place where they are situated or, in the case of isolated spots in the countryside, under the nearest village or town. Place names are listed alphabetically within each regional section together with the county name.

Map references are given against each place name. These refer to the colour maps at the back of the guide. The first figure is the map number; the letter and figure which follow indicate the grid reference on the map. Some entries were included just before the guide went to press and therefore may not appear on the maps.

ADDRESSES

County names are not normally repeated in the entries for each establishment but you should ensure that you use the full postal address and post code when writing.

TELEPHONE NUMBERS

The telephone number, exchange name (where this differs from the name of the town under which the establishment is listed) and STD code (in brackets) are given immediately below the establishment address in the listings pages of this guide. The STD code applies to calls made anywhere in the UK except for local calls.

PRICES

The prices appearing in this publication will serve as a general guide, but we strongly advise you to check them at the time of booking. This information was supplied to us by proprietors in the summer of 1992 and changes may have occurred since the guide went to press.

Prices are shown in pounds sterling and include Value Added Tax if applicable.

Some, but not all, establishments include a service charge in their

standard tariff so this should also be checked at the time of booking.

There are many different ways of quoting prices for accommodation and in order to make this as clear as possible and provide a basis for comparison we have adopted a standardised approach.

For example, we show:
1. Bed and breakfast. Price for overnight accommodation with breakfast – single room and double room.

The double room price is for two people. If a double room is occupied by one person there is normally a reduction in the quoted tariff, but some establishments may charge the full rate.
2. Half board. Price for room, breakfast and evening meal, per person per day and per person per week.

Some establishments provide a continental breakfast only in the quoted tariff and may make an extra charge for full English breakfast.

There is a statutory requirement for establishments which have at least four bedrooms, or eight beds, to display overnight accommodation charges in the reception area or at the entrance. This is to ensure that prospective guests can obtain adequate information about prices before taking up accommodation. When you arrive it is in your own interests to check prices and what they include.

A reduced price is often quoted for children, especially when sharing a room with their parents. Some establishments, however, charge the full price when a child occupies a room which might otherwise have been let at the full rate to an adult.

The upper age limit for reductions for children may vary according to the establishment and should therefore be checked at the time of booking.

Prices often vary according to the time of year and may be substantially lower outside the peak holiday weeks. Many hotels and other establishments offer special "package" rates (for example, fully inclusive weekend rates) particularly in the autumn, winter and spring.

Further details of bargain packages can be obtained from the establishments themselves or from the English Tourist Board and England's Regional Tourist Boards. Your local travel agent may also have information about these packages and can help you make bookings.

BATHROOMS

Each accommodation entry shows the number of private bathrooms available, the number of public bathrooms and the number of private showers. The term "private bathroom" means a bath and/or shower plus a WC en suite with the bedroom or a bathroom with bath and/or shower plus a WC solely for the occupant of one bedroom; "private shower" means a shower en suite with the

bedroom but no WC.

Public bathrooms are normally equipped with a bath and sometimes also a shower attachment. Some establishments, however, have showers only. If the availability of a bath is an important factor, this should be checked before booking.

MEALS

Where an establishment serves evening meals, the starting time and last orders time are shown in each entry. At some smaller establishments you may be asked at breakfast time or midday whether you will require a meal that evening. So, the last orders time for an evening meal could be, say, 0930 or 1330.

Although the accommodation prices shown in each entry are for bed and breakfast and/or half board, many establishments also offer luncheon facilities and this is indicated by the words "Lunch available".

OPENING PERIODS

Except where an opening period is shown (e.g. Open March–October), the establishment should be open throughout the year.

SYMBOLS

Information about many of the services and facilities available at establishments is given at the end of each entry in the form of symbols.

The key to these symbols can be found inside the back cover flap.

You may find it helpful to fold out the flap when referring to the entries.

ALCOHOLIC DRINKS

Alcoholic drinks are available at all types of accommodation listed in this guide unless the symbol UL appears. However, the licence to serve drinks may be restricted, for example to diners only, so you may wish to check this when enquiring about accommodation.

SMOKING

Many establishments offer facilities for non-smokers, ranging from no-smoking bedrooms and lounges to a no-smoking area of the restaurant/dining room. Some establishments prefer not to accommodate smokers and in such cases the establishment description makes this clear.

PETS

Many establishments will accept guests with pets but we advise you to confirm this at the time of booking when you should also enquire about any extra charges and any restrictions on movement within the establishment. Some establishments will not accept dogs in any circumstances and these are marked with the symbol 🐾.

Visitors from overseas should not bring pets of any kind into Britain unless they are prepared for the animals to go into lengthy quarantine. Owing to the continuing threat of rabies, penalties for ignoring the regulations are extremely severe.

CREDIT/CHARGE CARDS

Indicated immediately above the line of symbols at the end of each accommodation entry are credit/charge cards that are accepted by the establishment. However, you are advised to confirm this at the time you make a booking if you intend to pay by this method. The abbreviations are:

Access – Access/Eurocard/Mastercard

Visa – Visa/Barclaycard
C.Bl – Carte Blanche
Diners – Diners
Amex – American Express
Switch – Direct debit card

Where payment for the accommodation is made by credit card, proprietors may charge a higher rate than for payment by cash or cheque. The difference is to cover the percentage paid by the proprietor to the credit card company.

Not all proprietors make this additional charge but if you intend to pay by credit card, it is worth asking whether it would be cheaper to pay by cash or cheque.

When making a booking by telephone you may be asked to give your credit card number as "confirmation". You should note that the proprietor may charge your credit card account if you cancel the booking. If this is the policy, it must be made clear to you at the time you make the booking.

CONFERENCES AND GROUPS

Establishments which can cater for conferences and meetings have been marked with the symbol ♟; figures in brackets after this symbol indicate the number of delegates which can be accepted in the smallest and largest rooms. Rates are often negotiable and the price may be affected by a number of factors such as the time of year, number of people and any special requirements stipulated by the organiser.

National Crown Scheme

The National Tourist Boards in Britain operate a classification and grading scheme for all types of serviced accommodation, including hotels, motels, guesthouses, inns, B&Bs and farmhouses.

The purpose of the scheme is to identify and promote those establishments that the public can use with confidence. The system of facility classification and optional quality grading also acknowledges those that provide a wider range of facilities and services and higher quality standards.

Over 17,000 establishments are inspected under the scheme and offer the reassurance of a national Crown rating. The range of facilities and services provided is indicated by "Listed" or One to Five Crown symbols.

To help you find accommodation that offers even higher standards than those required for a simple Crown rating, there are four levels of quality grading, using the terms **Approved, Commended, Highly Commended** and **De Luxe.**
Establishments that apply for optional quality grading are subject to a more detailed inspection that assesses the quality standard of the facilities and services provided.

The initial inspection invariably involves a Tourist Board inspector staying overnight, as a normal guest, until the bill is paid the following morning.

The quality assessment includes such aspects as warmth of welcome and efficiency of service, as well as the standard of the furnishings, fittings and decor.

The standard of meals and their presentation is also taken into account. Everything that impinges on the experience of a guest is included in the assessment.

Tourist Board inspectors receive careful training to enable them to apply the quality standards consistently and fairly. Only those facilities and services that are provided are assessed, and due consideration is given to the style and nature of the establishment.

B&Bs, farmhouses and guesthouses are not expected to operate in the style of large city centre hotels, and vice versa. This means that all types of establishment, whatever their classification, can achieve a high quality grade if the facilities and services they provide, however limited in range, are to a high quality standard.

The quality grade that is awarded to an establishment is a reflection of the overall standard, taking everything into account. It is a balanced view of what is provided and, as such, cannot acknowledge individual areas of excellence.

Quality grades are not intended to indicate value for money. A high quality product can still be over-priced. A product of modest quality, if offered at a low price, can still represent good value.

The information provided by the combination of the classification and quality grade will enable you to determine for yourself what represents good value for money.

The quality grades apply to all the Crown bands. So, for example, a Listed or One Crown B&B or guesthouse can be Highly Commended, or even De Luxe, if its facilities and services, although limited in range, are provided to an exceptionally high quality standard.

The national Crown ratings that

appear in the accommodation entries in this "Where to Stay" guide were correct at the time of going to press.

Entries which do not bear a Crown rating may have applied for inspection but had not been inspected at the time of going to press.

What follows is a guide to the facilities and services you may expect to find at accommodation establishments with national ratings from Listed to Five Crown. Further information is available from the English Tourist Board (address on page 16), from one of the Regional Tourist Boards or from any Tourist Information Centre.

General requirements

All establishments are required to fulfil their statutory obligations, including the requirements of the Fire Precautions Act 1971 (if applicable), the Price Display Orders 1977 and 1979 (if applicable), the provisions of the Food Safety Act 1990 (if applicable) and to have public liability insurance.

All buildings, their fixtures, furnishings, fittings and decor must be maintained in sound and clean condition and be fit for the purposes intended.

LISTED
Bedrooms
1. Internal lock, bolt or equivalent on bedroom door.
2. Adequate measures to provide for the security of guests' property.
3. Reasonable free space for movement and for easy access to beds, doors and drawers. Recommended minimum floor areas, excluding private bath or shower areas, are: 60 sq.ft. single bedrooms, 90 sq.ft. double bedrooms, 110 sq.ft. twin bedded rooms. Family rooms: 30 sq.ft. plus 60 sq.ft. for each double bed plus 40 sq.ft. for each adult single bed plus 20 sq.ft. for each cot.

4. Minimum bed sizes (except for children's beds):
   single beds 6' x 2'6"
   double beds 6' x 4'
5. All beds with secure headboard or equivalent.
6. Mattresses in sound condition and either sprung interior, foam or similar quality.
7. Clean bedding and in sufficient quantity, with bed linen changed for every new guest and at least once a week. Bed linen other then nylon available on request.

A BOTTLE OF CHAMPAGNE, A POT OF CAVIARE AND A MINK HOT WATER BOTTLE...

Room Service

8. Beds made daily and the bedrooms cleaned daily.
9. Clean hand towel for every new guest and changed as required. Bath towels available on request.
10. Fresh soap provided for each new letting.
11. At least one external window and adequate ventilation. Opaque curtains or blinds on all windows.
12. Minimum lighting levels of 100 watts in single bedrooms and 150 watts in double bedrooms. Switches for room light by the door and bed or alternatively a separate bedside light. All bulbs, unless decorative, covered or with shades.

13. Carpet or bedside rugs or mats.
14. Wardrobe or clothes hanging space (with four hangers per person).
15. Dressing table or equivalent with mirror adjacent, bedside table or equivalent, adequate drawer space.
16. One chair or equivalent.
17. Waste paper container, ashtray (where smoking permitted), one drinking tumbler per guest.
18. A 13 amp socket or adaptor, electric razor point (or adaptor available).
19. Adequate heating available at no extra charge.
20. Access to establishment and bedrooms at all times for guests, unless any restrictions previously notified.

Bathrooms
1. At least one bathroom, adequately ventilated and equipped with:
◆ bath or shower
◆ wash handbasin and mirror (if any bedrooms without a wash handbasin)
◆ soap available at all reasonable times
◆ bathmat changed daily (in the case of private bathrooms/en-suite, the bathmat should be changed for every new letting and as required by guests).
2. At least one bathroom available at all reasonable times for every 10 resident guests (or for every 15 resident guests if washbasins in every bedroom) other than guests with private/en-suite bathrooms.
3. All bathrooms adequately heated.
4. Hot water available at all reasonable times.
5. No extra charge for baths and showers.

WCs
1. At least one WC, adequately ventilated, for every 10 resident guests (other than guests in bedrooms with private WC).
2. Toilet paper and sanitary disposal bin in each WC.

General

1. Provision of cooked breakfast (unless continental breakfast only advertised).

2. Dining/breakfast room (unless meals are served only in bedrooms).

3. Public areas well lit for safety and comfort, adequately heated and cleaned daily.

ONE CROWN

In a One Crown establishment you will find all the facilities and services required for "Listed" plus the following enhancements:

Single and double beds will be larger and nylon bed linen will not be used.

There will be a washbasin, with hot and cold running water at all reasonable times, either in the bedroom or in a private bathroom and there will be a mirror with light adjacent to or above the washbasin.

You will enjoy the comfort of at least one chair or equivalent per guest, with a minimum of two in family rooms. You will have access to your bedroom at all times.

At least one bathroom, with bath or shower, will be provided for every 10 resident guests – and at least one bathroom for the sole use of guests. There will be at least one WC for every 8 resident guests. Access to the bathrooms and WCs from bedrooms will not be through such areas as reception and lounge.

You will find a lounge or foyer area with an adequate number of easy chairs and you will have access at all reasonable times. A cooked breakfast will be available.

There will be a reception facility (or bell to call for attention), you will have use of a telephone and tourist information will be available.

TWO CROWN

A Two Crown establishment meets all the requirements of Listed and One Crown classifications and offers several additional comforts and services. All, by the end of 1993,

will have at least some rooms with a private bath or shower and WC.

The dining/breakfast room will be separate from the lounge unless meals are served only in the bedrooms. You can enjoy early morning tea/coffee in your bedroom – served on request unless there are beverage-making facilities in the bedroom. You may order a hot beverage in the evening, again available on request unless there are facilities in the bedroom.

There may be alarm clocks in bedrooms or else you can request an early morning call. If there is no TV in your room, you can be sure there will be a colour TV in the lounge, always provided that the establishment is in a signal reception area.

Double beds will have bedside lights or a single bedhead light, will have access from both sides and there will be a bedside table or equivalent for each person. Single beds will have a bedside or bedhead light. You will also find an electric razor point near a mirror and light.

You can request assistance with your luggage when you check in and check out.

THREE CROWN

If you require your own bath or shower with WC en-suite, the chances are you can arrange this at a Three Crown establishment because at least 33% (50% by the end of 1993) of the bedrooms have these facilities.

You will find an easy chair in your bedroom plus an additional chair if you have booked a twin or double room. There will also be a full-length mirror, luggage stand and fixed heating with automatic and individual control.

Tea/coffee-making facilities will be provided in the bedrooms on request (unless 24-hour room service is offered). Resident guests can also obtain a hot evening meal while, for early departures in the morning, a continental breakfast will be provided on request.

Should you need any assistance, you can talk to the staff or proprietor who will be available throughout the day.

You can also request a hairdryer, iron and ironing board and you will find shoe-cleaning facilities provided. A public telephone will be available unless there are direct-dial telephones

in all the bedrooms.

You will have access to the establishment and to your bedroom at all times.

FOUR CROWN

If Three Crown facilities are not enough, why not book into a Four Crown establishment and enjoy even more?

For instance, 75% (90% by the end of 1993) of all bedrooms have a private bath or shower and WC en-suite. You can relax in your room and watch colour TV or listen to the radio – and your room telephone will enable you to make external calls.

There will be a sitting area quite separate from a bar, TV lounge or games area.

If dining in, you will be able to invite non-resident guests (providing they are pre-booked) and you will be offered a selection of wines and a choice of dishes for each course; last orders will be 20.30hrs or later.

You'll be able to call room service for continental breakfast, drinks and light snacks between 07.00 and 23.00hrs while lounge service of drinks and snacks will

be available until midnight.

If the establishment has four or more floors, a passenger lift will ease the upward journey.

Writing tables will be available if comparable facilities are not available in bedrooms and additional facilities like laundry service, message-taking, newspapers and toiletries will be available on request.

You will find reception staff on duty during the day and evening while the proprietor and/or staff will be on site and on call 24 hours a day.

FIVE CROWN

If you check into a Five Crown establishment, you can expect the most of everything. Every facility of establishments up to the Four Crown classification will be there to enjoy – plus a few more.

Every bedroom will have private bath, fixed shower attachment and WC en suite. A bathsheet will be provided for each occupant and toiletries will be on hand in the bathroom.

There will be a writing table or equivalent with seat and the

direct-dial telephone will be capable of being used at both writing table and bed.

If your clothes need pressing, you can summon a valet and also avail yourself of the 24-hour return service for laundry and dry cleaning (except at weekends).

Room service of hot meals is assured from breakfast time to midnight while hot and cold snacks and drinks will be available at any time. If you decide to take breakfast in the restaurant, you can be served at the table and will be offered a choice of hot and cold dishes.

You will benefit from an all-night lounge service, there will be a night porter on duty and a shoe-cleaning service.

The restaurant will be open for breakfast, lunch and dinner and it will offer a wide selection of wines and dishes, with last orders for dinner at 21.00hrs or later.

Additionally, according to the nature of the establishment, you may find extra features, such as a cocktail bar, shop, hairdresser's, leisure facilities, secretarial services, etc.

HENRY VIII
ELIZABETH I
CHARLES II
GEORGE IV
AND
QUEEN
VICTORIA
ALL SLEPT
HERE

IT'S A FIVE CROWN!

WHERE TO STAY

National Accessible Scheme for Wheelchair Users

Throughout England, the Tourist Boards are inspecting all types of places to stay, on holiday or business, that provide accessible accommodation for wheelchair users and others who may have difficulty walking. Those that meet the criteria will display the new "Accessible" symbol at their premises and in their advertising – so look for the symbol when choosing where to stay.

All the places that display the "Accessible" symbol have been inspected by a Tourist Board inspector.

The criteria the Tourist Boards have adopted do not, necessarily, conform to British Standards or to Building Regulations. They reflect what the boards understand to be acceptable to meet the practical needs of wheelchair users.

The criteria may, in some cases, not be ideal, but the boards have been assured that wheelchair users would prefer to have a wider choice of places to stay than to be restricted to those, relatively few, places that make ideal provision for their needs.

The tourist boards recognise three categories of "Accessibility":

CATEGORY 1 – Accessible to all wheelchair users including those travelling independently;

CATEGORY 2 – Accessible to a wheelchair user with assistance;

CATEGORY 3 – Accessible to a wheelchair user able to walk short distances and up at least 3 steps.

At the moment the Tourist Boards are concentrating their inspections on hotels, guesthouses, inns, B&Bs, farmhouse accommodation and self-catering holiday homes. There are plans to extend the scheme to holiday caravan parks and visitor attractions in 1994.

The "Accessible" symbol will begin to appear at more and more establishments around the country during 1993 so please look out for it when touring. If you need information on establishments which meet the criteria before setting out on a trip, then contact a Tourist Information Centre in the area you are travelling to.

If you have special needs of any kind, we strongly recommend that you make sure these can be met by an establishment before you confirm your booking.

* The National Accessible Scheme forms part of the Tourism for All Campaign that is being promoted by all three national Tourist Boards. Additional help and guidance on finding suitable holiday accommodation can be obtained from:
Holiday Care Service
2 Old Bank Chambers, Station Road, Horley, Surrey RH6 9HW
Tel: (0293) 774535
Fax: (0293) 784647
Minicom: (0293) 776943 (24-hour answering)

What's on in England 1993

This is a selection of the many cultural, sporting and other events that will be taking place in England during 1993. Dates marked with an asterisk (✳) were provisional at the time of going to press. For details of local events please enquire at the local Tourist Information Centre.

JANUARY 1993

6–31 January
HOLIDAY ON ICE '93
Brighton Centre, Kings Road, Brighton, East Sussex

7–10 January
INTERNATIONAL HOLIDAY AND TRAVEL FAIR
National Exhibition Centre, Birmingham, West Midlands

7–17 January
LONDON INTERNATIONAL BOAT SHOW
Earl's Court Exhibition Centre, Warwick Road, London SW5

14–17 January
CRUFTS DOG SHOW
National Exhibition Centre, Birmingham, West Midlands

14–17 January
WEST LONDON ANTIQUES FAIR
Kensington Town Hall, Hornton Street, London W8

16 January
RUGBY UNION: ENGLAND v FRANCE
Rugby Football Union Ground, Twickenham, Middlesex

24 January
CHINESE NEW YEAR CELEBRATIONS
"Chinatown", Gerrard Street and Leicester Square, London W1

FEBRUARY 1993

12–27 February
JORVIK VIKING FESTIVAL
Various venues, York, North Yorkshire

20–28 February
BOAT, CARAVAN AND LEISURE SHOW
National Exhibition Centre, Birmingham, West Midlands

MARCH 1993

3–14 March
NORFOLK COUNTY MUSIC FESTIVAL
Various venues, Norwich, Norfolk

4–7 March
INTERNATIONAL PRACTICAL WOODWORKING EXHIBITION
Wembley Conference Centre, Empire Way, Wembley, Middlesex

6 March
RUGBY UNION: ENGLAND v SCOTLAND
Rugby Football Union Ground, Twickenham, Middlesex

16–18 March
HORSE RACING: CHELTENHAM GOLD CUP MEETING
Cheltenham Racecourse, Prestbury, Cheltenham, Gloucestershire

18 March–12 April
DAILY MAIL IDEAL HOME EXHIBITION
Earl's Court Exhibition Centre, Warwick Road, London SW5

19–21 March
INTERNATIONAL CLOWN CONVENTION
Bognor Regis, West Sussex

20 March
ROWING: HEAD OF THE RIVER RACE
Mortlake to Putney, River Thames, London

20 March–3 November
DURHAM CATHEDRAL – 900TH ANNIVERSARY CELEBRATIONS
Durham Cathedral, Durham

27 March
ROWING: OXFORD v CAMBRIDGE UNIVERSITY BOAT RACE
Putney to Mortlake, River Thames, London

APRIL 1993

1–3 April
HORSE RACING: GRAND NATIONAL MEETING
Aintree Racecourse, Liverpool, Merseyside

1–7 April
BRITISH INTERNATIONAL ANTIQUES FAIR
National Exhibition Centre, Birmingham, West Midlands

1 April–31 May
CORNWALL GARDENS FESTIVAL
Various gardens, Truro, Cornwall

7–13 April
HARROGATE INTERNATIONAL YOUTH MUSIC FESTIVAL
Various venues, Harrogate, North Yorkshire

9–12 April
DEVIZES TO WESTMINSTER INTERNATIONAL CANOE RACE
From Wharf Car Park, Wharf Street, Devizes, Wiltshire, to County Hall Steps, Westminster Bridge Road, London SE1

10–12 April
EASTER EGG HUNT
Leeds Castle, Maidstone, Kent

11 April
EASTER PARADE
Battersea Park, London SW11

11–12 April
BLACKHEATH EASTER KITE FESTIVAL
Blackheath Common, London SE3

12 April
WORLD COAL CARRYING CHAMPIONSHIP
Starts Royal Oak, Owl Lane, Gawthorpe, West Yorkshire

13–18 April
WORLD GYMNASTICS CHAMPIONSHIPS
National Indoor Arena, Birmingham, West Midlands

16–18 April
MORPETH NORTHUMBRIAN GATHERING
Various venues, Morpeth, Northumberland

22–25 April
HARROGATE SPRING FLOWER SHOW
Valley Gardens, Harrogate, North Yorkshire

MAY 1993

1 May
RUGBY LEAGUE CHALLENGE CUP FINAL
Wembley Stadium, Empire Way, Wembley, Middlesex

1–2 May
GOLF: LYTHAM TROPHY
Royal Lytham and St Anne's Golf Course, Links Gate, Lytham St Anne's, Lancashire

1–3 May
ROCHESTER CHIMNEY SWEEPS FESTIVAL
Various venues, Rochester, Kent

1–3 May
SPALDING FLOWER PARADE AND FESTIVAL
Spalding, Lincolnshire

2–3 May
BEXHILL ONE HUNDRED FESTIVAL OF MOTORING
De La Warr Parade, Bexhill-on-Sea, East Sussex

6–9 May
BADMINTON HORSE TRIALS
Badminton, Avon

6–9 May
BEVERLEY EARLY MUSIC FESTIVAL
Various venues, Beverley, Humberside

6–9 May
GOLF: BENSON AND HEDGES INTERNATIONAL OPEN
St Mellion Golf and Country Club, St Mellion, Saltash, Cornwall

7–30 May
BRIGHTON INTERNATIONAL FESTIVAL
Various venues, Brighton, East Sussex

8 May
HELSTON FURRY DANCE
Through the town, Helston, Cornwall

8–22 May
NEWBURY SPRING FESTIVAL
Various venues, Newbury, Berkshire

8–22 May
SHEFFIELD CHAMBER MUSIC FESTIVAL
Crucible Theatre, Sheffield, South Yorkshire

12–16 May
ROYAL WINDSOR HORSE SHOW
Home Park, Windsor, Berkshire

15 May
BARBON SPEED HILL CLIMB
Barbon Manor, Barbon, Cumbria

15 May
FOOTBALL ASSOCIATION CHALLENGE CUP FINAL
Wembley Stadium, Empire Way, Wembley, Middlesex

15–16 May
SAILING: WILSON TROPHY – WORLD DINGHY CHAMPIONSHIP
Marine Lake, West Kirby, Merseyside

19 May
CRICKET: ONE DAY INTERNATIONAL – ENGLAND v AUSTRALIA
Lancashire County Cricket Club, Warwick Road, Old Trafford, Manchester, Greater Manchester

20–22 May
DEVON COUNTY SHOW
Devon County Showground,
Westpoint, Clyst St Mary, Exeter,
Devon

21 May
**CRICKET: ONE DAY
INTERNATIONAL –
ENGLAND v AUSTRALIA**
Warwickshire County Cricket
Club, Edgbaston, Birmingham,
West Midlands

21–22 May
**SHROPSHIRE AND
WEST MIDLANDS
AGRICULTURAL SHOW**
Agricultural Showground,
Berwick Road, Shrewsbury,
Shropshire

21–23 May
**SOUTHERN COUNTIES
CRAFT MARKET**
The Maltings, Bridge Square,
Farnham, Surrey

21 May–6 June
**BATH INTERNATIONAL
FESTIVAL**
Various venues, Bath, Avon

23 May
**CRICKET: ONE DAY
INTERNATIONAL –
ENGLAND v AUSTRALIA**
Lord's Cricket Ground, St John's
Wood, London NW8

25–28 May
CHELSEA FLOWER SHOW
Royal Hospital, Chelsea, London
SW3 (Members only on 25 and 26
May)

26–27 May
**STAFFORDSHIRE
COUNTY SHOW**
Bingley Hall, Stafford,
Staffordshire

26 May–1 June
**BATTLE OF THE ATLANTIC
COMMEMORATION**
Various venues, Liverpool,
Merseyside

29–30 May ✳
AIR FETE '93
RAF Mildenhall, Bury St
Edmunds, Suffolk

29–31 May
**BALLOONS OVER
BASINGSTOKE '93**
War Memorial Park, London
Road, Basingstoke, Hampshire

29 May–6 June
CONISTON WATER FESTIVAL
Various venues, Coniston,
Cumbria

31 May
SURREY COUNTY SHOW
Stoke Park, Guildford, Surrey

31 May
WEYMOUTH TRAWLER RACE
The Harbour, Weymouth, Dorset

JUNE 1993

2–3 June
**BEATING RETREAT BY THE
HOUSEHOLD DIVISION**
Horse Guards Parade, Whitehall,
London SW1

2–3 June
SUFFOLK SHOW
Suffolk Showground,
Bucklesham Road, Ipswich,
Suffolk

2–5 June
**HORSE RACING:
THE DERBY** *(2nd)*
CORONATION CUP *(3rd)*
INTERNATIONAL DAY *(4th)*
OAKS STAKES *(5th)*
Epsom Racecourse, Epsom,
Surrey

2–5 June
**ROYAL BATH
AND WEST SHOW**
Royal Bath and West
Showground, Shepton Mallet,
Somerset

3–6 June
**ROCHESTER
DICKENS FESTIVAL**
Various venues, Rochester, Kent

3–7 June
**CRICKET:
FIRST TEST MATCH –
ENGLAND v AUSTRALIA**
Lancashire County Cricket Club,
Warwick Road, Old Trafford,
Manchester, Greater Manchester

4–6 June
**GREAT GARDEN AND
COUNTRYSIDE FESTIVAL**
Holker Hall and Gardens, Cark-
in-Cartmel, Grange-over-Sands,
Cumbria

4–13 June
GREENWICH FESTIVAL
Various venues, Greenwich,
London SE10

6 June
**ESSO BRISTOL TO
BOURNEMOUTH VINTAGE
VEHICLE RUN**
From Ashton Court Estate,
Bristol, Avon, to Undercliff Drive,
Bournemouth, Dorset

6 June–15 August ✳
**ROYAL ACADEMY OF ARTS
SUMMER EXHIBITION**
Royal Academy of Arts, Piccadilly,
London W1

7–13 June
**TENNIS: STELLA ARTOIS
GRASS COURT
CHAMPIONSHIPS**
Queen's Club, Palliser Road,
London W14

8–27 June ✳
POLO: WARWICKSHIRE CUP
Cirencester Park Polo Club, The
Old Kennels, Cirencester Park,
Cirencester, Gloucestershire

9 June
APPLEBY HORSE FAIR
Appleby, Cumbria

9–10 June
**CORPUS CHRISTI CARPET
OF FLOWERS AND FLORAL
FESTIVAL**
Cathedral of Our Lady and St
Philip Howard, Cathedral House,
Arundel, West Sussex

9–19 June
**GROSVENOR HOUSE
ANTIQUES FAIR**
Grosvenor House, Park Lane,
London W1

10–12 June
ROYAL CORNWALL SHOW
Royal Cornwall Showground,
Wadebridge, Cornwall

10–12 June
**SOUTH OF ENGLAND
AGRICULTURAL SHOW**
The Showground, Ardingly, Nr
Haywards Heath, West Sussex

11–27 June
**ALDEBURGH FESTIVAL
OF MUSIC AND THE ARTS**
Aldeburgh, Suffolk

12 June
**TROOPING THE COLOUR –
THE QUEEN'S OFFICIAL
BIRTHDAY PARADE**
Horse Guards Parade, Whitehall,
London SW1

12–13 June
FESTIVAL OF GARDENING
Weston Park, Weston-under-
Lizard, Nr Shifnal, Shropshire

12–13 June
**STEAM AND
TRANSPORT RALLY**
Wrotham Hill, Wrotham, Kent

12–19 June
**PILKINGTON GLASS
INTERNATIONAL LADIES'
TENNIS CHAMPIONSHIPS**
Devonshire Park, College Road,
Eastbourne, East Sussex

14–30 June
SIDMOUTH ARTS FESTIVAL
Various venues, Sidmouth, Devon

15–17 June
**THREE COUNTIES
AGRICULTURAL SHOW**
Three Counties Agricultural
Showground, Malvern, Hereford
& Worcester

15–18 June
**HORSE RACING:
ROYAL ASCOT**
Ascot Racecourse, Ascot,
Berkshire

17–21 June
**CRICKET:
SECOND TEST MATCH –
ENGLAND v AUSTRALIA**
Lord's Cricket Ground, St John's
Wood, London NW8

18–20 June
BEVERLEY FOLK FESTIVAL
Various venues, Beverley,
Humberside

19–20 June
**BIGGIN HILL
INTERNATIONAL AIR FAIR**
Biggin Hill Airport, Biggin Hill,
Kent

19–20 June
**FESTIVAL OF GARDENING
AT MIDSUMMER**
Hatfield House, Hatfield Park,
Hatfield, Hertfordshire

19–26 June
**BROADSTAIRS
DICKENS FESTIVAL**
Various venues, Broadstairs, Kent

20 June
RIPLEY CASTLE STEAM FAIR
Ripley Castle, Pateley Bridge
Road, Ripley, Nr Harrogate,
North Yorkshire

21 June–4 July
**LAWN TENNIS
CHAMPIONSHIPS**
All England Lawn Tennis and
Croquet Club, Wimbledon,
London SW19

22–23 June
CHESHIRE COUNTY SHOW
Tabley, Knutsford, Cheshire

23–24 June
LINCOLNSHIRE SHOW
Lincolnshire Showground,
Grange-de-Lings, Lincolnshire

26 June–10 July
**BOURNEMOUTH
MUSICMAKERS FESTIVAL**
Various venues, including Winter
Gardens Theatre, Exeter Road,
Bournemouth, Dorset

26 June–10 July
**THREE SPIRES FESTIVAL
OF THE ARTS**
Truro Cathedral, Truro, Cornwall

26 June–11 July
LUDLOW FESTIVAL
Various venues, Ludlow,
Shropshire

30 June–1 July
ROYAL NORFOLK SHOW
The Showground, Dereham,
Norwich, Norfolk

30 June–7 July
**SHREWSBURY
INTERNATIONAL MUSIC
FESTIVAL**
Various venues, Shrewsbury,
Shropshire

30 June–11 July
WARWICK FESTIVAL
Various venues, Warwick,
Warwickshire

JULY 1993

1–3 and 5–6 July
**CRICKET:
THIRD TEST MATCH –
ENGLAND v AUSTRALIA**
Nottinghamshire County Cricket
Club, Trent Bridge, Nottingham,
Nottinghamshire

2–11 July
**BIRMINGHAM
INTERNATIONAL JAZZ
FESTIVAL**
Various venues, Birmingham,
West Midlands

2–11 July
CAMBRIDGE FESTIVAL
Various venues, Cambridge,
Cambridgeshire

2–18 July
EXETER FESTIVAL
Various venues, Exeter, Devon

4–21 July
CITY OF LONDON FESTIVAL
Various venues, City of London

5–8 July
**ROYAL INTERNATIONAL
AGRICULTURAL SHOW**
National Agricultural Centre,
Stoneleigh, Nr Kenilworth,
Warwickshire

8–11 July
BRITISH ROSE FESTIVAL
Hampton Court Palace, East
Molesey, Surrey

8–17 July
**ST ALBANS INTERNATIONAL
ORGAN FESTIVAL**
Various venues, St Albans,
Hertfordshire

9–18 July
**YORK EARLY
MUSIC FESTIVAL**
Various venues, York, North
Yorkshire

10 July
**CRICKET: BENSON AND
HEDGES CUP FINAL**
Lord's Cricket Ground, St John's
Wood, London NW8

11 July ✳
**MOTOR RACING:
BRITISH GRAND PRIX**
Silverstone Circuit, Towcester,
Northamptonshire

14–17 July
**CLAREMONT LANDSCAPE
GARDEN FETE CHAMPETRE**
Claremont Landscape Garden,
Old Portsmouth Road, Esher,
Surrey

14–17 July
**SAILING: CUTTY SARK
TALL SHIPS RACE**
Newcastle Quayside, Newcastle
upon Tyne, Tyne & Wear

15–17 July
KENT COUNTY SHOW
County Showground, Detling,
Maidstone, Kent

15–18 July
GOLF: OPEN CHAMPIONSHIP
Royal St George's Golf Club,
Sandwich, Kent

15–18 July
**SOUTHERN CATHEDRALS
FESTIVAL**
Winchester Cathedral,
Winchester, Hampshire

16 July–11 September
**HENRY WOOD
PROMENADE CONCERTS**
Royal Albert Hall, Kensington
Gore, London SW7

17 July
**CUMBERLAND
AGRICULTURAL SHOW**
Rickerby Park, Carlisle, Cumbria

20–22 July
EAST OF ENGLAND SHOW
East of England Showground,
Peterborough, Cambridgeshire

20–31 July
ROYAL TOURNAMENT
Earl's Court Exhibition Centre,
Warwick Road, London SW5

22–26 July
**CRICKET:
FOURTH TEST MATCH –
ENGLAND v AUSTRALIA**
Yorkshire County Cricket Club,
Headingly Cricket Ground, St
Michael's Lane, Leeds, West
Yorkshire

23–25 July
ROYAL LANCASHIRE SHOW
Astley Park, Chorley, Lancashire

24–25 July
**RE-ENACTMENT OF
SIEGE OF BRISTOL**
Ashton Court Estate, Ashton
Road, Bristol, Avon

26 July–12 August
**SAILING: CHAMPAGNE
MUMM ADMIRAL'S CUP**
The Solent, off Isle of Wight

27–29 July
**NEW FOREST AND
HAMPSHIRE COUNTY SHOW**
New Park, Brockenhurst,
Hampshire

27–31 July
**HORSE RACING:
GOODWOOD RACES
(GLORIOUS GOODWOOD)**
Goodwood Racecourse, Nr
Chichester, West Sussex

29 July
AMBLESIDE SPORTS
Rydal Park, Rydal Road, Rydal, Nr
Ambleside, Cumbria

29 July–12 August
**HARROGATE
INTERNATIONAL FESTIVAL**
Various venues, Harrogate, North
Yorkshire

30 July–6 August
SIDMOUTH INTERNATIONAL FESTIVAL OF FOLK ARTS
Various venues, Sidmouth, Devon

31 July–7 August
SAILING: COWES WEEK
Cowes, Isle of Wight

3–4 August
BAKEWELL SHOW
The Showground, Coombe Road, Bakewell, Derbyshire

5–7 August
ENGLISH NATIONAL SHEEPDOG TRIALS
Whitby, North Yorkshire

5–9 August
CRICKET: FIFTH TEST MATCH – ENGLAND v AUSTRALIA
Warwickshire County Cricket Club, Edgbaston, Birmingham, West Midlands

6–8 August
PORTSMOUTH AND SOUTHSEA SHOW
Southsea Common, Southsea, Portsmouth, Hampshire

6–13 August
BROADSTAIRS FOLK WEEK
Various venues, Broadstairs, Kent

12 August ✳
APPLEBY AGRICULTURAL SHOW
Barley Field, Appleby Golf Course, Appleby, Cumbria

19 August
GRASMERE SPORTS
Sports Field, Stock Lane, Grasmere, Cumbria

19–21 August
SOUTHPORT FLOWER SHOW
Victoria Park, Rotton Row, Southport, Merseyside

19–23 August
CRICKET: SIXTH TEST MATCH – ENGLAND v AUSTRALIA
Foster's Oval, Kennington, London SE11

21–22 August ✳
GARLIC FESTIVAL
Fighting Cocks, Cross Roads, Bathingbourne, Isle of Wight

21–30 August
INTERNATIONAL BRASS FESTIVAL
Various venues, Wensleydale, North Yorkshire

22–29 August
THREE CHOIRS FESTIVAL
Worcester Cathedral, Worcester, Hereford & Worcester

26–28 August
PORT OF DARTMOUTH ROYAL REGATTA
Dartmouth, Devon

26–31 August
BEATLES FESTIVAL
Various venues, Liverpool, Merseyside

27 August–4 September
ARUNDEL FESTIVAL
Various venues, Arundel, West Sussex

27 August–5 November ✳
SUNDERLAND ILLUMINATIONS
Roker and Seaburn, Sunderland, Tyne & Wear

28–30 August
TOWN AND COUNTRY FESTIVAL
National Agricultural Centre, Stoneleigh, Nr Kenilworth, Warwickshire

28 August–4 September
GREAT DORSET STEAM FAIR
Tarrant Hinton, Blandford Forum, Dorset

29–30 August
NOTTING HILL CARNIVAL
Ladbroke Grove, London W11

2–5 September
BURGHLEY HORSE TRIALS
Burghley House, Stamford, Lincolnshire

3 September–7 November
BLACKPOOL ILLUMINATIONS
The Promenade, Blackpool, Lancashire

4 September
CRICKET: NATWEST BANK TROPHY FINAL
Lord's Cricket Ground, St John's Wood, London NW8

4 September
LOWICK AGRICULTURAL SHOW
Church Field, Lowick Bridge, Lowick, Nr Ulverston, Cumbria

4–5 September
**ENGLISH WINE FESTIVAL
AND REGIONAL FOOD FAIR**
English Wine Centre, Alfriston
Roundabout, Alfriston, East
Sussex

4–18 September
SALISBURY FESTIVAL
Various venues, Salisbury,
Wiltshire

8–10 September
**HORSE RACING: ST LEGER
FESTIVAL MEETING**
Doncaster Racecourse, Leger
Way, Doncaster, South Yorkshire

9 September
**WESTMORLAND
COUNTY SHOW**
Lane Farm, Crooklands, Cumbria

10–18 September
**SOUTHAMPTON
INTERNATIONAL BOAT SHOW**
Mayflower Park, Southampton,
Hampshire

11–12 September
**BEAULIEU INTERNATIONAL
AUTOJUMBLE**
National Motor Museum,
Beaulieu, Hampshire

16–19 September
**BLENHEIM INTERNATIONAL
HORSE TRIALS**
Blenheim Palace, Woodstock,
Oxfordshire

18 September
EGREMONT CRAB FAIR
Baybarrow, Egremont, Cumbria

24–26 September
GOLF: RYDER CUP
The Belfry, Sutton Coldfield,
West Midlands

OCTOBER 1993

1–31 October ✳
**WIRRAL INTERNATIONAL
JAZZ FESTIVAL**
Floral Pavilion, New Brighton,
Merseyside

6 October
**SOUTH WESTERN
DAIRY SHOW**
The Showground, Shepton
Mallet, Somerset

6–10 October ✳
HORSE OF THE YEAR SHOW
Wembley Arena, Empire Way,
Wembley, Middlesex

7–9 October
NOTTINGHAM GOOSE FAIR
Forest Recreation Ground,
Nottingham, Nottinghamshire

7–17 October
**NORFOLK AND
NORWICH FESTIVAL**
Various venues, Norwich, Norfolk

9–17 October
**CHELTENHAM FESTIVAL
OF LITERATURE**
Various venues, Cheltenham,
Gloucestershire

9–23 October
CANTERBURY FESTIVAL
Various venues, Canterbury, Kent

10 October
**WORLD CONKER
CHAMPIONSHIP**
Village Green, Ashton, Nr
Oundle, Northamptonshire

12–17 and 19–24 October
CHELSEA CRAFTS FAIR
Chelsea Old Town Hall, King's
Road, London SW3

18–22 October
**POWERBOAT RACING:
WINDERMERE RECORD
ATTEMPTS**
Low Wood Hotel, Low Wood Bay,
Windermere, Cumbria

21–31 October
**MOTORFAIR – THE
LONDON MOTOR SHOW**
Earl's Court Exhibition Centre,
Warwick Road, London SW5

22–24 October
**SOUTHERN COUNTIES
CRAFT MARKET**
The Maltings, Bridge Square,
Farnham, Surrey

28–31 October ✳
ROBIN HOOD PAGEANT
Nottingham Castle, Castle Road,
Nottingham, Nottinghamshire

NOVEMBER 1993

7 November
**LONDON TO BRIGHTON
VETERAN CAR RUN**
From Hyde Park, London, to
Brighton, East Sussex

13 November ✳
**LORD MAYOR'S
PROCESSION AND SHOW**
The City of London

29 November–2 December
**ROYAL SMITHFIELD SHOW
AND AGRICULTURAL
MACHINERY EXHIBITION**
Earl's Court Exhibition Centre,
Warwick Road, London SW5

DECEMBER 1993

16–20 December
**OLYMPIA INTERNATIONAL
SHOWJUMPING
CHAMPIONSHIPS**
Olympia, Hammersmith Road,
London W14

Booking coupons

➪ *Please complete this coupon and mail it direct to the establishment in which you are interested. Do not send it to the English Tourist Board. Remember to enclose a stamped addressed envelope (or international reply coupon).*

➪ *Tick as appropriate and complete the reverse side if you are interested in making a booking.*

❏ Please send me a brochure or further information, and details of prices charged.

❏ Please advise me, as soon as possible, if accommodation is available as detailed overleaf.

My name is: _____ (BLOCK CAPITALS)

Address: _____

_____

_____

Telephone number: _____ Date: _____

Where to Stay 1993
Bed & Breakfast, Farmhouses, Inns & Hostels

English Tourist Board

➪ *Please complete this coupon and mail it direct to the establishment in which you are interested. Do not send it to the English Tourist Board. Remember to enclose a stamped addressed envelope (or international reply coupon).*

➪ *Tick as appropriate and complete the reverse side if you are interested in making a booking.*

❏ Please send me a brochure or further information, and details of prices charged.

❏ Please advise me, as soon as possible, if accommodation is available as detailed overleaf.

My name is: _____ (BLOCK CAPITALS)

Address: _____

_____

_____

Telephone number: _____ Date: _____

Where to Stay 1993
Bed & Breakfast, Farmhouses, Inns & Hostels

English Tourist Board

Booking coupons

⇨ *Please complete this side if you are interested in making a booking.*

I am interested in booking accommodation for:

_____ adults and _____ children (ages _____)
Please give the number of people and the ages of any children

From (date of arrival): _____ To (date of departure): _____

or alternatively from: _____ To: _____

Accommodation required: _____

_____

Meals required: _____

Other/special requirements: _____

⇨ *Please enclose a stamped addressed envelope (or international reply coupon).*
⇨ *Please read the information on pages 424–428 before confirming any booking.*

⇨ *Please complete this side if you are interested in making a booking.*

I am interested in booking accommodation for:

_____ adults and _____ children (ages _____)
Please give the number of people and the ages of any children

From (date of arrival): _____ To (date of departure): _____

or alternatively from: _____ To: _____

Accommodation required: _____

_____

Meals required: _____

Other/special requirements: _____

⇨ *Please enclose a stamped addressed envelope (or international reply coupon).*
⇨ *Please read the information on pages 424–428 before confirming any booking.*

Booking coupons

⇨ *Please complete this coupon and mail it direct to the establishment in which you are interested. Do not send it to the English Tourist Board. Remember to enclose a stamped addressed envelope (or international reply coupon).*

⇨ *Tick as appropriate and complete the reverse side if you are interested in making a booking.*

❏ Please send me a brochure or further information, and details of prices charged.

❏ Please advise me, as soon as possible, if accommodation is available as detailed overleaf.

My name is: _____ (BLOCK CAPITALS)

Address: _____

_____

_____

Telephone number: _____ Date: _____

Where to Stay 1993
Bed & Breakfast, Farmhouses, Inns & Hostels

English Tourist Board

⇨ *Please complete this coupon and mail it direct to the establishment in which you are interested. Do not send it to the English Tourist Board. Remember to enclose a stamped addressed envelope (or international reply coupon).*

⇨ *Tick as appropriate and complete the reverse side if you are interested in making a booking.*

❏ Please send me a brochure or further information, and details of prices charged.

❏ Please advise me, as soon as possible, if accommodation is available as detailed overleaf.

My name is: _____ (BLOCK CAPITALS)

Address: _____

_____

_____

Telephone number: _____ Date: _____

Where to Stay 1993
Bed & Breakfast, Farmhouses, Inns & Hostels

English Tourist Board

Booking coupons

⇨ *Please complete this side if you are interested in making a booking.*

I am interested in booking accommodation for:

_____ adults and _____ children (ages _____)
Please give the number of people and the ages of any children

From (date of arrival): _____ To (date of departure): _____

or alternatively from: _____ To: _____

Accommodation required: _____

_____

Meals required: _____

Other/special requirements: _____

⇨ *Please enclose a stamped addressed envelope (or international reply coupon).*
⇨ *Please read the information on pages 424–428 before confirming any booking.*

⇨ *Please complete this side if you are interested in making a booking.*

I am interested in booking accommodation for:

_____ adults and _____ children (ages _____)
Please give the number of people and the ages of any children

From (date of arrival): _____ To (date of departure): _____

or alternatively from: _____ To: _____

Accommodation required: _____

_____

Meals required: _____

Other/special requirements: _____

⇨ *Please enclose a stamped addressed envelope (or international reply coupon).*
⇨ *Please read the information on pages 424–428 before confirming any booking.*

Booking coupons

➡ *Please complete this coupon and mail it direct to the establishment in which you are interested. Do not send it to the English Tourist Board. Remember to enclose a stamped addressed envelope (or international reply coupon).*

➡ *Tick as appropriate and complete the reverse side if you are interested in making a booking.*

❑ Please send me a brochure or further information, and details of prices charged.

❑ Please advise me, as soon as possible, if accommodation is available as detailed overleaf.

My name is: (BLOCK CAPITALS)

Address:

Telephone number: Date:

Where to Stay 1993
Bed & Breakfast, Farmhouses, Inns & Hostels

English Tourist Board

➡ *Please complete this coupon and mail it direct to the establishment in which you are interested. Do not send it to the English Tourist Board. Remember to enclose a stamped addressed envelope (or international reply coupon).*

➡ *Tick as appropriate and complete the reverse side if you are interested in making a booking.*

❑ Please send me a brochure or further information, and details of prices charged.

❑ Please advise me, as soon as possible, if accommodation is available as detailed overleaf.

My name is: (BLOCK CAPITALS)

Address:

Telephone number: Date:

Where to Stay 1993
Bed & Breakfast, Farmhouses, Inns & Hostels

English Tourist Board

Booking coupons

⇨ *Please complete this side if you are interested in making a booking.*

I am interested in booking accommodation for:

_____ adults and _____ children (ages _____)

Please give the number of people and the ages of any children

From (date of arrival): _____   To (date of departure): _____

or alternatively from: _____   To: _____

Accommodation required: _____

_____

Meals required: _____

Other/special requirements: _____

⇨ *Please enclose a stamped addressed envelope (or international reply coupon).*
⇨ *Please read the information on pages 424–428 before confirming any booking.*

⇨ *Please complete this side if you are interested in making a booking.*

I am interested in booking accommodation for:

_____ adults and _____ children (ages _____)

Please give the number of people and the ages of any children

From (date of arrival): _____   To (date of departure): _____

or alternatively from: _____   To: _____

Accommodation required: _____

_____

Meals required: _____

Other/special requirements: _____

⇨ *Please enclose a stamped addressed envelope (or international reply coupon).*
⇨ *Please read the information on pages 424–428 before confirming any booking.*

Booking coupons

⇨ *Please complete this coupon and mail it direct to the establishment in which you are interested. Do not send it to the English Tourist Board. Remember to enclose a stamped addressed envelope (or international reply coupon).*

⇨ *Tick as appropriate and complete the reverse side if you are interested in making a booking.*

❏ Please send me a brochure or further information, and details of prices charged.

❏ Please advise me, as soon as possible, if accommodation is available as detailed overleaf.

My name is: _____ (BLOCK CAPITALS)

Address: _____

_____

_____

Telephone number: _____ Date: _____

Where to Stay 1993
Bed & Breakfast, Farmhouses, Inns & Hostels

English Tourist Board

⇨ *Please complete this coupon and mail it direct to the establishment in which you are interested. Do not send it to the English Tourist Board. Remember to enclose a stamped addressed envelope (or international reply coupon).*

⇨ *Tick as appropriate and complete the reverse side if you are interested in making a booking.*

❏ Please send me a brochure or further information, and details of prices charged.

❏ Please advise me, as soon as possible, if accommodation is available as detailed overleaf.

My name is: _____ (BLOCK CAPITALS)

Address: _____

_____

_____

Telephone number: _____ Date: _____

Where to Stay 1993
Bed & Breakfast, Farmhouses, Inns & Hostels

English Tourist Board

Booking coupons

⇨ *Please complete this side if you are interested in making a booking.*

I am interested in booking accommodation for:

_____ adults and _____ children (ages _____)

Please give the number of people and the ages of any children

From (date of arrival): _____   To (date of departure): _____

or alternatively from: _____   To: _____

Accommodation required: _____

_____

Meals required: _____

Other/special requirements: _____

⇨ *Please enclose a stamped addressed envelope (or international reply coupon).*
⇨ *Please read the information on pages 424–428 before confirming any booking.*

⇨ *Please complete this side if you are interested in making a booking.*

I am interested in booking accommodation for:

_____ adults and _____ children (ages _____)

Please give the number of people and the ages of any children

From (date of arrival): _____   To (date of departure): _____

or alternatively from: _____   To: _____

Accommodation required: _____

_____

Meals required: _____

Other/special requirements: _____

⇨ *Please enclose a stamped addressed envelope (or international reply coupon).*
⇨ *Please read the information on pages 424–428 before confirming any booking.*

Booking coupons

⇨ *Please complete this coupon and mail it direct to the establishment in which you are interested. Do not send it to the English Tourist Board. Remember to enclose a stamped addressed envelope (or international reply coupon).*

⇨ *Tick as appropriate and complete the reverse side if you are interested in making a booking.*

❑ Please send me a brochure or further information, and details of prices charged.

❑ Please advise me, as soon as possible, if accommodation is available as detailed overleaf.

My name is: _____ (BLOCK CAPITALS)

Address: _____

_____

_____

Telephone number: _____ Date: _____

Where to Stay 1993
Bed & Breakfast, Farmhouses, Inns & Hostels

English Tourist Board

⇨ *Please complete this coupon and mail it direct to the establishment in which you are interested. Do not send it to the English Tourist Board. Remember to enclose a stamped addressed envelope (or international reply coupon).*

⇨ *Tick as appropriate and complete the reverse side if you are interested in making a booking.*

❑ Please send me a brochure or further information, and details of prices charged.

❑ Please advise me, as soon as possible, if accommodation is available as detailed overleaf.

My name is: _____ (BLOCK CAPITALS)

Address: _____

_____

_____

Telephone number: _____ Date: _____

Where to Stay 1993
Bed & Breakfast, Farmhouses, Inns & Hostels

English Tourist Board

Booking coupons

⇨ *Please complete this side if you are interested in making a booking.*

I am interested in booking accommodation for:

_____ adults and _____ children (ages _____)
Please give the number of people and the ages of any children

From (date of arrival): _____   To (date of departure): _____

or alternatively from: _____   To: _____

Accommodation required: _____

_____

Meals required: _____

Other/special requirements: _____

⇨ *Please enclose a stamped addressed envelope (or international reply coupon).*
⇨ *Please read the information on pages 424–428 before confirming any booking.*

⇨ *Please complete this side if you are interested in making a booking.*

I am interested in booking accommodation for:

_____ adults and _____ children (ages _____)
Please give the number of people and the ages of any children

From (date of arrival): _____   To (date of departure): _____

or alternatively from: _____   To: _____

Accommodation required: _____

_____

Meals required: _____

Other/special requirements: _____

⇨ *Please enclose a stamped addressed envelope (or international reply coupon).*
⇨ *Please read the information on pages 424–428 before confirming any booking.*

Advertisement coupons

⇨ *Please complete this coupon and mail it direct to the advertiser from whom you would like to receive further information. Do not send it to the English Tourist Board.*

To (advertiser's name): _____

Please send me a brochure or further information on the following, as advertised by you in the English Tourist Board's **Where to Stay 1993 Guide:**

_____

_____

My name and address are on the reverse.

⇨ *Please complete this coupon and mail it direct to the advertiser from whom you would like to receive further information. Do not send it to the English Tourist Board.*

To (advertiser's name): _____

Please send me a brochure or further information on the following, as advertised by you in the English Tourist Board's **Where to Stay 1993 Guide:**

_____

_____

My name and address are on the reverse.

⇨ *Please complete this coupon and mail it direct to the advertiser from whom you would like to receive further information. Do not send it to the English Tourist Board.*

To (advertiser's name): _____

Please send me a brochure or further information on the following, as advertised by you in the English Tourist Board's **Where to Stay 1993 Guide:**

_____

_____

My name and address are on the reverse.

Advertisement coupons

From (name): **(BLOCK CAPITALS)**

Address:

Postcode:

Telephone number: Date:

Where to Stay 1993
Bed & Breakfast, Farmhouses, Inns & Hostels   English Tourist Board

---

From (name): **(BLOCK CAPITALS)**

Address:

Postcode:

Telephone number: Date:

Where to Stay 1993
Bed & Breakfast, Farmhouses, Inns & Hostels   English Tourist Board

---

From (name): **(BLOCK CAPITALS)**

Address:

Postcode:

Telephone number: Date:

Where to Stay 1993
Bed & Breakfast, Farmhouses, Inns & Hostels   English Tourist Board

Advertisement coupons

➪ *Please complete this coupon and mail it direct to the advertiser from whom you would like to receive further information. Do not send it to the English Tourist Board.*

To (advertiser's name):

Please send me a brochure or further information on the following, as advertised by you in the English Tourist Board's **Where to Stay 1993 Guide:**

_____

_____

My name and address are on the reverse.

➪ *Please complete this coupon and mail it direct to the advertiser from whom you would like to receive further information. Do not send it to the English Tourist Board.*

To (advertiser's name):

Please send me a brochure or further information on the following, as advertised by you in the English Tourist Board's **Where to Stay 1993 Guide:**

_____

_____

My name and address are on the reverse.

➪ *Please complete this coupon and mail it direct to the advertiser from whom you would like to receive further information. Do not send it to the English Tourist Board.*

To (advertiser's name):

Please send me a brochure or further information on the following, as advertised by you in the English Tourist Board's **Where to Stay 1993 Guide:**

_____

_____

My name and address are on the reverse.

Advertisement coupons

From (name): (BLOCK CAPITALS)

Address:

Postcode:

Telephone number: Date:

Where to Stay 1993
Bed & Breakfast, Farmhouses, Inns & Hostels   English Tourist Board

---

From (name): (BLOCK CAPITALS)

Address:

Postcode:

Telephone number: Date:

Where to Stay 1993
Bed & Breakfast, Farmhouses, Inns & Hostels   English Tourist Board

---

From (name): (BLOCK CAPITALS)

Address:

Postcode:

Telephone number: Date:

Where to Stay 1993
Bed & Breakfast, Farmhouses, Inns & Hostels   English Tourist Board

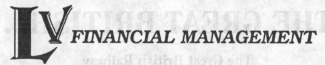

ALMANAC SERIES

English Castles ◆ English Gardens

England's castles and gardens are an integral part of its heritage. They provide a wealth of choice for the visitor. The pocket-sized Almanac guides include a selection of around 100 of the best-known locations open to the public.

Each of the individual entries is illustrated in colour and all the practical details a visitor needs to plan and enjoy a visit are provided. There is information on:

◆ *Opening times and admission charges*

◆ *Location and access*

◆ *Facilities for disabled visitors*

◆ *Special features*

Published in association with the English Tourist Board by Lochar Publishing.

Available in hardback from bookshops, price £6.99.

THE GREAT BRITISH...

The Great British Railway
by Tony Hall-Patch

The Great British Countryside
by Christopher Somerville

The Great British Soldier
by Philip Warner

The Great British... series presents a living history of British life:

The Railway – the development of both the engine and the rail system

The Countryside – how it has been shaped by geological and human influences

The Soldier – the changing lifestyle and experiences of the everyday soldier

◆ *Illustrated throughout with stunning photographs* ◆ *Packed with facts*

◆ *Recommends museums and locations of particular interest*

◆ *Contains a comprehensive gazetteer of the best of British museums*

Published in association with the National Tourist Boards for England, Scotland, Wales and Northern Ireland by David & Charles.

Available in hardback from bookshops, price £14.99.

Town index

The following cities, towns and villages all have accommodation listed in this guide. If the place where you wish to stay is not shown, the colour maps (starting on page 465) will help you to find somewhere suitable in the same area.

Index to Advertisers

You can obtain further information from any display advertiser in this guide by completing an advertisement enquiry coupon. You will find these coupons on pages 451–453.

MILEAGE CHART

The distances between towns on the mileage chart are given to the nearest mile, and are measured along the normal AA recommended routes. It should be noted that AA recommended routes do not necessarily follow the shortest distances between places but are based on the quickest travelling time, making maximum use of motorways or dual-carriageway roads.

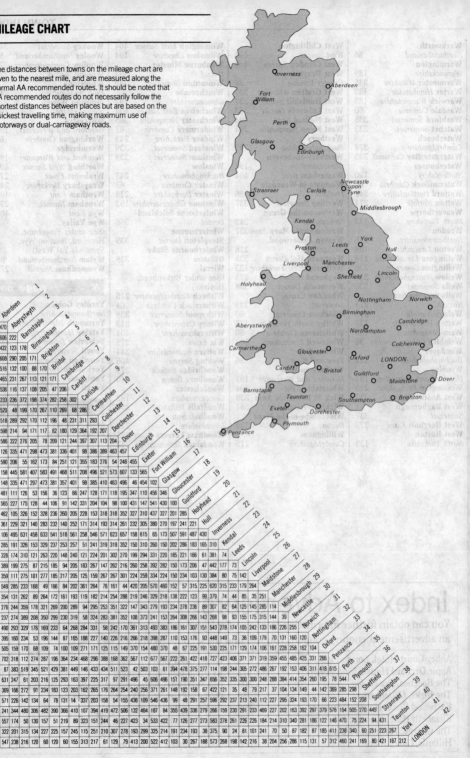

Index of towns on the chart:

1. Aberdeen
2. Aberystwyth
3. Barnstaple
4. Birmingham
5. Brighton
6. Bristol
7. Cambridge
8. Cardiff
9. Carlisle
10. Colchester
11. Dorchester
12. Dover
13. Edinburgh
14. Exeter
15. Fort William
16. Glasgow
17. Gloucester
18. Guildford
19. Holyhead
20. Hull
21. Inverness
22. Kendal
23. Leeds
24. Lincoln
25. Liverpool
26. Maidstone
27. Manchester
28. Middlesbrough
29. Newcastle
30. Norwich
31. Nottingham
32. Oxford
33. Penzance
34. Perth
35. Plymouth
36. Sheffield
37. Southampton
38. Stranraer
39. Taunton
40. York
41. LONDON

Mileage chart (distances in miles):

```
 1 Aberdeen
 2 470  Aberystwyth
 3 606 222  Barnstaple
 4 432 123 178  Birmingham
 5 608 290 205 171  Brighton
 6 516 132 100  88 170  Bristol
 7 465 231 267 113 121 171  Cambridge
 8 536 116 137 108 205  47 206  Cardiff
 9 233 236 372 198 374 282 258 302  Carlisle
10 520  48 199 170 267 110 269  68 286  Colchester
11 518 289 292 170 112 196  48 231 311 293  Dorchester
12 598 214  94 171 117  62 180 129 364 192 207  Dover
13 586 322 276 205  78 209 121 244 397 307 113 204  Edinburgh
14 126 335 471 298 473 381 336 401  98 386 389 463 457  Exeter
15 590 206  55 162 173  84 251 121 355 183 276  54 248 455  Fort William
16 158 445 581 407 583 491 468 511 208 496 521 573 607 133 565  Glasgow
17 148 335 471 297 473 381 357 401  98 385 410 463 496  46 454 102  Gloucester
18 481 111 126  53 156  36 123  66 247 128  71 118 195 347 116 456 346  Guildford
19 565 227 175 128  44 106  91 142 331 204 104  98 100 431 147 541 430 100  Holyhead
20 462 105 326 152 328 236 260 205 228 153 318 318 352 327 310 437 327 201 285  Hull
21 361 229 321 140 283 232 140 252 171 314 193 314 261 232 305 380 270 197 241 221  Inverness
22 106 495 631 458 633 541 518 561 258 546 571 623 657 158 615  65 173 507 591 487 430  Kendal
23 285 191 326 153 329 237 253 257  51 241 319 352 150 301 260 150 202 286 183 165 310   Leeds
24 328 174 310 121 263 220 148 240 121 224 201 302 270 199 294 331 220 185 221 166  61 381  74  Lincoln
25 389 199 275  87 215 185  94 205 182 260 258 392 282 150 173 206  47 442 177  73 259   Liverpool
26 359 111 275 101 277 185 217 205 125 159 267 267 301 224 259 334 224 150 234 130 384  80  75 142  Maidstone
27 549 285 233 168  49 166  84 202 361 264  76 161  44 420 205 570 460 152  57 315 225 620 315 179 264  Manchester
28 354 131 262  89 264 172 161 193 119 182 214 254 288 219 246 329 218 138 222 123  99 379  74  44  85  35 251  Middlesbrough
29 276 244 359 178 321 269 200 289  94 295 253 351 322 147 343 279 234 278 236  39  80  82  64 125 145 285 114  39  Newcastle
30 537 237 389 308 350 299 231 319  58 324 283 381 352 108 373 241 153 264 308 266 143 268  97 156 175 315 144  39  Norwich
31 490 293 329 176 169 233  64 268 284 331  58 242 170 361 313 493 383 186 161 307 151 543 278 174 105 242 133 186 255 255  Nottingham
32 395 160 234  53 196 144  87 165 188 227 140 226 216 266 218 398 287 110 153 176  93 448 149  73  36 139  70 131 160 120 207  Oxford
33 505 159 170  68 109  74 100 109 271 171 125 194 370 154 480 370  48  67 225 191 530 225 171 114 106 161 228 258 162 104  Penzance
34 702 318 112 274 287 196 364 234 448 296 388 168 362 567 112 677 567 222 261 422 418 727 423 406 371 319 359 455 485 425 331 266  Perth
35  87 383 519 345 521 429 381 449 146 433 434 511 523  42 503 103  61 394 478 375 277 114 198 244 305 272 486 267 192 153 406 311 418 615  Plymouth
36 631 247  61 203 216 125 293 163 397 225 317  97 291 496  45 606 496 151 190 351 347 656 352 335 300 300 248 288 384 414 354 260 195  78 544  Sheffield
37 369 166 272  91 234 183 123 203 162 265 176 264 254 240 256 371 261 148 192 158  67 422 121  35  48  79 217  37 104 134 144 142 369 286 298  Southampton
38 571 226 142 134  64  78 131  14 337 203 158  54 135 306 158  90 546 436  99  48 291 257 596 292 237 213 240 112 227 295 324 193 170  66 223 484 152 208  Stranraer
39 241 344 480 306 482 390 366 410 107 394 419 472 506 132 464 187  84 355 439 336 279 266 159 233 469 227 202 163 392 297 379 576 154 505 270 445  Taunton
40 557 174  50 130 157  51 219  89 323 151 244  46 227 403  34 533 422  77 126 277 273 583 278 261 226 226 184 214 310 340 281 186 122 146 470  75 224  94 431  York
41 322 201 315 134 227 225 157 245 115 210 307 278 193 299 325 214 191 234 193  38 375  90  24  81 101 241  70  50  87 185 411 238 340  60 251 223 267 212  LONDON
```

Colour Maps

Places with accommodation listed
in this guide are shown in black on
the maps which follow.

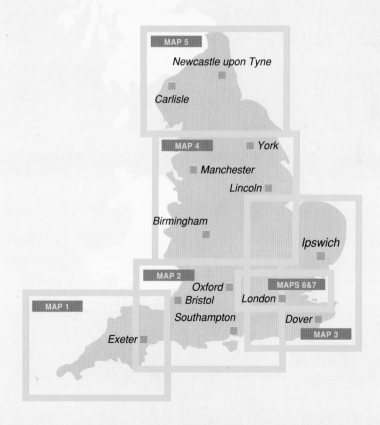

MAP 5

Newcastle upon Tyne

Carlisle

MAP 4   York

Manchester

Lincoln

Birmingham

Ipswich

MAP 2

Oxford

Bristol   London   MAPS 6&7

Southampton

Dover

MAP 1

MAP 3

Exeter

Map 1

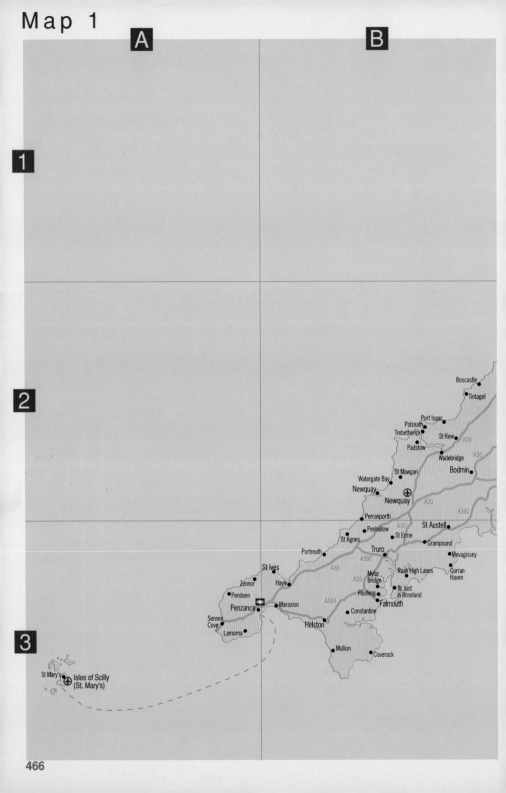

A   B

1

2

3

Boscastle
Tintagel
Port Isaac
Polzeath
Trebetherick
St Kew
Padstow
Wadebridge
Bodmin
St Mawgan
Watergate Bay
Newquay
Newquay
A39
A30
A390
Perranporth
St Austell
Penhallow
St Agnes
St Erme
A39
Grampound
Truro
Portreath
A390
Mevagissey
Ruan High Lanes
St Ives
Mylor
Bridge
A39
Gorran
Haven
Zennor
Hayle
A30
Pendeen
Flushing
St Just
in Roseland
Penzance
Marazion
Falmouth
Sennen
Cove
Constantine
Lamorna
Helston
A394
Mullion
Coverack

St Mary's
Isles of Scilly
(St. Mary's)

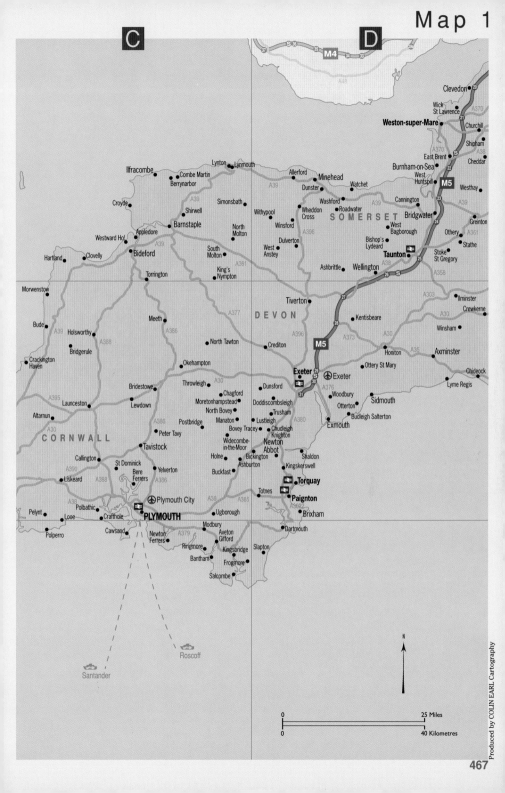

Map 1

Produced by COLIN EARL Cartography

Map 2

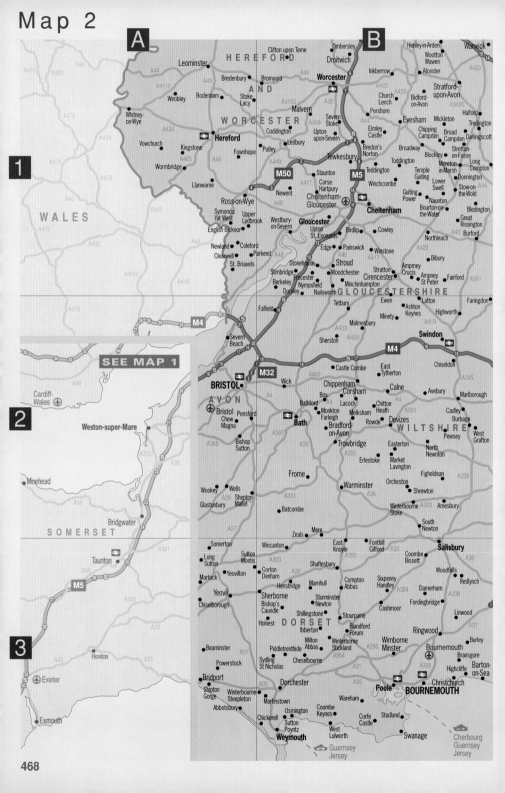

Map 2

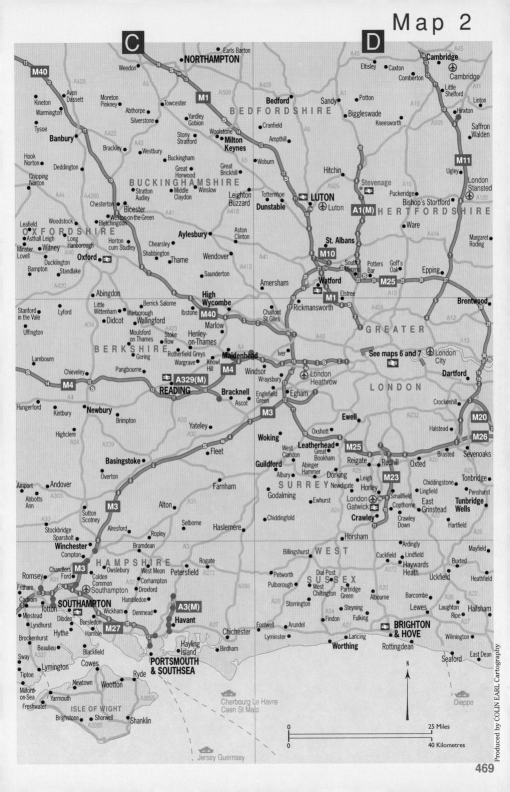

C   D

NORTHAMPTON
Earls Barton
Weedon
M40
Kineton
Avon Dassett
Warmington
Moreton Pinkney
Abthorpe
Towcester
Silverstone
Yardley Gobion
Tysoe
Banbury
Brackley
Westbury
Stony Stratford
Woolstone
Milton Keynes
Hook Norton
Deddington
Great Horwood
Buckingham
Great Brickhill
Chipping Norton
Stratton Audley
Middle Claydon
Winslow
Leighton Buzzard
Woburn
Chesterton
Weston-on-the-Green
Bletchingdon
BUCKINGHAMSHIRE
Totternhoe
Leafield
Woodstock
OXFORDSHIRE
Asthall Leigh
Long Hanborough
Horton cum Studley
Aylesbury
Aston Clinton
Minster Lovell
Witney
Chearsley
Shabbington
Thame
Wendover
Ducklington
Standlake
Oxford
Saunderton
Bampton
Abingdon
High Wycombe
Berrick Salome
Stanford in the Vale
Lyford
Little Wittenham
Warborough
Ibstone
M40
Chalfont St Giles
Uffington
Didcot
Wallingford
Marlow
Moulsford on Thames
Stoke Row
Henley-on-Thames
Lambourn
BERKSHIRE
Goring
Rotherfield Greys
Wargrave
Knowl Hill
Maidenhead
Iver
Chieveley
Pangbourne
M4
Windsor
Wraysbury
READING
A329(M)
Bracknell
Englefield Green
Egham
Hungerford
Kintbury
Newbury
Brimpton
Ascot
M3
Highclere
Yateley
Fleet
Basingstoke
Overton
Woking
West Clandon
Guildford
Leatherhead
Great Bookham
Amport
Andover
Alton
Selborne
Farnham
Abinger Hammer
Dorking
Abbotts Ann
Sutton Scotney
Alresford
Ropley
Haslemere
Godalming
Ewhurst
Stockbridge
Sparsholt
Bramdean
Chiddingfold
Horsham
Winchester
Compton
Rogate
Billingshurst
Chandlers Ford
Owslebury
West Meon
Petersfield
Petworth
HAMPSHIRE
Colden Common
Corhampton
Pulborough
West Chiltington
Romsey
Fritham
Southampton
Droxford
Hambledon
Storrington
Steyning
Cadnam
SOUTHAMPTON
Wickham
Denmead
A3(M)
Havant
Fontwell
Arundel
Findon
Totton
Bursledon
Hamble
Chichester
Lymister
Lancing
Worthing
Minstead
Dibden
M27
Hythe
Hayling Island
Birdham
Brockenhurst
Beaulieu
Blackfield
Cowes
PORTSMOUTH & SOUTHSEA
Sway
Lymington
Newtown
Ryde
Tiptoe
ISLE OF WIGHT
Wootton
Milford-on-Sea
Yarmouth
Freshwater
Brighstone
Shorwell
Shanklin

Cherbourg Le Havre
Caen St Malo

Jersey Guernsey

BEDFORDSHIRE
Bedford
Sandy
Potton
Cranfield
Biggleswade
Kneesworth
Ampthill
Hitchin
Stevenage
Eltisley
Caxton
Comberton
Cambridge
Little Shelford
Linton
Hinxton
Saffron Walden
Ugley
London Stansted
M11
Puckeridge
Bishop's Stortford
LUTON
Luton
Ware
HERTFORDSHIRE
St. Albans
M10
South Mimms
Potters Bar
Goff's Oak
Epping
Margaret Roding
Watford
M25
Elstree
M1
Rickmansworth
Brentwood
Amersham
GREATER
See maps 6 and 7
London City
LONDON
London Heathrow
Dartford
Windsor
London
Crockenhill
Ewell
M25
Oxshott
Halstead
M20
M26
Leatherhead
Reigate
Redhill
Oxted
Brasted
Sevenoaks
Leigh
M23
Chiddingstone
Tonbridge
Newdigate
Horley
Lingfield
Penshurst
SURREY
Smallfield
Copthorne
East Grinstead
Tunbridge Wells
London Gatwick
Crawley
Crawley Down
Hartfield
WEST
Ardingly
Mayfield
Cuckfield
Lindfield
Buxted
SUSSEX
Haywards Heath
Uckfield
Heathfield
Dial Post
Partridge Green
Albourne
Barcombe
Lewes
Laughton
Ripe
Hailsham
Fulking
BRIGHTON & HOVE
Wilmington
Rottingdean
East Dean
Seaford

N

Dieppe

Produced by COLIN EARL Cartography

0   25 Miles
0   40 Kilometres

Map 3

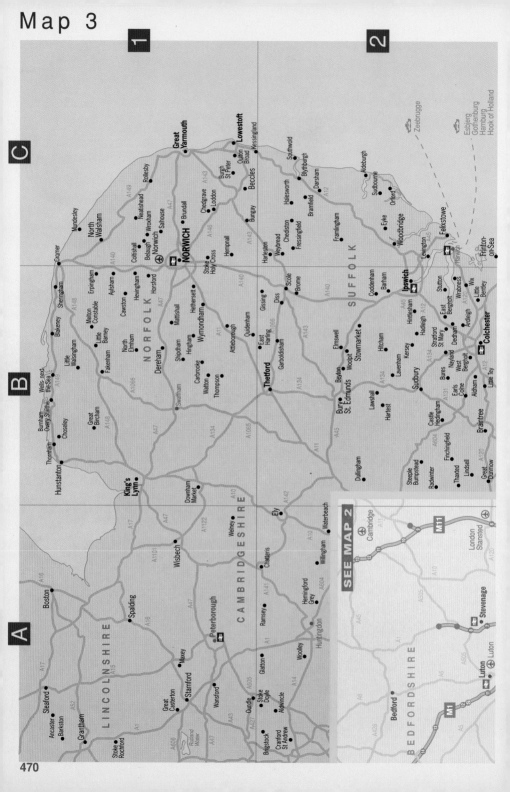

1

2

C

Great Yarmouth
Lowestoft
Zeebrugge
Esbjerg
Gothenburg
Hamburg
Hook of Holland

Kessingland
Oulton Broad
Southwold
Mundesley
Rollesby
Burgh St Peter
Beccles
Blythburgh
Aldeburgh
Chedgrave
Loddon
Halesworth
Darsham
Sudbourne
Cromer
North Walsham
Neatishead
A149
Wroxham
Brundall
Bungay
Bramfield
Orford
Sheringham
Erpingham
Belaugh
Salthouse
A143
Chediston
Weybread
Framlingham
Eyke
Woodbridge
Aylsham
Hevingham
Norwich
Cottishall
NORWICH
A148
Hempnall
Fressingfield
Lexington
A47
A140
Blakeney
Melton Constable
Cawston
Horsford
Stoke Holy Cross
Harleston
Scole
Brome
Coddenham
Barham
Ipswich
Stutton
Wrabness
Wix
Felixstowe
Frinton-on-Sea
Harwich
Little Walsingham
Little Barney
North Elmham
Hethersett
A140
Diss
Gissing
SUFFOLK
East Bergholt
Little Bentley
Colchester
A12
Wells-next-the-Sea
Fakenham
A1065
Mattishall
Shipdham
Hingham
Wymondham
Quidenham
East Harling
Elmswell
Hadleigh
Stratford St Mary
Dedham
Ardleigh
Burnham Overy Staithe
Choseley
Great Bircham
A148
NORFOLK
Dereham
Carbrooke
Watton
A11
Attleborough
Garboldisham
Thetford
Beyton
Woolpit
Stowmarket
Hitcham
Kersey
Nayland
West Bergholt
Thornham
Hunstanton
A149
Swaffham
Thompson
A134
A1065
Bury St Edmunds
Lavenham
Sudbury
Bures
Earls Colne
Aldham
Little Tey
King's Lynn
Downham Market
Lawshall
Hartest
Castle Hedingham
Braintree
A101
A142
A10
Dillingham
Steeple Bumpstead
Radwinter
Finchingfield
Thaxted
Lindsell
Great Dunmow
A120
Welney
A1122
Ely
Waterbeach
B

Wisbech
A1101
Chatteris
Willingham
CAMBRIDGESHIRE
Boston
Spalding
A16
A47
Peterborough
Ramsey
A141
Hemingford Grey
A604
Huntingdon
A

Sleaford
Ancaster
Bankston
Grantham
A52
A607
LINCOLNSHIRE
A1
A15
Great Casterton
Stamford
Maxey
Woolley
Glatton
A605
Stoke Doyle
A14
Oundle
Aldwincle
A605
Wansford
Brigstock
Cranford St Andrew
Rutland Water
A606
A43
A47
Stoke Rochford
A17

SEE MAP 2
Cambridge
A11
M11
London Stansted
Stevenage
A1
A505
A10
A5
Luton
M1
Bedford
A6
BEDFORDSHIRE
A421
A428

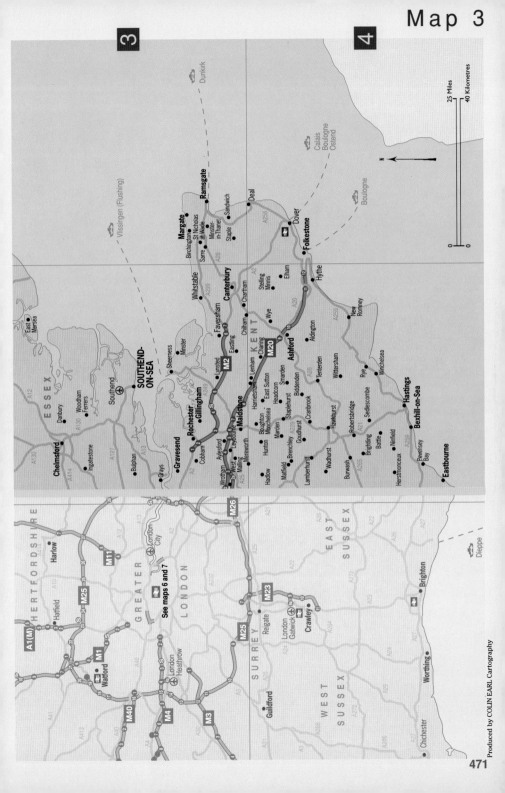

Map 3

3

4

25 Miles

40 Kilometres

N

0

0

Dunkirk

Vlissingen (Flushing)

Calais
Boulogne
Ostend

Boulogne

Dieppe

Ramsgate

Margate
Birchington
St Nicholas
at Wade
Minster-
in-Thanet
Sarre

Sandwich

Staple

Deal

Dover

Folkestone

Whitstable

Canterbury

Chartham

Stelling
Minnis

Elham

Hythe

Wye

Chilham

A20

Aldington

New
Romney

A259

Winchelsea

Rye

Hastings

Bexhill-on-Sea

Pevensey
Bay

Eastbourne

Faversham

Eastling

Charing

Lenham

East Sutton

Snarden

Biddenden

Cranbrook

Tenterden

Wittersham

Sedlescombe

Battle

Ninfield

Herstmonceux

Headcorn

Staplehurst

Goudhurst

Hawkhurst

Robertsbridge

Brightling

Burwash

Wadhurst

Lamberhurst

A265

A21

Harrietsham

East
Peckham

Marden

Brenchley

Mardesley

Hadlow

Matfield

Maidstone

Rochester

Gillingham

Gravesend

Cobham

Aylesford

West
Malling

Mereworth

Leybourne

Hunton

Broughton
Monchelsea

M2

M20

Ashford

A28

A2

KENT

Minster

Sheerness

**SOUTHEND-
ON-SEA**

Southend

Grays

A13

A127

Bulphan

A2

Wrotham

A25

M26

M25

M11

Harlow

HERTFORDSHIRE

A1(M)

Hatfield

A10

M25

Watford

M1

M40

M4

M3

London
Heathrow

A40

GREATER
LONDON

London
City

See maps 6 and 7

M23

M25

Reigate

London
Gatwick

Crawley

A22

SURREY

Guildford

A3

WEST
SUSSEX

Chichester

A27

EAST
SUSSEX

A22

A26

Brighton

Worthing

East
Mersea

Chelmsford

Ingatestone

Danbury

Woodham
Ferrers

A12

A130

A414

ESSEX

A130

A12

Produced by COLIN EARL Cartography

471

Map 4

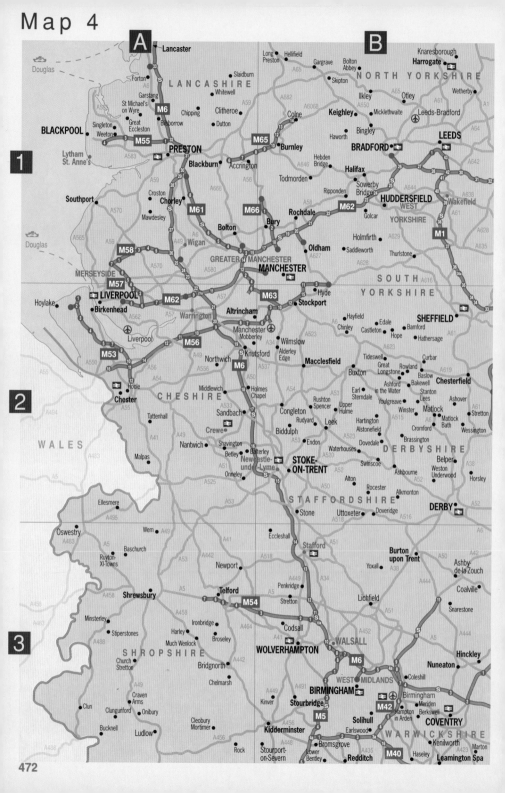

Map 4

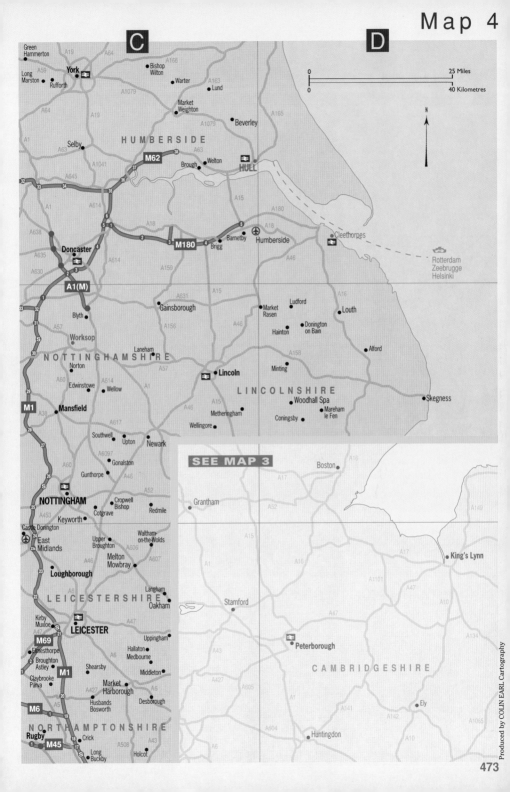

0 | 25 Miles
0 | 40 Kilometres

N

Green Hammerton
A19
A64
York
Long Marston
A59
Rufforth
Bishop Wilton
A166
Warter
A163
Lund
Market Weighton
A1079
Beverley
A165

HUMBERSIDE
Selby
A63
A19
A1041
A645
M62
A63
Welton
Brough
Welton
HULL
A15

A1
A614
A18
A180
A638
A635
A630
Doncaster
A1(M)
M180
Brigg
Barnetby
Humberside
A46
Cleethorpes
Rotterdam
Zeebrugge
Helsinki

A631
A15
A16
A159
Gainsborough
Market Rasen
Ludford
Louth
Blyth
A57
A156
A48
Hainton
Donington on Bain
Alford
Worksop
S
A158
Laneham
NOTTINGHAMSHIRE
Norton
Lincoln
Minting
A60
A514
A57
Edwinstowe
Wellow
A1
LINCOLNSHIRE
M1
Mansfield
A38
A15
Woodhall Spa
Skegness
Metheringham
Mareham le Fen
A617
Coningsby
Wellingore

Southwell
Upton
Newark
A6097
Gonalston
A60
Gunthorpe
A46
A52

NOTTINGHAM
Cropwell Bishop
Cotgrave
Redmile
Keyworth
Castle Donington
East Midlands
Upper Broughton
Waltham-on-the-Wolds
A606
Melton Mowbray
A607
Loughborough
A6
Langham
LEICESTERSHIRE
Oakham
A6
Stamford
Kirby Muxloe
LEICESTER
A47
M69
Uppingham
Enderby
Hallaton
Medbourne
Broughton Astley
Shearsby
Middleton
M1
Claybrooke Parva
Market Harborough
A427
A6
M6
Husbands Bosworth
Desborough
NORTHAMPTONSHIRE
Rugby
Crick
M45
Long Buckby
Holcot

SEE MAP 3
Boston
A16
A17
Grantham
A52
A149
A15
Peterborough
A47
King's Lynn
A1101
A47
A10
A47
A134
A43
Peterborough
CAMBRIDGESHIRE
A427
A605
A1
A141
Ely
A604
Huntingdon
A10
A1065

Produced by COLIN EARL Cartography

Map 5

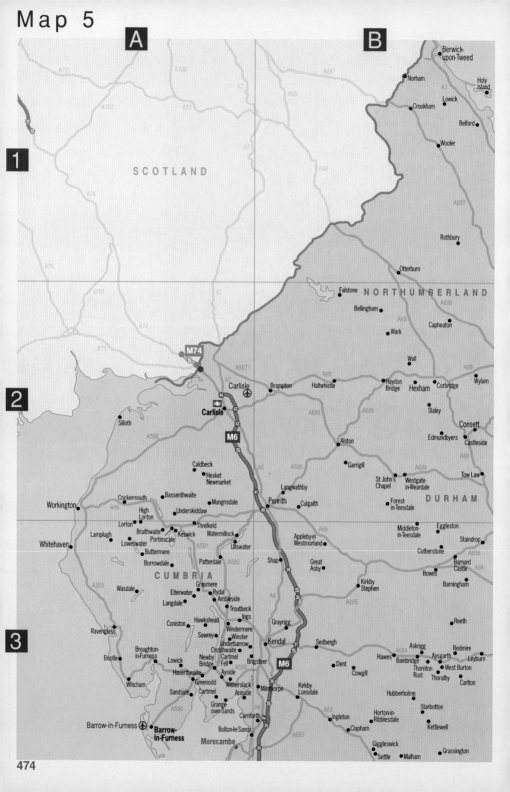

A   B

1

2

3

SCOTLAND

NORTHUMBERLAND

DURHAM

CUMBRIA

Berwick-upon-Tweed
Norham
Holy Island
Lowick
Crookham
Belford
Wooler
Rothbury
Otterburn
Falstone
Bellingham
Capheaton
Wark
Wall
Haydon Bridge
Hexham
Corbridge
Wylam
Haltwhistle
Slaley
Consett
Brampton
Carlisle
Edmundbyers
Castleside
Alston
Tow Law
Garrigill
St John's Chapel
Westgate-in-Weardale
Silloth
Langwathby
Forest-in-Teesdale
Caldbeck
Hesket Newmarket
Penrith
Culgaith
Middleton-in-Teesdale
Eggleston
Cockermouth
Bassenthwaite
Mungrisdale
Workington
High Lorton
Underskiddaw
Appleby-in-Westmorland
Staindrop
Lorton
Threlkeld
Cotherstone
Barnard Castle
Lamplugh
Braithwaite
Keswick
Watermillock
Bowes
Whitehaven
Portinscale
Ullswater
Barningham
Loweswater
Buttermere
Shap
Great Asby
Borrowdale
Patterdale
Kirkby Stephen
Wasdale
Grasmere
Reeth
Elterwater
Rydal
Ambleside
Langdale
Troutbeck
Ings
Ravenglass
Coniston
Hawkshead
Windermere
Grayrigg
Sawrey
Winster
Askrigg
Redmire
Bootle
Broughton-in-Furness
Underbarrow
Kendal
Sedbergh
Hawes
Aysgarth
Leyburn
Lowick
Crosthwaite
Bainbridge
Thornton Rust
West Burton
Newby Bridge
Cartmel Fell
Brigsteer
Dent
Cowgill
Thoralby
Carlton
Haverthwaite
Ayside
Whicham
Greenodd
Witherslack
Hubberholme
Sandside
Cartmel
Arnside
Milnthorpe
Kirkby Lonsdale
Starbotton
Grange-over-Sands
Kettlewell
Carnforth
Horton-in-Ribblesdale
Barrow-in-Furness
Bolton-le-Sands
Ingleton
Clapham
Barrow-in-Furness
Morecambe
Giggleswick
Grassington
Settle
Malham

474

Map 5

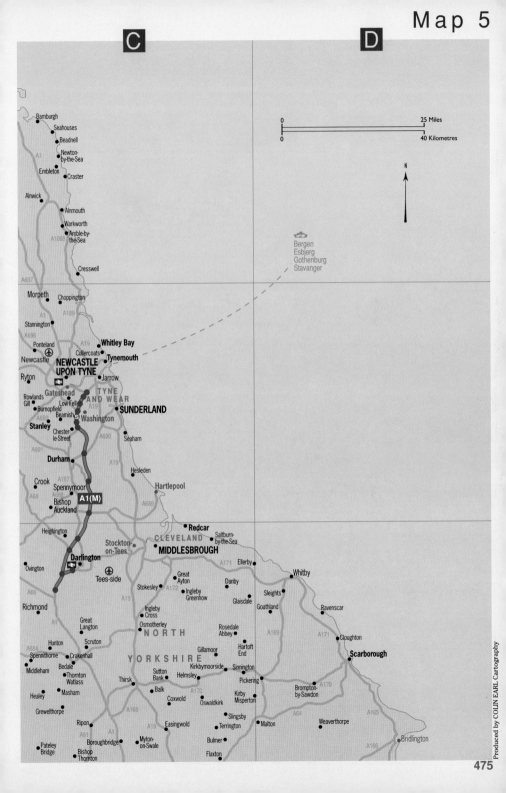

C

D

Bamburgh
Seahouses
Beadnell
Newton-by-the-Sea
Embleton
Craster
Alnwick
Alnmouth
Warkworth
Amble-by-the-Sea
A1068
Cresswell

A697

Morpeth
Choppington
A1
A189
Stannington
A696
Ponteland
A19
Whitley Bay
Cullercoats
Newcastle
NEWCASTLE
Tynemouth
UPON TYNE
Ryton
Jarrow
Gateshead
TYNE
AND WEAR
Rowlands
Gill
Low Fell
A19
Burnopfield
Beamish
Washington
SUNDERLAND
Stanley
Chester-le-Street
Seaham
A692
A690
A691
Durham
A19
Hesleden
Crook
A167
Spennymoor
Hartlepool
A68
A688
Bishop
A1(M)
Auckland
A689
Heighington
Redcar
Stockton-on-Tees
CLEVELAND
Saltburn-by-the-Sea
Darlington
MIDDLESBROUGH
Ovington
Tees-side
A171
Ellerby
A66
Great
Ayton
Danby
Whitby
Stokesley
Ingleby
Greenhow
Sleights
Glaisdale
Richmond
A19
Ingleby
Cross
Goathland
Ravenscar
A1
Great
Langton
Osmotherley
Rosedale
Abbey
A169
Cloughton
A171
Hunton
Scruton
N O R T H
Gillamoor
Hartoft
End
Scarborough
Spennithorne
Crakehall
Bedale
Y O R K S H I R E
Kirkbymoorside
Middleham
Thornton
Watlass
Sutton
Bank
Helmsley
Sinnington
Healey
Masham
Balk
Pickering
Brompton-by-Sawdon
A170
Grewelthorpe
Coxwold
Kirby
Misperton
Oswaldkirk
A64
A165
Ripon
A170
Slingsby
Pateley
Bridge
Boroughbridge
Myton-on-Swale
Easingwold
Terrington
Malton
Weaverthorpe
A61
A1
A19
Bulmer
Bridlington
Bishop
Thornton
Flaxton
A166

Produced by COLIN EARL Cartography

0   25 Miles
0   40 Kilometres

N

Bergen
Esbjerg
Gothenburg
Stavanger

Map 6

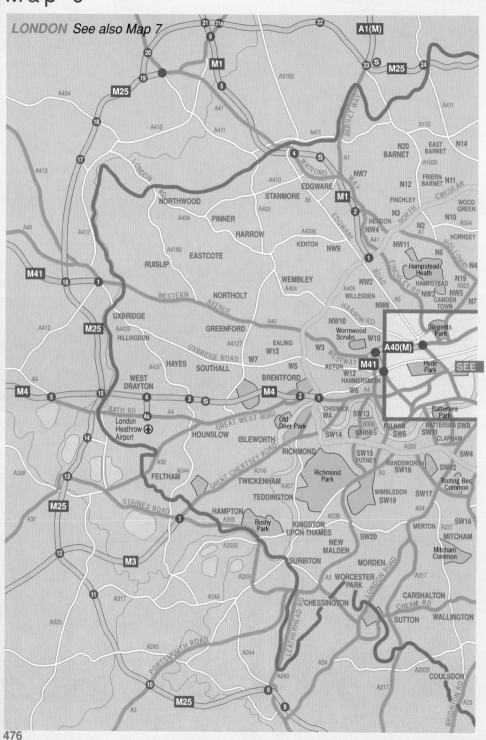

LONDON *See also Map 7*

Map 6

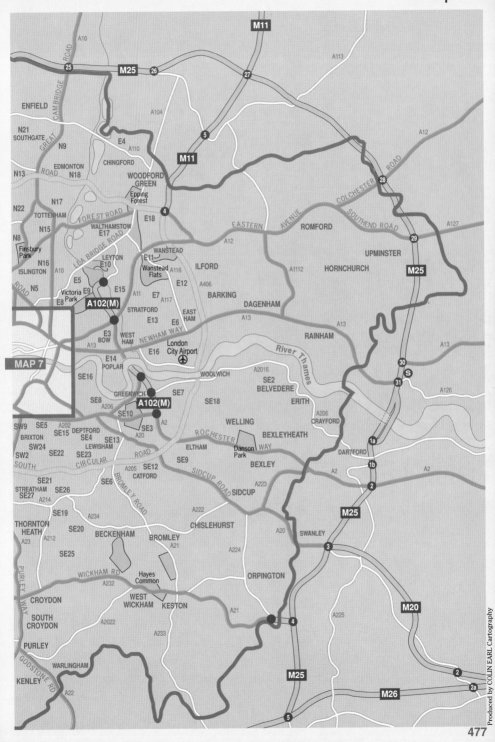

Map 7

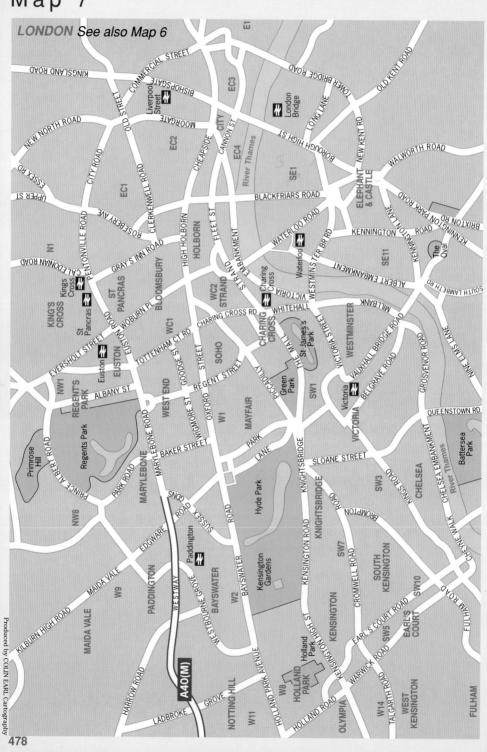

LONDON *See also Map 6*

KINGSLAND ROAD
COMMERCIAL STREET
BISHOPSGATE
E1
EC3
TOWER BRIDGE ROAD
OLD KENT ROAD
NEW NORTH ROAD
CITY ROAD
OLD STREET
MOORGATE
Liverpool Street
EC2
CHEAPSIDE
CITY
CANNON ST
London Bridge
LONG LANE
BOROUGH HIGH ST
NEW KENT ROAD
WALWORTH ROAD
ESSEX RD
UPPER ST
N1
ROSEBERY AVE
CLERKENWELL ROAD
EC1
EC4
River Thames
SE1
BLACKFRIARS ROAD
ELEPHANT & CASTLE
KENNINGTON PARK ROAD
BRIXTON RD
CALEDONIAN ROAD
PENTONVILLE ROAD
ST PANCRAS
GRAY'S INN ROAD
HIGH HOLBORN
HOLBORN
FLEET ST
VICTORIA EMBANKMENT
Waterloo
WATERLOO ROAD
WESTMINSTER BR RD
KENNINGTON ROAD
SE11
The Oval
KENNINGTON LANE
KING'S CROSS
Kings Cross
St Pancras
EVERSHOLT STREET
EUSTON ROAD
WOBURN PL
BLOOMSBURY
WC1
WC2
STRAND
Charing Cross
CHARING CROSS
WHITEHALL
ALBERT EMBANKMENT
SOUTH LAMBETH RD
NW1
Euston
ALBANY ST
TOTTENHAM CT RD
GOODGE ST
REGENT STREET
CHARING CROSS RD
SOHO
W1
ST MARTIN'S
St James's Park
THE MALL
Green Park
VICTORIA STREET
WESTMINSTER
MILLBANK
REGENT'S PARK
WEST END
WIGMORE ST
OXFORD STREET
MAYFAIR
PICCADILLY
SW1
Victoria
VICTORIA
VAUXHALL BRIDGE ROAD
BELGRAVE ROAD
GROSVENOR ROAD
Primrose Hill
Regents Park
PRINCE ALBERT ROAD
PARK ROAD
BAKER STREET
MARYLEBONE ROAD
PARK LANE
KNIGHTSBRIDGE
SLOANE STREET
SW3
KINGS ROAD
CHELSEA
CHELSEA EMBANKMENT
River Thames
Battersea Park
QUEENSTOWN RD
NW8
MARYLEBONE
EDGWARE ROAD
Paddington
SUSSEX GDNS
BAYSWATER ROAD
Hyde Park
Kensington Gardens
KNIGHTSBRIDGE
BROMPTON ROAD
SW7
CROMWELL ROAD
SOUTH KENSINGTON
SW10
CHEYNE WALK
FULHAM ROAD
MAIDA VALE
W9
WESTWAY
WESTBOURNE GROVE
PADDINGTON
BAYSWATER
W2
KENSINGTON ROAD
KENSINGTON
SW5
EARL'S COURT
KILBURN HIGH ROAD
HARROW ROAD
A40(M)
LADBROKE GROVE
NOTTING HILL
W11
HOLLAND PARK AVENUE
HOLLAND PARK ROAD
W8
HOLLAND PARK
Holland Park
KENSINGTON HIGH ST
HOLLAND ROAD
OLYMPIA
WARWICK ROAD
EARL'S COURT ROAD
TALGARTH ROAD
W14
WEST KENSINGTON
FULHAM

Produced by COLIN EARL Cartography

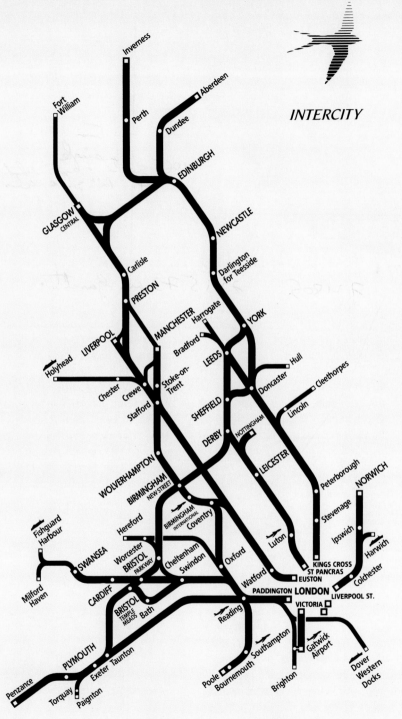

INTERCITY

© InterCity 1992/C (for BRB)

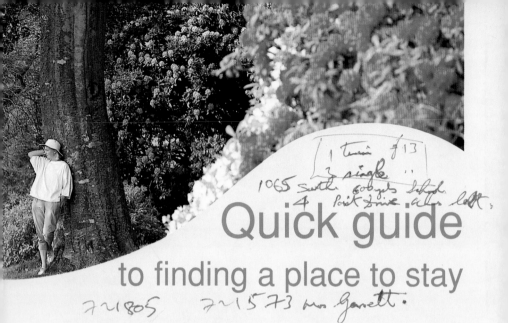

Quick guide

to finding a place to stay

This 'Where to Stay' *guide makes it quick and easy to find somewhere suitable to stay.*

Just note the place names in your preferred area and then use the town index to find page numbers.

1 **If you have a particular city,** *town or village in mind, simply check the town index (starting on page 457) to see if that place is listed. If it is,* turn to the page number given and you'll find information on accommodation available there.

When you have found suitable *accommodation, check its availability with the establishment and also confirm any other information in the published entry which may be important to you (price, whether bath or shower in en-suite rooms, children/dogs/credit cards welcome, months open, etc).*

If you are happy with everything, *make your booking and, if time permits, confirm it in writing.*

2 **If the place** *you want is not listed in the index – or if you have only a general idea of* the area in which you wish to stay – *turn to the colour maps (starting on* page 465). *The maps pinpoint all cities, towns and villages which have accommodation listings in the guide.*

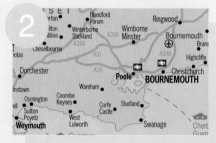